THE MAHABHARATA

THE MAHABHARATA
A MODERN RENDERING

Volume I

RAMESH MENON

Published by
Rupa Publications India Pvt. Ltd 2004
161-B/4, Gulmohar House,
Yusuf Sarai Community Centre,
New Delhi 110049

Sales centres:
Bengaluru Chennai
Hyderabad Kolkata Mumbai

Copyright © Ramesh Menon 2004

All rights reserved.
No part of this publication may be reproduced, transmitted,
or stored in a retrieval system, in any form or by any means, electronic,
mechanical, photocopying, recording or otherwise, without the prior
permission of the publisher.

ISBN: 978-81-291-1492-1

Seventeenth impression 2025

20 19 18 17

The moral right of the author has been asserted.

Typeset by Mindways Design, New Delhi

Printed in India

This book is sold subject to the condition that it shall not,
by way of trade or otherwise, be lent, resold, hired out, or otherwise
circulated, without the publisher's prior consent, in any form of binding or
cover other than that in which it is published.

Contents

Foreword xi
Acknowledgements xv
Preface xvii

BOOK ONE: Adi Parva — 1

On the banks of the Ganga — 3
A tale of two curses — 7
The river's son — 12
A scent of heaven — 15
A solemn vow — 18
Two princes — 26
Three princesses of Kasi — 29
Bheeshma and Amba — 33
Amba — 41
The solemn oath — 48
Satyavati's other son — 52
The blind night and the pale one — 55
In the dark — 60
The three princes of Hastinapura — 62
Kuntibhoja's daughter — 64
The blazing Deva — 67
A curse in the forest — 72
Pandu's yearning — 76
Kunti's unworldly lovers — 80
The sons of Pandu — 84
The sinister night — 90
Sweet, deadly spring — 96

The Pandavas come home	101
The seeds of envy	108
At Pramanakoti	112
Under the river	117
A master for the Kuru princes	125
Drona's story	130
The brilliant pupil	136
At the river	143
Ekalavya	145
A young man's dreams	154
Karna finds a master	157
The exhibition	166
The golden warrior	177
Drona's revenge	183
A father and his son	190
To Varanasi	199
The palace of lac	205
Fire	209
The tragic news	216
Flight through the jungle	220
A change of heart	223
Ghatotkacha	230
A sleepy town	234
A strange story	245
Encounter in the night	251
The spinning fish	258
'Share the alms you've brought'	268
The unusual wedding	276
Anxiety in Hastinapura	281
The council at Hastinapura	286
Vidura in Kampilya	292
A desolate gift	295
Miracle in the wilderness	301
Narada visits Indraprastha	307
Ulupi and Chitrangadaa	313
The crocodiles	320
The Raivataka hill	325

The holy yati	329
The yati and the princess	335
Cure for an illness	340
Balarama's anger	345
Draupadi's anger	349
The Yadavas come to Indraprastha	354
The hungry brahmana	357
The burning of the Khandava vana	365
BOOK TWO: Sabha Parva	**373**
Mayaa	375
Mayaa's sabha	380
Narada, the messenger	388
Yudhishtira's quandary	392
Krishna arrives in Indraprastha	398
Jarasandha	402
Girivraja	406
The blade of grass	411
The four quarters	418
The Rajasuya yagna	427
A cousin's anger	434
Dark omens	440
The green monster	445
Shakuni's plan	450
An anxious messenger	457
The game of dice	459
Shame	467
'Am I a free woman?'	472
The miracle and the oaths	476
Dhritarashtra's fickleness	485
The second game of dice	488
BOOK THREE: Vana Parva	**497**
The Sun's gift	499
The king's brother	504
The rishis' warning	509
Krishna swears an oath	516

Dwaitavana	520
The trials of Yudhishtira	525
Vyasa's advice	534
Arjuna's quest	539
The vetala	543
The Lords of light	548
Amravati	555
The weapons of Indra	560
The apsara Urvashi	562
The curse	569
The Muni Brihadaswa	577
Tirtha yatra*	586
To Badarikasrama	594
An old monkey	603
Where the saugandhika grows	612
Arjuna returns	618
Arjuna's story	622
The wondrous city	627
Hiranyapuri	633
Bheema's adventure	641
The riddles of Nahusha	649
Markandeya's lore*	655
The four yugas	661
The foolish brahmana	670
Duryodhana's ghosha-yatra	676
The shaming of Duryodhana	683
Despair	687
The powers of darkness	691
The Rishi Durvasa	698
Jayadratha	704
The lake of death	711
Yaksha prasna: the yaksha's riddles	716
BOOK FOUR: Virata Parva	**723**
The thirteenth year	725
Kanka, the gambler	730
Ajnatavasa	735

The cook and the wrestler	742
Karna's dream	746
The brahmana at noon	750
The queen's sairandhri	754
The besotted Keechaka	759
Ballava's night visitor	764
The long day	768
The angry gandharvas	770
Duryodhana's spies	776
Virata's battle	782
The prince and the eunuch	786
Uttara Kumara	790
Unearthly weapons	795
Dissension	799
The Kuru army	802
Arjuna	805
A gambler's blood	810
The Pandavas	816
A wedding in Upaplavya	819
Glossary	823
Appendix	837

FOREWORD
A note on Hindu time and the Mahabharata

'THREE HUNDRED AND SIXTY-FIVE HUMAN YEARS MAKE ONE YEAR OF the Devas and the Pitrs, the Gods and the ancestors.

Four are the ages in the land of Bharata: the krita, treta, dwapara and kali. The krita yuga lasts for 4800 divine years, the treta for 3600, the dwapara for 2400 and the kali for 1200; and, then, another krita begins.

The krita or satya yuga is an age of purity; it is sinless. Dharma, righteousness, is perfect and walks on four feet in the krita. However, from the treta yuga, adharma, evil, comes to the world and the very fabric of time begins to decay. Finally, the kali yuga, the fourth age, is almost entirely corrupt, with dharma barely surviving, hobbling on one foot.

A chaturyuga, a cycle of four ages, is 12,000 divine years, or 365 x 12,000 human years long. Seventy-one chaturyugas make a manvantara; fourteen manvantaras, a kalpa. A kalpa of a thousand chaturyugas, 12 million divine years, is one day of Brahma, the Creator.

8,000 Brahma years make one Brahma yuga; 1,000 Brahma yugas make a savana and Brahma's life is 3,003 savanas long. One day of Mahavishnu is the lifetime of Brahma ...'

The Great War, the Mahabharata, is fought at the very end of a dwapara yuga, the third age, just before the sinister kali yuga begins. Once, in time out of mind, the Gods created the kshatriyas to establish dharma, justice, in an anarchic world. Most royal kshatriya bloodlines can be traced back to the Devas themselves: in the most ancient days, the Gods came freely to the earth. But in time, generations, the noble race of warrior kings has grown arrogant and greedy. By the end of the dwapara yuga, they have become tyrants, and they are still practically invincible.

Krishna, the Avatara, and his cousins, the Pandavas, are born to destroy the power of the kshatriyas of Bharatavarsha (India) forever. This is what the Mahabharata yuddha, the war on the crack of the ages, accomplishes; and thus, ushers in the kali yuga, modern times. By the Hindu calendar, the Great War was fought some five thousand years ago.

The House of Kuru is one of the oldest and noblest royal houses. It traces its origins to Soma Deva, the Moon God. Timeless Hastinapura, the city of elephants, is the capital of the Kuru kingdom and one great king after another has ruled from here. The legend of the Mahabharata begins with King Shantanu of the Kurus, and how a son is born to him. But that prince, Devavrata, will never sit upon his father's throne. Instead, Shantanu's blind grandson, Dhritarashtra, will become king.

The main theme of the Mahabharata is the story of Dhritarashtra's sons, the Kauravas, and his brother Pandu's sons, the Pandavas, and the enmity between them. Dhritarashtra's hundred boys are evil princes, led by the eldest of them: the ruthless Duryodhana, who is a demon. Pandu's five princes are Devaputras, Devas' sons, born to fight for dharma in the world.

They are Yudhishtira, Bheema, Arjuna, Nakula and Sahadeva.

Almost every king in Bharatavarsha takes one side or the other in the Great War and ten million kshatriyas are killed. Dharma is established again on earth; but an age has ended and another has begun.

The Maharishi Vyasa, the poet of the Mahabharata, himself wanders in and out of the story. Unearthly beings—Devas, yakshas, gandharvas, nagas and apsaras—find their way into the story, as do demonic ones, asuras and rakshasas. The Mahabharata is set in a pristine and magical time of the earth. Its heroes and villains are all larger than life. The war itself is fought with occult weapons: the astras of the Gods.

Just before the war begins, the third Pandava, Arjuna, the greatest archer in the world, loses his nerve on the field of Kurukshetra. That perfect warrior cannot bear the thought of killing his cousins. Krishna, who is Arjuna's charioteer, expounds the eternal dharma to him. This exposition is the Bhagavad Gita, the Song of God. The Gita is the heart of the Mahabharata, its real treasure. At one level, all the rest of the restless action of the epic is a quest for the precious Gita and its stillness. The Gita is the Hindu's New Testament.

Senayor ubhayor madhye...between two immense armies, on the brink of a savage war, the Avatara sings his wisdom. To this day, Kurukshetra is holy ground for the Hindu because it was here that Krishna sang his immortal Gita, and here that he revealed his Viswarupa, his Cosmic Form, to Arjuna.

The original Mahabharata in Sanskrit is an epic poem of 100,000 couplets: seven times as long as the Iliad and the Odyssey combined. To record his epic for posterity is such a daunting task that Vyasa begs the elephant-headed God, Ganesha, to be his scribe. Ganesha has one stipulation: Vyasa must never keep him waiting, for even a moment, during the narration. The poet agrees and manages to keep ahead of his quicksilver writer, often with long digressions from his main story. Ganesha writes down Vyasa's legend with a tusk he breaks from his own face.

This is a modern prose version of Vyasa's timeless epic—the legend of the sons of Pandu.

Acknowledgements

THE LATE KAMALA SUBRAMANIAM'S MAHABHARATA IN ENGLISH WAS one of my main sources for this version of the epic. Her devotion was exceptional, and my debt to her is great.

After finishing my book, I discovered Kisari Mohan Ganguli's 12-volume translation. I have added some details from his work, which I found interesting and relevant – as footnotes, to the text of my book, and in an Appendix.

I must thank Vasantha Menon, Jayashree Kumar, Saugata Mukherjee, and Atreyee Gohain for their wonderful copyediting, and my publisher, Mr. R.K. Mehra of Rupa & Co., for his enthusiasm and support.

PREFACE
The Birth of a Poet

ONCE, IN MORE GRACIOUS TIMES, WHEN THE KSHATRIYAS OF THE earth were like gods, there was a devout sovereign of Chedi called Uparichara. Indra of the Devas gave him a marvellous vimana, a crystal ship that flew anywhere at his very thought. That king became known as Uparichara Vasu; for like the Vasus, he ranged the sky in his vimana.

Uparichara's wife was Girika, and she bore him five excellent princes. One morning, when she was in her fertile time, Queen Girika came to her husband and asked him to make love because she wanted another son. But he had to go into the forest to hunt some meat for a sacrifice to his fathers in heaven. Uparichara set out with his bow in his hand.

Earlier, his queen had come to him wearing the sheerest robe; the king did not realize how much she had aroused him, until he missed two red stags with his arrows. Uparichara came to a lotus-laden pool in the depths of the forest and, with Girika's lush body before his mind's eye, ejaculated onto a banyan leaf.

He folded the leaf, chanted a potent mantra over it and called his hunting falcon down from the sky. 'Fly friend, take this to my queen as swiftly as you can.'

As the falcon sped towards Chedi, a fishing eagle perched in a tree on the banks of the Yamuna saw him. The eagle mistook the banyan leaf for a shred of meat and flew at the falcon. The birds fought briefly in the air and the leaf fell out of the falcon's beak, down into the river.

Now, a year ago the apsara Adrika had flown down from Devaloka to swim in the Yamuna. It was the twilight hour, and when the nymph had been in the water for a while she saw a sage at the river's edge, at his sandhya vandana, his evening worship. The austere one sat motionless, his eyes shut fast. Adrika saw how radiant he was and lusted after him.

She swam close to where the rishi sat and playfully seized his ankles. Adrika thought that on seeing her beauty and naked body he would make love to her. She could not have been more mistaken.

The hermit's eyes flew open and he cursed Adrika, "You dare disturb my dhyana? Be a fish from now!"

At once the apsara had golden scales and a fish's body. The rishi rose and strode away. Neither of them realized that fate had a deep purpose to fulfil by their encounter. Adrika stayed in the river, devouring smaller fish when she felt hungry. She grew bigger and bigger. Soon she forgot she was an apsara and thought of herself as just a fish.

When the eagle set on Uparichara's falcon the banyan leaf plunged down into the midnight-blue Yamuna. Adrika swam lazily in the river. She saw the leaf strike the water and the king's seed being washed off. As it sank, shimmering, with a flick of her tail the fish darted forward and swallowed that seed.[1] At once she became pregnant.

In ten months she was so big she could hardly swim and only lay on the bed of the river. One day she was snared by a fisherman in his net. He drew her from the water, and she lay heaving in his boat. The fisherman cut the golden fish open with his knife. There was a flash of light and he saw the spirit of a nymph fly into the sky.

The man was blinded for a moment. But when he looked into the fish's belly, he saw two human infants: a boy and a girl lay there and gazed serenely back at him. The next day the fisherman arrived in the king's palace and told Uparichara Vasu how he had discovered the children. The man begged to keep one of them.

The king guessed how those twins had been conceived, and his queen still wanted another son. Uparichara Vasu kept the little boy and allowed the fisherman to take the girl. That prince born from a fish's belly was named Matsyaraja; in time, he would rule his father's kingdom as ably as Uparichara had. The fisherman raised the little girl in the wilderness as his daughter. A fortune-teller who read the lines on her palm said that, one day, she would become the queen of a great kingdom. The fisherman lived with that prophecy clasped close to his heart.

That dusky child's body always smelled of fish, and her father called her Matsyagandhi.

Some years later, the celibate Parashara, another immortal rishi on his pilgrimage, arrived on the banks of the Yamuna. It was a crisp winter morning. The sun shone pale and ethereal, and the river sparkled as if a million jewels had been strewn across her water. The fisherman in his hut sat at his morning meal of last night's fish and rice, when the austere figure loomed suddenly in his door.

"Take me across the river, I am in a hurry!" said Parashara ungraciously.

It was not the first time the profound one had passed this way and the fisherman recognized him. He called out to his daughter.

"Matsyagandhi, take our Muni Parashara across."

She appeared at the corner of the hut, sixteen and bright as a bit of winter sun. Breast buds strained like young lotuses against her green blouse; eyes like saucers set wide in her lean dark face gazed frankly at Parashara. Without a word, Matsyagandhi led the illustrious one to the wooden boat tethered to the riverbank.

As he followed the girl, the smell of her body invaded him: the raw smell of fish with which she was born; but instead of being repulsed, Parashara lost his heart to her. He who had felt no twinge of desire in the company of fawning apsaras in Devaloka, was overcome by the earthy whiff of the fisher-girl.

When she helped him into the boat, he held her hand longer than he needed to. She freed herself quietly and cast off. But he would not be so easily denied. As they moved out Parashara reached for her hand again and clasped it on the oar at which she rowed. She smiled at him, her huge eyes twinkling. She stopped rowing, though they were in midstream and drifting. But she did not withdraw her hand.

Parashara's presence and his dignity, which now suffered not a little for his visible excitement, attracted her. His hand quivered on hers. He leant forward awkwardly to try to kiss her. She smiled, dazzling him, and stroked his gnarled hand without inhibition.

In her husky voice she said, "Holy one, why do you want to do this? You a lofty brahmana descended from Brahma and I the daughter of a nishada: between us, this isn't proper."

Then she trembled, remembering—suppose he cursed her! At that moment her father hailed them faintly from the bank. He stood washing his hands outside the hut and wanted to know why they had stopped.

Parashara released the girl's hand. She rowed again while the rishi kept a watch on the fisherman, who stood staring after them, his eyes shaded. Again, the sage took Matsyagandhi's hand.

She said, "Brahmana, aren't you repelled by my smell? Muni, don't you know the Vedas say one should never have sexual intercourse during the day? And besides, my father can see us."

When Parashara was near enough to kiss her, she was reminded sharply of his great age, and both excited and dismayed by it. But he waved a slender arm over his head, his hand curled in an occult mudra. Instantly they were shrouded in mist and the fisherman could not see them any more. Then it began to snow!

It was dark on the boat on the river.

"Is that night enough?"

Little Matsyagandhi gave a cry of wonder. But being a virgin and still afraid, she said, "Yogin, you will enjoy me and go your way, but I will become pregnant. I will be ruined, the laughing stock of the world. And what will I tell my father?"

He cried hoarsely, "Give me your love and you will be famous forever among Devas and rishis. You will be known as Satyavati in heaven. Look."

Again a wizardly mudra from him, and she saw her body glow with a new beauty. Her limbs were lambent, her features finer, and the smell of her transformed so now she smelt of wild jasmine, lotus and other unearthly fragrances. In a moment they spread from her for a yojana. Her original, fishy musk had not vanished either; it became a sublimely erotic perfume, which fuelled his ardour!

Still, she hesitated. She restrained his wandering hand, so he cried, "Say whatever you want and it shall be yours. Quickly, you are driving me mad!"

After a moment's thought, she said, "If neither my father nor anyone else comes to know of this, if my virginity is not broken, if the son born of our love is a magician like you, and if I always smell as sweetly as I do now, then take me, O Rishi, and gladly!"

Parashara, famed across the three worlds, laughed aloud. He said, "This is God's will, Satyavati. All your conditions will be fulfilled, *and your son shall be the greatest poet the world has ever known.*"

He took her in his arms in that boat rocking softly on the Yamuna, while his magical snowstorm held up its opaque curtain around them. Impatient for him now that her fears had been allayed, she rowed to an island in the stream and moored there. And they lay together, unlikeliest lovers, heating the pale sand dry.

At last, after he drank deeply of her youth, and she of his age, Parashara rose to bathe in the Yamuna. With a last kiss on top of her head, he walked upon the water and out of her life.

And in the mystic dimension, no sooner had she conceived than she was in labour.

Her delivery was miraculous and quite painless. As soon as he was born, her lustrous boy, as handsome as Kamadeva, became a full-grown rishi, with a kamandalu in one hand, a smooth staff in the other and his matted, tawny hair lit in a halo. That newborn and exceptional hermit said to his mother, "We must go our separate ways. But if you ever want to see me, just think of me and I will appear before you." And he also walked away from her.

Since he was born on the dwipa in the Yamuna, Satyavati's son was called Dwaipayana. But later, he was to divide the holy Veda and to compose the sacred Puranas from ancient revelations. He was to become renowned as Veda Vyasa.

Vyasa composed the immortal Mahabharata and his disciple Vaisampayana narrated the epic for King Janamejaya of the Kurus, during his sarpa yagna, his snake sacrifice.[1]

---

1 See Appendix.

BOOK ONE

Adi Parva[2]

AUM, I bow down to Narayana, the most exalted Nara, and to the Devi Saraswati, and say *Jaya*!

---

[2]. See Appendix for a note on the beginning of the original text.

BOOK ONE

Adi Parva

ONE

On the banks of the Ganga

SHANTANU, FOURTEENTH KING OF THE KURUS IN THE AUGUST LINE of Manu and Bharata, was a keen hunter. Since his earliest years, the monarch of the race of the Moon was a solitary; and he hunted alone as well. He did not like to share the passion of careful tracking, the breathless chase, or the humming arrow. He did not care to diffuse the excitement and danger of the hunt by surrounding himself with courtiers or trackers. Hunting was rather like worship to him, a thing just between himself and the wilderness.

Shantanu was a young king at the time of which we speak. He had not married and the kingdom did not have an heir. It seemed he would never take a wife, for he had refused the most beautiful, most gifted princesses in all Bharatavarsha. Shantanu had always known that one day he would indeed marry, and the Kurus would have their crown prince. But only when the woman for whom he was waiting, the one who appeared so clearly to him in his dreams, came into his waking life.

Twilight, and the blue sky was dying in dark crimson and turquoise when Shantanu rode to the banks of the sacred Ganga. His horse frothed at the mouth, its flanks steamed. Shantanu had almost ridden him into the ground today, as if the king was possessed by a demon. He had come much farther than he had intended, and though he had set out at dawn, he hadn't a kill as yet. Once a leopard had eluded him, and twice a fine stag. The last arrow missed its mark by a hand's width. An archer like him should have turned home in disgust, on this luckless day when the gods of the hunt mocked him.

But Shantanu did not turn back. He pressed on, more determined than ever that he would not return empty-handed, not if he had to sleep out under the stars. He did not know it yet, but fate drew him on.

The sun was sinking at the crest of the western hills, when he arrived exhausted on the banks of the shimmering river.

"Ganga!" breathed Shantanu when he saw her: she who had fallen from the sky in pristine times. She was as wide as a sea and he could hardly make out her far bank. He dismounted and led his horse to the susurrant water's edge, where the river lapped at banks of green moss.

He knelt beside his beast and, bending down to the crystal flow, drank deeply, splashing his arms and face with the sweet water. Suddenly, the king became aware that he was not alone.

He turned and saw her: a vision swathed in the last rays of the saffron sun, her skin like soft gold. She appeared perfect of face and body. Her eyes were luminous, her black hair fell to her waist in a cascade, as she stood staring at him and made his blood quicken as no other woman ever had. And she was no stranger: she had visited his dreams since he was a boy.

They stood transfixed for an interminable moment, before Shantanu went softly towards her. Words failed him, but he held out his hands, wanting to say everything with that gesture.

She stood there, playing nervously with her black tresses. Her face mirrored the river uncannily; it seemed the water flowed across her sculpted features, as if the Ganga and she were one being, their rhythms the same, their souls.

Next moment, he drew her to him in the deepening darkness. He whispered, "I am Shantanu, king in Hastinapura. I cannot live without you, I want you to be my queen."

Her eyes wild, she said, "Oh I love you, my lord! But I must bind you with a condition, if I am to be your wife."

"Anything, anything at all; my life if you want it."

"You must never ask me who I am, nor question what I do, however terrible it may seem."

His hands parted the flowing garment she wore, which seemed made of river-moss, and he knelt before her to slake all the thirst of his young manhood, for the king was still a virgin. She breathed, "I will be your wife until you question me. But the day you do, I will leave you for ever."

"Never. I swear I will never question you, whatever you do."

Now her hands were peeling off his clothes, and the river swelled around them in a tide of flames. It seemed their bodies turned to water and fire, and they were lost in an ancient dream of love.

Shantanu brought her home to Hastinapura, the city of elephants, and she became his queen. For where he had found her, he called her Ganga. She was peerless: a perfect companion who knew his every whim, wise and just, modest and charming, and knowing how to keep her own counsel. Most of all, she was his love; and when they were alone together, Shantanu and Ganga slipped beyond time's confines and became other, magical beings.

A year passed, and one summer's evening Ganga told Shantanu that she was pregnant. There was celebration in Hastinapura, which lasted a month: that an heir would be born in the royal House of the Moon. It seemed to the king that he was hardly mortal any more. In his joy Shantanu chose to ignore the strange anxiety that gripped his wife during her pregnancy. He attributed her moody silences, and her refusal to see anyone for days, to just the fact that a woman is subject to many changes at such a time.

Winter was near its end, and there was spring in the air, when on a fine morning a messenger arrived breathless in his king's court. He came with the news that a fine son had been born to Queen Ganga. Shantanu sprang up from his throne and ran to his wife's apartment. Ignoring the guards, who were trying to convey something urgently to him, he burst into the room of labour, only to find it deserted.

He turned back to the guards and the sombre women of the harem.

"Where is she?" he cried. "Where is my son?"

The captain of the guards said, "My lord, the queen had hardly given birth when she snatched up the child in her arms and ran out. She said she was going to the river and forbade any of us to follow her, on pain of death."

Shantanu ordered his swiftest horse saddled. She had an hour's start, but she had gone by chariot. It was twilight again when the Kuru king came flying to the river's bank, to the very place where his love had first appeared.

The sun was sinking over the western hills. In that last light, he saw her standing at the candescent water's edge, her infant in her arms. She was speaking earnestly to the river in an old and fluid tongue. He couldn't understand a word she said, but suddenly he remembered some other words she had once said to him: "You must never question me, whatever I do, or I will leave you for ever."

Even as he leapt off his horse, she chanted a resonant mantra, lifted their baby high above her head and cast him into the swirling flow. Her cry echoed there as if she had torn her heart from her body and flung it from her.

She turned in the golden ghost-light and, as long as he lived, Shantanu would never forget the look on her face. Before he could roar the searing protest that rose in him, she ran to him and flung her arms around his neck. Her eyes raged at him, 'Remember your oath!'

She pulled him down onto the emerald moss and enfolded him in her currents. She made him forget everything in the velvet tide to her sea.

TWO

A tale of two curses

NEVER ONCE DID SHANTANU ASK HIS QUEEN WHY SHE HAD DROWNED their child, not even in their most intimate moments together.

In a year, she was pregnant again. Once more there was expectation and rejoicing in the kingdom, and once again, when she was delivered of a beautiful infant, she took the child to the river and threw him to the foaming currents. Again Shantanu followed her and found her at the water's edge. Once more she made him dumb with a look, smothering him with her loving so he dared not ask her why she had killed their baby.

Seven times in as many years, Ganga became pregnant: because her husband did not stop loving her. But living with his terrible secret, his heart died within him, day by day. They told the world their sons were born diseased from an old curse and had been given into the care of some rishis in the forest. This was near enough the truth, but Shantanu did not know that yet.

Like a serpent in its hole, his anguish coiled itself round his life. His hair turned grey and his face was lined. He tried to stay away from Ganga, but this he could not do; she was closer to him than his very breath and he could not live without making love to her. He bore his ordeal in silence, through the murder of seven sons.

But slowly Shantanu arrived at a crisis. What tormented him most, whenever he thought of it, was his queen's nonchalance at what she did, which was so monstrous. He often wondered whether she was not a rakshasi, a demoness. After all, her past was cloaked in mystery. Even on that first day they met, he recalled now in dark suspicion, she had made him swear he would never question her: on pain of losing her forever.

Yet, he also knew how gentle she was, even to the smallest living thing. How was he to reconcile these two Gangas? Shantanu was close to losing his mind, when his queen conceived for the eighth time.

The time of her delivery drew near and this time Shantanu waited night and day outside his wife's apartment. He listened, as he could not have done in the past, to her cries of labour as their child pushed his way out from her delicate body. It was the night's final yaama, the hour before dawn. Shantanu heard her order her chariot to the door, and he knew where she would go.

That night Shantanu rode to the river before her.

For an hour he waited by the murmuring water, until dawn caressed the eastern sky. It was the longest hour of his life; then he heard her arrive. By the first rays of the sun, he saw her alight from the chariot with their child in her arms. He stood hidden by a tree and she did not notice him in her urgency. She ran straight to the edge of the water, and as she lifted the baby to cast it into the lightening flow, all the sorrow of seven agonized years burst from him.

"Stop!" howled Shantanu, his voice echoing against the dawn. "You won't kill my son!"

It was as if he had struck her with an arrow. She turned in shock, a moan on her lips, and stood frozen as he ran up to her. Before he could snatch the child from her arms, she handed it to him herself. He was beside himself now, raging.

"What is this dreadful thing you do again and again? How can a mother cut off these innocent lives?"

She smiled sadly, "You have broken your oath to me. It seems you need this son of yours more than you do me. So be it; the curse has ended."

"What curse? What are you raving about, you murderess?"

He saw hurt flash in her eyes; then she took his hand, "My lord, hear my story before you judge me." Stroking his face so tenderly he thought his heart would break, she whispered, "Look, Shantanu, at who I really am."

She stood transformed before him. She was ethereal light and crystal waves at once: the tides of ages were contained in her. She was pure beyond belief, brighter than the rising sun. She was a Goddess. He drew back from her in awe—she who had been his wife for ten years, stood now, an immortal.

She said, "I am Ganga, the river of heaven and earth. The sins of men are washed in me."

Shantanu stood speechless. He wanted to kneel and worship her, but the child was in his arms and confusion stormed through his body.

In a moment, she returned to her human form. "Now you will believe me, and my tale of two curses.

"The first curse is the reason I came to you as a woman. Once, in a time you cannot remember, since this mortal body binds you now, you were another king. You were called Mahabhishek then."

As Ganga spoke, the memory of another life rustled at Shantanu's soul, and he saw what she described in a vision.

"Once Mahabhishek sat in Indra's court, the Sudharma, among the Devas. Those were days when heaven and earth were hardly apart from each other and kings of the earth went freely to the realms of the Gods. Ganga came there then, as she often did, and when Mahabhishek saw her he wanted her. When she looked at him, she also felt a powerful yearning. The Devas saw them quicken to each other and a hush fell in Indra's court."

As Ganga told her tale, Shantanu saw it all again clearly: he was swept back to that unearthly occasion.

How could an immortal like her, and he, a mortal king, come together? The Devas cursed them that they dared gaze at each other with forbidden desire, in the Gods' very presence. They cursed Mahabhishek and Ganga to a human life, when they would be a king and his wife for a time and satisfy themselves with each other's love.

"And I appeared before you at my water's edge one day," she said.

He asked in a whisper, "And the children? What curse was that?"

She said in her voice of tides, "Once the eight Vasus of heaven came down with their women to roam the earth."

With invisible bodies those immortals came, and saw a mountain where Vasishta the sage had his asrama. They saw Nandini, the muni's cow, with her calf beside her, cropping the grass that grew on a jade slope. They were besotted with that divine cow that lit up the mountainside with her lustre.

One of the Vasus' wives cried to her husband that she must have the creature for herself.

The Vasu laughed, 'Nandini belongs to the Rishi Vasishta, who is master of this mountain. My love, a human may escape death by drinking her milk. But we are already immortal; it is foolish to tempt the sage's wrath.'

But his woman would not listen. 'It is not for me, but for a mortal friend of mine that I want the cow. My friend is dearer to me than I can tell you and I don't want her ever to die.'

Taunted by their wives, who brought their husbands' manhood into question, asking how could they, who were Gods, fear a mere rishi, those Vasus came down like eight comets on that mountain and took Nandini and her calf from Vasishta's asrama.

But Nandini was like Vasishta's daughter; he could not live without her. The muni was a seer of time. He looked into his heart and knew the Vasus had taken his cow. When he saw how his gentle animal had been spirited away, crying out, her calf lowing in terror, his eyes blazed. With all the power of his long tapasya, he cursed the Vasus.

'Arrogant Devas, be born as mortal men!'

He felt drained. In their distant world, the Vasus became aware of the curse and they trembled. It was unthinkable for them, who were as free as light, to be bound in flesh. They flew to the rishi's feet, with Nandini and her calf, and cried, 'Muni, forgive us!'

But a rishi's curse was no trifle that it could be withdrawn. Moreover, the germ of a deep destiny was hidden in that curse; there were mysterious designs to be accomplished by it, on earth. Vasishta had grown calmer now and felt pity for the contrite Vasus.

He said, 'I cannot withdraw the curse and you must pay for what you did. But for seven of you let the curse be brief. You will spend nine months in the darkness of a mother's womb; but as soon as you are born you will meet your deaths and be free again.'

It was the eighth Vasu, Prabhasa, who had actually seized Nandini. He stood with his head hung before Vasishta. The rishi said kindly to him, 'You led the others to sin; you must pay more fully than they. Prabhasa, you will live a whole life as a man on earth and yours shall be a great human life. But now, Devas, go and find a woman who can be your mother in this world.'

The curse, and even its softening, had exhausted Vasishta. He had to find a lonely place to begin his tapasya once more. Taking Nandini and her calf with him, he disappeared from there.

Left alone on the mountain, the Vasus saw a sparkling spring that issued from a cleft in some rocks. They knew this was from where the Ganga flowed down into the world. It struck them that here, surely, was providence trying to show them their way ahead: who better than the river of heaven and earth to be their terrestrial mother?

They worshipped her on the icy mountain and, surprised at their being there, Ganga appeared before them. Already like children, the Vasus fell at her feet and cried, 'Devi, listen to the curse Vasishta has laid upon us.'

They told their tale by turns. At last, Prabhasa said, 'We beg you, O Ganga, take a human woman's form. Marry a king of the earth and become our mother. And as soon as we are born, cast the first seven of us into your waters. But I, Prabhasa, must suffer the whole span of a mortal life.'

Ganga ended her story softly, "With the other curse already hanging over me, Shantanu, and longing for you as I did, how could I refuse?"

Now Shantanu knew she was pure. He knelt before her and asked her forgiveness that he had doubted her. Then, without a word, he handed her the shining infant he held in his arms. Tenderly, she took the child, the Vasu Prabhasa, from him.

Ganga said, "When he is sixteen our son will return with you to Hastinapura. And one day, he will rule the Kurus."

Shantanu realized the time had come for her to leave him. He cried, "And you, Ganga? Will I never see you again? What if I come to the river? Won't you meet me here in secret, hidden from the eyes of men and Gods? Oh, how will I live without you?"

Briefly, she was sad. But then she stroked his face, and said, "Nothing is hidden, nor ever shall be. Our time together is past."

With the child in her arms, she vanished. Shantanu's cries rang against sky, forest and river. Again and again he called out her name; but she had gone. In a while, knowing his old life was truly over, he climbed wearily into the chariot in which she had driven here, and turned home.

THREE

The river's son

For sixteen years Shantanu lived alone like a hermit, in his palace. He turned all his attention to his kingdom. The rule of Shantanu, son of Prateepa, of the House of the Moon, was a just and prosperous one and his people were contented. More than anything else he was a sad man; but his very sorrow seemed to give Shantanu strength and wisdom, so his reign could be a finer one than before.

The king had one pleasure he still indulged in—hunting. But now Shantanu never killed any creature. He only watched their wild lives as an avid spy. Most of all, his hunting took him back to the place beside the river, where, to his mind, he had found and lost everything.

Whenever he came there he would grow strangely peaceful, as if he sensed her presence near him; though not once did she appear before him, for sixteen lonely years. But he would set himself down at the deep-flowing water's side, and lose himself in the murmuring of her currents and the mists that clung and drifted across her expanse. And it was as if she reached incorporeal fingers through daylight and darkness and took his pain from him.

Sixteen years passed, and one day Shantanu fell asleep beside the Ganga, dreaming of the past. He saw her standing before him once more, stroking his face with her cool hands, smiling at him, calling him with her eyes and with open arms. It was midday. Shantanu dreamt that the river had stopped flowing.

The king woke up and saw the dream was true—the Ganga was dry beside him! A short way upstream, all her water had gathered in a huge wave: froth-flecked and swelling higher every moment, but powerless to flow. Shantanu saw an exceptional dam across the river, which she could not breach.

It was a filigree wall of golden arrows, a brilliant net through which no drop of water passed. He heard a soft laugh at his back and whirled around. There she was, her face wreathed in a smile.

Shantanu cried, "So you've decided to take pity on me! Shall we go back to the palace? Shall we tell the people their queen has come home?"

But she said, "All that is past. When the sun sets on one day, who can call him back so you can live the same day again? There is no returning; not a moment may we retrieve. Turn your heart away from what is over."

Something in her voice startled him. He realized what she said was true; moreover, he felt changed himself by the years. Now that he knew who she was, he felt worshipful towards her. Shantanu struggled briefly with himself. Then, growing calm, he asked, "Why have you come back?"

"Do you see the river, my lord?" she said, a laugh in her fluid throat.

"Yes," he breathed. "Who has done this?"

He also smiled. He did not quite know why, except that a great happiness was dawning on him. Wryly, he added, "Who holds your tameless flow in check, which all my love could not bind?"

Before she could answer, there was a deafening report. The dam of arrows gave way and the immense wave that had built up behind it came roaring down the empty riverbed. A youth who shone like a God rode that cataract, effortlessly at its crest.

Ganga called out in her river-tongue to the boy. He turned towards them, laughing in exhilaration, walking on the water as if he trod solid ground. He gained the bank, ran flushed and breathless to the river-Goddess and flung his arms around her.

"Mother, did you see? I held the river up again!"

Only then, he seemed to notice Shantanu. He looked at the king with his great dark eyes, uncanny recognition sweeping across his heart. The young face was a picture of confusion, as delight and disbelief chased each other across it. Laughing, Ganga said, "My child, this is your father. And this is our son Devavrata."

The boy prostrated himself at Shantanu's feet. With a cry, Shantanu raised him up and embraced him.

Ganga said, "Devavrata is sixteen today and he knows everything a prince should know. Vasishta taught him the Vedas and Vedangas. Brihaspati taught him politics, and at my begging him, the bane of the kshatriyas, Parasurama himself, taught him archery.

"I do not think the Kurus will find a better heir for their ancient throne than my Devavrata. He is a kshatriya, my lord, take him with you to your kingdom of heroes."

The boy stood beside his father, bright with the sense of the destiny that was upon him. Though his eyes were full, he embraced his mother in farewell, unflinchingly. Smiling bravely, holding back her tears, Ganga vanished.

Arm in arm, father and son turned back towards Hastinapura and the future. Shantanu was full of joy.

FOUR

A scent of heaven

F OUR PERFECT YEARS WENT BY. SHANTANU NAMED DEVAVRATA Yuvaraja, the heir apparent; the people were delighted, because they saw what a prince Ganga's son was. Shantanu doted on the boy, and for his part Devavrata was a perfect son. He too was absorbed in his father, soon anticipating his every wish. Devavrata was mature far beyond his years; in their bond of love, the son was the stronger one. He bore the responsibility of their intense relationship.

Then one day Shantanu went hunting again. He was not lonely any more and he hunted far less frequently than he used to. But the habits of his youth seldom leave a man entirely and that day Shantanu came once more to the bank of a river. It seemed that, as in the past, a river would again play a fateful role in his life. However, this other day of moment he did not come to the Ganga. He rode instead to the banks of the Yamuna.

As his charioteer led his horses to the water to let them drink, an ineffable fragrance swept over the king, a scent of heaven that set his senses on fire. This scent on the breeze was so exciting that Shantanu had to seek out its source.

As he moved towards it, he wondered what exotic flower it was which had this effect on him. Had some gandharva in rut dropped a garland he had made for his love from unearthly blooms?

Shantanu rounded a shoulder of thick woods and found himself in a small clearing beside a bend in the river. He saw a rough hut of timber and thatch, with smoke issuing from its chimney. In front of that hut, sitting on a smooth slab of rock beside the Yamuna and dipping her feet in the midnight-blue water, was a young woman so fragile and beautiful it was hard to imagine how she was here in this wilderness. As Shantanu went nearer, desire woken in him by now, he realized that the heavenly scent, which had awoken his desire, was the fragrance of the young woman's dark body.

Some years ago another man had found the same young woman, much as she sat today, and the Rishi Parashara had also been overcome; though then she did not smell of heaven but of very earthy fish.

Now Shantanu stood right behind the young woman, whose name was Satyavati. He whispered, "Who are you?"

She looked up at him, and turned her eyes down quickly from what she saw in his gaze. The king felt faint now that he was so near her. Shantanu said again, "Who are you, lovely one? I am Shantanu, king of the Kurus, and I want you for my wife."

She did not seem surprised. Her eyes still turned down to the boat tied to the rock on which she sat, she said huskily, "My name is Satyavati and my father is the king of the fishermen on the river. I ply this boat across the Yamuna as a ferry."

He saw in her eyes that she was pleased with the idea of being his queen; though he doubted she knew a thing of what it would entail.

"Where is your father?" he cried impatiently.

She turned lissomly and pointed. He was loth to leave her for even a moment. But bending quickly to caress her cheek, he tore himself away and strode across to the fisherman's hut.

Inside, the old fisher-king, black, with unkempt locks hanging to his shoulders, sat hunched over his midday meal, savouring the fish his daughter had smoked for him on a spit. Deftly, he separated the flesh from the skeleton so no morsel fell on the ground. Without rising, the fisherman peered at his obviously noble visitor and waited for him to speak first.

Shantanu was in a hurry, and said, "I am Shantanu, king of the Kurus of Hastinapura. When I was hunting along the river, a scent like I had never smelt before swept over me. I followed it and found it came from a young woman. She says she is your daughter. Fisherman, I have come to ask you for her hand."

The fisher-king did not rise even when Shantanu said who he was. He merely listened, all the while taking the flaky flesh off the big fish's bones, with stained teeth. He squinted shrewdly at the king, then got up and went out to wash his hands. When he returned, he folded his palms to Shantanu. "Lord of the House of Soma Deva, my daughter could never hope to find a husband like you. I am happy to give her to you to be your queen."

Shantanu gave a shout of delight. But the fisherman stopped him with a look from heavy eyes, and said, "However, there is one condition I must impose, my lord, before she becomes yours."

"What?" cried Shantanu, certain he could easily satisfy any greed for wealth this crude fellow might have, even in his dreams.

Wiping his hands carefully on a square of rough cloth, the fisherman said, "A rishi told me that one day my daughter's son would be king of all these lands." The man's eyes shone with that prophecy he had cherished so long. "You can have my Satyavati, if you give me your word that her son will be king after you."

Shantanu gasped. What would become of Devavrata if he agreed to this man's condition, as he so frantically wanted to? In his mind he saw his son's face. He saw Ganga's face; he heard her say to him, "Here is your son, Shantanu. He is a kshatriya, take him with you to your kingdom of heroes."

The day of Devavrata's investiture as yuvaraja rose before his eyes. Yet the fisher-girl's unearthly scent made his heart falter. Without a word, and with an effort that took all his strength and all his love for his son, Shantanu turned and walked out of the hut without committing himself to the fisherman.

He wrenched his treacherous gaze back from where it strayed wretchedly to the girl, who still dangled her feet in the blue river, now humming a snatch of song as sweet as the scent of her. Shantanu trembled. He dragged himself to his chariot, and cried to his charioteer to ride home to Hastina, to go like the wind. But the fire Satyavati had kindled in his blood raged on.

FIVE

A solemn vow

Shantanu was a changed man after his encounter with Satyavati. He became morose and moody, and hardly saw even Devavrata anymore. At first his son was pained. Once his father doted on him. He wanted him at his side always, and spoke endlessly with his prince about anything under the sun he cared to, from the shapes of the clouds in the sky to the affairs of the kingdom Devavrata would inherit one day. Shantanu had been so happy with his son, every day of four wonderful years. But now he did not care to even meet him. Feigning tiredness or illness, the king turned Devavrata away when he came to see him. Or he said he was too sleepy tonight; they would speak tomorrow: which never came.

Devavrata guessed that something had happened to his father the last time he went hunting. After he saw Satyavati, Shantanu not only became dejected, he gave up the hunt. Soon Devavrata was more concerned for the king's health than hurt at his distant behaviour. But knowing his father's nature as he did, he was sure it would not be long before Shantanu confided in him. He was not mistaken.

One day the king sent for him. Even as Devavrata entered his chamber, his father fetched a sigh.

The youth said, "Some terrible grief consumes you, but you will tell no one what it is."

Avoiding his son's eyes, Shantanu said, "It is the burden I must bear as a king, the anxiety that feeds on my very life."

"What is it, father? Won't you speak plainly to me?"

"Oh my child, you mean more than a hundred sons to me. But the wise say that having just one son is like having one eye to see with. If you lose it, you are blind.

You are a kshatriya, by both your birth and your gifts. And kshatriyas must satisfy themselves with wars. Who knows what happens during any war: who lives or dies, or who is killed by a cunning arrow through his back? These are dark times and if, God forbid, something happens to you Devavrata, the kingdom will be without an heir. I cannot bear to think of it—that our bloodline will not be continued from father to son, as it has since time began; and some usurper will sit upon the throne of Hastinapura."

The father cast a canny look at his son, "Devavrata, I am full of fear when I think that you are an only child. Kuru was seventh in the line of Bharata himself; it is after him that our branch of the Paurava tree is named. The thought that our royal lineage may be broken robs me of my peace."

Devavrata stood quiet, suspecting the truth, waiting for his father to come out with it. Shantanu gazed outside through a lofty palace window. He said in a low voice, "Of course, I shouldn't like you to think I want another woman. I am only anxious for the kingdom. If an outsider takes our throne, that will be an end to everything, why, of Bharatavarsha herself. Perhaps in kali yuga such a thing may happen, but not now."

Suddenly Devavrata knew what he must do. He cried, "It will not, my lord! Give me leave." Bowing quickly, he strode out of the king's apartment. He knew what ailed Shantanu: it was that old and mighty illness, love.

The prince sought out the sarathy who had last taken Shantanu hunting, and came unannounced into his home. Briskly the yuvaraja said, "My friend, I have a question the king would like you to answer honestly. Where did my father go the last time you took him hunting, and whom did he meet?"

The old man smiled. A gleam in his eye, he said, "Are you sure, my prince, that your father would have me answer this?"

"It is imperative you do. The king has not been himself since that day, but languishes from some deep sorrow."

Still the man hesitated. Devavrata aimed a shaft in the dark, "Say old one, what woman was she?"

"She was a fisher-woman, but an extraordinary and beautiful fisher-woman. We found her beside the Yamuna, and not by seeing her at first but only by her unworldly scent."

He shook his head in wonder to remember that scent. Devavrata cried impatiently, "And?"

The man turned his eyes away. "The king was smitten by her. He went to her father and asked for her hand."

The old man paused, embarrassed. The yuvaraja said, "The fisherman was fool enough to refuse the king of the Kurus? Impossible."

"No, my prince, he was no fool. He took his time about answering your father, and proved shrewder than is good for any of us."

"Tell me what happened!"

"The fishermen's king, for so he was, said to your father that he could not hope for a better husband for his daughter. But he would only give his Satyavati to him if...my prince, don't make me tell you."

Devavrata's eyes flashed in warning, and the charioteer said, "He would give his girl to your father only if her son became the Kuru king after him. And he would not budge from what he said, that coarse and ambitious fool."

The sarathy grew silent, fearing the yuvaraja's anger. For a moment Devavrata was still as a stone; then he began to laugh softly.

"Is that all?" he cried. "Is this what stands between my poor father and his happiness? That I am the yuvaraja?"

Devavrata seized the sarathy by his arm. "Take me to where my father's sorrow began, so I can mend it. Come, at once!"

Without telling the king, even perhaps as Shantanu had hoped, his son rode to the banks of the Yamuna. Arriving, Devavrata sprang lightly from the chariot and took the old sarathy with him for a witness.

A yojana before they came to the river, the unearthly fragrance swept over them. They saw Satyavati sitting where Shantanu had first seen her, and to be near the scent of her body was so intoxicating, even Devavrata felt his blood quicken.

Turning her head when she heard their chariot, she stared with black eyes at the visitors. For a moment she caught her breath: she thought Shantanu had returned, but a life younger and so handsome! Her eyes shone. Devavrata ignored her. The sarathy pointed out the fisherman's hut and the yuvaraja strode towards it.

The fisher-king had just finished his meal when Devavrata burst in on him. "I hear you were arrogant enough to refuse my father your daughter's hand. Were you in your senses, or were you drunk on jungle brew and thought you were dreaming?"

The man cringed, but slightly; Devavrata saw he was dealing with a brazen soul. The swarthy fellow was quite calm, as he said, "I did not refuse to give my daughter to your father. My daughter is my only child and she is all I have." He paused, crossed to the window and spat a stream of scarlet juice from the betel-leaf he was chewing. Lowering his voice, he confided, "She is no common girl, my prince. She was not always as lovely as you see her today; nor did she smell so fine. Once she smelled powerfully of fishes, so I called her Matsyagandhi. And I feared I would never find a husband for her even among our own people."

Devavrata listened impatiently. But his curiosity was roused by the tale of Matsyagandhi, who was born smelling of fish but smelt of paradise now. For fear of being thought a liar, the fisher-king did not tell him how he had found his daughter. He squinted at his royal visitor, and saw he had his attention. The wild man went on, "But one day when she was still a slip of a girl, barely sixteen, a rishi came this way wanting to cross the river in my boat. He was so illustrious, his face and his hair, and he looked so ancient that I doubted he was a man of this earth.

"I was at my lunch and Matsyagandhi ferried the muni across. It was a fine afternoon and the old man stared at my daughter with piercing eyes. If he were not a sage, I would not have let her go with him alone. When they reached midstream, near that island, (he pointed through the door to an island in the stream), suddenly lightning and thunder gashed the sky, and a blizzard of snow swept the river. It was the middle of summer, mind you. I called out to them. But the thunder was so loud they could not hear me, and I had to run back indoors.

"That snowstorm lasted two hours. I fell into a strange slumber full of dreams such as I had never had before. When I awoke my Matsyagandhi stood beside me and she was like someone who had stepped out of my dreams. Not that her face had been transformed altogether, but it had been changed subtly as if with a few perfect touches. And now my plain girl was a ravishing beauty.

"The other marvel was that her old smell of fish was gone. In its place was the scent of heaven you smell now, spreading from her for a yojana on every side."

He paused again and scrutinized Devavrata's face. The river man was as sharp as he was ambitious. Seeing how full of haughty nobility this poor prince was, the fisher-king was not about to let this great opportunity slip through his fingers.

Devavrata had heard him out in silence. He was happy for his smitten father's sake that the girl was not entirely common, but had been blessed by a holy rishi; though the yuvaraja did wonder about the real circumstances of that blessing.

Devavrata said again, "Say, fellow, what you want and I swear you shall have it."

Passing his tongue over his lips, the black man said softly, "Whatever I want?"

"Yes! But hurry, I am growing impatient."

The fisherman drew a breath to steady himself. "I already told your father my only condition. I want no gold or jewels for myself, or horses or palaces. I only want my daughter's son to be king after your father's time."

Devavrata stood staring at him. Losing his nerve the man said, "Of course your father would not agree. So I also could not give him my daughter. As I have told you…"

But Devavrata held up a hand to silence him. "Listen to me, fisherman. *I, Devavrata, yuvaraja of Hastinapura, relinquish all my claims to the throne of my ancestors.* Your daughter's son shall be the next king of the Kurus. Are you satisfied now?"

At first the fisher-king gaped in disbelief. These were the very words he had hoped, against hope, to hear. Then he saw from the prince's face that the boy meant what he had said. The fisherman let out a long, slow breath. Growing bolder, he said, "I see, Yuvaraja, that your father's happiness is more important to you than his kingdom. But I must make sure Satyavati will not just be made brief use of, for as long as her youth lasts, and then cast out. Kshatriyas like you and your father have been known to do worse to folk like us."

Devavrata recoiled from the resentment he saw in the man's eyes. He held his peace, thinking of Shantanu. The fisherman went on,

"Yuvaraja, you are indeed as noble as fortune has made it possible for you to be. I have no doubt that not even the fear of death will make you forswear yourself." He stopped, and leaned forward. Devavrata could smell his rancid breath. The fisher-king hissed, "But what about your sons, my prince? Will they be as generous as you are?"

Devavrata did not understand what the fellow meant; but he was not about to leave him in the dark for long. Stuffing some thick tobacco into his mouth, the fisherman continued, "Devavrata, you are a great kshatriya. I have heard there is no warrior like you in all Bharatavarsha. Your sons will inherit your prowess; while my grandchildren will also be a king's sons, surely, but a fisher-girl's as well. How do I know your princes will not kill my grandsons and take the throne for themselves? Answer me that and my daughter shall be your father's wife." He grinned, and said, "Though, for sure, your father is old for her," with a leer that Devavrata ignored.

Without a moment's pause, the prince replied, "If you give your daughter to my father, I will do more than renounce the throne of my ancestors. Come!"

He seized the surprised fisher-king's hand and pulled him out into the sun. Throwing back his head, the prince cried in a ringing voice, *"I, Devavrata, swear before all you Gods of heaven and earth, in the name of everything sacred to me, in the name of my guru Bhargava, of my mother Ganga and eternal dharma, that I will never marry but remain celibate all my life!"*

In that moment's resonant silence it seemed the elements, and those who are the elements' deities—sun, earth, wind, sky and river—all fell hushed at Devavrata's vow. Then they heard faint music in the sky, and fisherman and prince were covered in a fine rain of flowers of light. These vanished in a moment, but their fragrance dimmed even the dusky Satyavati's scent. And now a name resounded all around, from earth and sky, from river, trees and rocks, from invisible throats.

"Bheeshma!" chanted the unearthly voices, *"Bheeshma! Bheeshma!"*

Because his oath was so awesome, so terrible, the oath he would never break. For a while, the fisherman was dumbstruck. But he was a son of the forest and, recovering quickly, he beckoned to Satyavati. When she came up, innocent as the wilderness, her father said, "Here, my prince, is your new mother. Take her to the king."

Without another word, not even pausing to say farewell to his daughter, the fisherman turned back into his hut, as if some weighty matter awaited his attention inside. As indeed it did; but he would not have gone to it so impatiently if he had known what it was. That same night death came for the fisher-king, as if everything he had been born for was fulfilled; or as if losing his fragrant daughter broke his heart.

Bheeshma, as we will call Ganga's son from now, took Satyavati back to Hastinapura in his chariot. All the way home the old sarathy never stopped muttering his astonishment, and his disapproval, while his yuvaraja urged him to go faster: his father's joy must not be delayed. It was that charioteer who spread the word like fire through the city: about Devavrata's vow and how the Gods themselves had named him Bheeshma.

In the palace, the yuvaraja ran to the king's apartment. Bheeshma bowed to Shantanu, and cried, "Father, put away your sorrow. I have brought her for you."

Shantanu had expected something of the sort, if not so quickly. Rising, the king said, "Who have you brought?"

"Satyavati."

"But her father wouldn't give her to me, unless...what have you done, Devavrata?"

"I have only renounced the throne and my manhood: they are as nothing to give if they can buy your happiness, why, your very life. My lord, you will not live another month without her."

"Oh, my son!" Shantanu sat down heavily; the world spun around him and his legs were weak. When he heard of the bargain his prince had struck with the fisherman, the king's guilt threatened to overwhelm his excitement.

Tears in his eyes, Shantanu said, "You are noble, and dishonour would break your heart. Otherwise I would ask you to take her back to her father." The king took his son's hand, "You have always been more like the father and I like the son. But my shame will not change that, because you are strong like your mother, while I am only a weak mortal.

"Yes, I confess I love the fisher-girl. And now, knowing what you have done for my sake, I will enjoy her as well as I can."

Shantanu paused; a wan smile lit his face. "I too have the punya of my celibacy of twenty years. I bless you, my son, with this father's blessing: *let death come for you only when you call him yourself.* For what you have sacrificed for me, you shall choose the hour and the manner of your own dying."

And so Shantanu, king of the Kurus, married the fisher-girl Satyavati in Hastinapura, with pomp and ceremony, and some unkind whispering among his subjects who, despite her unworldly aroma, compared the new queen unfavourably with Ganga. Most of all, the people were heartsick to hear that Devavrata would never rule them.

But time heals almost any wound and the kingdom settled down to its new circumstances. Even if Bheeshma never actually sat on the throne of Hastinapura, he would be the virtual king for many years, until Satyavati's son came of age. And so it happened. Shantanu gave up most of his powers to his son and immersed himself in his young wife, who delighted him with her wild simplicity, her passionate nature and, of course, the heavenly scent of her dark body.

Two sons were born to Shantanu and Satyavati, and they were named Chitrangada and Vichitraveerya. Their half-brother Bheeshma doted on them; it was he who raised them. Shantanu was too old, and also too absorbed in his queen, to raise them himself; and after the children were weaned, Satyavati showed no maternal possessiveness. She was genuinely glad of the love the powerful Bheeshma lavished on her boys.

Shantanu's last few years were deeply happy ones. Surrounded by a close and loving family, it was as if near his end time repaid the old king for whatever fierce sadness she had inflicted on his earlier life. And so, at peace, Shantanu of the Kurus was gathered to his fathers.

Chitrangada, Shantanu's older son by Satyavati, was still too young to become king. Bheeshma ruled Hastinapura as regent, if in his younger brother's name: for he had Chitrangada installed as yuvaraja even before Shantanu died. The reign of Bheeshma, the uncrowned king of the Kurus, was a halcyon season for the kingdom. It was as nearly perfect a time as it could be in those last days of the dwapara yuga, when darkness gathered ominously over the world.

But as if fate herself resented the prosperity of those years and the harmony and affection between Satyavati, her sons and Bheeshma, tragedy struck with no warning at the very heart of the royal House of Hastinapura. And its agent was a being not of this earth.

SIX

Two princes

THERE WAS A GANDHARVA WHOSE NAME WAS ALSO CHITRANGADA. For reasons of destiny more inscrutable than we can unravel here, one day this immortal decided to appear at the gates of Hastinapura. Splendid he was, as if his body was full of light. He was taller than any human, unimaginably handsome, and his eyes deep and luminous. His blue-black hair hung below his shoulders and he seemed made more of the stuff of dreams than of flesh and blood.

Chitrangada the gandharva appeared out of thin air one morning outside Hastinapura and blew a sweet blast on the golden horn he carried at his waist. When the astonished guard asked who he was, he cried in his fine singing voice, which was thick with the wine the gandharvas drink, "I hear a mere mortal has stolen my name! The apsaras of Devaloka laugh at me. I hear he is a prince, the yuvaraja of your city. If he is a kshatriya, let him come out and fight me. Tell him that only one Chitrangada will live to see the sun set today."

Bheeshma was away from his capital, visiting remote corners of the kingdom. For his honour as a kshatriya the yuvaraja Chitrangada had to accept the drunken gandharva's challenge. It was a month before he was to be crowned king of the Kurus. Frightened and brave, curious because he had never seen a gandharva before, though he had heard wondrous tales of them, Satyavati's son came out to face Chitrangada of heaven.

The gandharva waited for his namesake, whistling like a tree-full of birds so a crowd gathered. The birds of the air flew down to the trees outside Hastinapura. They knew this was song such as their own wild songs were first made from: the music of the Gods. When the human Chitrangada came out of the city-gates, the Elf grew quiet. His hands on slim hips, he stood glaring at the youth that dared use his name.

In a moment, the gandharva began to laugh. Satyavati's son saw how tall and wonderful the immortal was, his hair shimmering and his face full of soft splendour. The gandharva challenged Chitrangada of the earth.

"Mortal! You dare take the name Chitrangada, whose meaning you cannot even know. I say you are guilty of theft worse than of gold or jewels, or even kingdom." His beautiful face turned dark. "I see you are just a boy, so I will give you a chance to save your life. Declare that you renounce the name Chitrangada, which has been mine for eons. Kneel before me and beg my pardon, and I will give it to you. If you like, I will even give you a new name you can bear through your brief human years.

"This is your only chance to save yourself. If you fight me, you will die. Then what use will my name be to you? The choice is yours, boy."

Satyavati's son's eyes turned the colour of plums. He said, "You must indeed have lived for eons, vain gandharva, that you have grown so tired of your life. I am Chitrangada, yuvaraja of Hastinapura, and I know of no other Chitrangada. If you want to fight me for the sake of my name, I think you are a fool and deserve to die."

Chitrangada of Hastinapura drew his sword. The people gathered there hardly saw what happened next; it happened with such blinding swiftness that mortal eyes could not follow it. They heard a growl, as musical as the rest of his speech; they saw the gandharva's hand streak to his side. Next instant, they saw their prince keel over clutching his neck that had been pierced by a silver dagger. The Elf whistled softly and his slender blade flew back to its jewelled sheath. The yuvaraja's life went out through the neat wound in his throat. In a flash of light the gandharva vanished, leaving Hastinapura bereft, her destiny transformed.

Bheeshma was heartbroken. He had loved Chitrangada as his own son. Carefully, since the boy's infancy, he had groomed him to sit one day on the throne of the Kurus. He had taught him archery and the Vedas, politics and history, astrology and metaphysics, and everything else the yuvaraja knew. They had been so close. Now all that was left, after Chitrangada's body was cremated beside the Ganga, was an urn of ashes. Wondering for what crime of another life he was being punished with such torment in this one, Bheeshma floated those ashes down his mother's serene currents, towards the ocean which receives the remains of the dead.

His dreams shattered, Bheeshma began all over again with Satyavati's second son, Vichitraveerya. Whereas so far he had brought him up only to become his brother's loyal minister, now he groomed that prince to be a king. Bheeshma crowned the younger boy yuvaraja and continued to rule Hastinapura himself.

Chitrangada's death had fallen on him like summer lightning; but in a few years, Vichitraveerya grew into a fine young kshatriya and Bheeshma crowned him king. Vichitraveerya was a modest youth who worshipped his brother, and it was in Bheeshma's able hands that the real power in the kingdom of the Kurus still rested. The people, Satyavati, and Vichitraveerya himself were all content with this arrangement. It would never do that a younger brother ruled while his older and wiser brother was alive.

Some years went by, in peace and plenty, and they were kind to Hastinapura and her people. Then Bheeshma decided it was time Vichitraveerya married. News arrived in Hastina that the king of Kasi was planning a swayamvara for his three daughters, Amba, Ambika and Ambalika, all of them reputed to be beautiful and accomplished. From time immemorial, indeed ever since the two kingdoms had existed, it had been the unvarying practice for the princesses of Kasi to be given as wives to the princes of Hastinapura. Never had there been any question of a swayamvara. The slight did not escape Bheeshma: Vichitraveerya was not being offered the hand of any of the Kasi princesses because he was a fisher-girl's son. But Bheeshma was not about to let the matter pass.

SEVEN

Three princesses of Kasi

THE CITY OF KASI WAS FESTIVE: MANIKARNIKA, THE ORNAMENT THAT once fell from Cosmic Siva's ear, to be his special place on earth. Kasi was decked in colourful archways; her streets were choking with a million garlands. Singing, dancing crowds swung through her aisles.

In the hall of the swayamvara, a thousand of the most eligible kings and princes of Bharatavarsha had gathered. Each one had come in the hope that one of the princesses of Kasi would choose him to be her husband. The jewellery those kshatriyas wore caught the shafts of the morning sun and the sabha glittered. Jasmine-laden air eddied softly around those high born masters of the earth. Their refined laughter could be heard there, tinged with some anxiety.

Amba, Ambika and Ambalika were all named after the Devi who is Siva's consort. Wearing wedding finery they sat haughty and ravishing beside their father. The custom was that when the auspicious muhurta arrived and the planets were in their most benign places, the palace priests, who were avid at their ghatikas, the water clocks, would announce the hour. Each princess would then be given a garland of wildflowers, which she would drape around the prince or king she chose. It was age-old custom that a princess could choose her own husband, her vara. This was why the ceremony was called a swayamvara, meaning literally 'her own husband'.

The moment had arrived and the oldest princess, Amba, had just been handed her garland. Suddenly they heard chariot-horses' hooves outside. Silence fell when they saw who had arrived: it was Devavrata of Hastinapura. Some kshatriyas in the sabha snickered, though none too near Bheeshma.

"Has the celibate found his celibacy unbearable?"

"Isn't he a little old for this?"

"Has he decided to break his oath?"

"Who can blame the poor man? These princesses could shake the vows of the rishis of the forest."

Someone shouted, "I think you've left it a little late, Devavrata. Your hair has turned grey!"

And loud laughter. Bheeshma's eyes glinted dangerously. With a soft growl that froze the assembly, he said, "I rather think I am just in time."

Amba stood unmoving before the groom of her choice, the king of Salva. She had raised her hands to place her garland around his neck when Bheeshma arrived. Next moment, Bheeshma was a flaming immortal in that sabha. When he was just a stripling Ganga's son had dammed her flow with golden arrows; now he was a grown man at the height of his powers.

He was among them like some invasion. One moment they were mocking him and Amba was about to garland the king she had chosen. Then Bheeshma had seized not only that dazed princess, but her sisters as well, and swept them into his chariot in a blur.

As he went, he cried, "They are for my brother Vichitraveerya. They shall be queens in Hastinapura like their mothers before them. Come and fight me, Kshatriyas, show me your mettle."

Those were days when honour meant more than life itself. A throng of kshatriyas flew after Bheeshma. For a while it seemed he would outrun them and escape. But then he whirled his chariot round. His bow was raised and it blazed arrows at his pursuers in a storm. Every shaft found its mark, shattering chariots, piercing armour, and blood leaked on to the earth.

But there was a king that one of the Kasi princesses had actually chosen, and Salva gave Bheeshma a ferocious fight. He struck him with three scathing shafts. Roaring in surprise the Kuru plucked them out, and his blood gushed after them. In a flash he cut down Salva's chariot and killed that king's horses and sarathy. Salva stood exposed, and Amba shut her eyes and prayed for his life. But Bheeshma did not intend to kill a defenceless man. Growling deep in his throat, like some lion, he swung his chariot around again and rode back to Hastinapura.

The people of the city came streaming out of their homes. They crowded into the streets to see what Bheeshma had brought back. They set up a cheer when they saw the three princesses in his chariot: bashful, but two of them so excited by the romance of having been abducted by the magnificent Kuru. They were flushed with the battle that had been fought for them; what more could any princess ask for on the day of her swayamvara?

When the people of Hastinapura welcomed them exuberantly, asking their names and calling them their queens, Ambika and Ambalika began to wave back to that sea of friendly faces. They felt thrilled to be called queens, and no sooner had they ridden into it, than they knew Hastinapura was the city of their destiny. But Amba kept her head bowed.

Bheeshma thundered up to the king's palace and leapt down from his chariot. The princesses followed him meekly. He strode straight to Satyavati's apartment and knocked on her door. When she opened it, she saw him standing there with a rare smile on his face. He said, "Mother, look what I have brought for you."

"What is it, Devavrata?"

He moved aside and she saw the princesses behind him. He cried, "Daughters-in-law! Three of them from Kasi."

As they came forward to touch her feet, Satyavati saw how beautiful they were. Bheeshma said to a guard, "Take word to the king that his mother wants to see him urgently."

Vichitraveerya arrived, and when he saw Amba, Ambika and Ambalika he fell at Bheeshma's feet. Bheeshma raised him up like a child and embraced him. The young king saw blood on his brother.

"You are wounded! Mother, quickly, fetch warm water and ointment."

Bheeshma protested that it was only a scratch, but the king would not listen. Luckily Bheeshma's armour had endured the brunt of Salva's arrows. Vichitraveerya dressed his brother's wounds with the herbs his mother's women brought. When he had finished, a quivering voice said, "I beg you, give me leave to speak."

It was Amba, the oldest princess. Bheeshma said, "Speak freely, child. Have no fear, this is your home now."

Mustering her courage, she said, "When the lord Bheeshma stormed into the swayamvara and took us, I was in the very act of placing my garland around King Salva's neck. With all my heart I had chosen him to be my husband."

"Why didn't you speak out?" said Bheeshma. "You did not say a word, not even when I was fighting Salva."

She whispered, "I was robbed of my courage. And before I breathed freely again, we had ridden to Hastinapura."

Now Vichitraveerya said firmly, "It isn't right that I marry her if she has given her heart to someone else."

Bheeshma was relieved; he had hoped his brother would not make this an issue of kshatriya honour. Satyavati also agreed. Gently, Bheeshma said to Amba, "If what you say is true, you must not remain here."

He clapped his hands for the guard.

"Arrange for the princess Amba to have a royal escort. Prepare my own chariot for her, and let her be driven at once to Salva."

Such a smile broke out on the lovely Amba's face that the others laughed. Blessing them all, blessing Hastinapura, seeking Satyavati's blessing herself, Amba mounted the chariot and drove away. Little did she realize how short-lived her joy was to be.

EIGHT

Bheeshma and Amba

A RADIANT AMBA ARRIVED IN SALVA'S KINGDOM. FLUSHED WITH THE thought of seeing him, of being his queen, she alighted before the palace. She ran up the steps and was shown, but after an hour's wait, into a solemn court hardly full of the welcome she had expected.

"My lord," she cried happily, "I have brought your garland. I told Bheeshma I had chosen you for my husband, and he sent me to you with a royal escort. Here I am, take me for your queen."

She was overjoyed to see him and waited for him to rise and take her hand. But he remained sunk in his throne. A spasm of contempt twitched his lean face; he gave a short laugh.

More for his court's benefit than hers, he said, "Do you think I am a beggar that I would take you as alms from my enemy? Bheeshma seized your hand and carried you from your swayamvara. If that was not enough, he routed the rest of us as a lion would a jackal-pack. By kshatriya dharma, princess, the man who wins a woman in battle has made her his own." His voice quivered and she knew he cared more that Bheeshma had defeated him, than for her or what she felt.

Salva said coldly, "Go back to Bheeshma, perhaps he will break his oath for you. Beg him and see if he will marry you. As for me, I have no place for the refuse of my enemies, neither in my palace nor in my heart."

Lovely Amba's face crumpled. Hanging her head, she whispered fiercely, "Not that you have a heart for me to find a place in it."

Amba stalked out of Salva's palace. She went back to Hastinapura and came to Bheeshma. Strands of white streaked her hair as if she had aged ten years on her journey. Bheeshma rose in concern, "Why have you returned so soon?"

She raised her tearful face to him. Through clenched teeth, she said, "Salva turned me away. Yet, he enriched my knowledge of dharma. He said a woman belongs to the man who wins her in battle: it is the law of the kshatriyas. You took me by my hand, defeated the other kings and carried me away. Salva says I belong to you and no one else."

She broke down. She knelt at Bheeshma's feet and sobbed, "I cannot go back to my father's house. I have nowhere to turn, except to you. Noble Bheeshma, don't abandon me, don't let my womanhood be desolated. Take me to be your wife."

As Bheeshma raised her up gently, he realized what he felt for Amba was not only pity. He wanted to take her in his arms and keep her there forever. But instead, he said, "How can I marry you, child? I am too old for you. Besides, I have sworn an oath that I will be celibate all my life. I had better die than marry you, because if I break my oath I will not be able to live with myself."

She stood before him, so vulnerable, and he could hardly bear to look at her. Kindly as he could, and he knew how cruelly to her, he continued, "If you had just said a word to me in Kasi I would have left you behind. But fate is inscrutable. She deceives us effortlessly, time and again: as if we learn nothing from all the lessons she teaches and our hearts never grow quiet enough to master our own destinies.

"Rather than wait for me to marry you, princess, go back to Salva. He may change his mind in time and take you for his queen. He may already have thought better of his rashness."

But she said, "You don't know his heart. How quick his anger was when I stood before him, and how cold his hatred. I thought I would die. And you want me to go back to that man and beg him to marry me? Never! And he would never do it. You are too kind, Devavrata, and full of such lofty wisdom." Her eyes flashed. "But you are not kind enough to break your oath and unfortunately your wisdom is of no use to me. You never hesitated when you abducted me. Why can't you use the same courage now to save my life?"

She moaned as if an arrow was lodged in her flesh. His heart churning, Bheeshma said, "My oath is not for myself. My dharma is far beyond my own selfishness, and more important than your life." His voice grew hard, when he thought of Vichitraveerya and the future of Hastinapura. He said grimly, "Forgive me for what has happened if you can. You may remain here in our city for the rest of your life and your every comfort will be seen to. But as for marrying you, Amba, that I cannot do."

Bheeshma turned and walked out before he imperilled his soul by looking into her face again. Amba wept long and bitterly. She lived in Hastinapura for six tormented years. She saw her sisters, Ambika and Ambalika, become Vichitraveerya's queens. And she, the first of them, was alone, unwanted.

After six years, thinking anything was preferable to the purgatory in which she lived, she went to Salva again. He was even more savage with her. He laughed; did she really expect him to marry the concubine of Hastinapura? Further deranged by his cruelty, Amba went back to the Kuru kingdom. Now she focused all her frustration on Bheeshma; she held him responsible for ruining her life.

And one day, unable to bear her life in that city any more, she walked out. Her long hair left loose, she came like a mad woman down the palace-steps, walked out into the open and down the king's highway, while the guards stared at her. She went in her finery, unaware of her surroundings, as if some implacable purpose more potent than the world drew her on. Never pausing, she went towards the forest she had passed through when she rode to Salva. Amba had not abandoned her battle to persuade Bheeshma to marry her; she had decided to enlist the support of the rishis of the jungle.

The holy ones were alarmed at her coming. She was beautiful and full of virgin womanhood. The older hermits feared she would distract the younger acolytes. They were about to turn her away when a grand old mendicant, whose voice echoed under the trees, arrived in that asrama. When Amba saw him she gave a cry and ran to fall at his feet. That ancient with the long white hair and beard, whose name was Hotravahana, raised her up and embraced her. She sobbed like a small child against his chest. He was her grandfather, and once a king of Kasi. In his last years, he had taken to the forest and a life of tapasya.

When she had wept for a while, and he comforted her, she grew calmer. He drew out her story in agonized fits and starts, from the day of the swayamvara. When Hotravahana saw how obsessed she was with

Devavrata, he knew Bheeshma and no other man was his granddaughter's deepest destiny. She would have been unhappy even if Salva had married her. She was a passionate girl, and once Bheeshma had taken her hand, she had belonged to him.

Hotravahana said, "There is only one person in the world to whom Bheeshma will listen. Curiously, he is due in this asrama in a few days."

Amba and the other rishis wondered who that person was. But Hotravahana said they must wait and see for themselves.

Now that her grandfather was there, Amba was allowed to remain in the asrama. A few days later there was some excitement in that hermitage and some novices ushered in an extraordinary figure. He was tall and great; he was old and youthful at once. His hair was like a lion's mane; his face was calm, yet reflected the deep tides that moved in his heart. He was so godlike you felt he could set aside his human form at any moment, like a set of clothes.

The eldest rishis rose and prostrated themselves before him. The visitor seemed especially glad to see Hotravahana and embraced him warmly. Her grandfather brought Amba to the profound one, "Guru Bhargava, this is my grand-daughter Amba. She has a grievance which only you can redress."

Bhargava laid a hand in blessing on the distraught Amba's head. She felt a current of grace flow through her body. For a moment, she was faint with joy, as if he had removed her pain by his very touch. But the relief did not last. Bhargava stared at her, his eyes misting over with whatever he read in her sad face. Puzzled, he continued to gaze disconcertingly.

At last, he sighed and said in his deep, slow voice, "Ah child, you are stricken with sorrow." He turned to Hotravahana, "But tell me, old friend, who is he that makes her so sad?"

Hotravahana told him Amba's story. Bhargava was visibly startled when he heard Devavrata Bheeshma's name and he listened in some absorption. When Hotravahana had finished, Bhargava stared at the princess even more intently. Again his eyes grew dim as if he saw distant times and events, all far from the present, but to him as real.

Suddenly, as if making up his mind, he said, "I will tell Bheeshma to marry you. And how will he refuse his guru? Let no time be lost, you have suffered long enough."

Bhargava sent a young rishi to Hastinapura to tell Bheeshma his master wanted to see him. Bheeshma came immediately to the forest. The regent of the Kurus prostrated himself at his guru's feet.

Laughing happily, blessing his most illustrious pupil, Bhargava enfolded Bheeshma in a great embrace.

"Devavrata, my child, let me look at you! It has been so long. I often ask your mother about you. But she says she hardly sees you herself any more, but only hears of you from rumours on the wind, and the news of birds and men who come to wash their sins in her.

"You have grown so much. Why, you have grown into a man, Devavrata, and not a young one any more."

"Master, why have you sent for me? Is there anything I can do?"

Bhargava watched his disciple's face thoughtfully. He said, "Hotravahana is an old and dear friend of mine. He has never asked me for a thing, until today."

Bheeshma said, "You know I will do whatever I can."

"Devavrata, it is a mere trifle."

"Tell me, Guru."

Bhargava signalled Amba to come forward. When he saw her, Bheeshma grew very still. Bhargava said, "I believe you know this young woman?"

Impassively, his sishya replied, "She is the unfortunate Amba, a princess of Kasi. She was to marry the king of Salva, but fate played her false and I was fate's instrument." Bheeshma raised his eyes and looked into his master's face. "Salva wouldn't take her for his wife and she came back to Hastinapura. But I could not marry her myself, because of the oath I swore for my father."

"What oath is that?"

"That I would never marry in this life."

"A grave oath," said Bhargava slowly. "But there is no oath that may not be broken for one's guru. I command you now, Devavrata, you shall marry this princess. And I see in your eyes how much you would like to make her your wife."

Bheeshma said in a low voice, "Don't ask me to do this. You know how solemn my oath is."

"Yes, all heaven speaks of it and all the earth too. But I have given my word to Hotravahana that you will marry Amba. Would you have me break my word, would you mock your guru?"

Bheeshma said levelly, "Ask me for my life and I will gladly give it to you. But don't ask me to break my oath. That I cannot do, even for your sake."

"By the timeless laws of guru and sishya, which have come down the ages, you leave me no choice. I must curse you." But he was torn between anger and love for his pupil. He added softly, "Or else, you must fight me."

"I will fight you."

For a long moment, Bhargava stared at his disciple. Then he turned abruptly and made for a clearing in the forest, some yojanas away. For no battle should be fought near an asrama where rishis live and pray for the world.

Forbidding the hermits to come after them, Bheeshma followed his master. Amba's very life felt faint within her. She was sure Bhargava would kill the man of her twisted destiny. Who could face the Avatara in battle? Strong woman though she was, she clung to Hotravahana, trembling to think she was the cause of this. But her anger gave her strength and she told herself she did not care if Bheeshma died. It was only fitting, after the ruin he had made of her life.

Deep in the jungle, master and disciple arrived in a green clearing. With no warning Bhargava turned, quick as light, and shot a calescent astra at Devavrata. It flashed at him like a streak of lightning. But the sishya had been well taught. In a blur, quicker than the astra's flight, he doused it with a shaft of his own, of water. All this took no more than a moment: they were both such bowmen.

Hardly had fire and water subsided when Bhargava loosed his second missile, now plain and cold. But it was a weapon of illusion and seemed to fly at Bheeshma as a thousand arrows; but only a single one was real, aimed at his heart. He had less than a moment to spot that shaft and cut it down. Bheeshma sliced the real arrow in two and the others vanished around it.

Now Bheeshma shot an incendiary agneyastra at Bhargava. Across the clearing, the guru had abandoned his human form and was a figure of white light, illumining the darkling trees. With a varunastra, his master extinguished Bheeshma's arrow of a hundred fires. The two archers stood panting with their effort of will.

They rested for only a moment. Then, invoking more mystic astras, each one more potent and complex than the last, they duelled in the jungle's heart. For days they fought, the awesome master and his tremendous disciple. The earth shook and the Devas came out in their sky-chariots to watch.

Someone else watched, as well, hidden behind a banyan tree that grew at the edge of the clearing. Amba had broken away from the rishis and her grandfather, and followed Bhargava and Bheeshma. She watched them now, her mad eyes blazing.

Their duel became the world to the two warriors. It became a reflection of their spirits, of life and death. They were entirely absorbed, as munis are by their dhyana; battle to those two was no less than worship. Forest and sky lit up with the flares of astras. Amba stood petrified behind her spreading tree. Like her, the Devas in their vimanas did not stir, but were breathless spectators above.

For a while it seemed neither archer would prevail. Then Bheeshma invoked the praswapastra. That weapon would fuse the apocalyptic fires hidden within the most infinitesimal particles; it would consume the very earth.

Bheeshma drew his bowstring back to discharge the astra at his master. But two other figures appeared between the bowmen. Midnight was brilliant, as if day had dawned. The Devas put aside cloud coverings, drew back the veils of heaven and revealed themselves. The sky was full of shining craft and stern Gods who are beyond the understanding of men.

One of the splendourous ones who stood between Bhargava and his pupil was Rudra, tall as a tree. His skin was white; dreadlocks hung to his shoulders, with a moon-sliver hiding among them. His throat was blue, where he had once quaffed smoking poison, and emerald cobras twined themselves around his attenuated body. Beside him was Narada, the eternal wanderer, Brahma's son, old as the stars are.

In his voice deeper than the sky, Rudra said, "Stop, Devavrata of the dreadful vow! It is not written that you shall be the one to end this age. That time has not yet come, and the task belongs to another."

Bheeshma stood frozen. He did not hear Rudra, only waited for his hand to be free to loose the astra at his guru. Narada went near Bheeshma and spoke softly to him, calling him back to the world he was set to burn.

Slowly Bheeshma's breathing grew calmer, his knotted body relaxed. With a sigh, Devavrata remembered himself and lowered his bow. Vast relief surged through heaven and earth.

Rudra said to him, "You are the sishya, you must withdraw first."

Bheeshma bowed. He went up to the smouldering Bhargava. He laid his bow and his quiver at his feet, and knelt before his guru. Bhargava raised his pupil up and embraced him, crying, "My son, you are Bheeshma indeed! Even I could not vanquish you. My heart is full today, that I have such a sishya."

Bhargava cried across the clearing to Amba in the trees, "This man will give up his life, he will consume the world; but he will not break his oath. Princess, Devavrata will never marry you."

Amba gave a shuddering howl as of a wild creature shot with an arrow. She turned and ran from that place like a dark wind.

NINE

Amba

Running, sobbing as she ran, she hardly knew herself any more as she went. She stopped at times and bayed at the stars in the night sky like a she-wolf that had lost her mate. All she knew was the fire in her soul for revenge, consuming her. Bheeshma may be the greatest kshatriya on earth; but he had ruined her and he must pay for it with his life.

In the heart of a forest, where not even rishis ventured, she sat under a gnarled tree and began to pray. For a year she sat, unmoving, her body fed by just her hatred, worshipping Siva's son Karttikeya. Dirt caked her face and her hair hung to her waist in tangled jata. Her tapasya was so perfect that Karttikeya appeared before her sooner than he ever had for any other bhakta.

One day, a marvellous aroma filled the forest in which Amba sat in padmasana, the lotus-posture. The darkness she had grown accustomed to behind her eyelids shut fast was lit up like day. Her eyes flew open, and there he stood: the lucific Lord Karttikeya. In his hands, he had a garland of lotuses that were from no lake on earth. They glowed as if moonlight was hidden in them, and their scent spread through the forest like a blessing.

Amba fell on her face before the vision. She began to speak, "Lord..."

But he said gently to her, "I know, my child. I know everything and I know the boon you want. Look, I have brought you lotuses from a pool in my own garden. Whoever wears this garland around his neck will kill Bheeshma for you."

With a moan, she reached out and took the garland from him. The God vanished, leaving the trees dark once more. On her careen out of the forest, Amba bathed in a stream. Peering into the water when she was clean, she saw her penance had aged her.

Full of hope, she emerged from the jungle and went seeking her champion. She wandered into many kingdoms, and told her story to their princes and kings. In her hands was the fateful garland, which seemed to grow fresher every day. Those who heard her tale were not averse to fighting her cause. She was obviously noble and still very beautiful. But when she told them who it was they must kill when they wore her garland, they all refused her in alarm. Most of them dare not face Bheeshma in battle, and those who were bold enough would not. They said he was honourable and taintless; they would sin if they killed him.

Cursing them all, calling them cowards and eunuchs, she would storm away. Her lotuses remained as fresh as they had been when she received them, but her hope faded within her.

At last, almost broken in spirit, Amba arrived in the kingdom of the Panchalas, in Drupada's court. Once more, she told her story. She showed that king the garland that no kshatriya in Bharatavarsha dared take from her.

Strangely moved, Drupada heard her out patiently. But then, he also said to Amba, "Bheeshma of Hastinapura is a righteous man, I cannot fight him."

Her face twitched in rage. With a scream, she flung Karttikeya's garland at Drupada. But as if plucked up by an unseen hand, it flew away from him and landed around a marble pillar. Her howl of frustration echoing behind her, Amba stormed out.

Drupada held the garland that hung on the white pillar in awe and fear; not he, not anyone in his court ever touched it. They lit lamps before it and worshipped it at every sandhya of each day. That garland hung there, never fading, as fragrant as it had been when Amba first received it. It hung waiting for the kshatriya who would dare take it up and wear it.

Across wild plains, through mysterious forests, fording sacred rivers, and hardly aware of any of these, went Amba. Her face was set in a mask. Her eyes stared straight ahead, seeing nothing around her. She came to the foothills of the highest mountains in the world—the Himalayas, which are said to be the threshold between heaven and earth. Unworldly beings, elven gandharvas, centaurian kinnaras, knowing siddhas and charanas lived here. They renewed themselves upon the Himalaya, because these are the holiest mountains in creation.

Rishis also, hermits in solemn numbers, lived on the mystic slopes of the Himalaya. Some were lost in sweet oblivion, adrift on the ocean of the spirit that welled in their hearts. Others mortified their bodies in streams that carried ice floes down to the melting plains. They sat motionless, entranced in dhyana. Past them all, whether they were solitary or congregated in asramas, climbed Amba. She did not pause to greet them; perhaps she did not see them at all for the single flame that consumed her.

Up she went through the wooded foothills, crossing biting rillets. She climbed over the sheerest faces of rock and ice, which nimble kinnaras would have shunned for being too hazardous. Through breathtaking gorges, hidden in the naves of towering ranges, she climbed on and on, like a spirit who had lost her way in eternity.

Magical sunrises and sunsets lit the landscapes around her in reverberant colours, and her tiny form as she went along, at times crawling on all fours through sculpted snowdrifts. She had no eyes for their incomparable beauty; locked into her obsession, she plunged blindly on. At night unparalleled moons bathed her in ethereal lustre. Some nights, just the stars, seeming like small moons themselves at this height, shone down in distant kindness. But she hardly noticed that they sought to comfort her with their subtle influences.

On she went, while knots of sapphire-eyed kimpurusha fauns and their oread mates stepped out of caves embedded in the ice-faces of deep valleys and paused their pale orgies to stare at her. Grave siddhas heard her footfalls pass them, where they sat in meditation, often covered entirely by snow. Snowflakes fell off their eyelids as they blinked at the human princess. For princess she so obviously was who climbed along this secret way with darkness filling her heart to bursting. Once a young gandharva Elf whistled hopefully to her, his mellifluous note echoing off glassy slopes. But Amba did not hear him.

She went grimly past five mountains, one of them a secret, golden pyramid. She ate just wild berries on her white way. At last, she crossed the Himalaya and arrived at a solitary massif that thrust its peak at the sky to the north of the great range. Seeing that most sacred of all mountains, Amba's eyes softened. The lone mountain was her destination; here she hoped to find the redress she had not found anywhere else. She lay on her face in the snow and worshipped Kailasa, looming like a full moon before her. She called out, in agony and devotion, to the master of that mountain: Siva, Lord of Gods.

She climbed halfway to the summit of Kailasa and she was exhausted now. She made her home in a shallow cave, and began a tapasya fiercer than her penance in the forest. This one lasted years.

One day, when spring flushed on ice-bound Kailasa after a savage winter, Amba felt impelled to open her eyes that had seen nothing for a year but the inner spaces. There, in glory and in an eternal hermit's guise, stood Siva the Mahayogin. He smiled at her, while the emerald cobras he wore as ornaments on his ash-coated body twined around him.

With a sigh, Amba prostrated herself at the Lord's feet. Smiling, Siva said, "Stop your tapasya, my child, or you will melt all the snow on Kailasa! I have come to bless you with what your heart desires, and I see it wants just one thing."

Amba cried, "Who will kill Bheeshma?"

His eyes, which had seen the constellations begin, twinkled at her. "Why, you yourself, Amba, for nothing would please you more."

"I, my Lord? But I am no kshatriya, certainly not one to match Bheeshma."

"Not as you are in this life, but as you shall be in your next one."

She was dismayed. "But I will not remember anything of this life. What sweetness will revenge have if I don't know what it is for?"

But Siva, whose power turns the nebulae on their axes, replied, "But you will, Amba. You will remember every bit of this life, as clearly as if there was no break of death between it and the one to come."

Her cry of joy rang among precipices, and she fell to kissing his feet. She was light as a bird, when Siva had blessed her.

"Lord, where will I be born when I am dead?"

"Where a garland of lotuses hangs, waiting for you."

He melted out of her sight, leaving just the ineffable memory of his presence, and his boon. Feverish Amba built herself a pyre from dry branches. She kindled it with a twig she set alight with the power of her mind. With no thought for the pain of the flames, or of the deep passage of death, only pausing to murmur Siva's name, she walked into the blaze and was turned into ashes. They were redolent with her long austerity.

By Siva's grace, Amba was born again with no lease of time. Her spirit may have, otherwise, been condemned to a longer wandering in some realm of the dead; now it flitted through Yama's labyrinths like a bright swallow that knew its way through these mandalas. The flame of her purpose still searing her soul, she was born as the daughter of King Drupada of the Panchalas. She was born amidst celebrations in that kingdom and her father named her Shikhandin.

She was so thin as a child: as if she had been pared by some great rigour of another life. But her spirit was fierce and bold, more a male child's spirit. Her doting father would look at his daughter's intense face, with its dark burden behind her eyes, and he would think, 'Her expression is so familiar.' But, of course, he could not remember where he had seen her before.

One day, when she was just seven, her father brought Shikhandin into his court for the first time. She played quietly in the capacious sabha for a while. Suddenly the young princess saw the garland of lotuses that hung on a marble pillar, with incense and offerings set before it. She darted away from a group of indulgent courtiers and ran to that garland. Her eyes shone. Folding her small hands briefly to the fragrant thing, she plucked it off the pillar and draped it round her neck.

Drupada sprang to his feet. He shouted at his courtiers, "Fools! Couldn't you have stopped her? Shikhandin, put that garland back, it is not for children to play with."

But his daughter had grown very still. She had shut her eyes in some secret rapture when she draped the garland around herself. Now she opened them and her father was startled by what he saw there: such an adult look of triumph. Her sharp chin lifted up, she stared back at him. In the voice of Amba of old, Shikhandin said, "Drupada, I have been born as your daughter only to wear this garland."

A memory flared up in the king's mind—of a beautiful woman who years ago had spoken to him in that same voice. He dismissed the similarity as coincidence; but it would return to haunt him. Especially in his dreams, the tense, pale face of Amba, princess of Kasi, would coalesce with his daughter's; and the eyes were the same, burning with their single purpose.

Once she had put it on, Shikhandin refused to be parted for a moment from Karttikeya's garland. Drupada was unnerved by his dreams and at the thought of Bheeshma's wrath. Finally, the king grew convinced Shikhandin really was Amba and had returned just to seek the revenge she was obsessed with. When she reached puberty, her father turned the princess out into exile.

She went cheerfully, her precious garland around her neck, as if exile was a welcome step on her way to her only goal: Bheeshma's death. She retraced her steps of many years ago. As Shikhandin, Amba went back into the plumbless forest. The jungle probed her strange destiny with subtle feelers of flower and leaf, green vapours, animal eyes and intuition: all of which perceive time so differently from human senses. In its deep stillness, the forest had known she would return. Here Karttikeya had given her the garland she now wore as if it were part of her body. She sat in the same spot where Amba had once sat, so disturbed. Locked in padmasana, facing the east, she shut her eyes. Wrapped in the caress of the unearthly lotuses, she chanted Siva's holy name, ceaselessly, and his son Karttikeya's. The years slipped by, unnoticed. She was waiting for a sign, another boon.

One day, a yaksha of the race of tree-spirits, who pass through the twilights of the days between flesh and fleshlessness, was snared in a woodsman's trap close to where Shikhandin sat in tapasya. She was returning from her evening bath in the nearby stream, when she heard his subliminal cries echoing in the ethereal zone between day and night. Coming to that panicstricken being's help, she freed him with a mantra.

The grateful yaksha stayed with her until dawn, when he could slip back into his other world through a crack in the legends of leaves and birds, between darkness and light. That night she told him the story of her two lives. The wild being, with leaf-skin and bright bird's-eyes, was moved. He thought, surely, the hand of fate had snared him in the woodsman's trap.

The yaksha said in his uncanny voice, "I have a boon for you, if you want it."

Sensing a blessing from Siva, who is the Lord of the yakshas, Shikhandin readily agreed. An hour before dawn, in the night's last yaama, with just a touch of his green fantastic fingers the yaksha transformed Shikhandin into a man. Amba, princess of Kasi, lost her womanhood and the princess Shikhandin became prince Shikhandi of the Panchalas.*

And it came to pass that one day, years later, Shikhandi rode before Arjuna's chariot in the war on the crack of the ages, the Mahabharata yuddha on the field of Kurukshetra. Coming face to face with great Bheeshma, that prince cut him down with the first arrow that pierced him. Bheeshma knew Shikhandi had once been Amba of Kasi, the woman he loved. He would not raise his bow even to defend himself against her. This was the only way that invincible kshatriya could be killed, and the war would be lost if he did not die.

As he fell, shot with a hundred shafts, Bheeshma said, "Ah, these are all Arjuna's arrows."

Then he found the deepest one, lodged next to his heart. Feeling it gingerly, he breathed, "This one is Amba's."

When the sun turned north again, it was through that wound his spirit left his body and Ganga's son was free.

---

* Another story is that Sthunakarna, the yaksha, exchanges his own sex with Shikhandin, becoming female himself.

TEN

The solemn oath

KING VICHITRAVEERYA OF HASTINAPURA WAS PERFECTLY CONTENT to allow his half-brother Bheeshma to rule the Kuru kingdom, while he himself remained absorbed in his young wives Ambika and Ambalika.

It was a blessed time for them all. Satyavati was happy, and Bheeshma at doing what he did best—ruling ably. And of course, the king was more than happy. Day after day, you could hear him laugh with his queens in their royal apartment. The three of them would lie together long after the sun had risen, long after the moon had set, tenderly entwined. Or they would be out walking in their gardens, or hunting in the forest even as Shantanu once used to. Vichitraveerya was a poet and a musician. He composed and sang so beautifully the people of Hastinapura said their king was surely a gandharva minstrel born among them as a man.

But fate is seldom content to allow such earthly happiness to endure; and when only a few of those golden years had passed, she struck again at the heart of the Kuru kingdom. Vichitraveerya contracted a virulent consumption and died when he was hardly more than a youth.

For a black month Satyavati took to her bed and would see no one, not even Bheeshma. She lay without eating or drinking, and with grief devouring her. She entertained thoughts of taking her own life. But the truth was, that over the years, the fisherman's daughter had become too much of a queen to give up courage.

In her solitary mourning, she recovered from the first tremors of the tragedy. To her own surprise, Satyavati realized what disturbed her, most of all, was that Hastinapura had no heir. Vichitraveerya had died before he made a mother of either of his wives.

Rising at the end of a month, the fragrance of her body faded with sorrow, Satyavati called for some warm water. She bathed and dressed herself in crisp, fresh clothes. When she had eaten enough to give her strength to speak, she sent for Bheeshma.

His face lined and old—he also felt he had lost another son—Bheeshma came and stood silently before his stepmother.

She took his powerful hand in both hers. "Devavrata, all this is because of my father's greed. And of what use has your vow been? Even while they lived, my sons preferred to let you rule." She choked, "No one has ever prospered at the cost of another's misery. And in all time no one shall, though they may deceive themselves briefly that they do."

Bheeshma pressed her hand consolingly. Kneeling beside her, he said softly, "Mother I am not miserable. My life is a full and rich one. Only the grief of my brother's death savages me. But for the sake of the kingdom I must be calm and that pain will also pass."

He saw her eyes glowed in the falling darkness. Her tears had stopped, and she said to him, "And after your time, Bheeshma? Who will rule this kingdom after you? What will become of the people, their children and grandchildren? The unborn generations. Have you thought of that, Devavrata?"

She paused, then said, "The Kuru lineage must not perish for the sake of an oath sworn to a dead man." He knew what she was leading up to. Clasping his hand tighter, she went on feverishly, "It is time the Gods were appeased with justice in Hastinapura, before they visit us with more punishment. I have decided what must be done, and you must not refuse me. What I ask is only dharma."

"What do you want from me, mother?"

A smile trembled on her face. Her body's fragrance rose again, at the very thought of the justice she was going to see done. "Ambika and Ambalika are so young and their nature's needs are unfulfilled. You are Vichitraveerya's brother. You must make his widows your wives and the mothers of the future scions of the House of Kuru. You must do this for the sake of your ancestors, to preserve this line come down from Soma Deva. It is your dharma and your oath means nothing, anyway, after Vichitraveerya's death."

She stopped and waited for his answer. After a brief silence, during which he still stroked her hand, he said, "You are not yourself, mother. How can you ask me to marry my brother's wives, when I have sworn no woman will have any place in my life? You are unhinged with grief, or you wouldn't ask me this."

A sob shook her, and she let him hear it. "Chitrangada and Vichitraveerya are dead! What use is your oath any more? Can't you see the Gods are trying to tell us that it is you and your sons who must inherit the throne of Hastinapura? Devavrata, you must not let the line of Kuru die."

A tide of memory rose in Bheeshma's mind, in flashing clarity. He saw a thousand moments of his childhood with his mother Ganga. He saw her, he touched her; he smelt her sweetness, as if it were all happening again. He saw himself, a stripling, learning the Vedas and Vedangas from Brihaspati, and archery and politics from Bhargava. He heard his mother's voice telling him, "Learn well, my son, because you must be the greatest king who ever sat upon the Kuru throne."

The fine tide turned another bend in the maze of memory. He saw the times he spent with Shantanu: those perfect four years, before his father met Satyavati. He clearly saw the fateful day of his own visit to the fisher-king's hut beside the Yamuna: the day of his vow. And then, a brief darkness, before the clearest of all the memories rose.

Bheeshma saw Amba's face. He heard her begging him, not once but a hundred times, to marry her; and he heard himself refusing her again and again. Bheeshma knew why those last images roiled him. Deep inside himself, locked away safely out of harm's way, there nestled the secret that he loved her: that still his dreams were often of Amba.

Tears stung Bheeshma's eyes. The fisherwoman before him, for whose sake he had sacrificed his manhood, actually expected him to break his oath just because she asked him. When he had been prepared to kill his guru for that oath. And why? Because his master had asked him to marry the woman his soul cried out for! Bheeshma turned on his stepmother. His voice was quiet, but it was cold and haughty now.

"You don't begin to know me," he said, with contempt, "or what my dharma is. But then, how could you? Let me make this clear once and for all, so I never have to repeat myself."

She shivered at his tone. He drew a breath, and went on, "The earth may lose her fragrance, water its sweetness, the sun may lose his lustre, or the moon his enchanted coolness; Lord Dharma of the Devas may abandon the truth, but Bheeshma will never break his oath.

"My oath is everything I live by. That day at your father's hut my life changed forever. My oath is my truth, and truth for me is greater than all the anticipated rewards of heaven."

He was still speaking quietly; but if Bheeshma could rave, this was his raving. "Mother, please give up this foolishness, and think of a less absurd solution."

He turned and walked out of her room.

ELEVEN

Satyavati's other son

SATYAVATI DID NOT GIVE UP HOPE. WHEN SHE EMERGED FROM THE seclusion of mourning Vichitraveerya, she would at times summon the courage to speak to Bheeshma about an heir for Hastinapura. He was always busy with pressing affairs of the kingdom, and most often contrived to avoid her.

Yet, now and then, she did manage to waylay him along one of the interminable passages of the palace. And her eyes full of tears, she would implore him again. But Bheeshma was adamant. Other nobles of the sabha, those that dared, began to broach the subject, delicately, of an heir for the Kuru throne. In the streets, the common people began to ask what he had done to ensure the kingdom had an heir.

Early one morning, as the sun was rising and the birds all sang, Bheeshma was returning to the palace from the bathing-tank, when Satyavati accosted him yet again. Today he did not avoid her, but said with a smile, "I think I have the cure for your anxiety. When I rode out to hunt yesterday, I met a rishi in the forest and he reminded me of a custom we had all forgotten."

Her eyes lit up, "What is it, my son? Will you relent?"

The smile on his craggy face grew wider. "When a royal line is in danger of becoming extinct, ancient custom allows that a brahmana may be called in to father sons on the women of the threatened house. If you can think of a worthy brahmana, mother, your fears can be laid to rest."

Satyavati cried out as if he had stabbed her. Her eyes grew blurry and she ran from him, trembling with outrage. He stood staring curiously after her; she would always remain an enigma.

Came evening and Bheeshma, regent of the Kurus, was summoned to the queen mother Satyavati's chambers. Waving away her maids, she received him alone. Making him sit beside her, she said, "I have something to confess to you, Devavrata."

He saw the struggle in her eyes. Gently he said, "If it is so hard to tell, let it be, mother."

He rose to leave, but she took his hand. And once she managed to begin, it came tumbling out of her: her old secret. It was the tale of the Rishi Parashara and how, long ago beside the midnight-blue Yamuna, he had taken a mad fancy to a slip of a girl who smelled, in those days, not of heaven but of fish.

She stammered, she flushed and kept her face turned from him. But she managed to tell her story, ending with how Parashara blessed her. She had her virginity back, kept the new fragrance of her body and she bore a rishi for a son: Vyasa the poet, who was born on an island in the river as soon as she conceived him. He was full-grown in moments and illumined, and said to her, "Mother, our paths lead away from each other. But if ever you need me, just think of me and I will appear before you."

And he had wandered out of her life.

When Satyavati finished her story, she sat shyly before Bheeshma, her eyes turned from him. She knew how much he had sacrificed for her sake and feared his anger when he discovered his father had not been the first man in her life. But then, Bheeshma had always suspected the truth.

After a moment's silence, he took her hand kindly. When she saw he was not angry, she burst out with, "Devavrata, if you really meant what you said to me this morning, I will call my son Vyasa to sire the heirs of Kuru on Ambika and Ambalika."

Bheeshma greeted this imperturbably. "So be it, mother. I am adamant and, after all, the Muni Vyasa is your son. Summon him if the queens are ready to receive him."

When Bheeshma left her apartment, Satyavati chanted the mantra her first child had given her, a life ago, on the island in the stream.

Hardly had she said, "Vyasa my son, I have need of you," than a spirit light appeared in that chamber. As it grew brighter, a figure became plain at its core, dark as moonless nights, wild as forest's hearts, his beard and matted jata hanging coppery to his waist. His eyes smouldered and he looked altogether fierce.

He bent at her feet to take his mother's blessing. He embraced her and said affectionately, "How wonderful to see you again! But surely, you have thought of me today for some other reason besides a mother's love?"

Satyavati told him about her life in Hastinapura. He listened gravely, never interrupting. Finally, she came out with what she wanted from him. She said that, being a brahmana and also Vichitraveerya's brother, he was the one she had chosen to beget the Kuru heirs on Ambika and Ambalika.

For just a moment, Vyasa shut his heavy eyes in dhyana. Opening them, he said, "Why, it is the very least I can do for you who gave me life. But I have seen your daughters-in-law in my mind and, mother, they are so young. Hadn't you better speak to Ambika and Ambalika first? Their husband was a handsome youth, and I..." he smiled, and did not finish.

"I will speak to them at once."

She did not give him a moment to change his mind, but hurried away to Ambika's apartment, where that queen lay in mourning still, like a wilted lotus.

Satyavati dismissed the maids. In a fair delirium of hope by now, she explained her mission to the young widow. She brought tears to the girl's eyes. The shock of Vichitraveerya's death still lay on Ambika like a shadow, but Satyavati was in no mood to let her refuse what she asked.

"Just one night," she told her daughter-in-law firmly. "And remember he is a great rishi, so make him welcome."

Ambika sobbed. But what was being asked of her was her dharma. Besides, she was not being asked, but told: because the future of the House of Kuru was in her hands. As she went out, Satyavati turned at the door, "By the way, he is a little fierce-looking, but he is a gentle soul."

TWELVE

The blind night and the pale one

AMBIKA WAITED FOR THE STRANGER TO COME TO HER APARTMENT. Evening arrived; the world outside her window grew dark. Her maids came in and lit the lamps. Ambika grew increasingly dismayed at what she had to do. She crossed to the long mirror on the wall and examined herself in it: an old habit, would the strange man be pleased with her? Her fair body was boyish, with its small high breasts and lean satin flanks. She was not yet seventeen.

Came night and the soft dreaded knock at her door. Her hands clammy, Ambika went to answer it. Despite her wildest apprehensions, she was unprepared for the appearance of the man who stood in the passage. His coppery beard obscured most of his long face. He was jet black, his eyes were deep and so intense, and his manner altogether untamed. A whimper escaped her when she saw him standing there, tall and grim, from a savage world out there, full of dark jungles, wolves that bayed a shining moon, tigers that were evil spirits and hermits who flew ominously through the air. From the first moment she saw Vyasa, poor Ambika was lost.

She was so terrified she could barely wash his feet in the silver trough to welcome him, as she must. Her hands shook and she could not look up at his face. Yet when she thought about that night later, when she was alone, she remembered Vyasa had been patient with her. He was a far cry from the irascible rishi who took umbrage at the slightest fault and cursed one to be born as an insect or a snake in one's next life. Indeed, when she looked back calmly, she felt he had been full of a deep good humour.

But that night itself was a calamity, and it was only because of him they managed to get through what they had come together for.

She remembered later that he did not speak much; but when he did, his voice was soft and kind. Somehow, she did wash his fine feet, almost dropping the water for the wretched shaking of her hands. With a wry smile, a flash of white against his night-black skin, he took the silver pitcher from her and set it on a table. He took one of her small hands in his knotty one, calloused by his life in the wilderness, so full of grace.

Vyasa's was a reverberant presence, after the only other man she had known, the elegant Vichitraveerya. She found his stranger's touch overwhelming and the blood rose dizzily to her head. She longed to put out the lamps that burned in the room and were reflected in his deep eyes. But she lacked the courage. With not a word exchanged between them, he led her to the bed, gently but with an eerie detachment. How different, how unthreatening, love had been with Vichitraveerya. Through her tumult, she had sense of a part of Vyasa watching himself in this obviously unaccustomed role, and smiling inwardly.

But he was adroit when he peeled her clothes away from her slender body. With a quick sigh to see her naked, he lifted her easily on to the bed. He stroked her pale breasts. Ambika shut her eyes tightly from fear, and from something else as well: an excitement so yawning she would not admit to herself what it was.

She teetered between a dream and the reality of him, darkly potent above her, inside her. She felt his rough beard against her cheek, as he nuzzled her in deep tenderness. She clawed his back each time the swell crested in her head in a white flash. But though he loved her all night, with his rishi's great control and virility, not once did she open her eyes to look into his face.

Only when dawn flushed on the world, Vyasa spent himself into Ambika's body in a warm cloud streaked with lightning: the golden seeds of life. She lay in a swoon. He rose from her bed and, dressing himself, went out from her apartment.

Satyavati could not contain her excitement when Vyasa arrived in her chambers. She clutched his hand and cried with a fisher-woman's curiosity, "How was the night? Did you succeed?"

He said quietly, "Ambika will have a powerful son. The night was perfect, except for one thing."

She was anxious, "What was that?"

He grunted, "She was frightened and never opened her eyes to look at me."

"And?"

"Your grandson will be born blind."

She felt faint; she cursed the stupid girl. Sighing at her fate, Satyavati said, "Be comfortable here. I will take you to Ambalika tonight. She is a bolder child than Ambika; you will have no trouble with her."

Vyasa settled himself on the floor of the opulent room. He shut his eyes and began to meditate. Satyavati went to prepare Ambalika to receive Vyasa. She said to her younger daughter-in-law, "Your sister had her eyes shut all night, like the spoilt princess she is, and her son will be born blind. Don't you do anything so foolish."

Then she went off to give Ambika a piece of her mind. What did she think: that being with a rishi was like sleeping with a boy like Vichitraveerya? After all, Satyavati did know a thing or two about rishis and their love. She had not shut her eyes out on the island with Parashara. But she had been raised on the banks of a river, a child of nature; not a pampered princess in a palace.

Late that evening, there was a knock at Vichitraveerya's younger widow's door. Braver than her sister, and rather excited at the prospect of spending the night with another man, she opened it. Unlike Ambika, Ambalika had very little imagination; she had not worked herself up at all. But when that queen, who was barely sixteen, saw Vyasa in the passage she turned pale. She had never seen anyone as fearful as the black stranger who stood at her door.

Her excitement vanished; her gumption was gone. For fear of having a blind child, she managed to keep her eyes screwed open. Why, she managed to look at the rishi's face and to keep her voice steady, as she asked him in. But with each moment she spent with him, poor Ambalika grew paler and paler.

The way Vyasa made love to Ambalika was as direct as it had been with Ambika. He wasted little time and fewer words, before he drew the brave princess to him and plucked away her clothes. He picked her up and laid her on the bed. Though she was younger than her sister, her body was more rounded and womanly. She kept her eyes open; she even managed a smile.

But when he came to her, in a feverish mixture of fright and lust Ambalika turned white as a sheet. And so she remained all through the night. Because he had spent some of his passion on her sister, Vyasa was gentler with Ambalika. His lovemaking was slow and languorous. But while her body responded helplessly, some part of her mind could never reconcile itself to him. She remained blanched all night; though she never shut her eyes, not even in pleasure.

In the morning, Vyasa returned to his mother, waiting eagerly to hear his news. He said, "A handsome and bold boy will be born to your younger daughter-in-law. But he too shall have a defect."

"Why?" she cried.

"Ambalika didn't shut her eyes, though she wanted to. But she was so afraid she turned the colour of moonlight. Your grandson will be born as pale as his mother was when I was with her."

Satyavati groaned. Ah, these foolish girls, had they been taught nothing about life? She clasped her son's hand, and implored him, "You mustn't be angry with them, they are just children. I have another favour to ask you. After these two princes are born, you must come back again. You must go to Ambika once more. She will be a mother by then, and mature. You must give me your word."

Laughing, he gave it and went back into the wild world from where he had come.

In course of time, and a day apart, sons were born to the widowed queens of Hastinapura. Just as Vyasa had predicted, Ambika's son was a large and powerful infant; but he was born sightless. At his father's instance, the blind prince was called Dhritarashtra. The day after Dhritarashtra, an elegant, quiet son was born to Ambalika. There was no rich pigment in his skin: he was an albino. He was also given a name his father had chosen. He was called Pandu.

Using the mantra he had given her, Satyavati called Vyasa again and he appeared before her. She showed him his sons and how they were exactly as he had said, one blind and the other white. The rishi blessed the two children. But he showed no attachment for them: they might have been anyone's sons. He said, "Tell me why you called me, mother."

"I want you to spend another night with Ambika. I want a grandchild who is whole in all his parts. I had two sons and both died. If there had been a third one to rule Hastinapura, I wouldn't have to trouble you like this."

Vyasa said. "Prepare your daughter-in-law to receive me."

Satyavati went off to do just that.

THIRTEEN

In the dark

When night fell, Vyasa knocked for the second time at Ambika's door. It opened slowly and she stood there, now her face covered by a veil. No lamp burned in the room and he could see only dimly by the starlight that glimmered through the windows. When she brought the silver pitcher to wash his feet, he was pleased to see that her hands did not tremble. Unlike the first night he had been here, she bent and wiped his feet dry with a firm touch.

In a clear voice, she said, "Welcome, my lord, I have waited impatiently for you."

Vyasa was surprised! She had not uttered a word the last time; she had been so terrified. Now, to his growing astonishment, she came and sat near him in the dark.

She whispered, and there was eagerness in her voice, "I am glad you have come."

She took his hand and brought it to her breast. She had undone her blouse when she went to put away the water. He was pleased: she must have thought back on their first night together and decided she liked him. Yet, even as she lifted her veil and began to kiss him, and to caress him with some abandon, he remembered when she had shut her eyes that first night.

But tonight it was not he who stripped away her clothes and his own, but she. And she did not shut her eyes, he could tell even in the dimness. She was like another woman tonight as she ministered to him. Laughing softly in her deep warm way, she could not wait to lead him to her bed.

"You have changed," he observed quietly. "The last time, you were afraid."

She smiled in the night, stroking him, "The last time I had never been with a man like you before. I can't say the same tonight."

She laid him down and made such tender love to him until dawn Vyasa feared he would lose his heart to her. At the first flush of the sun on the horizon, she left him asleep and melted from the room. Vyasa slept for some hours and it was Satyavati who awakened him.

She was eager to know how the night had gone. "Did she shut her eyes again?"

Vyasa shook his head, smiling.

"Did she turn pale?"

"No," he murmured, "she did not."

Satyavati sighed in satisfaction. "So I will have a grandson who is neither blind nor pale."

"Surely you will, and he will be a boy of great wisdom."

"Oh, I am content!" cried his mother.

"But there is one small matter," mused her son. "It was not with your daughter-in-law that I spent last night, but her sakhi."

Ambika was summoned and confessed she had been so afraid that in her place, she had sent her favourite maid, who resembled her in build if not in temperament. Satyavati begged Vyasa, "You must visit Ambalika again, we must..."

But he cut her short in a voice that brooked no argument. "Three times is as often as a hermit may risk himself with a woman."

Vyasa went away from Hastinapura. He wended his way back to the Himalaya, where he sat in dhyana. It was to take him a long time before he had his serenity back. One night of the three he spent with a woman haunted him. He felt her velvet body against his; he tasted her fervid kisses. Worst of all, she had touched him deeper than the flesh. If ever Veda Vyasa came dangerously near falling in love, if perhaps he did fall in love, it was on the enchanted night he spent with Ambika's maid, whose name he never learnt. It took him years of tapasya before her memory receded from his meditation.

And she, simple, passionate woman, never forgot him for the rest of her days.

FOURTEEN

The three princes of Hastinapura

WHEN HE WAS BORN, VYASA'S THIRD SON HAD A LONG, GRAVE FACE from which soulful eyes gazed with an intuition and humour that bespoke intelligence far beyond the ordinary. They called him Vidura.

It fell once more to their uncle Bheeshma, who was no blood of theirs, to raise those princes. He also ruled the kingdom with wisdom and inspiration. Bheeshma became the boys' surrogate father and taught them everything they learnt as they grew. The princes were as different from one another as could be, and they were, each in his way, remarkably gifted.

Dhritarashtra, the oldest, was as strong as a lion. Pandu, the albino, was a master of archery when he was ten. And Vidura, the maidservant's son, was a prince of the intellect. He was serene, and his insight into men and the world was swift, deep and unerring. When they reached their youth, Bheeshma crowned Dhritarashtra yuvaraja of the Kurus. He had raised Pandu to become the Senapati of the Kuru army, and Vidura would be the king's main minister and counsellor. Slowly, Bheeshma began to entrust more and more power to the princes. Blind Dhritarashtra would never really reign because he could not see. So white Pandu gradually began to rule in his older brother's name, and to rule ably with the sage counsel of his brother Vidura.

The time came and Bheeshma turned his attention to the marriages of his wards. Subalu, the Gandhara king, had a lovely daughter who was a pious Siva-bhakta as well. The king of Madra also had a daughter of exceptional beauty. Bheeshma called Vidura and said to him, "The lineage of Gandhara and Madra are equal to ours, as no other line of these times is. Their princesses are fine girls. We must ask their fathers for their hands for Dhritarashtra and Pandu."

Bheeshma sent a messenger to the Gandhara king, who was reluctant because Dhritarashtra was blind. But when the princess Gandhari heard of the proposal, the God-fearing girl told her father she had had a dream in which Siva came to her and said she would marry a sightless king. She had no objection to marrying Dhritarashtra.

Escorted by her brother Shakuni, Subalu sent Gandhari to Hastinapura to become Dhritarashtra's queen. Her arrival in the Kuru capital created a stir among the people, and not only because she was so beautiful. Before she entered that city, the princess bound her eyes with a square of dark silk and swore never to remove that cloth as long as Dhritarashtra lived.

The wedding of Dhritarashtra and Gandhari was celebrated in Hastinapura. Then Shakuni returned to his father in Gandhara.

Some years after Dhritarashtra's marriage, the king of Madra held a swayamvara for his daughter Madri, to which a thousand kshatriyas came. But the moment pale Pandu stalked into the enclosure of that swayamvara the causes of all the rest were lost. The princess' eyes never left his face: she had been struck by the subtle lightning of the heart. When she was handed the garland of wildflowers with which to declare her choice, without a moment's hesitation she crossed the marble floor and draped it around Pandu's neck.

Bheeshma was pleased the Kuru household had been enriched by these two princesses, Gandhari and Madri. After the years of lonely trial, he felt gratified. But Madri was not Pandu's first wife.

FIFTEEN

Kuntibhoja's daughter

KING SOORA OF THE VRISHNIS, WHO WERE A BRANCH OF THE YADAVAS descended from Soma Deva, the Moon God, had a son and a daughter called Vasudeva and Pritha. Soora had a cousin who was like a brother to him. That king, Kuntibhoja, had no children and was obsessed by this lack. Soora, who had grown up with him, feared that Kuntibhoja was on the verge of either losing his mind or taking his life. He gave his daughter Pritha to his cousin, to raise as his own.

Kuntibhoja's dejection vanished like winter's frost on the mountain at the advent of spring. Pritha became his perennial spring, and he loved that charming girl more than anything else. She was his sun, moon and stars; she was his world, his universe. He named her after himself, because he could not bear to think that she was not his in any way. He called her Kunti. Kunti was exquisite; she was wise beyond her years. She was everything her foster-father could have wanted her to be. And best of all, she doted on him.

Kunti grew up in Kuntibhoja's palace and she grew more beautiful every day. The people and the kings and queens who saw her all said that nowhere in Bharatavarsha was there a princess like Kunti. Some said, surely, she was more suited to be the wife of a Deva in heaven, than the queen of a mortal king: they never knew how near prescience they came.

This was the dwapara yuga, when the world had not yet been shut away from Devaloka, as it would be when the kali yuga arrived. Immortal sages and luculent gods still came openly among men. Of course, the dwapara yuga was drawing to a close and darkness was falling swiftly over the earth. But those were still times when rishis like Vyasa and Durvasa lived in the sacred land of Bharata.

One day, the Muni Durvasa appeared in Kuntibhoja's city. Fate had brought him here, for he had a gift to bestow on the Vrishnis. There was a dramatic design unfolding in time, for which the holy one was chosen to be a catalyst.

Durvasa was often described as an amsa of Lord Siva, and his temper was legendary. So when that rishi came to Kuntibhoja's court, he was received not only with affection but trepidation as well: lest he was offended by some trifle and cursed the king and his kingdom. Of course, Durvasa was not nearly as temperamental as he was reputed to be. Yet, it was true that among the great sages this one was more easily angered than most: with him, it did well to err on the side of caution. And innocent as all mortals are of fate, Kuntibhoja entrusted the task of looking after his guest to his daughter Kunti.

Young Kunti, who was barely fourteen, fulfilled her difficult task so graciously that even Durvasa, a hard man to please, was delighted with her. The day before he left he sent for the young princess. It was late evening. Birds were roosting in their armfuls in the darkening trees outside. Durvasa sensed fate so near him, he felt he could reach out and touch her.

Kunti came in and he made her sit beside him. He laid his hand on her head, and said fondly, "Dear Kunti, what a special child you are. You have looked after me so well I have decided to give you a gift that none of your father's friends can match.

"I am going to teach you a mantra. It is old and powerful, and once you know it I will tell you what it is for."

He made the girl kneel before him. As she repeated the secret words after him, Durvasa felt the tide of destiny surge in his body; on its wave-crests rode resplendent kshatriyas of a strange future. For the life of him, the muni could not understand why he had decided to teach this princess a mantra that was certainly not meant for a child like her. But then, he understood little of why, in the first place, he had come to Kuntibhoja's city.

"Have you learnt it?"

Kunti nodded. She rose, sat beside him again and asked, "What is it for?"

For a moment, Durvasa did not reply. He was uncertain whether he should, after all, tell her what the incantation really was. Then he said, "It is a mantra for the Devas. Think of any Deva as you say it aloud, and he will appear before you."

She gave a delighted laugh. Durvasa spoke so gravely that a part of her believed him completely. But another part, which was still a child, just couldn't conceive that she could summon a God. Durvasa smiled at the princess, but he wondered what he had set afoot.

The next day, blessing Kuntibhoja and his wispy, adorable daughter, that profound sage went on his way.

SIXTEEN

The blazing Deva

A MONTH PASSED, AND KUNTI HAD ALMOST FORGOTTEN ABOUT Durvasa and his mantra. Her youth was flowering, her body filling out into womanhood. Warm new yearnings awoke in her. One day, fate took a dramatic hand in her young life.

It was spring, and dawn. Kunti had just woken up. The morning sun crept over the horizon and poured in through her window in a cascade of crimson and gold. She rose and sat on the edge of her bed, so she was drenched in that first light. Under her window, the river lapped at the palace walls, she also touched awake by the livid star. Kunti thought how wonderful it must be to be a naked river, embraced each dawn by a replenished sun. Every night must be like a death and each morning like a new birth: ecstatic! The birds in the trees sang as they have done every sunrise since there was a world.

Kunti felt her youth inflamed by the sheer magic of the hour. Like the river, she felt intimately caressed by the sun. She quivered with sensations she was certain were quite improper, and all the more delicious for being so. She felt as if burning Surya Deva held her in incandescent arms.

Kunti hardly knew how, but she folded her hands like a lotus bud and whispered Durvasa's mantra.

As the mystic words spilled from her lips, there was the strangest flash of light. Something extraordinary was happening to the stream of sun's rays that flowed in through her window. They had become intolerably bright and shone with a hundred colours. Kunti shut her eyes in terror. What had she done? Then she heard it, a low, but quite distinct sound: there was someone else in the room. Could it be...?

Her eyes flew open and she cried out—standing not five feet from her was a dazzling being whose body was a cool fire and his hair wavy flames. Kunti breathed, "Durvasa's mantra worked! I called and you came." Almost as if she was talking to herself, and he was just a dream. "Oh, how splendid you are, Surya Deva!"

He stood there, so implacable, his light blotting out the rest of the world. It was as if just she and he were alone together in a place that was not only her bedchamber, but also another world. She saw his eyes roving over her with a far from innocent look.

He, the God, said slowly, "What do you want from me?"

She knew what she wanted from him and wouldn't dare admit it. She mumbled falsely, "Why, nothing. I saw you rising, and you set the river alight and the birds all sang to you. I thought I would like you to come to me. So I said the mantra, and here you are."

"The Devas do not appear before mortals for their mere fancy. We come only when a great purpose of fate is to be fulfilled."

Kunti bit her lip, and whispered, "Deva, what do you want from me?"

"Young woman, I want you."

"Oh! How can you even think such a thing?"

But his eyes were grave and mocking. With a sinking feeling, she knew he would not relent. The cool Sun said, "The rishi taught you a mantra for childbearing. Perhaps he did not say?"

The Sun God clicked his tongue, and shook his head of spectral flames.

"But what will the world say if you give me a child? What will my poor father say? It will kill him if he knows I am not a virgin." Tears rolled down her face in a slow procession.

It is told that even the Sun, who has burned in the sky since before earth was made and is the witness of the world, lost his heart to young Kunti. He put his arms around her and unearthly warmth surged through her body, calming her. He stroked her hair and her face. Soon she began to forget all her fears; instead, she was on soft fire.

He assured her, "Our child will be born immediately and you will feel no pain. You will still be a virgin, and no one will ever know what happened between you and me."

He was invading her with his delirious warmth. Ripples of excitement flowed from some core of her that she had never known existed. She heard his assurances and knew he would not lie. Young Kunti gave a moan of sheer lust. She flung her slender arms round his neck and kissed him feverishly. That kiss coursed such dreams through her heart, dreams with the power of sun-flares. She hardly knew when he lifted her robe over her head. She did not hear herself cry out, as the God fastened his lips to her breast.

Kunti was borne far from herself, far from the earth. With him beside her, she flew in a burning chariot of the sky, through visionary mandalas. And made a woman by the Sun himself, she draped her legs around his neck like a wild-flower garland and a hundred tumults shook her.

When he had finished and rose away from her, she smiled gratefully at him.

"We are in another world, and no time passes on earth," said the God.

He placed his hand on her flat, young girl's belly. When she looked down, she saw her body there was full of light. "My son grows in you," breathed Surya Deva. The child in her grew swifter than time. In moments, with just a quavering of her loins, he was born. The father held the glorious infant in his arms.

"Look, he wears kavacha and kundala." It was true, their baby was born wearing golden armour and earrings. Already, the little one looked like his luculent sire.

The Deva went on, in wistful prophecy, "He will be the greatest archer on earth. He will be kind and generous to a fault, but proud and sensitive as well, because he is born to a twisted destiny. Yet, his fame will live in the world as long as the sun and the moon are in the sky."

Surya handed the child to its mother and vanished from her room as abruptly as he had come. Kunti tried her best to raise a spark of motherhood, but she was too young to feel maternal towards her fabulous child. The whole morning seemed like a dream, except for the baby she cradled in her arms, his long eyes still shut fast in the slumber of infancy.

Now that her supernal lover had gone, shame and fear returned sharply. The princess dreaded to think what would happen if the child was discovered. True, before he went she felt the God restoring her virginity. But how would she explain the infant with the golden armour and earrings?

She crossed to the window, thinking even to be rid of the child by flinging him out. She felt no twinge of anything maternal, only panic. Under her window, the river flowed as calmly as ever. As she stood there with the unwanted infant in her arms an idea stole over the princess Kunti, rather as the sun had.

In a fever of haste, she pulled a square of silk from among her clothes and swaddled her baby in it as securely as she could. From the next room, she fetched a sandalwood box in which she had received a gift the previous day. She set him down in it, making him cozy by stuffing its sides with more cloth. She fetched a long cloak, which she put on.

Hiding the box under the cloak, Kunti stole out of her apartment. Nodding perfunctorily to the servants she saw along the passage that wound down to the level of the river, she strode along. At last, with a whimper of relief, she came out through a side-door into the sunlit day. This was her private garden, at the bottom of which the river flowed through the palace grounds. She saw there was no one about.

Kunti broke into a run and reached the bank of the river. Under a tree that grew out over the water, she turned to make sure she was unobserved. Kneeling quickly at the current's edge, she was about to float the little box on the murmuring flow, when her sun-child opened his eyes and gazed up at his mother. He gurgled in his little throat and smiled at her. She bent helplessly to kiss him, and now tears streamed down her cheeks. Kunti floated the wooden box down the river.

She raised her eyes to the sky. She folded her hands to the burning Deva, and cried, "Watch over our son, let no evil befall him."

Young Kunti wept beside the river. As he floated out of her life, bobbing upon the bland current, she blessed her baby: "May all your paths be auspicious. May the lord of rivers guard you; may the lord of the air watch over you; may all the Gods protect you. And when I see you again one day, let me know you by your golden *kavacha* and *kundala*."

She sobbed after him, "How fortunate she will be who finds you and raises you. But oh, my son, I am not that woman."

The box with its precious cargo grew smaller; soon it was only a dark speck on the water. She cried after it, "God bless you, my child, God bless you!"

Her son was lost in the distances of the river. She stood gazing after him for a long time before she turned back to her father's palace. In a single incredible hour, her life had been transformed forever.

Everyone said a new maturity had come over the princess Kunti; it was time she married. She smiled and asked innocently how she, who lived such a cloistered life in her father's house, could mature so suddenly. But at nights when she slept, and whenever she was alone, an unvarying image haunted her dreams and her solitude. She saw a wooden box floating away from her. She saw the small, brilliant face of him who lay in that box and Kunti thought she would go mad with guilt.

SEVENTEEN

A curse in the forest

KUNTI SURVIVED THREE YEARS OF ANGUISH, EVERY BIT LIKE A princess. Then, the planets in the heavens changed their positions and her life changed as well.

Kuntibhoja held a swayamvara for his daughter. At that gathering of the most eligible kshatriyas on earth, she chose dashing Pandu of Hastinapura to be her husband. She draped her garland of wildflowers around his neck, with a prayer in her heart that he would fill her womb with a hundred sons: so she could forget the child she had abandoned on the river. Kunti was Pandu's first wife, and Madri, his second.

Because his brother Dhritarashtra, the nominal king, was blind, prince Pandu of Hastinapura was the virtual ruler of the Kurus. From his earliest boyhood, Pandu's natural vocation had been a soldier's. And when he was made Senapati, the Supreme Commander of the great Kuru legions, he found the perfect chance to give free rein to his martial genius. He took an army with him and ranged the length and breadth of Bharatavarsha.

Pandu conquered the Dasarnas, Kasi, Anga, Vanga and Kalinga. Magadha fell to him like a ripe fruit from a tree. When Chitrangada and Vichitraveerya had both died young, the cares of kingdom and the responsibility of raising his young nephews tied Bheeshma down to the palace. The world had said that the glory and the fortunes of the Kurus were waning. Pandu's triumphal march swiftly put paid to such speculation. Now they said this was the golden age of the Kuru kingdom, as no other time in the past. They also said that Pandu was the finest soldier of his day, his uncle Bheeshma had taught him well.

When the kingdoms around him were subdued to his satisfaction, and the talk about the waning stars of the Kuru House was silenced, Pandu decided he owed himself and his wives the pleasure of a sojourn in the forest. Like his forefathers, the pale prince was a keen hunter and he went to the Himalayas with Kunti and Madri. There, on the southern slopes of that mountain range, the three of them spent the happiest, most enchanted weeks of their lives.

Those were perfect days to which, years later, Kunti would look back: to find strength in them and to remind her that life was not only a grim struggle. Those were the days when the forest folk mistook the three of them for a Deva and his two women come down from heaven to sport in the world. But fate was waiting in time's wings with a curse.

In that same forest on the Himalayan foothills lived a rishi and his wife. Between long abstinences, they were enjoying an interlude of passion. It was spring. All the forest was at love, so too the hermit couple. One day, the husband decided that ordinary lovemaking in their hut hardly satisfied him. The muni turned himself and his woman into two deer in season, a stag and a hind. Musky desire took them and he mounted her in an open glade. This mating was so exhilarating that for days they were happy to be rutting deer.

One evening as the forest prepared to receive the night, Pandu saw the lustful pair. He saw the stag with magnificent antlers straddling his mate. The prince was arrogant with his recent victories at arms and time was ready to humble him. In the heat of the hunt, and quite forgetting the hunter's olden law that mating animals may never be made targets for arrows, Pandu shot the stag through his heart.

The creature fell with a bellow. Before Pandu's eyes the stag turned back into a man, the arrow sticking grotesquely from his heaving chest. His hind was also a woman again; by her devotion to him, she too lay dying in her husband's arms.

Blood bubbled at the rishi's lips. He said to Pandu, "You are a prince of the noblest house in the world. How could you do this?" His breath was stertorous and in his eyes was a legend of pain. "You saw, cruel Kshatriya, that we were at love. Yet you had the heart to kill me. How could you do this to the gentle deer of the forest?"

He lay breathless for a while. Then, with an effort that made his eyes roll up white, the rishi cursed Pandu, "The moment, terrible prince, you make love to a woman again, you will also die."

And with a sigh, the sage and his wife were gone, as if they had shared a single life. Pandu's roars echoed through the trees. That prince was the virtual ruler of the invincible Kurus; he had recently conquered most of Bharatavarsha. Now he was like a great tree in its prime that has been struck by lightning. Fate had nudged his carefree life into hell.

He ran back to Madri and Kunti. At first he couldn't speak, but stood panting before them, his eyes full of tears. At last, sobbing, Pandu told them what had happened. The three of them spent a night as long as a year, in dark silence.

At dawn, Pandu announced, "The world is no longer the place for me. I won't return to Hastinapura, but seek my detachment here in the forest. From now on, I must be a brahmachari."

He called the soldiers and ministers who had come hunting with him. He told them about the dying hermit's curse. He gave away all his possessions, sending detailed instructions for their disbursal through those dazed men. Pandu said, "Tell my mother, my brothers, my grandmother and, most of all, my uncle Bheeshma that I will never return to Hastinapura. Tell them Pandu has become a sannyasi."

Kunti and Madri had resolved to stay with their husband. They sent back their silks and ornaments to the city. And so, just when its star of fortune had seemed to be rising again, a curse darkened the destiny of the kingdom of the Kurus.

Hastinapura received the shocking news. It truly seemed that all the old sins of the Kuru ancestors were being visited on the present time. Ambalika was inconsolable. Satyavati retired into seclusion and offered incessant prayers to the Gods, who must still be wroth with her. As for Bheeshma, to all outward appearances he was calm; but privately, he railed against the long misfortune that had stalked him, ever since he came of age. It had cost him two brothers, and now a brilliant nephew.

Bheeshma found himself at the helm of the kingdom once again, and felt his heart must surely be made of stone. Any other man in his place would have succumbed, and either lost his reason, killed himself or become a hermit from grief. But none of these recourses was for him. It appeared he was destined to go on forever, if need be, shouldering his sad burden alone; and only he himself knew how time had savaged him.

There was one person in the kingdom who was some support to Bheeshma, a young man who carried an old head on his youthful shoulders: his nephew Vidura. Of course Vidura could never be king; not only was he a maidservant's son, he was no warrior either.

EIGHTEEN

Pandu's yearning

In the asrama in the forest of Satasringa, a jade valley nestled between Himalayan slopes, Pandu settled slowly to his new life. Often, in the cold nights, the wildness in his blood urged him to seek out one of his wives. But by God's grace, or because his time to die had not come, at the critical juncture either he himself or his women prevented the fatal contact. Some years went by in this struggle. But celibacy, even enforced celibacy, quickly brings strength and serenity; and so it did to Pandu and his wives.

Peace came over them. It became a habit, and in time, an easy one, to subdue the mortal enemy, desire, whenever she raised her seductive head. Many rishis came to Pandu's asrama; from them the prince learnt the art and the joy of dhyana, meditation. After the first year, Pandu began to accept his new life. Like a molting snake does its skin, he shed the memory of his violent past. The loyal Kunti and Madri also settled into their untimely vanaprastha. The years flowed by without any outward event, but in inner transformation.

Then the initial adjustment to the new life had been made. The first shock passed, of the change the rishi's curse had forced on them. But now, Pandu was gripped by a deep sorrow: that he could not have children. In his boyhood, his grandmother Satyavati had instilled the fear in him that no man who did not have a son could enter heaven when he died. She said only the most accursed men were condemned to childlessness.

Pandu found he could not meditate any more. When he shut them to still his mind, images of fantasial children danced before his eyes. It was as if destiny had taken a hand again, if a subtler one, in Pandu's life in the wilderness. Day and night, he saw visions of his wives with sons in their arms; in his dreams, he saw himself a proud father. His peace was gone.

Once he went to visit some munis that lived in tapasya in that forest. They were planning to cross the mountains to the Manasarovara, lake perched between heaven and earth, which Brahma once created with a thought, where the Parabrahman, the eternal Spirit, abides.

Pandu said to them, "Take us with you; we also seek the refuge of the Brahman."

But the eldest rishi replied, "That is not your way, Pandu, nor is it time for you to seek the Brahman. Besides, the princesses will not be able to make the crossing to the Manasarovara."

Pandu broke down and wept. He told them how he had become obsessed with the desire for a son. Among those rishis was an old man who was a visionary and saw through time. He said to Pandu, "I have looked into your future and I have seen you having not one, but five sons. They will not be ordinary children, but kshatriyas of destiny."

"How will I have sons with my curse?" asked Pandu.

"Your own mothers had sons after their husband was dead."

Pandu stood transfixed by the implication. Those rishis blessed him and went on their way to the lake of the Brahman. Pandu ran home in a fever of excitement. He called Kunti, who was the older and more mature of his wives.

He said to her, "I will find only hell when I die, because I have no sons. I cannot father children on you myself, but we can ask a rishi to help us. It seems to be the fate of the Kuru line."

Kunti turned pale. "You violate the chastity of my mind with this thought. I am your wife, Pandu, and that is a sacred thing. I would give up my life for that, and here you are asking me to have another man's child. Whoever he may be, the very idea is hateful to me."

He stared at her in a mixture of disappointment and a love he could not express. Her eyes turned down, she said softly, "If you think you won't find a place in heaven without having a son, here I am before you. Father your child on me and when he is born I will follow you out of this world."

"I am so desperate that I would do as you say. Only, I would not orphan my son as soon as he is born, but nurture and enjoy him. Kunti, listen to me, I also know something of the scriptures and the law.

"In the elder days, the golden ages of the earth, women were never bound to one man. It was only Rishi Uddalaka's son Swetaketu who forced the contrivance of marriage on women; and perhaps caused the fall of the human spirit. For when their holy freedom was restricted, women began to be secretive and deceitful.

"In our own house, Vyasa was called to father sons on our mothers. There is no sin in it, Kunti. Would you rather see me die of a broken heart than do as I ask?"

She stopped his lips with her hand. Kunti had remembered something, a boon given her long ago by another rishi. Slowly she said, "I have a cure for your sorrow."

"What is it?"

He hardly believed her. He was thinking instead of asking Madri to give him a child by a rishi, though she was even less likely to agree. Despair suffocated Pandu.

But Kunti was saying, "Many years ago, when I was a girl, Maharishi Durvasa stayed in my father's palace for a week and I looked after him. Though I did nothing very much, he was pleased with me."

"I am not surprised," murmured Pandu, whom she cared for so lovingly in the forest.

"Just before he left, he taught me a mantra and told me I could summon any Deva I wanted with it. I was too young then to understand what he meant; besides, I was too frightened to invoke a God. But I still remember the mantra as if he taught it to me yesterday. If you want me to, I can summon a Deva and the Kuru line will be blessed with a matchless prince."

She spoke half in jest and, of course, said nothing of how she had invoked the blazing sun. But her husband cried, "You must use the mantra today!"

He led her impatiently to their little hut. He called Madri out and told her they were going to visit all the asramas in the forest. They must leave at once, because today was the happiest day of his life! A bewildered Madri prepared to go with him. But she asked, "What about Kunti?"

"Kunti stays here!" cried Pandu. "She stays here and invokes Dharma Deva, the Lord of truth."

When Madri and Pandu had gone, Kunti stood waving after them for a long time. At last, alone and afraid, she turned back into the little wooden dwelling. Briefly, she regretted having told Pandu about the mantra. She trembled when she thought of the day the Sun God had appeared before her. But then, she remembered how miserable her husband was and thought how happy she could make him.

With a sigh, Kunti stood beside the fire of worship. Fixing her mind on dharma and the God who embodies eternal justice, she chanted Durvasa's mantra for the second time.

NINETEEN

Kunti's unworldly lovers

ALL NIGHT, UNTIL DAWN LIT THE HORIZON, THE QUIET DEVA STAYED with Kunti in the hut. How different he was from the fiery sun, but just as overwhelming.

The next morning Pandu and Madri returned. Pandu riveted his wife with a gaze full of one question. When she turned her face away shyly, and whispered, "I am with the Lord Dharma's child," he gave a shout that rang among the trees, as if he himself had fathered that child. All his melancholy vanished and never raised its head again the rest of his days.

Kunti was radiant in her pregnancy. Pandu and Madri pandered to her every whim, whether it was for sour mangoes or for a fish from the river. One day, when all the planets were configured in harmony, Kunti's labour began and she gave birth to a boy of uncommon serenity. As soon as he was born, he gazed back at his mother with calm, knowing eyes.

His heart bursting with joy, Pandu took that calm infant in his arms. An asariri, a disembodied voice, spoke out of the air, "Pandu's first son should be named Yudhishtira,* for he will be steadfast even in war. He will be the image of truth on earth and he will rule the world one day."

A year went by, with the blissful father and his wives absorbed in the growing child. One day Pandu took Kunti aside and said, "These

---

* The time of Yudhishtira's birth is given as the eighth muhurta, called abhijit, noon, of the fifth day of the waxing moon, in the month of Kartika, when the moon was rising in the nakshatra Jyeshta.

are dark times and Yudhishtira will have need of brothers, especially if he is to be a king. We must have a second son to be his support: to do his bidding, to love and to serve him."

Kunti gasped. "You want me to invoke another Deva?"

"There is no sin in it. Heaven is all awhisper in my heart, telling me to have another son. They say we must have a boy of unrivalled strength."

Kunti flushed. She could not deny, which mortal woman could, that the temptation of a Deva's vertiginous embrace was hard to resist. Since he spoke of strength, she guessed which Deva her husband wanted her to summon this time. The mere thought of that God made her quail.

"Pandu, I am afraid. Being with a Deva is more than any woman can bear."

"I will take Madri and Yudhishtira away to the rishis' asramas. Invoke Vayu now, he is the strongest Deva. Great Hanuman, who carried a mountain through the sky to save his Rama's life, was Vayu's son."

What she had feared was true: it was the Wind her husband wanted a son by, to be Yudhishtira's brother. Pandu said gently, "Think of the future, Kunti; think of Yudhishtira without a brother in this treacherous world. If he is to be a king, he will need more than friends to protect him."

She bowed her head, acquiescing. How could she tell him she needed little persuasion to invoke the Deva, that the very thought of lying in the arms of the tameless wind made her blood course? But she did say, "Let me go to higher reaches of the mountain. I fear our asrama may not contain Vayu Deva when he comes. Besides, I cannot be with him in the same house we live in with Yudhishtira."

The weather was clear and fine, and Pandu agreed. Kunti did not mention that she had felt shame even the last time, when Dharma was with her: shame, because it was herself she could not contain. If she must be with a God again, she would rather it were in a place in which she did not have to live, or ever return to.

Well before the sun set the same day, she set off by herself for the higher mountains above Satasringa. When she had climbed for an hour, she came to a depression between some large rocks. The view of the setting sun from here was spectacular. He, her lover once, bathed the white massifs all around in melting bronze and scarlet, ethereal violet and burning pink. The wind already swirled through the gorges, restless and powerful, as if that Spirit knew why she had climbed here and was impatient for her. She thought he caressed her with wanton fingers of air.

As the sun sank over immense ranges, Kunti settled herself in the declivity. The crags around her had stood like sentinels through lonely ages. The seasons and centuries had taken slow toll of them, with snow and sleet, rain and blizzard, warm days and icy nights. As the last ray of the sun broke across her face, and the wind plucked at her hair that she had left loose, Kunti said the mantra Durvasa had taught her. Today she said it aloud, calling Vayu the Wind God to her.

Suddenly, all the zephyrs and breezes stood still, breathless to hear those words. It seemed even the sun paused at the rim of the world, startled to hear the familiar mantra, now said to summon another God. To Kunti, holding her breath, it seemed an age passed of that surprised stillness. Then slowly, a tidal whispering of airs gathered in the sky. It spread around her in a tempest, until it whistled above her, below her, blowing from everywhere. Storm winds lashed the mountain as if to uproot it and blow it away.

Kunti shut her eyes in terror, and again, the stillness and silence. She sensed a flickering brightness in the growing dark and opened her eyes. Night had fallen. But before her stood an irradiant being, his body made of spinning airs. His hair, flowing back from his shining face, was a storm contained. His smile was glorious and the look in his eye entirely wild. She shook with fright: his presence was not a comforting one as Dharma Deva's had been, but one of tumultuary excitement, as when the Sun God stood before her.

She could see through his face and his body. He was a world of intense whispering, always restless, full of the strangest news of undreamt-of lands and seas across which he blew in a million breezes and winds, gales and cyclones, covering the earth. She stood rooted by the vibrancy of him.

At last, he spoke to her with surprising softness, "Don't be afraid."

Perhaps she moaned in reply, because she was speechless. He knelt quickly before her, and gathering her lightly in his arms, flew away to a luminous cave set high on a golden mountain. From there, he showed her some of his secrets. He showed her visions of the earth—how it was day somewhere else, always fleeting, like the wind, and how the round world turned steadily.

He gave her an ambrosial drink that calmed her, and soon Kunti felt easier in his company. She found him affable and gentle, though he was unnerving as well. When he had won her trust in the lofty cavern, and she did not tremble any more but wondered what it would be like to be in his gusty arms, he reached for her in the starlight.

TWENTY

The sons of Pandu

WHEN KUNTI RETURNED FROM HER NIGHT ON THE MOUNTAIN, SHE was with child again. Now she bore the son of the wind in her womb and she glowed with that boy, growing powerfully within her. Pandu could hardly wait for his son to be born. And when Kunti delivered her child, and he cried lustily for her breast, Pandu was not disappointed. His second son was a huge baby and the grip of his small hand was as strong as his voice was loud.

Once more, a disembodied voice spoke to them, "Let your son by Vayu Deva be named Bheemasena. He will be the strongest and most loving of your children."

And so it was. Little Bheema was so fond of his brother Yudhishtira that Pandu was delighted. From the beginning there was no rivalry between the two; rather, they seemed to complement each other's natures perfectly. Once, when their second son was just two months, Pandu and Kunti were out on the mountain with the children. They were returning to the asrama by a steep trail, a short way they used when they were tired. Kunti tripped over a root that had stretched itself across the narrow path, and Bheema flew out of her arms and fell onto a rock some fifty feet below.

Kunti ran screaming down the slope, certain her baby had been killed by the fall. His heart in his mouth Pandu went after her. But little Bheema lay gurgling happily; the fall had thrilled him no end but had not hurt him at all. The black rock on which he had fallen was smashed to bits, and there was not a scratch on him. Kunti snatched him up and he snuggled against her, while Yudhishtira watched with solemn eyes that saw everything with unwinking equanimity.

A happy year passed, and then Pandu grew restless again. He had been having strange dreams, in which he saw himself as the father of more children than two. He saw many Devas in his dreams; but most of all he saw one who was more majestic than all the others, because he was their king. Pandu was certain that greatest Deva spoke to him.

He called Kunti, and said, "I have been dreaming of Indra. He says we must have a son by him, a perfect kshatriya, greater than even Yudhishtira and Bheema."

She began to protest, but he laid a finger on her lips. With a sigh, and an inner quaver at the thought of summoning the king of the Devas, Kunti agreed to do as her husband asked. Now she went deep into a nearby forest, and inside a cave, invoked the Deva king with Durvasa's mantra. Indra came to her, stern and full of majesty. For all that, he was tender; and when he had calmed her first helpless anxiety, he was the most ardent of her unearthly lovers. Even as she lay delirious in his arms, she swore she would never use the mantra again.

In time, Kunti delivered her third and finest son. Once more, an asariri spoke to that forest family. "This is the child who will win undying fame for his father. He will become the greatest archer on earth, and conquer the world in his brother's name. Let him be called Arjuna." The heavens opened. They heard gandharvas singing little Arjuna's praises, and soft flowers rained down on them, swathing the hermitage in the scent of other worlds.

The night Arjuna was born, Indra came to Pandu in a dream. Now he spoke clearly to that kshatriya, "Tonight Vishnu's twin incarnations, Nara and Narayana, have been born into the world to cleanse it of evil. Arjuna is Nara, come again as a man. In Mathura tonight, Narayana has also been born. Hearken to the earth, Pandu, she sings the birth of dark Krishna."

Pandu awoke. It was past midnight and he heard the wind in the trees like a hymning sea, full of a celebrant rumour that a blue saviour had been born into the world, to purify it in blood. From far away, he thought he could hear a storm over a distant city at whose evil heart the newborn Avatara, his Arjuna's cousin, nestled. When Pandu fell asleep again, listening to the wind outside, prophetic dreams visited his sleep. He saw his sons fight a great war for the Blue God who had been born that night. It was an ancient war between good and evil, one that would destroy the race of kings forever. But when he awoke the next morning, he remembered nothing of his dreams.

The years were full and swift with the joy of his sons, and Pandu, hermit prince of the Kurus, could not have been happier. But when a year passed after Arjuna's birth, he called Kunti once more, and said, "There is a greed more irresistible than the avarice for wealth, and I am prey to it. How wonderful our three children are, but I am not satisfied. Kunti, use your mantra again; give me just one more son!"

But this time Kunti was firm. "Not the direst calamity should make one summon the Gods for more than three sons. Besides, I could not bear the coming of another Deva. I would die."

No matter how much he begged her, she would not relent. But Pandu's desire for more sons was soon to be satisfied. One morning, when Kunti had gone to the river, Madri came to him. She looked unhappy, and Pandu asked her, "Is something the matter, my love?"

And it all burst out of his second queen: the resentment she had harboured, and the envy. Madri cried, "The preference you have shown Kunti doesn't sadden me, because I know I am younger than she is. But can't I be the mother of at least one of your children? She has borne you three sons; can't she teach me her mantra so I can also fulfil my womanhood?"

"Kunti thinks of you as her own sister, she won't grudge you this," said Pandu.

But he saw Madri's face set hard. "She is my rival for your love. She has resented me since the day you brought me home. She never shows it in your presence, Pandu. But in the things she says and does when we are alone, she makes it clear she would rather have been your only wife. I will not beg her for the mantra. You must ask her yourself."

Pandu was only happy to go to Kunti and say, "If you won't have any more children, will you allow Madri to use the mantra? She says that you have three fine sons, may the Gods protect them, while she has none."

"Did she ask you for this? Is she willing?"

"She was afraid you might refuse if she asked herself."

Kunti laughed, "Why should I refuse my little Madri anything? But she has been strange lately, as if she resents me. I cannot teach her the mantra, but I can invoke a Deva for her, whichever one she wants."

Kunti took Madri to a secluded grove in the forest. She asked her to think of any Deva she chose. When she had murmured the words of power Kunti hurried away from that place, leaving Madri alone. As she went, behind her she felt the intense agitation of heaven and earth that heralded the coming of a God. Kunti and Pandu stayed awake most of the night in their kutila, thinking of Madri in the forest. Through the night they heard the wind moaning in the trees; it could have been the passionate whispering of a Deva. At last, near dawn, Pandu and Kunti fell asleep.

When Madri returned from the forest in the morning, a soft new radiance was upon her; her skin shone from whatever had happened in the night. But when they asked her excitedly who her Deva was, she would not tell them. "Let that be my secret," she said.

In course of time, Madri delivered not one but two beautiful sons. She wore a look of such smugness that Kunti finally realized how much the younger woman envied her.

The heavenly voice spoke in that asrama once more, "The sons of the Aswins will be the most handsome men on earth. Let them be called Nakula and Sahadeva."

No sooner were her twins born, than Madri's nature underwent a sad change. She did not have a moment to spare for Kunti's boys any more, but only carried and cosseted her own. Kunti treated all five princes equally, and fortunately the children made no differences among themselves. It was in none of their natures, and to Madri's chagrin, even her sons were more attached to Kunti than to her.

When the twins were a year old, Madri said to Pandu, "Tell Kunti to say the mantra again for me. Wouldn't you like to have more sons as handsome as Nakula and Sahadeva?"

Pandu went and asked Kunti, "Will you say the mantra once more for Madri? She has only two sons while you have three."

But Kunti's face grew dark. "She is always setting her boys apart from mine. Using the mantra once, she had twins. I dare not think whom she will invoke, if I say it for her again. Don't ask me to do this, my lord. Let us be content with the children we have."

And Madri had to be satisfied with her twins, and her position in the family, which was definitely of the second wife. But that asrama, set like a jewel in Satasringa, was the happiest place. Pandu's sons grew apace there, loved by all the rishis who lived in that valley praying for the world. Those masters of the spirit performed the rituals of naming and initiation for the five princes. It was with them that the young Pandavas had their earliest tutelage.

In Mathura, Kunti's kinsfolk the Yadavas were shocked to hear Pandu had been cursed. Now when he heard that Pandu was the father of five sons, Kunti's brother Vasudeva sent gifts for his nephews through his family priest Kashyapa. He also sent news of the birth of his own sons, Balarama and Krishna. Charmed by the Pandava princes, Kashyapa stayed on in the forest asrama for a while. He performed the upanayanams of the Devaputras.

The rishis all adored the young kshatriyas. So did the wild creatures of the jungle, where the boys ranged as freely as the wind and the sun: inseparable and wonderfully gifted.

In the same forest lived Sayyati's son Suka, as if fate had brought him here. This hermit was a fine archer, and he became the princes' first guru in the wilds. So, though they grew up far from a palace, they lacked little in their education: which kshatriya boy could have asked for better masters than Suka and their own father Pandu?

From the beginning, Yudhishtira was adept with a javelin and Bheema with a mace. Arjuna was far ahead of the rest with a bow and arrows; he shot with equal ease with his right and left hands. Though, in every discipline, they were no match for one of their brothers, the twins excelled as all-round warriors. They performed equally well with the mace and the javelin, the sword and the longbow.

In just a year, Suka told Pandu, "Arjuna is already as good an archer as I am. I have nothing more to teach him. I have never seen another boy blessed with such talent. A gift like his develops only over many lives, and is perfected in a final one." He paused, thoughtfully, "After which there are no more births or deaths, because the spirit has become immaculate."

Suka gave young Arjuna his own bow, and then went away to the highest Himalaya to continue his tapasya, in preparation to leave his body. Now that he had taught Pandu's third son everything he knew, his work in the world was accomplished. He passed beyond this earth and its affairs.

TWENTY-ONE

The sinister night

MEANWHILE, WHEN YUDHISHTIRA WAS BORN THE NEWS CAME swiftly to Dhritarashtra that Pandu had a son. The blind Kuru was king in Hastinapura, but he was always conscious that he was king in little more than name. He was still childless, and though he loved Pandu, he was unhappy that his younger brother had become a father before him. Kshatriya dharma was clear that the firstborn prince in each generation would become king. Gandhari was even more distraught than her husband to hear Kunti had a son, whose father, rumours whispered, was a Deva. She was most aggrieved because she herself had been pregnant for a year.

A year before this time, brought once more by destiny, Vyasa arrived in his son's sabha. Travel-worn and drawn, came the enlightened visitor. Gandhari looked after him in the palace; and even more than by her caring hospitality, Vyasa was moved by how she went with her eyes bound to share Dhritarashtra's blindness. Vyasa blessed her with a boon.

"You will have a hundred sons, each one as strong as Dhritarashtra."

But a pang gripped his heart even as he spoke, as if he was not blessing Gandhari but cursing her to a horrible fate. But then, she fell at his feet and thanked him joyfully, and he was consoled. Gandhari and Dhritarashtra found their love kindled by Vyasa's prophecy. One morning soon, the queen came to her husband, and taking his hand, placed it shyly on her stomach. She whispered, "Your son grows in here, my lord. Already I can feel he will be as strong as his father."

Dhritarashtra declared a celebration in Hastinapura. Nine months passed; Gandhari had to be confined in bed, where she lay in intense discomfort, and often in pain. Her child—or children if Vyasa's prediction was true—was monstrously heavy. The weight inside her was dark and leaden, and her dreams were so evil she was afraid to fall asleep.

At the end of a painful year came the news from the forest that Kunti was already a mother. Gandhari's screams rang through the harem; fate had cheated her. In agony anyway at her morbid pregnancy, the queen became hysterical. She struck herself again and again in her belly, until she began to bleed. As she fainted, she was aborted of a seething mass of flesh that was hard as a rock and stank of contagion.

Groaning dementedly in her bed, she ordered the putrescent lump cast into the forest. A maid was carrying the wretched thing out, when suddenly Vyasa appeared at the palace-gates. His face twitching, he accosted the young woman, and cried, "What is it? Where are you taking it?"

She drew back the cloth that covered the shapeless flesh. "My queen was aborted of this an hour ago."

Vyasa caught his breath. Seizing the maid's arm, hurting her in his urgency, he brought her back into the palace. The rishi shouted to the women of the harem, "Give me a hundred earthen vats of warm oil. Put them in a hidden chamber. Hurry! There isn't a moment to lose."

Gandhari appeared there, dishevelled and sobbing. She cried, "Muni, you said I would have a hundred sons, each as strong as my husband. Instead I have borne this putrid lump of flesh."

But Vyasa said, "Go back to your bed, woman. A hundred sons you shall have. The words of Vyasa Dwaipayana have never yet been proved vain."

When the earthen vats were ready in a cellar below the harem, Vyasa took the abortion down into that chamber. He sprinkled the flesh with cold water, and then patiently divided it with his hands into one hundred pieces. He gave them to a midwife to be immersed, each one in a separate vat of oil.

Gandhari also arrived in that room, in irresistible curiosity. She stood at the door, her bound face craning to the sound of Vyasa's fine hands at their strange work. The lump of flesh dwindled as he pinched off more and more thumb-sized bits. The queen counted every one from the sounds that were so clear to her powerful hearing. As he neared the end of his task, a wish flared into Gandhari's mind. "I will be the mother of a hundred mighty sons. Can't I have a daughter as well, a sister to those hundred?"

At that very moment, Vyasa had given the hundredth bit of flesh to the midwife. But he still had one final piece left in his hand. As if he divined her thought, her father-in-law said to Gandhari, "I have placed a hundred pieces of the flesh you bore in vats of oil. They shall be your sons. But I have one small piece left; let this be your daughter."

A hundred and first vat was called for, and Vyasa gave the midwife that final shred of flesh to sink in it. The moment this was done, a susurrus filled that cellar, as of countless bees buzzing. The startled midwife saw those hundred and one earthen vats glow dully, with a malignant aura. Vyasa came out of that room, and said quietly to Gandhari, "The future has been set in motion."

Blessing Gandhari and Dhritarashtra, that they may find the strength to bear the trial that lay ahead of them, Vyasa went away from Hastinapura. He wended his way back to the Himalayas, which are cosmic masters of the Spirit dwelling on earth as towering mountains. There, he would perform a tapasya to save the world. That rishi, who saw deep and far in time, already realized the danger those hundred vats contained, especially the first of them, in which the piece of flesh was somewhat larger than in the others.

The pieces of flesh grew into tiny human foetuses. They grew in those vats of oil as if in a hundred and one women's wombs. As they grew, their weird lustre filled the cellar, which Gandhari had sealed as Vyasa instructed her to. That light was like an evil sun risen in the bowels of Hastinapura.

Another year passed, and it was the same night when, in a faraway forest, Kunti gave birth to Bheema. It was a night when uncanny fires rose from the earth around the city of the Kurus and spumed into the sky in livid geysers. Wild beasts from deep jungles, wolves and black panthers with gleaming eyes, jackals and hyena-packs, came crowding and baying into the city's streets as soon as the sun had set. Crows, vultures and other birds of carrion flew down in teeming swarms and settled on the terraces of the palace. Twisting cyclones that are seen only out at sea, and other winds, dust-laden and flecked with sulphur, lashed the city of elephants. Squadrons of vampire bats, flown from some hell to greet their master to be born, obscured the face of the full moon. The planets hid themselves in the sky and a thousand spirit-hosts stalked the land, while it rained glowing, hissing drops of blood and flames. In the cellar below Dhritarashtra's palace, the first of the one hundred and one vats burst open with a report that reverberated through the passages and brought Gandhari and her midwife running.

When they unlocked the door and went in, the maid cried out in fear. There on the cold floor, in a pool of luminous slime, lay an immense child. His terrible serpent's eyes were wide open and stared at them unwinkingly. Those eyes belonged to a Demon of the pit that had taken a human form to become the bane of the earth. The child's body glowed with the same macabre aura that coloured the foetal slime in which he lay. The sinister infant gave a dismal cry and the poor midwife felt her blood turn to ice. That cry was not in the least human, but the long scream of a feral beast.

Outside, there arose the greeting of the night—the grunts, wails, howls, chatters, roars, growls, shrill ululations, the manic laughter and a million wing-beats of the animals and birds of darkness congregated to welcome their lord into the world. And he called back to them, his creatures, in a devilish voice that was all their voices at once: bat's screech, wolf's bay, hyena's deranged cackle, bray and growl, roar and howl, in vile cacophony.

At which din, the second vat burst open, and then quickly the third and the fourth; and then, two, three and more, all at once. Gandhari and the midwife shrank back in fear. Now the king came down into that chamber with Vidura. Vidura stood horrified to see those children of hell lying in their slime, while their creatures outside still howled their welcome through the shocked night.

Fortunately for them, Dhritarashtra and Gandhari saw nothing of what happened in that cellar; but Vidura's gaze never left the first and biggest of those hundred and one infants. That monstrous child grinned with needle teeth; his green eyes were on fire. Grunting like a pig, he had already managed to pull himself into a sitting posture. He sat fondling himself lewdly, while all around him the earthen vats continued to burst open, until the last one, from which a little girl was born. All those children howled back at the night, in a bizarre chorus.

Feeling suddenly weak, Dhritarashtra grasped Vidura's arm and said, "Take me out of here!"

But Gandhari stood rooted. Soft mother's joy was upon her, and she said to the midwife, "Give me my first son and my daughter. Don't you hear them crying? They are hungry."

She heard no wolf howl, no bat screech, or hyena cackle from her children's throats. By the sublime mystery of motherhood, she heard only human babies crying to be fed. She squatted on the floor and bared her breasts for her son and her daughter. They fastened greedy lips to her flesh and fed voluptuously.

In his lamplit sabha, Dhritarashtra shivered as if he had a fever. Wild visions of evil danced before his blind eyes. He saw crimsoned battlefields, where corpses lay piled like hills and blood flowed in rills. He saw them as clearly as sighted men see the light and the events of day. Only Vidura stood beside his brother, and he knew what this night presaged. Vidura already saw what must be the tragic future of their royal House, founded by Manu, the lawgiver, himself.

At last, Dhritarashtra said, "My son is a year younger than Pandu's firstborn in the jungle. Yudhishtira will inherit the Kuru throne."*

The jackals and wolves outside howled in long unison, and the night was alive with fear. The king leaned forward in his throne, and whispered, "But tell me, my brother, will my son rule after Yudhishtira's time? Vidura, I am terrified by the omens. The birds and beasts of death have flocked into Hastinapura's streets. Listen to the wolves baying! I am told occult fires leap into the sky from the earth's belly, and the very world quakes, as if in fear at my children's birth. What does it all mean, Vidura? Do my sons seem strange to those who can see?"

Vidura said softly, "The omens mean only one thing, Dhritarashtra: that your firstborn son will be the ruin of the House of Kuru. It is for him that the dog-packs bay and the wolves howl, and the bats of hell wheel in dizzy circles. The omens cry that he is the terrible one of whom the old prophecies warned. He will destroy everything that has been held sacred through the ages, and fetch doom to this holy land."

Dhritarashtra breathed, "What can I do to keep doom away?"

---

* This is the same day that Bheema is born in the forest.

"What you will not do, my lord. You can sacrifice your son. Kill him tonight."

The blind king gasped. Vidura went on, "The wise have always said an individual may be sacrificed for the good of the family, a family for the good of the village, the village for the country. And everything, even the world itself, may be sacrificed for the sake of the immortal soul. O my brother, it is for the soul of mankind that this monstrous child of yours has come from the depths of hell: to corrupt and to destroy. Kill him now, and I swear his brothers will be harmless. And you can enjoy them, ninety-nine fine princes. But him you must not leave alive."

But that child, of whom the darkest prophecies told, was Dhritarashtra's firstborn. Vidura was right to assume that his brother would never do what he asked.

The same night, a vaishya woman in Dhritarashtra's harem was also delivered of a son sired by the blind king. That child was named Yuyutsu. And so Dhritarashtra had one hundred and one sons, and a daughter whom they named Dussala. And his eldest, the Demon, was Duryodhana.*

As they grew into strapping young princes, the king was pleased with his powerful boys. He laughed in joy to think of the hundred of them, and Gandhari rejoiced as well.[3]

---

* Duryodhana is also frequently called Suyodhana, throughout the original text. Yudhishtira is also known as Ajatashatru, (he who has no enemies) and Bheema is often called Vrikodara, while Arjuna acquires ten names. Karna is called Radheya and Vaikartana, too.

3 See Appendix for the hundred names.

TWENTY-TWO

Sweet, deadly spring

Fifteen idyllic years passed in the forest of Satasringa. The sons of Pandu grew swiftly, and their brilliance with them. They hunted in those wilds, swam and fished in the rivers. They learnt the ways of the jungle-folk, and about the deep motions of the stars in the sky. They studied the Vedas and the other Shastras from erudite rishis in the asramas. But one day, fate seemed to decide that the idyll had lasted long enough.

Yudhishtira was fifteen winters old, when spring arrived once more with a burst of flowers on the trees. Bird-song trilled from countless vivid throats and heady scents wafted through the airy passages of the forest. After the long cold, the season of love had arrived again: mating time. The wild creatures were all in rut. Serpents came out of their holes and entwined. Elephant and mountain-goat, panther and wolf, the eagle on his eyrie, and the smaller birds in the lower reaches of the hills, butterflies in the air, fish in the frothy brooks and insects under mossy stones were all at love.

One morning, Kunti had taken the five young Pandavas to a nearby asrama. Pandu was alone that day; he had not seen Madri either. He decided to take a stroll in the scented woods and pluck some lotuses for his wives from the pools that brimmed with startling blooms. Humming to himself, he walked along the familiar cedar aisles. The air was crisp and clear, the spring morning perfect and, it seemed to that hermit prince, alive with a mystic loveliness. He strolled through the woods and arrived in a clearing where a stream flowed, from which they drew their drinking water, and bathed in its sparkling currents.

Walking into that clearing, Pandu saw Madri at a bend in the stream. He stood still behind a large cedar, and his senses throbbed with a fever he thought he had long since known the last of; which is why it took him so unawares. That morning, Pandu saw something he had not seen for eighteen years: a naked woman. Madri had just put away her clothes on a smooth stone beside the jungle stream. She stood for a moment, testing the water with her foot before she waded into it. The sight of her body, filled out lushly with the years, touched Pandu like wildfire.

He stood transfixed, his mind reeling at seeing her like that after so long. Suddenly, it did not matter to Pandu whether he lived or died. The sight of naked Madri as she waded into the stream, the sight of her hips and breasts, her long, smooth arms and, most of all, the darkness that nestled between her fair thighs was more than he could bear. It was more than he could tear himself away from and run from that place as if death was after him.

He saw her as a young man sees his first naked woman, and all that mattered was to possess this dream at once. Like a hunter stalking his prey, he darted from one tree to another, his eyes never leaving the woman as she bathed in the warm water. Until, he stood behind a pine not five feet from the stone on which her clothes lay.

She finished bathing. When she came out and began to dry herself, he gave a strangled cry and darted out from hiding. At first she also cried out. But when she saw it was he, she smiled. She was full of languor from her bath and pleased that he had been watching her. Then she saw the state he was in and grew afraid.

"My lord, you mustn't. The curse!"

Without a word, breathing hard, he seized her in arms that were still so powerful and forced her down on the soft grass. She flailed about to get free. But he was too strong, and then she herself was swept away by his urgency. Realizing that protest would be of no use, she prayed that after so many years the rishi's curse might not be potent. She shut her eyes and, with a moan, clasped him to her. He bared himself in a flash, thrust himself into her like fire and began to move on her convulsively, crying aloud in release.

But even as ecstasy swept over him, and Madri found her sharp joy, that pale prince was borne right out of his body. As if he could not bear the intensity of what he felt, clutching his wife, Pandu went limp in her arms. She lay briefly in her own swoon. But when she tried to move him off her, where he lay heavy and inert, Madri saw that her husband was dead.

Kunti was on her way back home with the boys. Hearing Madri's screams they ran towards the stream. Cradling Pandu in her arms, Madri heard them calling anxiously to her from across the water. Quickly covering her nakedness, she cried, "Kunti, leave the children and come alone!"

The boys waited at a distance, while Kunti ran over and saw what had happened. Her cry rang among the trees. Kneeling beside her dead husband, she turned fiercely on Madri. "How could you?" she wailed. "How could you allow it, you wretched woman?"

Angrily, she took Pandu's body from Madri and laid his serene face in her own lap. Madri sobbed, "He took me by force, I couldn't stop him. Believe me, Kunti, I couldn't stop him though I tried."

Gradually, Kunti's fit of sobbing subsided. Setting Pandu's head down gently on the grass she said, "Ah Madri, your deepest wish has come true: he chose to die in your arms rather than mine." Jealousy flashed in her eyes, where Madri had never seen it before. Kunti whispered, "It was you who saw the bloom of love on his face, you who knew him as a man again."

Her lips quivered, then she said quietly, "He died in your arms all right, but I will follow him to the land of the manes."

By now their sons came there and saw their father lying on the ground. They stood numb, until Kunti told them to carry Pandu back to asrama. Meanwhile, hearing the women scream, some rishis also arrived there. They went back to the asrama with the bereaved family. Kunti dressed her husband's body in his royal silks, which he had not put on for eighteen years. She laid him out in their garden, as if in state, on the rope-cot he had slept on.

There seemed to be a smile on Pandu's face. Her courage melting away at the sight of him lying there, Kunti knelt beside him again. Laying her cheek against his, she sobbed piteously. Yudhishtira stood near his mother, knowing their lives would never be the same again.

He said to his brothers, "We are orphans from today. It is fate's will and we must be brave."

But the younger children cried, and the rishis tried to console them. And now the strangest tussle began between Kunti and Madri: both of them wanted to commit sati on Pandu's pyre. It seemed their argument would lead to an unseemly altercation, when the sages intervened.

The eldest rishi said, "You are not only wives, but mothers too. Your dharma lies not with your dead husband anymore, but with your sons who are still young and need you. We have decided to take you back to Hastinapura. You will find welcome from the people of the city, if not from blind Dhritarashtra. Your sons are born to rule the world, and you must watch over them until the future is secure.

"We have heard that evil has been born into Hastinapura, as Dhritarashtra's sons. He may be a good man himself; but will he choose your princes over his own? Don't speak of killing yourselves, when there is so much you both still have to do in this world."

Kunti was mollified, and grew quiet. But Madri cried, "We cannot send our husband unattended into heaven. To be with him is our dharma, too. He died because of me, because he desired me more than his life. I cannot live without Pandu. I must follow him and make him happy."

With less conviction now, Kunti said, "I am his first wife, I must follow him. You look after the children."

But Madri took her aside. She clasped Kunti's hands, and said, "These children will have to walk through hell together, for they are born to greatness. If you die and leave them to me, I will never be able to treat them equally. I will favour Sahadeva and Nakula over the others. And how long will the strength of a house divided against itself last?"

"Surely, knowing this, you can overcome it?"

"If I wanted to live or to deceive myself, I would say yes, I could. But you and I both know that isn't the truth. For once let me be the first one with Pandu. You make no difference between your sons and mine; it is as if you are the mother of all of them. And they, even my twins, prefer you to me. You must endure this world for a lifetime still, and I must follow Pandu into the land of the ancestors."

She looked pleadingly at Kunti, "I beg you, give me this much. I will make a bad mother to these boys in the world. I will divide them, and help their enemies. But I will be a good wife to Pandu in Devaloka. Don't stand on your being his first wife; your place is here with our children and mine with our husband."

Kunti raised Madri up and embraced her. "You be the fortunate one today," she said.

Madri kissed her fervently and broke into such a smile that Kunti realized for the first time how much she loved dead Pandu. Madri blessed her, "Your sons will be masters of the earth, and you will live to see them rule."

Madri called Sahadeva and Nakula and said to them, "Kunti is your real mother, but I was childless and she let me adopt you both. Yudhishtira, Bheema and Arjuna are your brothers. All of you are Kaunteyas, Kunti's sons, and Pandavas, Pandu's princes. From now on Yudhishtira will have your father's place. Obey him without question, never displease him."

She hugged the five of them, kissing them again and again. Clasping Yudhishtira tightly, for a second time, she said, "Look after the younger ones, my prince. You will be king of the earth one day. I will watch you from heaven and blow my blessings down on the wind, my noble child."

Pandu's funeral pyre was ready, and the dead kshatriya was laid upon it. Madri took the rishis' blessings. She came to Kunti and now fell at her feet, crying, "If I have ever wronged you, forgive me, my sister!"

Kunti raised her up and she also wept, "I will miss you little Madri, because I have always loved you. But this is no time for tears. You are going to a happy place where you will be with Pandu. Go with my blessings, and may your name be remembered for ever."

Touching Kunti's feet a last time, smiling radiantly at her, Madri turned and mounted the heaped sandalwood. Her eyes shut and her face calm, she sat at Pandu's feet in padmasana, the lotus posture. One of the rishis handed Yudhishtira a burning torch and, with tears streaming down his face, that prince lit his father's pyre. It caught swiftly and saffron flames rose, licking the air. Just once Madri cried out when they first touched her and she felt a stab of fear. But then those flames were cool and did not hurt her at all. They caressed her out of her body; and across the great threshold Pandu stood, his arms opened wide to her.

TWENTY-THREE

The Pandavas come home

KUNTI WENT BACK THE WAY SHE HAD COME EIGHTEEN YEARS AGO, towards distant, by now alien Hastinapura. She went back with five sons, and escorted by an entourage of sages. They set out from Satasringa, and Kunti wept to leave the asrama in the forest where she had been so happy. They crossed the mountains that guarded the hidden valley and came to the lake Indrayamuna, shimmering in the setting sun.

They spent a night on the banks of the lake and went on again the next morning towards Gandhamadana, the fragrant mountain, said to be the gatekeeper to the realms of the Gods. Skirting that massif, they came to the lands of Chitraratha the gandharva. But they met no Elves, who range heaven and earth, and are as old, some say, as the world itself.

Coming down from that enchanted country, Kunti, her sons and the rishis finally came to the plains of Bharatavarsha, the young Pandavas for the first time. The princes were overwhelmed and prostrated to worship the sacred land of their ancestors. On they pressed and reached the banks of the Ganga. They bathed in her ritually, and offered tarpana to their dead father and Madri. After another three days' journey, the party arrived on the banks of the Yamuna. In the distance they saw the ramparts of Hastinapura reaching for the sun.

They forded the river in some ferries, whose boatmen stared at the strangers. Seventeen days after setting out from Satasringa, the Pandavas and their mother arrived at the gates of Hastinapura.

For a while the princes stood there, gazing, their hearts full of their father's legends of this noble city. Then with a deep sense of destiny, which the five brothers shared at that moment, Yudhishtira nodded to Bheema. Bheema stepped forward and rattled the city-gates, and their guards came running. Those soldiers saw that no army threatened them. It was only some rishis, with a regal woman, wearing widow's white, and five young men in foresters' garb. Their curiosity aroused, the guardsmen opened the gates of the city of elephants.

The soldiers bowed to the seers who accompanied the gracious woman. The young men had to be princes of a great kingdom; they were so splendid, though they were dressed like hunters.

The eldest rishi said to the guards, "Send word to Bheeshma and Dhritarashtra that they have visitors whom they must come out to receive."

The soldiers stared for a moment. Was the old man serious that the king and the regent of Hastinapura should come out to meet these travellers? But they received such a glare from the holy ones that they were afraid lest they were cursed to be born as dogs, or worse, in their next lives. The guards of the gates went to Bheeshma and gave him the sages' message. The patriarch gave a shout that echoed in the sabha. He rushed to Dhritarashtra, in his apartment with Gandhari, and cried, "Kunti has come home with her sons!"

Meanwhile, word spread like light through the city. The people came flocking out from their homes to see the princes and hear their news. Soon Bheeshma and the king, Vidura, Satyavati, Ambika, Ambalika, Gandhari, the sons of Dhritarashtra, in their finery, and a royal retinue with them, arrived at the city-gates. They saw Kunti in white and untold grief upon her. Yet she glowed like an arani with five flames around her. Her sons were clad in deerskin, but, unlike Dhritarashtra's pampered princes, they were radiant.

Bheeshma bent to touch the munis' feet and the rest of the retinue after him. The eldest rishi said loudly, so everyone heard him, "You all know that Pandu renounced the world because of a rishi's curse. He was living among us in Satasringa, with his wives Kunti and Madri. Five sons were born to this kshatriya family in the wilderness."

He beckoned and Yudhishtira stood forward, and after him, as each one was introduced by that sage, the other Pandavas. The holy one said, "This is Yudhishtira, Pandu's eldest son and the natural son of Dharma Deva."

Yudhishtira bowed, as a sigh went up from the crowd. Bheema stepped forward. The rishi said, "This is Bheemasena, Kunti and Pandu's second son, whose natural father is Vayu Deva. And this is Arjuna, who is the son of the king of the Devas, Lord Indra himself."

As each Pandava prince came forward, a wave of cheering rose from the people. It swept over Duryodhana like a tide of venom. His face grew darker and darker, with a rage he could only force deep down into his envious heart, where it lay ever after as cold murder. The old rishi said, "Here are the youngest Pandavas, Nakula and Sahadeva. They are twins, and their fathers are the Aswins of heaven."

When the cheering had died down, the muni resumed, "When Yudhishtira was fifteen, Pandu performed all the kshatriya rituals for his sons. The princes are versed in the Vedas, and the arts of war and statecraft. They now need masters of the royal way to teach them further."

There was such power in that sage's voice nobody dared interrupt him; but everyone was impatient to know where Pandu was. When the old man paused for a moment, Bheeshma said, "Lord, where are my nephew Pandu and Madri?"

"Seventeen days ago, Pandu was gathered to his fathers and Madri committed sati on his pyre."

He pointed to the covered litter they had carried with them from Satasringa. "We have brought the mortal remains of Pandu and Madri, so you can honour them with a proper funeral."

A shocked silence fell. Then a wail went up from the crowd, and Kunti began to sob. The people scrambled forward to pay homage to that simple litter in which Pandu's ashes lay. Only Dhritarashtra's sons stood apart, snickering among themselves.

Bheeshma wept. Pandu's mother Ambalika had fainted to hear her son was dead. Dhritarashtra stood stricken as a wave of memories swept over him: memories of a tender childhood, and of an endlessly patient and loving brother, through whose eyes, he, blind Dhritarashtra, had learned to see the forms and colours of the dark world. Dhritarashtra turned to Vidura, who cried like a boy, and told him to arrange for a royal funeral.

The eldest rishi said, "Don't mourn a kshatriya who has left you five sons like these princes. Take them into your palace and into your hearts. They are your charge from now; this is where they belong."

When that muni saw the expression in the prince Duryodhana's hooded eyes he felt a pang of fear. But he knew fate must take her course, inevitably, whatever it was. Those rishis raised their hands in blessing over Kunti and the princes, and next moment, vanished like a dream at waking.

With solemn rites, Pandu was laid to rest in the city of his fathers. Vidura called Vyasa to conduct the funeral. Through the chanting of Vedic hymns, the rishi sat plunged in thought. Finally, Pandu and Madri's remains were taken to the Ganga and consigned to her golden waters. They would flow to the ocean, and their souls would find peace. When Pandu's sons had performed tarpana for their father and mother, a feast was held to mark the end of the fast, and announce that the mourning was concluded.

After the feast, Vyasa went to see his mother Satyavati. He made her sit beside him and took her hand. He said grimly, "Mother, the days of joy are over; now begins the darkness that heralds the kali yuga. Sinister times are in store for the House of Kuru. Every day will be heavy with sin and the next day worse than the last one. The earth has outgrown her youth, and evil is at hand, evil that men have never known before.

And right here, in your own family, evil will take root among your grandsons." He leaned forward to whisper to her, "Most of all in the hearts of Dhritarashtra and his son Duryodhana, who is a devil. With births like his into the world, the very earth loses her innocence. She is defiled, and the days of corruption have arrived. Look into the eyes of your great-grandchildren, Dhritarashtra's sons. There is enough rapacity there to drag the earth down into hell.

"The sons of Pandu and the sons of Dhritarashtra will have enmity between them, which will end in a war like the world has never seen; a war that will destroy the power of the kshatriyas on earth, and usher in the end of an age. I had a vision of it as I sat upon the Himalaya: a war between dharma and adharma, light and darkness. Millions will fight and die, most without knowing the reason for their being born, or being slaughtered like beasts on a hunt."

Vyasa paused; he sighed and shook his head. Gently, he said, "Mother, you will not be able to bear what the future holds for your children.

I think it is time you left the city and went into the forest to seek your peace. So far, only noble spirits have been born into this august House as its scions. But Duryodhana and his brothers are not princes of dharma. They are creatures of evil come to destroy the world. Satyavati, go far away from this city. You belong to a quickly vanishing time, and your eyes mustn't see all that will come to pass here as surely as night follows day."

Satyavati was wise enough to know he spoke the truth. She had already watched with alarm what louts Dhritarashtra's sons, the young Kauravas, were growing into. Duryodhana had given his brothers and himself that name, which meant the sons of Kuru, to underline his future claim to the throne.

Satyavati called Ambika and Ambalika, and asked Vyasa to repeat whatever he had told her. Then she said, "I have decided to go away to the forest. If you both want, you may come with me."

She had guessed shrewdly at those women's sorrow in Hastinapura. Ambalika, of course, was shattered by Pandu's death and there was never any question of her not going. But strangely, Ambika, whose son was the king, was so saddened by what she had seen recently in the palace that she said she would go to the vana as well. Dhritarashtra hardly had time for his mother any more; he was so absorbed in his wife and his princes. And Ambika's grandsons, the Kauravas, treated her with less than contempt.

It had been a trying life for those sisters, since the day Bheeshma swept them up in his chariot on the morning of their swayamvara. They had never been able to forget what had happened to Amba. It had been an evil omen. Vichitraveerya, with whom they had spent the few happy years they had known, had died. Then came the nights with Vyasa, the thought of which made them tremble even now; and Satyavati's anger that both her grandsons, except Vidura, were born less than whole. The old woman had never stopped taunting them for that. Ambika and Ambalika were relieved to leave this city of their sorrows. Peace was all they craved, and they were eager to set out in pursuit of it.

When everything was ready, and all their possessions had been given away as alms, Satyavati called Bheeshma and said to him, "My son, today we say farewell in this world, you and I. I have decided to leave this unhappy city."

Recently, Bheeshma looked more anxious and drawn than she had ever seen him. He breathed, "Why, mother? Why do you want to do this now? Won't you stay and help me bear the burden?"

But Satyavati shook her head. "No Devavrata, I will not stay. Vyasa said to me there is nothing but doom in store for the House of Kuru, and I shan't be able to bear what must come to pass here." She lowered her voice, "All the evil.

"I am an old woman now, and of no use to anyone. And I am not brave anymore. I am like a fruit that is so ripe it is ready to drop from the tree and be received by the earth. Let me go and seek my peace, before it is too late."

Bheeshma had grown thoughtful, absent. He said slowly, "Doom. Is that what Vyasa said? Tell me what exactly he said; I must know, mother."

Word for word, she repeated what her son, the seer, had said. She saw Bheeshma's strong face grow pale; his lips twitched in anguish to hear the fate that awaited the royal House he had nurtured all his life.

When Satyavati finished, Bheeshma fetched a sigh. He rose stiffly and paced the room. Suddenly, he stopped and cried, "I too am willing to play the coward, for my courage deserts me when I hear what you say. I have never told you this, but the day you came into this house my father was so pleased that he granted me a boon. I can summon my own death at any time I choose. I think the time has come."

"No!"

He turned to her, puzzled, and saw her eyes flash as of old. Those two were closer than they perhaps cared to admit. Through the long, hard years the two of them had, quietly and bravely, shared the tragedies fate had chosen to visit them with. Theirs was a bond of two strong people. In moments of crisis they had felt free enough to say to each other what they could not tell anyone else, to speak their inmost thoughts.

But now, Satyavati had reached the end of her strength. And when she said she was leaving Hastinapura, Bheeshma realized what her being in the city had meant to him, and the loneliness she was consigning him to by going away. This would be the final trial, and the most difficult. He did not think he could bear it; but her eyes glittering, she brought him up as sharply as ever.

"I forbid it!" she cried. "You shall not even think of taking your life. Hastinapura has more need of you than ever, and you want to play the coward now?"

She came near and took his hand. "Listen to me, Devavrata. You are forgetting Pandu's sons. Who do they have in this godforsaken palace except you? I leave them in your care. From what my heart knows of the evil growing here, and from what Vyasa has foretold, the Pandavas are the only hope for this kingdom. Nurture them, Bheeshma. Don't dream of dying until dharma is firmly established in the House of Kuru, and Yudhishtira rules from its throne."

She paused, and smiled, "Once, I asked you to do something for me. You refused saying it was against your dharma because of the oath you had sworn. This time, it is surely your dharma that I am begging you to keep. Everything depends on you; Devavrata, don't derelict on your duty."

Bheeshma grew very still, and then he also smiled wanly. He nodded that he would do as she asked. At last he bowed and left her, and his eyes were moist with thoughts too deep for words. And so a chapter of fate's tale in Hastinapura ended, when Satyavati, Ambika and Ambalika left that city and went away to a distant forest, from where they never returned. And in course of time in that vana, after a long tapasya, they found their peace.

TWENTY-FOUR

The seeds of envy

T HE PANDAVAS SETTLED SLOWLY INTO THEIR NEW LIFE. FOR THE first time, they tasted the luxury of a palace, and the privileges of being princes. They accepted these with humility and grace. They were very different from Dhritarashtra's sons, who had known only this opulent existence: Pandu's sons had lived in the wilderness, which is a profound teacher. Besides, they had known the sorrow of their father's death, and Madri's.

Envy from the Kaurava princes could not be far behind. They burned with it, when they saw how kshatriyas and servants alike, and, most of all, the common people of Hastinapura warmed to their cousins. The Pandavas were always courteous and kind, while Dhritarashtra's sons were arrogant, wanton and often cruel. And when Duryodhana and his brothers found the Pandavas were altogether more accomplished than they were, and especially at arms, there was no turning back from the destiny that lay in store for them all.

Of the five Pandavas it was the second one, rumbustious young Bheema, whom Duryodhana saw as being the main threat to himself. So far, being the oldest among his brothers, Duryodhana had been a favourite of the Kuru patriarch Bheeshma, whom the Kauravas called Pitama, Grandfather. Suddenly, with the advent of the Pandavas, Duryodhana saw his pre-eminence with Bheeshma dwindle sharply. He felt the old man's affections were now shared too much; and as with everything else about him, Bheema's appetite for his grandfather's love was larger than life. Duryodhana was jealous of every caress or tender word with which Bheeshma favoured his ebullient cousin.

The other four Pandavas, especially the introverted Yudhishtira, were reticent when compared with Bheema. But he, young giant, suffered from no inhibitions. He took heartily to palace life, as if he wanted to make up for the lost years in the forest. There was a huge, innocent wildness about young Bheema that was irresistible. Everything he did or wanted was at least twice as much as all the others. And his energy was boundless, as he raged his exuberant way from dawn to dusk, and one day to the next, his eyes shining!

Pandu's second son was as restless as his natural father, the wind, and he was awesomely strong. When the Pandavas first arrived in Hastinapura, Duryodhana and his brothers had smirked at their simple attire and their rustic appearance. A few days went by and Duryodhana made the mistake of challenging Bheema to wrestle with him. He wanted to put the Pandavas in their place. The oldest Kaurava was by far the strongest of his own brothers, and he thought he would give the forest boy a sound lesson.

But this was a miscalculation. For a week, Duryodhana could hardly sit from the thrashing Bheema gave him. The bout had hardly begun and Duryodhana was flat on his back. Each time he got up, Bheema would knock him down again, effortlessly. It was the first time anyone had given Duryodhana a beating, and all his life he never forgot it. Seeing their brother humiliated, ten other Kaurava boys set on the Pandava, who was alone: Bheema routed the lot and they carried bruises for days.

After that, none of Dhritarashtra's sons dared cross Bheema, or any of the other Pandavas for fear of him. Indeed, most of the boys acknowledged that Bheema was by far the strongest among them; though not in front of Duryodhana. Bheema became the bane of Duryodhana's life, the despoiler of his youth. It was a hatred the Kaurava never grew out of. He spent his days hatching plots against his cousin, who was quite innocent of the undertow of real evil in their relationship. Bheema lived irrepressibly, from moment to moment, day to day—life was a wonderful thing, to be lived to the hilt and never to be brooded over. It was a game to play, perhaps to bury the sorrow of a father's death; and Bheema was certain that everyone else, even Duryodhana was just like himself.

Little did he know how obsessed the Kaurava had become with him, that the king's son spent hours thinking dark thoughts about him, how even his dreams were full of Bheema's ringing laughter. Duryodhana just could not accept his cousin, who had arrived in Hastinapura only to ruin his life. All Duryodhana saw these days was Bheema: hateful, happy, incredibly strong Bheema, everywhere. Bheema who ate twice what any other boy did; who could run like the wind, twice as fast as the others; who was stronger than any ten Kauravas; who was a bit of a bully and taunted his cousins, always daring them to a fight; Bheema who had quickly become his grandfather Bheeshma's favourite grandchild; who shook the Kauravas out of the fruit-trees in the palace orchards like mangoes; who pulled their hair, beat them at will, wrestled with any ten of them at once; carried tales about the Kauravas to each other, so they fought among themselves; Bheema who was fiercely loyal to his own brothers, and for whose sake no Kaurava dared touch any Pandava, though they were only five; Bheema who was the bane of Duryodhana's life, *Bheema whom Duryodhana wanted dead.*

For some time, Duryodhana seethed in silence, and the bile he was forced to swallow threatened to choke him. Then, there came to Hastinapura someone who was to fuel Duryodhana's envy of the Pandavas into tragic proportions. Gandhari's brother, Shakuni, arrived in the ancient city.

Plump Shakuni had cold, womanly hands, pale serpent's eyes and the hint of the serpent's hiss in the lisp with which he spoke. Duryodhana took to his uncle immediately, as if he had waited for him all his young life. Shakuni sharpened Duryodhana's sense of the future and what lay in store for him if Yudhishtira ever ruled Hastinapura; as seemed likely, since the Pandava was the oldest among the cousins, and ideally suited to be a king by his upright and serene nature.

Duryodhana had grown up all these years believing that one day the throne of the Kurus would be his. Shakuni whispered in his ear that he would be no more than the Pandavas' slave; is that what he wanted, he the king's son? Is that the fate he intended to allow his life to be mired in, and leave it a shallow, powerless thing forever? Or did he mean to stand up like a kshatriya to the injustice that was about to overtake him? And thus return his life, and his brothers' lives, to the destiny of being the Kuru king's sons.

Shakuni said, "The choice is yours. Will you be weak and allow events to overwhelm you? Or will you be strong, and mould events to your own will? Will you be a servant or a king?"

Duryodhana replied without hesitation, "I will be a king. I will rule the world and shape it to my will."

"Then Bheema is the one you must get rid of. He is Yudhishtira's strength."

"I know. But how?"

Shakuni seemed to examine his nephew closely, as if to discover if the boy was worthy; whether, when the time came, he would have the courage to carry out the scheme his uncle was about to suggest to him. Shakuni was a small man, the eyes in his closed face always restless with plotting. Nobody ever knew what Shakuni was thinking, though you could be certain it was no good. He also had the reputation of dabbling in the dark arts, of being something of a sorcerer; but again, no one knew for sure.

Now Shakuni moistened his lips with a slim tongue. He lowered his voice and said, "There is only one way, of course. You must kill Bheema. Without him the others are no match for you and your brothers."

Duryodhana gave a hiss of satisfaction: here at last was a counsellor after his own heart. The prince's eyes blazed. He clasped Shakuni's hand so fiercely even that evil one was a little unnerved. Duryodhana whispered, "I've been thinking the same thing for a year. But there was no one I could trust to help me, and keep his mouth shut as well."

"You have me now, Duryodhana; and if you want it, for ever."

"No one, uncle, will make a better minister to the future king of the Kurus. Tell me, Shakuni, how do we get Bheema out of the way? How soon can I sleep again at nights? When can I know that animal, my detested cousin, is dead?"

"We mustn't touch him here in the palace. It is too risky. Listen..."

TWENTY-FIVE

At Pramanakoti

WITH THE CONNIVANCE OF SHAKUNI, WHOSE IDEA IT WAS, Duryodhana arranged an outing to the river for the princes of the Kuru court: the Kauravas and the Pandavas. Suddenly, he seemed to have shed his resentment of his cousins, and took such pains over the excursion that Bheeshma was pleased. The patriarch thought Duryodhana had outgrown his envy; perhaps the future would not be as ominous as Vyasa had predicted.

At Pramanakoti on the banks of the Ganga, Duryodhana had a pavilion built, with smaller tents all round it, furnished with couches and silks from Hastinapura and a kitchen to rival the one in the palace. Bright flags flew over these and everything was ready for the outing. To be sure the Pandavas would not refuse to go to the river, Duryodhana made it a point to ask their advice on every detail: which cooks to take, where each tent should be pitched, how far from the main pavilion the kitchen should be, how many chariots they should travel in. He was so friendly the Pandavas were disarmed. They felt this was the beginning of a happier phase in their relations with their cousins.

It was a fine spring morning. The sky was clear, the sun shone down on the world and the people of Hastinapura came out of their homes as the youths set out, on elephants and in chariots, singing, cracking jokes and laughing. The people were pleased to see how free from rivalry their princes were. It boded well for the future.

After a merry journey, the young kshatriyas saw the river, wide as a small sea and winding away into the distance. When they arrived at

Duryodhana's sprawling pavilion, the boys dismissed all their attendants and charioteers, except for the cooks: this was to be an outing just for the princes, to celebrate their newly struck friendship. They entered the pavilion and it was hardly less than a palace. Everyone said how wonderful it was; this was their very own domain, a kingdom of the young. They hoped they would come back here frequently, free from elders, masters and tutors, and tiresome court rules and etiquette.

Quickly, in the gardens between carefully laid lotus-pools, they were at wrestling and other boisterous games; Bheema excelled at all of them. And soon they were hungry as only the young can be, and came roaring for food into the dining hall. A feast was already laid out on the long tables set end to end against the walls, vast quantities of princes' fare.

When they had eaten their fill out of their own plates, they began to feed each other, affectionately. No one noticed it was Duryodhana who began this, and strangest of all, he himself served Bheema. Yudhishtira approved, and the other Pandavas too. It seemed that finally the Kaurava had taken them to his heart. The guileless Bheema ate more than his fill from the plate of sweets, which Duryodhana fetched just for him and insisted his cousin finish every morsel. Bheema gorged himself on the delicious sweets, never knowing that deadly poison had been mixed in them. Earlier Shakuni had procured this nightshade from some forest gypsies, who were thieves and thought little enough of murdering anyone who crossed them. It was a slow-acting poison that Bheema had ingested.

When the meal was over, Duryodhana cried, "It's time for a swim!"

With loud yells, each one wanting to be first in the water, they raced one another to the river. They threw off their clothes as they went, and dived in naked as they were born. A lot of fine young manhood was on display in the golden afternoon. Most of them were fluent swimmers, and they raced one another to the far bank and back. Once more Bheema won by a long way, with Duryodhana just behind him. But the moment he came ashore, Bheema gave a sigh and flopped down on the warm sand. He felt so tired that he had to sleep.

Arjuna went up to him, "Are you all right, Bheema?"

Bheema waved him away, "It's so fine and warm here, I want to sleep for a while. I'll join you soon enough."

Duryodhana now said it was time for another round of refreshments; they should return to the pavilion.

"We haven't much time before sunset. Then we must head home."

He led the others back, shouting, laughing and pulling on the first set of clothes each one found. Often they were so ill fitting it provoked ribald jokes and fresh laughter. Duryodhana went into the kitchen to tell the cooks to bring out more food and drink. When the food arrived, no one noticed him slip out again. In the gathering dusk, he ran to the river where Bheema lay in a stupor of weird dreams. The Pandava lay paralysed by the poison, of which Duryodhana had fed him enough to kill an elephant.

Humming to himself, the Kaurava began to tie Bheema's hands and feet with some vine he had hidden in a tree. He wasn't sure that even the huge dose of nightshade Bheema had eaten would kill him. He decided to make sure the thing was done one way or another. Having bound his unconscious cousin firmly with the thick vine, Duryodhana rolled Bheema into the murmuring river, grown dark with the falling night.

For a moment the Kaurava stood anxiously scanning the water. With a mock salute, he bid farewell to his tormentor, "Goodbye cousin, and sweet dreams."

He turned and ran back to the pavilion, where the others were still at their food. No one noticed him come in; so he had never left for all that anyone knew. Soon it was night, and time to return to Hastinapura. Suddenly Yudhishtira asked, "Where is Bheema?"

Duryodhana replied casually, "When we last saw him he was asleep by the river. He must have woken up, found us gone and decided to get home before anyone else."

And no one gave it another thought. It would have been just like Bheema to go without telling them: he liked to be as unpredictable as he could. The rest of them, all the Kauravas and Pandavas, climbed into their chariots and on to their elephants and went back as merrily as they had come.

When they arrived, Yudhishtira went straight to Kunti. "Mother, has Bheema come home?"

"No. Isn't he with you?"

"We left him asleep by the river, and we thought he had come home on his own."

Kunti turned pale. "You must go back and look for him."

The four brothers rode back to Pramanakoti. Arjuna remembered where Bheema had lain down to sleep on the sand. Arjuna's sense of direction was uncanny in the moonless night; he led them straight to the spot. They lit torches and began to call Bheema's name, but only faint echoes above the river answered them.

Then Arjuna pointed to the sand at their feet. Clearly visible by the rushlights was the indentation of Bheema's heavy body where he had slept. And next to that were the marks where someone had rolled him into the water. It was too dark to do anything now. The river was cold and deep, and full of undercurrents that could pull them down. And if their brother had drowned, it was too late to save him.

Yudhishtira said, "We can't do any good here now. Let's go back and come again tomorrow. Mother must be in a panic."

They rode back to the city. It was near midnight when they came into Kunti's chambers. They found Vidura was already with her. One look at her sons' faces and Kunti's eyes filled with tears. She said desperately, "I am sure Duryodhana has killed Bheema. Oh, haven't you seen, Vidura, how Dhritarashtra's boy hates my son?"

Vidura said, "Calm down, Kunti. These are rash accusations."

But she was past restraint. "How can you say that when you know how greedy Duryodhana is for the throne? He always saw Bheema as the main obstacle in his way. How can I be calm when my son has been murdered?"

Suddenly, the mild Vidura was stern. "Long lives have been foretold for all your sons. The astrologers who read the stars do not lie. Even if Duryodhana tried to kill Bheema, I'm sure he isn't dead." He grew sombre, then, said gravely, "Even if Duryodhana has killed Bheema, it won't help you to accuse him. It will only put him on his guard. And then, he will be in a hurry to kill your other sons as well, from whom he perceives no threat so far."

Kunti shivered when she heard that, and grew quiet. Vidura said again, "My heart tells me Bheema will come back. Until then, you must remain calm. And most important, none of you must accuse Duryodhana."

Meanwhile, in another wing of the palace, Duryodhana and Shakuni were celebrating their successful enterprise with wine. Again and again, Shakuni asked, "Are you sure no one saw you when you rolled him in?"

"No one, Shakuni."

"None of your own brothers even? They can't be trusted to hold their tongues."

"Absolutely no one."

"Well, be sure you show none of this joy in the sabha tomorrow; or ever. At least, not until you are king. And you may not have to kill any more of your cousins. The others are weaklings; we can take care of them easily now the dangerous one is dead."

"I am a man today, Shakuni. Where are the women you promised me?"

Shakuni clapped his hands, and two young girls were brought in by a trusted servant, for the uncle and his nephew.

TWENTY-SIX

Under the river

His veins full of nightshade, Bheema sank like a stone in the river. Down he slid, along the smooth sides of the shallows, plunged in venom dreams. Pulled down by a wicked undertow he fell towards the riverbed, among phosphorescent mosses and lichens. Vivid fish swam curiously around him, wondering what this giant was.

But the river is a Goddess and she is mysterious. She was also, after a fashion, Bheema's great-grandmother. Many strange creatures lived beneath her currents, and becoming aware of the peril to Bheema's life, she stirred up some water-serpents that had their nests on the deepest bed of the river. She cried to them that a dangerous enemy had arrived in their midst. Those scarlet and green serpents swarmed around the unconscious Bheema, and began to sting him repeatedly. They sank their fangs in, squeezing pale snake-venom into his blood.

Bheema struck the bottom of the river, and he fell right through the sand into the world of the nagas. Normally, any man would have been dead as he plunged through the subtle threshold; so many snakes had stung him, and quite a few went down with him, their fangs still fastened to his flesh.

But Bheema did not die. Fate had intended him to fall into the secret realm below, and the Devi of the river knew this. Instead of dying, he seemed to recover with each sting. Colour flushed back into his face and the Pandava awoke with a shout in the kingdom of the nagas. Flinging off the vines that bound him, he seized the serpents and smashed their hoods against the emerald floor of the strange chamber he found himself in. As the river knew it would, the snake-venom acted as a powerful antidote to the kaalakuta Duryodhana had plied him with. The Pandava was quickly back to himself, and livid that these wretched worms had dared sting him.

He killed a hundred of them, and those left alive fled through an opening in the wall through which he could not follow them. Along smooth, narrow passages, their way lit by jewels on the walls, those serpents flew deep into the bowels of the earth, into the under-world of patala. They were the guardians of that hidden world, and the human had killed more than half of them.

They arrived in the august presence of their sovereign, Vasuki of countless coils, master of all nagas. Vasuki sat on his throne, which was a giant emerald carved into a seat, with two glimmering snake-wives entwined around him. His ministers sat around their king, and that sabha was as brightly lit as Indra's Sudharma by jewels embedded on walls, ceiling, floor, and at serpent-hood and throat. The snakes from the river bent their hoods at Vasuki's feet. That king now had a human form, green and brilliant.

Vasuki whispered so that chamber echoed with his voice, "My children, why have you come to me? What is the matter?"

The serpents of the riverbed gnashed their fangs and venom trickled from their jaws. Their leader cried sibilantly, "A man, sire, a young mortal. He sank into the river and the Devi stirred us. A thousand of us rose to meet him, and his hands were bound and he seemed asleep. We stung him fiercely as he sank. No ordinary man could have survived our stings, but this one woke up as if our fangs had tickled him.

"He broke the vine with which someone had tied him before they pushed him into the river, and he fell on us. He dashed us against the floor and the walls. He stamped our hoods with feet like tree-roots, and our brothers were crushed. Vasuki, he was a storm of death and his body seemed to be made of gusts of wind. Those of us who escaped the savage youth fled to you, my lord."

That snake bent his head low before his emperor. He knew that death was Vasuki's punishment for allowing a stranger into his kingdom. A long moment's silence fell, only soft snake breath filled the cavernous chamber. The queen serpents slid quietly away from their king. Vasuki's expression gave nothing away of what he thought. Silently, the naga emperor brooded. Then, to the relief of the river-guards, Vasuki's face was lit by a smile. He said in his rustling voice, "I think I know who this youth of yours is. Come, let us take a look at him."

And at once he was an awesome hamadryad, a hundred feet long and resplendent. His immense hood was tucked in, his scales shone and the jewel in his head was as big as a man's fist. Swift as eagles, the nagas and their king flew along the mazes of patala towards the chamber in which Bheema stood, panting, among the carcasses of a hundred snakes. Among those who went with Vasuki was an aged serpent Aryaka. He was his king's minister and Vasuki and Aryaka had exchanged a knowing glance when they heard the intruder being described; both of them suspected who the human youth was. Aryaka was also Kuntibhoja's grandfather.

They arrived at the emerald chamber. Bheema was now striking resounding blows at its walls. He saw no way to get out, other than to break them down. Vasuki peered through a panel on one of the walls; he could look in but Bheema could not look out.

The great naga said, "This is a welcome visitor! It is Bheemasena, Kunti and Pandu's son, and the wind's."

Aryaka shimmered to see his great-grandchild. In a moment, all the nagas had human forms again. At a secret word from their king, a whole wall to that chamber slid smoothly away. Bheema stood gaping at those serpent-lords. Aryaka cried, "My little son!" and clasped the Pandava in his arms.

Bheema was amazed. "What is this place? Who are you, old man, and who are these fine friends of yours?"

Vasuki laughed to see how fearless the Pandava was. He, too, came forward and embraced Bheema. "You may have heard of me, young Bheemasena. I am Vasuki of the nagas. Surely, fate has some important plan for us that you have fallen into my kingdom. I see you are as strong and as brave as I had heard, O son of Vayu. This old one here is your grandsire Aryaka."

Bheema knelt before them. What a story to tell his brothers in Hastinapura! Vasuki and Aryaka both blessed him. The serpent-king said, "I must give our guest precious gifts to take home. He is an honoured visitor and, from now on, always welcome in my kingdom."

The king touched Bheema's shoulder, and a delectable coolness coursed through the Pandava. The place where the naga had touched him glowed like dark jade. Vasuki said, "I declare you a friend of the nagas. Anywhere in the world my people will know you by my mark on your body. And they will help you, whenever you need them. But that isn't enough."

He clapped his hands. When two of his servants came forward, he said, "Give this youth treasure to his heart's content, gold, silver and jewels."

But Bheema was hardly moved by this. Vasuki laughed again.

"So," he cried, "he is truly a prince! Wealth means little to him. Then what would you have of me, Bheemasena? You only have to ask and it shall be yours, because I have already grown very fond of you."

Aryaka whispered in his king's ear, and Vasuki smiled. "I have something for you that you can treasure for ever."

"What is it?"

The Lord of the nagas said, "I have an amrita for you, Bheema. An elixir that will give you strength such as even you haven't dreamt of."

Vasuki nodded to one of his servitors who went off to fetch the nagamrita. It was made from snake-essences, and from arcane recipes handed down from generations of nagas, since the beginning of their race. Crushed jewels were mixed in that elixir, and venom as well, and other rare substances, all in exact measures: even a drop too much of this or that would kill the drinker instead of giving him superhuman strength.

The attendant returned shortly with a steaming chalice in his hands, which he gave to his king. The silvery amrita in the chalice was heavier than quicksilver, and Vasuki arched a long, slender brow. "You have brought a good deal of it. You obviously think this young kshatriya can drink twice as much as anyone else."

The serpent-king turned to Bheema, "This will give you the strength of a hundred elephants, for every draught you can drink. But it is a heavy potion; no mortal has ever drunk more than a sip before."

Aryaka made Bheema sit cross-legged on the floor, facing the east. Ceremonially, Vasuki handed the Pandava the chalice, its effervescent amrita streaked with colour.

"Drink slowly, prince. No man can hold more than a sip or two."

With a grin at his grandsire, Bheema drained the whole thing at a gulp. He handed back the chalice, and cried, "It's heavy all right, but tasty. Can I have some more?"

"Bring more nagamrita for Bheemasena! He must have as much as he can drink, and he will be as strong as the kshatriyas of the nobler ages."

More amrita was fetched. Bheema quaffed eight chalices. Then he began to feel drowsy. The nagas had already made a bed of dry moss and soft reeds for him. Bheema was helped on to it, yawning and his limbs heavy with the drink. Vasuki said, "Sleep deeply, sleep long Bheema. And as you sleep your strength will grow."

Murmuring his gratitude, Bheema fell asleep at once and began snoring. Posting a guard outside the room, Vasuki, Aryaka and the other nagas left. Eight days Bheema slept under the Ganga, one for each chalice of amrita he had drunk. The potion went to work on him, and he grew stronger with each moment he slept.

When Bheema awoke and stretched his limbs, he felt an enormous new power rippling through them and gave a roar of delight. Vasuki's guards went flashing away to their king. The serpent lords returned to the emerald chamber. Now they came with a hillock of food piled on silver salvers.

Bheema ate until the last morsel was gone. It was exotic and delicious fare, and he did not ask what any of it was. He was given water to drink and wash with. The nagas clothed him in soft garments, woven from white fabric that glowed in the dark. That cloth was made of mosses washed clean of their natural dyes. Bheema felt rather pleased with himself.

Vasuki said to him, "You are as strong as a thousand elephants now. May the Gods bless you; there are many trials ahead of you, and many battles you must fight."

Bheema knelt and thanked that strange and splendid king. Vasuki raised him up and embraced him, and Bheema's grandsire Aryaka did as well. In his hypnotic voice Vasuki said, "It is time you went home to your mother and your brothers. They have given you up for dead."

The Pandava bid farewell to his new friends. Old Aryaka's eyes were moist, and the king also seemed sad to see the charming human prince go. Bheema went through a tunnel with some of the nagas and up through a hidden trapdoor. They swam up through the river and into a sunlit day above.

Breaking the surface of the Ganga with a shout, Bheema saw he was in the same place where he had fallen asleep. Vasuki had told him how

Duryodhana had tied his hands and feet and rolled him into the water. He warned Bheema he should not confront Duryodhana; nor should he reveal anything of his adventures under the river. The best course was to be vigilant, and to keep the Kaurava guessing.

The nagas came ashore with the Pandava; they pointed to the colourful pavilion. Could Bheema find his own way home to Hastinapura? Of course he could, he cried. One by one, those magical beings embraced the Kuru prince and they dived back into the Ganga. Bheema saw that as they swam through the clear water, they turned into great snakes and flashed down, back to their nether world and their mysterious king.

When he was alone, Bheema threw back his head and gave an echoing roar. The sun was bright in the cloudless blue sky above him. It was a fine spring day and it was wonderful to be alive, especially now that he was so much stronger as well. Just let Duryodhana cross him again! But as he walked home, at leisure, the Pandava was thoughtful. He could hardly believe what he knew: his cousin had actually tried to kill him. He grew sombre. It dawned on him that the world was not what he had naively imagined it to be. Young Bheema had begun to grow up.

Then he thought of his mother waiting for him. He thought of his brothers and what a story he had for them. Bheema began to run towards Hastinapura as swiftly as his father of the air, so that the trees, the birds and animals on his way wondered at the uncanny little gale blowing past them. Its heart was invisible, because it went so quickly.

When Bheema returned, Kunti clasped him to her, sobbing, "My little son, I thought you were dead!"

At last she calmed down and let him go to his brothers. Yudhishtira had tears in his eyes and he also held Bheema long. Then Bheema hugged Arjuna and the twins. Kunti sent word to Vidura, whom she considered her only friend in the palace. When he came, he cried he had told them, hadn't he, that Bheema would be back safely. Vidura sat with Kunti and the Pandavas, and Bheema related all that had happened to him since he had fallen asleep beside the river.

He told them that Vasuki, who had eyes everywhere, said Duryodhana had poisoned him and rolled him into the water. Their suspicions were confirmed. But Vidura warned them, "Say nothing of what you know, but always be on your guard. Be friendly and wary, and at dinner tonight, watch every face and you will know who all were guilty of trying to kill Bheema."

That evening, Bheema appeared in the royal dining-hall with his brothers for the night meal, which was taken together with the king and the rest of the family. The smile of the past eight days froze on Duryodhana's lips and his face was a picture. Beside that evil prince, sat another whose mouth fell open as if he, too, had seen a ghost: Shakuni was obviously shocked and, if the Pandavas did not suspect Gandhari's brother yet, Vidura saw through him.

Duryodhana was forced to pretend he was also relieved that Bheema was back safely. But he saw in the Pandavas' eyes that they knew who had tried to kill their brother, and he lay low for a while. But not for long: the attempt by the river was by no means the last one he made on his cousin's life. He was responsible for many subtle 'accidents' in the palace, which befell only the second Pandava. But at times by good fortune, and often by his superhuman strength, Bheema always escaped unhurt.

Duryodhana felt he would go mad from the ravening hatred that fed on his heart, day and night. He took his brothers into his confidence and some of them, like Dusasana, hated the Pandavas as much as he did. Those hundred agreed readily with their brother, that their cousins were in their way. Eventually, the sons of Pandu must be killed.

There was one son of Dhritarashtra who was closer to the Pandavas than to his own brothers. He was not evil by nature, but a gentle youth and loving. He was Yuyutsu, the king's son by the vaishya woman, and had been born naturally from his mother's womb. He had been raised with his half-brothers, the Kauravas, and they thought of him as one of them. They never suspected Yuyutsu was a spy, which is exactly what the resourceful youngster became.

Yuyutsu pretended to despise Yudhishtira and his brothers more than any of the others did. Duryodhana made him privy to his incessant plotting to be rid of the five Devaputras. But Yuyutsu had decided his loyalty lay with the Pandavas. Despite his cousins' protests that he shouldn't risk bringing them word of Duryodhana's plots, Yuyutsu insisted on doing just that, often at some peril to himself. If he had been discovered Duryodhana would have killed him.

Somehow, with breathless midnight assignations, messages encoded in leaves, twigs and markings on tree-trunks and palace-walls, which no one but the Pandavas could decipher, Yuyutsu managed to warn Kunti's sons about all Duryodhana's schemes. As time went on, many of the Kaurava's most cunning plans to kill Bheema fell by the way almost as if the Pandavas had definite foreknowledge of them.

Duryodhana was certain there was a traitor in his camp. Shakuni and he often discussed who it might be, frequently with Yuyutsu himself present; but never did they think to suspect the real culprit, who had turned himself into an accomplished agent. The role he played was to last most of his life; until one day, on the battlefield of Kurukshetra, Yuyutsu would openly cross over to Yudhishtira's army. Only then would Duryodhana realize who the betrayer had been when they were children.

TWENTY-SEVEN

A master for the Kuru princes

ONCE, THE MUNI GAUTAMA'S SON, SHARADWAN, WAS STROLLING along a river's bank when he saw an apsara, Janapadi, bathing in the crisp water. Sharadwan had been celibate for a century, and he was a master of himself. But on that day the unexpected sight of the naked nymph unmanned him. Watching her, he spent his seed into a clump of river-reeds.

The apsara did not see the sage whom she had stirred, and both went their separate ways. But just a day later, two infants of unearthly splendour lay crying lustily in the bed of reeds. They were a boy and a girl, and their fine voices rang over the murmurant river.

One of King Shantanu's soldiers was passing by, when he heard those babies crying and, captivated by their beauty when he saw them, he took them back to Hastinapura. Shantanu was so taken by the twins that he adopted them, and raised them in his palace like his own children. This was some years before the return of Bheeshma and the advent of Satyavati. Since they were found in a bank of river-reeds, Sharadwan's twins were named Kripa and Kripi: God's grace.* Shantanu thought of them as fate's mercy to him, after Ganga left him and before he had Devavrata back.

Kripa and Kripi grew into noble children, and the story of how they were discovered spread across Bharatavarsha. On his wanderings, Sharadwan heard about the twins and knew they were the fruit of his

---

* Also, because Shantanu adopted them out of pity.

seed. One soft autumn day, that rishi arrived in Hastinapura and met Shantanu. The king was astonished to hear how Kripa and Kripi had been born.

Sharadwan lingered on in the city of elephants for some years, and taught his son Kripa archery. It is doubtful if he ever told the twins he was their father; he was an itinerant sage and not suited to the long responsibility of parenthood. Besides, the children seemed very happy in the palace and looked upon Shantanu as their adoptive father. They were hardly curious about their real origins, believing them to be irretrievable.

Kripa became a person of importance in the court of Hastinapura. With the instruction he had from Sharadwan, he was a master of weapons. In time, he was to become the first guru of the Pandavas and the Kauravas. Not only the sons of Dhritarashtra and Pandu were Acharya Kripa's sishyas, the young Vrishni princes of Mathura, and the Bhojas and Andhakas came to study under him in Hastinapura.

The princes of the Kuru House, the sons of Pandu and Dhritarashtra's princes, as well, were pupils of remarkable talent. They swiftly mastered all that Kripa had to teach them; and then, Bheeshma was worried. He knew the young kshatriyas now needed a greater teacher than Kripa, and was constantly on the lookout for such a man. He sent his scouts through all the kingdoms, across mountains and rivers, and into deep forests. But none of them was able to find a master for the Kuru scions. They all returned with the same impression: that perhaps a man like that did not exist in these dark times.

Yet, at last, a guru did arrive to teach the princes of Hastinapura, and he came of his own accord, brought by fate. As it turned out, he was even related to Kripa. But though he had lived in Hastinapura for some time no one knew about him. He watched the young Kurus, secretly; and they never saw him until he thought they were ready for his instruction.

One day, the Pandavas and the Kauravas went out of the city-gates to a favoured garden to play vita-danda. This game was played with two sticks, one short and sharpened at its ends, and the other stout and long. The long stick was used to twirl the smaller one off the ground by striking one of its pointed ends. While it was aloft, the player hit it a second time as hard and far as he could, while the others tried to catch it in the air. Bheema struck the little vita such a blow that it flew above the heads of the rest and landed in an old well in a corner of the garden.

The boys crowded round the well. Peering in, they could dimly see the vita, floating a hundred feet below them on dark water. Some of them cried that they should lower a rope and try and snare the little thing, while others said it would be easier to lower one of them into the well. Among the latter was Duryodhana, who wanted to send Bheema down. At first none of the youngsters noticed the stranger who stood under a mango tree and watched them intently.

Suddenly the stranger, who was a brahmana by his attire and the thread he wore across his body, spoke to them in such an arresting voice that the boys all turned to listen. He came nearer. They saw that, under shaggy brows, his eyes were like live coals. Though he spoke softly and slowly, his voice seemed loud to their ears.

"Kshatriyas, obviously you know no archery or you would easily fetch your vita out of the well."

One of the Kaurava boys said, "You are wrong, stranger. We are good bowmen."

The man came closer, and leaned over the mouth of the well. Yudhishtira ventured, "We are all archers, Brahmana, and disciples of Acharya Kripa. But what has archery to do with our vita?"

The tall brahmana turned his face to stare at Yudhishtira for a moment. His eyes roved over the others, one by one, and each prince was discomfited by the piercing regard. At last, he stopped with young Arjuna and his gaze remained fixed on that Pandava's face. Now when he spoke, he seemed to address only Arjuna.

"You say you are archers, sons of Bharata, yet you can't retrieve your vita with arrows."

Arjuna felt an extraordinary warmth suffuse him at the stranger's scrutiny. He felt the brahmana knew him well, even chose him somehow over the others. Arjuna said, "Can you retrieve our vita with archery?"

"Watch me."

"But you have no bow or arrows!" laughed one of the Kauravas. The stranger glared at him with his burning eyes, and the boy fell quiet. The brahmana cast around for a moment and pulled up a clump of sharp reeds that grew at the base of the wellhead. The princes looked on disbelievingly, many of them thinking the fellow was mad, and the others curious to see what he would do. Only Arjuna felt a complete faith in the stranger; he was certain the brahmana would recover the vita from the well. By sorcery, if need be.

Said the stranger, "These shall be my arrows. But first I will cast my ring into the well after your vita. And I will fetch them both out."

He slipped a golden, jewel-studded ring off his finger and threw it casually into the well. They heard a distant splash, and when they peered down they saw no trace of it. Unlike the buoyant wooden vita, the metal ring sank below the surface of the dark water.

Chanting a mantra under his breath, the brahmana began to stroke the reeds he had pulled up. They sprang erect in his long fingers, as if he had invested them with a fierce life of their own. Those reeds assumed the shape of green arrows, plumed at their base and with silvery arrowheads. Still he stroked them and spoke to them; until, they began to fly out of his hands, each attached to the next so they formed a rope of arrows. The green rope snaked out of his grasp and into the deep well.

Down the well shaft those reed-arrows flashed. In a moment, they flew up again into the sun and, like obedient creatures, brought the vita into the stranger's hands.

The boys were speechless. The brahmana smiled, "See how easy it is when you are an archer?"

Only Arjuna found his voice, "What about your ring?"

Again the stranger glanced intently at that prince. He detached one arrow from the rope he had made. He let the rest fall on the ground where, at once, they were common reeds again. He shut his eyes briefly and whispered more secret words. He cast the single reed down the well. This time they all heard it splash into the water. A moment passed when they thought the reed had sunk. Then they cried out, for up flew the reed-arrow and back into the strange master's hands. At its tip, his jewelled ring glittered. Calmly the intense brahmana took his ring off the arrowhead and slipped it back onto his finger. He discarded the reed, which collapsed limply on the ground.

Yudhishtira breathed, "Tell us who you are, Brahmana."

But the stranger only said, "Go to your Pitama Bheeshma and tell him what happened here. He will know who I am."

Not pausing for breath, the boys ran to the palace. There, shouting all at once in their eagerness, they tried to tell Bheeshma about the stranger. Laughing, their grandsire stopped them. He couldn't make head or tail of what they were saying. He asked Yudhishtira, who alone had held his peace, to tell him what had happened. Yudhishtira told him about the brahmana with eyes like coals, and how he fetched the vita and the ring out of the old well. Bheeshma's face lit up; he knew he had found the master for his princes. But he hadn't known that Kripi's husband Drona had come to Hastinapura.

Bheeshma went with the boys to the garden, where Drona waited. The two greeted each other cordially, and Bheeshma said, "Welcome to Hastinapura, Acharya. How is it I did not hear of your arrival?"

Drona replied with habitual directness, "Because I did not want you to hear of it yet, O Bheeshma, because misfortune brought me here, and because your princes were not ready for my instruction."

Bheeshma said, "So you will be their master. I came to ask you just that."

"I know. I have been watching your grandsons and they are all gifted boys. Some more so than others," his eyes sought Arjuna again in the throng of young kshatriyas. "Yes, I will be happy to teach them, as long as I am fed and treated with respect in the House of Kuru."

His deep eyes smouldered with defiance. Bheeshma took his arm and said, "Come, let us go in and speak privately. It will be easy enough to give you what you want. Here in Hastinapura, we honour men like you."

They went indoors, leaving the princes breathless with excitement that they were to have lessons at archery from the wizard.

TWENTY-EIGHT

Drona's story

In Bheeshma's chambers, Drona was served food and drink with the dignity accorded to any visiting king. When he had eaten his fill, Bheeshma said, "I read a sorrow in your face. Tell me what saddens you; what you say will not pass beyond these walls."

Drona sighed. He seemed to relax his guard, which, Bheeshma realized only now, had been raised all the while: as if he expected to be insulted at any moment.

Drona began, "As you may know, O Bheeshma, the Rishi Bharadvaja was my father and my mother was a river-shell. And for my exceptional birth, I am called Drona."*

Bheeshma knew all this. But he listened with interest, never interrupting, as the unusual brahmana unfolded his life's story.

"Bharadvaja learnt the secrets of the astras from his guru Agnivesha, who was the son of Agni Deva himself, the Fire-God. Agnivesha taught my father the mantra for the agneyastra of a thousand flames, those for the varunastra and the vaishnavastra, the aindra, the brahma and the siva, and a hundred great weapons more. When I was a boy, as old as your grandsons are today, my father taught me about the devastras and the mantras that summon them.

"At about that time, a kshatriya prince came to our asrama in the forest to have my father's instruction. He was the son of King Prihasta

---

* Bharadvaja sees the naked Apsara Ghritachi and ejaculates into a *drana*, a pot. Hence the name Drona. But here, perhaps, the pot or 'vessel' was a river-shell.

of the northern Panchalas. The boy's name was Drupada, and we became inseparable friends. We did everything together: studied the Vedas and archery and played at children's games. I thought we were like brothers and Drupada always swore that we were.

"Once he said to me, 'Drona, our friendship mustn't end here. When I am a king, you must come and live with me in my palace. My kingdom will be yours as much as it is mine. Only, we must be friends forever.'

"I thought I would never want for anything with a friend like Drupada. I embraced him, swearing it would be as he wanted.

"The years passed and Prihasta died. Drupada returned to his kingdom and was crowned. Around this time, also, my own father Bharadvaja left this world. It was then, if you remember, O Bheeshma, I first came to Hastinapura as a young scholar of the Vedas and married Kripi. Yes you must remember, though much has happened in both our lives since then."

Bheeshma nodded to say that he did indeed remember the marriage of Drona and Kripi. His father Shantanu had been alive then and was pleased to give Kripi away to as accomplished a young man as Drona.

"Kripi and I lived in the forest for some years, and our son was born in the wilds. At his birth he neighed in joy like a little horse, a small Ucchaisravas. And an asariri said to us, 'Let this child be called Aswatthama!'

"So we gave him that name. It was at this time I heard that Jamadagni's son, Parasurama Bhargava, was giving away all his possessions. I went to the Mahendra Mountain, where the Bhargava lived. It was my ambition to become the finest archer of our times, and I knew Parasurama was the one who could help me realize my dream.

"Over vast plains, I journeyed, and through dark forests, asking my way of hunters and hermits. At last, I stood at the foot of the Mahendra. I worshipped the mountain, and after climbing a week, arrived in a green glade near its summit. There I saw a fine lustre that began under a tall tree and reached for the sky. At its heart, seated serene, his eyes shut and his face blissful, I saw Bhargava. His presence was so awesome I trembled even to look at him.

"When I was quite near, without daring to make a sound I prostrated myself at his feet. For many hours, neither he nor I stirred. Then, I heard him speak to me. He did not speak in the truculent voice I had expected, but quietly and with affection, 'Who are you, my son? Why have you come to me?'

"Rising, and my own voice unsteady, I said, 'Lord, I am Bharadvaja's son Drona. I am a brahmana, though I was not born of a woman but in a river-shell.'

"'What do you want from me, my child?'

"'I have come for your wealth.'

"He threw back his great head and laughed. 'Wealth! I have no wealth, my poor boy, but only this body and my weapons. You have come too late. I have already given away all my gold to Kashyapa, which is why I am sitting here alone and in peace. What wealth can I give you, who am as poor as you see me?'

"'My lord,' said I, 'I have come to seek the wealth that is still yours to give.'

"He stared at me with his deep eyes. 'I have only this body and my astras to give you. You can have one of them. Which do you choose?'

"'Your astras, and mastery over them, my lord.'

"He laughed like spring thunder. I heaved a sigh of relief: obviously, he was pleased with me. I was already a master of conventional archery, as well as of the astras my father had taught me. But the weapons of Parasurama were far beyond anything I possessed. Yet, it did not take more than a month and he taught me all he knew. Bheeshma, you are Bhargava's sishya yourself. You know the astras are given by teaching their mantras to one whose spirit is strong enough to receive them.

"I came down from the mountain with my master's priceless wealth. Aswatthama was still very young. We lived on the hem of a village, and we were poor indeed. I had always believed that the poorer the life is materially, the richer it is in spirit. But all that changed one day.

"Aswatthama was out playing with his friends. Some of them were the children of rich parents, at least compared with us. I was passing by where they were playing their little games, and I paused out of sight behind a tree, curious to hear what they said to one another.

"One boy cried to my son, 'Do you like milk, Aswatthama?'

"Innocently, he answered in his lisping voice, 'What is milk? I've never even heard of it.'

"A silence fell on his playmates. Some of them sniggered cruelly among themselves, and began whispering to one another. Then one of them said to my boy, 'Aswatthama, milk is the most delicious drink there is in the world. Next to the amrita of the Devas, there is nothing to compare with milk. Come, we will give you some milk if your parents are too poor to afford it.'

"I waited to watch what happened next. I saw two of the older boys mix white flour with some water in a bowl and bring it to my son. My sweet child drained that sly cup in a gulp. He began a little dance in the street, singing, 'I've tasted milk today! The drink of the Devas!'

"My heart breaking, I slunk away from there. On the way I thought I heard someone say, 'There goes Drona, who says he is one of the greatest archers on earth. But his child drinks flour mixed in water and dances for joy because he thinks it is milk.'

"'Drona says he wants no wealth, but it is his son who suffers for his father's sloth.'

"'Drona does not know how hard it is to make a decent living. Only the blessed have wealth.'

"I might have imagined this conversation, as I walked home in a daze, but it did not matter if I had. When I reached our house, Aswatthama was already there. He was lying in his mother's lap and sobbing loudly, and Kripi's eyes were full of tears.

"'What happened?' I cried.

"'Aswatthama wants milk. He said his friends gave him some to taste and it was wonderful. But where am I to go for milk, when we have no money to buy any?'

"I cried, 'Enough of this wretched poverty! We are going to my friend Drupada's court, and you will see how rich we shall be. Don't delay a moment, we leave now.'

"I picked Aswatthama up and we set out for the Panchala kingdom. We arrived some weeks later, and we were tired after the long journey during which we had little enough to eat. I went directly to the palace. Saying that I was his boyhood friend and his guru's son, I asked for an audience with Drupada. I was told to wait outside. In a while, the guard came back and said I could see the king only after two days.

"I thought he wanted to give me untold wealth, perhaps even a palace, as soon as I saw him; that is why he had made me wait, while he made the arrangements. After all, Drupada once swore he would share his kingdom with me.

"Somewhere inside my head, a small voice insisted this was not the reason for my being kept waiting; but I was in no mood to listen to its cynical whispering. We spent two nights under a tree beside the road. I was full of nostalgic stories about our boyhood together, Drupada's and mine, and Kripi listened to them all patiently.

"Finally, the two days were over and I went to the palace for my audience with the king. My heart light with excitement, I was shown into Drupada's presence. There he was at last, seated high above me on his throne, wearing silken robes and a golden crown. I opened my arms wide and cried, 'Drupada, my friend!'

"But he did not rise from his throne, nor did he seem pleased to see me. He said, 'Destitute Brahmana, do you presume to call me "Friend"? Wouldn't "My Lord" or "Your Majesty" be more appropriate?'

"At first, I could not believe what I was hearing. But he went on remorselessly, 'Perhaps you are dull-witted now, Brahmana? Though I do not remember you as being a fool; but that was so long ago, Drona. That is your name, isn't it? See my memory is excellent. Yes, that was long ago, in another life. I was a student then, your father's pupil and maybe even your friend. But now, fellow, you are a beggar here and I am the king.'

"His face was flushed with pique. 'And you have the temerity to walk into my sabha and cry "Friend" to me! It seems you are an idiot, Brahmana. A king like me has a thousand friends like you, all wanting to live off him if they only could.'

"I was shaking, and my eyes saw nothing but a crimson mist. Hearing Drupada's voice so arrogant and mocking, I thought I would lose my reason. His words were like knives in my flesh, and I turned and walked out of his court. I picked up Aswatthama, and Kripi, who is wiser than I am, guessed from my face what had happened: it was even as she had feared. We left the Panchala kingdom and came here to my brother-in-law.

"I have lived for some weeks in Kripa's house as a welcome guest; but also, in truth, as a beggar. He told me as soon as I came that you were looking for a guru for your princes. But I asked him to say nothing of my arrival. I watched your grandsons to see if they were ready to learn what I have to teach them.

"This is my story, O Bheeshma. The truth is, I have as much need for pupils, to feed my family and myself, as you do for a master for your young ones. But you must understand that what I thirst after is to have revenge on Drupada one day."

His eyes shone with a hatred that verged on madness. Bheeshma saw how deeply the Panchala king had wounded this extraordinary brahmana.

The Kuru patriarch said kindly, "You have come to the right place, Drona. For being my grandsons' master in the House of Kuru, you will have all the wealth you want. More than wealth, you will have the honour you deserve. Wipe that foolish Drupada's memory from your heart for the present; it isn't worthy of being stored there. And when the time comes, I swear the Kurus will stand with you against him, be it even in war.

"Acharya Drona, I hand my wards, the princes of this kingdom, over to you. From this day, they are your charge. I have waited a long time for you, though I did not know you would be the one who came. Come, let me show you to your new home, and you can begin your lessons tomorrow."

Bheeshma rose and embraced Drona to solemnize their pact. Drona knew he had come to the city that would be his home.

TWENTY-NINE

The brilliant pupil

Bheeshma gave Drona a mansion to live in. It was no less than the home of any nobleman in Hastinapura, and the granary in its yard was always full. He gave the brahmana and his son fine clothes; silks for his wife and ornaments fit for a queen. Bheeshma said, "From now you are not only the guardian of my grandsons but of this kingdom."

Drona bowed and accepted the charge, though he knew it would be a heavy one. The Kuru princes were summoned. When they prostrated themselves at his feet, one after the other, Drona blessed them. That first day of their tutelage, he said to them, "I have a mission that is close to my heart. Swear you will help me accomplish my mission and I will make great kshatriyas of you."

There was a moment's silence, and no one spoke. They feared what impossible task he might ask them to perform. Then Arjuna stepped forward and said quietly, "I will do whatever you ask. I want to be a great kshatriya."

"Don't you want to know what I want from you?"

Arjuna shook his head. Drona knew his instinct had not betrayed him about this youth. He embraced the third Pandava, and from that day he was his master's favourite pupil. From that day, also, Arjuna was Drona's most brilliant sishya, and the most dedicated one; and his guru tried him harder than he did any other student.

The first years of the princes' education passed swiftly. Drona taught them not only the use of ordinary weapons, but initiated them into the secrets of the supernatural astras, each one ruled by a Deva. Not his brothers, the acharya's own son, Aswatthama, and certainly none of the others had the single-minded obsession for archery that Arjuna did.

Not a word or nuance of the guru's did that prince miss. He hung on his master's every flicker of instruction. During the bright fortnight of the month, Arjuna would be out all night, practising by moonlight. Drona watched him with satisfaction, and even more than Aswatthama he thought of this Pandava as being his spiritual son.

It was customary for the princes to rise before the sun and set out together for the river to fill their water-pots. They had to walk between the river and their acharya's house five times, before each one had filled the large urn kept for him in Drona's yard. Gone were their lazy, luxurious mornings for Duryodhana and his brothers. Drona's severe discipline and his intolerance of weakness soon began to make men of the spoilt Kauravas also. Yet, that master who otherwise made no difference between his own son and any of the others, made it a point to give Aswatthama a bigger water-pot than the ones the Kuru princes had.

The reason for this was subtle. Drona would never teach Aswatthama at home when the others were not present: all his students must have perfectly equal opportunity. But even the master was only human. If Aswatthama filled his urn before the rest, and came into Drona's morning class before them, there was no reason why he could not impart some little archer's secret to his son before the others arrived. Aswatthama would, indeed, arrive at the lesson before the Kuru princes; while they must make the trip to the river five times, he, with his bigger pot, had filled his urn in just four. As he had told all his students he would, Drona began his lesson as soon as his first pupil arrived.

This went on for a month and Arjuna chafed at it. He ran back and forth from the river, and arrived considerably ahead of his brothers and cousins. But he could never arrive until well after Aswatthama. Of course, he could not dream of accusing his master of being partial to his son.

At the end of that month, one day, Arjuna came for the morning lesson before Aswatthama did. Drona showed no surprise. Neither did he reveal if he regretted Arjuna's being early, or whether it was delight he felt; nor did he ask the Pandava how he had managed to come early today. The master merely began his lesson the moment his first pupil appeared before him. Soon, Arjuna not only caught up with Aswatthama, he outstripped him.

Drona knew his prize sishya had understood one of the cornerstones of his teaching: the astras were not meant only for war; once one made friends of them, they could be used for everyday purposes. Drona knew how Arjuna had managed to come earlier than Aswatthama. He had not been to the river at all; he had used the varunastra, of the lord of oceans, to fill his urn.

Months passed, and Arjuna's brilliance and his devotion to archery were unrivalled. Yet it always seemed that his acharya was out to set all the obstacles he could in just this disciple's path. And as surely as a river will sweep past a tree that falls across its course, Arjuna overcame these. He grew sharper and more tenacious, because he had to fight his way to every morsel of knowledge his master had for him. That was how his guru chose to teach him.

One day, Drona called the palace cook. He said, "You will never serve Arjuna in the dark, without at least a lamp burning beside him."

So sternly did he say this the cook obeyed him implicitly. Early one night of a new moon, Arjuna sat eating alone. He had been out practising his archery all evening, until there was no light left to shoot by. He sat next to a window in the dining room, with his food and a lamp burning before him. A gust of wind blew out the flame and he was left in perfect darkness. Still he ate on, his hand travelling instinctively to his plate and then to his mouth with the food he had picked up, though he could not see it. A smile spread on his face. The lesson had not escaped that boy of genius.

He finished his meal quickly, leaving half his food uneaten on his plate. He picked up his bow and quiver and ran out into the moonless night. The targets of the day still hung on tree-branches. Arjuna took up his position as usual, some fifty yards from them. His eyes shut, he fitted arrow after arrow to his bow and shot at those invisible targets, first with his left hand and then the right: he was perfectly ambidextrous.

When he had emptied his quiver, he went to see how he had fared. His accuracy had been significantly greater in the dark. He had brought every target down. With a cry of joy, he hung them up again. Now there was no time of the month when he could not practise his archery. From the pitched night behind him, someone applauded softly. Arjuna whirled around. The tall figure of his master stepped out into the starlight and embraced him.

"Every amavasya night, for a year, I have waited for you. At last you have come. Arjuna, I have never seen an archer like you. I swear I will make you the greatest bowman in the world. Yes, even greater than your guru, devoted child."

From that night on, Dronacharya held nothing back from Arjuna. Soon his students had mastered the basic skills of archery, and fighting with the javelin, the sword, the spear, the dagger and the little dart. Next, they learnt to fight from horseback, and to shoot, hew and thrust at moving targets. They went on to hand-to-hand combat, fighting each other with every conceivable weapon, except the astras.

Each student was blessed with different gifts. There was no one to touch Arjuna at archery. Being his father's son, Aswatthama was unmatched in the lore and the mantras of the devastras. Yudhishtira quickly proved himself a master charioteer; no one could come near him at either speed or manoeuvering. Bheema and Duryodhana's bitter rivalry found legitimate expression in the mace pit. Both of them were magnificently built, and their strength far exceeded their brothers' and cousins'. They were so evenly matched at the mace there was nothing to choose between the two red-eyed princes when they fought.

Sahadeva and Nakula were better swordsmen than all the others: when the twins faced each other, it was hard to tell who was faring better, especially when they wore identical clothes and armour.

But there was no complete kshatriya among them like Arjuna. He was a close second to the best in every other discipline, and he was far, far ahead of the others at archery. As for his foresight, his presence of mind and his devotion to his master, he was without equal by a long way. Young Arjuna's fame as a total warrior spread through the land. Soon Drona had more pupils than he cared to, many of them from the most far-flung kingdoms in Bharatavarsha.

The tale is told of a small competition Drona once held to test his pupils' skills at archery. He had the palace carpenter carve a green bird in wood, so it looked exactly like a little barbet. Drona called a young gardener who was the best tree-climber in the palace. He told him to secure the bird in a branch of a tall jamun tree growing in the acharya's own garden.

When this was done, the master summoned his disciples. He had a test for them, he said. He made the boys stand side by side, their bows armed with arrows and the strings drawn back. Ready to shoot at his word, the princes stood tensely, in a row, facing the jamun tree from a hundred yards away.

Drona said to his wards, "Relax perfectly and concentrate; this will not be easy. You must bring the bird down from the tree with a single arrow."

After another moment, he called, "Yudhishtira, come forward."

The eldest prince stepped smartly forward beside his guru. He raised his bow, and drew back the bowstring. Drona pointed at the lofty branch of the jamun, where, to the untrained eye, nothing except some blurry leaves were visible.

"Do you see the bird in the branch?"

"I do."

"What else do you see?"

"I see the branch, the tree. I see you, Acharya, and my brothers here."

Drona knit his heavy brows. "You may step back, Yudhishtira. You won't strike the bird with one arrow. Duryodhana, come forward."

Duryodhana stepped forward. Here was a chance to beat the Pandavas, since Yudhishtira at least had failed the acharya's test.

"Do you see the bird in the tree?"

"I do."

"What else do you see?"

"I see the tree, and you, Acharya."

Drona said, "Step back, Duryodhana, you will not hit the bird."

One by one, he called up all his pupils. All of them saw the bird in the tree, and besides they saw the tree and their master; and many saw their brothers and cousins as well. Drona made all of them step back, without letting them shoot at the bird. To each one he said, "You will not find the target with one arrow."

Just four princes were left who had not been called up: Nakula and Sahadeva, Aswatthama and Arjuna.

"Nakula, step forward."

"Do you see the green bird in the tree?"

"I do."

"What else to you see?"

"I see the tree, Acharya."

"What else?"

"Nothing else. I see nothing else."

"Step back. You won't bring the bird down with one arrow."

It was Sahadeva's turn. He saw the bird, the branch on which it was perched and nothing else. Drona said to Sahadeva, "Can you describe the bird to me?"

Slowly, the youngest Pandava said, "It is green. Its beak is red, and its claws are blue, I think."

"Does it have feathers?"

"I can't see the feathers."

"Is it a real bird?"

"I couldn't be sure, but it hardly moves."

"Sahadeva, step back."

Just Aswatthama and Arjuna remained.

"Aswatthama, step forward."

"Do you see the bird?"

"I do."

"What else do you see?"

"Nothing, I see only the bird." There was a murmur from the others. They were silenced at once by a look from Drona.

"Can you describe the bird?"

"It is green and made of wood, with a red beak and feathers painted on. It is motionless."

"And its eyes, are they open or shut?"

"I can't be sure. Shall I bring it down?"

"You will miss the bird, Aswatthama. Don't waste your arrow, step back."

Only Arjuna was left. He remained motionless in the archer's stance, alidha, with not a muscle moving.

"Arjuna, step forward."

A lithe step, such a fluid movement, and Arjuna had come forward a pace, without lowering his bow. Drona smiled. Already, this pupil was different from the rest even in the way he moved. Arjuna's gaze was fixed on the branch. He seemed perfectly relaxed, as if he could stand as he was for a week.

"Do you see the bird on the branch, Arjuna?"

"I do."
"What else do you see?"
"Nothing else."
"Can you describe the bird to me?"
"Its eye is open, staring."
"What else?"
"Its head is round."
"What about its wings, its feet?" asked Drona, in mounting excitement.
"I don't see the bird's body, only its head."
"Bring it down, Arjuna."

Arjuna's arrow took the bird through its eye and it fell out of the tree. There was silence among the princes as Arjuna lowered his bow. Drona embraced him and said, "When the time comes, you will vanquish my father's sishya for me."

The master turned to his other pupils. "How could you bring the bird down unless you saw it properly first? That is what you must learn: to see the target and nothing else. Archery is no less than dhyana. Only he who treats it as such, only he who is reposed in his archery and gives himself to it utterly, can be a master. Aswatthama, you may or may not have brought the bird down. But what if the bird was an enemy and an archer himself? If you did not kill him with your first arrow, you would be a dead man. As for the rest of you, you were all dead men against a real archer. Never think of yourselves as shooting at targets that do not shoot back. That isn't the way of the warrior."

In his heart, Drona thought, 'Drupada, my Arjuna will make you humble again.'

THIRTY

At the river

A FEW DAYS LATER, DRONA WENT WITH HIS PUPILS FOR A LONG RIDE and a bath in the Ganga. Evening was upon the world and the last light of the sun bathed the river and the woods in soft gold. The Ganga was a picture of calm, flowing with hardly a ripple. Drona entered the water first. He stood in the knee-deep shallows, saying a prayer to the setting sun, to his ancestors in Pitriloka, and to the Gods. The princes stood on the shore. They had laid their bows and quivers on the ground, because they must not bear arms while their guru offered worship.

Some dead logs floated downstream on the swiftly darkening current. The sun sank beyond the woods and the birds all sang together, as they nested in the living branches of the trees. Suddenly, the tranquility of the sylvan spot was shattered. One of the innocent looking logs on the river grew a demonic snout, gaping jaws, a bloated body and a lizard's thrashing tail. A primordial monster seized Drona's leg and dragged him into deeper water.

It was a crocodile, thirty feet long, and Drona cried frantically for help. Only Arjuna moved, and how he did! Bheema stood between him and his quiver. Yet, between Drona's first cry and his second, in a blur Arjuna had thrust his brother out of his way, scooped up his bow, pulled five arrows from his quiver and shot the armoured monster through its eyes and heart.

The beast sank, its dark blood staining the clear water. Its grip on Drona's thigh went slack and, crying out Arjuna's name, the brahmana swam ashore. Now, as if waking from a dream, the other princes ran to help Drona. Arjuna laid down his bow and quiver. He was as calm as if he had been at moonlight practice in the palace yard in Hastinapura. Not a thought had disturbed him, no flicker of doubt. He had merely reacted to the situation, quicker than thinking, perfectly, like the immaculate warrior he was.

Drona embraced Arjuna. Then he held him at arm's length, and gravely studied the prince's face. At last, he smiled, "I am going to reward you for saving my life. Purify yourself in the river."

He made his other disciples sit in a wide crescent. When Arjuna had bathed in the Ganga, Drona made him sit facing east in the twilight. The guru sat before his sishya. Drona held his arms stretched out towards Arjuna, palms open and facing up, and murmured a mantra. As soon as he said the hermetic words, a pulsing, unearthly radiance shone upon them. Enfolding the master and his pupil, it separated them from the rest of the world. Then a blinding stab of light and a golden arrow lay in Drona's hands, shining in the gloom like a strip of sun. Its shaft had four small heads, plainly visible, breathing.

The others watched with their eyes riveted to Drona's hands. Drona said slowly, "Arjuna, receive the brahmasirsa from me. It is the weapon of the Father of the worlds, and one of the greatest astras."

Once more, now softly so the others could not hear, Drona whispered the mantra for that weapon. He made Arjuna stretch out his hands, palms up, and say the occult words after him. The astra with four heads vanished from the master's hands, and it now lay in Arjuna's. Once more Arjuna repeated the mantra. The golden shaft rose out of his palms and melted into the prince's body, near his heart. He shuddered, and sighed deeply.

Arjuna prostrated himself at Drona's feet. The guru said, "You may never use this weapon against a mortal man. Because once you summon it, if its fire is not quenched on the one against whom you call it, it will consume the very earth. Only against a great Asura or a Deva turned to evil may you invoke the brahmasirsa."

Drona raised Arjuna up and embraced him again. Smiling, he said, "You shall truly be the greatest archer in the world. Yes, I swear it."

Arjuna glowed, and his brothers came and hugged him. But envy stung Duryodhana and the Kauravas like a serpent, and their faces were dark.

THIRTY-ONE

Ekalavya

B<small>UT</small> A<small>RJUNA WOULD NOT HAVE BEEN THE GREATEST ARCHER IN THE</small> world.

One evening, Drona was out alone in his garden, breathing the scents of lotuses growing in his tank, when a lithe figure darted out from the bushes and prostrated itself at his feet. Drona saw it was a young boy, who now turned up his face, darker than moonless nights, to gaze at him. Such reverence shone in those stark white eyes; Drona had never had a look like that from any of his disciples.

The boy had bathed before he came here, but he smelled of wild places. Drona felt sure that he would soon be caked with mud and leaves again from head to foot, tameless as the jungle that was his home.

He was drawn to the dark youth, who looked some three years younger than Arjuna. The brahmana said kindly, "Who are you, my child?"

In his musical dialect, the boy replied, "I am Ekalavya." And then, added in a whisper, as if he could hardly believe where he was, "And you are Drona. The master."

"Yes, I am Drona. Now say what you want from me."

"I am the son of Hiranyadhanush, king of the nishadas of the forest." His eyes never left Drona's face, as if to imprint every feature on his heart.

"Say what you would have of me," said Drona impatiently.

"Take me for your sishya, teach me archery!" The youth breathed his dream.

Drona sighed. "I feared as much. But I teach only kshatriyas, and a nishada could never learn along with them. The princes I teach will rule the earth one day. I am sorry, but I must refuse you."

He saw tears glimmer in the unwinking eyes. Ekalavya crouched there in silence. Then he said, "At least bless me once, Guru!" and laid his tousled head at Drona's feet.

Moved, Drona bent and placed his hand on the boy's head, "Bless you, child."

A smile as white as his eyes lit his long black face. Ekalavya cried, "Now I will not fail!" and, jumping up, he was gone.

Drona stood staring after him uneasily, and was filled with an unaccountable sadness. Kripi called from the lamplit doorway that the night meal was served, and he turned to go in.

Ekalavya flew through the forest like a joyful wind. A golden moon unfurled above him, engaging wakeful trees in supernal converse. He plunged on, deep into the familiar jungle, past trees who were friends, among whom he had grown and roamed since he was a child, out of whose branches he had shot fruit and birds with his wooden bow. This was the rarest night of his life: the great Drona had blessed him; now there was no dream the darkling child of the forest couldn't turn into reality.

He arrived in the very heart of the jungle, where even birds and beasts were rare visitors, and exotic plants grew in surreal profusion. Strange crocuses thrust phallic stamens at the moon, and resplendent lotuses mantled satin pools hidden away from the world as if they were too precious to be seen. Beside one of those inmost pools, Ekalavya stopped.

He was unconcerned by the time of night. He was used to hunting at all hours, with sight such as only those creatures have that depend on it for their lives. He began to scoop up wet earth from the mossy bank of the pool, its face alight with violet and crimson blooms in the flowing moon. He carried this earth to a tree that grew apart from its fellows, alone, much like intense Ekalavya himself.

Through the night he worked, pausing just once, briefly, to eat some lotus-stems. Under his fine touch, a figure began to take shape. On he worked, past the dawn, at times in silence, feverishly, at others singing softly in his wild tongue—of trees, birds and beasts that have never known restriction, but life, love and death, in perfect freedom and danger. He worked with absolute passion.

Past the feet and the long, powerful legs, grew the figure Ekalavya was making with such love; up past the erect waist and back, the deep, supple chest, right up to the neck. Then he began on its long arms, one hanging at the side, fingers almost to the knee, the other raised, its palm open in a blessing. When he finished the arms and the hands, it was evening of the next day. He fell asleep at the feet of his headless clay figure. But in his dreams, he saw, lucidly, the noble head he must still fashion.

He awoke at midnight and resumed his obsessive labour. By now his dusky skin was covered in pale clay, his curly black hair was streaked with it. While he had worked in frenzy on the body, now he was slower, more careful; it took him two days before he finished the head. He picked up his bow and bamboo-quiver, in which the arrows lay straight as bands of light, and hunted a young wild pig. He roasted it on a spit and devoured it hungrily. Then he slept, and now dreamt only of the face he had yet to make: most of all, the unforgettable eyes in that face, eyes like live coals.

He awoke again, and took up the light clay from the pool of lotuses. He scooped it up uniformly, leaving no ugly pit to mar the beauty of the wild spot. More painstakingly still, often pausing to shut his eyes to recall some tiny wrinkle at the corner of its mouth, Ekalavya worked on the stern, gaunt face. It took form under his subtle fingers and was eerily life-like. He was impatient to be done with his unfamiliar task. Only when he had finished making this figure could he begin with the other calling that raged in his blood, the one that would make his wild name immortal.

He toiled for a week, often sobbing in frustration when he had to break off some feature because it was not perfect. Most of all, the eyes eluded him. It was their expression he could not capture: because he wanted them to express all things, to be a mirror of the universe to him. Where else would he turn but to his master's eyes, when he wanted solace or instruction, approbation or love?

At last the figure was complete. Ekalavya went to the nearby jungle stream and bathed languorously in it. He came back to the clearing where the form he had made now stood, tall and commanding: its enigmatic eyes were alive, they looked at him.

The boy went to the pool and pulled up some lotuses from its surface. He tied their stalks together to make a garland. He came to the clay figure and draped the garland of lotuses around its neck. With a lump in his throat, he whispered, "Bless me, Guru!" and prostrated himself at the feet of his preceptor in the wilderness.

Ekalavya rose. With his hunting knife, which he used to carve the flesh of animals he killed, he cut a flat, round piece of wood from a dead log. Climbing nimbly into the tallest tree at the glade's edge, he secured the target to a high branch. He moved with the grace of a young jungle cat, lean muscles shimmering. He climbed down from the tree and walked to the opposite end of the clearing; now he could not see the target at all. With his guru's name in his fierce heart, the jungle boy raised his bow.

The years flowed by. In Hastinapura, the Kuru princes had their instruction from Drona, and Ekalavya studied with his earthen master in the forest clearing. Everyone said Arjuna was the finest archer in the world; the Pandava was confident of it himself, he knew even his great master thought so. One day, the princes went hunting in the forest with a hunting-dog, a lively animal with the keenest nose. They had come to hunt big game: a leopard, or even a tiger.

The restless dog dashed eagerly into the forest, and the princes went after it. Its nose to the ground, the beast ran on, exhilarated with all the marvellous scents this jungle was suffused with. That dog sniffed a thousand tales of wild lives and encounters, as clearly as if he saw them with his eyes: some fading, some fresh and vibrant. He was fervid on the trail. Snuffling in rapture, he plunged deep into the vana, where not even foresters and honey-gatherers ventured, and the princes were hard-pressed to keep up with him.

Then, ahead of them and out of sight, the dog stopped dead in his tracks, his hackles raised, growling. He broke into a frenzied volley of barking, so gaudy birds came flapping out of the trees. As if he had gone quite mad at whatever he had seen, he bayed, a long howl, a terrible, nerve-wracking sound.

Certain that the beast had found a tiger or leopard, the princes came running, their bows ready. Suddenly the dog gave a shrill yelp and fell silent. With Arjuna ahead of the rest, the young Kurus crept through the trees, thinking that a big cat had killed their dog and now lay in wait for them.

But they had hardly gone a few yards, when the dog shot out of the thickets, whining piteously in his throat. Crowding round the hapless animal, the princes saw what had silenced the poor brute. Round his muzzle, in circle as perfect as the petals grow out of a flower, the dog's jaws had been shot shut with seven wooden arrows.

Arjuna knelt beside the beast, and gently tugged the cruel barbs out one by one. The others saw his eyes fill with tears. They were not tears of sorrow, but envy! As he drew out those arrows, Arjuna's hands shook.

Once his jaws were free the wretched dog began to howl, and blood gushed from his wounds. Every prince there knew how unlikely it was that someone, anyone, could have muzzled their animal like this. It would take an archer of unearthly skill; because once the first arrow struck him, the dog must have turned and run from his assailant.

Just one person might, conceivably, have attempted such a feat—Arjuna. He may have been able to shoot four or five arrows in less than a moment. But seven? And so symmetrically? Not even Arjuna could have done it. Anyway, the hidden archer was not he.

Finally, Bheema breathed, "Who did this? Is Drona out in the jungle?"

His face taut, Arjuna stalked ahead into the dense forest and arrived in a bright clearing. There, shooting a tide of arrows at an invisible target on a treetop, with grace and skill that took even the Pandava's breath away, stood the wildest young man. He was dark and sinuous as a black panther; his hair hung to his shoulders in unkempt straggles. He wore a spotted leopard-skin, was covered in jungle mud and loosed his arrows as effortlessly as he breathed. He was surely no kshatriya prince; but then, no kshatriya prince on earth was the marksman this youth was.

Choking with envy, Arjuna cried, "Fellow, who are you?"

The youth turned. He was handsome in his untamed way; his eyes were fine and sharp. Lowering his bow, he brushed the hair that had fallen across his brow, and stood facing them. He was not in the least awed by the throng of princes, glittering with ornaments and carrying jewelled bows. He surveyed them with some slight interest. Arjuna repeated his question, desperately, "Who are you, archer?"

"I am Ekalavya. My father is Hiranyadhanush, king of the nishadas of this jungle."

Somehow, Arjuna controlled the trembling that had broken out over his body. "Who taught you to shoot like that?"

"At the target?"

Sensing the seismic tension between the youth and Arjuna, the others were silent. Arjuna said, "No, what you did to our dog."

White, even teeth flashed in a grin. "Oh, that. He annoyed me with his howling. I think he mistook me for a leopard."

"Who taught you archery?" cried Arjuna, his world crumbling around him.

"My master, of course."

"Who is your master?" the Pandava almost shouted.

"The greatest archer on earth."

Arjuna thought he would die from the pounding of his heart, the jealous coursing of his blood.

"His name, Nishada!"

"Why, Drona, prince. Who else would be my master?"

With a cry, Arjuna turned and fled from that clearing as if the black youth had shot him with an arrow. The other Pandavas and Kauravas followed Arjuna, some puzzled and others knowing. His eyes streaming hot tears, Arjuna flew back through the trees. At the edge of the vana, he leapt into his chariot and rode back to Hastinapura like one who would race the wind.

In the city, he drove straight to his master's house. Still sobbing, he stormed into Drona's presence. Arjuna stood red-faced and silent before his guru. Drona rose and came up to his favourite pupil. He saw tears flowing down the Pandava's face; he saw how the young kshatriya shook as if he had a fever.

"Arjuna, what is the matter? What happened to distress you like this, serene prince?"

Arjuna turned his face away from his acharya.

"Tell me what happened."

"You swore! You swore to me, Acharya, and you lied."

"What are you talking about? What did I swear?"

"You swore I would be the greatest archer in the world. But you lied, you lied."

Drona took Arjuna by the arm. "What are you saying, Arjuna? You are the best of all my pupils. Who is a better archer than you? No one on earth."

"Lies, lies, lies! Your sishya in the jungle, the nishada, is better than I am. I saw him today, Acharya, you can't hide him from me any more." He broke down and wailed, "He is so much better than me that he makes me look like a child."

Puzzled, Drona said, "Who is he in the jungle who is a better archer than you?"

"The nishada. Ekalavya."

Meanwhile, the other princes rode up to their master's house. They were also full of the wonderful archery of the youth in the jungle's heart: how he had sewn up the dog's mouth with seven arrows even as it ran from him, and how unerring his aim was when he shot at the target in the tree. They all agreed: not even Arjuna could match the nishada.

But Drona knew that Arjuna was the hope of the world; he was the prince who could save the future. And here he was, already on the verge of destroying himself. Drona saw how blankness filmed Arjuna's eyes and how he toyed with his clothes, as if his mind was on the edge of some trauma. To be the best bowman in the world was more important to the Pandava than his life. It would break his spirit if there were anyone better than he was; and in this case, not even another kshatriya but a mere hunter.

Drona knew his time was short. He said to Arjuna, "Come, let us go and see this nishada of yours."

The others wanted to go as well, but Drona was firm, "Only Arjuna and I will go to the forest."

They climbed into the Pandava's chariot. Hope flared up again in Arjuna, that somehow Drona would relieve his agony. He drove back as swiftly as he had come, racing the wind once more. When it could go no farther, they alighted from the chariot. His fabled poise in shreds, Arjuna dashed through the trees towards the place where the dog had received its incredible punishment.

They arrived at the hidden clearing. Drona stopped Arjuna, laying a hand on the prince's arm. At the far end of the clearing stood Ekalavya. He had blindfolded himself and had his bow in his hand. He stood very still, his body relaxed and alert. As Arjuna and Drona watched breathlessly, that youth burst into a blur of movement that not even their trained eyes could follow. It was movement from another dimension, unreal.

He stopped almost as soon as he began, and was still again. Yet he had shot ten arrows, drawing them from his quiver like lightning, and he had brought down eight birds from eight different trees. The ninth and tenth arrows had flown back to him, one with a lotus from the pool at the heart of the clearing, and the other with a fish from its water that had come up for a gulp of air.

Ekalavya set down the lotus and the fish; he undid the soft bark with which he had bound his eyes. Now he went from tree to tree, collecting the birds he had shot. He seemed satisfied, and sat down to pluck the birds and gut the fish, which was a big one. Drona stepped into the clearing with Arjuna.

The boy had his back turned. But he was on his feet in a flash and spun round, his bow raised with an arrow at its string. Then he saw Drona and such a smile broke out on his face. With a cry of sheer joy, Ekalavya fell at Drona's feet.

"Acharya!"

Drona felt his feet bathed with the youth's tears. He, too, felt a surge of tenderness. There was no mistake: this boy was better than Arjuna, he was the best archer on earth. Yet, equally, he was neither a kshatriya, nor was he noble. Arjuna would never have silenced an innocent dog as cruelly as this dangerous nishada had. The forest boy could become a great threat; someday, he could change the course of fate. Not recognizing Ekalavya from the brief encounter he had with him, many years ago, Drona raised him up and said, "Who are you, son? How do you call me your guru? I don't recall ever having seen you."

"I am Ekalavya. It was dark that evening in your garden, when I came and asked you to take me as your sishya. When I told you I was a nishada, you said you could not have me. But when I set my head at your feet and asked for your blessing, you gave it to me. You are my guru and you have stood beside me all these years, showing me the archer's way."

He led them to the solitary tree. Drona laughed when he saw his own image, now a little worn with sun, wind and rain, but still a remarkable likeness. The acharya turned to Arjuna and saw only burning resentment in that sublime prince's face. Drona sighed. He knew what he must do. Slowly, he said to Ekalavya, "So I am your guru, and no pupil has learnt better from me than you have."

His heart bursting with happiness, the boy stood before his master. His master was saying, "If you say I am your guru, Nishada, shouldn't I receive some guru-dakshina from you?"

Ekalavya cried, "Ask me for anything, my life is yours! At least, you will acknowledge I am your sishya if you take dakshina from me."

Arjuna still stood petrified, his eyes glazed. Sadly, Drona turned back to Ekalavya and said, "Give me the thumb of your right hand as my dakshina."

The smile never left that black youth's face. He said in his lilting tongue, "Archery is a thing of the spirit. My thumb is as nothing to give you for all you have taught me."

Arjuna did not say a word, though his master looked at him again to see if he relented. Ekalavya picked up the crescent-headed arrow that had fetched the lotus from the pool. Without a murmur, he sliced his thumb from his right hand and laid it, dripping, before Drona. He knelt at his master's feet for his blessing. It took Acharya Drona all his strength to keep his hand from shaking, as he laid it on Ekalavya's head. When he turned to look at Arjuna, he saw light in the Pandava prince's eyes again. The hollow stare, which did not see the world, was gone. Without another word to the kneeling nishada, they walked out of his life.

Ekalavya bound his bleeding hand with herbs mixed in a pack of mud. He set up his target again and began practising more rigorously than ever. Indeed, he quickly acquired incredible proficiency with just four fingers. But it was never the same; he would never be the matchless bowman he had been before.

Once more, Arjuna was the greatest archer in the world.

THIRTY-TWO

A young man's dreams

"Mother, tell me why I am so confused!" the sixteen-year-old was full of anguish.

"What is it, Karna?" said Radha, the charioteer's wife, pulling her son close and stroking his handsome face. "Why are you so upset on your birthday?"

Karna sighed. "Father has bought me a chariot today, and fine horses. But I don't want to be a sarathy! Why do I feel like this, mother? What is wrong with me?"

"What do you want to be, my child?"

His eyes shone. His voice full of soft excitement, he breathed, "An archer! Oh, my hands ache for a bow and arrows; night and day, I think of nothing else. How the blood surges in my body when I see a kshatriya with his bow. Mother, am I cursed? That I am full of this unnatural desire."

Radha was silent. He saw tears fill her eyes, and trickle down her cheeks. With a cry, the boy hugged her.

"Have I hurt you? I am sorry, I am so sorry! I would rather die than hurt you. Why are you crying, mother? Tell me!"

She said through her tears, "You talked in your sleep last night. You cried out, 'Ah, don't go! Don't go before you answer me. Tell me who you are, and why you haunt me like this.' Who was in your dream, Karna?"

He was silent for some moments. Then he shook his head and said, "It is the same dream, night after night, and I can't understand it."

"Tell me what it is."

"A woman comes to me while I am asleep. I can see her clearly, but she doesn't know that. She comes as I lie dreaming and she wears a veil across her face. But she is dressed in costly silks, and her manner and carriage are those of a princess. As she bends over me in the dream, her tears fall on to my face. I sit up and say, 'Who are you? Tell me who you are.' But she has vanished. Oh mother, someone must have cursed me! The woman in my dreams, the rush of blood when I see a bow."

Radha held him close as if she was afraid she would lose him. "Karna, I think the time has come when I should tell you something. It's a story, just like the ones you love listening to. It was sixteen years ago, a morning in spring, and your father Atiratha had gone to the Ganga to bathe. As he stood in the river, offering Surya-namaskara, he saw a glitter on the water as if the rising sun was pointing at something adrift on the Ganga. It seemed a treasure floated there and, borne by the tide, it came nearer.

"Your father swam across and saw it was a polished wooden box. He was amazed at what he saw inside it. Swaddled in silks, his thumb in his mouth, there lay the most beautiful baby. He slept peacefully, smiling in the sacred dreams of infancy. It was as if the Ganga had sung that child to sleep, with a lullaby he could not hear from his mother. He was a lustrous baby, like a bit of the sun fallen on to the river.

"Your father came running home, and cried, 'Radha! Look what I have brought you.'

"The child in his arms was so beautiful I could not take my eyes off him. 'Look at the kavacha and kundala he is wearing,' I breathed.

"The armour and earrings were golden, but made from a purer gold than any I had ever seen. I said in alarm, 'This is no ordinary baby; you've brought home the child of some Deva.'"

Her son Karna sat breathless beside her. His mother's every word tore down his world; he was being reborn in her story.

Taking his hand, she continued, "I said to your father, 'No human child can be so beautiful. He must belong to a God.'

"Atiratha still smiled at me in the joy of finding the dazzling baby. 'I found him floating on the river. Perhaps, he is indeed a child sent by the Gods to answer your prayers. My heart sings in me that he was born to be yours, Radha. I am going to call him Radheya, and he will be your son!'"

Karna gave a moan and hugged his mother. She said, "We saw the baby was swaddled in silks that only a princess would have. We decided that a princess had abandoned you, for reasons only she knew. But we could never understand the golden kundala and kavacha you came with. They seemed to be part of your skin, and grew with you.

"For your kavacha and kundala, we named you Vasushena. But your father always called you Radheya, and I named you Karna for your long ears. All that mattered to us was that we had a wonderful son. And for these sixteen years, we were lost in that blessing. But now you grow disturbed, and your hands itch not for chariot-reins but a warrior's weapons. Karna, you must have been born in some great kshatriya's palace, and here we have raised you in a humble suta's house. And all the wealth we have been able to give you is our love."

Her eyes were full again. "No, my son, it isn't any curse or perversion that makes you long to hold a bow in your hands. It is because of the blood that flows in your veins.

"Go, Karna, go into the world and seek out your real mother. I am only the lucky woman who raised you. But I am grateful to God that He gave me a son like you. You might leave me now, but the memory of these sixteen years will help me survive the sorrow the future holds."

Karna flung his arms around her and cried, "What are you saying? Are you also going to abandon me as she did? I don't even want to know who she is. I already have a mother, the best mother in the world!

"As for being a kshatriya, I must be one. That is why I long to be an archer, and now nothing will stop me. Bless me, mother. I must go and seek a master who will make me an archer."

"Oh, my child, may you be the greatest archer on earth!"

"And when I am, I will come home to you. Meanwhile, you must explain everything to father. He may not understand if I told him, especially today when he has bought me a new chariot and horses."

And so Karna, the suta's adopted son, set out on his sixteenth birthday to find a master who would teach him archery.

THIRTY-THREE

Karna finds a master

Hastinapura was famed the world over for the excellence of her archers, who studied under the great Drona. Karna went straight to that city. It was evening. The day's lessons were over, and he found Drona alone in his yard. The young man strode up to the master and saluted him. "Acharya, I want to learn archery from you. Take me as your sishya."

Drona looked curiously at the handsome youth. His instinct told him this boy was more than he seemed. He asked cautiously, "Who are you, young man?"

"I am Atiratha the suta's son. Karna."

At which, Drona knit his brows and said bluntly, "All my sishyas are kshatriyas, they have archery in their blood. I cannot teach a sutaputra."

Karna opened his mouth to speak, but no words came. How that 'sutaputra' scathed him. He glared at Drona as only a kshatriya could, turned on his heel and walked away. Drona stared after him. This was not how a sutaputra would behave; but then, the youth himself said he was a suta's son. Drona felt sure it was not the last he would hear of this charioteer's boy.

Meanwhile, Karna rode home, with the 'sutaputra' echoing in him like doom. He did not eat or drink anything for two days; nor would he answer his mother's anxious questions. Atiratha wisely left the boy alone.

From then on, this became a routine. Karna would announce to Radha that he was off to a distant town, or forest, where he had heard there was a renowned master of archery. But either the same evening, or after a few days, her son would return. He would look a year older, would answer none of Radha's questions and not eat for days. It was the same story each time: another guru had refused to take him in because he was a sutaputra.

At nights, Radha would hear him pacing his room, sleepless, or sobbing in the dark. But Atiratha refused to let her go to comfort their son.

"It's no use," the sarathy said. "He is meant to suffer until God finds a way for him. Who knows, it may be a better way, a greater master than he has dreamed of."

Then one day, he came to eat the morning meal with his parents and his eyes were alight. Radha sighed to herself. He had thought of another acharya to approach; and as surely as he went, he would be back soon, more desperate than ever. Radha had begun to fear her son might take his life.

But that morning Karna was uncommonly cheerful and his parents did not ask him where he was going. They were so relieved to see him back to his old bright self again. Embracing them, he said, "I won't be back for a long time. When I return I will be the best archer in the world, because I am going to learn from the greatest master. God was only leading me to him, that the others refused to take me in."

"Who is this acharya?" his doubtful mother asked.

"I will tell you when I come back!"

And he was gone. The previous night, Karna had a dream in which the mysterious woman, who he now felt certain was his mother, came to him again. She had whispered the name of the master to whom he was going. As he went along, Karna asked himself a thousand times whether he was not being foolish. He had heard about the master's legendary temper, and he would have to lie if he were to persuade him to accept him as his sishya. But Karna was prepared to take that risk. He had decided his life was not worth living, anyway, unless he could become an archer.

It was to no ordinary guru that Karna was going, but to an Avatara. He had decided to approach Parasurama Bhargava to teach him. Karna had a plan. Being a sutaputra, he was both a brahmana and a kshatriya; and of course, neither of these when it mattered. He knew how Bhargava hated the kshatriyas. A kshatriya had murdered his father Jamadagni, and Parasurama had let flow a river of warriors' blood.

He was calmed now, that his revenge was complete; and he had played no part in the affairs of the world since Rama of Ayodhya had confronted him. Bhargava sat in tapasya to purify himself of the sins of all the killing he had done. But Karna was wise enough, and worldly enough by now, to know that Parasurama would never teach a kshatriya. But if he told the master that he was a brahmana—that rarest of brahmanas, who wanted to be an archer—surely, he would not turn him away. And to say he was a brahmana was only half a lie.

After many days, Karna arrived on the tangled slopes of the southern mountain, Mahendra. After climbing for some hours, he saw a sequestered tapovana ahead of him. There, under a majestic banyan tree, he saw Bhargava, his eyes shut, like a flame. But he was quiescent now, all his vast energy turned inwards. His heart beating wildly, Karna approached the guru.

Parasurama sat lost to the world. Karna stood with folded hands, not daring to make a sound. At last, the Avatara's eyes fluttered open and gazed into Karna's deepest soul. Parasurama said, "Who are you, young man?"

Karna threw himself at Bhargava's feet, and cried, "Lord, I have come to you with my heart full of hope. Please don't turn me away, you also!"

Parasurama saw the youth was in tears. He said gently, "What is it you want from me, child?"

"Take me as your disciple. I am a brahmana, but I want to be an archer. And no master will have me, saying they teach only kshatriya princes. You are my last resort. If you don't accept me I will kill myself."

Parasurama laid his palm on the striking youth's head, blessing him. "From today, young Brahmana, you are my disciple. I will teach you everything I know. What is your name?"

"Karna."

Thus began the tutelage of Karna, son of Surya Deva and Kunti, adopted son of Atiratha the suta and his Radha. In many ways, those were the best days of his life. Holding a bow in his hands finally was like being born into his dreams. The cruel world paled, and all the times he had been called sutaputra. Karna was absorbed in learning from his profound and, he discovered, kindly master. He even forgot the woman of his dreams, and she never came to haunt him in Parasurama's asrama.

The guru discovered this sishya was an extraordinary pupil. He had never seen a young man as gifted as Karna; be it archery or the Vedas, the youth was completely devoted to whatever he studied. He drank thirstily at the profound font his master was.

Yet Karna thought of the archer's martial knowledge rather differently from what most young men did. To him that knowledge would make him powerful; power would bring fame; and fame meant everything to him, it meant honour to the sutaputra. What else was worth living for in this harsh world?

Came the day, after three years, when Parasurama said to his brilliant disciple, "The time has come for you to acquire the final gyana that any archer can have."

"What will I learn, master?" cried Karna, loving every challenge.

"The devastras."

One winter's morning, having bathed in the frothy stream, Karna sat before his guru just as the rising sun lit the horizon. Parasurama intoned the mantras that invoke the astras of the Gods of light. Suddenly the mountain air was full of awesome spirits bearing unearthly gifts of weapons. The astras appeared, phosphorescent before the master and his pupil. When Karna chanted their mantras, those weapons flashed into his body and from then on were his to command. Karna acquired all the astras that could be had in this world, even the brahmastra and the bhargavastra.

Parasurama embraced Karna. "It seems the Gods have blessed you; you are the best sishya I ever had. And what pleases me even more than your genius are your humility, your affection, and, most of all, your honesty.

"You are a master of the devastras now, an invincible warrior. I have one final piece of advice for you, which by itself is worth everything else you have learnt from me. You must use your powers only in the service of dharma. The other way, the path of sin, leads to death."

The sun was overhead. Parasurama said, "I am tired. Go back to the asrama and fetch a roll of deerskin. I want to fall asleep here, beneath this tree."

"Why wait until I fetch the skin? You can use my lap for a pillow."

Bhargava patted Karna's cheek. The sishya sat cross-legged under the spreading banyan and his guru lay with his head in his lap. In no time, he was asleep, snoring softly. Karna also shut his eyes, and was lost in anxious thoughts. His master had called him honest. But was he that? Hadn't he lied about being a brahmana? Wasn't his more a thief's way, than an honest man's? Then he thought, 'I lied only to learn from my guru. I have served him faithfully, and been a deserving pupil. He himself said I am the best sishya he ever taught; there is no sin in what I did.' But these tangled anxieties gave Karna no peace.

Suddenly he felt a searing pain in his leg and almost cried out. He dare not move lest he wake his master. He saw a strange insect had crawled on to his thigh. It was as big as his thumb and looked like a tiny wild boar. The creature had tusks and needle-sharp teeth, with both of which it now gouged out good mouthfuls of his flesh and champed on the raw meat and swilled the blood.

Karna was in agony. But he did not stir. His guru's arms lay across his own hands, so he could not move these either. Gritting his teeth, Karna sat on. Finally the blood from the insect's feast flowed on to Parasurama's face, and he awoke and sat up.

"Where did this blood come from?"

"An insect bit me," said Karna casually, plucking the offending creature from his skin and throwing it down.

Bhargava saw the wound in his pupil's thigh. He saw the black insect, covered in Karna's blood. Parasurama stared hard at Karna. Very softly, he said, "That thing tore at your thigh for a long time. The pain must have been intolerable, but you did not move."

"I would have disturbed you if I moved. I paid no mind to the pain."

"Pain?" Parasurama's eyes had begun to smoulder dangerously. "It must have been agony. But you didn't move."

"I didn't want to wake you," repeated Karna, growing confused at his master's accusing tone. He thought his guru would be pleased by his devotion.

But Parasurama was on his feet, his face a picture of suspicion. "You told me you are a brahmana, but no brahmana on earth could bear such pain. You lied to me, Karna; you are a kshatriya, aren't you? Tell me the truth!"

Karna stood shaking before his master. Parasurama breathed, "I have given the devastras to a lying kshatriya. For three years I kept you with me, taught you everything I know, and it was all a lie!"

Karna fell at his feet. "I am a sutaputra. I had to become an archer and no one would teach me. Forgive me, my lord. I am not a brahmana, but I am not a kshatriya either. The wise say that true knowledge knows neither caste nor creed. Be merciful, Guru, I couldn't bear it if you were angry with me."

The rishis are masters of their emotions; but at times, anger overwhelms the strongest of them. Parasurama was no exception. He was livid, blind with rage. Forgotten were Karna's humility, his devotion, his brilliance; all Bhargava saw was a betrayal, an aggression against himself, a violation.

Parasurama was an Avatara; he had sat for centuries in dhyana. Yet now fate stirred him more than he could bear. Bhargava cursed Karna: "One day, when you invoke the brahmastra, when you need it for your very life, you will forget its mantra. Why, that day you will forget the mantras of all the astras I have taught you!"

Karna knelt, aghast, before his master. "Oh, my lord, do I deserve this? You are too harsh."

As soon as he had cursed Karna, Parasurama's rage seemed to cool. He said more gently, "I cannot take back my curse. But it was seeking fame that you came here, for fame that you lied to me. Sutaputra, I bless you now that your name will be a legend across the earth, and men will say you were the greatest archer who ever lived."

For a moment more, the guru stared at his stricken sishya. Then he turned and walked away from him forever. For a long time Karna lay hugging himself, sobbing. Then, slowly, he rose and went down to the stream and washed his face. He bathed the wound in his thigh, where the fateful insect had gorged. Still moaning now and again, he made his way down the mountain.

The world around him assumed a miasmic quality, as Karna wandered along in a daze. He hardly noticed the lands through which he walked, eating if someone fed him, drinking if he came across a river or a stream. Otherwise, he was quite content to stagger on, starved and thirsty, not knowing where he was, not caring if he lived or died. Dark hallucinations beset him, visions of death. And now, the woman of his dreams appeared clearly to him, even while he was awake. He spoke feverishly to her, at times calling her mother and begging her to release him from his torment; at others, he cursed her for his wretched fate. People of the villages and towns he passed blindly through, would stare at the bizarre wayfarer, who, with his fine bow and quiver, seemed to be a noble kshatriya. Plainly, he was demented with some unbearable sorrow.

At last, he arrived at the western sea and collapsed on a deserted beach. Only gulls screamed above him, as he lay in a swoon, lost in the ebb and flow of the waves. At nights, when the tide came in, he allowed the silver foam to wash over him as if he hoped the sea might wash away his pain. During the day he lay on his back, staring at the azure sky above him. The sound and the touch of the waves were like sacrament to him. Slowly, the ocean began to heal the wound in his heart.

One day, when he rose from a dreamless sleep, he felt impelled to worship the rising sun. When he had done this he felt hungry again, ravenous. He scrabbled about in the shallow water and caught some crabs, which he broke open and ate raw. But their scant flesh only whetted his raging hunger. Out of the corner of his eye, some way off, he saw a pale animal's form flash across the beach. His hand moved quicker than his mind. Before he knew what he was doing, he seized up his bow and shot an unerring shaft at the beast he thought was a deer.

He saw the creature fall with a bellow. Karna ran towards his kill, salivating at the prospect of a feast of venison. To his horror, he found he had killed a white cow. The barb stuck like a curse from her side. She gazed at him from her great soft eyes, full of pain, before she shut them forever. Now a brahmana appeared, fell across the dead animal and set up a loud wailing. He sobbed over the cow as if he had lost his own child.

"I didn't know she was a cow," cried Karna. "I thought she was a deer and I have been starving for a long time. Forgive me, Brahmana; I swear I will give you a hundred cows for the one I killed."

"Cruel, ignorant Kshatriya, if you kill a man's only child can you give him another one in its place? The cow was like my own daughter. I curse you, heartless warrior! When you face your deadliest enemy in battle, your chariot-wheel will become mired in the earth. When you get out to free it, your enemy will cut you down when you least expect to be killed. Just as you have my cow today."

Without another word, the brahmana walked away. Karna's roars echoed across that empty beach, so the gulls wheeled away in alarm. He fell on the sand and rolled about in a frenzy, howling with the brahmana's curse. Great healing from the sea had come to him today, and this morning he had found his God, his ishta devata: the splendourous Sun. He had thought his troubles were over. How wrong he had been.

In a while, the panic drained from his body and he sat staring numbly across gray waves. Above him, storm clouds had gathered like some dark portent. A realization dawned on young Karna. For the first time, he admitted a terrible truth to himself: from the very beginning, his life was a cursed one. He had been born into this world only to expiate some terrible sin from another birth. Fortune would never smile easily on him. What other men took for granted, like an ordinary childhood and a hereditary vocation, were chimerical for him. He was a freak of nature, a damned child of the earth. He must find the strength to accept that, to bear it manfully.

Karna sat sombre, as a drizzle began. Then the heavens opened and torrents lashed the beach, the solitary warrior and the carcass of the cow he had killed. He sat on, drenched to the bone. And then, he thought of the one person he loved more than anyone else, she who loved him like her very life. Karna thought of his mother Radha. Tears welled in his eyes; he rose and set out on the long way back home.

Such a welcome she gave him. She clasped him to her, laughed and cried, and babbled everything she had wanted to say to him all these years he had been away. She kissed him again and again. Then his father embraced his son. Atiratha had new respect in his eyes when Karna told them he had been Bhargava's disciple and was now a master archer himself.

But he did not tell them about Parasurama's curse or the curse of the brahmana on the beach. Karna had left home a boy; he returned a man, who knew he was not one of fate's favoured children. Not all his mother's love could remove the twin curses that hung over him. But if he told her about them, it would break her heart. Karna kept the secret locked away inside him like some dangerous treasure.

He stayed at home for a month after his return. Radha saw how thin he had grown and never stopped feeding him. Then one day, he said he must go and seek his fortune in Hastinapura. In that city they would recognize him for what he was: the greatest bowman on earth.

And so, Karna, natural son of Kunti and Surya Deva, adopted son of Atiratha and Radha, the Pandavas' eldest brother, though they would never know it while he lived, set out for the capital of the Kurus, where his destiny lay in wait for him like an ominous shadow.

THIRTY-FOUR

The exhibition

ONE MORNING, DRONA CAME TO MEET BHEESHMA, DHRITARASHTRA and Vidura in court. "My lords, the Kuru princes are ready to display their skills to yourselves and the people."

Bheeshma was enthused. "Let us have an exhibition."

Dhritarashtra said, "Ah, today I curse my blindness. But Vidura will sit beside me and describe everything as if I saw it all with my eyes. Acharya Drona, let us prepare for an exhibition like Hastinapura has never seen before. Vidura, have a stadium built where the princes can show their skills. As soon as the stadium is complete, find an auspicious day for the exhibition. Let every convenience be placed at Drona's disposal, and let Hastinapura be alight with the news!"

Drona hired the finest artisans in the kingdom to build the stadium. In the shastras of vaastu there were exact specifications for such an edifice: which direction it should face; where the royal stands should be built, and where the popular ones; how long the arena should be, and how wide; and other fine details relating to the planets above and the spirits of the earth.

Drona and Vidura chose a site just below the king's palace, and had it sanctified. A huge labour force was collected and, the day after the consecration, work began under Drona's watchful eye. With that force toiling day and night, expertly, the stadium was completed in less than a month; even though the workers had to meet the acharya's exacting standards.

All the lofty stands were complete—the king's enclosure, those for the nobility, separate stands for the women of the palace, and those for the common people. Drona came to the court again and announced that a date had been fixed for the exhibition, a week hence. The princes were preparing for the display.

Drona said, "There will also be a friendly tournament between the princes to make the exhibition more exciting."

"Let word be sent among the people, informing them of the date," said Dhritarashtra.

Came the day of the tournament. It was a brilliant morning, not a cloud in the sky, and a golden sun shone down as if to bless Hastinapura. Well before dawn the people began to throng the gates of the stadium. Some had spent the night under the stars outside the enclosures. They lit fires, sang songs and discussed the prowess of the different participants— whether Aswatthama was the best marksman, or Arjuna, by far; whether Bheema, the Pandava, was the strongest with the mace, or if it was Duryodhana, the Kaurava.

With dawn, the gates were thrown open and a sea of people surged into the stadium to secure places on the wooden and stone steps, which were their stands, canopied with bright canvas to keep away the sun's heat, and the rain, if by some mischance it came down. And as in any crowd, each prince had his partisans. There were those who said, "There is no archer on earth like Arjuna. We have come to watch Arjuna perform with his bow."

"All the Kuru princes are great kshatriyas," cried another. "We have come to watch them all."

Someone else had a different view of things. "The world knows that Drona cares just for one disciple. This exhibition is only to show off Arjuna's skills; the others will serve as foils for him."

"Do you think Drona is a fool that his intentions are transparent to one of your feeble wit?"

There was some irate shouting from the aggrieved party. But just then a hundred deep conches boomed around the arena, silencing the crowd. A covered passage led straight from the palace to the royal enclosure. And now the Kuru Pitama, the august Bheeshma, walked up that passage. His white hair and beard shone in the sun. The people rose to their feet, and called out his name. The patriarch was all smiles today, as he waved to acknowledge their greeting. He took his place on a throne beside Dhritarashtra's central one. Once more, the crowd fell to speculations like a murmurous sea.

The conches resounded again, and again they were on their feet. Along the royal passage came Dhritarashtra, with Gandhari, Vidura and Kunti. The king came on Vidura's arm, and Gandhari on Kunti's. The people took up their names one by one, including Pandu's, and the sky echoed with their chanting. Dhritarashtra was also smiling today, as he raised his arms to greet them. Vidura helped him to his throne.

Kripa followed the king, the queen and Vyasa who had come to watch the exhibition; and then, the retinue of Kuru nobility. The women were shown to their own enclosure to the left of the king's. Settling again, the crowd was full of gossip about the grand men and women of the Kuru House. Romantic secrets were aired in loud whispers, by those who spoke as if they were go-betweens in every affair. Political rumours floated in the sunlit air, wafted along by a tolerant breeze.

The conches echoed again and a hush fell. The people craned to another entrance below the royal enclosure, which led directly onto the white river-sands that had been brought in cartloads to fill the arena. The crowd took up a new cry, "Drona! Drona! Drona Acharya!"

Wearing a crisp white robe, his grey hair down to his slim shoulders, his tread lithe and firm, and his son Aswatthama following five paces behind him, the master strode into the arena. Raising his hands to quiet the excited crowd, he said, "Welcome friends, good people welcome! Your majesties, Dhritarashtra, Gandhari, Bheeshma Pitama, Muni Vyasa, noble Vidura, Acharya Kripa, I welcome you all to this exhibition by the Kuru princes."

The conches sounded again, and Dhritarashtra rose to honour the gurus, Kripa and Drona. In that glittering stadium, the king rewarded the two masters lavishly with gold and jewels. In the background, the Vedas were being chanted without pause since daybreak. When he had formally feted the acharyas, Dhritarashtra cried, "Let the exhibition begin!"

The crowd roared like the sea when a full moon rides her waves. Out of the warriors' passage issued a phalanx of servants, with the Kuru princes' weapons. The crowd gasped to see the bows and quivers, maces, swords and lances, gleaming in the sun. The weapons were set down on a long table. Perfect silence fell over the arena, and then Yudhishtira walked out on to the white sand, leading his brothers and cousins, in order of their age. The stadium rang with the Pandavas' names and the Kauravas', from different sections of the crowd.

Fanning out in a circle the princes walked around the arena, waving to the people. Then Drona called them back to him. The young kshatriyas bowed to their masters and, at their acharya's signal, picked up their bows from the table. Standing in a lotus formation they pulled on their bowstrings in unison, until the stadium and the sky above rang with that sound. The crowd began to clap and cheer lustily, but the thunder of the bowstrings drowned its most strenuous efforts.

When they stopped, Drona announced, "The Kuru princes will now show you their skills."

A hundred horses' hooves drummed the earth. A gate at the southern end of the stadium was flung open, and a hundred brightly caparisoned steeds from the royal stables entered. As they cantered around the hem of the white sands, the princes mounted them effortlessly. A revolving target had been set up at the heart of the arena. As they rode around it, the Kauravas and Pandavas shot arrows at that wooden target carved like a little boar. Not a shaft missed its mark and the crowd erupted in cheers. Faster and faster the horses flew, now galloping round at blinding speed. Still, not an arrow failed to find its mark. Soon the little wooden boar looked like a porcupine.

Nimbly as they had mounted them, the princes leapt off their horses and the animals galloped out of the stadium amidst tumultuous applause. Now the princes took the crowd's breath away with mock fights from chariots, horse- and elephant-back. They fought hand to hand with sword, spear and dagger. These mock fights were so lifelike, one imagined the youths were locked in mortal combat. But not a drop of blood was spilt; not a scratch broke any prince's skin, though they hewed powerfully at each other, with roars to make the crowd's hair stand on end.

Only when they put down their swords and bowed to their guru did the people of Hastina stand up as a man and applaud the display that had rather unnerved them. All the speculations that the exhibition had been organized just to show off Arjuna's talent were forgotten. Arjuna had hardly taken part yet and the crowd was enthralled by what it had seen so far. The skills of the Kuru princes, all of them, exceeded the most imaginative expectations.

A beaming Drona held up his hands for silence. "Now Duryodhana the Kaurava and Bheemasena the Pandava will give us an exhibition of mace-fighting."

It was common knowledge in Hastinapura that there was no love lost between Bheema and Duryodhana. As the princes stepped into the middle of the arena, already some of the people yelled the dashing Duryodhana's name, and others rooted for Bheema.

Drona cried, "This is no duel between enemies, only an exhibition." He looked meaningfully at the combatants, so they remembered this as well.

Drona stepped away and, bowing briefly to each other, the two mace-fighters began to circle one another, the maces shining in their hands. Those gadas were weapons that few men could even heft. But Bheema and Duryodhana carried them as if they weighed nothing, as if they were limbs of their own bodies. For a while they circled, their gazes locked.

At first a hush fell on the crowd and you could hear it breathe. Then some of Duryodhana's supporters began to chant his name, "Duryodhana. Duryodhana. Duryodhana."

Promptly, others cried, "Bheema! Bheema! Bheema!"

Duryodhana lunged forward like a striking cobra, and swung his gada viciously at Bheema. The chanting stopped at the ferocity of that blow. But for all his bulk, Bheema was as quick as his adversary; his mace rose in a flash to block his cousin's stroke. The weapons rang together, sparks flying from them, and the sky echoed with a thunderclap. Silence again in the stadium. Just the two immense kshatriyas circled each other warily, their eyes on fire with feelings far from those proper to an exhibition. The crowd was silenced by the elemental force of that first blow. The air was charged with the cousins' antagonism.

Bheema bent his knees and struck out, low and savagely. Duryodhana leapt into the air so the tremendous stroke whistled harmlessly under his feet. As he descended, he struck Bheema squarely across his back. Bheema had no time to block that blow; but it was delivered from a defensive position and did not hurt him. Yet he staggered two paces and the crowd gasped. Spinning round like a pirouetting dancer, astonishingly graceful for his size, Bheema struck back at once—a backhanded, one-armed blow that landed high on Duryodhana's shoulder and fetched a cry from him.

The people were agog, and now there was no more circling or holding back from the princes. With fierce yells and roars that were uncannily like those of real battle, they hewed at each other with breathtaking speed and power. When they paused to wipe the sweat from their glistening bodies or dripping faces, their supporters shouted their names. The mace-fight was like a duel out of pristine times, when kshatriyas were scarcely human, but godlike. Besides, there was the eerie feeling that this was just a rehearsal for another duel these two would fight some day; and then, to the death of one of them.

More than the awesome blows Bheema and Duryodhana lashed out with, the palpable hatred between them was a shadow looming over the crowd. Vidura sat at Dhritarashtra's elbow, describing each blow, every parry, to his brother who sat as absorbed as anyone that watched with his eyes. His imagination conjured as magnificent a spectacle for him as the actual contention below.

Drona frowned. He said to Aswatthama, "They will kill each other if they continue, and they are dividing the people between them. Stop them."

Aswatthama ran forward and cried, "Stop! Drona commands you to stop fighting!"

But Bheema and Duryodhana seemed not to hear him. The crowd was on its feet once more. The duellists were figures in a dream of titans. Their eyes blazed and their maces rang together still, as if they were powerless to stop themselves. Aswatthama leapt between them, risking a blow which could fell him, or worse. He held on to their fighting-arms, while they growled and struggled to push him aside and fight on.

Drona shouted, "Stop at once! This is an exhibition."

Still bristling, Bheema and Duryodhana stepped back from each other and lowered their maces. And when they bowed to the crowd, the cheer that went up was deafening.

Dhritarashtra cried anxiously to Vidura, "What is happening? Why does the crowd roar?"

Vidura replied, "Drona has stopped the princes. They seemed to become carried away."

Bheema and Duryodhana set their maces down and stalked out of the arena to the enclosure where the other princes sat. Drona raised his arms to call for quiet. When the shouting for the mace-fighters died down, he announced, "Now Arjuna will show us his prowess with the longbow."

Not all the people had really enjoyed the tension of Bheema and Duryodhana's duel, and as Arjuna strode into the arena there was just one name on everyone's lips.

"Arjuna!" they cried. "Arjuna!"

The third Pandava wore burnished mail; he was like a dark cloud lit by the evening sun. Drona said, "This is my disciple Arjuna, dearer to me than my Aswatthama. He is Indra's son, Pandu's son and Kunti's, and he is as valiant as Vishnu."

The crowd hummed with anticipation. Arjuna's name was already a legend in Hastinapura: it was said he was the greatest archer ever.

"The son of Kunti!" they cried.

"The son of Indra!"

"The guardian of the Kurus!"

In the women's enclosure, Kunti could scarcely see her prince since her eyes were full of tears. Like a young lion Arjuna walked slowly to the centre of the arena of sand. He held his bow in his hand; twin quivers, brimming with arrows, were strapped to his back.

Dhritarashtra turned to Vidura, and asked, "Why are the people shouting?" as if he had not heard Drona or the crowd.

"Arjuna is about to show his skills with the longbow." Vidura's eyes were also full.

It is told that though the king's heart simmered with envy, he smiled as guilelessly as only the blind can, "Ah Vidura, the three flames sprung from the lamp, Kunti, have brought me fortune, joy and protection!"

And in her place beside Gandhari, Kunti felt so secure today. She felt certain no misfortune would ever befall her sons or herself. They had come home from the wilderness and found a place in her husband's city, and in the hearts of its people.

Arjuna bowed to his guru Drona, to Bheeshma and to his uncle, the king. Then he began a display of archery that would have remained imprinted forever on the minds of those who saw it, except that something happened after he had finished to put his stunning exhibition in the shade.

Standing at the edge of the arena in alidha, the archer's classic stance, Arjuna began. He stood utterly still, eyes shut, a silent mantra on his lips. Without opening his eyes, he shot five arrows, quick as thoughts, into the mouth of another wooden boar which Aswatthama had set spinning at the heart of the arena. Only when Aswatthama held up the little boar did the crowd roar its appreciation.

The Pandava had already moved on to the next part of his display. Invoking Agni, God of fire, he shot a common enough arrow into the sky. But this was an uncanny shaft: it flew so slowly, as if it hung on every hand of air it traversed. Then it began to glow as if someone had ignited it. It flared up, blazing now, and growing more fiery each moment. And soon not only the arrow but all the sky above the arena was aflame: a conflagration on high!

The crowd cowered.

Arjuna invoked another astra. A silver, sparkling shaft flashed up from his bow. At once the sky was a sea, with waves risen in it to put out the inferno of the agneyastra: tidal waves of the varunastra Arjuna had invoked with the mantra of the God of seas.

The fire in the sky was drowned. The firmament was an inverted ocean. The crowd was speechless; all save Vidura and Kunti, who described every moment of Arjuna's performance to the blind king and Gandhari. Kunti could hardly keep the pride she felt out of her voice.

Arjuna never paused. He was like some dancer, moving in a blur to inaudible music. Another light-like arrow, a parjannyastra, and the waters in the sky billowed together into rumbling storm clouds. The next missile flew up like a long mirage. A tempest rose on high, blowing the clouds away and leaving the sky as chaste as when the day had begun: spotless cyan, and the warm sun shining in it.

After a moment, the crowd found its voice again: its cheers shook the stadium. But Arjuna the dancer, Arjuna the sublime bowman had not finished. Rising onto his toes, he shot another clutch of arrows, now straight down into the sand of the arena. They plunged out of sight. This was the astra of the earth, the bhauma. A crack rent the air, the ground at Arjuna's feet was cloven and a deep passage revealed. He walked down into that tunnel and the earth closed above him.

Another, subterranean, report rang out, and the earth opened again; but now across the arena. The bhaumastra flashed up and lay on the ground. A smiling Arjuna walked out of the opening, and it closed behind him. Not a ripple on the white sands showed where he had entered the earth or emerged. The arrow flew up with its own will, and into one of the quivers strapped to Arjuna's back.

By now the crowd was almost delirious. But the Pandava still had not finished. His bowstring sang again, and all at once there were mountains that thrust their way up out of the sand, towering peaks of ice and snow. They stood there so majestic and real. And the crowd still sat around them, though that arena was hardly big enough to contain a mountain range! All were lost in the archer's miracle.

Another magic arrow, the antardhanastra, and both Arjuna and the mountains vanished and the arena was bare. When the Pandava reappeared he was tall as a hill himself, a giant looming over the stadium. Then, in a flash, he was a little homunculus no bigger than a man's thumb, and Aswatthama had to point him out to the crowd, which was past cheering now, it was so overwhelmed. Minuscule Arjuna shot a tiny arrow and a golden chariot appeared, drawn by horses out of a fantasy. Himself once more, Arjuna rode in that ratha, waving to the crowd.

As he flew round the arena, he flung an empty quiver high into the air. Before it fell to the ground, switching his bow from hand to hand, he shot twenty-one arrows into that quiver, filling it perfectly. It was then that the earth shook and the crowd trembled.

First the people thought it was another of Arjuna's wonderful astras. But he himself stopped his chariot, leapt down from it and stood staring towards the stadium gates. Again the thunder echoed there. Some of the crowd looked up at the sky to see if a storm was brewing. But above was unbroken, clear blue, falling away to the horizon on every side.

Dhritarashtra asked Vidura, "What is that noise? What astra does our nephew summon now?"

"It isn't Arjuna who made the sound of thunder."

The crowd realized the thunder came from the gates. The Pandavas had gathered around Drona. Nearby, his heart stirred powerfully by an intimation of fortune, Duryodhana also stood, with his brothers and Aswatthama beside him. Again and again the defiant noise echoed at the gates to the arena, always drawing nearer.

Drona said, "It is a bowstring being pulled. But only the greatest masters can make their bows sound like this."

A startling figure stalked haughtily in through the lofty gates. His armour shone like treasure and his golden earrings seemed to be made of two drops of the sun. Such was the presence and authority of the stranger, the crowd fell hushed. Like a golden lion, like a Deva, he walked calmly onto the white arena. One look at him and the people of Hastinapura knew that here was a great warrior if there ever was one. They saw how the very sunlight seemed to enfold him, as if in special grace, and how extraordinary his armour was. Was it armour or his golden skin? His hair fell on his shoulders in dark waves. The bow in his hand and the sword at his waist glittered as brightly as his eyes.

The archer stood at the heart of the arena; you could hear the breeze rustling in the trees outside the stadium. With the assurance of a warrior who has no equal, he gazed unhurriedly around him—at the royal enclosure, the stands of the people, at the Pandavas and the Kauravas, at Arjuna and Drona. Almost with contempt.

Not even Drona spoke. Now the stranger bowed quickly to the blind king, to Drona and Kripa. In a voice to match the sound of his bowstring, the golden warrior said to Arjuna, "Pandava, I see you are conceited with the paltry tricks you just performed." Such a mocking smile was on his noble, but also strained and sad face. "If your guru allows me, I will repeat every feat of yours, with my own refinements."

There was a murmur from the people. The instinct of fortune swelling in him, moment by moment, Duryodhana stood riveted. He stared at the newcomer as if he was an old friend, from another life perhaps. Drona could not refuse, at least for the curiosity that consumed him. Who was this archer he had never heard of, who claimed he could match Arjuna?

"Show us your skills, stranger."

Bowing again to Drona, Karna began a display that wiped the very memory of Arjuna's earlier feats from the minds of the people. His fires were fiercer; his ocean in the sky was vaster, brighter. His rainclouds, into which he resolved that sea, were darker, more threatening and streaked with lightning. The gale he summoned to blow away those clouds howled louder than Arjuna's wind. The report with which the earth opened for his bhaumastra was more deafening. The tunnel that lay at his feet, which he also went down into, was paved with glimmering jewels. The mountains he caused to appear were Himalayan, and made Arjuna's mountains seem like hillocks. And when he grew before the people they could not see his face, because it seemed to be hidden in the sun. His chariot not only flashed along the ground but flew through the air. And he shot nine arrows into the mouth of the revolving boar and forty into the quiver he tossed up.

When he had finished and stood radiant before them, the crowd was beside itself. Bheeshma smiled to see the shock on Drona's face. There was no doubt that his pupil had been eclipsed by the golden warrior. Duryodhana ran forward and clasped the stranger in his arms. He cried, "Welcome to Hastinapura, O greatest archer on earth! From today, I, Duryodhana, am yours to command and the kingdom of the Kurus yours to enjoy. Let us be friends always!"

And there was genuine warmth in that greeting. Duryodhana not only sensed that here was the man who could tame Arjuna for him, he also felt uncanny affection for the golden-armoured archer: as if they shared an ancient pain, from before this life.

Flushed with triumph, Karna said, "We shall see today who the greater archer is, Arjuna or I. I, Karna, challenge him to a duel."

Arjuna's face was crimson. "How dare you come uninvited to our tournament?"

"It is a tournament, and all are welcome to show their skills at such exhibitions. Or did Arjuna think it was arranged just for him? But I am challenging you, Pandava. Do you accept my challenge? Or would you rather admit that I am the better archer?"

Arjuna roared, "Come braggart, I will send you to your fathers in hell!"

Coolly, Karna retorted, "Why fight with words, which are women's weapons. Let us speak with arrows."

Arjuna pulled on his bowstring in fury. Abruptly, dark, bluish clouds scudded into the sky. It was Indra, the God of rain, looking down on his son Arjuna with a blessing. Then, a single shaft of the sun pierced those clouds and lit the golden warrior.

THIRTY-FIVE

The golden warrior

KARNA STOOD BATHED, JUST HE, IN THE GOLDEN BEAM OF THE SUN. Arjuna stood darkling under his father's clouds. And suddenly Kunti realized who the stranger was. She remembered the day when she had floated her first born down the river of the past. She remembered the kavacha and kundala he had worn. Blood rushed to her head, and Kunti fainted. Vidura called for some salts. He guessed it was the sight of the stranger that had upset her. Kneeling beside her, he held the sharp salts under her nose and her eyes fluttered open.

Vidura was startled when he saw the look on her face. Tears in her voice, she began to blurt out something. But an instinct warned Vidura: Kunti must not say anything in this public place, least of all with Gandhari so near. Placing his hand across her lips, he shook his head, "Rest now, this is not the time to speak."

He helped her sit up and gave her the salts to sniff again. Clasping her pain to her like a serpent's sting, Kunti steadied herself. She said to Gandhari, "I don't know what came over me."

"Are you better now?"

"I am well now." Once more, Kunti began to describe what went on below to the blindfolded queen. Patting her hand, Vidura returned to Dhritarashtra's side. In the arena, Kripa, who was an expert in the etiquette of duelling, had stepped between the two warriors hungry for a fight.

Kripa announced, "Karna, a proper introduction is in order. Here before you, ready for battle, stands Kunti Devi's third son Arjuna the

Pandava, of the royal House of Kuru. Now you tell us your own ancestry, young Kshatriya. Who is your father and to which family do you belong? You know that no prince will duel with an adversary of lesser lineage than himself." He smiled, "No more than he will marry a princess from an inferior kingdom."

The crowd laughed. But Karna was crestfallen. His handsome head was bent like a lotus in a storm and his face was red with shame. As far as he knew he was not Arjuna's equal by birth, by a long way. A sigh rose from the crowd, and then jeers and catcalls came from the sections loyal to the Pandavas. Arjuna stood haughtily before Karna, a sneer on his lips, and another, altogether inexplicable emotion in his heart: one he would feel every time he was face to face with this man. But he would never know, until it was too late, that it was the blood in his body responding to a brother.

Then, like a king cobra uncoiling, Duryodhana sprang up and cried in his deep rough voice, "My lord, the oldest dharma says that kings are of three kinds: those who are born kings, those who become kings by their courage, and those who vanquish a king and so become kings themselves. I submit, my lord, that a king of the second sort is not necessarily a kshatriya. Not only kshatriyas are valiant but other men as well, as they are blessed by God."

A powerful passion was upon Duryodhana; his chest heaved. "Valour is not the birthright of just the kshatriyas. But if Arjuna means to make it a condition that Karna is a king before he fights him, then so be it!"

The crowd had grown silent. Whatever could Duryodhana mean? The dark prince said, "The kingdom of Anga, which is ours, has no king at the moment. We are happy to create our new friend Karna the lord of Anga! Once he is crowned, let Arjuna find no excuse for not fighting such a worthy adversary."

You could hear your own heart beat in that stadium. Karna's head jerked up and his eyes filled with incredulous hope. Duryodhana smiled at him. Then he turned and crossed to the royal enclosure, where he stood with his head bowed before Bheeshma and Dhritarashtra, waiting for their approval.

Bheeshma was more proud of his prince than he had ever been. He nodded his head, giving his blessing. Then he put his hands together and applauded Duryodhana's gesture. At which the entire crowd burst into loud cheering, calling out first Duryodhana's name and then Karna's.

When Vidura told Dhritarashtra that Duryodhana stood before him for his approval, the blind king smiled. He raised both his arms and cried, "You have our blessing for your noble deed, my son. Karna deserves to have a kingdom; let him be lord of Anga. The people are eager to watch the contest between Arjuna and him."

A messenger ran hotfoot to the palace. A golden throne was fetched out to the stadium, and everything else that was needed for a coronation: holy water, grains of rice, incense, flowers, chamaras—silken whisks—and the white parasol that was the emblem of a king of the earth. The court priests were already present. Duryodhana took Karna by the arm and brought him to the dais on which the throne was set. The other Kauravas showered rice-grains and flowers on him, as, with just a glance of hesitation at his new friend, Karna ascended the throne amidst deafening cheers from the crowd.

The priests began to chant the Vedic mantras for a coronation. Water from the ocean and the rivers of Bharatavarsha was poured over Karna's head. The white sovereign parasol was raised above him, and the crowd was on its feet. Finally Duryodhana set a crown on Karna's head. He pulled his own sword from its sheath and gave it, haft-first, into Karna's hand.

The Kaurava stepped back a pace and said, "Now, mighty Karna, you are king of Anga, and Arjuna is just a prince. Let him not refuse to fight you anymore on pain of being known as a coward."

The crowd was breathless. Karna rose in a daze. Choking, he said to Duryodhana, "I am not sure that I deserve this honour, my prince. And even if I do how will I ever repay you for what you have done today?"

For a moment, Duryodhana stared at Karna. Then he cracked a smile, "We have never seen an archer like you. Such a warrior deserves to have much more than insignificant Anga. Why, to me it seems you could rule the world!" He paused, then, gazing levelly at Karna, said, "As for repayment, there is one thing I want in return for the small service I have done you. I want your friendship."

Meeting his gaze, Karna laughed and said, "That is already yours."

The two embraced each other before that crowd. Some of the people cried, "Duryodhana, yours is a noble heart. You are truly a Kuru prince."

But others held their peace. They saw that the Pandavas were slighted by Duryodhana's gesture. Then, everyone was startled to see an old man, who walked with the help of a stick, pushing his way through the crowd. His wrinkled face was wreathed in a smile. He came straight into the arena and, when Karna saw him, he gave a cry of joy and ran to him. Atiratha, the suta charioteer, hugged his son and said, "What fortune, my child!"

Karna knelt at the old man's feet and set the golden crown of Anga there. Atiratha cried, "Prince Duryodhana, I bless you! You have a great heart."

Now the Pandavas were full of scornful smiles. Bheema cried, "Sutaputra! You aren't man enough to die at Arjuna's hands. Go and ply your whip; it suits you better than a bow."

The Pandavas and the sections of the crowd loyal to them laughed. A spinning weakness threatened to overwhelm Karna. He stood mute and lifted his eyes up to the Sun, Surya who was his God. Kunti's eyes welled again when she saw her son praying to his own father like that, never knowing the coruscant Deva was his sire.

Once more Duryodhana sprang up in his place. He was like a bull-elephant in musth, about to trample a forest pool brimming with lotuses. He roared at Bheema, "Cousin! You are a kshatriya, but you demean your birth; why, what you say would demean a beggar. Valour isn't the preserve of just the kshatriyas."

He raged now, and the seething crowd was his true audience.

"Take the greatest rivers and warriors, and their sources are mysterious. It is the greatness they swell into during their course through the world that counts. Moreover, the births of the greatest men have always been obscure. Why, the most awesome fire, Badava, is to be found below the ocean, where it slumbers until the apocalypse, when it erupts to consume heaven and earth.

"Think of the origins of our own gurus, Drona and Kripa. One was born in a river-shell, the other in a bank of reeds. Think, for that matter, of the birth of our own fathers and of our uncle Vidura. Think of your own births, O Pandavas, who were never Pandu's sons. The world knows your mother took three lovers, whoever they were, and you three were born!

"Who are you to talk of origins and lineage? That you pour scorn on this hero, who from his qualities, why, from his very face, is more of a kshatriya than you or I.

"I say Karna deserves to be lord of the earth! And if you were not blind, Bheema, you would see that too. On every feature of this noble stranger, I see greatness stamped. I don't care whose son he is: to me he is a kshatriya and among kshatriyas he shall live!

"Now tell your highborn brother to fight the king of Anga. Of course, if he dares to."

But then, abruptly, night fell; it was too dark now for a duel. But Karna had stolen Arjuna's thunder today. Moreover, Duryodhana's gesture towards the brilliant stranger had endeared him to the crowd, which now filed its way out of the stadium praising the Kaurava prince. No one spoke of Arjuna's feats tonight. Duryodhana knew the appearance of Karna was the best omen in his life. He felt certain that from now on his fortunes would change for the better.

By torchlight, through the festive streets where singing and dancing broke out, it was the heroes of the evening who led the procession: Karna, king of Anga, and his friend Duryodhana, the Kaurava prince. They walked with arms linked, glowing with their friendship so well struck.

Bheeshma seemed pleased; perhaps because Drona's arrogance had been shorn a little today. The patriarch walked behind Duryodhana and Karna, with a gleam in his eye. He greeted the people as if every one of them was his own child. But Drona walked at the very end of the procession, and hid his face from the glare of the torches. Vidura, too, was pensive beside Drona.

And behind Vidura walked the humbled Pandavas, solemn, even sullen. Yudhishtira managed to greet some of the crowd. Yet even he was shaken today. He had always felt that his position and his brothers' were unassailable because of Bheema's strength and Arjuna's peerless archery. But Duryodhana was at least Bheema's equal; and today the Kaurava had made a friend who was clearly Arjuna's equal. Karna had appeared like a dangerous comet in Yudhishtira's sky, and the eldest Pandava was far-seeing enough to realize this.

Behind Yudhishtira walked Arjuna, stiffly, sweat on his face and his hands clammy. His spirits were lower than they had ever been since the day he saw Ekalavya. But Karna was not Drona's pupil and the acharya could not ask him for his thumb. Beside Arjuna walked the young giant, Bheema; and he was also too angry to greet the people who were, anyway, busy lionizing Karna and Duryodhana. His hands were clenched and his mouth set in a tight line. He was smarting under Duryodhana's assault on him.

Of course, what really hurt him was that every word his cousin had said was true. Bheema had never felt so small in all his life, or so petty. His heart burning with shame, his face red in the torchlight, he walked behind Yudhishtira, with a sombre Nakula and Sahadeva behind him. So grim did the usually ebullient Bheema look tonight, that none of the people dared approach him.

THIRTY-SIX

Drona's revenge

Drona saw how Arjuna had become subdued and withdrawn after the exhibition. The princes' education was complete; their guru called them all, Pandavas and Kauravas, and said, "Your siksha is complete. Now give me my dakshina."

They saw the deep fire in his eyes.

Bheema said, "We can never pay you back for everything you have taught us. But say what you want, Acharya; we will move the earth for you."

"All the wealth of the Kurus is at your disposal," said one of the Kaurava princes.

Drona turned on him and snapped, "It isn't wealth I want. All my needs are already seen to." A wistful look came into his eyes. "It is revenge I want, much sweeter than all the wealth in the world."

Yudhishtira said evenly, "What revenge, Guru? We will give our lives to get you whatever you want."

A spasm of darkness twitched on Drona's face. "I want you to bring Drupada to me as a prisoner. Go to the Panchala kingdom, defeat him in battle and bring him to me alive. But remember, it was said no archer on earth could match Drupada." He paused and looked at Arjuna, then, added softly, "Somehow, I don't think that is true any more. Well? Will you give me my dakshina?"

The Kuru princes, Kauravas and Pandavas, cried together, "We will!"

Bheeshma, Vidura and Dhritarashtra supported Drona's cause. An army was mustered. With the young Kurus at its head, and Drona himself going with them, that force set out for the Panchala kingdom. Exhilarated at the prospect of a real battle, they rode to Drupada's capital. Their acharya was the most excited of them all, like his pupils had never seen him before.

When he saw the army from Hastinapura surround his city Kampilya, Drupada was puzzled. He had no quarrel with the Kurus. But he was a kshatriya too, and a great one. In no time, his legions were ready to repulse the invaders. Outside the city-walls Kuru horsemen took their positions for the attack; but the Kaurava princes were almost coming to blows, each one was so eager to lead the first charge. Drona was having trouble keeping them calm, and now the Pandavas won their first battle. Not that their blood wasn't up as well, but the sons of Pandu behaved with composure. The five of them stood aside quietly under a tree.

Duryodhana wanted to lead the first onslaught; Yudhishtira, the eldest prince, said he had no objection. When the Kaurava force charged the Panchala army, the Pandavas stayed back with their guru. Arjuna's dejection of the past weeks fell away from him. He was confident, "Drupada will prove too much for our cousins. They have no archer who can face him."

Drona murmured, "Let us wait and see", but he knew Arjuna was right. The brahmana knew what a warrior Drupada was. He also knew his own fortunes had changed; he could feel it in his body. Let Drupada tire himself against the Kauravas. Then Arjuna could go into battle.

Weapons flashing, chariots thundering, their roars deafening, the Kaurava legion charged the defending Panchala force. The front-line of the defence fell to Duryodhana, their heads crushed by his mace blows. His brothers were terrible around him, and it seemed the Panchalas would be quickly overcome.

The Kauravas breached the front gates of Kampilya. On horseback and in chariots, they stormed up the streets, felling Drupada's soldiers at will. They gained the central square of the Panchala capital. The sides of his chariot bloody, a triumphant Duryodhana was about to hoist the Kuru flag there. Suddenly, deep sea-conches boomed and the palace-gates flew open. From them rode Drupada in a white chariot, like a wheel of fire.

Cutting down everything in his way he came and his arrows were a wave of wizardry. His chariot, too, was not less than magical: it seemed to be everywhere at once. Now the blood-soaked square rang with the screams of Kuru soldiers mown down like stalks of wheat. His horses were so swift it seemed there was not one Drupada, but a hundred, a thousand of him. By himself the Panchala king was like an army of Yama. Not an arrow left his bow but it claimed an enemy life; and his shafts flowed in torrent.

The flag fell from Duryodhana's fingers. He saw there was no Kaurava who could remotely match the Panchala king. Duryodhana called out to his brothers to retreat. They turned their chariots and fled before Drupada razed the army between himself and them, and came for their lives.

Only Dusasana, Duryodhana's fiercest brother, stood his ground briefly. Dusasana wounded Drupada from a side with a sizzling salvo like hot light. The Panchala king broke the bow in that prince's hand, and shot the helm off his head. The Kaurava fell on his chariot-floor, and screamed at his sarathy, "Fly for our lives!"

Armed with staves, knives, household pestles, and whatever else they could lay their hands on, the common people of Kampilya came roaring out of their homes. They fell on the last stragglers of the Kaurava army. Even as they clubbed and hacked them to death, victory conches blasted and drum-rolls resounded in Drupada's jubilant city. Drupada himself felt ill at ease. He chose not to pursue the fleeing Kauravas and finish them off outside his walls. Instead, he remained within his gates as if he were a coward.

Meanwhile Duryodhana and his brothers came howling before Drona, "You didn't warn us about Drupada! There is no archer like him on earth. We couldn't stand against him, no one can."

Seeing how they trembled, doubt clutched at Drona. He thought he might have overestimated the Kuru princes. Perhaps the time had come for him to take the field himself against Drupada.

Then five young kshatriyas stepped out from under a tree where they had been waiting patiently. They touched their guru's feet, and said, "We will attack Drupada now."

Arjuna and Bheema glowed with anticipation, but none of the frenzy the Kauravas had shown. Laying his palm on their heads, Drona blessed them. Arjuna said, "There is no need for Yudhishtira to come with us. We four will bring Drupada back to you."

Duryodhana and his brothers laughed. Dusasana cried, "Four of you where a hundred of us failed! Bid farewell to your brother and your guru before you go."

Duryodhana nudged his brother to make him stop, lest Drona held the Pandavas back. The Kaurava was sure Drupada would kill the four foolhardy Pandavas. Then Yudhishtira would be at Duryodhana's mercy; he may not even need to have him killed.

Drona said, "Yudhishtira, you will be king one day; you mustn't ride into this battle. You others beware of Drupada."

Bheema, Arjuna, Nakula and Sahadeva climbed into their chariots. Drona asked, "Won't you take the army with you?"

Arjuna replied, "We will go by ourselves."

Bheema blew a blast on his conch, rattling the masonry on Drupada's ramparts. Roaring then, a pride of young lions on their first hunt, their manes flying in the wind, their bodies shining, Devaputras that they were, the four Pandavas flew at the gates of Kampilya.

Bheema rode in front. The very sight of him, a titan with a huge mace gleaming in his hands, made Drupada's soldiers break ranks and run. But he was on them like an angry force of nature, smashing down elephants and horses, hewing down footsoldiers, blood flying, screams ringing. The Panchala ranks parted like a school of minnows for a whale. Their courage broken, they fled even as the vanaras once did in Lanka, when Kumbhakarna came to battle. In moments, a way was clear between Arjuna and Drupada.

Drupada raised his bow and arrows flared like thoughts from it: the same livid stream that had put the Kauravas to flight. But it was an archer of a different calibre who now faced him in that wide city-square. Arjuna, the son of Indra, confronted the Panchala king. From Arjuna's bow a tide of arrows rose, and drowned Drupada's stream in the air. The Pandava prince matched the Panchala king shaft for shaft, and beat him back.

Drupada's kshatriyas, all fine archers, surrounded Arjuna's chariot and covered him in fire. But then it seemed unearthly power was upon the Pandava prince: they did not see his shafts anymore, but a river of light seemed to flow from his bow. Most eerily, they no longer saw

Arjuna himself. He was just a ghostly blur; his archery seemed to have absorbed him bodily.

Yet, screams of death rent the air. The river of light was made of deadly arrows, and every one took a life. Drupada's kshatriyas had always thought their king was a matchless bowman; but this prince's archery was godlike, and the fear he brought unbearable. They either fled from him or perished.

Roaring to keep his own courage, and in fact awestruck by Arjuna's genius, Drupada charged the Pandava. As Sambara the Daitya once charged Indra, Drupada plunged at Arjuna, hoping to shatter the young man's nerve.

A thunderclap exploded in the space between the two rathas, then six more. Smoke billowed around Drupada's chariot. When that king looked up from that moment's destruction, he saw his sarathy and horses were dead, and his flagstaff cut down. Now he felt the bow in his hands, the jewelled weapon given him by his master Bharadvaja, riven by a silver shaft. Arjuna stood facing Drupada, and the king trembled with shock. No other archer on earth could have done this to him. Arjuna's bowstring was drawn to his ear and his next arrow aimed at Drupada's heart. With a moan, the Panchala prepared to die.

Then Arjuna dropped his bow and leapt down from his chariot. In a flash, he was at Drupada's side, his sword across the king's throat. Like three legions Bheema, Nakula and Sahadeva held the Panchala army at bay. Arjuna hauled Drupada into his own chariot. The shame Karna had wrapped him in falling away like a dream, the Pandava rode back to his guru with his prisoner.

Now Bheema had leapt down from his chariot; gripped by bloodlust, he was slaughtering Drupada's soldiers like helpless children. Arjuna swerved his chariot towards his brother and cried, "Drupada is related to the Kurus, Bheema! Leave his army. Let us take our dakshina to the Acharya."

Reluctantly, Bheema lowered his bloody mace and, dissatisfied though he left a hundred corpses behind him, rode out of the city. Roaring, the brothers issued from the smashed gates of Kampilya. When the Kuru soldiers saw Arjuna bring Drupada out with a sword at his throat, they rushed forward again to have revenge for their earlier rout.

Drona saw Arjuna ride towards him with his captive. Arjuna pulled Drupada down from his chariot and marched him to Drona. Drupada breathed, "You! I should have guessed."

"Yes. These are my sishyas."

Tears stung Drupada's eyes. That proud kshatriya stood with his head bowed before Drona. Drona had forgotten nothing of his own humiliation by the Panchala. He savoured the moment silently.

Then, he said, "You once said that friendship was possible only between equals. It seems to me that today you have need of my friendship. Today, my old friend, we are not equals. When you spat on our friendship, Drupada, I stood helpless before you, with nothing I could call my own. Time has come a full circle.

"Now it is you who have nothing, Drupada; your kingdom is not yours anymore. My pupils have crushed your army. Arjuna's sword is at your throat and not even your life is your own. One word from me and he will kill you. But we brahmanas, even the poorest among us, are forgiving. You and I spent some happy years in my father's asrama. I have never forgotten those years, Drupada. Here, I offer you my hand once more in friendship. Remember this hand holds your life in it. Take it Panchala, be my friend."

His heart dying within him for shame, but never showing a trace of it, Drupada took Drona's hand. The brahmana was so happy he forgot his anger and embraced Drupada. Drona cried, "You said that friendship can be only between equals. Well, I will make an equal of you, you poor pauper. To prove that I still want to be your friend, I return half your kingdom to you!"

No kshatriya would have committed that foolishness, but would have killed Drupada for fear of his revenge. Drona was a brahmana; he thought naively that everything was forgiven. He cried, "Look, there is the Ganga. I return all the lands south of it to you, to be your kingdom. All the Panchala lands north of the river I will keep for myself." He laughed, "So that we can always be equals, and thus be friends!"

Drupada returned Drona's embrace. "Drona, let us be friends for ever."

Drona had tears in his eyes. Drupada thought, 'Ah, the young Arjuna is a peerless kshatriya! I must have a daughter whom he will marry. And, of course, I must perform a yagna and pray for a son as well, who will kill Drona for what he has done today.'

Drupada ruled his remaining kingdom from Kampilya, in the province of Makandi, from the Ganga upto the banks of the river Charmanwati. Drona ruled the northern Panchala lands with all its towns and people, the country called Ahichatra. It was the Pandavas', and especially Arjuna's, guru-dakshina to him.

THIRTY-SEVEN

A father and his son

Dhritarashtra was king of Hastinapura and the Kurus. But the people knew it was Pandu's campaigns that had extended the boundaries of the Kuru kingdom as far as they were now. Besides, Yudhishtira was older than Duryodhana. The Pandava was noble, steadfast and utterly honest. Against his own wishes, Dhritarashtra crowned his brother's son yuvaraja of the Kuru kingdom, the heir apparent. Yudhishtira quickly proved himself wise and discerning, far beyond his years.

One day, shortly after the humbling of Drupada, Drona called all the Pandavas and Kauravas. The acharya seemed distressed. The previous night, he had a prophetic dream in which a horrible war of the age was revealed to him, and his own role in it. Dismayed by what he had seen, Drona assembled all his pupils in his yard.

It was to Arjuna that he said, "I received the brahmasirsa from my guru Agnivesha. And my master had the astra from Agastya Muni."

He paused to show how serious he was. "Only to you, Arjuna, have I given the secret of that weapon. For if you summon it, it can destroy the world. I know your heart is strong. I know you will never lightly invoke the ayudha that bears the heads of Brahma. Yet I have given you a great gift in the brahmasirsa, and I now demand a special dakshina from you."

Arjuna said quietly, "My life is yours if you want it."

"That I know. But what I want from you is that you swear an oath to me, something that may be harder to pledge than your life."

"Tell me what it is, Acharya."

"If you know what I want you may not give it even to me. First swear that whatever I ask you will give me, unconditionally."

Arjuna drew a deep breath. "I swear it in your name, and by all that is sacred to me."

"I want you to swear that if some day, I face you in battle, you will fight me without reserve. Even to the death of one of us."

Arjuna cried out softly, the other princes gasped; but Drona stood waiting. At last, Arjuna nodded wordlessly.

Now Drona smiled, and said to the others, "You are all witnesses to his vow. He must honour it at any cost."

For a year more, Drona kept just Arjuna near him, as his most remarkable disciple. He taught him secrets and refinements to his archery, beyond the grasp of any other pupil, including Aswatthama. Avidly Arjuna learnt those subtle and complex lessons from his guru. Finally, one day, Drona called his favourite sishya. The master appeared exceptionally relaxed and he made Arjuna sit beside him. They were alone together.

Drona said, "Your tutelage is complete. This last year has been invaluable, and now I think I can proclaim that my sishya Arjuna is the greatest archer on earth."

Arjuna glowed. The Pandava had grown with each day that passed: not only in skill but in spirit. At last, he felt he had put Karna, the only threat, behind him.

Drona said quietly, "Yet, if I were to tell the world that you are the greatest archer in it, Arjuna, I would be lying."

Arjuna gave a start: so Karna was still better than he was. His face grew dark. Drona laughed, "I am not speaking of Karna, but of another." His voice was wistful. "Another like whom there has never been any archer in all time, and never shall be."

"Who is he, Acharya?"

"Your own cousin, Arjuna: Krishna of the House of Vrishni. Your mother has a brother called Vasudeva. Krishna is his son." He smiled and shook his head. "Though in truth he is no one's child but his own; for he has no beginning or end. He is all things and all men. He is the Avatara, and he knows about you and longs to see you."

Arjuna felt a surge of elation, as if Krishna's was the name he had been waiting all his life to hear. An ecstatic current coursed in his heart, as if everything meaningful in his life was enshrined in that name. It was an unprecedented emotion that swept over the young Pandava, one he could not explain at all. As for jealousy, Arjuna felt no trace of it, as he had with Ekalavya and Karna; he only felt an uncanny joy.

From far away, recalling Arjuna from the reverie he had lapsed into, Drona was saying, "Humility is a great thing, Arjuna, much greater than archery."

In a year of being yuvaraja, Yudhishtira won the people's hearts. Now another guru came to teach in the court of Hastinapura. He was as much as a master with a mace as Drona was with a bow and arrows. He was Krishna's older brother Balarama. Bheema and Duryodhana were quickly his best pupils. Indeed, Drona had begged Balarama to come to Hastinapura for the sake of those two princes.

Though Bheema was as gifted as Duryodhana, the young Kaurava became Balarama's favourite. Very soon, word in the palace had it that Duryodhana was as dear to Balarama as Arjuna was to Drona. Duryodhana basked in that affection. He was devoted to this guru, particularly since the great Yadava openly preferred him to Bheema.

Meanwhile, Sahadeva became exceptionally proficient at the Vedas and other, more arcane, lore; of these, also, Drona was a master. Nakula was always treated like the youngest among the Pandavas; though, in fact, he was born before his twin. Nakula was an adept with unusual astras, and a master charioteer.

Arjuna was inspired by the tales he heard in Hastinapura about his father Pandu's valour. His taste for battle had been whetted in Kampilya and his kshatriya blood cried out for more. He set out with his brothers and an army to conquer some of the other kingdoms of Bharatavarsha.

The Pandavas slew Sauvira, who had once kept a force of marauding gandharvas at bay during his long yagna. Arjuna humbled the Yavana king, a warrior whom even Pandu had not been able to subdue. He killed Vipula, who had humiliated the Kurus, chasing them countless times from his kingdom. The Pandava vanquished Dattamitra also, who was a greater kshatriya than any of the above.

Legend has it that Arjuna and Bheema, in just two chariots and with no other army, overcame the kings of the east who fought with ten thousand rathas. They also defeated some kings of the south. The Pandava brothers came home to Hastinapura with the spoils of war—gold, jewels, horse and elephant in thousands, as not even Pandu had in his finest days.

So far, Dhritarashtra had done his best to be a father to his brother's sons; but envy, and not love, is the most powerful force in any kingdom. Now that the Pandavas were no longer children, and their deeds so overshadowed those of his own sons, envy began to consume Dhritarashtra. It began to rule the blind king.

More even than Arjuna and Bheema's military triumphs, what turned Dhritarashtra's heart against his nephews was what the people of Hastinapura were saying. The Pandavas were being extolled at street-corners and in the people's councils. Everyone was saying that Yudhishtira should be made king.

"Dhritarashtra was never really a king. Once there was no choice but to let him rule, at least in name; while Bheeshma and Vidura attended to the real task. Now we have Yudhishtira. Let him be king. He is young and honest, and all the elders think highly of him."

"He will care for Dhritarashtra's sons like his own brothers."

"More than can be said of the king's sons."

"Arjuna has added immeasurably to the kingdom."

"It is only dharma that Yudhishtira becomes the king."

Duryodhana had many spies in Hastinapura. They were unhappy their prince was being reduced to such insignificance in the kingdom, and brought word to him of what the people were saying. Duryodhana came to see his father. Always partial to his firstborn, Dhritarashtra took his hand and made him sit close to him.

"Your hand is cold and you are trembling! What is it, my child?"

"You have brought us all to the edge of ruin. I told you it was foolish to make Yudhishtira the yuvaraja. Do you know what all Hastinapura is saying? Do you know what the people want?"

Dhritarashtra's blind face twitched, "Tell me what the people say."

"They want you to give the throne to Yudhishtira. That is what your precious people want!" hissed his son.

His blindness had taught Dhritarashtra the value of patience. Growing anxious at his son's mood, the king said, "You will achieve nothing by anger, Duryodhana. When you can't control yourself, how can you hope to control outside events?" He sighed. "My poor child, there is something you are forgetting. Though I was the king, Pandu conquered most of the lands we rule from Hastinapura today. How can I forget these Pandavas are my brother's sons?

"Yudhishtira deserves every shred of praise with which he is showered. Alas, it is true that being blind I have never been much of a king. The throne of Hastinapura does seem cursed, and no real king has sat on it after Shantanu. Even I have dreamt of Yudhishtira becoming the great ruler this kingdom deserves. I have prayed that, with his brothers beside him, he will restore the fame of the Kurus. And I had hoped against hope that my own sons would become loyal ministers and commanders in this kingdom, you also just like Yudhishtira's brothers; and find your glory in that."

With a cry, Duryodhana wrenched his hand away. He began to pace the floor in a fever. Dhritarashtra said gently, "I am sad to see you so full of hatred, especially towards your cousin Bheema. Think at least of your own best interests, Duryodhana. Yudhishtira is already enthroned in the hearts of the people. To oppose him would be dangerous."

A howl came from his son. He screamed at his father, "Enough! Oh, how craven your blindness has made you. I know why these honeyed words spill from your lips, though not from your heart, my lord." He laughed. "You think we may be overheard! I made sure there is no one here besides you and I. Now listen to me carefully: this is my last word to you.

"If Yudhishtira becomes king, his son shall also be king one day. The Kuru kingdom will pass on to the sons and grandsons of Pandu, and the line of Dhritarashtra will fade into a lowly, subservient one. What you are asking, father, is that your sons, the heirs to the throne of Hastinapura, renounce their pre-eminence forever and become dependants of the Pandavas.

"I am the king's eldest son. I would rather die than eke out the rest of my life as Yudhishtira's servant, and Arjuna's servant, and that gluttonous Bheema's slave!"

Duryodhana said with finality, "Father, I know you love me. I was raised as a king's firstborn son, and I must be a king as well. Nothing less will do. If you cannot give me the throne, but decide that I must depend on the Pandavas' charity, I will kill myself."

Kneeling abruptly and laying his head in Dhritarashtra's lap, Duryodhana wept. The king stroked his head. "Ah, you are making yourself miserable for nothing, my child. Pandu was gentle and loving. He was generous to a fault. Yudhishtira has taken after his father, and he has already made a matchless conquest. He has won the people's hearts. All the Pandavas are popular. Bheeshma, Vidura, Kripa and Drona are inordinately fond of them. The Pandavas' wellwishers and friends are past counting. It would never have done to make enemies of them. It was after deep reflection, Duryodhana, that I crowned Yudhishtira yuvaraja."

The king paused and moistened his lips. "Our ministers and commanders are loyal to Yudhishtira. They were all Pandu's men once, or their fathers were. Our army is Yudhishtira's army. Won't they kill us for the Pandavas' sake? Don't be rash, my child. Think of every consequence before you act."

Duryodhana smiled. His father did not know how long, how carefully he and his confederates had been plotting to have the kingdom for themselves. The inmost circle of the conspiracy consisted of Duryodhana himself, Dusasana, and Shakuni, its scheming mastermind. Lately another warrior, bound in gratitude and friendship, had joined them: Karna.

"I have also thought of what you are saying, my lord. We have distributed lavish gifts, in secret; we have made quiet endowments of land and property. The treasury, the counsellors, and most of the army commanders who matter are with us.

"As for Pitama Bheeshma, he will never take sides between the Pandavas and the Kauravas. It seems to me that deep sorrow and tiredness, which have little to do with us, weigh on him. I have seen him so often, walking alone on the banks of the Ganga. I watched him from hiding. I could have sworn he was talking to himself or to the river, and his eyes were full of tears. Once, when I was a child, I ran up to him and asked, 'Why are you crying, Pitama?'

"You know how fond he is of me. He took me onto his lap, and ruffled my hair. 'I am just so tired, little one. I am crying from tiredness.'

"'Then why don't you rest, Pitama?'

"He laughed aloud. 'Rest! Ah, my child, I am afraid rest is not for me. No, not for a long time, I fear. Yet, that time will also come, the time for rest; and then, I shall be well after that.'

"He gave me another of his rare smiles, set me down, and told me to run along and play.

"Pitama's heart is full of a sorrow beyond all our paltry concerns. When the Pandavas first came to Hastina, Bheema was a bully. Bheeshma never said a word to him. Later, I tried to kill Bheema a few times." Dhritarashtra gasped. His son continued coolly, "I am certain that in good time Pitama knew this. But not once did he mention it."

Duryodhana drew a deep breath. "Now for the other powerful men in the sabha. Being jealous of Arjuna, Aswatthama is my friend. He will stand with me, and so Drona will never oppose me. Not because he agrees with me, or because he does not love Arjuna better than me, but because he loves Aswatthama so much. Acharya Kripa is Aswatthama's uncle, and he will not go against Bheeshma and Drona.

"As for the last one: Vidura loves the Pandavas too much ever to take my part. Why, if things came to a head Vidura would abandon you for them. Father, what can one son of a maidservant do by himself? He will preach to you about dharma when he discovers our purpose. Let him talk, you enjoy his sermons anyway!"

Dhritarashtra sat very still, chewing his lip slightly. He waited to hear the crux of what his son had in mind.

Duryodhana was pacing the room again like a tiger. He stopped in front of the king. "I have a plan. Send the Pandavas and Kunti away to Varanasi. Let Yudhishtira be out of sight for one year. In that time, I will win the people of Hastinapura to me; and if Hastina is won, the rest of the kingdom will follow. Like children, the people have short memories. By the time the Pandavas return," he paused ominously, "if they return, they will find Hastinapura has begun to love Duryodhana. My cousins' time in the sun will have ended."

He fell silent. Then seeing his father sombre, he grasped the king's hand and cried, "You must do this for me! If you do not, you will be killing me as surely as if you cut me down with your sword. Remember all you have to do is send the Pandavas and Kunti to Varanasi. The rest I will take care of."

He gave Dhritarashtra's hand a last squeeze and walked out. Dhritarashtra sat alone for a long time. He knew his son well enough to realize he was in deadly earnest. He would not hesitate to take his own life if he could not be king. Then again, he would not hesitate to have the Pandavas' lives, and their mother's, too, if that could give him the crown. Dhritarashtra knew that, very likely, Duryodhana had already arranged that his cousins would never return from Varanasi.

The choice before Dhritarashtra was clear: the life of his own son or those of his brother's sons. He did not hesitate to make his choice. The truth was that he, also, had long harboured secret envy of not just his nephews, but of his dead brother. Pandu had lived such a full and resonant life compared to his own blind, desolate one.

Dhritarashtra did not doubt what Duryodhana said was true: they must either be rid of the sons of Pandu or resign themselves to obscurity and powerlessness forever. Dhritarashtra sent for the wily Kanika. He sent for this particular counsellor, knowing what the ruthless old man would advise. After all, Kanika was among Shakuni's inner circle.

Dhritarashtra decided to throw caution to the winds. When Kanika sat before him, he said, "Are we alone, my friend?"

Kanika sent out a guard who stood at the door and shut the heavy thing. He came back to his king. "Now we are alone, my lord."

Today Dhritarashtra seemed full of urgent purpose, and a new darkness. He leaned forward and whispered, "Kanika, how is an enemy best demolished? With compromise or by aggression?"

Kanika stroked his close white beard. Two shifty eyes glinted, a smile touched his lips. "I see you are arriving at wisdom, my lord. For too long you have been kind to the Pandavas, and loving and avuncular towards them. I am happy to see that finally you realize the threat they are. I am not mistaken in what I surmise?"

Dhritarashtra smiled his deceptively vulnerable smile. "You are as shrewd as ever, Kanika. But tell me, what should I do?"

"Pretend to love them, as you have done all this while. Kings must be hypocrites at times. But don't be carried away by your own pretence. Remember they are the enemy!" Kanika's voice was a serpent's hiss. "The only cure for an enemy as dangerous as the Pandavas is death. And kill them soon; in my opinion, you have already left it too long. A young sapling is easy to cut down, not a full-grown tree. Every day, each moment, Pandu's sons grow stronger because the people love them more. Strike swiftly, before it is too late."

Dhritarashtra sat very still. At last, he heaved a sigh, as if Kanika had shown him the way. Kanika rose softly and left. Dhritarasthra sat alone once more. He did not brood any longer on what he should do, only how he should do it. The king had irrevocably decided that the Pandavas must be got out of the way. He would send them to Varanasi. What Duryodhana did with them there was his affair.

THIRTY-EIGHT

To Varanasi

Cunning courtiers, instigated by Duryodhana, came to the Pandavas and began to praise the city of Varanasi to the sky. They said, "Why don't the yuvaraja and his brothers go to Siva's city for the Pasupati festival this year?"

The Pandavas had no inkling of the plot being hatched, and they felt no desire to visit Varanasi. Duryodhana himself never mentioned Varanasi to his cousins. He went to his father and said, "The Pandavas have heard so much about the Pasupati festival they are keen to visit Varanasi."

Dhritarashtra called Yudhishtira and his brothers. "I hear you want to go to Varanasi, but feel delicate to ask me."

Yudhishtira began to protest, but the king cut him short. "It seems I must force you to enjoy yourselves. So be it: I order you to go to Varanasi. Go on a holiday, my sons; go for a whole year. Take Kunti and a retinue with you, and gifts for the priests, musicians and the people of Varanasi, as befits the Kuru yuvaraja."

Yudhishtira saw through his uncle: Dhritarashtra wanted them out of Hastinapura for a year. He was helpless to resist. He bowed to the king, and said, "We will prepare to leave, my lord."

Yudhishtira restrained a smouldering Bheema and an irate Arjuna from committing any discourtesy. He realized the Pandavas must always be in the right, and visibly.

Yudhishtira came to Bheeshma. He hoped the Pitama would intercede on their behalf. Drona and Vidura were with Bheeshma when the sons of Pandu arrived in his presence.

Yudhishtira said, "The king wants us to live in Varanasi for a year. Pitama, you are our father, our mother and our guru. We are your children, bless us."

Yudhishtira's tone contained a world of insinuation; Bheeshma gave no sign he understood.

Yudhishtira continued, "The king wants us to spend a year in Varanasi worshipping Siva Pasupati, who burned the Tripura with his astra. Pitama, we are fortunate to have an uncle who loves us so much."

Bheeshma was certainly aware of Yudhishtira's sarcasm. Yet, at this crucial juncture, Duryodhana was proven right in his judgement of what the patriarch's reaction would be. Perhaps Bheeshma could not dream of the evil Dhritarashtra and his son were plotting. He had also seen enough of life to know that all things take their course in this world, inevitably. No one could subvert destiny; her purposes were always deeper, wiser and more inexorable than man's. Besides, in those days, Duryodhana was still a restrained prince, at least with his elders. He hardly wore his restless ambition on his sleeve. On some pretext or other, Bheeshma might have rescued the Pandavas from having to go to Varanasi. He did nothing of the sort; indeed, he also seemed pleased at the idea.

Yudhishtira could not accuse the king of plotting against him. He had done the best he could, and he, too, was wise enough to know that if fate took his brothers and himself to Varanasi, then to that city they would go. Bheeshma said, "My blessings go with you, children."

Yudhishtira replied, "Your blessing will keep danger away from us."

"Let all the Gods be with you. Go joyfully and in peace."

Kunti and the Pandavas prepared themselves to leave. When they were ready, they came to take their leave of the elders in the king's court. Bheeshma, Dhritarashtra, Drona, Kripa and Vidura blessed the princes; and so did Gandhari and the other women of the palace. The Pandavas set out grimly for Varanasi. They sensed Duryodhana's hand behind this journey and they knew they could be in danger.

Some weeks before the Pandavas left, Duryodhana and Shakuni heard that Yudhishtira had agreed to go to Varanasi. There was a Purochana in the court that was a trusted man of Duryodhana's. The Kaurava accosted Purochana one day, and steered him to a quiet corner.

"The world will soon be mine, Purochana. Share it with me! You know the thoughts I keep in my heart. It is the hour of my opportunity, and of my need as well."

Duryodhana gripped Purochana's arm, and whispered, "The Pandavas leave for Varanasi in a few weeks. You, my friend, must fly within the hour to that city. Your mission there is simple. You will build a palace for the Pandavas on the outskirts of Varanasi.

"Spend whatever gold you must, hire as many men as you have to. Complete the palace before the Pandavas arrive. It must be a jewel of a mansion, full of the rarest artifacts, replete with every luxury that should grace the home of the heroic Pandava princes."

Purochana stood wonderingly before Duryodhana. Why was he building a palace for the cousins he hated? Duryodhana's serpent eyes glittered. He pulled his man closer and hissed, "But that palace must be built of resin and hemp, wax and lacquer! Its walls must be coated with oil and tallow, then plastered over with mud, and painted. Use your own masons and carpenters, men that can keep secrets. Pay them well: so no one suspects anything is wrong with this beautiful palace, with the finest furniture and silks, the softest beds in which our cousins and their dear mother can sleep. Scent it richly with perfume and incense so the flammable stuff is well disguised."

He paused. Purochana asked, "And then, my prince?"

"And then, meet the noble Pandavas as a friend and well-wisher. Tell them you have built a palace for them at Bheeshma's instance. Make sure our cousins don't stay anywhere else."

A thin smile played on Duryodhana's face. A muscle on his cheek fluttered. "Let them live in the palace for some days; let them begin to enjoy themselves. Then on a moonless night, when they are all asleep, Purochana..." he paused again, and glanced around to be sure no one overheard.

"Yes, my prince? What shall I do on a moonless night?"

"Set fire to the lacquer palace, of course, you fool! Kill them in their sleep. Make sure all the doors and windows are locked from the outside. Make it seem like an accident, and be sure none of them escapes. The palace must burn down swiftly, completely, and the Pandavas with it."

Even Purochana was taken aback. Then being the killer he was, Duryodhana's man to his evil core, he squeezed his prince's hand and cried, "A plan that can't fail! No one will suspect a thing. Especially when they see how Duryodhana grieves for his cousins, who perished in such a tragic accident. And so far away from you."

Duryodhana said quietly, "Poor bereaved Duryodhana shall sit reluctantly on the Kuru throne. And his faithful friend Purochana will not be forgotten when he is king."

He embraced Purochana fiercely, then said, "Purochana, God speed! And don't fail me."

Duryodhana turned and walked away. His last words were spoken with such soft menace Purochana knew the price if he failed the dark prince. Duryodhana was as ruthless as he was ambitious; Purochana did not intend to fail him. He went home and hastily put together some clothes and other things he needed. Then, in a chariot drawn by Duryodhana's own horses, with a casket of gold given him by the prince, Purochana rode like the night wind to Varanasi, Siva's timeless city.

Three weeks later, everything was ready for the Pandavas' departure. They bid farewell to their elders and, climbing into their chariots, rode from Hastinapura with heavy hearts.

The people came in a crowd to see them off. They realized why Yudhishtira and his brothers were being sent away for a year, and came out in anger against their blind king. "Why does Dhritarashtra want to send Pandu's sons away from the capital?"

"Like his sight, Dhritarashtra's wisdom is also gone."

"The king hopes we will forget the Pandavas and take Duryodhana to our hearts. He is foolish; Yudhishtira will be our king!"

The crowd took up the chant, "Yudhishtira will be our king!" as the people followed the Pandavas' chariots out of the city-gates.

Some of the older citizens went up to Yudhishtira and said, "You need not obey your uncle if he means you harm. You are the heir to the Kuru throne. Why should you go to Varanasi?"

"We are with you. We fear you may find danger in Varanasi."

"Ah, this is a sad day, and Bheeshma is as blind as the king."

"Don't go, Yudhishtira! The people are with you."

Some of the citizens cried, "Let us go with the Pandavas!"

Yudhishtira stopped his chariot and climbed down from it. They thronged noisily around him. He held up his hand for silence.

When the crowd was quiet, Yudhishtira spoke quietly to the people. "Our uncle Dhritarashtra has our father's place in this world. It is my dharma to obey him. My friends, we are not going away forever. We will always be with you in our thoughts, and we will return to you as soon as we can. But now, just as our dharma is to go to Varanasi, yours is to bless us and send us on our way."

He wanted to pacify not just the crowd but his impetuous brother. Bheema was already for defying Dhritarashtra, and what the people said was stirring him. "Today, my friends, you must return to your homes without making this parting harder. Yet, a day may come when your dharma will be otherwise. Let us not be hasty, but wait for that day."

The yuvaraja went among the people. He embraced as many of them as he could, clasped the others' hands. He sent them home, taking their hearts with him.

Finally, the last citizen had gone back. Now Vidura put his arm around Yudhishtira's shoulders and, to the astonishment of the others, spoke to him in the dialect of the mlechchas: the coarse barbarian tongue that only very few yet understood.

"The blind one has lost his way. Remember that once corruption enters the heart all values perish. There is no limit to what a corrupt man will do." Vidura sighed. "You are honest, my son, and intelligent too. It is a time of danger and you must be on your guard. I speak from secret knowledge: heed what I say.

"There are weapons more deadly than swords and arrows. Even in the bitterest winter, the clever rat knows how to be safe from the cold by burrowing under the ground. Though he seems apparently helpless, and guileless too, the clever man knows how to protect himself."

Vidura looked around him with sharp eyes. He lowered his voice, though it was unlikely that anyone else there could understand the harsh mlechcha speech. "Fire is a more terrible weapon than the sword. A man should guard himself against fire as the rat does against winter: by burrowing. Having escaped the fire, the stars always shine above to show you the way ahead. And if your wits are about you, who can harm you?"

Yudhishtira stood listening intently to the riddles in which his uncle spoke. Obviously, Vidura felt he could not be too careful, and continued cryptically, "The fire cannot reach you in the heart of the jungle. It is the best place to hide when you want your enemies to think you are dead."

He embraced his nephew, and said, "Don't be afraid. All fares well with those who have restrained their minds!"

Bowing to Kunti, hugging the other Pandavas, Vidura turned back to Hastinapura. Yudhishtira climbed into his chariot and they set out. Kunti rode in the first chariot with her eldest son. When they had gone a short way in pensive silence, his mother laid a hand on Yudhishtira's arm. "What did Vidura say to you? He used the mlechcha bhasha. Is what he said to be a secret from me as well?"

Yudhishtira put his arm around her. "Our uncle warned me against fire. He also said our path would be clear by the stars. I always feared treachery in Varanasi; now I am certain of it. We must be on our guard. Vidura hinted that we would find help, and he said the danger is not immediate. He spoke twice of rats burrowing under the earth. I am not sure, mother, what he meant."

They rode for eight days and came to the holy city of Varanasi, which was part of no earthly kingdom and ruled by no king anymore. Varanasi belonged only to the Lord Siva.

THIRTY-NINE

The palace of lac

Once, an age ago, during his time of misfortune, King Harishchandra of the race of the Sun had sought refuge in Varanasi. Now the people of that city washed their streets clean, set them out in arches and banners, draped these with garlands, and flew bright flags from their rooftops. No one stayed home on the day the Pandavas arrived in Siva's timeless city, and Kunti and her sons received a tumultuous welcome.

They were brought to the old palace in the heart of the city. When they had been in Varanasi for ten days, and the initial strangeness of the place had begun to fade, Purochana came to see them. He told them about the new palace he had built for them.

"It wouldn't have been proper to take you there when you had just arrived. Now the people will not mind if you move to the new palace. It is built on the edge of the city, and you will have more privacy."

Yudhishtira became suspicious the moment Purochana said that Bheeshma had ordered the palace built: the patriarch had not mentioned it. Yet, the Pandava could not refuse to live in it without good reason. He went with Purochana, but he was on his guard.

The first thing Yudhishtira noticed was the moat around the little palace, with sharp stakes in it. Purochana said with a laugh, "No thief can get in, unless the front door is opened to welcome him."

Yudhishtira wondered why stakes lined the moat next to the inner walls as well. It seemed to him the moat was as much to prevent those within the palace from leaving, as to keep intruders out. His eyes never leaving the princes' faces, Purochana showed them around proudly.

The incendiary lac, fat and resin, with which the walls of the mansion were filled, had been plastered over and painted. The walls had been smoked with incense. The Pandavas seemed to notice nothing amiss, as they went from room to room, admiring the lofty ceiling, and the fine views of the city and the jungle behind the palace.

Yudhishtira announced, "My brothers and I will be happy to move here. It is the better-appointed dwelling, and we will certainly have more privacy. Let our possessions be fetched straightaway from the old palace, I see no reason to return to it. We thank you, Purochana; your labour will be rewarded."

The delighted Purochana hurried off to have the Pandavas' belongings brought to the palace of lac.

As soon as they were alone, Yudhishtira took Bheema aside.

"Do you smell anything strange?"

Bheema sniffed the air, and his eyes grew round. "What is it?"

"Lac, tallow and resin, I think." Yudhishtira tapped on the walls with his knuckles, and they made a hollow sound. "This is what Vidura was trying to warn us about. Beware of fire, he said. If I am not wrong this Purochana is Duryodhana's man, and he has built this palace with every incendiary material he could find. And surely one night the good Purochana will set fire to this wonderful palace and cremate us inside it."

Bheema's face was a picture. "We must return to the old palace at once! With the moat full of stakes, we will be caught like rats in a trap here. We cannot wait, Yudhishtira: what if he starts his fire tonight? This place will burn like straw."

Yudhishtira laid a hand on his hasty brother's arm. "We mustn't be rash, whatever we do. This is a carefully laid plan. I doubt that Purochana will be in any hurry to set us on fire. He won't want the people to say the Pandavas were killed as soon as they arrived. He will bide his time, at least a month, or more, before he shows his hand.

"He is not the only one who knows what he is doing. Vidura knows about the plot; he got wind of it in Hastinapura. He will not sit idly, while we are killed. So let us be wary, but for the present, let us wait rather than be caught out in haste. We have a long way to go; we must think where that way leads. We must think beyond this house of lac."

Bheema did not agree. "You are forgetting what sort of men Duryodhana and his friends are. Our cousin does not think twice, and never did, to kill anyone. He is not going to let what the people say deter him, not for a day. He wants us dead, and his way to the throne cleared; and the sooner the better.

"I am not for waiting. I say strike back at them. Let us take fire to Hastinapura and finish them when they least expect it. Arjuna by himself is enough for the lot. And if he isn't, I will go with him and tear them limb from limb."

His eyes shone at the prospect. Then he growled, "Curse them! They have destroyed our peace of mind. We shall not be able to sleep until we kill them. That's what I say and I think I am right."

Yudhishtira smiled, and stroked Bheema's head, as one might an impulsive boy's. "It isn't just this house of lac we have to consider, but our situation. That will not change. Vidura said that beyond the fire our way lies clear under the stars. Now I think I know what he meant. For a moment, just suppose we die in Purochana's fire. Our uncle will put on a great show of grief. 'Ah, my brother's sons are dead! They were like my own children, the hope of my old age. All five of them are gone in one fell stroke. Oh, fate is so cruel to me.'

"With his blind face, in which no one can read the truths of his heart, he is the perfect hypocrite. Pitama Bheeshma is righteous. Yet there is a part of him so detached, so enigmatic: as cold as his grandsire Himavan. He will be sad we are dead, even heartbroken. But he won't blame Dhritarashtra, or punish Duryodhana for murdering us. Drona and Kripa will be sad, as well; neither will avenge our deaths. They will not dare point a finger at the king and his son."

"What are you trying to say, Yudhishtira? Tell me plainly!"

"If we leave this place now, we will always have to be on our guard because our enemies will know we have discovered their intentions. After that, we shall never be certain how or when they strike at us. And strike they will. We will have no peace, and they will have every advantage.

"The other choice we have is to accuse Duryodhana and the king openly. That would be foolish, Bheema: an unequal battle for which we are not prepared. They have given out such favours and wealth of late in Hastinapura that they have enough men of influence in their keep. We shall be humiliated. It is never the common, honest citizen who decides the outcome of these struggles for power, but always those who manipulate the people in crowds. If we accuse Dhritarashtra and Duryodhana, it will be like the fledgling flying against the grown eagle, the beggar waging war on a king. They are prepared for every exigency—Duryodhana, Dusasana, the wily Shakuni, the king, and all their friends in and out of the court. In our innocence, we have only just learnt what they intend; at the moment, the advantage lies with Duryodhana and his father."

Bheema was growing impatient. "We are sitting in a house of lac, and you are talking politics. For heaven's sake, and all of ours, say what we must do!"

"Calm yourself, Bheema, that is the first thing you must do. As for the rest, we must watch and wait; let our enemies believe that we suspect nothing and are ripe for burning."

"Do you mean to sacrifice us to Duryodhana?" cried Bheema.

"Not at all," laughed Yudhishtira. "I assure you, we have time. Vidura will not fail to help us. Wait just a week; and let us tell the others, and keep watch in turns every night. Whoever sets fire to this mansion has first to come to the front door. Let one of us always keep vigil beside it, until either this week is over or we hear from Vidura."

Reluctantly, Bheema agreed. Yudhishtira mused, "Suppose we find a way, or Vidura does, by which we can make Duryodhana believe we have died in the house of lac? Suppose we let it burn down and escape secretly. Then, surely the advantage of the next surprise will be with us and not our cousin."

Bheema was not entirely convinced; but deep down, he trusted Yudhishtira's judgement more than his own. They told the others what they feared. They agreed Yudhishtira's was the best course open to them. Each night, with no lamp burning, the brothers took turns to keep watch at the front door.

It was a strained and anxious time. Often, they felt truly like rats in a trap. They kept each other's spirits up, especially Bheema, who joked and laughed even more than usual. Nobody who visited them, least of all Purochana, suspected anything of the anguish they endured during their first week in the house of lac. When, years later, they looked back on those days they felt that was the beginning of everything that followed.

FORTY

Fire

On the sixth day of that anxious week, a quiet man with a long face and keen eyes arrived in the palace of lac. In a soft voice, he said, "Your uncle Vidura sent me. I am a miner; I tunnel under the ground for precious stones."

Yudhishtira glanced at Bheema. He said nothing yet, because he must be sure the man was not a spy. After a moment, the miner went on, "Vidura said to me, 'Duryodhana means to immolate my nephews in a house of lac in Varanasi. Go and help the Pandavas.' So I have come."

Though they found themselves warming instinctively to the taciturn miner, the Pandavas waited for some sign that they could trust him. Suddenly remembering, the miner brightened and said, "Fire is a more terrible weapon than the sword. Against fire a man should guard himself as the rat does against winter, by burrowing."

Vidura's very words to Yudhishtira outside Hastinapura, and the miner spoke in the rough mlechcha bhasha. Yudhishtira rose and embraced the man, "Welcome, friend! We had to be sure Vidura sent you. These are days of conspiracy, and our cousin means to kill us. Did you notice the smell in the air?"

The miner nodded, he was not a man who missed much. "I will dig an underground passage out of here, through which you can escape on the night Purochana sets fire to this place. Duryodhana will believe you are dead, and you will have the advantage over your enemies. The people will also suspect foul play and turn away from Duryodhana. You will gain an advantage twice over, and time as well, says your uncle Vidura who loves you."

The miner began his task at once. He prised away a flagstone from the central courtyard, and started digging. He said his tunnel would lead to the banks of the Ganga. The only trouble was that Purochana was always in the lacquer palace. He pretended to be an eager servitor; while, in fact, he was spying. And of course, he was waiting uneasily for a moonless night.

It was not possible for the miner to dig his tunnel while Purochana was about. Every day, the Pandavas went hunting with Purochana as their guide. While they were away, the miner worked feverishly.

For two weeks he toiled: by day, while the Pandavas were out in the forest with Purochana, and by night as well, when Purochana returned to Varanasi to sleep. The miner barely slept a few hours daily, and Duryodhana's man never suspected a thing. In fact, the miner made friends with Purochana. He even made him think that he, too, was Duryodhana's man sent by him to keep an eye on the Pandavas, and on Purochana himself.

The tunnel was finished sooner than they expected. The miner's task had been providentially halved: some twenty feet down he struck a natural subterranean rock-tunnel that led straight to the river. All he had to do was excavate his way up through soft earth, and make an opening for the Pandavas and Kunti to come out. By this stroke of luck, he was also able to make a much longer passage.

One night, the miner took Yudhishtira and his brothers a short way down the tunnel to show them how it led into the ground. Meanwhile he also took to drinking with Purochana on some evenings in Varanasi. He won the assassin's confidence by speaking slightingly of the Pandavas, and praising Duryodhana. And once Purochana confided to the miner that an astrologer had told him the Pandavas should be very careful of their lives on the night of the coming new moon.

The next morning the miner warned Yudhishtira. The Pandava said, "Amavasya is a fortnight away. Before that we must set fire to the palace ourselves, with Purochana in it, and escape."

Kunti said, "Let us have a poor-feeding in ten days. We will invite Purochana also, and get him drunk until he falls asleep."

"And we set fire to this cursed palace and escape!" cried Bheema, hugging her. "Our enemies should beware of our mother."

Arrangements were made for the poor-feeding. There was one problem: when the house of lac burned down Purochana's body would be found among its ashes, but not the princes or Kunti's remains. Word would reach Duryodhana in Hastinapura and the Pandavas' advantage would be lost.

King's daughter that she was, Kunti had a solution for this as well. It was a terrible solution. But they all agreed, after a lot of hard thought and discussion—the miner insisted desperate measures were unavoidable—that it was the only way to mask their escape. If Duryodhana became suspicious that they were still alive, he would hunt them down relentlessly and have them killed by one agent or another.

Kunti had taken to feeding a nishada woman and her five dark sons, who came occasionally from the forest to visit her. She invited them to her feast for the poor. That night, Kunti was especially attentive of this woman and her grown sons. She took them away from the rest of the crowd into an inner room. There she not only fed them sumptuously but plied them with some very strong liquor, which the miner bought in Varanasi.

Bheema drank with Purochana that night. Now Bheema could drink as much as five men and feel just slightly merry. Obliged to keep up with the unusually friendly prince, Purochana was soon so drunk that he passed out even before he tasted Kunti's delicious cooking.

The feast ended, and all the guests left: all save Purochana, and the nishada woman and her five sons, who were also unconscious. One of those wild youths was a giant like Kunti's Bheema. A strong wind had risen over the river and the jungle beyond it. It whistled around the lacquer palace.

The Pandavas gathered in the courtyard where a trap door, covered by a flagstone, led to escape and anonymity: the inscrutable future. Bheema said, "The walls will burn so quickly we may not all have time to get away. The rest of you go down into the tunnel. I'll light the fire in Purochana's room and join you in a moment."

Bheema ignited the torch he carried in his hand. When his brothers and Kunti had climbed down into the darkness of the tunnel, he crossed quickly to Purochana's room. The man lay on his back, snoring. Bheema said, "Farewell, Purochana old friend. Sleep now for ever."

He stepped out of the room and applied his torch to the door. In moments, huge tongues of flame leapt across the walls and the ceiling. Bheema had thought he might have to apply his torch to some of the other rooms as well. When he saw how the fire caught and spread, he ran for the tunnel.

As he scrambled down the tunnel-mouth and secured the trapdoor behind him, the flames had engulfed the palace. They burned hungrily, devouring the willing stuff of which the murderous edifice was built. The vats of ghee stored in the kitchen erupted.

In the dimness, Bheema asked, "Won't they find the tunnel when the palace has burned down?"

Yudhishtira held his torch up to the ceiling of the underground passage; smoke dribbled in from above. He pointed to some wooden rafters. "Those will fall when they burn, and the ceiling will cave in and debris from the palace will fill the tunnel. Rocks and earth will fall, blocking it halfway to the river. Our friend the miner is a cunning craftsman. Not even if someone looks for a tunnel will he find it. But let us fly, before the roof falls on our heads."

They set off by torchlight. The tunnel led steeply down at first, before straightening towards the river. The air was thin here. When they had gone a short way, Kunti and all her sons, except Bheema, felt dizzy. Behind them, the fire raged.

The people of Varanasi were woken from sleep by the crackling of great sheets of flame, and the sound of rafters crashing down. They came running out of their homes and stood shocked, watching the lacquer palace burn like an immense firework. Walls and ceiling fell noisily with explosions of sparks.

"Duryodhana planned this."

"And his father knew."

"Alas, Kunti has perished with her sons."

"A curse be on Dhritarashtra. He will pay for this sin."

"Even Bheeshma did nothing to stop it."

"A murderer rules us, and his murderous son will rule after him."

"Drona and Kripa were blind to their dharma."

"Vidura loved the sons of Pandu, but even he did nothing."

"Nemesis will stalk the Kuru kingdom."

They wept that they themselves could do nothing to save their princes. Until the treacherous palace had burned down completely, and the piles of embers began to subside, the people of Varanasi stood and watched in horror under a flame-lit sky.

Some hours ago, when the Pandavas and Kunti started down the tunnel they were overcome by dizziness, except Bheema who had once drunk the nagamrita. Yudhishtira, Arjuna, Sahadeva, Nakula and Kunti sat down and gasped that they could not go a step further. The first rafters and stones came down, shaking the tunnel ominously. At any moment, the whole thing would collapse, doing Duryodhana's work for him.

With the strength of the elemental Vayu, Bheema now picked up Kunti and his brothers. Yudhishtira and Arjuna sat on his shoulders. Kunti perched on his neck. Then the titan scooped the twins up in either arm. While the others clung to him, stupefied, Bheema loped down the miner's tunnel. Just in time: as he set off, he heard part of the tunnel's roof, which lay under the lacquer palace, come crashing down.

The son of the wind streaked down the secret passage. He carried his mother and his brothers as lightly as his natural father may have some leaves. Like the wind, he arrived at the end of the tunnel. Like a gust of air from the earth, he burst out of the branch-and-leaf covering that hid the tunnel-mouth beside the Ganga. He sprang out into the woods with Kunti and his brothers.

Midnight was laden with the scent of wildflowers and lotuses that floated on the river. The others stirred from their swoon. They drew deep draughts of clean air. Bheema set them down gently on the grass. They were south of Varanasi now.

When they looked back, they saw the northern sky lit up. Gigantic tongues of flame reached for the stars, and Kunti shuddered. Ahead of them the Ganga flowed, lapping serenely at her dark banks. They imagined the river spoke to them, saying, 'Like my waters, all things must pass and be forgotten.'

They stood on the banks of the river, not knowing how they would cross her. Their way lay across the water, into the thick jungle beyond, and oblivion. Then a voice spoke from the night, startling them. The brothers drew their swords.

A thin, very tall man stepped out from behind a tree, into the light thrown all the way here by the fire. "You must be the Pandavas and their mother. I thank God that you have come. This is the night Vidura told me to wait for, when I would see the white palace burning like a hayrick."

"Who are you?" asked Yudhishtira, mistrustfully.

The man ignored the question. "The lord Vidura gave me gold to wait here every night with my boat. I have been here three months, and I was beginning to think you would never come. Tonight I had fallen asleep, when suddenly I heard the fire crackling. I knew this was the night, and God be praised, here you are."

Yudhishtira asked again, "Who are you, fellow? We don't know you."

The man cracked a big-toothed smile. "So you are careful, my prince; that is a good thing, because these are dark times. But listen to this."

Now he spoke in the mlechcha bhasha, "He survives who knows fire doesn't harm those that hide in the hearts of jungles."

Yudhishtira took his hand warmly. The man said, "You will be safer across the river, and the sooner we set out the better."

He led them to a boat tethered to some rocks. The Pandavas noticed his skin glowed softly in the dark, and wondered if he had gandharva blood in him; and his boat was the strangest, sleekest craft. It was made of a dull metal, and was flatter than any boat they had seen. It had no oars or sail.

The mysterious boatman helped them aboard, Kunti first and then her sons. He smiled when he saw how the Pandavas stared at his craft. "My boat is not ordinary, my princes? You wonder how it will cross the river without oars or sails. But tonight, my passengers are more extraordinary than my father's boat!"

The night was moonless, and they did not see what he did with some levers near the stern. The boat began to hum. Slowly, with life of its own, it set off across the river, gliding along, hardly rippling the velvet water.

"It is best if I don't set you down directly across. We will go upstream, where the jungle is wilder and few men venture. So the good Vidura said I should."

He worked the shining levers beside him. The strange boat leapt forward, flying easily against the current while the boatman steered it casually with his left hand. He smiled to see their astonished expressions. "Cast off your despondency, my friends! As swiftly as my boat, your evil time will pass."

They went half an hour, and they could no longer see the glow in the sky where the palace still burned. The night was black and the jungle loomed forbiddingly. A breeze sprung up in the trees, and blew into their faces.

The boat slowed and, at the boatman's expert navigation, came to rest softly against the far bank of the Ganga. Above them bright stars hung in the sky, but ahead lay the jungle and utter darkness.

When he had helped them ashore, the boatman bowed, "My lord Vidura, who is wise and prescient, says that Duryodhana, Shakuni, Karna and all the Kauravas will taste bitter defeat one day. Yudhishtira will sit upon the throne of the Kurus, with his brothers around him. Vidura says he waits impatiently for that day."

The man of the night bowed again. He turned back to his boat, and it hummed with life once more. He veered it round and set off into the dark, and soon the night swallowed him. He had a long way to go back to Hastinapura, to tell Vidura his mission was accomplished.

The Pandavas knew it was not safe to rest where they were: anyone on the river could see them. With a prayer in their hearts, they plunged into the jungle, picking their way through it by rushlight. Hunting owls and other creatures of the night, nocturnal ones with luminous eyes, stared down from the trees at the intruders.

FORTY-ONE

The tragic news

Two hours before dawn, the palace burned down completely. Only embers remained, glowing in the night like thousands of fiery eyes. The place was still too hot for anyone to look for bodies, and the people of Varanasi decided to return to their homes. They would come out the next morning, when the embers had died and they could begin a search of the gutted building.

All night, the miner had mingled with the crowd. He was a little worried lest the opening into the tunnel was exposed by the fire. Now, when the crowd dispersed, he stayed back. Wrapping himself in a blanket he had brought, he stole among the ruins of the palace. The heat singed him, but he was determined to level the mouth of the tunnel. The closest investigation in the morning should not reveal the secret of the underground passage. He carried a spade in his hand.

The miner knew exactly where the trap door was, and made straight for it through the haze of heat. He arrived at the courtyard. A slow smile spread on his face as he scrabbled in the smoking debris with his spade. The roof of the tunnel had caved in, but its entrance had been covered evenly with fallen masonry and burnt timber. It was miraculous: as if the place had been diligently levelled, so no one could ever tell, not the miner himself, where the tunnel-mouth had been.

The miner saw where Purochana, what remained of him, lay on the floor beside his bed, where he must have fallen screaming when tongues of fire licked him awake from his stupor. With small regret, the miner saw the charred remains of the poor nishada woman and her sons. He wondered fleetingly if the Pandavas and their mother would ever pay for that sin. With grim satisfaction, he left the ruins of the lacquer palace. His task was fulfilled, and he set out for Hastinapura to bring Vidura news of the Pandavas' escape.

Came dawn, and the people of Varanasi returned to the house of lac. Only ashes remained of the palatial mansion. These were barely warm, because the morning dew had extinguished any living embers. Now the import of what had happened struck the crowd with full force. The women wept, some beat their breasts. Curling their tongues, the older ones ululated shrilly as was the custom. They knew it was not just five princes and their mother who had perished in the night's fire: it was the future of the Kurus.

The people went through the charred remnants of the palace. Some cried, "Here is the murderer, Duryodhana's man. At least he got what he deserved."

"I hope he died slowly."

"And screaming in pain, with no escape," said one of the women in anger. She was not far from the truth.

They saw the remains of the nishada woman and her sons. The women's wailing grew louder; none of the men was dry-eyed either.

"Let us take news of his success to the blind king," it was decided, "and may his joy be short-lived. May the people's curses darken his destiny and his sons' with sorrow and evil."

The news came to Hastinapura. When the messengers from Varanasi stood before the king, they said coldly, "Kunti and her sons were burnt alive in the palace they lived in."

The king sprang to his feet, almost falling. A howl of anguish tore its way out of him, shaking even the messengers. Dhritarashtra was an actor. His heart was awash with joy, but his blind eyes leaked tears and he staggered as if someone had struck him. Dhritarashtra's grief was like the autumn cloud, which is full of thunder but brings no rain. It was like the tears of the crocodile.

"Ah! Today I feel the grief of my brother Pandu's death again. I must have been a great sinner in my past lives that I have to suffer like this now."

His head bowed, clever sobs shook his powerful frame; it seemed grief had overwhelmed him and he could not speak. Then he appeared to gather courage. "Let my soldiers and our kinsmen fetch the remains of Kuntibhoja's daughter and her valiant sons from Varanasi. Let our coffers be opened, and food, clothes and gold be given generously to the poor."

The tragic news spread through the city like the fire of an astra. Later, Dhritarashtra and Gandhari, Bheeshma, Drona and Kripa, Vidura and the elders, the nobility of Hastinapura and the commanders of the army came to the banks of the Ganga to offer tarpana to the souls of the dead. All save Dhritarashtra, his sons and their coterie mourned sincerely. Many wept as if they had lost their own flesh and blood. The nishada woman and her sons had a funeral they could not have dreamt of.

Most stricken was Bheeshma. He cried without pause since he heard the news. He did not speak a word; his heart was truly broken. He was too old to bear such grief any more; he felt death at his elbow. Everyone knew Vidura loved the Pandavas like his own sons. They were all too shocked to notice how controlled he was.

Bheeshma offered tarpana in the river. Then he stood apart from the other mourners, wracked, wondering how he would live through this day. He had braved many deaths: his father's, Chitrangada's and Vichitraveerya's. Then, Pandu also had died. But this was more than just the sudden death of five princes and their mother; this, Bheeshma knew, would prove to be the end of the Kuru kingdom. There was no hope left in him, as he stood whispering Yudhishtira's name like some mantra. "Yudhishtira, you should not have died. You were to be king."

Vidura appeared at Bheeshma's side. The patriarch sobbed pitifully. Vidura put an arm around him, and led him out of earshot of the others. Though he had intended to keep his secret to himself, he now decided to share it with the elder. He was afraid that, otherwise, the old man would die of grief.

Gently Vidura said, "Pitama, give no sign on your face of what I am about to tell you." Bheeshma turned swollen eyes to Vidura. "Pandu's sons did not die in the fire at Varanasi. I arranged for their escape."

Bheeshma began to tremble, and Vidura held his arm tightly to remind him that he must give nothing away.

At the river, having committed himself irrevocably to evil, Dhritarashtra was offering a hypocrite's tarpana to his nephews. He wailed loudly and called out the Pandavas' names, as if to call them back from the dead. "Yudhishtira, hope of my old age, why have you abandoned me? Oh, Arjuna, Bheema, Sahadeva, Nakula! Kunti, my sister, what curse has fallen on us? Dear God, have mercy."

Vidura whispered to Bheeshma, "It was my brother, Duryodhana and Shakuni who plotted to kill the Pandavas. They built a lacquer palace and told Purochana to set it on fire."

"Murder! Ah, Dhritarashtra."

"Kunti and her sons are in Siddhavata, the southern jungle across the Ganga. Let them remain hidden for a while. When the time comes they will return, and we shall live to see them become lords of the earth. But we must be patient."

Bheeshma squeezed Vidura's hand, "The secret is ours, my heart is at peace. Keep me informed."

Vidura turned to leave him, but Bheeshma drew him back. Embracing him as if in grief, the patriarch said, "My son, the House of Kuru will always be in your debt."

FORTY-TWO

Flight through the jungle

Using the stars to guide them, the Pandavas went south through the jungle. The trees grew closer together, and soon the vana was so dense it was difficult to go on. They had reached the deep Siddhavata, and they were tired and thirsty. Kunti sat down under a tree. "I can't go another step."

Their eyes closing, panting, the twins, Yudhishtira and Arjuna also sat beside their mother. Bheema stood before them, as fresh as if he had just had a sleep.

Yudhishtira said, "The land crawls with Duryodhana's spies, we are still too near Varanasi. If Purochana escaped the fire, they will already be on our trail. If they find us here, no one will ever know how we died. We must press on, and be far from here when the sun rises."

With an effort, he tried to get up. His legs gave way, and he fell back. Arjuna said, "I cannot stand either. You will have to carry us, Bheema."

Bheema smiled. "I have never been tired since I drank the nagamrita. Come, let us go."

Bheema picked up his mother and his brothers again. When they sat securely, it seemed to them, though it may have been their imagination, that Bheema grew even taller. He set off through the forest as if he had wings on his heels from his father Vayu.

The night breeze, full of mysteries, blew into their faces as the son of the wind bore them through the Siddhavata. Kunti and four of her princes slept. Pushing down trees that came in his way, loping easily over hillocks that loomed in his path, the fifth flew south.

Flight through the jungle

He hardly realized how far he went. When dawn broke, he had gone eighty yojanas. Suddenly, he felt tired. He stopped, and set his brothers and his mother down. Waking, Kunti cried, "Oh, I will die of thirst! Water, you must find water."

Feeling ashamed, Bheema picked the others up again and set off in quest of water. On they plunged through the thick jungle, and saw no water anywhere. Once or twice Kunti swayed where she sat, and Arjuna or Yudhishtira held her, or she would have fallen off. Finally, near noon, she could not bear her thirst any more.

"Put me down at once! I will not go another step until I have drunk some water. I don't care if the Kauravas find me. I must rest."

Ahead was an old banyan tree and Bheema set them down under it. He stood for a moment, attentive to the noises of the jungle. Then a smile creased his face.

"Mother, listen! Water birds."

Kunti was in tears. She, too, strained her ears, but heard nothing. The other Pandavas slept against the great roots of the banyan, their lips dry, their eyes shut over parched dreams. Bheema said to his mother, "Before you know it, I will be back with water."

As she laid her head in the crook of her arm, he sped off into the gloom ahead. Now Bheema went so swiftly, he resembled a wild zephyr of the woods: a forest spirit flying towards the dim sounds of the water birds.

He broke into a clearing, and shouted in delight to see the fine lake stretched across it end to end. He also felt desperately thirsty. Bheema plunged into that sparkling lake, overgrown with lotuses in colours he had never seen before.

Standing in the cool blue water, he drank deeply from cupped hands and strength flowed back into his tired body. Laughing aloud in exhilaration, he splashed about for a while. Then, soaking the upper cloth he had worn, saturating it, he raced back through the jungle to where he had left his mother and brothers.

He found them in the same stupor. Gently, he made them sit up and squeezed some precious water into each one's mouth. They moaned and opened their eyes briefly, and fell asleep again. He saw that colour returned to their cheeks, and their lips were moist once more. It seemed to him they slept more peacefully, and their breath flowed evenly.

Bheema sat watching them. When he looked at his regal mother, still so beautiful, lying on the rough earth under the banyan, tears welled up in his eyes. Bheema began to speak softly to himself.

"I am cursed and a sinner, for I see my mother Kunti, daughter of Kuntibhoja of the Vrishnis, daughter-in-law of Vichitraveerya of the Kurus, Pandu's wife, and the Pandavas' mother, sleeping like a beggar in the forest. She bore the Devas' sons in her body, Indra, Vayu, and Dharma's. Yet, here she lies on the rude earth, and our enemies thrive!"

He sighed, and muttered on. "Ah, blessed are those whose relatives are not envious. Duryodhana, do not think the Gods smile on you, vile cousin. If Yudhishtira had not stopped me, your father, Karna, your brothers, Shakuni and you yourself would be floating down the Ganga as ashes, and your spirits haunting the mazes of naraka."

He clenched his hands at the pleasant thought. Then, to console himself, he whispered, "The sources of great rivers, like those of great men, are often obscure—some hidden crevice high on a mountain. But in the fullness of time, the world sees their glory. So, too, shall it be with us."

Bheema took heart from this thought and, growing quiet, sat in lone vigil over his family in that deep jungle.

FORTY-THREE

A change of heart

Bheema did not know it, but he had carried Kunti and his brothers into a rather terrible jungle. A rakshasa called Hidimba ruled this vana.

Fortunately, when Bheema went to find water, Hidimba and his sister Hidimbi were both asleep in a tree, hanging bat-like from stout branches. Earlier they had feasted on a fine sambur stag—Hidimba had leapt on from above and fastened sabre-like fangs in its throat. They lived off wild game, mainly: any animal whose warm blood they could drink, and flesh they could rend from the bone, and soft, glutinous marrow they could suck out. Hidimba and Hidimbi ate deer, wild pig, bison, tiger, and even elephant. But no meat was as succulent as man, or any other creature's blood as sweet to drink.

Hidimba, the arboreal rakshasa, was huge and sinister. As Bheema sat forlorn beside his sleeping family, a bird's sharp song roused the demon from dark dreams. As he stirred, the most alluring scent wafted into his nose: the scent of living human flesh. For just a moment, he thought he was still dreaming. Then, with a hiss of foul breath, the rakshasa came fully awake. His eyes gleamed as he pulled himself up by hand-like feet onto the branch from which he had been hanging.

Sniffing the jungle air, he rubbed his eyes and then woke his sister. She also smelt the aroma on the breeze, which made her brother drool.

Hidimba grinned hideously. "Can you smell them? At least four or five of them. The vana devatas are pleased today that they have brought us such a feast. It has been a long time since we drank human blood, gnawed human bones, and sucked soft human brain out of foolish human skulls."

She, too, was snuffling the air in excitement. Her brother said, "You hunt today, Hidimbi. This is not only the sweetest prey but the easiest to kill. They may die of fright just to see you drop out of the trees. Go enjoy the hunt. If any of them runs, call me and he won't get far."

Her eyes afire in the leafy dimness, Hidimbi set off, swinging through the treetops. Hidimba lay back with a sigh, shutting his eyes again so he could smell the human scent more deeply, and let his mind savour the images it conjured of a bloody feast.

Quick as a flying-fox, gliding between the trees with wings outspread, Hidimbi sped through the forest. She arrived above Bheema at his vigil. He sat on a fallen tree-trunk, his hands on his great thighs, staring dully ahead of him.

The rakshasi crouched on her branch and gazed at him, and at his sleeping mother and brothers; then helplessly back at Bheema again. Hidimbi, on her hunting perch, looked down at Bheema below her, lost in his sorry thoughts, and suddenly she trembled. The human male was more beautiful than any creature she had ever seen, or even imagined. He was more magnificent than her rarest dreams; he was godlike. Her eyes roved over his deep chest, his slim waist and his great arms, caressing him already with her gaze. Lithe as a wolf, she thought, but more powerful than a tiger, than ten tigers.

She breathed even harder, her heart beat more quickly than when she hunted. Powerless against the strange feelings surging in her, she moaned and her clawed hands shook like leaves in a wind. Crouched in her tree, Hidimbi felt she had become the quarry and he below her, so ineffably handsome, was the hunter. A transformation came over the rakshasi: she shivered as with a fever, and fell helplessly in love.

Her brother was forgotten, and the savage thing he had sent her for. Looking at Bheema, any thought of killing him left Hidimbi: she must have him for her lover, or she herself would die.

She dropped lightly down to the ground. Softly she approached him, and as she did, she was not a rakshasi any more. Instead, with sorcery, she had turned herself into a dark human beauty. Her face shone with what she felt, and her form was perfect! She was tall and curvaceous; he could encircle her waist in his hands. Her breasts were high and full, and her hips flared. Dark as night, and as enticing, clad in a chaste white garment that set off her skin seductively, enchanting Hidimbi came up to Bheema.

Bheema looked at her, and his heart went straight out of him and melted into her. She smiled and he wanted to take her in his arms, and lay her down right there beside his mother and brothers.

Not looking directly at him, she said softly, "Who are you, mighty one? Hasn't anyone warned you about this jungle? Did no one tell you this is Hidimba vana?"

A pleasant heat suffused Bheema. "Hidimba vana? Who is Hidimba?"

"My brother, the rakshasa who sent me to bring him your warm carcasses. He sits on a tree, licking his lips that he will drink your blood."

Bheema laughed as if nothing could be more amusing. Her eyes straying to the sleepers under the tree, Hidimbi said, "Who are they? She is beautiful still, though she is not young any more. What is she to you?"

"My mother, and my brothers. But tell me, lovely one, how is it you stand talking if your brother sent you to kill us and bring us to him warm?"

The dusky beauty flushed; he saw her delicate body quiver. His gaze roved shamelessly over her. She whispered, "I came to feast on your flesh. But when I saw you, something strange happened to me."

"And what is that?"

She blurted desperately, "I fell in love with you! Come away with me. I can fly through the air. I will take to the mountains. We shall be lovers forever among hidden caves where Hidimba will never find us. Come, my love, we must fly. My brother will be here any moment, it has been months since he drank bright human blood."

She glanced nervously over her shoulder. Bheema said, "My mother and brothers are more precious to me than my life. And you want me to fly away with you, leaving them at your brother's mercy?"

"We will take your mother with us. I can grow twice as tall as I am now and carry her."

"And leave my brothers, who love me more than their lives?"

Neither of them noticed that they were not alone any more. In the branches of a nearby mango tree, a long hirsute fiend crouched among the ripening fruit, his eyes slitted at what he heard.

Hidimbi had tears in her eyes. "I didn't mean to upset you. I am lost in love with you, Kshatriya: more than ever now, when I hear what you say. I will bear you, your mother and your brothers, too, through the sky. But we must go!"

In his tree, Hidimba's eyes blazed, and he gave a low chuckle at Bheema's reply.

"Can't you see they are sleeping? They have had a long journey and I will not disturb them. I am not afraid of your brother. I am Bheema, the wind's son, and fate has brought me here today to rid this jungle of its devil."

He took her hand and placed it on his arm.

"Feel these arms. Aren't they strong enough to kill your brother?"

Bheema laughed in excitement at her silken touch, and she sighed to feel how strong he was. She let her hand wander across his chest. She leaned against him, and whispered, "Yes, yes they are."

Bheema began to draw her to him, her lips parted for his kiss, when Hidimba dropped down from his tree with a hiss. Hidimbi sprang up, her eyes full of panic. Hidimba stood growling before them, tall as two men, his pale fur standing on end, his glare crimson.

He screeched at Hidimbi, "Weren't you afraid when you gave the human your love? I lay in my tree, thinking you were sinking your fangs into his throat, and here you have become someone else for him. In his arms already, and plotting my death."

He was terrifying, now the one creature he trusted in the world had betrayed him. "You have broken my heart, Hidimbi. I will kill you first, drink your blood and smear myself with it. Then I will eat these others, and you can meet your lover in Yama's land."

Hidimbi whimpered. With a roar, Hidimba rushed at her, but Bheema sprang up and shoved him back. The rakshasa was astonished; every man he had met before had fled from him.

Bheema was a head taller than any other man, but the pale vampire towered over him. Yet, Bheema's eyes shone at the prospect of battling this beast that stood there, long ears twitching, claws extended, the fangs in his white bat's head glistening in such sun that pierced the gloaming of the forest.

Bheema said, "Come, Rakshasa, you and I will go a way off and fight, so my brothers and my mother aren't disturbed."

Hidimba hissed at him like a great lizard. Bheema went on, "Strange creature, pray if you know how, for the hour of your death has come. From today this forest will be safe for those who would pass through it." The Pandava spoke quietly. "I am going to crush your ugly head as if a wild elephant trampled on it, and you will be carrion for the jackals and hyenas you have been feeding on, and for vultures and crows." Hidimba was too startled to retort. "Rakshasa, your sister will watch me drag you across the earth as the lion does an elephant he has killed."

Now Hidimba gave a shrill laugh, and Hidimbi clutched Bheema's arm. "Your opinion of your own strength is high indeed, human. Match your fine words with blows. I am thirsty, great-mouth, and only your blood will quench my thirst."

With a roar, the rakshasa flew at Bheema. Bheema caught the claws of the flying monster in hands stronger than tree-roots, and the creature howled as the Pandava dragged him away from the sleeping Kunti and his brothers.

Some way off they fought: the son of the wind and the beast spawned in darkness. Bheema also roared in exhilaration. Like bull bisons, they charged each other, colliding so the earth shook under their feet. Kunti and her sons awoke anyway and sat up. They saw the lovely Hidimbi; through the trees, they saw Bheema battle a pale beast winged and tailed like a monstrous bat. Arjuna, Yudhishtira, Sahadeva and Nakula were on their feet in a flash, and ran towards their brother.

Kunti asked Hidimbi, "Who are you? Are you an apsara or a gandharvi? Your beauty is not of humankind. Are you the goddess of this jungle? And why are you here, watching the rakshasa and my son fight?"

"My brother sent me to drink your blood. When I saw your son, I fell in love with him. My brother was angry and wanted to kill me, and now they fight."

Meanwhile, Hidimba uprooted a tree and cast it at Bheema like a lightning bolt. Bheema stood his ground and the tree shattered against him. Hidimba flew through the air and seized Bheema by the throat. The fiend was strong, and Bheema tired. They flailed about, the Pandava avoiding the curved fangs the rakshasa wanted to sink into him.

Arjuna pulled on his bowstring. "Let me have him, Bheema."

"Why must two of us kill this insect?"

"Night falls swiftly, and he will be ten times stronger with darkness. You must kill him before the sun's rim touches the western mountain."

With a growl, Bheema flexed himself against Hidimba and there was the dreadful sound of the rakshasa's elbows and shoulders breaking. Hidimba set up a demented wailing. His short arms hung useless at his sides, and terror sprang into his eyes.

Bheema said, "Rakshasa, let me tell you who I am before you die. I am Bheema, and Vayu Deva is my father."

He lifted the rakshasa and whirled him round over his head. Bheema flung Hidimba down on to a rock, bursting his bat's body asunder: the neck broken, the wings and back smashed, black blood flying everywhere, the monster's final scream echoed through the jungle at the sinking sun. Bheema roared and roared his triumph. He kicked the rakshasa's corpse repeatedly, mangling it; he dragged it about, and danced round it in frenzy.

Yudhishtira ran forward to embrace his brother and Bheema went limp in his arms. The others made him lie down, while the twins rubbed his tired limbs. Yudhishtira was overjoyed after the slaying of Hidimba.

"How lucky I am to have brothers like you! Why, with you four at my side I am as strong as the Devas."

Arjuna, Sahadeva and Nakula smiled. Having slept deeply for a time, they felt revived and confident again. The sight of Hidimba's body, lying beside the rock against which Bheema had broken him, picked up their spirits even more.

Yudhishtira said, "This forest is full of darkness and anguish, from the years Hidimba ruled it. Let us leave this place behind us."

Bheema rose, and Kunti and her sons set off through the darkening jungle, where a rough trail led through the trees. They had quite forgotten Hidimbi. Now she called to Kunti, "Devi, what will become of me?"

Yudhishtira and Kunti turned. Hidimbi said, "I have lost my heart to Bheema. I will kill myself if he leaves me like this." She turned imploringly to Kunti, "Devi, you are a woman. I have forsaken my own nature for love. Make him understand how I feel."

Kunti looked at Bheema, and he blushed and looked away. The other Pandavas smiled. Kunti said, "Well, it seems Bheema would like to make you his wife."

Bheema looked at Yudhishtira and opened his mouth to speak. No words came. Yudhishtira put an arm around his brother. "I am older than you and you think you must not marry before I do. But the heart observes no such convention, and the heart must be honoured."

Bheema looked at Hidimbi and she at him. Both dropped their gazes, their eyes shining.

FORTY-FOUR

Ghatotkacha

Hidimbi led the Pandavas to a sylvan lake called Salivahana. With amazing speed, skill and some magic, as well, she built a cozy, wide-windowed cottage for them on its banks. Then, she said to Kunti, "Let me take Bheema away with me for a while. But every night, I will bring him back to you."

Kunti blessed them. Hidimbi took Bheema by the hand and flew up into the sky.

The lovers had not so much as touched, since Hidimba interrupted their first embrace. Now, as she flew through the air with him, their lips sought each other. They kissed until Hidimbi, wild for more than kissing, flew down into a forest that was hardly a place on earth.

The trees and flowers that grew here were softly radiant and the air was full of quiet wonder. Pale mountains rose steeply all around them. Bheema saw they had alighted in a valley that had surely nestled here, pristine and undiscovered, since the world began.

Beside a pool covered with lotuses the Pandava warrior and his beautiful rakshasi lay together on a bed of satin-soft grass, and were lost in sweet delirium. Hidimbi's cries echoed from the encircling mountains.

When they did not make love or sleep, Hidimbi bore her husband through the air to many marvellous, unsullied places; and the earth conspired to make their ardour more climactic. Under thousand-year-old nyagrodha trees, which all but spoke, they lay together; and upon eagle's eyries on the dizziest peaks, their naked bodies bathed in the gold and vermilion of sunrise and sunset, or the silver light of the moon that gazed down on their delicious exertions.

Every night, Hidimbi faithfully brought Bheema back to his mother and brothers. For an hour or two, they returned to the cottage on the banks of the Salivahana, where they would eat with the others: wild game that Arjuna and the twins hunted, or fish from the lake. As the days and months flashed by, a shadow of sorrow fell over the love of Bheema and Hidimbi, and they could find no reason for it. One day Bheema said to her, "I fear our time together is nearing its end."

Lying upon him in languor, she nodded, and her eyes were tear-laden. Softly, she said, "Our destinies lead away from each other because there is much that you still have to do in the world of men. But I am with your child, and we mustn't part until he is born."

Bheema's roar shook the sky. He lifted her in his arms and danced about, naked as he was. Then moved by sharp desire, that now she was his own flesh, he laid her down again tenderly. Later that night, they returned to the cottage. They saw another visitor had come to meet Kunti and her sons: a grandsire and mentor, Vyasa Dwaipayana.

He had heard how the house of lac in Varanasi had burned. With a seer's insight, he knew the sons of Pandu had not died. Asking their whereabouts from wild beasts and birds, he found their sanctuary. As the moon rose over the hills, Vyasa shared their evening meal. When they had eaten, they sat on the cottage steps watching Soma Deva ride on the still mirror of the lake.

Vyasa said, "In seven months Hidimbi will bear Bheema a mighty son, a grandchild of the jungle and the wind." He paused, and seemed to peer into the future. "The boy's valour will be a legend through the ages. Do not call Bheema's wife Hidimbi from now, for she is not a rakshasi any more. Call her Kamalamalini; she is as lovely and true as a lotus."

Bheema took her hand in the silvery night. Vyasa continued, "When Bheema's son is a year old, you must leave the forest. Kunti, my child, put away your anxiety. These troubled times are only passing clouds against the firmament of your sons' destiny. I, Vyasa, say to you, your princes are born to rule the world, and Yudhishtira to be its emperor.

"Evil appears to triumph just for a day, and then dharma must prevail again. The darkest yaama of night is just before the dawn. Be calm, be brave: these trials are only to strengthen your spirits. Fear nothing, you are never alone. All the rishis of the world are with you, and the Devas who are these princes' fathers stand by you always. There is deeper and more careful design behind your travail than you imagine."

Seven months went by after Vyasa's visit: months of love for Bheema and Hidimbi, and of beauty, but poor peace, for Kunti and her sons. Though the green asrama reminded them of their early years with Pandu, anxiety never left their hearts.

Then Hidimbi delivered a large infant, dark as his parents. He did not cry when he was born, but gazed back at his mother and father, his uncles and his grandmother with grave eyes. He had not a hair on his head, and with his enormous ears, it truly resembled a smooth water-pot. They named Bheema and Hidimbi's son Ghatotkacha.

Ghatotkacha was no ordinary child, and at the end of the first month of his life, he was a full-grown youth. Time for him was another, extraordinary stream.

Just as the growth of his body was prodigious, so was his mind's. The weeks Ghatotkacha spent with his father, his uncles and grandmother were like years; and by their love for him, they were drawn into his fabulous time. Those were joyful days, and full of sorrow as well: they all knew how few these days must be. What filled their hearts, more than Ghatotkacha's phenomenal gifts, was his loving nature.

He learnt wrestling from his father, archery from his uncle Arjuna, and mastered them with swiftness which, if anything, exceeded that of his growth. But Ghatotkacha had a favourite among his uncles in that asrama: Yudhishtira.

The half-human, half-rakshasa boy never tired of sitting at Yudhishtira's feet and learning the Shastras and the Vedas from him, imbibing them with astonishing speed and seldom an interruption. He would sit raptly with his big eyes fixed on the eldest Pandava's tranquil face, and drink in everything he heard.

With his uncles for masters, Ghatotkacha quickly became a complete warrior and a youth of deep learning as well.

One day, when just a few months had flitted by, Vyasa returned to the asrama on the lake. Bheema and Hidimbi knew the hour of parting had arrived. Ghatotkacha knew it was time to leave his father, his uncles and grandmother. Hidimbi clung to Bheema. No words would come from her; she only wept, her heart breaking. Bheema clasped his woman and his son in his arms and sobbed like a child.

At last, tearing himself away, he said, "Wipe your tears, my love, you have our son with you. Whenever I want to see you, I will think of you and you must come to me at once. Don't cry any more or I shan't be able to go with my brothers, who have need of me still."

They both knew that he would not call her, for a long time. Not because he would not want to, but if he did, another parting would be unbearable.

Vyasa said gently, "Put on valkala and disguise yourselves as wandering hermits. Twist your hair into jata with the juice of the nyagrodha. There is a town called Ekachakra not far from here. That is where you must go for the present."

When they had disguised themselves to look like itinerant brahmanas, they bade farewell to Hidimbi and Ghatotkacha. Then, wrenching themselves away, following Vyasa through the forest, they made their way sadly towards Ekachakra.

They journeyed across clear, chatty streams and still, bright glades that seemed to have been painted on to the earth with a God's brush-strokes. They passed through numinous jungles, full of invisible presences, hidden kinnaras and vidyadharas, and other wood spirits. At last, they saw before them a warm, picturesque valley and in it a fine little township. Ekachakra was a collection of perhaps two hundred dwellings. Smoke issued lazily through their chimneys and curled up into a vacant sky.

Vyasa led them to the house of a brahmana he knew where he had already arranged for them to live. When the brahmana welcomed them, and showed them a sunlit, airy room where they could stay, Vyasa said with a smile, "Ekachakra is a quiet town, but I think you may find some liveliness here before long. Live, meanwhile, by alms, as brahmanas should. And I will see you again in a few months."

Then he went away.

FORTY-FIVE

A sleepy town

KUNTI AND HER SONS KEPT MUCH TO THEMSELVES AND LIVED BY begging for alms. The people of Ekachakra took readily to the quiet youths and their mother; but those town-folk were no fools. Whenever they met together they said, "These are no itinerant rishis, but high-born kshatriyas. Perhaps they are in flight from some danger."

"Yet they are not arrogant, nor are they condescending."

"Their devotion to their mother is wonderful to see. Let them remain among us for as long as they want."

Though the people of Ekachakra accepted them warmly, anxiety was never far from the Pandavas' minds. They would go out for alms in the morning. How alien to their royal natures this begging was, but it made them humble, and taught them about the world. As soon as their begging-bowls were full, they would not delay a moment but hurry back to Kunti, lest any of Duryodhana's agents wandered into the little town.

Often with tears in her eyes, Kunti would divide the food her sons had begged. Bheema would always get half of everything the brothers brought, and the rest was shared equally among the others. And they were not unhappy, though for Bheema the food was never enough and he grew rather lean.

Nearby there lived a potter who became friendly with them. He grew especially fond of Bheema, who helped him carry loads of hay; he was sad to see the young giant waning from not getting enough to eat. This potter was an intelligent man, and something of a comic. One day he arrived at the Pandavas' door with a begging-bowl he had made for Bheema, three times the size of an ordinary one.

The next day, Bheema went begging for alms with his outsized bowl. Giggling to see him with the huge thing, the women of the town filled it to the brim, some of them with amorous looks at the strapping brahmana. Then on, those women began to cook a little more food, and the big brahmana would oblige them by splitting firewood or doing heavy work around their houses. He was careful not to become otherwise involved, despite all the subtle and flagrant invitations he had almost daily. Some mild flirtation was harmless enough, and Bheema did not deny himself that pleasure.

One morning, just Bheema and Kunti were at home in the brahmana's house, when they heard loud sobs from the next room, where their host lived with his family. Kunti raised a finger to her lips: the brahmana and his wife were crying.

Kunti had grown very fond of the man, his wife and their two children: an older daughter and a young boy. She came to listen at the closed door that divided the brahmana's house.

She heard him say, "Curse this treacherous world! Curse this life, its roots are only torment and misery. Woman, years ago I said to you let us leave this accursed town. You answered that you were born here and here you would live. And now...oh, now death is upon us and there is no escape."

His wife said, "Death is certain for all that are born. Don't grieve, I will go in your place."

Her husband gave a louder cry still. "How can I sacrifice your life for mine?"

"The rishis of old have said that women should never be killed. If the devil won't hesitate to kill a man, he may not kill a woman. I have borne your children, and my nature's deepest needs have been satisfied. Death holds no terror for me, I will go to the rakshasa."

Hearing the word rakshasa, Bheema sat up in the next room. Now the daughter of the house, a girl of twelve, ran to her parents, hugged them and wiped their tears. "My brother is just four. He will die if either of you leaves him at this tender age. The son of a family is its soul, and the soul must be nurtured.

"Let me go to the rakshasa. You are more precious to me than my own life, and I will feel no fear or pain."

All three clung together and sobbed. Then the little boy stopped his thoughtful game in the yard. He was a tousle-haired, beautiful young fellow. He ran in and lisped, "Don't cry."

He held a long blade of grass in his hand. Brandishing his green sword, screwing up his face in the sweetest snarl, he cried, "I will slay the rakshasa!"

The other three hugged him and began to laugh. Kunti walked into their room. She said, "I couldn't help overhearing you. You spoke of a rakshasa and some terror he held for you. Share your grief with me, perhaps I can be of some help."

The brahmana sighed, "Alas, we are beyond help. For this week our turn with Baka has come."

"But tell me anyway: to share a burden is to make it lighter. The least we can do in return for all your kindness is to listen to the reason for your sorrow."

"Devi, your heart is kind, but death has come and knocked at our door today. Yet, as you say, to share a burden is to lighten it. So, listen to our story if you have a mind to.

"Our first misfortune is that our king is an imbecile—inept, weak and callous. The second followed upon the first, thirteen years ago. The rakshasa Baka came down from the northern ranges, and found a dry cave to his liking on yonder mountain.

"It was a terrible day when Baka first descended on Ekachakra. He came like Yama. He killed anyone he could, drinking their blood, flinging half-eaten corpses around him. Then he went back to his cave and slept for a month. Again he awoke, hungrily, and came roaring down on us for a feast.

"When he had come and gone a dozen times, our elders met together and decided to go to Baka with a proposition. They climbed to his cave, and said, 'Great Rakshasa, we have come with an offer. Every week we will cook a cartload of food, and send it to you. In return, you must promise not to attack our town.'

"Greed stirred in Baka's eyes. He was lazy and, besides, he loved human cooking. Yet, he loved human flesh and blood better. In chaste language, the rakshasa said to the elders, 'Your plan is excellent, but

I have some conditions. The food you send me must be tasty. And each week I will eat the bullocks and the driver of the cart, as well.'

"The elders stood trembling: any moment Baka may tire of talking and fall on them. They quickly agreed. 'Each week, a different household will supply a cartman and bullocks. But Baka, there is one other matter: as long as we send you the food, you must agree to be our guardian. Not only must you never come yourself into our town, you must protect us from any other danger.'

"Baka thought about this for a moment. He said pityingly, 'Have you no king to look after you?'

"'Our king is wanton and an idiot. Ours is a cursed generation.'

"'Very well, if I enjoy the food you send me—if it is not too spicy, or too bland—I will protect your town. Be sure the bullocks that draw the cart are fat, and the rice you heap on it forms a hill. If I am still hungry after eating what you send me, I will come to Ekachakra. Go now, and send me a cart of food this evening.'

"Thus we began to feed the rakshasa every week, and had his protection in return. Each week a different household provides the cart, the bullocks and the cartman."

His face like ashes, he whispered, "This week the turn is mine."

Kunti listened sympathetically. The brahmana continued, "Devi, if I take the cart to Baka and he eats me, my wife and children will starve. If my wife goes in my place I will die of grief, and my children will be orphans. So we have decided all of us will go, and die together."

He paused, and his eyes were full again. "But despite all the philosophy in the world, life is sweet and the thought of dying dreadful."

The brahmana fell silent. Now Kunti said brightly, "Brahmana, you have been kind to us and the time has come to repay your kindness. I have five sons. I will send one of them, the second one I think, to Baka with the cart of food."

"Oh no! You are my guests. How can I send your son to die in my place? Devi, don't add to my grief."

Kunti smiled at her host. "My second son is not an ordinary boy. Trust me, I am not sending him to his death. My child was born blessed by the Devas." She leaned forward now and whispered, "He has superhuman strength; he will kill Baka and return safely. You prepare the food and the cart, and leave the rest to my boy."

The brahmana and his family listened round-eyed. It seemed they had come to the brink of death and been reprieved. Kunti said, "Just one thing. You must never reveal my son's secret to anyone, or he will lose his strength."

After a moment's silence, the brahmana said, "If what you say is true, this is a miracle. If you are sure your son will come to no harm, we accept your offer. Not a word will pass our lips about who went to Baka with our cart."

Kunti went back to Bheema and told him about Baka the rakshasa, and how she had offered to send him in the brahmana's place. He hugged her.

"Thank you, mother! I have felt so restless here, and now I can have a good fight again. More than that," his eyes shone, "the brahmana's wife is an unearthly cook, and tomorrow I will have a cartload of her food to eat."

Kunti laughed to see he was drooling. "Come, let us give them the good news."

The brahmana embraced Bheema, and blessed him a hundred times. Bheema was embarrassed, and said to the man's wife, "I hope your cooking is as good as ever, or I might change my mind."

Tears in her eyes, the woman said, "I swear you would never have eaten food like you will tomorrow. I am going to begin cooking now, and I will make a meal fit for a prince."

Kunti and Bheema exchanged a smile, and went back to their own room. Almost immediately, the other Pandavas returned with the alms they had begged. Yudhishtira saw Bheema sitting in a corner, and looking very pleased. He took Kunti aside in the yard. "Bheema has the look he used to get whenever he was planning some mischief against Duryodhana and his brothers. Do you know why?"

Kunti was washing the vessels from which they ate. "This time I've begun the mischief myself."

"You?"

Kunti made him sit beside her on the stone steps. She told him about Baka, and the brahmana's plight. She told him she had asked Bheema to take the cart of food to the rakshasa the next day.

"What?" Yudhishtira's face was red: for the first time in his life, with anger at his mother. "Have you taken leave of your senses, O my mother? We escaped through the tunnel only because of Bheema. We have come this far just because of him; and now you want to send my brother as an offering to Baka? Oh, Kunti, you have been terribly impulsive or you wouldn't have dreamt of such a thing."

Kunti took his hand, but there was an edge to her voice now that pulled him up sharply. "Do you think, Yudhishtira, that your love for Bheema is greater than mine? Do you really imagine for a moment that I would sacrifice a son of mine to a rakshasa? It does you little credit that you think your mother is a stupid woman.

"My Bheema is Vayu's son. You were not there when I conceived him. When he fell from a cliff, as a baby, the rock on which he fell was smashed and he didn't have a scratch on him."

Yudhishtira already looked chastened. Kunti had not finished. "Bheema drank nagamrita when Duryodhana pushed him into the river, and it made him even stronger. You saw how he carried us through the jungle, how he killed Hidimba, even when your brother was tired.

"Yudhishtira, none of my sons was born to die at the hands of an insignificant rakshasa. They were born to rule the world beside their eldest brother, who seems to have lost his wits for the moment that he judges his mother so harshly. I was only trying to repay the brahmana's kindness."

Yudhishtira knelt before her. She took him in her arms, and his eyes were full that he had hurt her. She wiped his tears tenderly, saying, "I don't blame you, my son, this furtive life is wearing us all down. But we have a long way to go before we return to Hastinapura."

Yudhishtira went to the brahmana and said, "My mother told me about Baka. I am happy we can help you, it makes our time here fruitful."

Their host was pensive. "Tell your mother she can still change her mind. I do not want your brother to die in my place. You don't know Baka, how strong he is."

"No mother would send her son to his death. You do not know my brother; he is stronger than you can imagine. Don't fret needlessly, the rakshasa will die tomorrow."

After working all night, the brahmana's wife finished cooking an hour before sunrise. When, at cockcrow, Bheema, Kunti and the others came out into the yard, they saw the brahmana loading the last of the food on to his bullock-cart. Bheema's face was a sight as he sniffed that hill of rice, covered thickly with mouth-watering curries.

He cried, "I must be off at once! What if Baka grows hungry and comes down the mountain?"

Without further ado, Bheema mounted the cart. With a crack of his rope over the bullocks' backs, he set off as the first flush of dawn lit the eastern sky.

Soon he passed the edge of town and was alone with the cart of food. As Bheema urged his sleepy bullocks towards the forest-mantled foothills on the horizon, he helped himself to the food. He ate with relish, occasionally singing the cook's praises to the lightening sky. He sang she had the most gifted hands in the world. Her spices were delectable, and how she mixed them into her curries was sheer sorcery. Her rice was the longest-grained and the most fragrant in Bharatavarsha, and so on. Enfolded in the aromas of the good woman's cooking, transported by its flavours, Bheema went slowly along. It was months since he ate such a meal, and he did not hold back.

Suddenly, he had a thought that made him shudder. When he arrived at the mountain, looming ever closer now, he would have to kill Baka. Then he would be unclean with the rakshasa's blood, and he would not be able to finish the food! Bheema stopped the cart. He tethered his bullocks to a tree, and really fell to.

For an hour or two, the Pandava sat gorging himself at his ease, as the sun rose into the sky; and once, did he imagine it, or did he hear a rakshasa's hungry roar far away? It did not bother him. When he had finished three quarters of the hillock of food, Bheema felt drowsy. He gave a ringing belch of absolute contentment, and lay in the shade of the cart to catch a brief nap.

He awoke in an hour, feeling better than he had since he last ate in the lacquer palace. Climbing back on the cart, he urged his bullocks forward, to their surprise: they had thought he wanted them to go slowly, the slower the better. Now Bheema was hungry for battle. Shouting at the bullocks that they were laggards, he stood up on the cart-head and whipped them on smartly. They flew across the flat land, arriving sooner than they liked in the dark woods that grew around the base of the mountain.

A dirt track, disused once Baka began living here, wound its way through the trees and up the gloomy slope. Bheema set his bullocks on that trail. The poor beasts would rather avoid this menacing mountain; after climbing a short way, they stopped obstinately. The Pandava realized he would have to carry them if he wanted to go on.

The careen from the place where he had last eaten had made him hungry again: just enough to polish off half of what remained on the cart. With a sigh and a brief curse at the bullocks, Bheema climbed down and tied them to a sturdy tree: so they would not bolt with the rest of the food, at the first sign of the rakshasa. He climbed back on and began to tuck in to what was left of the rice.

For a while he ate ruminatively, thinking that only now, at his second foray, could he really taste the nuances of the marvellous cooking. As he demolished the last quarter of the rice, savouring each morsel, he began to call out to the rakshasa.

"Baka!" bellowed Bheema, as he ate, "O Baka, come for your meal! The cart from Ekachakra has arrived, the bullocks and the cartman are here!"

Nothing stirred. Bheema continued to eat and, intermittently, to call out the rakshasa's name. Some time passed, and then the bullocks grew terribly restless. They tossed their heads and lowed, looking fearfully at the thick woods and the mud trail. Bheema ate on, with never a glance over his shoulder. Between mouthfuls, he still sang out Baka's name from time to time.

The birds in the trees had fallen ominously quiet. The woods had grown perfectly still. The bullocks were frantic. Their eyes showed white with panic, as they tried to break the rope and escape what they sensed in the dimness behind Bheema: the thing that had crept up on huge feet, and now stood glaring at the cart with burning eyes.

This was how Baka always received his cart of food and the cartman. He enjoyed stalking them, as a cat does a lizard. Baka was enormous. He made Hidimba seem mansized. His head was in the trees, as he stood quite naked and motionless, only his strange phallus twitching with the lust of the hunt. He saw what Bheema had done to the food. The rakshasa's hairless body quivered. His crimson organ subsided like a distraught serpent, and rage replaced excitement in his tiny eyes.

Bheema first became aware of Baka by his stench, borne on the breeze like a pall of death. Breathing through his mouth until he grew accustomed to that stink, Bheema continued eating. Baka gave a low growl and stepped out of the trees. He was covered in dried blood and his own filth. He wore a necklace of skulls and bones of the men and beasts he had eaten, and a crown of vultures' feathers. His hair hung below his shoulders like a woman's, and he had woven jasmine flowers into it. He was a bizarre sight, and the bullocks nearly broke their necks to get away. The rope held.

Baka padded up behind Bheema and stood glowering, his pale face pinched in fury. At last, thinking to frighten the human glutton out of his wits, Baka gave a louder growl. The poor bullocks danced in fright. Bheema did not turn around. He ate on: the last of the food he was meant to have brought for Baka.

The final mouthful down, the Pandava belched again. He yawned and stretched. Now Baka cried in his high lisp, "Dare you eat my food?"

Wiping his mouth, Bheema turned around. Baka saw the human was unafraid, and that his eyes glittered disconcertingly. Bheema said coolly, "Just look at you, Baka. You are so like the rakshasas in my mother's stories that you could have stepped out of one of them. You are fat and useless with living off the town. Why, you could not hunt any more if you wanted to. I think, Rakshasa, that you are fat enough for killing. Though you stink so much, that not the vultures and jackals would like to feed off your carcass."

With a screech, Baka aimed a blow at Bheema that would have torn any other man's head off his neck. Bheema let it land on him, while the bullocks bucked and bellowed. The rakshasa's blow did not so much as knock Bheema over.

With a howl Baka ran off and wrenched up a tree. Roaring like ten tigers now, he hurled it at Bheema, as his kind do when they fight each other in jungle-hearts. The wind's son raised an arm, and the tree smashed into slivers against it.

Fear gripped him now and Baka roared louder. Never had he encountered anyone of the puny race like the specimen before him. He pulled up more trees, and flung them at the Pandava like spears. By now the rakshasa frothed at the mouth as terror drove him mad. Laughing in his face, Bheema also began to pull up trees and cast them back playfully at the demon.

Baka saw Bheema's body grow bright; his sinews were made of eddying airs that rippled with the power of Vayu who wears down mountains. Baka thought he saw Bheema big as the sky, laughing at the rakshasa that he dared challenge him.

Quickly, the place where they fought was denuded of its trees. Bheema's laughter grew louder, and Baka's roars and screeches more desperate. The naked devil's black blood flowed, mingling with the filth in which he was caked. When the last tree was too far to reach, with the longest howl yet Baka turned into a pack of silver wolves. Bheema struck them with a sapling as if he was beating a dog, and yelping, Baka resumed his own form.

By now, he had no hope the dreadful human would flee. He rushed at Bheema, as he might rush into the jaws of death. Bheema seized him and snapped his spine like an elephant would a cane of sugar. Birds flew screeching into the air at the report, and the rakshasa's dying scream.

The bullocks had fallen silent, knowing with sure animal instinct that their cartman would prevail. Now he came to them and they nuzzled against him. Then there were other sinister presences in the woods and the bullocks grew restive again. Bheema saw a knot of smaller rakshasas, Baka's people. They had watched the battle and were in dread of Bheema.

He cried fiercely, "Leave this mountain or I will kill you all!"

He took a threatening step towards them; they fled howling, and never came again to those parts.

Flushed with victory, and all the fine food on which he had gorged, Bheema hauled the rakshasa's broken body to the cart and lifted it on. He turned his bullocks around and pointed them back to Ekachakra. As they trundled along, Bheema leant his head against dead Baka's thigh and he was soon snoring under the westering sun.

Night had fallen when Bheema arrived in Ekachakra. He stopped the cart at the edge of town, rolled Baka's carcass off and left it at the city-gates. Quietly, he went back to the brahmana's house. His mother and his brothers hugged him; the brahmana and his wife fell at his feet.

Bheema said to the brahmana, "Remember, don't breathe a word to anyone."

Kunti had hot water ready for her son's bath. As he went in for it, he turned back once more. With a grin, he said to the brahmana's wife, "I hope we don't have to wait for another rakshasa before I taste your cooking again."

He went in, bathed, and then fell asleep, digesting the awesome meal he had eaten like some python. As he slept, he smiled in a sweet dream of the food. His mother and his brothers sat watching him fondly for a while, and then they slept too.

The next morning, a commotion broke out in the sleepy town of Ekachakra, when someone found Baka's body at the gates. The townfolk soon discovered whose turn it had been to feed the rakshasa, and they thronged the brahmana's house. They wanted to know how Baka had died.

The brahmana said, "Yesterday, I sat crying with my wife because it was my turn to take the cart of food to Baka. Suddenly a young brahmana came to me and said, 'Friend, do not grieve. I will take the cart for you and, what's more, I will kill the rakshasa.' He assured me he was far stronger than any rakshasa on earth, and I need have no qualms about letting him go in my place. Sure enough, this morning my bullocks and cart had been returned, and Baka's body lay at our gates."

All that day there was singing and dancing in Ekachakra and offerings to the Gods. No one suspected who the rakshasa-slayer was. The Pandavas continued to live peacefully in their grateful host's house, and Bheema frequently had the most inspired dishes sent to him by the brahmana's gifted wife.

FORTY-SIX

A strange story

SOME WEEKS PASSED AFTER THE KILLING OF BAKA. ONE EVENING, AS twilight fell in Ekachakra, a handsome mendicant arrived at the door of the brahmana with whom the Pandavas lived. Always hospitable, the brahmana took the traveller in for the night.

When the visitor had bathed and eaten, he sat in the lamplit courtyard and began to regale his host with a fund of stories from his obviously incessant wandering. Many of these touched upon the holy tirthas of Bharatavarsha. The host begged the muni's permission to call his other guests, because surely they would be enthralled by his fabulous lore.

Soon, Kunti and her sons also sat raptly round the raconteur. The Pandavas were keen to hear what the world said about the burning of the lacquer palace in Varanasi. It was only later the stranger came to that.

He began with some glowing accounts of miracles he had either heard about or seen at the blessed tirthas; and he was a gifted pauranika. Then, he changed tack suddenly. "Tonight I am abroad on a royal mission. A king has sent me, and others like me, across the length and breadth of Bharatavarsha with a very special message, meant just for one kshatriya's ears."

Sahadeva asked, "Who is the king? And the kshatriya?"

Yudhishtira said quietly, "Let us also hear your message, Muni."

The wanderer retied his topknot with slim hands, and began. "I am abroad on a mission for King Drupada of the Panchalas."

The Pandavas all gave a slight start. If the mendicant noticed in the lamplight, he gave no sign of it. "Drupada has sent me to spread the word about his daughter Draupadi's swayamvara in Kampilya. Did you know the lovely Draupadi and her brother Dhrishtadyumna were born not from a woman's body, but a fire?"

"Tell us about them," urged Kunti, an inkling of destiny alive in her.

"It is a long story. Are you patient enough to hear it through?"

They all nodded. The mendicant said, "Once there were two childhood friends, Drona and Drupada. Both studied under Drona's father, the Rishi Bharadvaja. While they were students, Drupada swore that one day he would share his kingdom with Drona."

The Pandavas knew this part of the man's tale well. They did not interrupt him. He came to Arjuna's guru-dakshina, and how the prince humbled Drupada in Kampilya. What the muni said next astonished his listeners.

"Even in defeat, Drupada was full of admiration for young Arjuna. He said, 'There is no kshatriya on earth like Arjuna. I must have a daughter to marry him.' At that time Drupada pretended all was forgiven between himself and Drona, but it was then he conceived an implacable hatred for the acharya."

His audience sat up; they did not know this. "It was as if the hatred flew out of Drona's heart into Drupada's, and it was a demon that gave him no peace.

"But Drona was Bhargava's disciple, and a master of the brahmastra; no warrior on earth could kill him. Drupada left his city and wandered dementedly through a jungle, muttering to himself, 'A son to kill Drona and a daughter to marry Arjuna!'

"For weeks, he wandered, possessed, until he arrived at a lonely asrama in the very heart of the jungle. Two rishis called Yaja and Upayaja lived in that asrama. Drupada managed to tell them what he wanted.

"'My hatred is a fire that consumes me moment by moment. Drona is a master of the brahmastra. He was not born of a mortal woman, and no man on earth can kill him.'

"He paused, then changed his subject without warning, as the sages listened to him with grave attention. 'Arjuna is a peerless kshatriya! He came to my gates, and he vanquished me. There is no archer like him in the world. I wish he were my son or, at least, my son-in-law. But I have no daughter for him to marry, and even if I was to have one now, she would be too young for the Pandava.'

"Drupada began mumbling sadly to himself again. Yaja said, 'Serve us for a year, and you shall have a son to kill Drona and a daughter to be Arjuna's wife.'

"For a year, Drupada served the two rishis in the vana, and at the year's end, they performed a putrakama yagna for him. The munis sat chanting powerful mantras beside the flames of a sacred fire. It was high noon, and Drupada and his wife sat behind them. After some hours of chanting, Yaja poured some libation on to the flames. Candescent colours danced in that fire. Then it blazed up, blinding, and the flames were slabs of white light, piercing the sky.

"It seemed the earth had been subsumed into a more exalted realm. Drupada heard unworldly music. As he sat there, in transport, a crystal chariot rose out of the white flames, and in it sat a godlike youth of some fourteen summers.

"He was a kshatriya in shining armour. He carried unworldly weapons, and his face seemed as if it was carved from stone. The chariot emerged from the flames, the youth in it smiled at Drupada and his wife. The Panchala king could not contain a cry of joy: he knew Drona was as good as dead. A voice spoke out of heaven, 'This prince will kill Drona, and bring glory to the Panchalas.'

"When Drupada wanted to go and embrace the youth in the chariot, Upayaja restrained him. The yagna fire was full of colour and light again, and another miracle was unfolding among its flames. They sprang white once more, and higher, and abruptly grew still as if arrested in time. The burning stillness assumed a human form. There were long, dark arms there, a perfect head flowing black tresses. As Drupada, his wife and the rishis watched, stunned by her incredible beauty, her skin dark as night, her face and her body so perfect they were from a more pristine time, a young girl stepped out of the white light. Now a common fire burned again in Yaja's sacrificial pit.

"Once more, an asariri spoke in the jungle's heart, 'The dark one will be the most beautiful woman in the world. She is born to fulfil a divine purpose, she will be the nemesis of kshatriya kind.'

"Her fragrance filled that glade like the scent of a great black lotus. Drupada's queen cried to Yaja, 'Muni, let these children think of me and no one else as their mother!'

"Yaja said, 'So be it. Call your son Dhrishtadyumna. And let your daughter of destiny be named Krishnaa, for her dark skin.'

"But her father loved her so much that soon she was not called Krishnaa any more, but Draupadi, Drupada's daughter, and Panchali,* princess of the Panchalas."

The wandering ascetic paused. Bheema said softly, "So Drupada became a father of twins. But, good Brahmana, I have heard Dhrishtadyumna is Drona's sishya."

The man laughed. "Drona knew Dhrishtadyumna had been born to kill him. The acharya also knew that no man escapes fate. He took Dhrishtadyumna to be his sishya, and taught the fire-born prince like his own son.

"Let me come back to my mission. It has to do with the Pandavas, the nephews of blind Dhritarashtra who is king in Hastinapura."

Not a muscle moved on any of the brothers' faces.

The storyteller continued, "Dhritarashtra is the scion of an ancient House, in which only noble kings have been born since time out of mind. But not the blind one. He did not treat his dead brother's sons as he should, far from it."

He lowered his voice, as if the night had ears, "Dhritarashtra sent the Pandavas to Varanasi, on the borders of his kingdom. He did not want Pandu's son Yudhishtira to rule after him, but his own son Duryodhana, who is a devil. In Varanasi, Duryodhana built a palace of lac for the Pandavas and their mother Kunti. One night, as they slept, he had it set on fire and burnt them alive inside. He cleared his own way to the throne.

"Drupada was shocked; he seemed deranged by the news. If Arjuna were dead, how would he marry Draupadi? Strange, indeed, was the scene in the palace of Kampilya: Drupada mourned the Pandavas as if they were his sons.

"His guru said to him, 'My lord, Yaja and Upayaja are maharishis, and your children were born from their fire. The munis knew why you wanted a daughter. They would not deceive you, and lay waste Draupadi's life.

"Have it proclaimed all over Bharatavarsha, that a swayamvara will be held for the princess, and that there will be a test of archery for the

---

* She was also called Yagnaseni, since she was born from the sacrificial fire.

kshatriyas who would compete for Panchali's hand. I am certain the Pandavas are alive and in hiding somewhere. Wherever he is, Arjuna will come and win Draupadi's hand.'

"Friends, I was also sent forth by my lord Drupada to spread the word of Draupadi's swayamvara. So here I am, telling you about it. And, who knows, Arjuna himself may be listening!" He gave a laugh, but his eyes were shrewd in the flickering light. It was midnight and the hermit rose. He yawned and went in, saying nothing would keep him from his bed any more.

Their host and his wife followed their guest. Kunti and her sons sat on for a while in the open, with the night breeze playing on their faces. They sat in silence, and those young men's hearts beat wildly with visions of a dark princess.

Then, Kunti said, "We have been in Ekachakra for too long. I am tired of seeing the same four walls, the same pots and pans and begging-bowls, the same yard, the same trees, the same mountain."

She saw her sons' eyes light up with desperate hope. She felt sorry for them: so young, so manly, and no means to express either youth or manliness. "I think fate brought us here to rid Ekachakra of Baka. Now that is done, why shouldn't we move on?"

"But where to, mother?" asked Yudhishtira, innocently.

"Why not to Kampilya? I have heard it is a great city, and the princess Draupadi's swayamvara promises to be an event. It will be so refreshing to walk through the streets of a great city, in a thronging crowd. Besides, the archery promises to be exciting. I am for going to Kampilya…that is, unless you have some objection."

She laughed in the fetching, young girl's way she had whenever she was amused at her sons. In one voice, her five princes cried, "Let us leave tomorrow!"

Then, blushing, they avoided each other's eyes. Each one knew what obsessed his brothers and himself: a dark face they longed to see, black velvet skin they longed to touch. Yudhishtira knew she was meant for his brother Arjuna, but he could not get her out of his mind; and Yudhishtira's thoughts of Draupadi were not chaste at all.

Yet, what the eldest Pandava felt in the brahmana's yard, as the moon sank in the west, was a delicious anticipation in the depths of his body, a warm lake of sensation he shared with his brothers. Strangely, there was no conflict in it, but only an inexpressible deepening of their closeness: a vibrant, golden bond, past words.

"We'll leave first thing in the morning," said Kunti. Rare excitement was upon her as well, as she went in to sleep for a few hours before they set out.

Long after she had gone, her sons sat on under the stars. They sat wordlessly, when all the night birds, owls and bats, and even the breeze, had slept.

Finally, they also turned in, Yudhishtira last of all. Now they lay awake in the dark and the dusky Draupadi still tormented them. Yudhishtira did not sleep, nor Bheema, Arjuna, Sahadeva or Nakula. They lay tossing in their beds, waiting for the dawn.

FORTY-SEVEN

Encounter in the night

THE NEXT MORNING, SHORTLY AFTER DAYBREAK, KUNTI AND HER sons came to their host the brahmana to say farewell. They found the travelling bard, last night's inflamer, already gone. When the brahmana's wife heard their guests were leaving, she begged them to wait for just an hour: she wouldn't let them go without cooking some food for the young man who had saved her family. Bheema was delighted. Kunti and her sons spent that hour with the brahmana and his two children, while the wife got busy in her kitchen.

The meal was ready and packed in an earthen vessel tied in a cloth. Embracing their host, the Pandavas and their mother set out. The people of Ekachakra came out to say goodbye. Some of the women had tears in their eyes as they waved to Bheema. The Pandavas passed through the gates and walked on without looking back, it was inauspicious.

Across sweeping plains with fields bright as a parrot's feathers the wayfarers went, happy to be out of the friendly but dreary town they had lived in for so many months. They tracked the sun towards Kampilya. Soon the day grew warm and they rested in some airy woods, and ate the meal the brahmana's wife had sent.

When they had eaten, sleep came over them. The princes had not slept all night long, and Kunti just a few hours before dawn. They lay in the shade of a large nyagrodha tree, with no walls or ceiling to cage their dreams. The brothers all dreamt of a dark and bewitching face, its eyes full of fate.

It was growing on evening when Yudhishtira awoke, before the others, and he saw a profound rishi had joined them. With a knowing gleam in his eye, Vyasa said, "Sweet dreams, I hope, my son?"

Yudhishtira awakened the others. The princes prostrated themselves at Vyasa's feet, and he blessed them. The maharishi said, "The way ahead leads straight to Kampilya, and fortune awaits you there, all of you. I see darkness lifting away from your lives; days of joy are around the corner of time. You will soon forget the evil months you have passed through. Be of good cheer, I will see you in Kampilya!"

He strode off into the trees and actually seemed to vanish. Kunti and her sons made their way again towards Drupada's capital. Singing among themselves, more hopeful than they had ever been since the burning of the house of lac, they journeyed on, by day and by night, passing through virgin forests and across glimmering plains, fording gushing streams. In their mood, they were intensely sensible of the sights, sounds and scents of the lands they went through, as if only now that they headed for Kampilya they had eyes and ears for nature's lavish beauty.

One night, as they walked through a forest, Arjuna led the way with a rushlight in his hand. The moon had risen above them, and they heard the Ganga flowing ahead. They heard other noises, as well: unearthly voices and wonderful laughter; someone was bathing in the river.

As they went nearer, abruptly all the sounds ceased. Nothing stirred. They thought they must have heard animals drinking at the river; only the breeze had made them seem like golden voices.

Yudhishtira said, "My body is hot and tired. I am going to bathe."

"Let's all bathe," said Bheema. "The water smells so sweet."

They approached the river, when suddenly a luminous chariot appeared from the trees, like a full moon. Two horses were yoked to it, and they were not of this earth. Their skins glowed in the dark, green and copper, and their manes seemed to be made of tongues of silver flame. Kunti and her sons could not be sure if those horses' hooves touched the ground.

At the helm of the chariot, stood the most marvellous being. He was taller than any man of the earth. Woven with flowers and full of light, his hair hung to his shoulders. His dark face was keen and sharp, and his wide eyes glittered angrily at them. For a moment, he stood glowering, and behind him in the trees were other forms, dim and bright. The princes of Hastinapura fancied they were female forms.

The chariot-rider raised a hand and cried in his ringing voice, "You cannot approach the river! The twilight hours are only for the yakshas, gandharvas and rakshasas. We kill witless mortals who dare trespass here at this time."

Arjuna heard his haughty tone and cried, "Who are you to lay down laws for the river waters that are free?"

"I am Angaraparna the gandharva!" said the Elf, more imperiously still.

"Sky-rover, no one has any right over the ocean, the Himalaya, or the Ganga. Not by day or night, or twilight."

The gandharva bristled. He cried fiercely, "Begone mortals! I came to the river to bathe with my women; you may not approach the water until we have finished. Go peacefully, before you annoy me. This vana is named after me, and not merely men but yakshas and rakshasas dare not come here. Humans, begone!"

Arjuna laughed at him. "Your threats don't frighten us, not even at this twilight hour of your strength."

With a cry of anger, the gandharva raised his bow. It was an arc of light in his hands. Quick as light, he drew arrows from his quiver and began to shoot at them, especially at Arjuna. Now Arjuna, too, was a blur: he struck aside the immortal's fiery stream of arrows with his torch.

The gandharva paused in his archery that would have razed a small army. His arrows all lay extinguished at Arjuna's feet. The dark human said, "Angaraparna, your archery is very pretty, and about as potent as wave-froth. But you are not of our earth, and I will show you what sort of archer I am with a weapon of the sky."

The gandharva waited, amused, confident the human's arrows would be puny. Arjuna took his bow from Bheema, who had been carrying it for him. Indra's son called to his adversary across the moonlit glade, "Gandharva, I charge this arrow with the astra of Agni. It is Brihaspati's weapon, given to me by my master Drona. Let us see you stop my arrow."

With a resonant mantra, Arjuna shot his astra at the gandharva. It did not travel as swiftly as a common shaft, but seemed to linger in the air as it flew at the glowing chariot. Angaraparna waited with a mocking smile on his lips. Midway between Arjuna and the gandharva, the astra took fire.

Angaraparna cried out in amazement; his women in the trees screamed. In a sheet of flames, Arjuna's agneyastra flashed between the unworldly steeds and struck the chariot. The ratha erupted, and Angaraparna was flung headlong from it.

The chariot—from which Angaraparna got his name, 'Scorching Chariot',—burned down. The shining horses bolted into the trees. Arjuna strode up to the stunned gandharva, seized his lustrous hair and dragged him to Yudhishtira.

Three tall, incredibly beautiful women ran out from the trees: the gandharva's wives, their faces and bodies shimmering, their hair touched with starlight. The tallest came boldly up to the Pandavas. She said in her voice so full of music, "Noble ones! I am Kumbheenasi. I beg you, spare my husband's life."

The others remained behind her in the shadows. The princes heard their stifled sobs, and saw their delicate bodies tremble. Arjuna held Angaraparna by his hair, and the gandharva was still dazed. His chariot was a mound of ashes.

Kumbheenasi knelt at Yudhishtira's feet. She grasped his hand in her soft palms, knowing at a glance that he would decide Angaraparna's fate.

"Kind Kshatriya, spare my husband!" she sobbed.

Yudhishtira turned to Arjuna, who still stood red-eyed. The older Pandava said, "Let him go, Arjuna. You have proved your point, and who would kill a man that needs a woman's protection?"

Arjuna scowled at Angaraparna, as if he would dearly prefer to kill him. He released the Elf's hair, and the gandharva fell back on the grass. He gave a long moan, and slowly stood up. He was taller than Bheema. Now he bowed low, with folded hands, to Yudhishtira and Arjuna.

With a rueful smile, Angaraparna said, "I renounce my name! I am humbled and my chariot is ashes."

He laughed. It seemed merriment was so much part of his nature that not the shame of defeat could stifle it. Impulsively, Angaraparna took Arjuna's hand and cried, "I must repay your kindness! I would have killed you, but you spared my life when you could have had just revenge. I will give you the secret power of the gandharvas, the chaksushi is mine to give."

Before Arjuna could protest, the gandharva placed his fingertips on the Pandava's temples and whispered a mantra in his ear. Arjuna's body began to tingle with a most extraordinary sensation. Angaraparna was saying, "The chaksushi sets the gandharvas apart from you humans."

Liquid sight was upon Arjuna, as if a hidden eye had opened inside his head at the gandharva's mantra: a fabulous, mystic eye. Visions swept the Pandava prince, and all his rage of a moment ago melted away. A beatific smile lit his face.

Angaraparna said, "Now you can see into all the worlds, Kshatriya, and whatever you like on any of them."

Arjuna's eyes were alight at what he saw. Then, remembering himself, he willed the uncanny visions to stop, and to his surprise, they did. Arjuna looked at the tall being before him in some awe.

The gandharva had already flashed on to his next concern. "I also want, O Kshatriya, to give you and your brothers a hundred horses: steeds like mine foaled in the homelands of the gandharvas. They appear at the very thought of he who owns them, and so do they change their colour, or their speed. Look."

Next moment, a herd of wild horses stood on the banks of the river. They were like no horses of the earth, shimmering and of many colours. The Pandavas stood enraptured, as their new-found friend said, "My horses are lean, Kshatriyas. But they never tire, and they run as swift as thoughts!"

Arjuna thought this had gone far enough. "I cannot accept your gifts, wonderful though they are. I have nothing to give you in return."

Angaraparna bowed solemnly again. "To meet a great man is always a joyful thing. Besides, you have given me an inestimable gift—my life! Yet, if you want to repay me for what I gave you, teach me the secret of the astra that made my chariot ashes."

"So be it!" laughed the Pandava. "I will teach you the secret of the astra, and take your chaksushi and your horses."

Arjuna taught the gandharva the mantra for the agneyastra, and the immortal shone to receive it. In return, the Pandava took the horses, fleeter than the wind. The two of them embraced, crying, "May our friendship last for ever!"

Then, curious, Arjuna said, "Tell me, friend, why did you attack us? We are kshatriya princes, not thieves or brigands."

The Elf was solemn. "Unannounced, without care for proper time or rite, you wander these forests. You do not know where you should venture, at what hour. My women were with me; I was honour-bound to attack. But tell me friend, in truth, who are you?"

Yudhishtira replied, "We are the Pandavas, hiding from our enemies."

Angaraparna gave a long whistle, melodious as a birdcall. He embraced each of the princes again, and bowed deeply before Kunti.

"I am glad! I am exceedingly glad you are alive. One day you five will rule the world; it is not right that you roam the wilds without a priest to guide you. Kings and princes must have priests. Tapatyas, no kshatriya can conquer the earth without a brahmana beside him."

Arjuna said, "We are Pandavas and Kaunteyas, all right. But why do you call us Tapatyas?"

"Once, with the help of his guru, the brahmarishi Vasishta, the ancient king Samvarana regained the kingdom he had lost. With that muni's help, also, Samvarana won the hand of his beloved, Surya's daughter Tapati. In time, Samvarana and Tapati had a son. They named him Kuru, and he was your ancestor. And so I call you Tapatyas."

Arjuna said, "For the time being, let your beautiful horses remain with you. I will take them when my brother is a king. Now, wise friend, tell us if you know a brahmana who will be our priest."

"A rishi who does tapasya in this very forest. He is Devala Muni's younger brother called Dhaumya, and his asrama is yonder."

He pointed deeper into the jungle. After their piquant encounter, the Pandavas and Kunti bid the gandharva farewell and went the way he pointed, in search of a priest.

Dhaumya's asrama was a simple and austere dwelling, next to a jungle shrine called Utkochaka. He was a serene muni, tall, spare and bearded; and his eyes shone with wisdom. The princes prostrated themselves at his feet. When he had blessed them, he made the Pandavas and Kunti sit comfortably on seats of darbha grass, and fed them sweet fruit and some soft and delicious roots.

Already, uncommon empathy sprang deeply between them. Dhaumya said, "Tell me, Brahmanas, if brahmanas you are, who you are and why have you sought me out in this jungle where no man ventures?"

Yudhishtira replied, "Muni, we are the Pandavas of Hastinapura, whom the world believes dead. We have come to you because we want a priest and a guru. For, one day we hope to return to our father's city and rule the world from there."

Dhaumya smiled, and grew very quiet. Finally, he asked, "And where are you heading now?"

"To Kampilya."

This seemed to satisfy him. "If you truly want me to be your priest, I am willing."

Suddenly, they had a strong sense that the darkness that had shrouded their lives for two years had lifted away. Dhaumya did not take long to collect his spare possessions. By the light of a new dawn, they set out together for Kampilya.

FORTY-EIGHT

The spinning fish

After some days of walking through jungles full of exotic birds and beasts, tangled valleys full of flowers, and past lakes brimming with lotuses and swans, they arrived in southern Panchala, Drupada's kingdom; and a day later in Kampilya, that king's capital.

Inside the city, preparations were in full swing for the princess Draupadi's swayamvara. The Pandavas found a friendly carpenter who was willing to take in five brahmanas and their regal-looking mother, and they began living in a room he gave them.

As in Ekachakra, the princes still lived off alms. Like any mendicants, they went begging each morning and returned by midday with the food they gathered. Kunti divided what they brought among her sons. As they roamed the thronging streets of Kampilya, the princes heard from the people:

"Drupada has no doubt the Pandavas are alive. The rishis have told him Draupadi will be Arjuna's wife."

"The king has a mighty bow that few men can even lift. A wooden fish hung a hundred hands in the air is the target. The fish spins at great speed, and only the archer who brings it down with an arrow will win Draupadi's hand."

"The archers may not aim directly at the fish, only at its reflection in a trough of water."

"Drupada is sure only Arjuna can shoot the fish."

"A man who is meant to be dead!"

"We can hardly wait for the day."

The Pandavas, and Arjuna himself would go quietly among the people, listening to all this. The princes too waited impatiently for the day of the swayamvara.

Meanwhile, kshatriyas from all over Bharatavarsha had arrived in Kampilya. They came from kingdoms far and near to try their luck with the bow and the spinning fish. Besides, Drupada's hospitality was legendary.

Even before the Pandavas, the Kauravas had come to Kampilya, with Duryodhana and Karna. The Yadavas—the Bhojas, Vrishnis and Andhakas—had arrived in the city, heroic kshatriyas all. Among the Yadavas was dark Krishna of Mathura, Vishnu's Avatara, whose life was to become inextricably involved with the Pandavas' lives. They were destined to become his warriors of light one day, most of all, Arjuna.

At last, the momentous day dawned, bright and clear, birds singing in the trees, and all Kampilya was up with the sun. The arena of the swayamvara was an unforgettable spectacle. Every seat was taken. Brahmanas and rishis sat in their enclosures. The common people had thronged in thousands into the immense stadium: gaudily attired, as was their way, garlands round their necks, perfume in their clothes and on their skins, excited beyond measure.

The finest sight was the enclosure of the kshatriyas who had come to vie for Draupadi's hand. It was filled with the noblest warriors in Bharatavarsha: each a lion, every one a rival today.

They say the Devas of heaven had gathered in the sky in invisible vimanas, and peered down to watch Draupadi's swayamvara. Five kshatriyas disguised as brahmanas, their faces covered by heavy beards and masked with ashes, their hair matted in jata, also found their way into the arena. They mingled with the other brahmanas, and were careful not to enter or sit together.

Deep sea-conches sounded, calling the feverish crowd to be silent. Drum-rolls rose and faded, and rose again, as the crowd fell hushed and all eyes were riveted to the arched entrance from the palace.

For a moment, everyone in that stadium was breathless for the princess Draupadi's arrival; then, her brother Dhrishtadyumna led her in. She wore resonant red silk, golden ornaments, and flashing jewels. All these paled before her dark, mysterious beauty. A sigh rose from the crowd when she walked in. She was, beyond doubt, the most beautiful woman in the world. She was more, she was unearthly. Yet, there was something fateful about her as well, something frightening: beauty like hers did not belong in this world.

The Pandavas' wildest fantasies, which had their way with them since the travelling muni told them about her, did Draupadi no justice. She was lovelier than all their imaginings. Like everyone else in the arena, Pandu's sons sat like infatuated boys, their eyes never leaving her face.

The crowd had fallen silent in awe of the dark princess. You heard only the drone of the priests chanting mantras, as they poured libation over the ritual fire. At the heart of the arena was a dais, and now Dhrishtadyumna climbed onto this platform.

The fire-born prince's voice was muted thunder, as he announced, "We have come together for my sister Draupadi's swayamvara. Here is a bow, and here are five arrows. Above me is a matsya yantra, just visible through the opening in the screen below it. At my feet is the vessel of water in which the archers must aim at the spinning fish's reflection. My father, King Drupada, has said that he who brings down the fish shall have my sister's hand."

Dhrishtadyumna turned to Draupadi now, and named the kings and warriors who had come to try to win her.

"Duryodhana, prince of the Kurus, among his brothers. Karna, king of Anga, Duryodhana's dearest friend, now said to be the best archer in the world. Drona's son Aswatthama, and Duryodhana's uncle Shakuni."

One by one, Dhrishtadyumna pointed out the great kshatriyas: Jarasandha, Shalya, Bhagadatta.[4] Draupadi hardly looked at them, because her eyes always sought another face in the crowd.

"Balarama of the Vrishnis, and beside him, Devaki's son Krishna, who the wise say is the Avatara."

Draupadi bowed slightly to dark Krishna, who smiled back at her. His eyes were so different from all the others', so knowing and friendly. Krishna would take no part in the test of archery, said Dhrishtadyumna, nor his brother Balarama or any of the other Yadavas. He passed on to Jayadratha, king of the Sindhus, then to Sishupala, lord of the Chedis, and on to the rest.

---

4 Several other kshatriyas are named here. See Appendix.

There was a reason why Krishna would not compete for Draupadi's hand. In his immaculate heart, he knew why this ravishing princess had been born into the world: to be his own agent, to help catalyse what he himself had come for. To rid the earth of her burden, the arrogant sway of the kshatriya. This was the very end of the dwapara yuga, and it was written that the next age, the kali yuga, would be ruled by the sudra, mysterious are the ways of time. He, the dark deliverer, would become the bane of the kshatriyas, who must not survive to dominate the coming and lesser age. Krishna had come to end a yuga.

Moreover, knowing all things, he knew the Pandavas were not dead. His eyes also roved the swollen crowd in search of his cousins, who would become his soldiers in his war against evil. Though Kunti was his father Vasudeva's sister, Krishna had never seen the Pandavas before. He had no doubt that as soon as he did he would know them, even in a crowd like this one. While every other gaze in the arena was peeled to the stunning Draupadi, Krishna's ranged the jostling tiers for the sons of Pandu.

Meanwhile, Dhrishtadyumna invited the first kshatriya archer to try to bring down the fish. The great bow had come into the House of Panchala in times out of mind, days when Gods moved openly in the world, and kshatriyas were hardly less than Devas. It was the Kindhura, and it had not been fashioned on earth. Only the most exceptional archers of this dwindled time could hope to even lift that bow, let alone string it and shoot with it. The Kindhura's bowstring sparkled as if it was made with thousands of minute diamonds.

As the first archer mounted the dais, Draupadi and her twin climbed down and stood a small way off. This prince was a handsome young kshatriya. He was the first aspirant and the crowd cheered him loudly. Grinning, Yuyutsu, whom Duryodhana had sent to test the bow, strutted briefly on the dais, his body glowing with the oil with which he had rubbed himself. Raising his arms for silence, he said a brief prayer. His eyes strayed helplessly to the bewitching Draupadi. Yuyutsu bent quickly, and clasped both his hands around the bow.

Krishna by then spotted five brahmanas, whose eyes never left Draupadi, not even to glance at Yuyutsu: as if they focused on an archer's target! He pointed them out to his brother Balarama, whispering, "Look, they are here. Like live embers covered in brahmanas' ashes."

Poor Yuyutsu was having a hard time. The muscles stood out on his arms and his back, beads of sweat on his face. That bow would not budge. At last, with a cry of frustration, he gave up and stood panting. A rueful smile and a wave at the crowd, and Yuyutsu climbed down. The crowd cheered him for his effort, and the other kings for his failure. Draupadi's eyes shone with satisfaction. Krishna watched his Pandava cousins. Each of them sighed in relief that the bow was truly such an awesome one. The Avatara smiled to himself. Only he knew something of the long hard way that lay ahead of that supernaturally beautiful princess and her suitors.

The next kshatriya approached the platform. The common folk of Kampilya snickered among themselves; the mighty Kindhura would easily resist this mawkish prince, who was far too young anyway. Surely enough, after a valiant effort, he also failed to lift the bow from its pedestal and returned rather shame-faced to his place. But the crowd cheered him anyway, one spark crying, "Come back next year, son!"

But not all the warriors in that swayamvara were as easily frustrated by the Kindhura. There were many tremendous kshatriyas among them; Sishupala was the first. He was Krishna's cousin and the Pandavas' as well. He was a pale man, a giant, known as the Bull of Chedi.

A hush fell over the arena. Sishupala rose from his place, his head clean-shaven and gleaming in the sun, and his eyes shone as well. If any kshatriya so far seemed capable of lifting the bow, stringing it and, perhaps, even bringing down the spinning fish, it was this bull-like man.

For a long moment, Sishupala stood very still on the dais, breathing deeply and his eyes shut. Then he bowed to Draupadi and, with a smile on his haughty face, picked up the Kindhura quite easily. The crowd moaned. With no effort, Sishupala pulled the glittering bowstring taut and secured it.

The silence deepened on the crowd. Anyone who looked closely would have seen that Draupadi's hands shook. Sishupala picked up his first arrow, and the princess was as tense as his bowstring. The king of Chedi drew the string to his ear and, taking aim in the silver trough at his feet, shot his first arrow at the fish. He missed by the width of a sesame seed. Only Krishna saw Draupadi visibly relax; and then she was tense again, because Sishupala picked up his next arrow.

The spinning fish

Again, he missed so narrowly he took the crowd's breath away. But when he shot his second arrow, the bow came alive and, with a crack like thunder, flung the archer down. The crowd roared.

Groggily, Sishupala rose to his feet. The Kindhura had drained him. He staggered towards the bow, but now he could not lift it. He bowed quickly to the crowd and, hanging his head, walked back to his place.

Draupadi's eyes were alight, as if her life had been spared. Next came Jarasandha of Magadha, powerful king and Krishna's inveterate enemy. He, too, picked up the bow with no effort and, peering into the silver vessel, shot four arrows at the fish while Draupadi held her breath as if the shafts were aimed at her heart. She was praying. She had never set eyes on Arjuna, about whom she had heard so much from her father, and she was praying that only he would bring down the fish. Now, in fierce reality, Jarasandha missed the spinning thing four times by no more than a breadth of a mustard seed. Each time, Draupadi felt her heart stop beating, and every arrow took a lifetime to travel between Jarasandha's brutal hands and the target. She felt she lived and died four lives.

Dhrishtadyumna touched her shoulder and whispered, "It is twice as hard to bring down the fish as it is to string the bow."

Jarasandha could not shoot the fifth arrow, and Draupadi heaved another sigh. Duryodhana rose next, and his was a potent and sinister presence. Draupadi shivered to look at him; his hooded eyes raked her. She felt alone and vulnerable, as if he stripped her naked with those dreadful eyes.

Duryodhana also strung the bow effortlessly. The people of Kampilya were terrified lest this devil win their princess. Dhrishtadyumna, who knew what a monster Dhritarashtra's son was, quailed at the thought of his sister married to him. Duryodhana picked up his first arrow and sent it humming at the fish. The world stood still. Then, the very crowd sighed: the evil prince had missed. He missed again, and twice more. He shook with rage, as if the contest had been contrived just to humiliate him.

Duryodhana's last arrow missed the fish by the breadth of the little finger on a man's hand. With a tigerish growl, he let the bow fall. He bowed stiffly to the crowd, but no one clapped. Well aware of the ominous effect he had, he turned to Draupadi and smiled blandly at her.

She looked away. Seething, Duryodhana stalked back to his seat. This princess had touched his malignant heart as no other woman ever. Night after night, he would dream of her face and her dark body, as he saw it now, naked in his mind's eye.

Krishna missed none of this, and he knew the conclusion to which it would lead one day. Today was only the sowing of a seed. When it was grown, the plant of hatred which sprang from that seed would choke all kshatriya kind, and have the heads of countless kings for its fruit.

Now Karna of Anga rose from his place beside Duryodhana, and the Kuru camp erupted in wild cheering. This was the man Draupadi and Drupada feared the most. He was lithe and sleek, a warrior of presence and power, said, after the burning of the house of lac, to be unquestionably the best bowman on earth. His tread was soft, his quietness resoundingly assured, as he approached the dais like a hunting tiger.

The golden armour he had been born with, which was part of his very skin, shone dully beneath his pale silk shirt. The crowd fell quiet. Karna did not so much as glance at Draupadi, and her blood ran cold. Unlike all the others, he did not mount the platform straightaway. Truly like a stalking feline, he walked round and round the stage, studying the spinning fish from every side and angle.

Five princes, disguised as brahmanas, shivered as they watched Karna. Sweat broke out on their bodies. They knew he was the one who could find the target. Karna's concentration was elemental. Even blue Krishna was tense, looking on with anxiety in his eyes. The Avatara knew this archer was the only real danger.

Leisurely, Karna padded around the bow, the water and the fish, many times, unravelling the riddle of the revolving target. At last, he seemed satisfied and a smile touched his lips. Now he gave Draupadi a searing look, as if she were already his. She knew this was not just arrogance but the confidence of an immaculate archer. She felt as if a demon had embraced her.

Karna climbed the dais and paused at the foot of the bow. He turned his face to the sky, where the sun was at his zenith. That warrior seemed to pray. Then a light touched his graceful body, and he picked up the Kindhura in his left hand.

Dhrishtadyumna and Draupadi stood at the foot of the dais, not five paces from Karna as he fitted the first arrow to the string. Draupadi's heart was in her mouth, as he began to draw the bowstring to his ear. He bent to peer into the water at his feet. Above him, the fish glittered strangely now, and seemed brighter than ever: as if the sun lit it up for this archer. It even seemed the fish did not spin any more but hung still, grown big as a whale, so a child could shoot it.

Draupadi felt as if someone was choking her. She was certain Karna would bring the fish down. She wanted to scream, to flee. The string was drawn back now, the arrow aimed at the fish's eye.

Draupadi heard a voice from the crowd. Perhaps it was the blue Yadava's voice, but she could not be sure. Everything was a whirl, her life spun round with the wretched fish. The voice was saying, inside her head, "How can a princess like you marry a sutaputra?"

A moment before Karna shot his arrow, Draupadi cried to Dhrishtadyumna, "I will not marry a suta!"

Karna lurched as if someone had struck him; still, his arrow shaved the fish. Now his poise was shattered, and he flashed Draupadi a look of untold hatred. His hands shook, and his assurance was in shreds.

A murmur hummed through the crowd when Karna missed his mark. The people had been sure he would strike the target. Only Dhrishtadyumna and Karna heard what Draupadi said. Karna found the bow in his hands had grown intolerably heavy. It was all he could manage to shoot the next four arrows, but he had no hope of finding his mark. The Pandavas breathed again. So did dark Krishna, who a moment earlier had his eyes shut, and seemed to Balarama to have been plunged in dhyana, as if he was sending his very thoughts out to someone.

Karna climbed down, burning with the insult. Kuru voices were raised in anger, "This target is impossible. We have been brought here to be made fools of."

"If Karna can't shoot the fish, no archer on earth can."

The kings who had not yet tried the bow now refused to mount the dais. Silence fell on the arena. What would become of Draupadi? Drupada could not hold another swayamvara with honour, nor could he make the archer's test simpler. Would Draupadi remain unmarried and a virgin? Such beauty wasted!

Then, like a flame from ashes, Arjuna stood up in the enclosure of the brahmanas. Krishna nudged Balarama. Arjuna began to walk towards the dais; a murmur rose among the brahmana elders.

"This is madness. The best kshatriyas in Bharatavarsha have failed to shoot the fish, and this brahmana stripling dares approach the bow."

"He will bring ridicule on us all."

"Stop him."

To some others, the brahmana youth, his hair tangled in wild strands of jata, his face covered entirely in a thick beard and white ash, seemed radiant and strong. They cried, "He looks determined. Let him have his chance."

"There is no shame in failing here. Not even Karna of Anga has succeeded."

"He seems a poised young man."

"He seems powerful, let him try. He may cover us all in glory!"

The elders saw there was little to be lost, and everything to gain. Sensing uncommon strength in the dark brahmana, they now said, "Let him have a turn, if it is allowed."

Arjuna walked up to Dhrishtadyumna, and said quietly, "It seems the target is beyond the kshatriyas here. Is a brahmana allowed to shoot at the matsya yantra?"

The kshatriyas squirmed, though not for a moment did anyone imagine the young brahmana could bring down the spinning fish, when the likes of Jarasandha and Karna had failed. Some Kaurava princes cried mockingly, "Let the fool try. He doesn't know what a great bow this is."

"Let him lift it first."

Dhrishtadyumna raised his hand for silence. He said to Arjuna, "A brahmana may certainly try to shoot the target. Anyone may try, be he a brahmana, a kshatriya, a vaishya or even a sudra. And you have my word, the man who brings down the fish will have my sister for his wife."

Of course, the reason for this was that Drupada had no idea in what guise Arjuna would come to the swayamvara. Arjuna bowed to Dhrishtadyumna. He turned to Draupadi, and bowed to her; suddenly, she felt pierced, ah sweetly, by a shaft of love. She felt all her panic, that one of the kshatriyas may actually succeed, melt away when she looked into this young man's eyes. Draupadi felt fate move in her in a tide; she felt she already belonged to the brahmana. She began to pray that, whoever he was, he should not miss the fish. She did not care any more if Arjuna came to claim her. All she knew was that she had been born for this dark brahmana.

The spinning fish

More graceful than Karna, Arjuna mounted the platform. He made a pradakshina, walking around the Kindhura. The only one so far to do this, he folded his hands to the ayudha. To the crowd's amazement, the young brahmana prostrated before it: as if he was worshipping his destiny.

Krishna leaned forward, his hand tight on Balarama's arm. Draupadi's heart fluttered madly again; but now, every beat a prayer that the brahmana would not fail. Even Dhrishtadyumna found himself hoping, inexplicably, that the dark youth would succeed.

Arjuna rose again. He stepped up to the bow and lifted it. He strung it, and still he was completely calm. Some rowdy kshatriyas, who had been drinking in the morning, had clapped and booed when Arjuna prostrated himself. They fell silent at the ease with which he picked up the bow and strung it. And the silence turned deafening when, hardly pausing to aim in the water, the young brahmana shot the five silver arrows in a blur: the shafts flashing up, one after the other, all in a single moment.

The fish fell, pierced along its length by five arrows. Into perfect silence fell a fragrant rain of barely tangible flowers, from Devaloka; there was subtle music in the sky. Only Krishna heard it or saw the fine petal-shower, for the commotion that erupted in the stadium, especially from the frenzied brahmanas.

Drupada on his throne saw what had happened. He heard the deep bass of conches, the thunder of the drums of Panchala, as Draupadi, graceful as a black swan on water, glided up to Arjuna and draped her garland around his neck.

The crowd began to sing and dance, as the Pandava took his bride's hand and came down the platform steps. They were like Indra and Shachi, like Agni and Svaha, Vishnu and Lakshmi, Surya with Usha, like Kama and Rati, Siva with Uma, like Rama with Seetha, Nala and Damayanti.

Drupada was excited. But he was not sure the young brahmana was Arjuna; though he was brilliant, all right, and a better archer than Karna today. Dhrishtadyumna did not know who the young stranger was. As for Draupadi, she did not care: whoever he was, from now he was the lord of her heart and her life.

FORTY-NINE

'Share the alms you've brought'

But now, an uproar broke out among some of the humiliated kshatriyas: Sishupala and Duryodhana, Karna and the Kauravas.

"Drupada has slighted us! The swayamvara is not for brahmanas."

"If no kshatriya could shoot the matsya yantra, Draupadi should have killed herself."

"It must never happen again. We must make an example of this wretched swayamvara."

Those royal kshatriyas were shouting now, and Drupada grew afraid. One of the Kauravas cast a blazing look at the Panchala king, and yelled, "We can't kill a brahmana. So let us kill Drupada and his son!"

"Let us throw Draupadi into the agni kunda."

Roaring, the furious kshatriyas rushed at their hosts. The young brahmana stood in their way. He lifted the Kindhura and strung it. Another brahmana appeared at his side. He was a giant, strangely familiar; but both their faces were covered by thick beards and ashes, and their hair matted in jata. Besides, they could not be who they might have been; the Pandavas were dead.

Bheema pulled up a tree as if it were a tender plant, and stood, huge and menacing, beside Arjuna. Yudhishtira, Nakula and Sahadeva, who had set out towards the carpenter's house to tell Kunti the news, heard the kshatriyas roaring and ran back. Now five brahmanas faced the angry kings.

Perhaps, Duryodhana was suspicious for a moment: how uncannily familiar these brazen priests looked. But the Pandavas had died in the house of lac; their remains had been recovered and floated down the Ganga. Next moment, outraged by the insults of the kshatriyas, and emboldened by the five that dared confront the kings, all the brahmanas in the stadium surged forward in a throng, brandishing their staffs and kamandalus.

"We are with you, brothers!" they cried. "We will teach these arrogant kshatriyas a lesson today."

"You are not alone! Every man of us will fight beside you!"

Smiling, Arjuna said to them, "Thank you, brothers. But my friends and I are more than a match for these; don't worry, our brahmana honour will be safe."

He asked them to move back. In a moment, with bowstrings twanging, a battle began. The five 'brahmanas' were indomitable, and the crowd cheered their heroes lustily.

Arjuna's arrows were like flaring thoughts, though he did not shoot to kill anyone. Her eyes bright, Draupadi stood beside him, clutching his deerskin. When Arjuna and his brothers had beaten back the kshatriyas' first onrush, Karna came to join the fray. After years, Arjuna and he faced each other again. Now Karna did not know whom he fought; of course, neither dreamt they were brothers.

Arjuna had never forgotten the exhibition in Hastinapura; he was desperate to beat the king of Anga. Karna was keen to fight the brahmana who had brought down Drupada's cunning fish. Yet, there was no malice in his heart, nor any real fervour to defeat the young brahmana. Karna knew that but for Draupadi's vicious taunt, he, too, would have found his mark. Indeed, he felt strange affection for the brahmana, never knowing who he was.

They fought fiercely, pressing each other hard. Arjuna was cool, knowing his adversary; and Karna grew more and more amazed with every arrow they exchanged. Exhilarated at discovering this youngster, excited that, like himself, the youth was not a kshatriya, Karna cried encouragement to him as they fought. "Well done! You take my breath away."

His delighted laughter rang across the arena, though slowly he had to give ground to the youngster, who was perhaps a shade quicker than him. Still Karna was exultant, arrows flying from his fingers like light.

"Tell me who you really are, young man! Are you Vishnu himself, or at least Indra? For I am Karna and no archer on earth can match me except Arjuna; and he is dead. Who are you, young Brahmana?" roared Karna.

Two arrows like lightning scorched his face. "Are you my lord Bhargava? Are you my master?"

Arjuna called levelly across that arena of humming arrows, "I am not Bhargava, Indra or Vishnu. I am just a brahmana, and I learnt archery from a brahmana. Let us fight seriously now, Karna, I say I am the better bowman."

Just then Bheema lifted the gigantic Shalya high into the air and flung him down, shaking the ground. Shalya fainted. Bheema could have killed him if he chose, but Shalya was Madri's brother, Nakula and Sahadeva's uncle. All the other kings there, who had taken no part in the fighting, crowded round to watch.

When Shalya was beaten, Arjuna grew inspired. He severed Karna's bowstring in a flash, and the king of Anga stood defenceless before him. Bowing, and knowing the young man would not kill him where he had just found a bride, Karna withdrew.

Meanwhile, the duel that amazed the Pandavas themselves was the one between Yudhishtira and Duryodhana. Their mild older brother had vanished, and a fierce kshatriya stood in his place: one who remembered Varanasi well. Quickly, the Kaurava's bow was broken in his hands, and his arms lacerated by Yudhishtira's arrows. Duryodhana fled.

Now the other kings began to mumble dangerously among themselves.

"Who can vanquish Karna except Arjuna?"

"Who can fling Shalya down but Bheema?"

"Let us discover who these brahmanas are. Let's ask them their gotra and lineage."

Krishna knew it was time to intervene. "The brahmana won Draupadi fairly. All of us heard him ask Dhrishtadyumna if a brahmana could try his skill.

"Dhrishtadyumna said, 'Anyone can try his skill: a brahmana, a kshatriya, a vaishya or a sudra. And if he brings down the fish, he shall have Draupadi for his wife.'

"No kshatriya raised his voice to object; we were so sure a brahmana could never bring the fish down. To seek battle with the stranger now is not befitting noble men as we are all meant to be."

Not only because of the truth of what Krishna said, but also because they knew what implacable warriors the five brahmanas were, the kshatriyas retired. All the brahmanas celebrated, thronging around their young heroes.

Finally, breaking away from the crowd as they went through the streets of Kampilya, the Pandavas and Draupadi arrived at the carpenter's house. Kunti sat alone inside, anxiety having its way with her. Her mother's instinct warned her that her sons were embroiled in violence of some kind. She was imagining all sorts of terrible things.

Then she heard footsteps and Yudhishtira called cheerfully, "Mother, come and look at the bhiksha we've brought today."

Without even looking through the open door, Kunti called back in relief, "In the name of God, all of you must share the alms you've brought equally among yourselves. And enjoy it."

The brothers were shocked. Only then, did their mother rise and come out. When she saw Draupadi, the day's alms, she gave a soft cry. Then she saw how unbelievably beautiful the young woman was and she broke into a smile.

Yudhishtira said, "Mother, Arjuna won the princess Draupadi at the swayamvara. She is the bhiksha I meant."

Ignoring this for the moment, Kunti came forward and took Draupadi in her arms. "I've always wanted a daughter, and now I have one!"

Draupadi, her heart on song to hear who had won her, touched Kunti's feet, "Mother."

Later, Kunti took Yudhishtira aside. "My son, what have I done? I have never told a lie in my life. Yet, I said, 'In the name of God, share the bhiksha you have brought equally among yourselves, and enjoy it.'"

Yudhishtira had a strange look in his eye. But he said, "Don't worry, mother, nothing will come of it."

He quieted the wildness in his blood that threatened to overwhelm his reason, the wildness dark Draupadi ignited in him. Yudhishtira said to Arjuna, "You won her. Before this goes any further, take her hand and marry her."

His other brothers were obviously uncomfortable, disturbed. Yudhishtira himself avoided looking at Draupadi, for the fire in his veins. Arjuna knew what went on in his brothers' hearts. More, he saw how strangely Draupadi looked at them: he saw she wanted all five of them, and she was desperately troubled.

That critical moment could have changed their lives. It could have torn them one from the other, if Arjuna had chosen to be selfish. But Arjuna said quietly, "Yudhishtira, what you say isn't kshatriya dharma. You are the eldest; you must marry first. After you Bheema, and then I, and Nakula and Sahadeva last. Consider this, and also what would be best for all of us."

Yudhishtira was acutely aware of how his brothers stared at Draupadi, and how she gazed back at each of them. Not just one, but all including himself! Yudhishtira decided that what his heart cried out for and the best course for them were the same. He glanced up at Kunti, who nodded slowly at him, reading his thoughts. The others never took their eyes off Draupadi.

Yudhishtira said, "Mother has already shown us the way. She is our guru, and she said to share the princess equally among us. It is as if God spoke through her lips. If none of you objects, I see hers as being the truest way. It is obvious that all of us love Panchali. Let her not divide us, but bind us forever."

Such relief broke out on his brothers' tense faces and Kunti's face as well. They laughed when they saw Draupadi also smiled. Just then, they heard a low cough at the door and, turning, saw two splendid kshatriyas standing there. One was Balarama, who had been Bheema's master at the mace, and the other, the fabulous Blue One, they had never seen before. He came smiling and easy among them, and touched Kunti's feet first, then Yudhishtira's and Bheema's, too.

"I am Vasudeva's son Krishna," said he.

It was an auspicious moment, and his presence filled that dwelling and their hearts. Yudhishtira knew he was much more than what he said, and breathed, "My Lord!"

Krishna's black eyes shone at him. Moving quickly, he now embraced the cousin for whose sake he had most come, the one born on the same day as him. Krishna clasped Arjuna to him. In that moment, Arjuna knew his life had changed forever, and more profoundly than by his winning Draupadi's hand. The Lord of his destiny had walked in through the door, and Arjuna knew this unmistakably. He was full of uncanny faith. Now he knew all their battles would be won, and one day Yudhishtira would surely sit upon the throne of Hastinapura.

His eyes full of tender mockery, Krishna said brightly, "I am so happy to see my aunt Kunti at last. And my cousins alive, who are said to have died in Varanasi!"

Yudhishtira asked, "How did you know us, when you have never seen us before?"

Krishna smiled. "Even if it is hidden by ashes, fire glows. No one but the Pandavas could have done what you did today." He was quickly grave. "But I mustn't stay here any longer, in case I have been followed; and you must be careful not to be discovered for a while. I fear Duryodhana may already be suspicious. It is not yet time for you to show yourselves. You must wait until the kshatriyas have all left Kampilya."

One by one, he embraced them again and, with a last dazzling smile, left with Balarama. Already Arjuna yearned to be with him again.

Meanwhile, Drupada was distraught. He had arranged the swayamvara just for Arjuna's sake. Now a brahmana had won his precious daughter. What kind of life would she have with him? An unaccustomed one, anyway. The youth was noble, surely, and such an archer! Yet, he was not Arjuna but a mendicant.

Drupada called his son Dhrishtadyumna, the only one he trusted implicitly.

"I was certain only Arjuna could win your sister's hand. I should have never held the swayamvara. I am ruined, my jewel is flung on a dust heap."

"Draupadi is my twin, and she and I are as close as life and breath. I know in my very blood that fortune has befallen her. Let me find out more about these brahmanas."

Dhrishtadyumna arrived unnoticed at the carpenter's house. Quietly, he stood under a window at the back of the dwelling, listening to whatever he could hear from inside.

Towards dusk, four of the five brahmanas went out with their begging-bowls. Night was falling when they returned with food that they set before a striking woman who was obviously their mother. She now spoke to Draupadi, "My child, keep a portion for the Gods, which we can give to any brahmana who comes for alms. Of the rest, give half to our Bheema."

Draupadi smiled at the young giant, who blushed fiercely. 'At least she is smiling; she can't be unhappy,' thought her brother at the window.

The mother went on, "Divide the rest equally among the rest of us."

Dhrishtadyumna stood watching as Draupadi divided the alms, and then sat down herself to eat. She had never seen anything but opulence since the day she was born, and now she seemed perfectly happy in one room with the five brahmanas and their mother. Why, she was radiant.

When the humble meal was over, the brahmanas spread beds of kusa grasses on the floor and settled down for the night. They lay side by side, their heads pointing east, while their mother lay above their heads and Draupadi at their feet, still blissful. Her avid brother could almost hear the sigh on her lips. After the momentous day, the two women fell asleep quickly. The young men lay awake for a while, and what they said to each other in the dark brought a smile to Dhrishtadyumna's face.

Those five 'brahmanas' spoke not of Vedas, yagnas and mantras, but of the devastras, the weapons of the Gods. And they spoke so expertly, that if there was any doubt left in Dhrishtadyumna's mind who they were, it vanished. Leaving them to their quiet, knowing discussion, he melted back into the night and walked briskly back to his father's palace, as a warm moon rose above the trees.

Dhrishtadyumna strode in to his father's presence. That king sat tense and alone, crying from time to time. His son was smiling as he came in. He embraced Drupada and cried, "They are not brahmanas! They are five, and there is a regal woman with them who is surely Kunti Devi. Draupadi is so happy that the dark-skinned one who won her can only be Arjuna. The one who uprooted the tree is Bheema, and Yudhishtira broke Duryodhana's bow. The other two are so alike they have to be Nakula and Sahadeva.

"Father, they spoke of ayudhas and astras all the time; they must be the Pandavas. The prophecy is not belied, my lord. Arjuna won your daughter's hand!"

Drupada's face lit up. Yet, he hardly dared believe his son; he thought this was too good to be true. The next morning, he sent his palace purohits to the carpenter's house, with costly gifts. He sent this message to the 'brahmanas':

'We must discuss the arrangements for Draupadi's wedding. It would be best if you came to the palace.'

The Panchala king was faint with hope; but could he believe that the rishis' prophecy was so wonderfully fulfilled? Torn between faith and anxiety, Drupada waited in his palace.

FIFTY

The unusual wedding

Noon, the next day, and the Pandavas, Kunti and Draupadi arrived at the palace in the chariots Drupada sent them. Drupada rose from his throne in excitement. After the formal greetings were over, Draupadi led Kunti in to the women's apartments. Drupada noted how at ease the brahmana woman and her five sons were in a palace.

A meal was announced. Drupada had arranged for the young men to sit on silken chairs, and to be served in plates of gold and silver. Seeing how naturally they accepted this courtly hospitality, the Panchala king grew more certain they were kshatriya princes. The food itself, brought on shining salvers, was no vegetarian fare as brahmanas are used to. There were rich and exotic meat preparations, mutton, fish, pheasant and venison, and Drupada watched the young men relish them.

After the meal, the king shrewdly led them past the armoury and their eyes lit up to see his weapons. He took them to a private room, where, finally, Dhrishtadyumna and he were alone with the brothers.

When they were comfortably seated, Drupada said, "Who are you, Brahmanas? We have seen how brave you are, but beyond that we know nothing about you."

Yudhishtira knew the time had come to declare themselves. "My lord, we are not brahmanas at all, but kshatriyas. We are brothers, and we are the sons of Pandu of Hastinapura. I am the eldest, Yudhishtira. This is Bheema, and my brother who won your daughter's hand is Arjuna. These twins are Nakula and Sahadeva, Madri's sons."

Dhrishtadyumna, who had been staring hard at the ash-masked brahmanas, gave a cry, rushed to Bheema and hugged him. Drupada could not speak for a while. He took Yudhishtira's hand, and tears stood in his eyes. Finally, composing himself, he said, "My cup of joy is full today. Tell me how you escaped from the lacquer palace. And where have you been all these months?"

When Yudhishtira told him, in some detail, Drupada cried, "You mustn't fear your cousins any more. My kingdom is yours, and my army."

They spoke about Dhritarashtra's betrayal, and Duryodhana's conspiracy; then, Drupada said, "We must make the arrangements for the wedding, without delay."

Yudhishtira replied, "I am Pandu's eldest son. I must marry first."

Without hesitation, Drupada agreed, "My daughter will not find a nobler husband than you."

But Yudhishtira smiled, "My lord, I mean no disrespect, but five of us will marry your daughter. She will be the wife of all the Pandavas."

Shock leapt in Drupada's eyes. "But that is impossible! A man may surely take more than one wife. But who has heard of a woman having more than one husband? It is immoral, against the dharma the ancients have laid down for us. I cannot imagine how you even think of it. No good will come of this, Pandava, it is a sin."

"We five have always shared everything, so nothing ever divides us." Drupada began to interrupt, but Yudhishtira said, "Hear me out, my lord. My mother has never spoken a falsehood in her life. When we arrived at the carpenter's house with Draupadi, Kunti said, 'In the name of God, share the bhiksha you have brought equally among yourselves, and enjoy it.' Draupadi was the only bhiksha we had brought, and to us our mother's word is more sacred than the Vedas.

"I have heard of more than one instance when the great rishis shared the same woman. The Muni Jatila's daughter had seven husbands; and there have been many others, none of them sinners, but holy men."

There was a knock at the door and Vyasa appeared there, timely as ever. Drupada rose to welcome him. Yudhishtira and his brothers were sombre, because Drupada's reaction to their proposal had been one of such dismay. As Vyasa settled among them, all eyes turned to the muni. He said nothing, only sat quietly, waiting for his host to open the conversation.

"My lord, your arrival couldn't have been more opportune," said Drupada.

Vyasa murmured, "Perhaps that is why fate has brought me here."

Sighing anxiously and certain the sage would never countenance what the Pandavas wanted, Drupada told Vyasa what Yudhishtira had said. The king ended, "You are an embodiment of dharma, Muni. You tell me, how can I allow this and still preserve my daughter's honour?"

Vyasa was quiet for a moment. Then, he said, "Drupada, as you say, recent custom does not allow a chaste woman to marry more than one husband."

Drupada smiled: Vyasa was his ally. But the rishi continued, "Yet, if you ask those who know about ancient times—times far more righteous than these—it was not exceptional for a woman to take more than one husband. Indeed, it was the rule rather than the exception in the nobler ages, when the earth was peopled by fewer men and women. And remember, only the truest man can even think of sharing his wife with another, be it not his own brother."

Drupada was full of anxiety again. Vyasa went on imperturbably, "The five brothers may marry your daughter, and the Gods will bless them. Drupada, the marriage of your fire-born child to these Devaputras was ordained long ago. Let me tell you part of an old story.

"Once, in the elder days, a muni had a beautiful daughter. Some karma from another life cast a shadow over her and she could not find a husband. In desperation, she fashioned an earthen Sivalinga and sat before it in tapasya to remove the curse from her life and win a man. Dark was the karma that lay over her, and she sat in penance for many years. One day, when she had all but given up hope, the Lord came to her in glory."

"Siva said, 'Tell me what boon you want.'

"Her heart full of longing, the young woman cried, 'Grant me a husband, merciful Siva, give me a husband! Give a husband, a husband is what I want, a husband and nothing else.'

"Siva said, 'I take your sin from you, and you shall have five husbands.'

"She gasped, 'Lord, one husband is all I want!'

"Illustrious Rudra said, 'You asked me five times for a husband. Five husbands you shall have,' and he vanished.

"Your daughter Draupadi is the young woman before whom the Lord appeared. You will in no way break dharma by this unusual wedding. It is blessed by Siva, and no sin will come from it."*

Drupada inclined his head, bowing to fate and to God's will. "So be it then, Muni. If Siva himself has willed it, who am I to flout his will? All five of you shall marry Draupadi, and with honour."

On an auspicious day, when the moon was in the nakshatra Rohini, where he is exalted, the strange wedding of one peerless princess to five matchless princes got underway in Drupada's palace in Kampilya. That king had made the most elaborate arrangements. All his relations and ministers, the rishis and the common people of the Panchala kingdom were invited. It was made known that the omniscient Lord Siva had blessed the extraordinary wedding.

Their brahmana disguises abandoned, the Pandavas arrived in royal finery, with Kunti and Dhaumya. When the sabha sat, Dhaumya lit the sacred fire. He sanctified it with libations to Agni Deva, who conveys the offerings made in this world to the other Gods. Dhaumya sanctified the occasion by chanting the mantras meant for just such a wedding.

The auspicious muhurta was announced, and Dhrishtadyumna brought in his sister, so breathtaking today, destiny plain on her perfect face. Yudhishtira took her hand and led her round the fire seven times, and they were man and wife. Later, after the first day's feast, the Pandavas retired to an apartment in the palace where they were now living.

The next day, again at an auspicious hour, the people all gathered in the kalyana mantapa, and today the mighty Bheema and the lovely Draupadi were married. Again, the princes returned to their apartment.

On the third day, Indra's son Arjuna, greatest of archers, married Drupada's daughter. On the fourth day, Nakula took her hand; and on the fifth, his twin Sahadeva, Pandu's youngest son married the beautiful Panchali.

With Agni as his witness and tears of joy in his eyes, Drupada blessed his daughter's husbands and gave them each a hundred chariots, five hundred horses, a hundred elephants, a hundred sakhis, garments of

---

* Vyasa also tells the story of how the five Pandavas are five Indras of previous kalpas, who were petrified by the Lord Siva for their arrogance. King Drupada sees a vision of them as such, illustrious.

rare silk, and gold and ornaments to fill a treasury. Secure in Kampilya, since Drupada, Dhrishtadyumna, Krishna and his Yadavas were with them, the Pandavas lived among the Panchalas for a time with Panchali.

It is told that, on the five nights she first spent with a different Pandava prince, the princess was a virgin for each of her husbands. The love of those six was more fervid for their being five men and one woman. Draupadi was the happiest woman on earth, and her husbands the most contented of men; though, as always, the malicious and the envious gossiped, and the imaginations of the wretched were full of obscene visions.

Borne on the tongues of gossip, word of the reappearance of the Pandavas and their marriage to Draupadi flew to Hastinapura, and pierced their enemies' ears like poison.

FIFTY-ONE

Anxiety in Hastinapura

Vidura was overjoyed when he heard the news. He went straight to Dhritarashtra. Either he could never really believe his brother was party to what had happened in Varanasi, or he wanted to rub a little salt in the guilty king's wounds. Vidura walked into the chamber of private audience and said, "My lord, I bring the most wonderful news!"

Dhritarashtra knew Duryodhana had gone to Kampilya to vie for the hand of the princess whose dark beauty was a legend throughout Bharatavarsha. His heart blazing up in hope, he cried, "Tell me the news, Vidura!"

"Twice blessed is the House of Kuru."

"Ah!"

"Call for a celebration. Drupada's daughter has become part of our family."

"Well done, Duryodhana!"

"Duryodhana, my lord?"

"Yes, surely he won Draupadi's hand?"

Vidura laughed. "Perhaps I heard the good news before you. Haven't our spies told you yet?"

Instantly, the king's face was a mask; not even his brother could see through him when he was like this. A smile flickered on his lips, though this was a very different smile, if one could read it: one to hide the doubt that gripped him. Dhritarashtra said slowly, "No spies from Kampilya have come to me yet. Tell me, Vidura, you are dithering."

Vidura took his brother's limp hand.

"Kunti and her sons are not dead. Arjuna won the lovely Panchali's hand. And all five of them have taken her for their wife, as in the old days."

Not a twitch of his palm betrayed anything of what Dhritarashtra felt. The bland smile still played on his face, though it took all his guile to keep it there. He said mildly, "Good fortune indeed! Let our goldsmiths make the finest ornaments for the princess. Let those ornaments be set with the most precious jewels in my treasury. The sons of Pandu are as dear to me as they were to my dead brother. No, truly, they are dearer to me than to him: for I have watched them grow here in Hastinapura. Drupada is a formidable ally to have. He is a more powerful king than ever, and his kinsmen are strong, especially his sons."

He paused for a moment, then, asked very softly, "But tell me Vidura, how did they escape that terrible fire? And where have they been since?"

"The people are saying they died in the fire, and were reborn miraculously in a far country. And for a while they roamed the earth as brahmanas, not knowing who they were."

"Is that what they are saying?" mused the king.

Suddenly, the passage outside rang with footfalls, as two grim warriors strode along it and into the king's presence. Riding hard, they had just arrived from Kampilya, where they had been humiliated by some brahmanas. Duryodhana and Karna entered the king's chamber.

Dhritarashtra was saying to Vidura, "Ah, today is the happiest day of my life. Not only have my brother's sons returned to me alive, they come bringing a beautiful bride, and the alliance of her great father and brother. Which king in Bharatavarsha would not be proud to have Drupada and Dhrishtadyumna for his kinsmen?"

Duryodhana and Karna stood stunned. Vidura nodded to them briefly, triumphantly. He said to the king, "May such wisdom always dwell in your heart, my lord. Now your son has come to see you, and I will leave you together. I must visit the jewellers for Draupadi's trousseau." He turned and left the royal presence.

Dhritarashtra ordered his guards to leave them. When they had gone, he held out his hand to his son. At first, Duryodhana did not take it.

Dhritarashtra said softly, "You misunderstand me again, my child. Karna, explain to him that what a king says is not always what he feels in his heart. My son is too hotheaded. He becomes angry without considering why I spoke to Vidura as I did."

"Why did you, father?" cried his son.

"Why should I let Vidura, who loves the Pandavas, know how I truly feel? Least of all, I will make him privy to my feelings. Let him think that I, too, am a kindly old fool. So when I strike, he will be taken unawares. But what do you intend now, that the enemy has escaped your fire?"

Duryodhana knelt before his father. He took the king's hand and kissed it. He said, "I misunderstood you, my lord. Forgive me, I am upset. That bungling fool Purochana let us down. My cousins are back among the living, and more powerful than ever by marrying Drupada's daughter."

"You cannot recall what is past; think what you will do next. Have you a plan? The Pandavas know we are their enemies, they are dangerous now."

Duryodhana was bristling with plots; he listed them excitedly. "Let us drive a wedge of envy between the sons of Kunti and Madri's twins: have our agents poison Nakula and Sahadeva's minds. We can bribe Drupada, Dhrishtadyumna, and their ministers in Kampilya. Buy them with whatever wealth it takes."

Neither Dhritarashtra nor Karna said anything, so he plunged on to his next plan.

"We will send our subtlest spies to Kampilya, and they shall befriend the Pandavas. Our men will win their confidence, and fill their minds with how dangerous it will be for them to return to Hastinapura, since we, their enemies, are so well prepared. They must be convinced the Panchala kingdom is the safest place for them to remain."

Still, Karna and the king said nothing. Duryodhana had not exhausted his plots to be rid of his cousins. He had thought of nothing else, since he heard they were still alive.

"What if we have them seduced by the most beautiful women we can find in our kingdom, and turn Draupadi against them? Discord sown within the home is best of all. Break their hearts first, then finish them off!"

No reaction came from his father or his friend. Duryodhana said, "But the finest plan, and the one nearest my heart, is to kill Bheema.

Snare him with friends, wine and treachery, and cut his throat. The Pandavas are nothing without their beast.

"Even Arjuna's assurance is three parts because Bheema stands behind him, and just one because of his own skill. Arjuna by himself is not a fourth the archer our Karna is. With Bheema at his side, he feels invincible. I say kill Bheema and victory is ours."

His voice was tremulous when he thought of killing Vayu's son. Dhritarashtra was quiet, and Karna shook his head doubtfully. Duryodhana cried, "You are shaking your head, Karna! Have you a better idea?"

"These devious plans won't rid you of the Pandavas. You forget that now they are bound not only by Kunti, but by dark Panchali as well. You will never divide them. As for seducing them with women, you saw Draupadi: what man who sleeps in her bed would even look at another woman?

"As for Panchali herself, she chose them when they were poor, she will not abandon them. Besides, a woman always likes to have more than one husband, and she has now five."

"Buying Drupada and Dhrishtadyumna with wealth you can forget. Drupada is known for his frugality, and so is Dhrishtadyumna. They are not men you can buy.

"As for killing Bheema, I am certain that after Varanasi the Pandavas are on their guard against treachery. No, my friend, none of these schemes will work. Besides, they are worthier of your uncle Shakuni than a kshatriya like you. There is only one sure way for us: the way of the warrior. Let the future not say Duryodhana was a coward.

"I hear Krishna of Dwaraka may come to Kampilya with his Yadava army, to help Yudhishtira take Hastinapura. I am told the Yadavas are hardly mortal, and that any of them, especially Krishna's own blood among them, could easily have shot the matsya yantra; but Krishna forbade them to compete. We must arrive in Kampilya before the Yadava legions do.

"Duryodhana, the direct way is the best one. We have such great kshatriyas in our army. Why should we resort to women's methods? Aren't you with us, and I, and your hundred brothers? You yourself say Arjuna is not my equal. Let us kill them in open battle, and then rule the world without remorse."

Karna also trembled with what his fiery nature yearned for: battle, savage and honourable. But now, Dhritarashtra said, "Karna, you speak as every warrior should. Yet, I am not certain yours is the best course. We have to contend with the people of Hastinapura; by now, they have heard the Pandavas are alive. We have to take Bheeshma, Drona and Vidura with us on this matter. We cannot act alone."

Surprisingly, Duryodhana agreed, "So be it. But let us not waste time."

Duryodhana and Karna had already anticipated that, after Varanasi, Dhritarashtra would insist on having the elders of Hastina with him. If there was to be a confrontation, the two friends were prepared for it. Between them, they had agreed it would be politic for Karna to espouse the cause of war in the court. It would keep Duryodhana in the background, and, at this stage, that was wise.

The king said, "If you are ready, I will call the sabha."

"We are ready," said Duryodhana and Karna together.

Dhritarashtra sent a guard to summon an immediate council of elders and ministers in the king's court. Duryodhana and Karna retired to a corner to confer in whispers, of which Dhritarashtra missed not a word with his acute hearing. In half an hour, the guard returned to say the sabha was sitting, and awaited the king.

"Come," said Dhritarashtra, "let us go. Only, remember I cannot show open support for your cause yet. But the day will come, I feel sure it will."

He did not speak with any enthusiasm. Their young blood alight for swift action, they followed him through the lofty passages of the palace to the hallowed sabha of the Kurus.

FIFTY-TWO

The council at Hastinapura

Every seat in the sabha was taken. Bheeshma and Drona were there, waiting for the king, so were Kripa, Baahlika, Somadatta and Vidura, and all the others whose opinions mattered in the kingdom, who wielded influence among the people.

Dhritarashtra needed no help to find his way to his throne. He walked in regally and took his place. The others sat after him, Duryodhana and Karna side by side. These men were mostly greybeards, though recently, at Duryodhana's instance, some younger kshatriyas had been admitted into this elect council. Karna was one; most of the others were Duryodhana's brothers.

The news had spread swiftly, and all the men in that court knew what they had come to discuss. Among them were those who supported Duryodhana, and others were delighted at the Pandavas' resurrection; even if they dare not show their delight for fear of the blind king and his ruthless son.

Dhritarashtra said solemnly, "Pitama Bheeshma, you have heard the joyful news, I presume. Would you like to say what you feel? We must keep in mind that Pandu's sons vanished mysteriously, leaving us to think they were dead; and their even stranger conduct in Kampilya."

Bheeshma rose today, as he never had before. He did so to emphasize the gravity of this council. He began to speak, and his tone was unemotional as always, but there was no doubt about what he said.

"The time has come for justice to be done, or fate will turn against this kingdom. We have been given a second chance by time, as few peoples ever are. God be praised the Pandavas and Kunti are alive. We must not seek a confrontation with them, for whatever reason, real or imaginary. They have given us no offence, no cause to make enemies of them, though they may not say the same of some of us.

"Dhritarashtra, Pandu and you are both my nephews, and I have always loved you equally. Death has robbed us of Pandu, but his sons are with us. They are as dear to me as you are, Duryodhana. In my eyes, they have as much right to this kingdom as you. No, they have more right, because Yudhishtira is older than you are."

He paused. A sigh quivered through his great frame, and his eyes may have been moist. "But, alas, what has so far only happened in other kingdoms, to other princes, seems to have taken root among us Kurus as well. Perhaps we have been cursed for a forgotten sin of some ancestor; perhaps, for some sin of our own. One thing seems certain: Duryodhana and his brothers and Yudhishtira and his brothers will never be able to live together in peace, under the rule of the eldest of them.

"So, this is what I say to you. Duryodhana, do not carry your hatred of your cousins any further. Give up half the kingdom to them. By God's grace, there is enough for both of you, and even He will condone such a division, knowing that bloodshed is the only other choice.

"Hear me well, Duryodhana. You stand at a crossroads in your life and in history. What you decide today will bring you either everlasting fame or eternal infamy. My son, in the end a man's strength is his honour, his reputation: what other people know and say of him. Take the noble path of conciliation, you will not regret it. Otherwise..."

He paused, and now his voice choked, "Otherwise, the doom I fear, the doom foretold for this kingdom, and indeed for all the sacred land, will come to pass. Strife will rule us, and the days of peace will vanish forever from Bharatavarsha. Listen to me, Duryodhana. I have lived many more years than you have, and I love you. You are young, and there is so much you do not understand. Yet, everything depends on what you do.

"If you choose selfishly, evil will take us all. If you make the right choice, the choice of dharma, you will be remembered forever as a kshatriya who saved his kingdom in a time of crisis. We are all friends here; all of us wish the Kuru kingdom well. All of us know, Duryodhana, that your reputation is tainted after what happened at Varanasi; and your father, the king's, as well.

"A man dies not when his spirit leaves his body, but when his reputation perishes. You have been given a rare opportunity to redeem yourself; seize it with both hands. Fortunately for you, Purochana is dead and can tell no tales. If you give Yudhishtira half this kingdom, you will clear your name with our people. They will know you have returned to the way of justice. They will celebrate that now they have not one but two princes of dharma to rule them when your father's days are over."

The patriarch was overcome. Wiping his eyes, he said, again, "Duryodhana, only you can save us from the evil you have invited into this land of truth. Give the Pandavas half the kingdom, or there will be hell to pay on earth."

Bheeshma sat down heavily, as if he already knew Duryodhana would ignore his warning. And that prince had avoided his grandsire's gaze all the while he spoke, occasionally turning to whisper something to Karna, even to share a smile with his friend.

There was a brief silence in the sabha. Then, expressionless as ever, the king said, "Acharya Drona, what do you think?"

Drona rose like a dark flame. His voice was firm, and there was no doubt in it when he spoke. "My lord, it is the sacred duty of anyone whose advice is sought on so solemn a matter that he speak only what he believes to be the truth. I agree with what Pitama Bheeshma has said. The Pandavas must have an equal share in the kingdom. It is dharma, and if dharma is not observed, retribution will overtake us.

"Let us have done with this hollow debate. We all know what the right thing to do is. Let a messenger go straightaway to Kampilya, bearing gifts for the Pandavas and their bride, for Drupada and his sons. Let him say how happy you are at their return, and then let him ask them to return to Hastinapura. Welcome your nephews with open arms, Dhritarashtra, and set Yudhishtira upon the throne of his fathers. It is not only I, but the people of the kingdom who want this.

"It is your dharma, my lord, to care for your brother's sons. Waste no more time on pointless discussion. Decide who you will send as your messenger, and let him set out at once."

Drona had hardly finished, when Karna jumped up and cried to the king, "I am amazed that you honour Bheeshma and Drona as your wisest counsellors! I find it strange indeed that the counsel they give is against your own interests and those of your son, the yuvaraja Duryodhana. This is craven, hypocritical advice, my lord. These men seem more like enemies than friends.

"Mine is the way you must choose: the straightforward path of battle and bloodshed, and kingdom and glory won by arms!"

No one had ever dared speak against Bheeshma and Drona before in the Kuru sabha. Duryodhana's pale eyes scanned the faces of all present, to determine who was with him, who against, and who could be bought to his side. Karna went on fiercely, "My lord, you are wise enough to decide for yourself who speaks in your interest, and whose advice is alloyed with cowardice."

He sat down and exchanged a glance with Duryodhana. The die was cast. Drona said, "Young man, you speak from envy and you have a malicious tongue! You dare point your finger at the Pitama and me. You are so full of hatred, you hardly know what you are saying. If we don't do as Bheeshma has said, ruin will come to the Kurus sooner than you imagine."

Karna was ready to speak again, but Vidura was up before him. "Dhritarashtra, hear what I have to say also."

The king turned his sightless face towards his brother's voice. Vidura said, "You have no counsel sager than Bheeshma's and Drona's. In age and experience, wisdom and sincerity, there is no one in the kingdom to match them. How can these mere boys, Duryodhana and Karna, full of youth, full of pique, and of little wisdom, hope to advise you better than Pitama or Acharya Drona? How can you take Karna's hotheaded counsel seriously? He hardly understands how grave these deliberations are."

Vidura's eyes flashed. "What Karna advocates, the way of war, may seem more pleasant to a father's heart. You must not be tempted again. I am your brother, and I have no fear in telling you that your name and your honour are covered in shame after the palace in Varanasi burned. What the people say does not reach your ears, because you are the king. I have heard what they say, and it does not augur well for the kingdom.

"Fate has indeed decided to give you another chance, as she does so seldom. Grasp it with both hands, Dhritarashtra. Call the Pandavas back, set Yudhishtira on the Kuru throne and wash the taint of sin from yourself. This is a heavensent opportunity; do not squander it, as these impulsive, ignorant boys want you to. Let Pandu not look down from heaven and curse you, Dhritarashtra. Remember what a happy childhood the three of us spent together: let the love we shared as children guide you now."

Dhritarashtra's hands shook slightly; but his brother knew him better than anybody did, and he noticed the sign at once. Sensing victory, Vidura pressed on.

"My lord, apart from being the way of dharma, what Bheeshma, Drona and I advise is also the most sensible course. The Pandavas are Kurus like us, we want no war with them." He lowered his voice, "Moreover, the sons of Pandu are invincible. Was it Karna or Arjuna who brought down the spinning fish? Was it Shalya or Bheema who prevailed, Duryodhana or Yudhishtira?

"Remember that Drupada, who once routed the Kauravas, is now with the Pandavas, and his son Dhrishtadyumna, too. Balarama, Krishna, and the Yadavas have allied themselves to their cousins. Dhritarashtra, you know who Krishna is. It would not only be evil, but foolhardy as well to challenge the Pandavas now."

For some reason, as his brother spoke, the blind king's mind was filled with a terrible vision of a certain night, many years ago, when his son Duryodhana was born. Once more Dhritarashtra heard the jackals and wolves baying in the streets of Hastinapura; he heard the wing-beats of a million bats, wheeling in black swarms over the palace. He remembered what Vidura said to him on that dreadful night, when the wind howled like a demon through the trees:

"Kill him before it is too late, Dhritarashtra. The omens all cry that your son will be the ruin of this holy land."

But how could he kill his own son? Now he realized what Vidura had meant, and a chill fell on his heart. For once, Dhritarashtra was happy his eyes were blind: that no one could read in them the terror he felt.

Vidura said, "Listen to the sagacity of Bheeshma and Drona; save us all from doom." He sat down, amidst loud murmurs of approval from everyone in the sabha, except Karna and Duryodhana, who sat with their faces dark, sensing defeat.

The king did not show his panic, by a flicker. He was cornered, helpless but to do what the elders asked. And if truth were told, he was glad of being able to salve his own conscience. Dhritarashtra said, "I endorse whatever Bheeshma, Drona, and Vidura have said. I know they speak with my welfare at heart, and that of this kingdom. What they say is no less than the truth. We are thrice blessed that we have such counsellors, who are the equals of Dasaratha's son Rama."

The king was frightened to hear what the people were saying about him: that he was involved in the attempt on the Pandavas' lives at Varanasi. He knew whatever he said today would be heard beyond the palace-walls, and among the people. How foolish he had been even to think of following the insane counsel of Karna and Duryodhana. Dhritarashtra sensed a perfect chance to redeem himself, and he was canny enough to seize it.

"The Pandavas are not just my dead brother's children, they are like my own sons. They are ceratainly entitled to an equal share of this kingdom. I had already decided that before I called this sabha. I wanted to be certain the rest of you felt as I did. Vidura, there is no one better than you to go to Kampilya to bring our nephews home. Take gold, jewels and the finest silks with you, my brother. Make haste."

The king rose and swept out of the council, leaving everyone more than a little surprised at the swift turn of events. Duryodhana and Karna left after him, burning with young men's hot shame.

FIFTY-THREE

Vidura in Kampilya

Vidura came to Kampilya and Krishna was already there, with Balarama and the Yadava army. When he saw Vidura came laden with gifts from the Kuru king, Drupada came out of his palace to welcome him. The Panchala king led the visitor into his sabha, where Vidura's nephews waited for him like five young lions. With them was a Dark One whose presence filled the palace, and Vidura's heart as soon as he saw him.

Yudhishtira ran to his uncle and embraced him. The others followed. Vidura wept as he clasped them to him. He loved them like his own sons; he had missed them, and been anxious for them. Talking all at once, in excitement, the Pandavas and their uncle, who had saved their lives, were re-united. Krishna stood by thoughtfully, watching them.

Vidura was introduced formally to Krishna, who bowed to him as an elder. The sage Kuru had the most inexplicable feeling that he knew the Dark One before him: that he had always known him, in dreams and lives gone by. He felt a mysterious surge of joy; Krishna's black eyes shone at him, and they were so knowing.

Vidura ordered the servants who had come with him to fetch the lavish gifts he had brought from Dhritarashtra. Yudhishtira received his quietly, as did Drupada and Dhrishtadyumna.

Vidura said, "I bring Dhritarashtra's best wishes. My brother asks me to remember him fondly to you all. Bheeshma and Drona send their greetings, and their blessings. They say it is our great fortune that you, O Drupada, have become our relative."

He paused for just a moment, then said blandly, "The Kaurava princes send their greetings as well. Most of all, the people of Hastinapura are overjoyed the Pandavas are alive, and married to the most beautiful young woman in the world! They are impatient to have the sons of Pandu return to their father's kingdom, with their bride. The king is also delighted that you escaped death. He says he cannot wait to see his beloved nephews again, and embrace them."

It took all Vidura's long experience in the Kuru sabha to keep a straight face as he said this. Krishna, who saw no need for such restraint, smiled broadly at the lie. Bheema's face was a picture. Arjuna bit his lip and his eyes glittered. Yudhishtira was composed, but when he glanced at Krishna a smile tugged at the corners of his mouth. Balarama gave a short, cynical laugh, which the rest ignored. Drupada remained impassive, as he had to, being the host.

Vidura went on easily, his eyes also smiling, if not his lips. "The noble Kunti and her sons have been away from their home for many months. Hastinapura eagerly awaits their return. Persuade them to come home with me, my lord."

Drupada bowed to Vidura. Formally, he said, "The alliance between our two kingdoms also brings me joy. However, dear Vidura, it is not for me to tell the Pandavas if they should return home with you or remain here with us, where they are more than welcome. I think the decision is for Yudhishtira to make. And his cousins, Krishna and Balarama, are here to advise him better than I can."

Turning to Krishna, who had been silent until now, Drupada asked, "Krishna, what do you say?"

"I think they should go back to Hastinapura."

The Pandavas were startled. Arjuna stared at Krishna; Yudhishtira seemed troubled. Krishna said, "That is my opinion. But let Drupada decide what you should do."

Drupada said, "I agree with Krishna. You should return to Hastinapura, and see what the future holds for you. Discover what Dhritarashtra truly intends. Besides, Krishna's concern for the Pandavas is even greater than Yudhishtira's!"

Krishna was still smiling. "My cousins fear for their safety. I will go with them to Hastinapura, and guarantee their wellbeing."

"If you come with us, we will return to Hastinapura," said Yudhishtira at once.

Vidura went in to meet Kunti. She cried, "Ah, Vidura! We would have been dead but for you. I say a prayer for you every day."

Vidura said, "Bheeshma and Drona want your sons back in Hastinapura. The people are ecstatic that the Pandavas are alive. Dhritarashtra has relented, at least since circumstances exposed him. Krishna and Drupada endorse the idea: you and your sons must come home."

Kunti was grave with concern. "I am not sure if it is the wise course. Dhritarashtra and his sons hate my princes. Won't they try to kill them again?"

"They dare not; the people will rise up against them. They did not expect the people to speak out as they did after the house of lac burned down. They did not think fingers of blame would point at them as openly as they have. Dhritarashtra, at least, has learnt his lesson.

"Now Drupada's daughter is your sons' wife, and Krishna is with them. You must not be afraid. Your sons are princes of destiny; no harm will come to them. They shall soon be lords of the earth."

And so the Pandavas set out from Kampilya, with Kunti, Krishna and Balarama, and with two armies, one of Panchalas and the other of invincible Yadavas. With Draupadi and Vidura, they set out for Hastinapura.

FIFTY-FOUR

A desolate gift

Messengers rode before the Pandavas to Hastinapura; and when they arrived, the city was waiting for them, agog! The people had laboured for three days to prepare the city of elephants for her princes' homecoming. The street-corners were adorned with festive arches; garlands of every bloom of the season hung everywhere in a riot of colours. The streets had been swept and washed, sprinkled all along the princes' way with scented water and strewn with rose petals. Incense hung in the air.

The people had turned out in crowds. They thronged the city-gates where they had seen the Pandavas off to Varanasi, and the sky resounded with their joy. They had hardly slept all night, but sat around fires they lit to keep warm.

Came dawn, full of bird-song: a crystal morning. An hour before noon, a shout swelled from the crowd beyond the gates, and those who stood high on the battlements, a cry that was taken up from the city-limits to the doors of the king's palace.

"The Pandavas are here!"

Trumpets and conches blared, and a roll of drums crackled like spring thunder on the ramparts and down in the streets. The people joined in with firecrackers, five-, ten- and a hundred-thousand of them strung together, and heady songs and frenzied dance. Fate had not betrayed them, after all: their princes of light had returned from the dead to fulfil their destiny.

A wave of clapping and cheering arose when the Pandavas rode into view, with Krishna and Vidura, Kunti and Draupadi; a wave that broke into the subtle vaults of the sky.

"Yudhishtira will sit on the throne of Hastinapura!"

"He will rule us like his own children."

"Pandu has come back from the dead, to rule as his son."

A sea of hands reaching out in love to touch them, as the five kshatriyas alighted from their chariots and walked through the triumphal archway over the gates. Taking the dust of the road, the princes marked their foreheads with it as if with holy ash. The crowd surged around them, shouting all their names, Vidura's and Kunti's; and Krishna's, as well, when they knew who he was. Most of all, they cried out the name of the princess Draupadi. They cried that they would have her climb down from her palanquin and see the face of their future queen.

Vidura tried to quieten them, and Bheema began to glower at those who shouted loudest. Then, she stepped out of her covered litter and at once all the noise subsided. A sigh went up from the crowd; never had they seen anything to remotely rival her dark beauty. The old people in the crowd came forward and blessed her. They said that, surely, she was lovely enough to be their princes' wife!

"Let the Pandavas and their queen be with us for a hundred years!" cried someone, and a roar went up from the rest.

Two of Dhritarashtra's milder sons, Vikarna and Chitrasena, and Drona and Kripa met the Pandavas at the gates. The princes embraced their cousins formally; perhaps curious if these two had conspired to burn the lacquer palace. They turned to their gurus, and prostrated themselves at their feet. Drona and Kripa had tears in their eyes.

In a royal train, with the people of Hastinapura beside themselves on both sides of the road, Pandu's sons were led to their uncle's palace. Dhritarashtra stood at the towering main door, with Bheeshma at his side. The princes touched their feet: Bheeshma their grandsire's with devotion, and the king's, wondering what went on in his heart. Krishna stood by quietly, with a ready smile for anyone who greeted him.

Duryodhana's wife, a princess of Kasi once, came out to receive Kunti and Draupadi. She had with her the wives of some of the other Kauravas, and they all touched Kunti's feet, then, led both the women in to Gandhari's palace next to the king's. Tall, very regal, her eyes bound with dark silk, Gandhari was waiting to meet them. She rose and reached out graceful arms to find them. She embraced Kunti, and when Draupadi knelt at her feet, she raised up the young bride by her delicate shoulders and embraced her as well.

Gandhari, the bhakta, had the gift of prescience since she had bound her eyes. The queen shivered when she clasped Draupadi to her, as if a cold fire licked her heart. As clearly as if it had already happened, she knew: 'This woman will be the death of my sons.'

Gandhari blessed Kunti and Draupadi, and gave instructions for them to be taken to Pandu's old palace where they would stay.

The Pandavas came into their father's house to rest after their journey from Kampilya. When he was alone with his cousins, Krishna said, "I will wager anything the blind king will not give you a fair inheritance. His words are warm, but his heart is cold."

After the noon meal, Dhritarashtra summoned another council in his court. Krishna went with his cousins to this sabha. Once more, the Kuru elders were all present. Bheeshma, Drona, Vidura and Kripa were there, as well as the others that were influential in the kingdom, and Duryodhana, his brothers and Karna. When the Pandavas had been welcomed ceremonially, the king began what he had to say.

"Yudhishtira, the Kuru kingdom is what it is today only because of your father's campaigns." A murmur of approval rose from the sabha. "But to my sorrow there has been some dissension between yourself and my own son, the yuvaraja Duryodhana. Everyone here knows what anguish this causes me. But I have decided to make a clean end to it."

He paused, then sighed, "It seems this ancient kingdom must be divided. So be it, for we shall be just. Yudhishtira, I hereby give you half the Kuru kingdom to rule. Duryodhana will have to wait for his inheritance, since I am still king in Hastinapura. From now on, all the lands of Khandavaprastha, which of old was the capital of the Kurus, Pururavas, Nahusha and Yayati's capital, shall be yours. Restore it and rule from there. Not a foot of land more or less shall there be between your kingdom and the one that remains with me. I hope this satisfies you. Tell me what you feel, you and your cousin Krishna."

Dhritarashtra turned his face to where the Pandavas sat. Krishna glanced at his cousins, and a sardonic smile lit his dark face. He said nothing yet. None of the Kuru elders, all of whom obviously supported

Dhritarashtra's plan, dared look at Krishna: not Bheeshma or Drona. Only Vidura did.

Yudhishtira rose from his place and crossed to the king on his throne. Taking his uncle's hand, he said, "I have always done your bidding. I see no reason to change that now. We will go gladly to Khandavaprastha."

A smile dawned on Dhritarashtra's face also. "Vidura, my brother, let no time be lost. Ah, I am a happy man today that I will see my Pandu's son become a king. A heavy burden has been lifted from my heart, let the city prepare for the coronation!"

Still avoiding Krishna's mocking eyes, Bheeshma and Drona said, "Let it be so."

Yudhishtira turned to Krishna. "Krishna, won't you say something?"

Dryly, Krishna said, "We understand your eagerness, my lord Dhritarashtra, better than you think perhaps. We are all keen to see Yudhishtira become a king. So let no time be lost."

Just then, the kshatriyas at the back of the sabha rose, for a revered figure had entered. Vyasa was among them once more. He strode in, crying, "I have come to name an auspicious day on which my grandson may be crowned!"

On the day Vyasa chose, Yudhishtira was crowned with deep and solemn ceremony. As he stood dripping with the waters of the abhisheka, Bheeshma and Drona, Kripa, Dhaumya, Vyasa and Krishna blessed the new king.

"May you conquer the earth!"

"With the Rajasuya and Aswamedha!"

"May your life be a long and glorious one!"

"Rule the kingdom as wisely as your sires!"

"May your fame spread through the world like the scent of flowers on the wind!"

There were such celebrations in the streets of Hastina; the feasting and drinking began while the sun was at his zenith, and went on until dawn, with singing and dancing by torchlight in the festive night. Only Duryodhana seethed, and those loyal to him—his brothers, Shakuni, Karna, and some others. Perhaps, it was to pacify his son that Dhritarashtra called Yudhishtira to him the day after the coronation.

Embracing his nephew in cold arms, the king said, "You are now the lord of Khandavaprastha. Go to your kingdom and restore the old city. Begin your rule, O king. Bless you, my son, may your life be a long and joyful one."

Yudhishtira knew that he was being sent away quickly for fear that the people may demand he rule from Hastinapura. Already, there had been some shouting to that effect after the coronation. He also knew that Khandava was a desolation ever since the rishis of the once lush jungle there had cursed Budha's mercurial son Pururavas. Nothing grew in Khandava except thorns. No birds or beasts lived in that wasteland; it was as arid as a tract of hell.

However, for just one reason Yudhishtira was hopeful: Krishna was with him. Each day in the Dark One's company was a miracle. The Pandava felt certain there was nothing his cousin could not do if he chose. Yudhishtira would have gone anywhere if Krishna went with him. He would have gone to the ends of the earth, and beyond. He believed there was no place in swarga, bhumi or patala, of which his blue cousin was not the master.

Besides, Yudhishtira was most of all a man of peace. He would avoid a confrontation as long as he possibly could. He knew that staying on in Hastinapura would eventually lead to a conflict with the Kauravas. He was not afraid; but he hated the thought of bloodshed and would prevent it at any cost. He knew he was, in fact, being banished into a desert. He preferred that to war with the sons of Dhritarashtra.

Taking leave of their friends in the city of Hastinapura, taking leave of their elders and their gurus, of their cousins and their uncle the king, the Pandavas set out for Khandavaprastha, with Kunti and Draupadi, Krishna and Balarama. Droves of the common people came to the gates of Hastinapura, with all their possessions packed, and ready to go off into the wilderness with the princes they adored.

Yudhishtira said to them, "My friends, it is a wild and uncertain land to which we are going. Let us first establish ourselves there and we will send for you. Meanwhile, live in peace in your homes."

There were those who wouldn't listen to him, and these, some hundred families, set out with the Pandavas, preferring the desolation they had heard about by now to the false comfort of Dhritarashtra's city. Their hardy leader cried to Yudhishtira, "You are our king now and we will go with you. We will come back to Hastinapura only when you return to rule from here as you should."

Fortunately, not everyone was as adventurous. Otherwise, most of Hastinapura would have emptied itself to follow the Pandavas into the wilderness. As it is, most of the people remained behind, swearing they would go to Khandavaprastha the day they had news that it was at all habitable.

FIFTY-FIVE

Miracle in the wilderness

WHEN THEY HAD RIDDEN TWO DAYS, THEY REACHED THE END OF greenness in the world, and saw a wasteland before them that stretched to the horizon and beyond. They knew they had arrived at the frontiers of Yudhishtira's kingdom. Certainly, in extent, the land of Khandavaprastha was equal to the rest of the Kuru lands. Looking at that desert, Yudhishtira wished it were much smaller: so there would be less of it to salvage from the curse of old.

The Pandavas and the brave people who had come with them stood silenced at the edge of that waste.

Only Krishna smiled. "I fear it is even worse than we expected from your loving uncle." He sighed, and said irreverently, "And to think that old man Bheeshma sanctions this, and your guru Drona, and all the other cowards except Vidura. Ah, death is not far from them, and they rush into its arms."

He saw how near tears his cousins were. He said, "Dhritarashtra is like the fool who admired the beauty of the streak of lightning, until it fell on him. He forgets he will reap the harvest of the evil he sows." Krishna took Yudhishtira's hand. "But not you, gentle cousin. Why should you reap the bitterness your uncle has sown? Come, let us enter your vast kingdom; for vast at least it certainly is." He lowered his voice to whisper to Yudhishtira, "And we shall see what we can make of this desolation, to frustrate the blind one in Hastinapura."

Yudhishtira looked sharply at him, but Krishna had already ridden ahead into the wilderness. Yudhishtira rode after him, and the others followed, numbly, wondering what the Avatara could do with such monstrous barrenness, where only the rishis' curse thrived.

On they rode, deeper into that dead land. As dusk fell around them, Krishna stopped his chariot and gave a shout.

"Look! The ruins of Khandavaprastha."

Fallen walls in the growing dimness, among which only lizards scuttled and snakes had nests; battlements and turrets, palaces, once eminent surely, but now tangled with thorny plants that survive in desert's hearts; deep moats and pools, which must have once been full of clear water, lotuses and birds, now full of dust and sand; streets where only the wind ventured; flanking those streets tumbledown mansions in which not even ghosts lived: these were the ruins of a magnificent city, the capital of Yudhishtira's ancestors.

His noble face alive with determination, Yudhishtira said to Krishna, "I am glad my uncle gave me this ruined land for my kingdom. At least, now we have a challenge before us. I am grateful for a destiny that tests us."

Krishna smiled at him like the sun. "The time of the rishis' curse is finished! Because your heart has been moved by this place. You did not know it, but it was foretold that life and prosperity would return to Khandavaprastha when a Kuru king yearned to heal the cursed land."

The sun was setting, and they had journeyed long and hard. They were exhausted and the task ahead seemed formidable, even impossible. Krishna advised, "Let us eat now and sleep. We are tired, and easy prey for despair."

They lit fires, and the cooks prepared a meal. When wine had been drunk copiously and the people and their princes had eaten, when the last firelight song had been sung, they fell asleep among the ruins of Khandavaprastha, some in their chariots, others on makeshift beds on the bare streets, under great stars hanging in a moonless sky.

At midnight, only Krishna was awake, touched by starlight, caressed by a breeze that had sprung up suddenly. He rose softly and stood among his sleeping cousins and their people who were devoted enough to follow them into this lost land. He made a secret mudra over the sleepers. At once, they were plunged in dreams like paradise. They would not awaken until he wanted them to.

The Avatara stood alone in the main street of the cursed city, as if at a crossroads of heaven and earth. He raised his arms skywards, until they were full of stars, and his body began to shine, brighter and brighter, until it was incandescent. Krishna turned his face to the sky and called in a tongue older than the suns that burned there, "Indra, I summon you!"

Silence. Nothing stirred for a moment, not the breeze, and it seemed even the stars did not pulse any more but froze at his words. Then, the firmament took light. Even as if there had always been great light there, but hidden; as if Krishna's words pulled back a veil from across heaven's blinding face.

A being whose body was made of unearthly lustre flashed down from the sea of splendour that was the revealed sky. He stood in the forlorn street of Khandavaprastha, where her princes slept, unaware of the miracle about to unfold around them. Indra, king of the Devas, stood before Krishna; and of the two, Krishna was the more lustrous.

Indra said, "Lord, how can I serve you?"

"Dhritarashtra has been generous enough to bestow this cursed land on Yudhishtira. You see the young king and his brothers asleep among their people. When they wake in the morning, let the curse have ended. Bless this land, make it fruitful." Krishna paused, "Let Khandavaprastha be named Indraprastha after you, O Deva: for you must raise this city again, in greater glory than it ever knew in the past."

Indra said, "The time of desolation is over. It was foretold that when you came to the city and called me here, the curse would end and Khandavaprastha would live again. Look, here comes Viswakarman."

Another luminous figure appeared beside Indra, out of the very air. With folded hands, Viswakarman, the divine artisan, stood before Krishna. "Command me, Lord."

Krishna said, "Fashioner of continents, the time of the curse has ended. Raise Indraprastha from Khandavaprastha's ruins, and let these lands be second only to Indra's own."

Viswakarman grew into a mist of light. He spread his ethereal body across the ruined country. Like time's ragged shroud, the curse lifted away from Khandavaprastha and a city of wonder emerged around Krishna and Indra, with glimmering towers, towering battlements, imposing mansions and resplendent palaces. The mantle of dust vanished from the city and fine new streets, paved with crushed jewels, appeared under the stars.

There were ample parks in Indraprastha, full of green plants, and herds of gentle deer. At Viswakarman's touch, the dry pools were all full of clear water, on which the stars were reflected between white lotuses, vermilion and violet ones, and flocks of water birds that slept with their heads tucked under their wings. Scented orchards and gardens flanked those streets. A deep moat, also full of the clearest water, ringed the impregnable outer walls. Those walls were like Garuda's wings, outspread.

A breeze of healing and renewal arose around Indraprastha, and all the thorns and the creatures of the desert were redeemed in it, and blown away, out of the earth. Across the arid wastes, dense green forests sprang up, with hills, wooded valleys, and rivers gushing through them. All sorts of wild creatures lived under the trees, and drank from charmed pools of sweet water, covered with pale and dark lotuses, some as dusky as Krishna. The arms of the trees were heavy with nesting birds of every feather.

When he had done, in a brief hour, what Krishna had asked him to, Viswakarman came to the Avatara again. "Khandavaprastha is restored, and it is greater than it ever was. Krishna, its coffers are full."

Krishna raised his hands in blessing over the two immortals, and bowing to him, they vanished. The stars shone down on a fabulous city and her princes asleep, strangely, in the open street.

Dawn came stealing over the horizon, over verdant hills that encircled the city of wonder. With first light, every bird in the trees of Indraprastha and the forests around it burst into song. The Pandavas, Kunti and Draupadi awoke, and the brave folk who had come with them. They thought their dreams had come true!

The desert had vanished, the waste of thorns and ruins where they had lain down sadly to sleep last night. They found themselves in the streets of a city which was surely not of this earth. Lush trees, lotus-pools and fine mansions were all around them; the streets glittered with jewel-dust. The birds sang in the trees as if it was the first day of creation: which, for them, it was.

As in a dream, the Pandavas and the others rose and began to walk along the dazzling streets. Yudhishtira whispered to his brothers, "Krishna has done this."

Laughing like a boy, Bheema cried, "Or we have died and gone to heaven!"

There was no sign of Krishna, not until they wandered to the end of the highway on which they had been asleep. Rounding a corner, they saw a palace so glorious that they stopped still, to stare. On the highest of the crystal steps leading into it sat their cousin with a gleam in his eye. He rose when he saw them and, flinging out his arms, cried, "Welcome to the palace of the master of Indraprastha. Yudhishtira, king, welcome!"

Then they knew this was no dream, and they ran up those steps and knelt before him. Laughing, he led them into that ineffable palace. Not Krishna himself could fault what Viswakarman had created: sweeping halls with unreachable ceilings, floors of polished stone that seemed like clear water, real pools laid in scintillating marble, and innumerable passages, all leading to sprawling apartments.

When they came out, breathless, on to an open terrace, they saw that overnight the desert had bloomed as far as their eyes could see. Thick green forests stretched away forever on every side. Bheema's delighted roar rang among the battlements, giving mighty voice to what his brothers and all the people felt.

Thus, Krishna raised a magical city and an emerald wilderness for the Pandavas, out of desolation. They had their first glimpse of his uncanny powers. The sons of Pandu and their queen began living in the palace, and the people who had come with them naturally occupied the finest mansions, nearest it. For their courage and loyalty, Yudhishtira gave them lands and wealth past their dreams.

Vyasa appeared in Indraprastha out of the blue, as usual, and Krishna asked him to perform the rituals of graha pravesha, and to bless the city in the wilderness. When the Pandavas had begun to settle into their new domain, one morning Krishna went to meet Yudhishtira in his apartment, awash with golden sunshine. Krishna embraced the king and said, "The time has come for me to return to Dwaraka, there is so much I have to do there."

"No!" cried Yudhishtira.

"I am always with you. If you need me, just think of me and I will come to you quick as a thought. But now I must go."

Yudhishtira hung his head, and nodded mutely. The others were forlorn to learn their cousin was leaving. They had begun to think of him as part of their lives, of themselves. They came with him to the city-gates. Krishna embraced them all and, cheerful as ever, cried, "Enjoy Indraprastha!"

Then he rode off without a backward glance.

Word of the miracle in the wilderness spread like fire. Soon, more people arrived from Hastinapura, and, indeed, from all over Bharatavarsha, to see for themselves the wonder Indraprastha was said to be. Those who came invariably stayed on, and became Yudhishtira's subjects. They realized that nowhere else on earth was there such a blessed city or such a noble king.

Folk of every ilk and persuasion came to Indraprastha: learned brahmanas, industrious vaishyas, valiant kshatriyas and gifted sudras; and, with their diverse talents, they quickly made that city the cynosure of the world. In Hastinapura, Duryodhana simmered with envy. He blamed his father for what he saw as a terrible humiliation for himself. Instead of thorns and dust, the detested Pandavas enjoyed a city of marvels, to which the people of Hastinapura were flocking, abandoning Dhritarashtra's capital in droves.

Karna, Duryodhana, his brothers and Shakuni all blamed the blind king and the elders for showing softness to the sons of Pandu, when they should have sent an army to crush them in Kampilya.

FIFTY-SIX

Narada visits Indraprastha

Some days after Krishna left, the Pandavas sat together in an airy room full of the orient sun and bird-song from the trees in the palace garden, when they heard the plucking of a vina in the passage outside. The timbre of that lute was so exquisite, and the playing so effortless, so inspired, that Yudhishtira said, "It is Narada Muni."

The name was hardly out of his mouth when the rishi himself stood at the door: slender, bright and quite ageless. Narada was as old as the world. He was Brahma's son, born at the beginning of the kalpa from the Creator's pristine thought. From an ancient curse he was a wanderer always, who appeared in the unlikeliest places to perform, in his inimitable way, the Lord's more difficult tasks; tasks that only an expert in human nature could accomplish. Because of his subtle, gossipy methods, Narada was known as a troublemaker. However, the truth was that he was a canny sage and perhaps the greatest bhakta of the Lord Narayana, whose ways are always inscrutable.

Yudhishtira washed the holy one's feet, and made him sit in a place of honour. Narada's voice was youthful, and his face a young man's; but he was older than they could imagine, and they could tell as much from his astonishing conversation. For example, he would speak of Siva's wedding to Parvati as if it had happened yesterday; and, of course, he had been there. So also, primeval legends those princes had heard from their gurus: Narada spoke of them with easy familiarity; he had seen it all happen.

He chatted with the Pandavas like an old friend, but the princes knew their brilliant guest was bound neither by time nor place, and travelled freely through both, as he liked. He spoke about kingship and war, love and children, about his meetings with Vishnu, his conversations with his father Brahma, and even of fathomless Siva. All his observations were embellished with vivid anecdotes, and the princes listened entranced.

For the first time after Krishna left, Yudhishtira was in a fine mood. He called for Draupadi, so she could have Narada's blessing. When she came, Narada cried, "How beautiful she is, my princes! How perfect."

Draupadi knelt before him, and he blessed her affectionately. When she had gone, Narada knit his brow and grew thoughtful. Yudhishtira asked, "Has something disturbed you, my lord?"

"I was reminded for a moment of Sunda and Upasunda."

"Who are they?"

"Not are. Were. They are, alas, dead." He fell silent again, knowing someone would press him to tell them more.

Sahadeva obliged. "Why were you reminded of them seeing Draupadi?"

Narada sighed. There was work to be done here, and the Lord's work was always so delicate. He must tread carefully. They must never know that he had met Krishna yesterday, and the Dark One had sent him to Indraprastha.

"Indraprastha is such an excellent city. Go and see my cousins there, O Muni."

And only as he left,—he had travelled by rishi patha, magical skyway, as all great sages did—was he told what Krishna wanted him to do in Indraprastha. The Lord never sent you anywhere just to admire the scenery, however wondrous a city and its environs may be. After all, Narada had some experience of the Lord's ways, for longer than anyone else did. He was his shrewd and far-seeing messenger.

So here he was in Indraprastha, sighing. He shook his slim head, and said, "They were brothers just like you, and they loved each other quite as much as I see you five do. But they both fell in love with the same woman. She was beautiful and dark-skinned, like your Panchali. She was a gandharvi called Tilottama." He lowered his voice, "And they killed each other because of her, though they had agreed to share her love."

The Pandavas shivered. Narada went on, insouciantly, "The trouble began when one day Upasunda, the younger brother, walked into Sunda's bedchamber, and saw his brother and Tilottama making love. He could not bear it and, later that same night, challenged Sunda to a duel. After a bloody fight, Sunda killed Upasunda. But then, he was horrified by what he had done and ran his sword through his own heart."

The Pandavas sat as if they were made of stone. Knowing he had their attention, Narada said, "You five brothers also share one woman, and such a beautiful woman. You must be careful she does not become the unwitting cause of your falling out among yourselves. For, my precious princes, you are the agents of a great destiny. And it would not do if you were to fight one another, instead of the evil ones who are your enemies."

Suddenly, his eyes were old as stars. "Just think how pleased Duryodhana and Shakuni would be, if you five were to fall out over Draupadi. You would do their work for them, and they could rule a world with no-one in it to oppose them." He lowered his voice still further, "Remember, as long as you stand together you are invincible. If you are divided, your enemies will cut you down very quickly.

"I am not saying there is jealousy in your hearts, or that you compare yourselves to one another. What I do say is that you are not ordinary men, by a long way. The future of the world depends on you five, and you must guard yourselves against the most unlikely contingencies."

Arjuna asked, "Tell us how, Muni."

"I have a way. But you must all approve of it, because it is a hard way."

Bheema said, "Tell us what it is, Narada."

"I suggest that each of you, beginning with Yudhishtira, keeps your dark queen for a year. During that year, she shall be exclusively the wife of one brother. If anyone intrudes on their privacy during that year, the intruder must go on a tirtha-yatra for twelve years, and not see Panchali for that time."

The Pandavas glanced at one another. Yudhishtira said, "We will do as you say, Muni. Bless us so we may be strong."

Narada did so, and, having accomplished what he came for, the itinerant was on his way once more, blithe as ever. News of her husbands' resolve came to Draupadi, who went into the prayer room to ask for the Gods' blessing for them all. Then she moved into Yudhishtira's wing of the palace for the first year.

The new arrangement appeared to be working well, until, one day fate took a hand in Arjuna's life. Fate arrived as an irate brahmana, whose cows had been stolen. Arjuna was sitting on his balcony that balmy morning, basking in the sun, when he heard the brahmana's voice below him.

"Pandavas, all the world has contempt for a king who levies a sixth of his kingdom's yield as tithe, and does nothing to protect his subjects!"

Arjuna leaned over his terrace. "What is the matter, Brahmana?"

"My cows have been stolen in broad daylight. Help me, Arjuna!"

"Thieves in Indraprastha? I am coming."

Then Arjuna remembered his weapons were in Yudhishtira's apartment, where the king was with Draupadi. Coming out into the courtyard between his wing of the palace and his brother's, Arjuna hesitated. How would he enter Yudhishtira's apartment when his brother was alone with the queen?

The brahmana cried. "The thieves will reach their homes with my cows!"

Arjuna stood in a quandary. The brahmana said in disgust, "As his brothers, so too the king! Like all kshatriyas you live off the fat of the land, and neglect your dharma to protect those that depend on you. When I came to Indraprastha, I thought Pandu's sons were different from Dhritrashtra's; but I see all you kshatriyas are the same."

The man began to walk away, when Arjuna seized his arm and cried, "One moment, Brahmana! Let me fetch my bow."

Deciding it was his dharma to help the brahmana, to his own cost if need be, Arjuna ran to his brother's apartment. The front door was not locked and he walked in. There was no guard posted, there was no need for one. Beyond the door, lay a small waiting room, and beyond that was another room where the weapons were. Arjuna paused, with his hand on the second door.

He knew Yudhishtira's bedchamber lay beyond the private armoury. He hesitated, knowing if he passed the second door, he must go into exile as well. He heard the frantic brahmana cry, "Arjuna has vanished into the palace, leaving me standing here like a fool! He is afraid of the thieves. Ah, what the world has come to these days. And they say Yudhishtira is a great king."

Arjuna pushed open the inner door. He heard Draupadi and Yudhishtira together; he heard her moan. Mustering his courage, Arjuna mumbled, "There is a brahmana in trouble outside. I came for my bow and arrows; forgive me."

He seized his bow and quiver, and ran out. There had been no answer from the next room; but he heard Draupadi draw her breath sharply. Shaking, Arjuna came out into the sun, where the brahmana was about to walk away again.

Knowing he had just sentenced himself to twelve years of exile, Arjuna said, "Come, show me where the thieves took your cows."

In a lather to retrieve his herd, the brahmana ran ahead already. Smiling at the man's alacrity, and his belly that flapped ahead of him, Arjuna followed at a lope. They came to the city gates, where the cows had been lifted. The herd's tracks were still fresh on the soft ground, and, telling the brahmana to wait for him, Arjuna followed them into the jungle.

As he sped through the trees, tears stung his eyes. It was all he could do to keep his mind on his task. With the herd, the cattle-thieves couldn't go as quickly as he did, and it did not take him long to catch up with them. Soon, he saw the rumps of fine white cows through the trees, and driving them on were three forest bandits, hurrying through the jungle's twisting avenues.

The bandits saw nothing of Arjuna. As they plunged along, suddenly a hundred arrows whistled around them. Some missed their heads so narrowly the thieves could feel their breath; others flashed down at their feet so they jumped into the air. They ran faster than ever. Stranger missiles flew after them, arrows that howled like bhutas and burned like fire-serpents.

The bandits left the cows and fled through the jungle. Arjuna sent a few more blistering shafts after them, crying, "I will kill you if you ever come back!"

He rounded up the cows, and took them back to the brahmana. It had been so easy, too easy almost. Arjuna knew fate had tricked him: the stolen cows had been a pretext, he was meant to leave the comfort of Indraprastha.

He came shyly to his brother, and stood with his head bent. Yudhishtira hugged him. "I hear you recovered the brahmana's cows. He is telling all the city what a kshatriya you are."

Arjuna stood downcast. At last, he said, "I came into your apartment when you were alone with Panchali. I must go on a pilgrimage for twelve years."

"No! You came only because you had to fetch your bow and quiver. I did not mind. Besides, it is never a crime for the younger brother to come into his older brother's chamber. If I had come into yours, that would be different. You must not leave Indraprastha, not for a day."

Arjuna was unmoved. "You are letting your love for me sway your judgement. I have often heard you say there is no room for compromise in dharma. Don't make me waver from the truth, I must go."

Yudhishtira sighed, and said quietly, "Go with my blessing, then, if you must. Take some of our brahmanas and sutas with you. They will make the tirthas come alive with their legends. Meet mother, our brothers and Panchali before you go."

Arjuna bowed to his king, clasped him once more and went to meet the others. Kunti and Draupadi wept, and begged him to reconsider; his brothers said that, because of the circumstances, he could not be held to the oath. Arjuna was adamant, and early next morning he set out with a group of brahmanas and pauranikas.

The sun was mellow in a clear sky as the pilgrims headed towards the Ganga. They meant to track the river back into the Himalayas, to her source.

FIFTY-SEVEN

Ulupi and Chitrangadaa

Climbing without rest, save at night, in a month Arjuna and his party arrived at the source of the Ganga. Near that hidden spring the water formed a crystalline lake, the Bindusaras; and on its mirror-smooth surface grew lotuses that might have fallen straight out of Devaloka. Arjuna decided to stay a while beside the lake on the Himalaya.

The brahmanas lit a fire, and made their offerings to Agni. Then they built simple shelters for themselves and began living there. They could not have chosen a better place for their worship. Soon the very air was laden with mantras, which mingled with the delicate scents of lotuses that unfurled, day and night, to rhythms neither of sun nor moon, but more subtle and mysterious: perhaps, the rhythms of unknown stars deep in the sky.

Arjuna lived contentedly there for some months, without any excitement or incident. During the icy winter, they lit fires and sat round them, singing stirring bhajans late into the night. The pauranikas had an inexhaustible fund of sacred tales; and Arjuna found solace in them, apart from pleasure.

Winter began to turn to spring, and the Pandava felt restless. He felt the urge to move on. He stayed, knowing he would be given a sign when the time actually came.

The days grew warmer, as the migrant sun drifted north once more. Every day Arjuna went to the lake where the river sprang. So far, he had neither heard nor seen anyone else there, save at times his own brahmanas. When spring had arrived and the trees all burst into bloom, one morning the Pandava came to the lake with the rising sun and prepared to light a fire for his worship. When the wood was stacked, dry twigs and branches, he dived into the water to bathe before sitting down to pray.

He was not aware that, for days now, someone had been watching him, from hiding among the trees or from under the transparent lake. The crisp water closed smoothly around him; by now, Arjuna was used to the first shock of cold.

He swam out a good way across the lake. He had seen some new lotuses of spring, their petals the colour of blood. He was being watched closely, but never knew it. With powerful strokes, he swam to the resonant blooms. He pulled up one of the crimson flowers, its stalk trailing the sparkling surface of the water. The sun was just peeping above the horizon.

As he reached for another lotus, an irresistible force seized him and pulled him under water. Arjuna was a strong swimmer, but there was no escaping whatever held him. Taking a deep breath, he submerged helplessly. As he went, he peered down to discover what dragged him down and saw nothing.

The deeper he went, the stronger grew the pull. Arjuna hurtled along and briefly lost consciousness. Curiously, he never felt threatened as he plunged past indigo serpents watching him out of knowing, lidless eyes. Unconscious, he fell straight through a magic opening on the bed of the lake, quite as Bheema had in another place, many years ago. The secret portals that lead down into the patalas are numerous, and many of them lie under water.

When the Pandava came to his senses, he found himself in a jewelled chamber whose walls seemed to be made of living moss. Clusters of glow-worms on the walls and ceiling cast their warm light through the room. Arjuna saw a fire of sacrifice just like the one he had stacked ashore; but this one was already kindled. He still had the two vermilion lotuses in his hand.

Arjuna sat before the fire and poured oblation into it. He still felt no sense of any danger. On the contrary, he felt welcome in this strange place, and he knew the fire had been lit for him. He was entirely at ease, and took his time over his worship.

When he finished, he opened his eyes and saw a young woman before him. Her skin shone softly, a half-smile was on her arched lips; her slanted eyes were full of shy desire. She wore a sheer gown made of silver fish-scales and fine threads of moss. Arjuna could see her slender body underneath, young breasts with long, dark nipples, and hips that flared away from a reed-slim waist, where she wore a glowing ruby in her deep navel.

Understanding now, Arjuna laughed. "Who are you, impetuous temptress? And where have you brought me?"

She had watched him for months, in his asrama and in the water, and she had waited impatiently for spring to arrive. Her voice was full of river-eddies, as she said slowly and quite regally, "I am Ulupi. My father is the Naga Kauravya, born in the line of Airavata, and he is a king of nagaloka. We are in my father's palace."

Feigning innocence, Arjuna asked, "But why have you brought me here, princess?"

She did not answer, but a blush spread from her neck down her sinuous body, and she turned her eyes down. He knew this was the first time she had done anything like this, and his heart went out to her. "You haven't answered me, Ulupi."

"I have watched you for many days now, stranger. I am not married, and I am a virgin still. I love you and want to give myself to you freely, as our women do before we marry." She turned her extraordinary eyes on him now, "Spend one night with me, Kshatriya, make a woman of me. That is all I ask. I see you are a man of destiny, and you will not stay with me forever."

"Ah princess, I wish I could, but I am sworn to brahmacharya. We five brothers swore an oath in Indraprastha, and that is how I came to the mountains."

He told her about Draupadi and his brothers, the vow, and his twelve-year exile. She heard him out in silence, then said, "You have sworn not to see Draupadi during your exile. But I am not Draupadi, O Arjuna, and if you will not have me I shall kill myself."

She slipped off her robe fluidly, and stood naked before him. Arjuna rose and took her in his arms. At just his touch, she began to tremble uncontrollably. When it passed, she smiled at him, and he began to kiss her hungrily, her lips, her fluted throat and her breasts. She took his hand and led him out of that room.

She took him down a winding passage and into another chamber, with a tall ceiling, embellished with a profusion of corals. At the heart of that wide room was a bed canopied with strings and strings of shining moon-pearls. As Ulupi led Arjuna to her bed, a door slid shut behind them. The only light in that room was from a thousand pearls. She reached for him in the dimness. She stripped away the cloth he wore around his waist, and began to caress him in a fever, crying strange deep cries. She stroked him with her petal hands and moistened him with her river lips, until, with a cry of his own, he lifted her in the velvet dark and laid her down on the soft bed. Helpless for the storm they were both in the eye of, Arjuna took her tenderly, fiercely. She writhed and screamed under him, and locked him in smooth legs strong as serpents.

A day and its night passed in wild lovemaking, and in languor and snatches of sleep in between. Came the dawn, and Arjuna said to Ulupi, "I must go now, or I will never be able to leave. The brahmanas must worry about me. This is the first time I have been away without telling them."

Sad and brave, radiant with the love they had made, Ulupi swam to the surface world with him through the portal on the bed of the lake. The sun was just rising, and the mountain birds were waking to hymn the morning. Arjuna plucked two more crimson lotuses and swam ashore. A last time she came to him, and he kissed her long and deep on the banks of the Ganga.

Her eyes brimming, she said, "I have a boon for you, my love. No harm will ever come to you while you are in water: in sea, lake and river you shall be invincible."

She clung to him briefly and then, with a sob, tore herself away. Ulupi dived back into the lake, cleanly as a water snake, cleaving its dawn-lit surface with hardly a ripple, and she was gone from his life. Only the taste of her lingered in his mouth, and the memory of her passion in his body. With a sigh, Arjuna made his way back to the asrama.

He had the sign he had been waiting for; he told the brahmanas it was time to move on. Later the same day, they packed their scant possessions, bid farewell to the hermitage that had been so hospitable, and, after worshipping the spring of the Ganga one last time, they climbed higher up the mountain.

Through white valleys they went, under peaks on which the snows of winter were still melting. Sunset and sunrise here were pristine spectacles that reminded a man, as nothing else on earth, of the immortality of his soul.

They visited the asramas of Agastya, Vasishta and Bhrigu, and each day the weather grew warmer and more clement. Their hearts full of the wonder of the Himalayas, they came down again into the plains of the Ganga. Arjuna and his party journeyed east. By now, all of them looked like sannyasins, with matted jata and thick beards, and they came to the tirthas in Anga, Vanga and Kalinga.

The brahmanas grew weary of wandering, and in Kalinga, they bade Arjuna farewell. He was determined to see all of Bharatavarsha, at least as many of its tirthas as he could. Walking on, alone, Arjuna came to the looming Mount Mahendra. Taking his time, climbing leisurely, pausing to rest in charmed valleys full of spirits, and on the banks of frothing rivulets, hunting his food in game-rich forests, Arjuna passed over the Mahendra. He turned south along a beach where once, more than seven hundred thousand years ago, at the beginning of the dwapara yuga that now neared its end swiftly, a distraught blue saviour had come with his brother and an army of monkeys: in search of his wife whom an awesome Demon had abducted.

Briefly, Arjuna worshipped Sri Rama of old and, then, the one whom Rama himself had worshipped here: Mahadeva Siva. Now he turned south, and walking along the shoreline, leaving his prints on damp sands, Arjuna found his way to the kingdom of Manalur, where king Chitrasena welcomed him.

At first, Arjuna stayed in Chitrasena's palace for a month. It was a year since the Pandava had been in royal surroundings, and he allowed himself to be tempted by the luxury of the palace in Manalur. He never told the king who he was, and pretended to be an itinerant rishi, as he seemed by his appearance and his saffron robes.

After a month, Arjuna left Manalur abruptly and wandered to the sea again. He lived in seclusion by the waves that washed dim tidings ashore from the corners of the earth, and the wind that bore the cries of gulls, and starlight full of prophecy. Arjuna was plunged in indecision, wondering whether to return to Manalur: for, he loved Chitrasena's daughter Chitrangadaa.

This princess had a secret: she was ugly. However, she was a gifted sorceress. Chitrangadaa had lost her heart the moment she saw Arjuna; she turned herself into a ravishing beauty to seduce him.

Finally, the Pandava went back to Manalur and sought audience with the king. Chitrasena received the handsome young mendicant to whom he had taken such a liking. The king said, "I thought you had left us, young Muni. I am glad to see you back."

Arjuna was quiet for a moment, then, said, "My lord, I am not who you think I am. I am Pandu and Kunti's son Arjuna."

Chitrasena rose in amazement. Arjuna said, "I left here to test myself: if what I had begun to feel in your palace was mere fancy or something more…"

The king was a shrewd man, and guessed what he meant. "And you found your heart didn't allow you to remain away?"

"I love your daughter, and want to marry her."

Chitrasena cried, "Which father would not give his daughter to the greatest kshatriya on earth? Yet, Arjuna, there is a condition I must insist on before I give Chitrangadaa to you. Since time out of mind, the generations of our House have been blessed with just one child. Chitrangadaa is my only child; she is the one who must continue our line. Only if you agree that your child by my daughter will remain here in Manalur with me, and in time be the king or queen, can I give Chitrangadaa to you."

The Pandava agreed without hesitation. The next day, Chitrangadaa became his wife, and for three years, Arjuna lived with her in Manalur. He never knew what she really looked like but believed her to be as beautiful as she had made herself for him with her maya. One morning, when she awoke at his side, Arjuna saw her aglow. "You are so happy this morning, Chitrangadaa. Share your joy with me."

She said, "You are going to be a father."

There was rejoicing in Manalur; but suddenly, Arjuna was restless again. He yearned for his brothers and for Indraprastha; and now, strangely, more than anything else, he longed to see Krishna. It was as if fate's work was complete once Chitrangadaa conceived, and it was time for Arjuna to move on.

Yet, he waited until his son was born, and that day Chitrangadaa was so weak after her labour that, for the first time, Arjuna saw her as she really was. He felt betrayed, and decided he must leave Manalur the same night. Past midnight, the Pandava stole out of the city and set out south again. Now he wanted to bathe in the sea at the southern tip of Bharatavarsha.

Tradition was not broken in Manalur. Like all her ancestors, Chitrangadaa of Manalur would have only one child, great Arjuna's son.

FIFTY-EIGHT

The crocodiles

Arjuna went from tirtha to tirtha, and each one purified him. He sat in dhyana in the hearts of unknown forests, under great trees that had themselves stood rooted in tapasya for an age; he felt renewed, and at peace. The years flowed by. Once, he came to a jungle where he found some friendly rishis. Arjuna stayed with them for a few days, and heard the mythic lore of the south from them. When he told them he was on a pilgrimage to the holiest tirthas of Bharatavarsha, they advised him on the best route to take so he would miss none of them.

But he noticed they left out five of the most sacred river-fords, where, in bygone days, the greatest sages had sat in tapasya and been rewarded with visions of the God they worshipped, and with boons. Arjuna asked the hermits why the route they charted for him did not lead to those five pilgrim's fords.

One of them replied, "There is a savage beast at each tirtha, which drags bathers down and devours them."

Another said, "Many hunters have tried to end the curse of the crocodiles. But they all failed, and many were killed themselves."

That set Arjuna's kshatriya blood coursing. "I am not afraid of crocodiles. If you show me the way to the nearest tirtha, I will bathe there."

The eldest rishi said, "These are not ordinary crocodiles. If you bathe at any of those tirthas, it will be your last ablution."

Arjuna laughed, "The crocodile that seized my guru Drona once was not ordinary; but I killed it. Besides, I have a boon that I will be invincible in water. Show me the way to the tirtha, Munis, and you yourselves shall bathe there soon."

The hermits took him to the nearest ford. One of them said, "The creature has never been seen ashore. The only way to find it is to enter the river."

The munis remained at a safe distance from the water. It was late afternoon. Removing the cloth he wore across his chest, Arjuna folded it on a dry rock. The Pandava dived into the current, and began to swim with easy strokes.

The rishis stood anxiously, prayers on their lips. They were certain they would see the handsome kshatriya pulled down by intractable jaws, and his blood stain the limpid water. They did not have long to wait. Arjuna cried to them, "There is no crocodile here, Munis! Come and join me, the water is fine and warm."

The next moment, a creature big as a whale broke surface behind him. The rishis shouted a warning, but too late. A leviathan's jaws closed round the Pandava's waist and, without a splash, the armoured beast dragged him under the river.

Below the water, Arjuna saw the creature that had seized him was a crocodile all right; but this was no crocodile such as he had seen or heard of before. It was a giant of the deeps, a dragon that belonged in the plumbless sea. As he went down, he saw Ulupi's smiling face before him. He heard her say, "You shall be invincible in water, my love. It is my boon to you."

As the monster dragged him to the riverbed, Arjuna felt a tide of new strength course into his body: as if the river knew he was a blessed one, and took his side against the predator. Arjuna seized the crocodile's jaws in his hands, and, easily as opening a baby's fist, wrenched open the maw that could have swallowed a small island.

For a moment, the beast was startled. Arjuna seized it by the neck and snout, clamping its jaws shut. He kicked his legs and swam powerfully towards the surface and the sunlight that creature loathed. The crocodile threshed about and tried to beat the terrible human off with its whiplike tail; but Arjuna was stronger. Inexorably, he rose into the daylight, and there, with arms like time, he dragged the giant lizard into the shallows.

Now the rishis began to cheer him, though still from a safe distance. In shallow water, the crocodile went limp in his arms. With hardly a struggle, it allowed itself to be hauled ashore, where it lay heaving for breath. Arjuna stood panting beside the dying creature when suddenly, the hermits gave a shout.

A transformation came over the scaly monster: in a flash of light, the huge lizard turned into an unearthly woman! Her delicate body shimmered; her hair cascaded from her enchanting head, dark and full of fascination. She was taller than Arjuna; she folded her hands to him in absolute reverence. Of the demon crocodile, there was no trace.

"Who are you?" cried Arjuna.

In a voice out of dreams, she replied, "I am an apsara of Devaloka, mighty Kshatriya."

"But how were you the monster, or are you still one deceiving me?"

She laughed, and it was a heavenly sound. Arjuna smiled at his own suspicion; no demoness could laugh like that, so full of joy. The apsara said, "The monster was what I became when I was cursed. Once, my four friends and I came down to earth to bathe in this river. We saw a rishi at his tapasya. We challenged one another to tempt the holy one from his dhyana.

"By moonlight, we came to him, singing softly, dancing, and wearing not a stitch on ourselves. For a long time, he sat unmoving. Then his eyes fluttered open, and we thought he had succumbed. For a moment, he gazed at us in the warm light of the moon, and we wondered which of us he would choose first. He was obviously a man of power, and we all yearned to lie with him.

"After staring at us for a moment, he cursed us. 'The Gods have not made you beautiful to disturb a rishi's dhyana. You are arrogant and I will take your beauty from you for a hundred years. Become ugly lizards from now and man-eaters, for your spirits are vulgar and rapacious. A hundred years should shear some pride from you. One day, a kshatriya will come to this place and free you from my curse. Until then live only in the water, and feed on whatever you find in it.'

"He rose and walked away. We stood naked, burning with shame, and we felt ourselves turn into the beasts we became. We heard ourselves hiss and growl at each other and the land was made of fire, so we fled from it into the river. We had become so fierce we would have devoured one another if we had stayed together. My friends swam away from here and they haunt four other tirthas.

"I beg you, Kshatriya, free them as well."

There were tears in her eyes as she told her story, and now, she surely seemed as humble as she was beautiful. Arjuna said, "Apsara, I was going with the munis to the other tirthas anyway. Come with us, if you like, and find your friends again."

In a few days, on the banks of the same river, but four fords upstream, not one but five apsaras stood gratefully before Arjuna. In more or less similar fashion, he had freed them all from the rishi's curse. Some say the nymphs rewarded Arjuna, spending five nights of abandon with him in the forest. Whatever the truth, he did not tarry long with them or they in the world. They were impatient to return to Devaloka, from where they had come a hundred years ago for a bath in the river.

When they left him, the Pandava longed to see his son and returned to Manalur. He stayed a month with Chitrangadaa and her young prince, Arjuna's first child, whom they named Babhruvahana. On an auspicious day, Chitrasena held a solemn ceremony in his sabha, during which Arjuna formally presented his son to that king, saying, "My lord, now free me of my debt: I give you my son to be your heir."

He set out again and went south once more. Travelling from tirtha to tirtha, crossing the western mountains, he came into Kerala and, finally, to the southern-most tip of Bharatavarsha, where he bathed in the sea at sunrise and sunset.

Now his heart yearned for home and, not stopping anywhere, he journeyed north along the western coast, along pristine beaches where few men had ever set foot. Arjuna went north with the wind in his face and the tide echoing in his body: the crash of waves against stark promontories, and their wash over virgin sands in silver grottoes where he spent many nights under stars hanging like lanterns above. Full moons streamed wild longing into his blood, and set his fantasies alight.

An extraordinary passion possessed him, as he made his way slowly up the coast and came at last to Prabhasa. Here, were those that may still recognize him. He let his hair hang loose, and his beard down to his waist. He smeared himself thickly with ashes, covered his chest with string upon string of rudraksha beads, which are the Lord Siva's tears of mercy for the world. He carried a trisula in his hand, and walked through the streets of the blessed city as a yati, a wild Sivabhakta.

His heart played strange tricks on him. Memories from his youth, which he had thought long buried, rose, fresh and untamed, in his mind: memories of when Krishna's cousin Gada came with the other young Vrishni boys to learn archery from Drona in Hastinapura. Gada had described Krishna's sister Subhadra vividly to Arjuna. The adolescent Arjuna had fallen in love with her then, without seeing her but only from hearing Gada's warm descriptions.

Prabhasa was just a short way from Dwaraka, city in the ocean, where Krishna ruled. Arjuna the yati dreamt incessantly of his cousin, the ravishing Subhadra. In Prabhasa, she became his obsession, a sweet mania; it was as if she called him to her, subtly, irresistibly. He knew he must either escape from this country at once, or go to Dwaraka and make her his wife. Otherwise, he would lose his mind beside the sea.

At nights, Arjuna sat under a giant banyan tree at the heart of Prabhasa, pretending to be lost in dhyana, while, in fact, visions of Subhadra gave him no peace. The greatest kshatriya on earth was vanquished by an insane love: for a woman he had never set eyes on! One evening, in despair, he sat under the immense awning of the tree and began to think of Krishna. Arjuna remembered his blue cousin's parting words, as he left Indraprastha, 'Think of me, and I will come to you.'

For the first time since he arrived in Prabhasa, Arjuna actually sat meditating. Not a hundred yards away, the sea was all fluid thunder; and then it began to pour. In flashes, the setting sun also slanted his crimson and gold through the torrents of the sky. Night fell, and it rained on. Arjuna sat unmoving, soaked through, his heart frozen around one frantic desire.

FIFTY-NINE

The Raivataka hill

On Dwaraka, also, it was pouring. Waves climbed over the outer walls, and spilled into the streets of the city of miracles, which the Devas had raised in the sea for the Avatara. Krishna was with his wife Satyabhama tonight. It was past midnight, and they lay together, after love.

Then Krishna grew restless. He rose and paced the room; often going to the windows that looked out at the lashing storm outside. Satyabhama lay quiescent, watching him. Suddenly her unpredictable husband began to laugh.

"What is it, Krishna?"

"I was thinking what love does to the greatest men. My valiant cousin Arjuna has been on a pilgrimage throughout Bharatavarsha. He has purified himself at all the holiest tirthas, and now he has come to Prabhasa disguised as a yati, his beard down to his chest and jata hanging to his shoulders.

The mighty Pandava sits under an old banyan tree, soaked to the bone and staring at the sea. But it isn't a call of the spirit that has brought him to Prabhasa." He smiled in the dark, "I fear he is unhinged with love, and too shy to come seeking love's satisfaction here, in Dwaraka. So he sits drenched in the storm, and calls for my help."

"Whom does he love in Dwaraka?"

"My sister Subhadra, about whom Gada told him when he was a boy, and he has never forgotten her. Poor Arjuna suffers; let me go to him and put an end to his misery."

"Now?"

"What better time?"

He pulled on his clothes and kissing her stole out into the squally night. Satyabhama sighed, but knew better than to protest or worry about him. She turned on her side, and was soon asleep.

Thunder and lightning gashed the midnight sky over Prabhasa, and Arjuna sat numb in the furious storm. He hardly saw the jagged whiplashes of lightning; he barely heard the heartstopping thunder. He did not mind the walls of rain that fell from the dark sky, and breached the canopy of his tree. Once he began to think of Krishna, Arjuna found he had some respite from the relentless visions of Subhadra that tormented him.

A towering bolt of blue lightning briefly connected sky and earth. It fell into the sea, lighting up the swollen waves for an electric moment. Then, all was darkness again, and the thunder, which followed on winged heels of the serpent lightning, erupted among the clouds. When the last echoes of that awesome peal died, out of the perfectly black night a voice spoke to Arjuna, "I wonder, cousin, if your thoughts really suit your hermit's garb!" and the familiar laugh, full of tender mockery.

"Krishna!"

Arjuna jumped up and, next moment, they were hugging each other in the storm.

Arjuna cried, "So at last you heard I was here."

Krishna murmured, "I couldn't sleep for hearing you call me."

Seeing the amazed look on the Pandava's face, he laughed and hugged him again. Now Arjuna did not shiver with the wind that ripped across sea and land, but with the thought that his uncanny cousin may have known his other, more intimate fantasies.

"But come, we can't stand out here all night. Let me bring you closer to Dwaraka, though not yet to the city, not until tomorrow."

The Pandava allowed himself to be led to the gleaming chariot that stood nearby, a chariot he could not fathom, this night or ever. He had often imagined it flashed not only over land, but flitted through the air, as if the exotic thing belonged to another order of reality. Yet, he could never be quite certain.

They came to the Raivataka, to the side of the hill away from the storm and the sea. Krishna led Arjuna to a dry cave, and settled him there.

"For another night, then; tomorrow you will come to Dwaraka. But first, there is someone I would like you to see, here on Raivataka."

Krishna's eyes twinkled at the Pandava. "Someone I rather think you want to see yourself."

He would say no more however Arjuna pressed him. Yawning and saying that he was no yati and Satyabhama would be waiting for him in bed, Krishna went off into the night. Exhausted, but at peace, Arjuna fell asleep in the cave. He dreamt all night of a young woman he had never seen before.

When he awoke the next morning, Arjuna went down to a stream that sprang nearby. He bathed in the crisp water, and, standing in the swift flow, performed Suryanamaskara. As he left the stream, he heard voices round the corner of a rough trail that wound its way to the summit of Raivataka. They were full of cheer that the sky had cleared so miraculously; last night, they had been certain there would be no feast today.

"Krishna made the storm pass!" said one young man who had come to prepare for the feast.

Arjuna hid from the Yadavas. He skirted the path and climbed above them. He hid behind a boulder perched conveniently above the flat clearing where the feast was to be. He sat watching the Vrishnis at their outing. The view from here was spectacular, out over a smoky sea stretching away to the curved horizon. The air had been washed so clean by the night's rain, Arjuna fancied he could see out of this world into other realms.

The clearing below him, on the hill's broad shoulder, was obviously a favourite spot for the Yadavas. There was a temple at the heart of the clearing, and around it pavilions for a banquet in the open. There were rows of stone tables and seats, on which the servants sent in advance now laid plates of silver, and cushions of down and silk. Other Yadavas arrived, and, with them, mule-carts laden with piles of fragrant food. Quickly, the tables were heaped with all sorts of delicacies, as the mild sun rose higher.

Arjuna heard singing round the corner of the path, and the tinkling of women's anklets. Peering around his rock, he saw a small throng of Yadava women. They were dressed for the occasion, and carried lamps and offerings for the deity in the little temple. They were resplendent in the sun. When Arjuna saw the young woman who led the others up the winding path, his chest grew tight and he felt short of breath. She pierced him like a streak of last night's lightning. All his daydreams about Subhadra vanished: Arjuna was on fire for this young beauty, whoever she was.

The Pandava almost fell on to the path when, suddenly, a laconic voice said behind him, "I fear, my good Yati, the thoughts in your heart don't suit your hermit's garb at all."

Krishna stood smiling at him. How he had climbed here, Arjuna could not imagine. The only way was the one by which the Pandava had hauled himself up; and he would certainly have seen his cousin if he had come that way. Behind Arjuna's back was a sheer cliff that fell a hundred feet. But this was Krishna, and one quickly learnt not to inquire too closely what he did, or how. Moreover, Arjuna only had just the one question that came tumbling out the moment he saw Krishna.

"Who is she?" he whispered desperately.

"Who?" asked Krishna, innocently.

"She who leads the puja," breathed the Pandava.

Krishna laughed softly. "That is my half-sister Subhadra. She is Balarama's sister. You like her, do you, Arjuna?"

Arjuna clutched Krishna's hand and said hoarsely, "I love her! I love her so much it makes me mad just to look at her. I feel as if my body and soul are on fire. I must marry her, Krishna, and you must help me."

Arjuna's eyes never left the lovely Subhadra below, as she performed the arati to the God in the temple. Krishna smiled, "Ah, poor Yati, you are truly lost. I will help you, isn't that my dharma? Come, climb down from here when no one can see you and go back to your cave. Sit there in dhyana, deep dhyana, Yati!" He paused. "Until you are discovered. Then be brave: give no sign of who you are to anyone or your cause is lost. Not even Balarama will recognize you as long as you do not give yourself away. Be perfectly calm, Arjuna, and watch what happens."

The Blue One gave a sigh. "After all, of the different kinds of marriage, the one of love is the highest. You must make her fall in love with you, as you have with her. I will go and mingle with the others. You sit very still in your cave, with your eyes shut, as if you have seen or heard nothing. Lost in samadhi, Arjuna, which should not be too hard, seeing how you have someone to meditate on now.

"My brother Balarama is the man for you, he can never resist a holy yati."

SIXTY

The holy yati

THE NEXT INSTANT, KRISHNA HAD VANISHED, AND ARJUNA COULDN'T fathom how he had gone. Shaking his head, he crept down to the cave, which lay below him and round a bend in the path to the little temple. Unobserved, he settled himself just within the cave-mouth, crossing his legs in the lotus posture. He held his trident in his hand, shut his eyes, and, apparently, he was lost in dhyana.

Beyond the bend in the path, the feast was underway; but soon, Balarama came down the trail alone. He saw the yati, and ran to him with a cry.

'Swami!'

The yati sat motionless, and it seemed, unaware of Balarama. Krishna's brother stood silently before the marvellously wild-looking yati. He saw how handsome the young hermit was, his body ash-smeared and bright with tapasya, years of it no doubt. His hair was tangled and unkempt, and his beard hung down over his chest. Though masked with ashes, his face was noble and serene. Balarama stood rapt, a worshipful smile on his lips.

Kritavarman, Samba, Pradyumna, Gada, and some others came down the path, calling Balarama's name. He turned and raised his finger to his lips: couldn't they see the yati was in deep meditation? They, too, gathered curiously round the ascetic.

For a while, the tapasvin did not stir, though inwardly Arjuna trembled lest any of his cousins recognized him: not the youngsters but Gada, Balarama himself, or one of the others who had studied archery with

Drona in Hastinapura. In a while, he realized none of them had, because of the beard and the ashes.

Arjuna sniffed the air to show he had become aware of them. He sighed, as if he was emerging from samadhi, the soul's trance. He fluttered open his eyes, and smiled slightly at the Yadavas. In fact, he longed to laugh at their faces, but a flaring thought of Subhadra prevented him from folly.

With a cry, Balarama prostrated himself at the yati's feet.

"Welcome to Anarta, holy one! We are blessed that you have come."

Arjuna only smiled, as beatifically as he could, and prayed none of them would see through his disguise. Gada was already staring at him. Yet, when Balarama rose after the yati had blessed him, Gada, and, one by one, all the other Yadavas prostrated themselves before him. Arjuna blessed them all, giving each one a pinch of ash he scraped off his skin.

Seized with reverence, and certain he had seen the yati before in his dreams, Balarama cried, "May we ask from whence your holiness has come? And how long you intend to stay?"

Arjuna gave a loud sigh: of relief, but it passed for a sigh of regret at being disturbed. The Yadavas quailed a little. The yatis, especially the Sivabhaktas among them, were known for the virulence of their tempers and their devastating curses. Fortunately, this one seemed amiable.

He now spoke in a rough voice. "I have travelled over the world. I have seen countless tirthas, and never have I spent more than three nights at any of them, even the holiest. Now the monsoon is here. Clouds for tonight's downpour already fill the horizon. I fear I will not be able to move on until the rains have passed. But I shall be happy on Raivataka; four months of rain will pass like four days, while I sit in dhyana."

Just then, someone else came round the bend in the path, whistling like a tree full of birds. It was perfect timing. Balarama cried, "Look Krishna, the holy one has come to us on the day of our feast!"

"And not a cloud in the sky, since he came," murmured Krishna, with a grin.

"Take his blessing!" hissed his older brother.

Krishna touched the yati's feet, and received his pinch of ashes. Balarama said reverently, "He has ranged the world before he came to us. He means to spend the monsoon on Raivataka, but I am not happy leaving him here. Water will flow into the cave, and even a bolt of lightning may fall on him, as he sits in samadhi. You are always the bright one, Krishna; what shall we do?"

Willing himself not to laugh, Krishna said, "Who am I to give my older brother advice on a religious matter? You must decide what we must do with the swami."

Balarama swelled up, and said quickly, "I have it! Virgins should serve holy men: it brings them noble husbands later. Let the yati stay in Subhadra's garden, and let her see to his needs till the rains last."

To Arjuna's amazement, Krishna stiffened, whispered to Balarama, "A word in private please, brother," and led him outside.

"What is it, Krishna?" Balarama was impatient to install the yati in Subhadra's garden.

"Is it safe to have the stranger living near our sister? Remember we know nothing about him. He is a bit smooth-tongued for my liking. His body is too soft to have known too much penance." Krishna shook his head doubtfully, "Subhadra is young, and the yati is just the sort to impress her. But of course, you have already thought of that."

Balarama was livid, exactly as Krishna knew he would be. "How dare you think of the yati with such wretched suspicion? Are you blind, Krishna? The light of the atman shines from him, and you are worried about Subhadra. I should make you beg his forgiveness. But I will let it pass if you take him to our sister's palace, and tell her to look after him."

Now the other Yadavas came out to the brothers. Krishna turned to them, smiling. "Good works should never be delayed! Come with me Pradyumna, and you, Gada. Let us take the holy one to Subhadra."

He went and bowed to the yati again, and, with a wink, said, "Swami, I beg you, come with me to my sister's garden. We have decided you must stay there until the monsoon passes. I am sure she will become devoted to your worship, and see to all your needs, whatever they are. If you are pleased with her, only give her a vara at the end of your stay."

Vara, of course, meant both boon and husband; but none of the Yadavas dreamt Krishna referred to the second meaning. Pradyumna and Gada went down the Raivataka with Krishna and the yati, and then in their chariots to Dwaraka. His first sight of Dwaraka by the afternoon sun transfixed Arjuna: not even Indraprastha could compare with it.

Like the dream of a God, the ocean-city rose from the waves, her mansions shining, her terraces and ramparts reaching for the sky. Her outer walls were smooth as glass, like a hallucination by the setting sun. The yati caught his breath audibly, and the Yadavas glowed with pride.

Krishna asked, "Do you like our city, my lord Yati?"

The yati replied softly, "Indeed, my son, yours is the most beautiful city I have seen in all my wanderings. Why, it seems Indra's Amravati has fallen out of Devaloka and into the sea of Bharata."

"I hope you will be happy in Dwaraka."

"We shall see what fate has in store for me."

At the edge of the sea a gleaming bridge rose out of the waves, a yojana long and made, it seemed, of fine crystal; but the chariots passed lightly over it and into wondrous Dwaraka. As they rode through the tall gates, Arjuna felt he was truly on the inside of a dream. Even more dreamlike than Indraprastha's were the streets and stately homes here, and the people were all as majestic as the kshatriyas with whom he rode. They waved as the chariots sped along towards Krishna's palace, which by itself was another city within Dwaraka. Here, his legendary harem of a thousand queens was housed, each one in a different palace, and each, it was rumoured, with her very own Krishna!

The yati was overwhelmed, but kept his composure. When they arrived at the Blue God's palace, Pradyumna and Gada left Arjuna with Krishna, who led him up white marble steps and down wonderful passages. At his apartment, Krishna instructed his guards that under no circumstances were the yati and he to be disturbed.

Entering, and arriving at the polished door to an inner chamber, Krishna knocked. Two bewitching women opened that door. Krishna drew Arjuna inside, to the amazement of Satyabhama and Rukmini: he had never brought a sannyasi into their apartment before. He tended to keep all holy men at a distance saying that most of them were common rogues, these days. Now, he not only brought this utterly wild-looking yati right in, but shut the door after him. Krishna stood beaming, as if he had done something quite special.

In his teasing way, he said to his wives, "Go on, bow to the swami. Can't you see what a great man he is? He has roamed all the sea-girt earth before coming to Dwaraka, and you don't even care to take his blessing?"

Knowing there was some mischief afoot, but helpless, Satyabhama and Rukmini prostrated themselves at the yati's feet. He grunted, and, scraping two pinches of ash from his chest gave it to them.

Krishna broke into peals of laughter. He flung his arms round Arjuna and cried, "Ah, women, women! Don't you know who this is? You have heard so much about him: from me, from all the Vrishnis who have been Drona's disciples. Why, his name is a legend in Dwaraka, and you still don't..."

Both lovely queens cried together, "Arjuna! Welcome to Dwaraka!"

Rukmini asked, "But why the yati's attire, Arjuna? Why do you hide your handsome face with a beard and ashes?"

Krishna said, "The good yati has fallen in love with our sister Subhadra, and wants to win her hand in secret. So, we will take his holiness to her private garden, and she shall attend to his every need, just as my brother Balarama wants her to."

The women laughed, excited at the thought. Satyabhama said, "You will find no better brother-in-law in all Bharatavarsha!"

"I could not agree more: which is why, my good queens, we must take our swami to Subhadra immediately, and leave him in her tender care so he can work his charm on her. Our cousin has no time for the likes of us; his heart is elsewhere, and we must convey him thence."

Arjuna was the solemn yati again, as Krishna led him through the amazing passages once more, some winding their way through the palace itself, and some, elegantly covered, through shady gardens under the sun. At last, they arrived at a secluded quarter of the queens' harem, and a mansion that stood apart.

Krishna gave Arjuna a moment to compose himself, before he knocked on the ornate door to Subhadra's palace and walked in with a nervous yati in tow. Soon, Subhadra herself stood before them, even more ravishing so near. Arjuna's heart drummed out of control, and the yati had lost his voice.

At first, Subhadra saw only Krishna, and cried gaily, "Well, this is a surprise! To what do I owe this rare pleasure?"

Krishna stood aside, so she saw the yati behind him. Subhadra did not know why, but her heart gave a lurch, as the holy man stared at her so strangely. Krishna allowed that moment to sink in, and it seemed the yati and the princess were locked into each other's gazes, and could not stop staring.

Krishna coughed softly. "Swami, this is my sister. Subhadra, the yati has roamed all the earth, and been gracious enough to accept our hospitality for as long as the rains last. Balarama told me to bring him to you; he asks you to look after his every need, to anticipate them if you can. Our brother says that he has never met anyone as holy as his worship."

For once, the feisty Subhadra seemed to have lost her tongue. She still stood staring at the yati, who did not take his eyes from the princess' face. Finally, Subhadra said, "Of course I will look after the holy one. Come, Swami, let me show you to my garden where you can stay. A part of it is roofed and the rain will not bother you."

Krishna said, "We are honoured by your visit to our city. Don't be shy, my lord; ask Subhadra for whatever you want, and she will be happy to give it to you."

Arjuna gave a start at Krishna's tone, and the images it conjured in his lovesick mind. Folding his hands to the yati, with a cheery wave at Subhadra, Krishna went off leaving them together.

SIXTY-ONE

The yati and the princess

THE DAYS OF THIS MONSOON WERE THE HAPPIEST ARJUNA HAD known in a long time. True, Draupadi was his first love; yet, Panchali did not belong only to him, but his brothers as well. Arjuna had changed during his lonely journey through Bharatavarsha. It was the first time he had been apart from his brothers and his mother for so long. He had grown to become a man, his own man.

Subhadra found herself drawn powerfully to the yati; but he was an ascetic, and sworn to brahmacharya. Any woman was an obstacle on his chosen path: she could only impede his progress. Yet, despite herself, Subhadra felt an impossible attraction for him.

She wanted to be with him, as much as she could; she told herself she was only carrying out her brothers' instructions. If her heart beat faster than she had ever known it to, when she was near the yati, or when she caught him looking at her from across the garden with his intense eyes, that was her affair. She could not help herself, and she was the only one who knew about it.

Did the yati know, or suspect, how she felt? She could not tell; but she noticed that, whenever she was in the garden, he did not meditate but turned his gaze on her. Once or twice, she fancied he stared at her in a most wanton manner; but then, she knew better.

At first, crowds of people would come to Subhadra's garden to meet the yati. Balarama told everyone he saw to go and seek this sannyasi's blessing. Arjuna grew annoyed at the lines that formed outside the princess' palace. He complained to Krishna, and the Dark One forbade any more visitors. He said the yati must have time for the tapasya for which he had come, which would bless them all if only they would leave him to it.

Uncannily, those first few days when the people came, real miracles did occur in Dwaraka: the sick were healed, the despondent regained cheer. Balarama said triumphantly to Krishna, "Didn't I tell you at one look he was a holy man? And you were worried to leave him alone with Subhadra!"

When word of his own powers filtered back to Arjuna, he was puzzled. Then he realized the miracles must be Krishna's doing. He was relieved when Krishna announced the yati had taken mowna, a vow of silence, to pray for the world.

Another name was renowned in Dwaraka, long before the yati arrived: the name of Arjuna the Pandava was a legend in the city of the Yadavas. In schools of archery, youngsters were told, "You must become as good as Arjuna."

"If you are half the archer Arjuna is, you will be a great bowman."

When children fought among themselves, they would puff up their chests and cry, "Not even Arjuna is as good as I am! What chance does a worm like you stand against me?"

When Yadava elders blessed their grandchildren, they would lay a hand on the young ones' heads and say, "May you grow up to be like Arjuna."

When a woman was expecting a child, the older women of the family would crack their knuckles against their heads, to ward off the evil eye, and say, "May you have a son like Arjuna!"

It was in this city Subhadra had grown up, and she had been infatuated with Arjuna ever since she could remember. When she was a little older, Krishna would tell her about their cousin: how noble he was, and how lovable, because there was still a child in him though he was such a great kshatriya. Then, there was her cousin Gada who knew Arjuna since he was a boy. Gada painted the Pandava in the most romantic colours. This was not out of any sense of mischief: Gada implicitly believed these cousins of his were born for each other.

Rukmini of Vidarbha had fallen in love with Krishna before she ever laid eyes on him. So it was with Subhadra: she had given her heart to

Arjuna. Since she was a girl, she would make it a point to meet any traveller from the north, at first from Hastinapura, and later from Indraprastha. She would press them for any scraps she could glean about her secret flame. She knew the Pandavas had married Draupadi; but this only excited her strangely, and she loved Arjuna even more. She would lie awake at night, tormenting herself with visions of the dark Panchali in his arms. It was delicious torment.

So now, when she felt these powerful stirrings whenever she was near the mysterious yati, Subhadra was dismayed. After all, her heart had been given long ago, to Arjuna. She told herself her frustrated love for Arjuna had turned into a spiritual inclination. If she could not have the Pandava, she would renounce the world: hence, her attraction for the yati.

One day she sat with the yati, in a companionable silence. She had just brought him his morning meal, and she sat daydreaming of Arjuna. She had developed this queer habit since the yati came to her garden; whenever she was with him, she found her mind turned ineluctably to thoughts of Arjuna.

Suddenly, she realized why this was so: she had begun to impose the image of the yati onto her fantasies of Arjuna! She gave a shiver when she caught herself doing this. Then, it struck her, *'What if he is Arjuna?'*

Near her the yati sat very still, breathing evenly, smiling slightly from a deep wellbeing that might have been mistaken for spiritual bliss. In fact, he was surreptitiously inhaling the delicate scent of her body, and was intoxicated with it. She was glad that, today, he had not turned his burning gaze on her; then, she would grow confused and breathless, and excuse herself quickly. This morning the yati was serene, and she could gaze comfortably at him out of the tail of her eye.

She gazed, and she thought, 'All the descriptions I've heard of Arjuna fit the yati perfectly, except for the beard and the jata.'

She tried to imagine him without the beard and jata: he could well be Arjuna! Subhadra looked at the yati's chest. It was a warrior's deep chest, and his arms were muscled, too strong to be a brahmana's arms. She looked raptly at him, the conviction growing on her that he was Arjuna; which would explain so much, especially her own feelings. His shawl slipped from his shoulders, and she almost cried out when she saw abrasions not just on one arm, but on both: marks of a bowstring! Subhadra knew Arjuna was ambidextrous.

Then, she told herself angrily, 'Arjuna is no sannyasi! I am losing my mind over this yati. He cannot be Arjuna, however much I would like him to.'

Yet, the nagging suspicions, or hope, persisted. One day, unable to bear it any more, she decided to have this thing out with the disturbing hermit.

"Swami, they say you have travelled the length and breadth of Bharatavarsha. Tell me about some of the places you saw, specially the tirthas."

It was a beginning. In good time, she would steer the conversation round to the matter in her heart. As Krishna had warned Balarama, the yati was an eloquent man. He was happy to describe his wanderings through the land of Bharata, dwelling on each tirtha he had visited and the journey to it. At least, she was near him while he kept this up.

It became a habit with both of them: after the morning meal, Subhadra sat with the yati, and he described every outlandish place to which he had been. She grew more absorbed than ever in the yati. Occasionally, she would ask him a probing question, and he would answer with a smile. He did not realize where this was leading, until one morning, out of the blue she asked, "My lord, have you ever been to Indraprastha?"

He gave a slight start. "I have been in marvellous Indraprastha."

"Do you know the king Yudhishtira and his mother? Kunti Devi is our aunt, and the Pandavas are our cousins."

"Indeed, I know them well," said the yati quietly.

Not looking at him, Subhadra said, "I hear my cousin Arjuna is on a pilgrimage not unlike your own. Have you perhaps encountered him on your travels?"

The yati seemed to hesitate for a moment. Then he turned to face her. "I know Arjuna. If you are curious about him, I can tell you where he is at this moment, and why."

He was staring at her, and she felt weak. In a low voice, she asked, "Where is he?"

For another interminable moment, the yati waited, still staring as if he would drink her into his soul with his eyes. Then, he whispered, "Arjuna has fallen in love with the most beautiful woman in the world, and he has disguised himself as a yati to be near her."

Subhadra began to tremble. He leaned forward quickly and took her hand. "Haven't you known me yet, my love? I am Arjuna. Subhadra, marry me! I can't live without you."

He pulled her to him and kissed her like fire. With a cry, she jumped up and fled.

From that day, Subhadra fell ill. She stayed in her bed, burning with fever. She was listless and anxious, as if she had a deep shock, or as if she stood at some yawning threshold of her life and was terrified to cross it.

When the princess no longer came out to see him in the garden, Arjuna confessed to Krishna what had happened. Krishna felt it was best if he did not meet her for some time. He consoled the Pandava, saying all the signs were favourable: Subhadra also certainly loved him, but he must be patient for a few days.

The next day, Krishna set a subtle plan in motion. He sent Rukmini to meet Arjuna. When the yati saw a woman's figure approaching him across the cloistered garden, he thought it was Subhadra. He jumped up and ran to her; his face fell when Rukmini uncovered her head.

Rukmini laughed. "I am sorry to disappoint you, holy one! I have come to tell you that Subhadra is unwell, and wastes from a mysterious illness that no physician in Dwaraka can fathom. Perhaps, a yati has the remedy for my sister-in-law's illness? Krishna thinks you do."

A teasing smile never left her face, and poor Arjuna felt acutely embarrassed.

Now she said more seriously, "Krishna asks you to be ready to abduct our Subhadra. He will let you know when." She flashed another smile. "I didn't know that holy yatis kidnapped young women!"

And Rukmini left Arjuna alone and terribly restless.

SIXTY-TWO

Cure for an illness

THE WOMEN OF THE PALACE IN DWARAKA WERE ANXIOUS ABOUT Subhadra. No one knew what the real cause of her sickness was. Krishna's mother Devaki was the most worried. For ten days Subhadra hardly ate, nor spoke a word to anyone, but lay in her bed staring glassily out of the window, or at a burning taper at nights.

One day, Devaki called Krishna and Balarama.

"I am at my wits' end about Subhadra. None of the physicians knows what the matter with her is. Oh, Krishna, what shall we do?"

She began to sob. Krishna took her hand, "Mother, let us go to Sankhodara and spend a fortnight praying to Lord Siva. Someone has cursed us, and the curse has fallen on Subhadra. I am sure a Rudra puja will see her well again."

Devaki agreed. Balarama went off to arrange for the trip, and tell the boatmen of Dwaraka to be ready. Krishna went to see Subhadra. He sent her women out of the sickroom and, taking her hand, whispered, "We are going to Sankhodara to perform a Rudra puja for you. We shall be gone a fortnight. The twelfth day from today is an auspicious day, my sweet sister: for you to marry the man you love!"

She gasped. Krishna stroked her cheek. "There is no other cure for love, my child. You must go with your heart; and don't be afraid, he loves you as well."

Kissing her gently, he left her. Krishna went out into Subhadra's garden where the yati sat with his eyes shut, seeing only the face that haunted him. He, too, had hardly slept since he confessed his love to her, ten days ago. She had never come back to see him since, and he did not dare ask for her. He knew she was unwell, and no one had discovered what her sickness was. Arjuna was worried; where was Krishna when he needed him most? It seemed the Blue One had left him to his own devices, to suffer.

Thus, when Krishna appeared beside him that day, the yati began to babble his woes to his cousin. Krishna laid a hand on his shoulder to quieten him, as he might with an excited child. Sitting beside the yati on the clipped grass, he said, "There is to be a puja on the island of Sankhodara. We shall all be gone for a fortnight."

He saw the alarm in Arjuna's eyes, and continued, "Only my sister Subhadra will remain behind in Dwaraka. She isn't well enough to travel."

He paused, and the yati clutched his arm. Krishna was smiling now, in his teasing way. "I am told by my brahmanas that the twelfth day from today is very auspicious. They said to me it is particularly suited for a gandharva vivaha."

It took a moment for what he said to sink in. The yati's eyes shone. Krishna went on, "I'll leave my own chariot for you. Carry her away, Arjuna! It's something a kshatriya may do without dishonour. Besides, at least one of the bride's brothers approves.

"I mustn't stay too long now, or I will be of no use to you later, when the Yadavas want to take arms against you for kidnapping our sister. I fear my brother Balarama will be the most incensed of all, that yet again that lofty intelligence of his has led him straight into trouble."

Laughing at the thought and hugging Arjuna, Krishna left. The next day, Balarama came to the yati and prostrated himself at his feet. "We are leaving for Sankhodara today to perform a puja to Rudra. Bless us, Swami."

The yati laid his palm on Balarama's head, and if that hand shook slightly, it was from an urge to burst out laughing. Balarama said, "Have a care for my sister while we are away, O Yati. As long as you are here, I am not afraid to leave her behind."

The yati said gravely, "I pray for her at every sandhya. My prayers have never gone unanswered yet."

"I thank you, Swami! It is our good fortune that you came to us, or I dare not think what would have happened to my sister. I am certain your presence has already prevented the worst."

"The curse upon her is powerful, it drains even my strength. It is best you go to Sankhodara quickly, and petition Lord Rudra. I am sure your sister will have recovered when you return."

Balarama bowed again, and left without turning his back on the yati.

Thus, the yati and the princess he loved were more or less alone in Dwaraka. For ten days after the Yadavas' departure, they saw nothing of each other. But at midnight of the eleventh, Subhadra heard a furtive scraping at her window. She leapt out of bed, stepped over a maid sleeping on the floor, and was at the window in a trice.

She caught her breath when she saw the yati's face framed in the moonlight. He smiled so tenderly at her that her malaise left her just to see him. When he reached for it, she gave him her hand. His eyes were so full of concern she was relieved: for, every other time, she had seen only desire in them.

Gently he said, "Oh, my love, you shouldn't torment yourself like this. I have always loved you, since I was a boy."

Finding courage now, she replied shyly, "And I have loved you, Arjuna, since I can remember."

He kissed her hand fervently. "It is time for the guard to change, and we mustn't risk being caught tonight. Bring a chariot to the garden gate tomorrow, and we will never be apart again. I am told you are as much of a rathika as I am. You take the reins so I have my hands free for the bow Krishna left me."

He saw her eyes glistened with tears. She bit her lip, and nodded bravely. "An hour before noon, I will be there."

Impulsively, she raised his hand to her lips and kissed it. Then she vanished back into the room. Slowly, he went back to the moon-drenched garden, but he knew he would not sleep.

Subhadra did not sleep much either; but her sickness was gone, as if the yati's touch had cured her. She lay awake, the wonder of her love kindled. She did not try to resist it, but allowed it to fill her body like a new life. Subhadra was not frightened or ill any more: she was a woman who knew what she wanted. She could not wait for the sun to rise and

Arjuna to carry her away. It took all her restraint not to go out to him in the garden at once.

The sun rose, at last, after a long night for the lovers. To the delight of the women of the palace, the princess Subhadra seemed to have recovered from her sickness. She was up at dawn. She bathed, dressed in fresh clothes and wore flowers in her hair. Once more, she took his morning meal out to the yati and spent some time alone with him. The women said among themselves that it was surely a miracle: the puja at Sankhodara had worked.

An hour before noon, Subhadra announced her intention to go for a drive around the ocean-city. Her sakhis told her Krishna had left his horses and chariot for her.

"Which horses?" asked Subhadra, who knew all of them by name.

"Saibya, Sugriva, Valahaka and Meghapushpa."

The princess smiled; her brother had left his favourite steeds for her. She said, "Have them yoked, and the chariot brought to the garden gate. I must tell the yati I am going out."

Meanwhile, in the room at the bottom of the garden, a transformation not far short of the supernatural had come over the yati. He stood in front of a silver mirror, inspecting how he looked on the day of his wild wedding, his gandharva vivaha. The matted jata was shorn, the beard shaved. The unkempt appearance had vanished, and the saffron robes been discarded. Wearing the prince's silks given to him by Krishna, dashing Arjuna of Indraprastha stared back at him from the polished silver.

His face was older than it had been when he last saw it beardless. Otherwise, it was him all right: Kunti's son Arjuna, the Pandava. Satisfied, he turned away from the mirror. He lit a lamp in the corner of that room and, kneeling before it, laid his brow on the floor in worship. Then he heard the clatter of horses' hooves on the road outside, and Subhadra calling, "Come Yati, I am ready for you!"

Arjuna emerged, and Subhadra's women's mouths fell open when they saw a glorious kshatriya striding from the room into which the dishevelled hermit had gone. One of them breathed, "It's Arjuna!"

They bowed to him, giggling, because they knew what had happened. He went calmly to the street and climbed into the chariot beside Subhadra.

With a cry, she cracked her whip and the fine horses flashed forward, making straight for the gates of Dwaraka. The drawbridge lay across the waves, and in moments, the lovers were out of the ocean-city, on the mainland and flying north towards Indraprastha.

SIXTY-THREE

Balarama's anger

THE GUARDS AT DWARAKA'S GATES SAW THE CHARIOT FLIT PAST them. Thinking the princess was being abducted by the dashing kshatriya, they tried to stop the ratha; but they did not give chase because the kshatriya looked dangerous. Then, again, he could not be abducting the princess: she held the horses' reins and whipped them to go faster. No doubt, they would return by evening.

Evening came, and there was no sign of Subhadra or the prince. Word spread through Dwaraka that the yati Balarama had brought into Subhadra's garden was Arjuna, and the Pandava had eloped with the princess. They said he had taken her for his wife in gandharva vivaha, which was rare, but acceptable.

A small company of soldiers was dispatched to Sankhodara. They rode a way up the mainland and blew on conches and horns. On the island, the Yadavas heard these and, winding up their puja since the alarm they heard was for extreme danger, rowed back immediately to Dwaraka.

At the city-gates, a nervous guard commander broke the news stammeringly to Balarama. Balarama's roar shook the walls of the ocean-city; it made the guardsmen turn pale. The great Vrishni turned on his brother. Balarama was shaking. He knew he had been made a fool of, and he knew who had made a fool of him.

"Krishna!" he roared. "You did this!"

The Blue One was prepared for the attack: he looked aghast at the accusation. "I did this? Who warned you about the yati on Raivataka?

Who said it would not be wise to keep him in Subhadra's garden? Let me remind you: it was I. I said he was too handsome and smooth-tongued to be trusted. But someone scoffed at my fears, and was furious that I dared suspect the yati. That was you, my lord. This is entirely your doing!"

Balarama howled at this. His eyes crimson, he said in a softer voice, "I am your brother, and I have known you since we were children in Vrindavana. You can deceive the world, but not me. Ah, Krishna, what have you done this time?"

Krishna shrugged. Balarama cried, "But perhaps it is not too late. If we fly towards Indraprastha, we can overtake them before they arrive. I will kill Arjuna and his brothers, and burn their city down. Fetch my chariot, I will ride alone!"

The guard commander ran to obey him. Now Krishna knew there was real danger. When his slow brother was roused, no one could stop him, except perhaps Krishna himself. He laid a hand on Balarama's arm, "You mustn't be so angry, they are our cousins. Let us think calmly about what has happened."

He led Balarama to a sea-swept stone seat, and, perching at his side, said, "You think Arjuna abducted Subhadra; but from what we hear, this isn't quite true. Our sister called for the chariot, and the guards all agree that she held the reins, not he. Shan't we seem fools, if we take war to the Pandavas and discover Subhadra went willingly with Arjuna?"

He paused, then mused, "And, if you think about it, our sister has made off with the finest kshatriya on earth."

Balarama growled to disagree, but he was beginning to calm down. Krishna went on, "Arjuna is a prince of the House of Kuru, a descendant of Manu and Bharata. His mother is our aunt, and his natural father, Indra himself. I take his love for Subhadra not as an insult, but an honour.

As for his valour, apart from you perhaps, there is no one on earth like Arjuna."

Krishna did not say it in so many words, but the implication was there: if Balarama pursued Arjuna, and the Pandava defeated him in battle, the honour of the Yadavas would be in tatters. And the outcome of a duel between his brother and their cousin need not be a foregone conclusion in Balarama's favour.

Balarama was breathing more evenly now; the angry glitter had left his eye. He saw reason in what Krishna said, though he still suspected his brother had contrived the entire escapade.

Krishna said, "There is no dishonour to anyone in a peaceful solution. Let us send after Arjuna and Subhadra, and have them married in Dwaraka. Subhadra will be happy, and Arjuna; so will the Pandavas, the Yadavas and I." He smiled. "And I am sure you will be happy as well."

For a moment, Balarama hesitated; then he also broke into a smile. "Ah, you are right as usual! But I am certain you planned this whole thing."

The resentment had gone from his voice. The big Yadava was most of all a good-natured man, and as long as there was no dishonour in what had happened, he was content to have Arjuna and Subhadra brought back and married formally. So, when the guard commander returned with his chariot, Balarama said to him, "Ride, my friend! Catch up with Arjuna and Subhadra and fetch them back to Dwaraka. Say that Krishna and Balarama want to see them married properly. Tell them we bear Arjuna no grudge, and we are happy at our sister's choice of a husband. Fly! Or they will pass out of your reach."

The surprised guard commander looked nervously at Krishna. When the Dark One nodded, he saluted them both briskly and rode off like a sea-wind after the princess and her abductor. Or was it the other way, and she was the abductress?

Meanwhile, once the lovers had ridden beyond the borders of Krishna's kingdom, Anarta, they slowed. They stopped the chariot often to kiss. When desire blazed too high, they would ride again, while the wind cooled their ardour. Then, they would slow and embrace. They could hardly wait for night to fall, so they could wrap themselves in covers of darkness and make love in the wilderness. After all, they were man and wife now by gandharva vivaha, the ritual of abduction.

The guard commander from Dwaraka caught up with the lovers' chariot. Arjuna heard him long before he came into view, and the Pandava waited with his bow in his hand. But the soldier came in peace, and when Arjuna saw he came alone he lowered his weapon.

The guardsman jumped down from his chariot, and folded his hands. The friendly soldier cried, "Felicitations to you both! I bring greetings from my lords Balarama and Krishna. They beg you to return to Dwaraka and be married with proper ceremony."

Subhadra asked, "Is my brother Balarama not angry?"

"He was at first, princess. But Krishna spoke to him, and now he is keen that you return and stay as man and wife in our city."

Arjuna said, "Tell my cousins we will spend tonight in the wilds, for we wish to be alone. Tomorrow we will return, and be married formally in Dwaraka. Nothing will please me more."

Bowing, the soldier climbed back into his chariot, and rode back to Dwaraka with the wind whistling around him. When he arrived, preparations were already in full swing, and the ocean-city was being decked out like a bride herself for the occasion. Krishna had been certain that, if sued with peace, Arjuna would return.

The young lovers spent the night of their gandharva vivaha in a familiar cave on Raivataka, where Arjuna had first seen the woman of his dreams without knowing who she was. The moon peered in on their sweet exertions through the cave-mouth.

SIXTY-FOUR

Draupadi's anger

THE NEXT DAY, ARJUNA AND SUBHADRA RODE BACK INTO THE OCEAN-city to a warm welcome. Balarama had forgotten his anger and greeted Arjuna with a huge embrace. The Yadava bowed elaborately, crying, "Bless me, Swami! We are honoured you have returned to our midst."

The kalyana mantapa for the wedding had been erected on the outer walls of Dwaraka, and the sea smashed against them a hundred hands below. With solemn ceremony, Subhadra, princess of the Yadavas, was married to Arjuna the Pandava. Krishna joked to his cousins, but out of Balarama's hearing, that it was amazing indeed to see a couple marry twice in two days, and once after they had spent a night together.

But the people of Dwaraka were overjoyed to have their princess married to the kshatriya who was such a legend among them. It was a romance unparalleled since their own Krishna carried Rukmini away on the day she was to marry Sishupala. The Yadavas were pleased at the new bond with the sons of Kunti, who was after all one of them: a Vrishni herself. This marriage would bring fortune to both kingdoms, and the sons born to Arjuna and Subhadra would be magnificent kshatriyas.

Arjuna remained in Dwaraka for a year after he married Subhadra. When the year was over, and only one last twelve-month remained of his exile, he felt the need to return to the wilds and live in solitude once more. Since his exile was a punishment, as well, he thought he should spend its final months away from the luxury of palace life in Dwaraka, and the Yadavas' lavish hospitality. A year in the forest would also prepare Subhadra for her new life in Indraprastha.

Subhadra and Arjuna were in love; the time they spent in a little asrama in Pushkara, which is sacred to Lord Brahma, passed like a dream. A year flew by and it was time to return to Indraprastha. Arjuna thought of Draupadi, and he feared her anger when he took Subhadra home. Though Panchali had five husbands, she had never forgotten which Pandava won her at her swayamvara: the one who had shot the spinning fish. Just a shade more than the others, always, Draupadi loved Arjuna, and she was possessive of him.

It was the end of spring, when Arjuna rode into Indraprastha with Subhadra. They had worn simple, rustic clothes in Pushkara, to go unnoticed, and were now dressed as a gypsy cowherd and his wife. Yudhishtira, Bheema, Nakula and Sahadeva came to the palace-steps to receive them.

"Arjuna!" cried Yudhishtira, and raised him up when he knelt at his feet. Tears in his eyes, the king embraced his brother. Then Subhadra knelt before him; Yudhishtira blessed her, a little awkwardly.

Meanwhile, Bheema enfolded Arjuna in a hug and would not release his brother. "How we have missed you!" cried the titan. "And here you are at last, and come home with such a lovely wife."

Bheema whispered to Arjuna, "You had better be warned, Panchali is beside herself with jealousy."

Then the twins were hugging their brother. Sahadeva cried, "But don't wait here any longer. Mother is impatient to see you, and Draupadi, too; though she has been in a black mood since she heard you married Subhadra."

Nakula said, "We have word from Dwaraka. Krishna and Balarama are coming here soon."

Arjuna took Subhadra in to Kunti's apartment. His mother had been waiting. She rose with a cry, and he fell at her feet. She raised him up and clasped him to her. Then she asked, "Where is she? Where is my little niece?"

Subhadra had never seen her aunt, and now she had become her daughter-in-law. Shyly, she entered the room, still wearing her gopika's clothes. Kunti hugged her as if she was her own daughter. She made her sit beside her, and gave her the silks and jewels, and all the special things she had kept for her since she heard the news.

Kunti kissed Subhadra again and again, crying, "How lovely she is, a jewel from the sea!"

Then, she was grave, and called Arjuna to sit near her. Kunti said softly, as if she was afraid she might be overheard, "Panchali has been angry since she heard. She hardly eats, or speaks to anyone. You must be tactful with her; she imagines the worst, especially since Subhadra is your cousin."

Arjuna blanched. Kunti went on, "It is fortunate you are fair, my child, or she would have compared herself to you. But Panchali is noble; she is only angry because she has never seen this girl like a bit of the moon. Draupadi grew in a house where she was constantly told she was the most beautiful woman in the world; and now she has five husbands, who tell her the same thing.

"Perhaps it is time she met an equal. But go humbly to her, Subhadra, everything depends on your first meeting. Go dressed as you are, as a gypsy rather than a princess. She will find it easier to accept you." Kunti frowned, "Everything depends on her liking you at first sight. Everything."

"I think I should go alone to her first," said Arjuna.

"Yes, but don't expect any welcome. That will not come until she has seen Subhadra. But, as you say, you had better see her first."

His heart in his mouth, Arjuna came to Draupadi's apartment. The door was ajar, and he walked in. She sat near a window, drying her long hair in the sun that fell in on her. She sat with her back to him, unravelling the knots in her tresses with fine dark fingers, and she was more bewitching than ever. He felt the familiar tautness in his stomach.

He stood gazing at her. For a long moment, Arjuna let a swirl of feelings overwhelm him, as he stood silently, staring. She was not aware of him yet; then, he coughed softly. Draupadi spun around, and the smile froze on Arjuna's face. Her eyes were red with crying, her face puffy without sleep. She rose slowly, very regally, and she was breathing hard. He took a step towards her, "Panchali…"

Her eyes flashed at him. He saw she was trembling, and she said in a terrible voice, "Why have you left her for even a moment? I don't need your pity, go where your heart is. When you tie a second knot, the first one is loosened."

She stood there, her face pale, her lips twitching. Arjuna said, "I am where my heart is."

But she cried, "Leave me alone!", ran into the next room and slammed the door.

Tears in his eyes, Arjuna went back to his mother's apartment. Kunti said, "She is angry, isn't she? It will pass. If she likes Subhadra, everything will be all right. You must go humbly to her, little one. When she sees how lovely you are, she will forgive Arjuna."

Arjuna's hands were clammy. He was far from sure that it would be as easy as his mother thought. Yet, they must try, and Subhadra, who was no less noble than Draupadi, was not reluctant to placate her, as any other princess would have been. At least, Panchali would know the younger woman did not want to threaten her position as queen of Indraprastha.

Arjuna sighed, "The only way is for you to go to her."

Subhadra rose and went bravely with the maid Kunti called to show her the way. The sakhi took her to Draupadi's door, and then waited nervously for the princess to enter by herself. With a smile, Subhadra walked in; this was her life now, and she knew she had to win Draupadi over.

Draupadi was not in the room where Arjuna had seen her, and the inner door still stood shut. With a silent prayer, thinking of Krishna, Subhadra knocked on it. There was silence from within. She waited a moment, then knocked again. A voice in which there were tears, demanded, "Who is it?"

"Krishna's sister. May I come in?"

Another silence, then, Draupadi asked, "Are you alone?"

"Yes."

Subhadra knew the other woman must have been frantically setting her appearance right. Another long moment passed, and then Draupadi opened the door and stood, dark and awesomely beautiful, before Subhadra. Subhadra gasped when she saw Panchali, and her eyes clearly showed what she felt. She smiled sweetly and said, "I am Subhadra, and I want to be your sakhi." Then, she added quite spontaneously, "You are even more beautiful than I had heard!"

Draupadi stared at Subhadra for a probing moment. At last, the ghost of a smile dawned on her lips. She said, "And so are you."

Then, Draupadi held her arms open; Subhadra came to her and, next moment, Panchali was kissing her and crying, "You are so exquisite I can't resist you myself! Then how could poor Arjuna?"

She took the younger woman's hand and led her into her bedroom.

An hour later, Arjuna came anxiously to Draupadi's apartment, worried that she may have been as savage with Subhadra as she had with him. He found Subhadra wearing a priceless sari in crimson silk, and Draupadi's most treasured jewellery. The two women sat chatting and laughing together like sisters!

Arjuna stood astonished at the door. Draupadi saw him and fell silent, casting her eyes down. Subhadra turned and saw him. She whispered to Draupadi and, brushing past Arjuna, went out, shutting the door behind her.

The blood pounded in Arjuna's body to be alone with dark Panchali after so long. She, too, had waited impatiently for him, determined to fight for her place as his first wife, and, equally, resolved to give in if she saw no other way. Now, she had no battle with Subhadra.

After a moment's silence, she rose. With a soft cry, she was in his arms. Her hands were on him in a familiar frenzy, that they had both lived without for twelve long years.

SIXTY-FIVE

The Yadavas come to Indraprastha

A FEW DAYS LATER, BALARAMA, KRISHNA, THEIR WIVES AND A COMPANY of Yadavas arrived in Indraprastha. Nakula and Sahadeva came to the gates to receive them.

The people of Indraprastha flocked into the streets to welcome the one who had raised their city in the wilderness. Of course, now that city was many times as populous as it had been when Krishna was last here, twelve years ago. Many of the Kurus had never seen the Dark One about whom they had heard so much, who lived in legendary Dwaraka on the sea, and whom the world called the Avatara. The women of Indraprastha were excited. They crowded the balconies and rooftops, and showered wildrose petals on him as he rode by in his chariot, waving to them.

The women saw he was handsomer than they had dreamt, and even more mysterious. They favoured him with sultry glances and inviting smiles; even shy housewives were strangely overcome. He smiled at them, and the men of Indraprastha never noticed the intimate exchange.

At the palace, Yudhishtira, Bheema and Arjuna waited on the shining steps. Yudhishtira ran to Krishna like a child and embraced him; and then Bheema and Arjuna. Balarama was warmly welcomed. Bheema, especially, was pleased his master had come. Ceremoniously, Balarama gave the gold, and the ornaments seldom seen in the world, the thousand chariots, the thousand horses, and the thousand virgins, all of which they had brought as Subhadra's dowry, to Yudhishtira.

Inside the palace, Kunti was waiting for them with Draupadi and Subhadra herself, looking radiantly happy. When they all sat together,

Yudhishtira said, "I hope you have come to stay with us for some time."

Balarama replied, "Ten days we shall spend together, Yudhishtira, and may they be joyful. But after that I must return home, and the others with me."

There were protests from the Pandavas. "Why only ten days, after coming all the way from Dwaraka?"

Balarama held up his hand. "Let me finish, cousins. We Yadavas also have enemies we must fear, and our women and children are at home. It would be dangerous to leave Dwaraka unprotected for more than ten days. If word goes abroad that Krishna and I are away, there are those that will seize their chance to attack our city." He paused, "But Krishna can remain here with you as long as he likes."

The Pandavas' faces lit up. A delighted Yudhishtira said, "You can't imagine how pleased I am."

Merry as always, Krishna replied, "I am happy to stay, Yudhishtira." He glanced at Arjuna, and added cryptically, "These are momentous times, and your city is the eye of the coming storm."

When they pressed him to explain, he would only say, "Everything will be made plain in good time; for time reveals all things to all men. Now we are hungry after our journey. We hear the cooks of Indraprastha are the finest in the world, and wonder if they deserve their reputation."

Bheema sniffed the air, and cried, "Food is served!"

Arm in arm, and all of them except Krishna quite innocent of what the future held, they went in to the banquet prepared by the gifted cooks of Indraprastha's palace. Bheema had lured these men away from Hastinapura and almost every other kingdom. He wanted the cuisine to be exceptional and eclectic: and to please any guest that came to their city, even from the remotest corner of Bharatavarsha.

Krishna and Balarama were seated at the head of the king's table; and served in golden and silver dishes, the fare was every bit as delectable as reputed. Bheema glowed when he saw how his guests enjoyed the meal, and he made a point of asking each Yadava if he liked the food. Bheema's appetite for compliments was as insatiable as it was for the food itself.

Ten days of swimming in the sparkling pools of Indraprastha, hunting in the forests around the city, feasts every evening supervised by the son of the wind, marvellous entertainment every night in the halls of the palace and in the open, music and dancing in courtyards where fountains plashed under the moon and the stars: ten perfect days and nights flashed by, and too quickly it was time for Balarama to return to Dwaraka.

Yudhishtira and Bheema came to the older Yadava and pleaded with him to stay. And they were so keen, and Balarama was having such an excellent time, that, when Krishna added his voice to theirs, his brother was persuaded to remain for another fortnight. But at the end of those fourteen days, it was time to go back. Balarama set out for Dwaraka, leaving Krishna behind with Yudhishtira and his brothers.

Colourful flags waving, and a thousand conches booming under the sky, the force from Dwaraka set out for home, flowing over the land like another great river: with Balarama at its head and the legion of Yadava heroes behind him.

SIXTY-SIX

The hungry brahmana

SUMMER CAME ONCE MORE TO BHARATAVARSHA AND THE HEAT WAS intolerable. In Indraprastha, Krishna and Arjuna were to be found in each other's company: the Avatara and the bhakta. From dawn until late into the night, they would sit drinking and talking, or, at times, enfolded in a shared silence, not needing words to commune.

Often they hunted together, for boar and deer, in the woods near the city.

Early one morning, Arjuna came to Krishna's room. "Shall we go to the river today, and spend a day in the Khandava vana? They say the forest is cooler than anywhere else."

Krishna was enthusiastic. "I've heard so much about the Khandavaprastha. I haven't been on the banks of the Yamuna for years, and I grew up beside her."

They set out within the hour. The party included Draupadi, Subhadra and Satyabhama, Bheema and the twins, other members of the family, the palace-cooks and a cart full of provisions and vessels for them to ply their craft. They journeyed leisurely through the comfortable warmth of the early morning. As the heat of the day began to grow fierce, they saw a forbidding jungle loomed ahead, its old trees reaching for the sky with dark arms and fingers of branch and leaf.

Subhadra shivered. "What an evil place it seems."

Draupadi said, "I hope we won't be going too deep into that jungle."

Arjuna laughed, "Not you, certainly, the Khandava is no place for women. But after we have eaten, Krishna and I may explore it for a while."

Krishna said, "But let us get to the first trees, or this heat will be the end of us."

The sun beat down, and they now drove their chariots hard to find shade. Suddenly, Sahadeva, riding in the van of the party, shouted, "Look, the Yamuna!"

Meandering into the dim forest, was the midnight-blue river. Krishna gave a cry, and forged ahead of the others and came first to the river. As if meeting an old friend, even an old love, he knelt beside the Yamuna and, excited as a child, began to speak to her! He not only spoke but craned to listen to her smoky water, as if she whispered back to him and he knew her fluid tongue.

The others arrived to find him under a kadamba tree whose branches grew out over the water, and a deep wistfulness had come over him. He sat lost in his mood. Satyabhama came and sat briefly beside him; but she saw he would rather be alone, and went back to Draupadi and Subhadra.

The servants cleared some level ground near the river, and set up tents. The food carts were unloaded, and the cooks were soon at their fires. The Kuru men stripped off their clothes, and plunged into the cool water. The women, also, had come prepared. They went off a short way with their sakhis, and they too swam in the caressing flow.

Krishna sat plunged in a reverie. The Yamuna beside him had loosed a flood of memories from his boyhood. This river was a part of him, a part of his earliest, happiest years. In his mind's eye now, he saw his father Nanda's house of logs built on the hem of another deep jungle along the Yamuna's course: the Vrindavana. He saw the gypsy cowherders' crescent-shaped settlement. Enchanted by the Yamuna, Krishna was borne back to those green days when he roamed the jungle and the riverbank, wild himself, a friend to deer and tiger, jackal and elephant, and all the free creatures of the earth.

He saw his mother Yasodha at her hearth; he thought she turned and smiled at him. He had not had the heart to say farewell to her, when he left Vrindavana all those years ago, left so suddenly for Mathura. His mind turned another corner in the precious maze of memory, and now he was not a boy any more, but a dark youth, irresistible. He saw himself in the heart of Vrindavana, in a hidden glade full of jasmine, fragrant as heaven. He was not alone there, but with she who was as lovely as the forest in spring. Krishna saw her face. The pain he thought he had grown out of was still sharp.

Thinking of Radha again, today beside the darkling river, Krishna's heart filled with ecstatic memories: of stolen hours of forbidden love in the forest, when a throbbing moon bathed the trees in silvery magic. He had never loved anyone else as he had her. He knew he would never see her again in this life; it was a curse he carried. He saw her face, her naked body filmed in dew, lying beside him on Vrindavana's velvet grasses. He could hardly bear the anguish; or wait for everything he had come for to be over, and his life to end. He felt her presence so clearly under the kadamba tree: Radha waited for him across the threshold of death.

At last, Krishna tore himself away from his dream of the sweet, irretrievable past. He joined the others in the river; and he was himself again, full of high spirits. He challenged Bheema to race across the Yamuna, and beat him by lengths.

The cooks announced food. They had laid on a banquet in the wilds, because Bheema would have no less. Everything tasted so fresh out in the open and, after a vigorous swim, they all ate more than they should. When the meal was over, the cool tents beckoned. The sun was overhead now, and the heat fiercer than ever on a full stomach. The kshatriyas and their women retired to the tents, and quickly fell asleep.

Krishna said to Arjuna, "Let's explore the vana."

The two of them set off into the towering, ominous jungle. As they went along, the trees grew closer together and their branches intertwined like so many lewd spirits embracing. They felt this forest was a single, somehow terrible being. Soon, hardly any light penetrated the thick awning above, and Krishna and Arjuna sensed sinister presences all around them, and an aura of implacable evil. The air was still, dank vapours hung heavy; no breath of breeze had stirred here for years. This jungle was the home of many malignant creatures, and fell spirits that had lived here through the ages, their malevolence spreading through the earth. It was a forest of ghouls and demons.

Arjuna shivered, "I feel suffocated! Let us find the river."

They struck out again towards the Yamuna and, quite abruptly, emerged from the breathless, perpetual night of the Khandava into a bright glade where the dense growth of trees parted to let the blue river flow through. Here the meshed roof of branches was broken, and the summer sun lay upon the clear water. Krishna and Arjuna sighed in relief. Back in the darkness, they had felt countless leering phantoms crowding them, probing them, stroking their very souls with obscene fingers.

They saw a large punnaga tree growing beside the river. Great roots curled above the ground, and the cousins sat in its shade, beside the susurrant Yamuna. They sat in silence, listening to the river murmuring along.

Here in the open the day was warm again, and the two kshatriyas drifted off into a light slumber. They had hardly dozed for half an hour when, roused by a sharp instinct, both of them awoke together. They saw the strangest being standing before them. He was tall as a sala tree, and he was a brahmana. But such an extraordinary brahmana! His bare body glistened like molten gold in the sunlight. His eyes, long as lotus petals, were red as flame-hearts, and so were his flowing hair and beard, tinged green. He had matted locks and wore rags, but glowed as if a fire burned inside him.

Krishna and Arjuna rose and folded their hands to the uncanny one. He stared back at them, breathing heavily, his eyes like sunsets. Krishna said, calmly as ever, "Greetings, Brahmana, how may we serve you?"

In an exceptional voice—as if a hundred wood-fires crackled in his throat—the brahmana said, "I am hungry!"

Arjuna said innocently, "Our cooks will make anything you want to eat."

The brahmana looked at him for a moment, as he might at an imbecile child. "My hunger is not easily appeased. I am Agni! I want to devour this accursed Khandava vana with all its evil birds and beasts, trees and plants, spirits, serpents and demons. I know who you are, and I have been waiting for you. You are the ones to help me."

"How is that, O Agni?" asked Krishna.

"I have my reasons for wanting to devour the Khandava,[5] and the weal of the world is one of them. For centuries, I have longed to burn this vana; but Takshaka, the serpent-king, lives in the heart of the Khandava, and he is Indra's friend. Whenever I send my tongues of

---

5 See Appendix.

flame to lick up the jungle, Indra unleashes a thunderstorm to put out my fire. Many times this has happened, and I have no answer to Indra's torrents.

"I know you two are masters of the devastras. This jungle is a seething nest of evil; you must help me exorcise it. The monsters that breed in the darkness of the Khandava are abominations upon the earth. Long ago, this was a pure and taintless forest; but for thousands of years now, its heart has turned to darkness. There is only one way to end the breeding night that thrives under its canopy. To burn it down! If your astras can hold off Indra's rain, I will raze the jungle in a day, and satisfy my hunger, which feeds on me that it cannot feed on the vana.

"I ask you this favour, and I will give you anything in return."

They were astonished to hear what the Fire God wanted. With a laugh, Krishna cried, "We will help you, Agni! But first, we need some weapons and a chariot."

Arjuna said, "We have astras, and we can hold off Indra's rain; but, Deva, I have no bow to loose the astras I command. I have no quivers, and my chariot and horses are too slow for your task."

Arjuna was certain the advent of Agni was, also, a pretext for him to receive a gift of weapons from the God of fire.

Agni turned to Krishna, "Tell me the weapon you want."

The Dark One murmured, "A Chakra would serve me well."

Agni bowed gravely to both of them. He folded his hands to the west, in the direction of the ocean. He shut his eyes and began to chant some words in a divine language that Arjuna did not know and Krishna had not heard in this lifetime; but the Avatara understood it. Agni stood rapt, and the arcane mantra flowed resonantly from him. The Yamuna paused to hear it.

Then, another sound arose, as of waves crashing against a rocky shore. For a moment they thought the river had risen, but then a great, fluent lustre shone there: light in rippling waves, light in a crystal tide. Another Deva stood before Agni, as tall and unearthly as himself. His body was translucent; his hair seemed to be flowing water, every strand a river. His raiment was of moss, lichen and colourful plants that grow in ocean-deeps. He wore incredible pearls and corals, carried a trident in his hand, and a thousand brilliant fish clung to him in adoration. He seemed to be in this world and another, at once.

The two Gods greeted each other in the tongue in which Agni had summoned Varuna, Lord of oceans and keeper of the pristine weapons of the earth. Varuna bowed to Krishna and Arjuna, who bowed back to him, quite wonderstruck.

In his voice of tides, Varuna said, "After an age, my friend Agni has called me with the Samudra mantra. It must be a task of destiny he summons me for."

Agni said, "You know how long I have wanted to consume the Khandava vana; but Indra has always prevented me. These kshatriyas are Arjuna and Krishna, whom we know of. They have promised to help me, but they have no weapons with which to contain Indra. You have Soma Deva's ayudhas, given to you when the earth was young. Let these warriors have the Moon's weapons, and a chariot swift as the mind."

Varuna said, "I have brought them, I knew the time had come. And the kshatriyas may keep the weapons for the span of their mortal lives, after which they must be returned to me."

"What have you brought?" cried Agni.

Varuna made a mystic mudra, and another supernatural light shone there: the river seemed to become part of another world. The Ocean God said, "Look!"

An incandescent chariot materialised at the heart of the light; four horses were yoked to it, whiter than the snow on Kailasa, their manes like moonlight. They tossed their long heads and whinnied. On the chariot's golden banner flew a legendary flag with the image of a hero from an ancient race that had vanished from the jungles of Bharatavarsha: Chiranjeevi Hanuman, the immortal vanara, bhakta of Sri Rama of old! This same chariot, in time out of mind, had helped the Devas win their very first war against the Asuras. It stood there, pulsing with life, bright as a new cloud lit by the rising sun.

Varuna led them to the ratha, and Arjuna drew a sharp breath: on the chariot-seat, lay a golden bow, encrusted with jewels. It was a prodigious weapon, and Arjuna was sure he saw it breathe. The Pandava had the strangest feeling that the ayudha recognized him!

Varuna opened his arms, like a sea parting, to that primeval weapon. He said, simply, "Gandiva."

They gasped at that name: who had not heard of the legendary Gandiva? It was the Moon's bow, which Brahma had wrought before the earth was made, and given to Soma Deva, his favourite son. No warrior who wielded the golden bow could be vanquished in battle. Beside the Gandiva, lay two silver quivers that shimmered so delicately they seemed to be made of moonbeams.

These were the Moon God's inexhaustible quivers; the arrows that welled from them were as numerous as water-drops in the sea. The oceans of the earth would dry up before these quivers were empty. By now, Arjuna was melting in gratitude. He bowed to Varuna and Agni, and made a solemn pradakshina around the chariot. At last, he picked up the weapon that lay in it.

It was alive in his hands! It spoke to his deepest heart, and the Pandava felt a tremor of exhilaration. He strapped on the quivers, light as wishes: at once, they were full of shining arrows. Arjuna prostrated himself before Varuna and Agni. They blessed him and, as he rose, Varuna vanished.

His hands shaking for joy—what greater prize could any kshatriya have than this bow?—Arjuna gingerly strung the Gandiva. As soon as he stretched the string from one tip to the other, the weapon rumbled like a cloud full of spring thunder. The Pandava's heart sang to hear that sound. When he had fastened the string, he pulled on it and the tremendous twanging made the earth quake under their feet. Arjuna threw back his head and laughed in absolute delight.

Now Agni came up to Krishna. Something terribly bright lay in his flame-like hands: an irradiant disc. Agni said, "This belongs to you, I have only fetched it into the world: the Sudarshana Chakra, my lord."

Krishna held out his hands, and Arjuna saw the disc spin out of Agni's palms and into the Dark One's. Krishna raised his right hand, with his forefinger pointing at the sky. The Chakra was so fine it might have had no thickness at all, but only one side, if such a thing could be! Now it flashed up and poised itself, a blinding wafer of light, above Krishna's finger.

Krishna bowed to Agni and, when he folded his hands to the God of fire, the Chakra disappeared from sight. Yet, it was with the Avatara now, in the world, and he could summon it when he chose. Krishna said, "Now we shall surely contain even Indra."

Arjuna climbed into the white chariot. Krishna climbed in beside him, and took the reins. Arjuna cried, "We are ready, O Deva, burn the forest as you will!"

Agni roared, and the brahmana was transformed into an immense figure of flames.

The burning of the Khandava vana

Roaring from his mouth of flames, Agni began to consume the Khandava vana. Flashing between tree and tree, setting them ablaze like tinder-sticks, in no time the calescent Deva set half that forest alight. His hands were fire, his body, his hair and his face. His breath spewed a yojana of white flames.

He cried to Arjuna and Krishna, "Follow me! Not a bird, beast or plant must escape. They are all evil spawn."

They flashed along beside him in the supernal chariot, the white horses keeping up effortlessly with Agni's coruscating pace. They saw he had a careful plan how he would burn the forest, so no creature escaped from it. First, the Fire God flew round the hem of the vana in a vast circle, setting alight all the outermost trees. The flames then licked in, towards the heart of the Khandava in an ever-thickening ring.

Agni roared his joy as the jungle caught and burned, and Krishna drove his chariot quick as thinking: round and round the conflagration, to make sure no beast escaped. But the birds of the forest flew up into the air to flee the inferno. Among them were vampire bats big as wolves, and bigger pterodactyls, survivors from another age. No avian of those raucous swarms escaped. Like rays of light, Arjuna's arrows brought every one down, and they perished with the other vile denizens of the Khandava, shrieking as they burned.

Having joined the ends of his ring of fire, Agni moved into the deeper forest. Flames of many colours—green, blue, red and every shade of orange—licked at the trees and the grasses, setting the brooding darkness aglow. The roof of the jungle collapsed to the onslaught of walls of fire, and the sun broke in with a vengeance, and the wind, fanning the flames.

Agni blazed on, and the screams of the creatures of darkness rang above his roars: screams of not only of thousands of animals, but rakshasas, pisachas, bhutas, yakshas and nagas, as the flames found them. Slavering demon faces, revealed briefly in the sheet-flames, dissolved with chilling howls and shrieks, as succubus and incubus, ghoul and goblin burned. For the rest, all the living fled deeper into the jungle. There was a stampede of evil species, flying in panic, with no hope of escape.

The stagnant pools and slime-covered lakes, across which no breath of air had stirred a ripple for centuries, began to bubble and evaporate in viscid fumes that rose into Devaloka. All their creatures, fish, crabs and tortoises, perished. On high, there was soon a commotion. The Devas flew to Indra their king, and cried, "Is the world ending, that Agni consumes the Khandava vana?"

Indra peered down and saw the forest burning. He growled in annoyance, but this was not the first time Agni had tried to burn the Khandava. Indra summoned his storm troopers of the air. Black clouds amassed in towering legions above the burning forest. As far as the eye could see, rumbling thunderheads filled the sky and it grew dark as night.

Agni cried, "Indra knows the forest is burning. Here comes his storm!"

The sky was riven by a terrific streak of lightning. A clap of thunder shook heaven and earth. A terrific gale sprang up and howled through the trees. The throbbing clouds opened, and an impossible rain fell out of them.

Agni howled. The rain was thick as arrows, each battering drop the size of a fist. At first, the blaze in the forest was so intense that Indra's downpour never reached the burning trees, but turned to steam in the white heat.

Indra, master of rainclouds, roared in the sky in a battery of thunder. At once, the clouds in the firmament were twice as dense: Pushkara and Avartaka joined the fray, their lightning fiercer than anything so far. Now the rain from those clouds was as if a sea fell out of the heavens. Across the jungle the leaping flames hissed and sputtered, and began to die, doused by the flash flood from the sky. It was as if the apocalypse,

Badava, which ends the world, had encountered the deluge, Pralaya, in which time drowns.

Agni hissed and screeched in frustration. The sky filled with billowing black smoke, cracked through with jagged lightning. Agni wailed, "Help me, Krishna! Arjuna, help me now!"

Arjuna raised the Gandiva, and it was an arc of golden light in his hands. Krishna drove his white horses in a dream of perfect chariotry; standing tall in the ratha, Arjuna loosed a river of arrows at Indra's storm. The shining river held up the storm, so not a single drop of rain fell to the earth! Again Agni's fire crackled and blazed; flames leapt up in exuberance, devouring tree and darkness. The Khandava burned like the fire from Siva's third eye.

The canny storm now tried to fall elliptically, to bend its way around the shield of arrows in the sky. Arjuna turned his aim lower, and in a moment enveloped all the vana, top and sides, in an impenetrable dome. Agni's flames licked at this cupola.

Indra's friend Takshaka, the serpent-king, for whose sake the Deva protected the Khandava, was not in that jungle at all; but Takshaka's son Aswasena was, and so was Aswasena's mother. They slithered here and there in terror, seeing no way of escape. From above, Indra watched their plight. As the flames closed on them and the heat grew unbearable, Aswasena's mother cried to her son, "I will divert Arjuna, and Indra will help you get away."

Before Aswasena could protest, his emerald mother, Takshaka's queen of winged serpents, flew up as if to breach Arjuna's dome of arrows. In a flash, Arjuna brought her down with three livid shafts, her cry ringing in the burning air. At that moment, Indra loosed a deluge that breached the roof of the dome directly above Arjuna's chariot. The water fell on him like a stone, and Arjuna fainted. Before Krishna could revive him, Aswasena had streaked out of the Khandava. He was the only creature of the forest to escape.*

Arjuna cursed Aswasena. "You have escaped your destiny like a coward! Your name shall be reviled through the ages."

---

* In another version, the mother snake swallows Aswasena to protect him. But Arjuna decapitates her as she tries to fly out of the burning forest. Aswasena escapes, vowing revenge someday.

Agni and Krishna cursed that serpent as well. Furious that Indra had tricked him, Arjuna now carried the battle into the sky. His astras came flaring into Devaloka. Torn between pride that this kshatriya was his son, and anger that a mortal dared attack him, Indra loosed a vayavyastra from above, a weapon of winds. A hundred hurricanes came screaming down on Agni's forest-fire.

They blew out the tallest pillars of flame, as the vayavyastra whistled around the Khandava, snuffing Agni's furnace. Arjuna loosed a torrid agneyastra at the vayavya. The screaming winds took fire themselves, and lit the trees again. Agni sprang up joyfully, and now he paid tribute to his warriors: some of his loftiest flames looked like Arjuna, and some, like Krishna, were deep blue.

Krishna drove the white chariot like light through the blazing forest. He held the reins in one hand, and with the other, he hunted the creatures of darkness: the bhutas, pretas, pisachas, rakshasas and yakshas that infested the Khandava. He hunted them with his spectral Chakra, which desiccated spirits, goblins and demons, and their cries echoed among tree-tall flames.

Arjuna shot three more fiery astras straight into Devaloka. Beside himself, Indra seized up his Vajra, the thousand-jointed thunderbolt, and started down from Amravati. He would teach these mortals a lesson! The other Devas went before him: Yama with his glowing staff, Kubera with his dreadful mace, Skanda with his lance of fire, Twastha with his mountain, Surya with his flaming dart, and Mrityu with his gleaming axe.

A river of arrows from the Gandiva greeted them in the ethereal akasa between heaven and earth. Then there was Krishna's Chakra, wheeling everywhere, nitid and inexorable, barring their way down. The Devas fled back to Indra, crying, "There is no way past the mortals' weapons."

"These kshatriyas are terrible!"

"Who are they? They strike fear in us!"

Indra smiled inwardly; but he had to take battle down to the upstart humans that dared put the Devas of heaven to flight. Indra knew who Krishna was, that there was no standing against the Avatara. Once, years ago in Vrindavana, he had suffered a humiliating defeat at the Blue One's hands.

But Arjuna's mettle was yet to be tested. Roaring above the storm, Indra plucked a jagged peak from Mount Mandara with hands of light. Carrying it aloft—perhaps to show Krishna it was not just he who could bear mountains in the sky!—the Deva king appeared above the Khandava vana and hurled his missile down at the human warriors like a bolt of lightning.

It flew down the sky, darkening the day, taking fire as it came like a comet. Quicker than seeing, Arjuna turned his arrows at the peak of rock and ice. He smashed it into dust, and scattered the dust everywhere in a fine rain.

The planets wobbled in their orbits at Indra's roar. The king of the Devas raised his thunderbolt, made in forgotten times from a rishi's bones of adamant. He drew back his arm to cast the Vajra at Arjuna, when an asariri spoke from the sky, "Takshaka is not in the Khandava vana, and the jungle is fated to burn today. It was written among the stars before the earth was made, and nothing can save it. You have helped Aswasena escape; you can do no more.

Arjuna and Krishna are Nara Narayana. No one can vanquish them. It is not natural for a father to fight his son; stay your hand, Deva. Salvage some honour before they humiliate you completely."

Indra lowered his Vajra. For a moment, he sat very still on his white elephant, Airavata treading air. Then he came down to the Khandava and stood before Arjuna and Krishna in a scintillating form. The kshatriyas climbed down from their chariot and folded their hands to him.

Indra said, "Not all the Devas together could have done what you both have. Ask me for any boon."

Arjuna quivered with excitement to see his father. He stood staring at the God of light. Indra said again, "Ask me for any boon, Kshatriyas, and it will be yours."

He looked at Krishna, who shook his head. Indra turned to Arjuna, who fell at his father's feet for his blessing. Indra laid his palm on his son's head, then raised him up and embraced him. Yet again, the Deva said, "I am proud of you, Arjuna, ask me for any boon."

Arjuna hesitated; he glanced at Krishna, who nodded at him. The Pandava cried, "Bless me with every astra you have power over!"

Indra threw back his illustrious head, and laughed. "You will have all the astras you want! But not yet, my son. When Siva gives you his own Paasupatastra, you will have my astras from me. So it is written, I believe, and so it shall be."

He turned to the inscrutable Krishna. "Krishna, is there nothing you want from me today?"

And Krishna said, "Let Arjuna always be my friend, through eternity."

"So be it."

Indra raised his hand over them once more, and vanished as if he had been an illusion. Just then, they heard a cry. A noble Asura—none they expected to find in this vile Khandava, but a great Demon of the ancient race, tall as two men—came flying through the clearing where Arjuna and Krishna stood beside the white chariot. He ran with huge strides, his face twisted in a grimace, his dark eyes full of fear. Roaring after him, flew Agni, man-shaped again, but gigantic, flaming arms outstretched to clasp the Asura and make him ashes.

That Asura was Mayaa, demon builder and awesome genius, who once made the Tripura in the sky. He had come to visit his friend Takshaka. Agni had burned down the serpent-king's cave palace, and Mayaa fled through a back door with the Fire God in pursuit.

When Krishna saw the fleeing Asura, he raised his Chakra to take off the fugitive's head. Mayaa ran to Arjuna, and cried, "Arjuna, save my life!"

Strangely taken with that dark and magnificent being, Arjuna said, "No one shall harm you."

Krishna gave a shout of surprise, but he lowered his hand and the Chakra vanished. Agni also turned away from Mayaa, sparing his life because Arjuna had given him sanctuary. In a wink, the Asura escaped from the burning forest.

Some say Agni burned in the jungle for a fortnight before the Khandava was razed; others claim the Fire God raged so fiercely he consumed the vana before the sun set that same evening. Perhaps, the truth was that the burning of the Khandava occurred in a subtler dimension of time and event, a transcendent zone.

Anyway, all that was left of the evil forest was ashes, which the wind scattered across Bharatavarsha. The earth was exorcised of the sinister vana and its evil creatures and spirits. Arjuna now had the white chariot, the Gandiva and the magic quivers that fate meant him to have: for the war on the crack of the ages, which he must fight one day.

His hunger appeased—with boundless animal flesh, to him nectarine rivers of blood, marrow and fat—Agni came back to Krishna and Arjuna as the bright brahmana once more. He glowed now with the satisfaction of the ample meal: like a contented guest after a wedding banquet! He laid his hands, cool flames, in blessing on the warriors' heads.

Agni said, "Today's feast would never have been but for you both. Krishna and Arjuna, I bless you: may your most cherished dreams come true!"

They bowed to him with folded hands, and he, too, vanished before their eyes like mist before the sun. Arjuna and Krishna were alone together. Exhausted by their adventure, they walked slowly to the river, dark now with twilight. The last rays of the setting sun lit the few clouds that straggled in the sky: like lamps at evening puja. Behind them in the jungle, livid embers still smouldered here and there; but otherwise, all that day was like some dream. A breeze sprang up over the Yamuna, full of the scents of night-blooming lotuses, and it blew the last wisps of smoke out of the razed forest. It blew soft calm into the two kshatriyas' tired limbs.

The cousins washed in the river, and offered sandhya vandana to the Gods. Then they sat in silence on the roots of the stalwart punnaga, where Agni had first approached them. The God of flames had spared just that one tree, as if he had known they would want to sit under it after the forest had burned down. They sat listening to the midnight-blue river murmuring by.

Krishna said, "It is time we returned to the others. They would have seen the fire, and heard the screams. They must be anxious for us."

As they walked back leisurely towards the Kuru camp, they did not notice the tall figure that followed them at a discreet distance. Just before they arrived at the camp, a voice hailed them from the night and the looming figure approached.

BOOK TWO

Sabha Parva

AUM, I bow down to Narayana, the most exalted Nara, and to the Devi Saraswati, and say *Jaya*!

ONE

Mayaa

H<small>E</small> CAME OUT OF THE DARKNESS, AS KRISHNA AND ARJUNA WALKED wearily back to the Kuru camp near the Yamuna. They saw Mayaa, the Asura, had recovered from the terror of Agni chasing him through the blazing Khandava vana. Laying his head at Arjuna's feet, he said, "You saved my life. Let me at least tell you who I am."

"Who are you, friend, living in the Khandava?" asked Arjuna.

"I am Mayaa of the Asuras, and I was the architect of my people. I built the Tripura in the sky, which Siva burned with his astra. I am in your debt, Kshatriyas; you must let me repay your kindness. Is there anything I can do for you?"

They saw his skin shone in the falling night, and his great eyes were deep and honest. The language he spoke was chaste, of an old strain seldom heard in the world any more, and a far cry from the crude dialects of the rakshasas of the day. He was a noble being, from another time.

Fascinated by Mayaa, Arjuna said, "I am happy I could be of use to you, but I never take anything from someone I have helped."

"I am deeply in your debt; there must be something I can do for you. Anything at all, you only have to name it."

"It is enough to have you for my friend. You must not feel obliged to me."

However, Mayaa insisted. "I must show my gratitude, or I will have no peace. It is no common favour you have done me, you have saved my life."

In the gloom, Arjuna saw the Asura's eyes glistened with tears. Krishna knew something of Mayaa, that he was among the great Sivabhaktas of all time, and a learned Asura to whom Surya Deva revealed the Surya-siddhanta, the secrets of the galaxy. The Dark One said softly to Arjuna, "He is noble and sincere. You mustn't disappoint him."

In a moment, Arjuna said to Mayaa, "Do something for Krishna here. That will please me more than anything else."

Mayaa bowed to the Avatara. "What can I do for you, Lord?"

Krishna grew thoughtful; he saw the germ of fate in the moment. He remembered the task for which he had been born: to remove the burden of evil from the earth, to destroy the power of the race of kings. He saw a vast battlefield heaped with corpses, and a skin of blood congealing on it. Krishna felt dizzy for a moment. He sensed the chance to sow a cunning seed of envy, and set the stage for an apocalyptic war. They were no accidents of circumstance: the appearance of Agni or Mayaa, or the burning of the Khandava. Krishna saw fate's hand in the day's extraordinary happenings.

He said to the Asura, "I have heard of your genius, Mayaa. Build a sabha for Arjuna's brother Yudhishtira in Indraprastha. Let it be as wonderful as your own court was, in the Tripura."

They saw how Mayaa's eyes misted over at the mention of Tripura. He had been a great king himself, once, in time out of mind, before Siva's astra consumed his cities in the sky and his people. Mayaa said slowly, "My skill isn't what it used to be, and this age does not support true grandeur. But I will do my best."

Krishna laughed. "I think the best you can do, even today, will be more than enough for us. But combine the finest styles of building known to the Devas, the Asuras and to men; let your sabha take inspiration from both ancient times and new. Let it be unique." Krishna paused. "Above all, Mayaa, *let it be the envy of those who set eyes on it!*"

Arjuna looked startled, but Mayaa received this calmly. With a smile, the Asura said, "So it shall be, Dark One, and may it serve your purpose."

Already, images of a majestic sabha for Indraprastha rose vividly in Mayaa's mind. How he had longed to create something visionary; but who would ask an Asura trapped in the wrong time, an age of humans, to build for them? And he was no longer a king of his people that he could build a court for himself. Eagerly, he seized the chance to use his gifts once more.

These were jealous and dangerous times, thought Mayaa. By now, he knew who the Blue One was. He would build just what Krishna wanted: a sabha to be the cynosure of the world, a sabha that would launch the greatest war of these times. A war to end a yuga with, and accomplish an Avatara's mission in the world.

Mayaa saw before his eyes, floors paved with candent jewels, gleaming domes and towers; walls depicting timeless legends of the Gods in great panels; friezes encrusted with rubies and diamonds, emeralds, sapphires, cornelians and pearls like this age had never seen. He saw gold and silver, employed subtly, tastefully, and the most resonant wood available in the jungles of Bharatavarsha. Mayaa saw all this in moments, as a tide of inspiration swept away the cobwebs from his mind.

They arrived at the camp to find the Kuru party had returned to Indraprastha. They rode back to the city in Varuna's chariot, swiftly as the night wind, bringing Mayaa the Asura with them. The guards at the gates shivered to see the darkly resplendent being with Arjuna. They drove through the streets of Indraprastha, and saw how appraisingly the Asura took in the sights of the city.

They brought Mayaa to Yudhishtira, who rose to welcome the mysterious guest, whose presence was so mythic, so out of place in these times in which he did not belong. Mayaa's eyes smouldered with ancient fires.

The Asura bowed deeply to Yudhishtira. "O King, your brother has asked me to build a sabha for you in Indraprastha. I have accepted the offer as eagerly as a thirsty man does a drink of water. For I have not built anything since the Tripura was torched from the sky."

He stroked a pillar near him, appreciatively, and let his eye rove over the hall in which they sat. Mayaa went on slowly, "Viswakarman has created a magnificent city for you. It will be an honour and a challenge for me to best my old rival in his own city, and show that Mayaa is still the greatest builder."

The others smiled; what did they know of that rivalry? They had not seen the wonder that had been the Tripura: triune, ineffable cities of the air, circling the earth. He would create a sabha for them that would make the rest of Indraprastha seem ordinary. Why just the kings of the world, he would build Yudhishtira a court to make the Devas envious.

Mayaa spent a week studying Indraprastha and its environs, before he decided on the site where he would erect his sabha. Dhaumya was asked to find an auspicious day for the construction to begin. He performed a puja on that day and chanted Vedic mantras to purify the site. The excavation began, to lay the foundations. Like Viswakarman, Mayaa worked with magical powers; but he believed in manual labour too. He knew the hard old way always gave an edifice more depth and grace.

Krishna came to Yudhishtira and said, "I must leave for home. There is much to be done in Dwaraka."

Yudhishtira looked stricken. "You are the star that guides our destiny. While you are with us, we are free from doubt and fear, and see our way ahead clearly. Stay a while longer, Krishna."

Bheema said, shyly, "We shall be lost without you."

Sahadeva whispered, "When you go, it is as if our life leaves us." Nakula nodded agreement with his twin. Arjuna was the most forlorn.

Krishna insisted, "If you need me, only think of me and you will find I am with you always. For I leave my heart in your care. But I must return to Dwaraka now, there are others who need me too."

They sorrowing, and he beyond sorrow, Krishna bid farewell to his aunt and his cousins. One by one, he embraced them, and last of all, he came to Arjuna and Subhadra. They were out in the sun now and Daruka, his sarathy, had brought Krishna's chariot to the palace steps. Krishna clasped Arjuna to him, and the Pandava wept. Finally, the Dark One turned to Subhadra, embraced her and said cheerfully, "May I have my chariot back now?"

He had a smile out of his sister and, then, she also began to sob. The people of Indraprastha had filled the streets to bid farewell to the Avatara. Yudhishtira said to Daruka, "Friend Daruka, we have a custom in Indraprastha that when Krishna leaves us, I drive him to the city-gates. So, allow me..."

Daruka got down from his place, and the king climbed up to the sarathy's seat. Arjuna and Bheema climbed into the chariot, with silken chamaras in their hands, and Nakula and Sahadeva held the white parasol over Krishna and Satyabhama. They drove through the streets, and the people thronged the ratha, in a sea, reaching out to touch the Avatara. On their way to the city-gates, they passed the site for the sabha and saw Mayaa. He ran up and folded his hands to Krishna, who raised a hand in blessing over his dark head.

They arrived at the gates and still Yudhishtira drove the chariot, like a man in a dream he did not want to wake from and find his cousin gone. Krishna said, "Yudhishtira, stop. You have a long walk back to the palace, and you are not dressed for walking."

Reluctantly, the king obeyed. The Pandavas alighted from the chariot, and Daruka climbed back on. A last time, Krishna got down and embraced his cousins. Then he got into the Jaitra again, and said, "Come Daruka, we must go or we will stand here for ever."

Bowing to the crestfallen Pandavas, the charioteer flicked his reins and his horses sprang forward, knowing they were heading home to the city in the sea. The Pandavas stood gazing after the chariot until it was out of sight. Still, they stood on. Finally, Yudhishtira turned back, and the others followed him in silence.

In their minds, they followed Krishna's chariot all the way back to Dwaraka, and their deepest thoughts remained with their blue cousin, long after they had ceased to be aware of it.

Soon after they were out of sight of Indraprastha, Daruka turned back to his dark master with a question in his eyes. Krishna nodded to him and, next moment, the unearthly horses rose steeply into the air, and they flew the rest of the way to Dwaraka with the wind in their faces.

TWO

Mayaa's sabha

Day by day, Mayaa's sabha took shape in Indraprastha. He had brought expert craftsmen from distant parts to work on the edifice. They were silent men and mysterious, who preferred to keep to themselves. They built a colony of hutments around the sprawling site, and ventured into the marketplace only to buy themselves food. They did not mingle with the people of the city, and Mayaa was pleased that this was so. He felt it kept their minds on their task, which was an undertaking of inspiration.

First, Mayaa erected a huge, skeletal wooden dome. He shrouded it with rough canvas to keep the sun, the wind and the rain out. Below this dome his men laboured, by day, and often by night. Mayaa himself was one possessed, as he plunged himself into the enterprise, body and soul. He ate little and slept less. Often, in the nights' last yaama, just before dawn, he could be seen stalking the streets of Indraprastha, alone, talking to himself, talking bare some nuance of design.

Rumour had it that, at times, Viswakarman, who eagerly watched the progress of the sabha, joined Mayaa during these nocturnal strolls, to analyse some delicate problem of structure or aesthetics, for hours. One day, Mayaa came to Arjuna, who was the only outsider he allowed under the covering dome. He said, "When the Tripura burnt I salvaged some precious things from the inferno, and buried them under the Bindusaras, near Kailasa and Mainaka. I want to use those treasures to embellish your sabha."

Arjuna thought how much more contented the Asura was, since he had begun working. He was absorbed, as if nothing existed any more except his sabha. Arjuna said, "What can I do to help you?"

"Give me some men to go with me, to carry back what I need."

Arjuna agreed readily, and Mayaa set out for the Bindusaras, lake of water-drops. Once when, at Bhagiratha's long prayatna, the Ganga fell in a starry torrent on to the earth, no one could bear her awesome fall. She was arrogant that it would be the end of the world. Then Siva stood up from the Himalaya, tall as the sky, and he caught the falling river in his jata, and contained her at the root of a single strand of his hair. Ganga's pride was broken: struggle as she would, she could not escape from Siva's head. Bhagiratha begged Siva to let the river flow in the world, for his ancestors' sake. The Lord released her, drop by painful drop, to flow as a blessing upon the earth, and absolve men who bathed in her of their sins.

Where Siva released the river of the sky from his head, a lake formed, which belonged as much to heaven as the earth. It was on the shores of the Bindusaras that the Rishis Nara and Narayana once sat in tapasya. It was beside the same lake that Arjuna had sat in dhyana, beneath it Ulupi had seduced him.

One night of a full moon that illumined the Himalayan landscape like a mystic's vision, the Asura Mayaa arrived at the Bindusaras with the men Arjuna had given him. The lake lay like a sea before them. It was a still winter's night, a silvery day, and snow lay all around like white fire. Here and there, a thin film of ice covered the water.

What is night for men is day for the Asuras. As soon as he arrived at the Bindusaras, though it was midnight and they had come a long way, Mayaa waded into the icy water. It was thousands of years since he was last here, but he swam unhesitatingly to the middle of the lake. His men sat watching, awed by the beauty of this luminous place poised between swarga and bhumi. Mayaa paused a moment, quite near where Arjuna had plucked the scarlet lotuses. He swam on with powerful strokes.

The Asura seemed like some aquatic creature from another world. He was a strange one, all right; he had hardly said a word to any of the fifty men that had come with him. He seemed wrapped up in thoughts too deep to share, of times so different his companions could not have imagined them. They thought he was the loneliest being in the entire world: a derelict from another age condemned to live in a diminished time.

Yet, now, in the midnight waters of the Bindusaras, the Asura seemed to come alive. He dived under the surface of the lake, and was gone interminably. Then he broke water with a shout that shattered the primeval silence of the white valley.

"They're here!" cried Mayaa. "My treasures are still here."

He held his hand up above his head. Something crimson and renitent shone in it like a piece of the rising sun. Mayaa swam fluently back to the shore. He showed them the object in his palm: it was a giant phallic ruby, a reverberant Sivalinga. Those men had never heard that, among all Sivabhaktas, Mayaa was among the very greatest.

Briefly the Asura shut his eyes in prayer, then said, "My Lord Siva has kept my treasures safe. Come, we must build a raft in which you can bring ashore what I dive for."

With fifty skilled men this was quickly accomplished. Soon, so many parcels—carefully wrapped in oilskin—lay in a pile beside the lake. Mayaa would not allow anyone to undo these and look inside. Most of them shone even by the light of day, as if there were cold fires burning within. Some of the parcels were so heavy, though small enough, that it took three men to carry a single one.

When Mayaa had retrieved the last of the parcels, they set off down the mountain. Not far from the lake, along the loftiest section of a mountain-trail, the chariots from Indraprastha waited. Lading these with the treasures of Tripura, Mayaa and his party rode home. The Asura's eyes shone with memories of the days when he had been a king of his people.

Back in Indraprastha, Mayaa had his treasures carried safely to the dome of secrecy that covered his growing sabha. To no one did he yet show what was in those parcels, which had lain for an age in a jade cavern under the Bindusaras. Just one of them he brought into Yudhishtira's palace, to Arjuna's chambers. Mayaa called Bheema and Arjuna there.

As he untied that large parcel, the Asura was smiling, as he so seldom did. When he had peeled away the rough oilskin, the Pandavas saw an emerald-and-saffron silken layer inside; the cloth was so rich, they had never seen its like. When Mayaa undid the silk as well, and laid the package bare, Bheema and Arjuna rose in awe to stare at what lay within.

Delighted that the princes were enchanted, Mayaa picked up the shining mace he had uncovered. Its knobs were golden, its haft jewelled and, when the Asura hefted it, it rumbled like a thundercloud. This was no common gada, but a weapon as old and powerful as the Gandiva. Giving that mace gravely to Bheema, Mayaa said, "May you be invincible in every battle you fight. May you kill your greatest enemy with this gada one day."

When Bheema received the weapon, it was alive in his hands; he felt its implacable spirit touch him. Mayaa turned to the battle-conch, the sankha that lay on the silk cloth, its presence filling the room. The Asura held the whorled shell out to Arjuna and said, as if it were an old and valued friend, "This is the Devadatta. When you sound him, not just your enemies but the earth will tremble; for he is a great spirit of the ocean."

Arjuna embraced Mayaa emotionally. "I was the lucky one on the day we met!"

Now, Mayaa began to give his sabha its final touches. Night and day, he toiled, obsessed that his creation should be perfect. In a tide of visions, intricate plans came to him under the lofty dome that still shrouded the great court. At last, after fourteen months of ceaseless labour, one night Mayaa came to Yudhishtira, and said, "Your sabha is ready. I will dismantle the covering dome tonight, and you may see it in the morning. I have consulted Dhaumya, tomorrow is an auspicious day."

When the sun rose the next morning, a gleaming miracle stood revealed before the palace of Indraprastha. Guarded by eight thousand stone kinkaras, Mayaa's edifice had columns of gold and silver, terraces of crystal, and the Pandavas knew it was by far the most magnificent sabha in the world. It made every other royal court on earth seem like stalls beside a great temple. Why, Mayaa's sabha made even the rest of fabulous Indraprastha seem ordinary.

It was ensconced in sprawling gardens, in which flowers of every kind—kalhara, madhavi, mallika, kuravaka and kadamba, among others—bloomed all together, many unseasonally: as if the sabha was part of a transcendent realm. Enchantment lay upon every part of it.

Pools full of ethereally clear water dotted the gardens. As Mayaa led Yudhishtira and his brothers around,* they saw these pools had floors and banks of blemishlessly white marble. The marble banks were set with clusters of pearl, and flights of crystal steps led down to the water. In the water were lotuses made of jewels, some of them solitaires as big as a dove's eggs. Among these, were real lotuses, fish, tortoises and water birds.

At the lofty doors to the sabha itself, as Mayaa led them in, after the chanting of sacred mantras, was another pool. This was inlaid with precious stones, exactly like the rest of the floor. By a trick of the light that fell on it, the water in the pool reflected the marble of the ceiling so perfectly, that at first the Pandavas mistook it for solid floor. Yudhishtira nearly stepped into it, and Mayaa drew him back.

The spectacular central hall of the sabha was elegant as a work of nature, surrounded by countless little terraces. It was lambent with jewel-light: deep emerald and ruby, scintillating sapphire and diamond, dusky coral, mystic amethyst, chrysoberyl and moonstone, and other gems no longer found in the world, secret stones set in the walls, ceiling and floor. All you saw was their light, never the stones themselves, unless you inspected the crevices in which they were craftily embedded.

At the head of the sabha, which was six thousand cubits square, was a raised marble platform. On this dais were five crystal-and-golden thrones, encrusted with the most exceptional and auspicious gemstones. These thrones were perhaps the finest reflections of Mayaa's imagination. Each one was different from the others, and each created for a particular Pandava prince.

Mayaa said, "Do you know which throne is for each of you?"

Yudhishtira's throne was obviously the biggest one, in the centre of the platform; but, with no hesitation, the other princes followed Yudhishtira on to the dais, and each one sat in his own throne.

---

* Yudhistira feeds ten thousand brahmanas, come from all over Bharatavarsha, madhuparka, fruit, roots, pork and venison before he enters the sabha. The greatest of them go in and sit with him in that court. Asita, Devala, Satya, Sarpamali, Mahasira, Arvavasu, Sumitra, Maitreya, Sunkaa, Vali, Vaka, Daivya, Sthulasira, Vyasa and his disciples, Suka, Sumanta, Jaimini, Paila, Parvata, Markandeya, Savarna, Bhaluki, Galava, Janghabandhu, Raibhya, Kopavega, Bhrigu, Harivabhru, Kaundinya, Babhrumali, Sanatana, Kakshivat, Ashija, Nachiketa, Gautama, Painga, Varaha, Sunaka, Shandilya, Kukkura, Venujangha, Kalapa, and Katha are some of the names mentioned.

Mayaa cried in delight, "So there was no mistake!"

There were a thousand other marvels in that sabha; and even the Pandavas, who had lived in the grandeur of Hastinapura, and the splendour of Indraprastha, were awed by it. Charming little passages led away from the main hall, to numberless smaller halls and atriums. There were other rooms for study and recreation; and up marble-and-wooden flights of stairs were elaborate apartments for each Pandava's relaxation and pleasure. Mayaa's sabha could easily serve as another palace in Indraprastha.

The outer walls were so sensitive to light the sabha seemed like an entirely different edifice, at different times of day. The people would say that in the evening you would not recognize it for being the same court it had been at dawn. And on the night of a full moon, it seemed to float on air and, surely, to belong to another, supernatural world.

Yudhishtira turned to the Asura and, bowing to him, said, "Now we can begin to imagine how glorious the Tripura must have been, and why its legend has survived the passage of ages."

Knowing this was the highest praise he could have, Mayaa also bowed. He said, "The Lord of Indraprastha deserves no less. If you are pleased, I am satisfied."

He could see they were more than pleased: they were entranced by his creation. None of them yet realized what envy it would stir in some hearts, and that envy would catalyze the greatest war. Yudhishtira and his brothers wandered around the sabha for hours, as if they could never have their fill of it. The next day, there was a feast to celebrate its completion; the poor were fed, gifts and gold given to them.

Mayaa came to Yudhishtira, and said, "My work here is complete. I must return to my family."

Yudhishtira took him back to the palace. Knowing the habitually solitary Asura would want to leave Indraprastha as soon as he had finished his task, the Pandava king already had several gifts ready for him. At first, Mayaa was reluctant to accept any of them, saying they owed him nothing; it had been his privilege to build the sabha. However, the Pandavas would not hear of this, and finally Mayaa left Indraprastha laden with treasures for himself and his family. Many of these were heirlooms fashioned in Devaloka and handed down the Kuru generations from sires of old.

Each Pandava came and embraced the Asura, and they wept when he left Indraprastha. Though Mayaa was a taciturn and essentially lone being, he had won their hearts with his generosity and his genius. Engraved on a fine silver sword Yudhishtira gave him, were the words: *To the greatest builder of all.*

Arjuna went beyond the gates of Indraprastha to see Mayaa on his way. Suddenly, the Asura had tears in his eyes as he grasped Arjuna's hands. "May your life always be filled with sweetness. I will never forget you, noble prince, or that you saved my life."

Arjuna's eyes were full. "I will think of you whenever I see your sabha. And when I ride into battle, taking my life in my hands, I will think of you: when I blow on the Devadatta to strike fear in my enemies."

They embraced, and the quiet Asura turned and walked out of Arjuna's life. The Pandava never asked where he was going: if Mayaa had wanted Arjuna to know, he would have told him.

A few weeks after Mayaa left Indraprastha, Yudhishtira and his brothers held a banquet in the new sabha, to which kshatriyas from other kingdoms were invited. Those who came said that truly Indraprastha, with the jewel at its heart, the Mayaa sabha, was no less than Indra's Amravati in Devaloka. The fame of the city in the wilderness spread throughout Aryavarta, and especially of the court Mayaa had built.

All the kings of the earth came to see the wonderful sabha, except Dhritarashtra and his sons. It was like a slap in the blind king's face. He had sent his nephews into a desert, thinking he would consign them to oblivion. Now, the renown of Indraprastha was greater than that of Hastinapura. The desert had bloomed; and the Mayaa sabha was the crowning humiliation for the Kauravas. Dhritarashtra and his sons could hardly bear the envy that burned them.

Not only kings, but holy seers from the tallest mountains and the deepest jungles came to see Mayaa's sabha. Many young kshatriyas, who came with their fathers, remained behind in Indraprastha to study archery with Arjuna. One of the finest of these was Satyaki, Krishna's cousin from Dwaraka. Chitrasena and Chitrangadaa came to Indraprastha with Arjuna's son Babhruvahana. They were welcomed, and stayed for some months.

It was a time of plenty, a time of fortune, a time when Indraprastha was a vibrant centre of activity and learning. The Pandavas' cup of joy brimmed over. Subhadra gave birth to a splendid son, whose arms were long, his chest broad and his eyes as large as a bull's. They named him Abhimanyu. He was a brilliant child, and quickly became his uncles' favourite. In course of time, Draupadi, too, had five sons: one from each of her husbands. Yudhishtira's boy was Prativindhya, Bheema's was Sutasoma, Arjuna's Srutakarman, Nakula's son was Satanika, and Sahadeva's prince Srutasena.[1]

Those were halcyon years. The dark and anxious days of the lacquer palace were forgotten, the furtive months in the jungle, and Ekachakra where they ate by begging alms. It seemed destiny smiled on the sons of Pandu, and their worst days were behind them.

But darkness and misfortune, the soul-makers of this world, were gathering themselves once more below time's apparently secure horizon. Surrounded by every luxury, and protected by the most powerful army and allies on earth, the Pandavas would not have dreamt they would soon be homeless wanderers in the wide world again, exiles from their wonderful city.

Meanwhile, the wheel of fortune turned towards its very zenith. The advent, once more, of Narada Muni in Indraprastha was to begin this final ascendancy.

---

1 See Appendix for a description of Abhimanyu and Draupadi's sons.

THREE

Narada, the messenger

ONE MORNING, THE ITINERANT NARADA ARRIVED IN INDRAPRASTHA. The people in the streets saw a spectral pathway in the sky. It flashed down into Yudhishtira's palace where the king sat with his brothers.

Hearing the outcry in the streets, they came out on to a terrace and saw the dazzle in the sky. Next moment, Narada stood smiling before them. Once it had delivered its slender traveller, the ethereal path dissolved.

Yudhishtira knelt before Narada, and the Devarishi placed a lean brown hand on his head. He blessed the others, one by one, and Narada said in his lively way, "I have heard Mayaa has built you a sabha in Indraprastha. I have come to see your sabha, Yudhishtira."

Yudhishtira was happy as a boy. The sage's feet were washed and he was offered madhurparka. Yudhishtira took Narada to Mayaa's sabha and showed the muni around. Narada was full of praise, even whistling softly at this or that marvel. He was obviously something of a connoisseur, since he noticed every nuance in that edifice without having them pointed out to him. When they returned to the palace, Narada said, "Mayaa has excelled himself. His own sabha in Tripura was hardly so wonderful."

Yudhishtira said, "Swami, you range through all the realms. You must have seen other sabhas like ours."

Narada laughed. "I have been in the halls of Yama in the darkness, and Varuna's below the waves, Indra's in Devaloka, and those of Brahma, Vishnu and Rudra, which are past describing. Would you hear about Indra's sabha in Amravati?"

"Yes, we would!"

"The Sudharma is made of light and crystal, in equal parts, and those who come and sit in Indra's sabha are all illustrious ones. Indra's throne is carved out of a single ruby, a jewel of incalculable power. But a king of men shares Indra's throne, and sits beside the Lord of the Devas."

"Who is he?" cried Bheema, hopefully.

"Harishchandra of the Suryavamsha," said Narada, and saw disappointment on their faces.

Changing the subject, with another purpose in mind, Yudhishtira said, "Tell us about the other sabhas, and the kings of the earth who sit in them today."

"The court of Yama is splendid, but swathed in the twilight of patala. The kings that live in Yama's halls are joyful; yet, their joy is tinged with sorrow. Yayati lives with Yama, and Nahusha," said Narada the wanderer, thoughtfully.

"And who else?" asked Nakula, eagerly.

Narada named a hundred great sovereigns of old, now passed on from the earth, among them the Pandavas' distant ancestors. Inexorably, at the end of those hundred, he came to the later kings of the Kuru line. He named Shantanu, and finally, said the name they had been desperate to hear: their father Pandu's. The princes' eyes were full; but in his blithe way, Narada passed on to some stunning descriptions of other unearthly sabhas.

Varuna's fabled court under the waves he told of, and turned the Pandavas' minds away from their father. The muni recounted his adventures in the mountain kingdom of Kubera, for whose sake Siva came to live on Kailasa, which is next to Kubera's ice-city, Alaka, where he keeps the Nine Treasures and the pushpaka vimana. Brahma's many sabhas, Vishnu's court in Vaikunta and Rudra's in Sivaloka, Narada said were ineffable.

"But these are all sabhas in Devaloka, or upon the borders of heaven and earth. But, Yudhishtira, of the sabhas in this world of men there is none to rival yours, not remotely."

A silence fell, and the Pandavas were lost among glowing visions of the courts Narada described, so eloquently, and of the Gods that sat in them. But another matter, closer to home, nagged their hearts, and at last Yudhishtira cried, "Muni, I had always thought the kings of the earth went to Devaloka when they died. From what you say, most of them are still with Yama. You said that Harishchandra shares Indra's throne in Amravati, and surely, he was a devout kshatriya. But our father was no less valiant or pure. He never told a lie in all his years, and was always willing to sacrifice his life for his brothers and his people. Yet, Pandu remains in Yama's halls, while Harishchandra sits beside Indra in the Sudharma. Why, O Narada?"

"Truly, there is nothing to choose in valour or purity between your father and Trishanku's son Harishchandra. Yet, there is another difference. Recently I was in Yama's realm, and I met your father. Pandu said to me, 'Muni, you wander the earth in freedom. When you meet Yudhishtira, tell him that if he undertakes a Rajasuya yagna I shall also enter Indra's swarga, with Shantanu and his sons. Tell him he must perform the yagna that sets one king apart from the rest, and makes him a king of kings.'

"That, dear Yudhishtira, is the difference between your father and Harishchandra. Harishchandra performed the Rajasuya yagna; he was an emperor. But neither you nor your ancestors are, yet."

Yudhishtira avoided Narada's eyes, twinkling at him. The rishi knew how diffident the Pandava was, and always more concerned with dharma than power or glory. He knew that, now, Indraprastha's master would anguish for days over the Rajasuya: could he possibly succeed at such an ambitious venture, should he embark upon it at all?

Gently, Narada said, "Yudhishtira, it is your father's fond wish that, with your mighty brothers beside you, and Krishna's blessings upon you, you should subdue every kingdom of Bharatavarsha. All the rishis say, if any king on earth can attempt a Rajasuya yagna in this yuga, he is Yudhishtira."

"But Muni..." a hundred doubts reared their heads in Yudhishtira's mind.

Narada cut him short. "This is your father's wish, Yudhishtira. I am only Pandu's messenger."

Yudhishtira's thoughts turned back to his boyhood, and he saw his father's face before him: Pandu, who had loved them so much, though they were not his natural sons. Yudhishtira was back in the asrama in Satasringa, and for the first time, he realized his father had died a frustrated man. If any man had been born to be a king it had been

Pandu; but fate had never made him more than his brother's General. Yudhishtira knew beyond any doubt that Pandu wanted to fulfil himself through his sons; and only the fulfilled went to Indra's realm of light.

There was no escape from it, and Yudhishtira saw his brothers' faces shine at the very thought of the imperial yagna. The Rajasuya would be the natural culmination of their years of tutelage under Kripa and Drona, a crowning trial of their worth as kshatriyas. On Bheema's face, on Arjuna's, on Sahadeva's and Nakula's Yudhishtira saw no trace of the doubt that tormented his own heart. They were superbly confident.

But he knew it was a momentous decision to make, and did not commit himself.

FOUR

Yudhishtira's quandary

NARADA STAYED ON FOR SOME DAYS IN INDRAPRASTHA. YUDHISHTIRA was full of anxiety after he heard what Pandu wanted him to do. Yudhishtira had always been singularly free of ambition. When Krishna raised Indraprastha in the wilderness, the Pandava had been more than delighted with his share of the kingdom. Mayaa's sabha had enthralled him: but only as a wonderful new toy excites a child.

Yudhishtira nursed no grievance against his cousins in Hastinapura or his uncle Dhritarashtra. He was pleased to be far from them, and with the peace he enjoyed in Indraprastha. He had no desire to have revenge on the Kauravas: not for having tried to murder his brothers and himself, not for the exile in Ekachakra, not for Dhritarashtra having given him a wasteland for his share of the kingdom. Yudhishtira asked nothing more of life than what he had.

Now he heard his father was still in Yama's halls, and he could only attain Indra's domain if the Pandavas performed a Rajasuya yagna. Yudhishtira's serenity was destroyed. Wild plans of conquest stirred in his gentle heart. He saw his father's face in his dreams, and Pandu spoke sadly to his son, "You must perform a Rajasuya yagna. It is almost the end of the dwapara yuga, and this is our last chance to reach Devaloka."

Yudhishtira's days were troubled, and his nights sleepless. When he knew the dream would not fade and leave him in peace, he reluctantly called a council in the Mayaa sabha. Vyasa also appeared in Indraprastha at this time.

Yudhishtira's quandary

When the sabha sat, Yudhishtira said, "Narada tells me my father remains in Yama's kingdom with his grandsire Shantanu. Pandu sends word that only if we undertake a Rajasuya yagna will our ancestors gain Devaloka. I have given it deep thought, but I failed to arrive at a decision. The Rajasuya is no ordinary yagna. There is no sacrifice on earth as rare or as difficult; how many kings in all time have successfully performed a Rajasuya?

My fear is, are we worthy of the royal yagna? Are we pure enough, strong enough? I need your advice, my friends, I cannot make up my mind."

He turned first to Dhaumya, who said with no hesitation, "You tread the path of dharma, Yudhishtira. To my mind, there is no king on earth more suited to undertake a Rajasuya."

Yudhishtira turned to his grandfather Vyasa. The old rishi said quietly, "My son, it is in your destiny that you will perform the imperial yagna."

A knowing muni that lived in Indraprastha cried, "You will not fail, Yudhishtira. Your fathers will soon be in Devaloka!"

Another said, "A man who plunges thoughtlessly into any endeavour is usually doomed to fail. But he who ponders the nature of his venture, who introspects conscientiously, weighs his own strengths and weaknesses, his resources against his needs, will succeed in whatever he decides to do. And you, Yudhishtira, have thought hard before you even called us here."

Yet another sage smiled, "And you still haven't decided if you will perform the yagna!"

It seemed his brothers agreed with the rishis. When Yudhishtira looked at them, he saw they were flushed with excitement. And which kshatriya would not be? He shared their keenness; but it was not his nature to be carried away by his emotions. He was the king; he must consider every possible pitfall before he embarked on the great enterprise. He knew that if they began and could not complete the yagna, it would break their hearts.

The choice was his, perhaps even because he was so cautious; and he could not make up his mind.

Yudhishtira said doubtfully, "It is only an emperor who may perform the Rajasuya yagna. Yet, Munis, my heart is becoming set on it. But will

I succeed? I must first become the sovereign of every kshatriya in Bharatavarsha, a king of kings."

Now Vyasa said, "You will never decide, one way or another, until you have sought the advice of someone who is not among us today. You had best send word to him and ask what he thinks."

A smile lit Yudhishtira's worried face. Narada volunteered, "I will take word to Krishna that you need him urgently." His eyes grew wistful. "It has been so long since I saw him, anyway."

When Narada arrived in Dwaraka, stepping out of the air with a song on his lips, another messenger, altogether more bedraggled and anxious than the good muni, had just finished delivering a petition from ninety-eight kings. They begged Krishna to come and set them free from the dungeons of Girivraja, where Jarasandha of Magadha had imprisoned them. Their crime against him was that they did not pay him tribute, remaining loyal to dark Krishna instead.

When Krishna had killed own uncle, Kamsa, he had made an implacable enemy of Jarasandha. Kamsa had been a favourite pupil of the king of Magadha, and his son-in-law besides. Jarasandha brought several armies to the gates of Mathura, and Krishna and his Yadavas decimated each one. Every time, to Jarasandha's chagrin, Krishna spared his life: so he could muster more fell legions for the Dark One to slaughter. The Avatara had been born to rid the earth of her burden of evil; and, ruled by his obsession to kill him, Jarasandha served Krishna's purpose.

Now, Krishna thought time was ripe for Jarasandha to die. For it was time the mantle of evil passed on to another spirit of darkness, a demon born into another generation: Duryodhana.

Krishna knew that most of his own battles on earth were over; it was time others fought in his name, especially, his cousins in Indraprastha. He knew one day they would fight a war on the brink of two ages, a war to end all others; and with that war, the kali yuga would begin.

However, immediately, Jarasandha meant to sacrifice the captive kings as soon as they numbered a hundred. He meant to cut their heads off and offer them to Siva. There was an outcry among the Yadavas when the incarcerated kings' messenger brought their message to Krishna's sabha.

"We must march against Jarasandha, and free the ninety-eight!"

"We have spared the Magadhan's life too often!"

"Since we moved to Dwaraka, he brings no more armies against us. Why should he live another day?"

A hundred yojanas from Raivataka was the valley of Girivraja, in which Jarasandha had his capital. The day he heard the Yadavas had abandoned Mathura, that king stormed out of his court and, roaring so the hills around Girivraja trembled, hurled his mace at Dwaraka. Ninety-nine yojanas that glittering weapon flashed through the sky, and fell just outside the gates of the sea-city; and Dwaraka shook. Since that day, Jarasandha left Krishna and the Yadavas alone; now, he had imprisoned Krishna's allies.

Balarama thundered, "You have spared his life too long, Krishna. The wretch must die!"

Krishna did not commit himself. Then Narada arrived, merry and tuneful, ecstatic to see the Blue God again. Krishna rose to receive Brahma's son.

When the Avatara had washed the sage's feet himself, and made him sit in his own throne, he said, "The worlds are free from fear, now your worship ranges over them! How may we serve you, Mahamuni?"

Narada replied, "My Lord, it is not as if anything is hidden from you, ah, not in any of the worlds. Yet, since you want to humour an old man, I will tell you why I have come. Your cousin Yudhishtira is distraught, because I myself sowed a seed in his mind that has sprouted into a grand ambition."

Krishna gave a shout of laughter. "As you ever subtly do! Sometimes to lead evil ones to their doom, and at others to show the kshatriyas of dharma the path to glory."

Narada flushed happily. "My work is only as you please, my Lord. It is you I serve."

"You are far too modest, Muni. Tell me, Narada, what ambition has sprung in my peaceful cousin's heart? Ambition is alien to his very nature. There must be some powerful reason why Yudhishtira has suddenly grown ambitious!"

"He is full of anxiety, Krishna: should he or shouldn't he, will he or won't he perform a Rajasuya yagna? He is anguished, and seeks your advice."

Krishna whistled like a bird. "So, at last, my cousin begins to sense his own destiny. But tell me, Muni, what did you say to him to turn him against his own peace-loving nature?"

"I only did the work of a messenger. I merely conveyed what his father Pandu said to me: that neither he nor Shantanu, or Shantanu's sons could rise from Yama's mazes into Indra's realm, until Yudhishtira performed a Rajasuya yagna."

"How timely you brought this message to Yudhishtira!" cried Krishna. "I have always thought, sagest of sages, that it isn't the messages you bring, but the flawless timing of your arrivals that is so remarkable."

Krishna turned to the messenger from the captive kings of Girivraja. The Yadavas' attention had been deflected from their fervour to ride, at once, to crush Jarasandha.

Now Krishna said, "We have two messengers, my lords, calling us to different places, both with urgent need. On the face of it, their missions seem exclusive of each other, but I wonder if that is truly so. I wonder if Indraprastha is not the way we should be heading to answer the summons from Girivraja."

The messenger from the ninety-eight kings and the rest of the Yadavas looked perplexed. Only Narada smiled. Balarama said heatedly, "How can we save the kings from that madman by going to Indraprastha?"

"It is true," smiled Krishna, "that Jarasandha is mad. Yet, as far as I know, he is also invincible. You have always accused me of forcing you to spare Jarasandha's life, many times, when you held it in the palm of your hand outside Mathura. The truth, Balarama, is that not even you could have killed him, because of a boon he has from his foster-mother, the rakshasi Jara. Jarasandha can only be killed by the one born to kill him."

Krishna looked around him at his Yadavas. He said softly, "My lords, you are so keen to take our legions to Girivraja. But I am afraid, if we do, we will find defeat at its gates."

They began to protest. Krishna said, "I promise you Jarasandha will die, and he will die without our having to take an army to Magadha." He turned back to the messenger, "Friend, your kings will not perish; they will soon be free. Go and tell them not to be anxious. I never fail those who give me their trust." He turned to Narada, "My lord, I will go first to Indraprastha, for the way to Girivraja leads through there."

Yudhishtira's quandary

There were some murmurs in the sabha, and Balarama still seemed confused. But Krishna had made up his mind, and nobody would trifle with that. Time and again, his judgement had been uncannily vindicated; and the obvious way been shown to be the path to disaster. His methods were mysterious, like no one else's, but they were invariably effective.

Krishna set out again for Indraprastha.

FIVE

Krishna arrives in Indraprastha

THE PANDAVAS CAME TO THE GATES OF THEIR CITY WHEN THEY heard Krishna had arrived. They brought him into Indraprastha just as he had left, with Yudhishtira taking Daruka's chariot-reins. Krishna went to his aunt Kunti, who received him like another son; and that is how the Avatara felt when he was here: that he was among his brothers.

Krishna arrived in the late morning, and he had travelled all night. He said he needed an hour's rest before he sat with Yudhishtira to consider the matter that had brought him here. They showed him to the royal apartment, kept just for him. It faced the Mayaa sabha, and no other guest ever stayed in these rooms.

"Arjuna, come sit with me. I don't want to sleep, just to stretch myself for a while."

Avatara and bhakta were closeted together for an hour. Arjuna told Krishna about his brother's state of mind: his keenness to perform the yagna, for Pandu's sake, and his anxiety that it was a task beyond him.

Then Yudhishtira arrived, and he was indeed full of conflict. Falteringly, he began, "Narada must have told you my father wants me to perform the Rajasuya. I gave the matter long thought, and asked the wise men of Indraprastha for their counsel. They all say I should undertake the yagna, and my brothers agree with them.

"I am far from being as confident as they are.

"I fear some want to please me, and others, who love me, don't consider our weaknesses, especially mine. Then there are those who want to see me become an emperor for their own ends, and they don't calculate the dangers of embarking on such a venture from selfish reasons. My brothers are as keen as I am to perform the sacrifice. But Nakula and Sahadeva are still young. Bheema and Arjuna are kshatriyas in the purest sense: for them, there is no higher achievement than a Rajasuya yagna.

"Krishna, you are beyond all other counsellors, and I place my faith in you. Attachment and affection do not sway you; your judgement is immaculate. I am torn between what my father wants, and a host of doubts that plagues me. Tell me what to do."

Krishna laid a hand on his cousin's arm. "Yudhishtira, you have all the qualities an emperor needs, and I, too, would be delighted to see you become lord of the earth. But before you become emperor of Bharatavarsha, every kshatriya across the land, north and south, east and west, must submit to you. There is another king who himself aspires to the title of emperor: Jarasandha of Magadha will never acknowledge your sovereignty.

"He has imprisoned ninety-eight kshatriyas in his dungeons below Girivraja. When they are a hundred, he means to sacrifice them to Siva on the night of a new moon. Anyone who frees those hundred will have their loyalty; and since he must first kill Jarasandha to do this, he shall qualify to become an emperor.

"If the Magadhan dies, none of his friends, Sishupala, Dantavakra, Salva, Rukmi or Paundraka will dare stand against you. As long as Jarasandha lives, Duryodhana and his brothers, Karna and the Kaurava host will be his natural allies; together, they will oppose your Rajasuya. They will perhaps even defeat you in battle. As I see it, the key to our enterprise is Jarasandha. None of the others is the great leader he is.

"I think, Yudhishtira, the first step towards your Rajasuya is killing Jarasandha. As long as he lives, you cannot succeed."

Yudhishtira sat nodding thoughtfully. When Krishna finished, the Pandava gave a sigh of relief. "Nobody else could have given me such sage advice. When you Krishna, my strength, my refuge, are so dubious of our success, I should not dream of going ahead. We would end in a disaster from which we could never recover.

"What the ancients say is so true: the greatest kings have all been men of peace. Anyway, in my heart, I was never for the grandiose enterprise, and I am pleased to abandon it. Thank you, Krishna, you have cleared my confusion!"

Krishna smiled at the other Pandavas. He shook his head that Yudhishtira had misunderstood him.

Bheema cried, "Any great enterprise must seem difficult at first. What we cannot achieve with armies, perhaps we can with craft. With Krishna and Arjuna beside me, I can kill Jarasandha. I have the strength, my brother has the will to prevail, and Krishna shall be our wisdom. You make too much of Jarasandha, I say it will be easy to kill him!"

Krishna shook his head again. "If you really think it will be easy to kill Jarasandha, then you never will. Yama himself has not been able to take the Magadhan out of this world. Jarasandha is a Sivabhakta, and he has the Lord's blessing. Besides, he is a munificent king whose subjects love him."

Bheema looked rather crushed. Then Krishna added, "Yet, it seems he has lost his mind: to think of sacrificing a hundred kshatriyas to Siva is a madman's plan. We shall have the destinies of a hundred kings and their prayers with us. If we go armed with caution, I believe we will succeed."

But Yudhishtira cried, "Ah no, Krishna! You are like my very heart, and Bheema and Arjuna, the eyes on my face. I will not send you three into peril, just because I want to be an emperor. How will a man live without his eyes and his heart?"

He grew more sombre than ever. "The thought of the Rajasuya fills me with foreboding. I say we should abandon the whole thing, before it is too late and we are hopelessly snared in this absurd ambition."

Arjuna had sat quietly. Now he said, "We are kshatriyas; it is our dharma to help the oppressed. Or are we craven, when it comes to facing a powerful enemy?

"Truly, Jarasandha is powerful; they say he is as strong as a thousand elephants. Yet, mere strength seldom endures, when it is not founded in dharma. Even Siva will never countenance the blood sacrifice Jarasandha intends. Yudhishtira, nothing will make your kingship seem more impotent and shameful than ignoring the ninety-eight kings' plea for help."

He paused a moment, then, said, "Besides, Krishna wants us to kill Jarasandha; he wants you to perform the Rajasuya. For me that is enough. I am for going at once to Girivraja."

Krishna himself seemed plunged in thought. But his thoughts had nothing to do with the demon of Magadha. They reached beyond

Girivraja, into the deeper future. He smiled as if Arjuna's averment of devotion touched him, but was quaint, and amused him as well. Krishna said, "That was said like a true kshatriya and a prince of the race of Bharata. And like Kunti's son; you, too, Bheema."

He turned to Yudhishtira, and he was cheerful again. "Cousin, this life on earth is a very brief one. Death lurks around every corner. It may come today or tomorrow, by bright day or in the pitched night, from within or without. Avoiding a battle of dharma never prolonged anyone's life, but it always cost a man his honour: which is a fate worse than death.

"Life flits by, Yudhishtira, and waits for neither you nor me. In life, there is no time for hesitation and too much deliberation. They serve no purpose but to divide the mind against itself. The thing is to act, swiftly, as the time demands."

The Avatara's eyes were grave again, frightening if one gazed into them. "Jarasandha is powerful; not the Devas or the Asuras would challenge him easily. But he is tired of his life. He calls his death eagerly, or he would never have imprisoned ninety-eight anointed kings of the earth.

"It is also time, Yudhishtira, that you and your brothers became the protectors of the world. Your time to rule all Bharatavarsha is near, the time of the destiny for which you were born."

Yudhishtira seemed moved. "Krishna, if you say we should fight Jarasandha, of course we will. Let our army prepare to ride to Girivraja."

"No army. Just Arjuna, Bheema and I will go. Uninvited, we will enter the enemy's house. Jarasandha is a proud kshatriya; he will not refuse us single combat if we challenge him. I think I know which of us he will fight, if we give him the choice between us three. The one he chooses must kill him, or die in the attempt."

There was laughter in his black eyes, "And what shame is there in dying a hero? Such a man finds swarga for himself." A smile tugging at his lips, he said to Yudhishtira, "Well, my lord, do you trust me enough to send your brothers to Girivraja with me?"

"I do, Krishna! But tell me for my curiosity, how is Jarasandha so powerful? What is the secret of his power?"

SIX

Jarasandha

JARASANDHA'S FATHER, BRIHADRATHA'S, FAME WAS LIKE THE LIGHT of the sun that falls across the earth. He was a just king, and he married the twin daughters of the king of Kasi, whose beauty and virtue were a legend. Brihadratha had everything he wanted, but he did not have a son to continue his royal line. There was no yagna he had not performed to get an heir, but to no avail.

Finally, in despair, he went into the jungle with his queens. They wandered in the wilderness for months, living on fruit and roots, hunting occasionally. One day, they saw the Rishi Chandakausika's asrama.

The distraught king began serving the hermit, like a common sishya. Chandakausika was moved by Brihadratha's sincerity. The king never told the rishi who he was; he did not ask him for a boon. One sweltering day, Brihadratha sat before the sage in the shade of a mango tree, when a ripe fruit fell into the muni's lap. Chandakausika gave the mango to Brihadratha and said, "Give this to your queens, and they will bear you a son. Return to your kingdom now. Your place is not in the forest but upon the throne of Girivraja."

Brihadratha prostrated himself at the sage's feet. Then he ran to his queens with the precious fruit. That king had two wives, like mirror images of each other, and he had only one mango. He cut the fruit in two with his sword, and gave a half to each of the women.

The three of them spent that night in love, and when they returned to Girivraja, both queens were pregnant. Nine months passed; the twins went into labour at the same time, and both delivered together. It was midnight of the night of a new moon, when not even the breeze stirred in the trees and the world seemed enveloped in a hush, when each queen gave birth to half a child. He would have been an enormous baby had he been born whole; but, as it was, he was lifeless, cloven by fate.

No one thought of the rishi's boon; or how wisely he had blessed the king and his wives: there would never be jealousy between them, since both would be the natural mothers of the same son. Instead, the queens wailed, the midwives wept. And without showing the bisected child to his father, the palace maids swaddled the two halves of a prince in silk, and left them at the edge of the jungle, in the dark night.

When he heard what had happened, Brihadratha thought this was as a lesson to him: a warning that he would never have a son; it was not written.

In the jungle outside his city, a miracle was unfolding. Jara, the rakshasi, had woken from a deep slumber to the howling of wolves, and she was ravenous. In her slouching, creeping shamble, she set out on her nightly hunt. She sniffed the air; there was not a breath of wind tonight, to carry the scent of any warm-blooded animal. Her eyes were keened for the slightest glimmer from other eyes in the darkness. But all she caught were some mice, which she gobbled; they only whetted her appetite.

Moaning softly, the rakshasi stalked on through the black forest, down the hill-slope, and she saw Girivraja before her. Usually, she never came this far; she was terrified of Brihadratha's guards. Suddenly, the sweetest, most unlikely scent invaded her flared nostrils. She stood hunched, sniffing hard, and she was sure the delicious aroma came not from within the city, but from outside its gates. It was the scent of human flesh.

Drooling, Jara crept forward. The smell of flesh mingled with that of fresh foetal blood was driving her wild. Soon, she scrabbled in frenzy through the undergrowth, and found the two parcels of swaddling. A human woman had miscarried, and abandoned her abortion in the night. Quickly scooping up the two warm wet parcels, the rakshasi scurried back into the deeper forest, whimpering in anticipation of a feast.

Her eyes alight, Jara undid the bloody swaddling of the first parcel. She gave an amazed chuckle: in it, lay half a huge human child. She mumbled to herself, "He would have a made a fine rakshasa, but there is only half of him. I wonder whose child he is."

She untied the other parcel. She wanted to lay out her banquet and feast her eyes, before she tore at it with claw and fang. She hissed in surprise when she had uncovered the second parcel. She began to laugh. As she gazed at the contents of the two parcels by starlight, she felt a wave of pity for the cloven infant. Crooning to the lifeless baby instead of devouring it, she held the halves, one by one, to her breast.

Jara whispered, "How handsome you would have been if only you were born in one piece! My, you would have been a great kshatriya, little one."

Tenderly, she placed the divided infant in her lap, both pieces together. "Let me see how handsome you would have been if you had been born whole."

The rakshasi joined the two pieces together in her lap. There was a flash of light. A powerful charge surged through her hands, as if she had clasped a streak of lightning. She sprang up with a cry, ready to run from the eerie sorcery. But the light had vanished, and Jara saw that the two halves had joined miraculously, and a lusty human baby lay at her feet. He stared up at her with shining eyes, and she saw he breathed. He was alive!

Now the rakshasi had a vision: she saw who the child was, and how he had been born. Poor Jara, all her hunger vanished. She did not have the heart to eat the child to which she had given life. She picked him up, and slouched towards the gates of Girivraja, as dawn reached its fingers over the horizon.

Brihadratha's guards were astonished to see the apparition at their gates in the early dawn: a rakshasi carried a strapping infant in her arms, and she claimed the child was the king's son. The guards sent word in to the palace. Just then, a holy man appeared there; it was Chandakausika. The rishi and the rakshasi clutching a child in her arms were shown into the king's presence. Chandakausika confirmed Jara's story, and said the prince should be named Jarasandha—'joined by Jara'—since but for her he would have rotted in the wild.

When the king rewarded Jara, fed her a bloody meal of raw goat's meat, and gave her freedom of Girivraja to visit Jarasandha whenever she wanted, she shambled back into the jungle.

Chandakausika said to Brihadratha, "Your son is no common child. He will have many strange powers as he grows. He will be awesomely strong, and a great king of the earth. He will be invincible: not the Devas or the Asuras will be able to kill him in battle. He will be the greatest Sivabhakta of his times, and the Lord will bless him."

In Indraprastha, Krishna said to Yudhishtira, "It won't be easy to kill him even now, when he has turned away from dharma. I have heard Jarasandha has seen Siva with his own eyes."

Yudhishtira asked in a whisper, "How will we kill him?"

The Dark One smiled. "No man, even the most gifted, may live beyond the time given him. I know how he can be killed."

Arjuna, Krishna and Bheema set out for Girivraja. Yudhishtira was anxious, but he did not let doubt prevail over his faith in the Blue God.

SEVEN

Girivraja

Disguised as snataka brahmanas, who know the vedas—young men who have completed their gurukulam, but are not grihasthas, householders, yet—Krishna, Bheema and Arjuna set out from Indraprastha. They crossed the deep Sarayu and the swift Gandaki, and the solemn Kalakuta mountains, on their way east to Mithila. They arrived at the borders of Mithila and saw the Ganga, laden with men's sins, flowing out to her lord, the ocean.

They forded her in a tribal's reed-boat, and they went south until they came to the banks of the Sona whose waters are golden. Crossing that river and pressing on, they arrived in fertile, bountiful Magadha. They struck out into the heart of that land, where a ring of five hills called the Goratha, chariot of cows, encircled a great city: Girivraja, the invincible Jarasandha's capital.

They stood on one of the peaks that ringed the city, and saw why Girivraja was impregnable. It was impossible to bring horse or chariot to attack it. Only a winged steed could cross the guardian hills that fell sheerly into the valley in which Girivraja lay.

Krishna said grimly, "It is the enemy's fortress. We must be full of aggression now!"

He tore some rocks off the Chaityaka hill, on which they stood, and hurled them down into the valley below. Bheema and Arjuna joined him; until their kshatriya blood raged and their roars echoed among the hills. Their spirits roused, they came down ferally into the valley and to the city-gates. Like three dangerous beasts of prey, Krishna, Arjuna and Bheema came to Girivraja.

Just outside the city stood a stone temple, an ancient shrine to Siva. The three kshatriyas entered its sanctum and worshipped the God of Gods. When they felt his blessing clearly, they came out and approached Girivraja.

They did not enter at the gates, but scaled the outer walls; and soon three unusual snataka brahmanas were swaggering through the streets of Jarasandha's capital, looking for trouble. They snatched some garlands off a flower-vendor's stall, and when he began to remonstrate with them, they silenced him with a low growling in their throats. They did not pay for the garlands, or say a word.

With the garlands draped around their sandal- and ash-coated bodies, they walked colourfully through the streets. People stared at the strangers, who were dressed like snatakas but had the physiques and the haughty demeanour of kshatriyas spoiling for a fight. Like a pride of lions, the three sauntered through Girivraja, daring anyone to accost them.

Meanwhile, evil omens appeared over the city. The brahmanas who read these signs saw birds of the air flying queerly, in wheeling, panicstricken swarms. Sacrificial fires spluttered and died, and purulent smoke issued from the embers. The priests grew alarmed, and, turning to their almanacs, found the planets were in precarious aspects.

The brahmanas came anxiously to the king, and said, "Sinister omens have gathered over Girivraja's destiny. You must perform a mrityunjaya homa at once; your life is in danger."

Jarasandha said, "Make arrangements in the palace temple. I will come there straightaway."

Even as the king of Magadha sat at the ritual, meant to turn death away, three warriors come to kill him arrived at his opulent palace. They did not enter at the gates. He was their enemy, and a kshatriya must never enter an enemy's house openly, but by stealth. Again they scaled the walls and stalked into Jarasandha's chamber of audience, in disguise, garlanded, and smeared with ashes and sandal-paste.

Word came to the king that three snataka brahmanas sought audience with him. His guard told Jarasandha of the trio's unusual entry into his palace. The king sent them madhurparka, milk and honey, and asked them to wait for him.

It was midnight, when the homa was completed, and Jarasandha came to meet the visitors, who had aroused his curiosity. He bowed to the strangers. His shrewd eyes appraised them. He saw their brahmanas' attire: sandal-paste and saffron garments, tall tilakas on their foreheads. He also saw the marks on their muscled arms made by bowstrings. He saw how splendidly they were built and knew these were no brahmanas but kshatriya warriors.

But he said warmly, "Welcome to Girivraja! It is strange that snatakas come to my palace wearing sandal-paste and garlands. It is stranger they choose to enter by scaling my walls. This isn't the way that friends arrive.

"And, friends, you refused the madhurparka I sent you. Yet, you are welcome. I see warriors' physiques under your ash and sandal-paste, battle-scars on your skin, and the marks of bowstrings on your shoulders. I wonder if you are brahmanas or kshatriyas. But whoever you are, you are welcome in Girivraja!"

Krishna smiled. "It is indeed the friend who enters at the gate, and the enemy that comes over the wall. The kshatriya is not known for sweet words, but his deeds. We have come to challenge you."

Jarasandha peered at them in the lamplight. "But who are you? Why do you want to challenge me, when I do not recall ever having harmed you? You say you are my enemies. How can you be my enemies when I have not set eyes on you before? I have many enemies, certainly, but none that I have never seen. Tell me who you are."

Krishna replied, "You have made prisoners of ninety-eight kings, and you mean to slaughter them in Siva's name. We are your enemies because you want to sacrifice these kshatriyas like animals."

"I have defeated every king in my prisons in battle. Their lives are mine, in dharma."

He still peered curiously at them in the deep night. The certainty grew on him that he had seen the strangers' spokesman before. He knew that ash- and sandal-coated face, and those black eyes full of transcendent mockery. He cried, "But tell me who you are, and where you have come from."

Krishna said softly, "I am Krishna of Dwaraka. These are my cousins Bheema and Arjuna. We have come to tell you to let the captive kings go free, or face any of us in single combat. Of course, if you are not afraid to, after the Yadavas routed you eighteen times outside Mathura."

Jarasandha's eyes blazed. Then he began to laugh, a silent shaking of his great body which turned to echoing peals. "There is more than one version of those eighteen battles. People say for fear of me you hide out at sea, behind Raivataka. Yet, you come here to challenge me in Girivraja. The thought is amusing, cowherd."

His eyes glinted. "Krishna, you dare come here and tell me what I should do with my prisoners. Have you forgotten who I am? Cowherd, I am Jarasandha. I fear no one in the world, and no one has ever vanquished me.

"You have come to your deaths. Tell me, how shall we fight? Army against army, or hand to hand? How many of you will fight me at once? All of you? Two at least? Or were you thinking of sending home for some more brothers and cousins, if I agreed to fight you?"

Still smiling equably, Krishna said, "Choose one of us, Kshatriya. Which one will you fight?"

Jarasandha sneered at them. "You will be poor antagonists, all of you. You, Krishna, are a known coward; I will not fight you. This Arjuna, who sits beside you like a fawning puppy, is just a boy. I am not in the habit of doing battle with children. As for this big fellow here, well, at least he looks like a man. He seems well built enough, so the fight may not be entirely one-sided.

"Bheema, I will fight you, and if I win let both your kingdoms become mine! If I lose, my kingdom will be yours."

Arjuna and Bheema glanced at Krishna, who nodded. Bheema said nothing; he rose and bowed, accepting the Magadhan's challenge. Now he had seen the enemy, felt his awesome presence and power, Bheema was more circumspect. But Jarasandha, who had never known fear in his life, felt a shiver of terror in his blood.

He said quickly, "Rest well tonight, enemies, and tomorrow we shall fight. After I have killed Bheema, both Indraprastha and Dwaraka will be mine, and you shall be my subjects. Tonight is your last night of freedom. Is there anything I can send you to make your night warm?"

Krishna replied, "Just a bed will do."

Jarasandha insisted, "You are my guests. I could not have hoped for greater fortune than your coming here like this, especially you, cowherd. You shall have wine and the best food in all Bharatavarsha, the finest women, too. Enjoy them, Bheema, this is your last night in the world. We begin at noon tomorrow."

He rose abruptly and left them. Warm, indeed, was Jarasandha's hospitality and, while the two Pandavas and Krishna were awash on it, later that night, Jarasandha himself attended an unusual ceremony: he had his son Sahadeva crowned king of Magadha. He could not stop thinking of the omens seen in his city, and icy foreboding laid its fingers on his heart.

But when he came to fetch his guests the next day at noon, no trace of fear remained on the Magadhan. He was just a superb kshatriya now, his mighty body oiled and glistening for the day's combat, his confidence supreme. After all, despite the omens, who could possibly know how he, whom Jara had joined, could be killed? He was convinced no one knew that secret, and so no one could kill him.

EIGHT

The blade of grass

THE NEXT DAY, AT NOON, JARASANDHA LED BHEEMA TO A COURTYARD in his palace, and a wrestling-pit full of white river-sand. The Magadhan said, "Which weapon do you prefer?"

"The mace," replied Bheema.

A selection of the finest maces was fetched, and Jarasandha allowed Bheema first choice. Krishna smiled, "It is a pity you flung away the mace that made you invincible. I have it in my palace in Dwaraka."

"I am still invincible, cowherd. And that mace will shortly be mine again, and your Dwaraka along with it."

It was time to begin and, maces clutched in hands powerful as thunderbolts, the giant combatants began to circle each other. The sieved sand sparkled like crushed diamonds under their feet. With a roar that welled from his belly, Bheema struck out wildly at Jarasandha's head. Quicker than the eye, the king evaded the stroke and Bheema staggered forward a step.

In a flash, Jarasandha swung a sharp half-blow at him from behind. It crashed into Bheema's back and he almost fell; and if he had fallen, Jarasandha's next blow would have killed him. But the legs of the son of the wind were as strong as trees. Bheema swivelled on his heels, and struck back at Jarasandha: a looping blow that began near the Pandava's feet, curved up and took the Magadhan smartly on his arm, fetching a cry from him.

Jarasandha roared, "You are strong, Pandava! And not half as dull as you look. This may turn out to be a better fight than I had thought."

Bheema kept his eyes fixed on his adversary's, ignoring what he said, just as his master had taught him to. The eye, Balarama had told him, never lies. Like two beasts from the earth's dim past, they circled in tense ritual, always seeking an opening to strike at. It would be an instant's relaxation, a fleeting weakness: that was all, because these two were great mace-fighters. But that moment was all they would need to make a kill.

Patiently, they circled. After his first blind swing, no further rashness came from Bheema. The thought sobered him that, if he had fallen, it would have been an end to everything. As they circled, they seemed to grow in stature, until they towered over the white arena.

Like summer lightning, Jarasandha aimed a savage stroke at Bheema's chest. Now Bheema was a blur of evasion and, quick as thinking, he struck back at the Magadhan. Just in time, Jarasandha raised his mace-head, saving his face. The two maces burst apart with the force of that blow, and Jarasandha's laughter rang through his palace.

"Well done, Pandava! I shall enjoy this duel. Fetch us more maces. Or would you rather fight hand to hand?"

Bheema stood there, and not a word out of him. But his eyes shone as brightly as Jarasandha's. He raised his arms in front of his chest to show he was ready to fight barehanded. Again, they circled, warily, changing their inner rhythms, adapting to the new form of combat. They knew it would be a serious mistake to imagine that fighting barehanded would be less dangerous than with maces. Both kshatriyas' hands were weapons hardened with years of striking rocks, crushing them. A blow from those hands could fell not just a man, but an elephant.

Meanwhile, their roars had fetched the people from the streets of Girivraja to the wrestling arena. Word flashed through the city that their king and a stranger were battling to the death, with their kingdoms set as stake. The people, brahmanas, kshatriyas, vaisyas, sudras, and even women and the aged came running to watch the stranger die. It was seldom, nowadays, that anyone came to challenge Jarasandha. This stranger must be a fool, or he must be tired of his life.

But as they arrived, they heard whispers that it was their old enemy Krishna who had come to challenge their king, and his cousin Bheema was the one Jarasandha was fighting. Soon they saw how evenly the two were matched. Why, if Jarasandha had been any other kshatriya, Bheema would have killed him by now. But Jarasandha had a boon from the Lord

Siva that he could be killed in just one way; and, of course, no one knew that secret.

This was the first day of the month of Kartika. The combatants had used a hundred holds and locks, vicious kicks to the marmas of the body, and blows, flat-handed and close-fisted, all at stunning speed. Any of these would have killed any other opponent, except three or four men on earth. But Bheema and Jarasandha knew the proper block and parry for each blow, every kick and iron lock; and no harm came to either.

With lowered heads, they butted one another like fighting rams, and shuddered with the impacts. They kicked each other with feet like thunder, and blows like whiplash lightning, and, invariably, these fell harmlessly on other parts of the body than they were meant to. Both were gifted, superbly trained, and each stronger than a bull-bison. In different ways, neither of their strengths was merely human.

The noise of their duel was like electric storms, like cliffs crumbling into the sea. At dusk, a conch blared, announcing an end to the day's combat. The warriors embraced each other and left the arena, and the crowd dispersed. And now, Jarasandha the ferocious antagonist was transformed into the most gracious host. The adversaries returned to the Magadhan king's palace for nightlong revelry, and the cordial exchange of drunken pleasantries and insults.

Late that night, Arjuna said wryly to Krishna, "This enemy is a better host than most of our friends."

Full of the delectable wine served at Jarasandha's table, cosseted by the loveliest women from his harem, Krishna agreed with feeling, "May Bheema kill him slowly, over many days."

So it turned out. For twenty-six days, all that month of Kartika, the two titans fell at each other for three hours every afternoon, with maces they swiftly broke, and then with bare hands. Each day, at dusk, they returned to the palace, bruised, often bloody: returned to dice and wine, delicious food, song and dance, uninhibited gaiety and the most luscious women. Indeed, it seemed that with every day the two kshatriyas' spirits improved.

Krishna said to Arjuna, "I see now why this Asura is such a favourite of Siva's. Twenty-six days, and his hospitality and generosity continue unabated." The Dark One sighed. "He is a magnificent kshatriya."

But at crack of dawn on the twenty-seventh day of the fluctuating duel, Krishna came to see his cousin Bheema in his room. Bheema had grown strangely close to the lord of Girivraja: as if the fight to death they waged daily bound them together with invisible thongs.

Krishna said, "Tomorrow is amavasya, the day he has been waiting for. His kind is strongest when the moon is new. You must kill him today, Bheema, or he will kill you tomorrow. Watch me for a sign, and I will show you how to finish him. It is time he died, or Yudhishtira will never perform the Rajasuya, and your father will remain in Yama's labyrinths.

For Pandu and Yudhishtira, for the kings in his dungeons, who I believe are a hundred now, and for this earth, who has borne his burden for too long: you must kill Jarasandha today."

Bheema smiled, "I have grown fond of him; he is great-hearted. But he is old, and he is tiring. I will kill him, Krishna: for your sake as well as for all the others'!" Bheema knelt at Krishna's feet, and the Dark One blessed him.

Five sets of maces were quickly shattered that afternoon. The king and his palace guest fell on each other with bare hands. Yet, they were more cautious than ever, both conserving their ebbing energies: only the one who endured would live. Suddenly, Bheema began to feel unaccountably strong, as if someone was infusing him with unearthly power. With this new strength, he swung an iron fist at the Magadhan. Caught unawares by a sickening blow, Jarasandha fell with a cry.

In a flash Bheema was on him, his knee planted on his enemy's chest, his vast hands round his throat to choke life out of him. Jarasandha's face turned purple, but he did not die. At last, Bheema released the thick throat, and turned desperately to Krishna. Jarasandha sat up, laughing, and struck Bheema a dreadful blow.

Bheema roared and sprang forward to clinch with him. Now, the Pandava was full of doubt as they circled, with immense arms locked. Bheema knew he had been within a whisker of killing Jarasandha. But he had not died, when Bheema had choked him for so long that his heart must have stopped beating. As they circled, breathing heavily, Bheema saw Krishna smiling at him. The Avatara held a blade of grass in his hands, and he tore it along its length.

The strange strength coursed through Bheema's arms again; he understood the meaning of the blade of grass. In a blur, he tripped

The blade of grass

Jarasandha into the sand, damp with their sweat. Quick as thinking he seized the king's ankles, one in each hand. Jarasandha's eyes flew open in shock, and a roar of alarm erupted from his lips. Bheema tore that king in two from his anus to his crown; and his steaming intestines, his faeces, heart, liver, spleen, all his innards spilled on to the white sand.

The crowd was petrified that the impossible had happened: Jarasandha was dead. Bheema gave a roar of triumph, he ran to Krishna and Arjuna to embrace them. But there was the queerest look in Krishna's eyes and, as Bheema flung his arms round his cousin, he heard a sound that froze his blood. The crowd was shouting its king's name again.

'Jarasandha! Jaya, Jarasandha!'

Slowly, Bheema turned, and his cry of terror at what he saw in the wrestling-pit echoed across the city. The torn halves of Jarasandha's body had joined themselves together; all his spilt organs had packed themselves into place again. There was a flash of light like the one when Jara, the rakshasi, once joined two pieces of a baby together and gave a huge prince life. The lord of Magadha rose from the dead, and laughing as if the tearing of his body had been a delightful jest, he advanced on Bheema again.

Bheema stood rooted. Wasn't it possible then to kill this terrible king? What point was it fighting if the demon would not die after being torn in two? As the grinning Jarasandha beckoned to him to come into a clinch again, Bheema turned in despair to Krishna. Arjuna looked as mortified as his brother did. But Krishna stood smiling, as if nothing extraordinary had happened. He held another blade of grass in his hands; who knew where he had come by a blade of grass? As Bheema watched him, amazed, again Krishna ripped the green blade in two; and now he crossed his hands and threw the torn halves in opposite directions.

Once more, Bheema felt the eerie strength surge through him. He leapt back into the wrestling-pit and charged Jarasandha. The king was taken aback; he had thought the Pandava's nerve would break when he saw that Jarasandha of Magadha rose from the dead. Bheema seized him and, hefting his bulk over his head, began to whirl him round.

Jarasandha roared with laughter. "Prepare to die when you have finished your little game!"

Bheema let him down suddenly, and seized his ankles. Planting his foot at the fork of his legs, Bheema tore him in two again, in a flash, so he had no time even to scream. Out spilled the warm and bloody innards. Bheema stood panting. Still holding one half of the giant body in each hand, he glanced uncertainly at Krishna. Krishna crossed his wrists.

Crossing his arms, Bheema flung the two body halves in opposite directions, so each one lay with its back to the other. Now they did not join and Jarasandha did not rise from the dead. His people shouted to him to come back, not to abandon them, O great king. The pieces of his corpse did not even twitch. Their king, Lord Siva's bhakta, would never rise again.

Krishna's celebrant cry rang through Girivraja: the roar of a triumphant God! Now he ran to embrace Bheema, who collapsed exhausted in the Dark One's arms. They paid the dead king every homage, but there was panic in the palace of Girivraja. Panic gripped the ministers and courtiers: what would become of them?

The customary shock that follows the death of a mighty sovereign seized the city, and the streets of mourning. The people knew their kingdom had been the stake for the duel. Would Magadha become part of Indraprastha? Would Yudhishtira come to rule Girivraja, or would Bheema or Arjuna become its king?

Krishna's first concern was for the hundred royal captives. He had them released from the fetid catacomb under the palace, where Jarasandha held them.

When those kshatriyas emerged into the clean night air, they saw dark Krishna effulgent and four-armed before them, and they knelt before him. When they had thanked him, repeatedly, for saving them from being brutally sacrificed, they asked what they could do for him in return.

Krishna said, "It was Bheema who saved you. His brother Yudhishtira wants to perform a Rajasuya yagna, and become emperor of Bharatavarsha. See you give him your support."

The hundred swore, "Yudhishtira is already our emperor!"

Krishna turned his mind back to Girivraja. At midnight of the day his father was torn in two by Bheema, Jarasandha's eldest son, another Sahadeva, found himself king in Magadha. No condition was attached to his kingship, except that he recognised Yudhishtira as his emperor and ally. Jarasandha's ministers retained their positions of influence.

Having achieved the impossible in Girivraja, Krishna set out for Indraprastha with an exuberant Bheema and Arjuna, and the chariots laden with the gold and jewels that Sahadeva sent with him.

When they arrived at the gates of Indraprastha, the three of them raised their sea-conches and blew clarion blasts on them, so the walls of that city shook. Yudhishtira came out from his palace. Tears streaming down his face, he hugged his brothers and his cousin. "This is a miracle, Krishna. We could have never killed Jarasandha without you."

Krishna replied, "Don't balk at the Rajasuya any more."

Yudhishtira made them recount the battle between Bheema and Jarasandha, day by day, blow by blow, again and again; as if he could never hear enough about the enemy's strength, and Bheema's valour. And Bheema never tired of telling the part when he had the shock of his life: when, after he had torn Jarasandha in two the first time, his body joined itself together and that king stood laughing at the Pandava.

"That is when I was sure everything was lost." Then he would sigh, "But Krishna was with me, and Jarasandha's time had come."

Krishna said to Yudhishtira, "I must go back to Dwaraka, and you must send your legions to the four quarters, with your brothers leading them. Declare yourself emperor of Bharatavarsha, and collect tribute from all the kingdoms for your sacrifice. With Jarasandha dead and a hundred kings already having sworn allegiance to you, your task will not be hard. When Bheema, Arjuna, Sahadeva and Nakula ride home in triumph, I will also come with the Yadavas from Dwaraka. And we will perform the great yagna, so your father and his fathers ascend into Indra's heaven."

With quiet satisfaction, that his most implacable enemy, Jarasandha, was dead, Krishna came home to Dwaraka.

NINE

The four quarters

In INDRAPRASTHA, EXCITEMENT WAS IN THE AIR. THE RAJASUYA YAGNA was on everyone's lips. From being some ruins in a wilderness of thorns, this city would soon be the focus of Bharatavarsha, her emperor's capital. Vyasa arrived, and he advised Yudhishtira on every detail of the sacrifice.

"You must first receive tribute from all the kings of Bharata. Let your brothers go forth and subdue the four quarters in your name. Only an emperor may perform the Rajasuya yagna."

Arjuna elected to go north, Bheema east, Nakula west and Sahadeva to the south. No king could resist Arjuna's advent; most preferred to acknowledge Yudhishtira's sovereignty without a battle that they could only lose. As Arjuna went north, the name Vijaya—the victorious—followed his triumphal progress.

Salva, the Sivabhakta and sorcerer whom Amba once chose, barred his way. Salva was a friend of Kamsa and Jarasandha, of Rukmi and Sishupala of the old conspiracy that had opposed Krishna from the start. But he was no longer the dauntless kshatriya he had once been. Since news of Jarasandha's death spread, every king of that alliance was forced to reconsider his position. It was as if their heart had been carved from them.

Salva had heard that Bheema had torn Jarasandha in two. He thought Arjuna's arrival in his kingdom was a fine opportunity to take revenge on the Pandavas. It was not to be. Arjuna won the day in a humiliatingly brief encounter. Quite simply, no army on earth could stand before his unearthly archery.

Salva, also, had to send Yudhishtira tribute. But he did not attend the Rajasuya; nursing his shame, he swore to strike back. He was convinced Krishna was the moving spirit behind these Pandavas. They were nothing without their blue cousin; he was the real enemy. Salva swore he would avenge himself on Krishna for Jarasandha's death and his own defeat. And indeed, he would try; but not yet.

Arjuna marched on, and came to the northern-most city in Bharatavarsha. The Demon Naraka, the son of Bhumi Devi and the Varaha, once ruled Pragjyotishapura in the mountains. Krishna killed Naraka, some years ago, and his son Bhagadatta was now king in his father's city of sorcery perched between heaven and earth.

Krishna had breached Pragjyotishapura, flying out of the sky on Garuda. Arjuna arrived by tortuous mountain trails, with his army from Indraprastha. He sent word to Bhagadatta that he should pay tribute to Yudhishtira or be prepared to fight him. And because he was a great kshatriya himself, Bhagadatta came out of his city to face Arjuna in the valley in which Pragjyotishapura was built.

Eight days, the two fought. Eight nights, the mountains lit up with other suns risen over them: the light of livid astras. Arjuna extinguished Bhagadatta's final missile, and it fell in a shower of embers on to white peaks. Bhagadatta came before the Pandava and gave up his city of black crystal.

"Your father was my friend, Arjuna, and Pandu could never have vanquished me in battle. You are a greater kshatriya than he was. What shall I do for you?"

Before his own army, before the people of Pragjyotishapura, Arjuna prostrated himself at Bhagadatta's feet. The Pandava said humbly, "Bhumiputra, Son of the Earth, my brother Yudhishtira means to perform a Rajasuya yagna in Indraprastha. We shall be honoured if you attend."

Bhagadatta embraced Arjuna and cried, "I shall be honoured to come!"

Arjuna left Pragjyotishapura, laden with treasures, many wrought in the elder ages. Bhagadatta gave him the golden vessels of Varuna, the very ones with which the Lord of the ocean performed his own Rajasuya, in time out of mind, the infancy of the earth. But Bhagadatta never forgave Arjuna for defeating him.

Arjuna rode towards Ramagiri, the mountain where Rama had lived for some weeks of his exile. The waters of its lake were sacred; for, precious Sita had bathed in them. It was on Ramagiri that Arjuna first fought the Trigarthas. After a long and fierce encounter, he had their measure and they fled from him. But their enmity was to last until he killed them all in the war on the crack of the ages.

The Trigarthas called themselves Samsaptakas from then. They swore to kill Arjuna, and became Duryodhana's allies.

Still further north went Arjuna, and he saw the peak of Meru before him in the virgin light of dawn. It seemed the massif wrapped itself in a cloak of gold and crimson and, then, offered the light of the sun back to the star. Arjuna stood chastened at the foot of Meru. He could feel the mountain's spirit, replete with the eternal Brahman.

Full of a sense of primordial time, and deep peace, Arjuna prostrated himself before golden Meru, from which the continents unfurl like petals from the corolla of a lotus. At last, the Pandava wrenched himself away from that holiest mountain, and turned back to the harsh world and its endless conflicts. Before he turned south, he prayed fervently that he would have the fortune to return to this place, some day, when all his battles were over.

As he went, he saw how the lower slopes of Meru were overgrown with the verdant jambu vine, in vivid bloom now, with orange and vermilion flowers splashed everywhere, in places like blood on a wounded warrior. The jambu was especially sacred to the eldest mountain rishis, some of whom lived for thousands of years. The land of Bharata is called Jambu Dwipa by the siddhas and charanas who are not mortal.

Though he was a kshatriya, Arjuna was always drawn to solitary places, and to silence. There still remained one mountain he must see before he went back: Gandhamadana, the fragrant one, gatekeeper of Devaloka! Having paid homage to that great spirit as well, Arjuna turned home to Indraprastha, to bring Yudhishtira news that the northern quarter had been conquered in his name, and worship offered to Meru and Gandhamadana.

Arjuna came home laden with treasure from all the kingdoms he passed through, and he was called Dhananjaya, winner of wealth.*

---

* Several other conquests are enumerated in detail in the original text for Arjuna and his brothers.

Meanwhile, Bheema had set out towards the countries of the rising sun. Through Panchala he went, and came to Mithila where its king resisted him: but not for long. Soon, carrying tribute from vanquished Mithila, he came to Chedi, his cousin Sishupala's kingdom. Since the Dark One had carried Rukmini away on the day she was to marry that prince, Sishupala had been Krishna's mortal enemy. He had fought outside Mathura eighteen times, in every army Jarasandha brought to Krishna's gates; and more than often, Krishna had spared his cousin's life.

Bheema expected Sishupala to meet him with an army at the gates of Chedi. Instead, a warm reception awaited him. The streets had been hung with garlands and perfumed with elephants' ichor and incense, to welcome the Pandava. In some surprise, Bheema allowed himself to be feted in the most effusive fashion. It occurred to him that Sishupala was only testing the wind after Jarasandha's death.

But such was the hospitality of the 'Bull of Chedi' that Bheema became convinced Sishupala was, also, genuinely affectionate. Finally, the time came to leave.

"Be sure to come to the Rajasuya, cousin!"

"How could I not come?" cried Sishupala, and Bheema naively imagined a new bond had been forged. He felt sure that Krishna and Sishupala would also bury their enmity.

On to Kosala, Ayodhya, and a hundred other, lesser kingdoms rode the son of the wind. They all paid him tribute for his brother in Indraprastha: some after battle, which was inevitably short and one-sided, and others without resistance, coming out to receive the kshatriya at their gates, yielding to him without a blow being struck.

At last, Bheema came to Magadha, to hidden Girivraja, and Jarasandha's son, young Sahadeva, received him with respect and promised to be in Indraprastha for the Rajasuya. Bearing wealth from the eastern kingdoms, Bheema returned home to a hero's welcome from Yudhishtira.

A month later, Sahadeva came home as well, carrying treasures from the south. He had defeated Dantavakra of Jarasandha's old conspiracy, Srenima, Vinda and Anuvinda, the brothers of Avanti, and Neela of Mahishmati in the deepest south of Bharatavarsha.

Then, Sahadeva arrived on the shore of the southern sea, and stood upon a lonely beach on a silvery night as the waves dinned their thunder at him. Across these waves, lay the island of Lanka, where a noble king of an olden race of rakshasas still ruled. That king, Vibheeshana, belonged to an age when men lived for thousands of years, and were altogether more splendid than the men of these lesser days could imagine.

Vibheeshana was the Rishi Pulastya's son, and the legendary Ravana's brother. Once, when Ravana held Sita a prisoner in Lanka, Vibheeshana had begged his brother to return her to Rama, or doom would visit their island. Blinded by passion, and deluded by the flattery of fawning courtiers, Ravana turned on Vibheeshana, accusing him of cowardice and treachery.

Vibheeshana fled Lanka, and joined Rama. When Ravana died after a savage war, Rama crowned Vibheeshana king in Lanka. With mighty Hanuman, Vibheeshana also flew to Ayodhya in Kubera's pushpaka vimana for Rama's coronation. Long ago, Rama had left the world; but Chiranjeevi Vibheeshana still ruled Lanka when, one night, Sahadeva the Pandava came to the southern tip of Bharatavarsha, and stood gazing across the surging foam, with the wind whistling around him.

Sahadeva felt he must invite Vibheeshana to the Rajasuya yagna. But he was no Rama, and his army had no awesome vanaras in it, who could build bridges across the sea, or leap a hundred yojanas across the phosphorescent waves. As he stood on that shining beach, Sahadeva had an inspiration. He shut his eyes and called the name of another fabulous being, for whom oceans and mountains were no obstacles.

Sahadeva had hardly called his name under the flowing moon, than his nephew Ghatotkacha appeared before him. He was so much like Bheema; but taller, slimmer, and his head still hairless and smooth as a ghatam, a water-pot. Sahadeva clasped Ghatotkacha to him, and the rakshasa knelt before his uncle for his blessing.

Sahadeva said, "On Lanka lives a great rakshasa, who was a bhakta of Rama of Ayodhya. Yudhishtira's yagna will not be complete unless Vibheeshana attends it. Can you fly to him, my child, and say that I beg him to come to my brother's sacrifice in Indraprastha?"

Ghatotkacha bowed and, easily as a bird, the young rakshasa rose into the sky and flashed away over the sea to the island like a green jewel. With his grandsire, the wind, blowing around him, Ghatotkacha glided along quite like a certain vanara, who was also a son of Vayu, had done an age ago.

As he flew by the light of the setting moon, Ghatotkacha saw a slender necklace of stone and wood laid across the waves. It was broken in many places now, but stretched from the shore of Bharatavarsha, across the horizon, all the way to Lanka. It was Nala the vanara's bridge: the Nalasetu over which Rama and his monkey legions crossed into Lanka.

Dawn was breaking on the eastern sky, when Ghatotkacha saw Lanka ahead of him: a jade island glimmering in the sleepy ocean. Down flew Ghatotkacha, smoothly as a bird. Now he saw that some mountains thrust their way into the sky from the island. Seeming actually to float above them, was a city that appeared to be made of fine crystal, its towers and mansions sparkling.

Ghatotkacha thought that not the hidden rakshasa cities of the north were as wonderful as Vibheeshana's capital set like a sapphire in the hills. He remembered Viswakarman had once built this city for terrible Ravana.

Ghatotkacha landed in Vibheeshana's courtyard. At once, a patrol of stern rakshasas surrounded him with dark weapons drawn. He had never seen ayudhas like these; they were old, and of strange appearance. Not, of course, that had he chosen to fight them, those weapons would have been of any use to Vibheeshana's guard against Ghatotkacha. He was the wind's grandson. He would have smashed them down even as another Vayuputra had done their ancestors, thousands of years ago.

As it was, unlike Hanuman, Ghatotkacha had come in peace and with a message of friendship for Vibheeshana. He smiled at the soldiers who accosted him, and folded his hands to show he meant no harm.

"Look, he is a rakshasa!" said the leader of the guards.

"Indeed I am, uncle, of the northern strain of our people," replied Ghatotkacha, speaking the old tongue fluently.

Vibheeshana's was a just kingdom and he was a king of dharma. Not since Rama came to Lanka had the island known war of any kind. Vibheeshana had been content to rule his own people, and to return Lanka to the path of truth from which Ravana had torn it. Perhaps, Vibheeshana's rule was not as brilliant or ambitious as his ten-headed brother's had been. But it was a reign of peace and had heaven's favour.

The palace guards brought Ghatotkacha before Vibheeshana, who said gently, "You are one of our own people, young man. Tell me, who are you and what brings you to Lanka?"

Ghatotkacha folded his hands to the great king on his throne, which seemed to be carved out of a single crimson coral. Vibheeshana looked as old as a mountain. His eyes shone affectionately at Ghatotkacha, and his face was a map of lines. His presence was one of fathomless stillness.

Ghatotkacha said, "I am Ghatotkacha, my lord. I am Hidimbi and Bheema's son, Vayu's grandson, and a nephew of Yudhishtira, who is Krishna's cousin and ally. My uncle Sahadeva waits on the southern shore of Bharatavarsha; he sent me. The Pandavas mean to perform a Rajasuya yagna in Indraprastha. Sahadeva begs you to attend the sacrifice."

As he spoke, Ghatotkacha studied Vibheeshana's serene face and was reminded of Yudhishtira. He saw the same nobility and purity, the same slow thoughtfulness; and their kindly eyes were so alike.

After a moment, Vibheeshana said, "You are welcome to Lanka, Ghatotkacha. We grant you freedom of our city. I want to hear all about the Pandavas and their dark cousin. We are told Krishna is the Avatara who has come at the end of the yuga: the one born into the House of the Moon. I hear he is my Rama returned to the world for its deliverance. Come, my son, sit near me and tell me about your uncles."

Thinking how gentle this king was, more a human being than a rakshasa, Ghatotkacha sat beside Vibheeshana and recounted the lives of the Pandavas. He began with the times of Bheeshma the patriarch, the son of Ganga; and in a while, he had brought the Lord of Lanka to the southern shore of Bharatavarsha, where Sahadeva waited. Whenever Ghatotkacha spoke of Krishna, he saw how intently the king listened, as if he hung on every word. Vibheeshana saw another dark face in his mind, a face long since vanished from the earth.

When Ghatotkacha finished, Vibheeshana said, "Tell your uncles I will be honoured to come to Indraprastha for their Rajasuya yagna. Meanwhile, will you take a few gifts from me for the Pandava king?"

Vibheeshana thought, 'How can I not come to Indraprastha? At least to see your face, Krishna.'

The few gifts turned out to be a small treasure, mainly of jewels from another yuga, whose worth could not be estimated in these times: auspicious pearls, corals, rubies, blue sapphires and emeralds big as eggs. Receiving these in a silken bag, Ghatotkacha knelt before Vibheeshana for his blessing. The king laid his palm on his head, then, drew him up and embraced him.

"You are a worthy nephew of your uncles, and a worthy son of your father. But come, let me show you from where another uncle of yours once leapt out of Lanka."

Vibheeshana led Ghatotkacha on to an open terrace, and showed him a place in the stone floor where two great footmarks had been filled with gold and sparkling gemstones. There was an offering of incense and fresh flowers before them.

"This is from where Hanuman of the vanaras, who was another son of Vayu, leapt across the sea. And how Lanka shook! A yuga has passed since then. Today, Ghatotkacha, you must leap from here, and we will record your coming as well. Let it remind us that he who came as Rama has been born again into the world."

So, from quite near where Hanuman once leapt, Bheema's son flew up with a roar into the cyanic blue, and flashed back through the sky to Sahadeva. In Lanka, the rakshasas marked the place from where he leapt.

Sahadeva received his nephew excitedly. Truth to tell, when he had sent Ghatotkacha to Lanka he had not been sure if Vibheeshana still ruled there. Now, the young rakshasa had returned with gifts worthy of an emperor, and Vibheeshana's promise that he would attend the Rajasuya. Blessing Ghatotkacha, hugging him, Sahadeva sent him back to the secret forests from where he had come, to his mother. Ghatotkacha vanished before Sahadeva's eyes just like a dream.

North rode the Pandava, along the eastern coast of Bharatavarsha, until he reached the Pandya kingdom; and Chitrasena received him. Sahadeva spent a few days with Chitrangadaa and Babhruvahana. Having invited them to the Rajasuya, the son of the Asvins came home to Indraprastha, laden with carriage-loads of tribute.

Nakula was already back, and Bheema and Arjuna, too. Nakula had gone only to Dwaraka, to invite Krishna and his Yadavas formally. Almost on Sahadeva's heels, Krishna arrived in Indraprastha. He came with his army, like a sea, and his wives riding in golden palanquins borne on chariots. When Yudhishtira met Krishna at the city-gates, as always he embraced the Blue One and wept for joy. One by one, the others welcomed their incarnate cousin.

In the palace, Draupadi and Subhadra received Krishna, Rukmini, Satyabhama and Jambavati. Kunti was there, with tears in her eyes. She knew that without her dark nephew, the Rajasuya yagna would have remained a dream.

Krishna had brought a thousand gifts. Yudhishtira took him to the treasury. When the Dark One saw the gold and jewels spilling over from great coffers, he said, "It is time for the yagna. Now you are an emperor by your wealth, also; an emperor by the purity of your heart you have always been. If your coffers are as full as this, I am sure your granaries must overflow. Why, all Bharatavarsha seems blessed since your brothers rode through it, proclaiming you a king of kings.

"Don't delay anymore, Yudhishtira; you have all the means for the Rajasuya. Let your brahmanas decide on an auspicious day for the sacrifice to begin."

Yudhishtira turned silently to face his cousin, and Krishna saw his eyes fill again: with gratitude, and worship. With a laugh, he embraced Yudhishtira.

TEN

The Rajasuya yagna

Yudhishtira called a council of his ministers and advisors, and all the kshatriyas of Indraprastha, in the Mayaa sabha. Veda Vyasa was there. Unlike the last sabha he had called, when he was so full of doubt, today the Pandava exuded assurance.

"My cousin Krishna and my grandfather Vyasa agree it is time for us to perform the Rajasuya yagna. I have called you here to assign tasks and responsibilities to each of you.

Nakula my brother, you must go to Hastinapura, to Bheeshma and Drona, to Dhritarashtra, Kripa, Baahlika, Somadatta, Bhoorisravas and our cousins, Duryodhana and his brothers. Go to every one, and invite him respectfully on my behalf. Do not forget Gandhari's brother Shakuni, and his sons. And don't forget the noble Karna, and Aswatthama."

There was a murmur in the sabha. But the excitement of the occasion was such that no one objected to inviting even their enemies, men who had tried to murder the sons of Pandu. Krishna hid a smile. Only he, and perhaps Vyasa, saw what lay in store, in the future. The Pandavas could only think of honour and glory; any thought of tragedy was far from their minds.

Yudhishtira went on, "Tell our elders and our kinsmen we await their arrival eagerly, and they shall not be guests but sacrificers themselves."

He turned to Sahadeva, "You, Sahadeva, must collect everything that Dhaumya and his brahmanas need for the yagna: the grain, the vessels and the gold. Send Arjuna's sarathies, Indrasena and Pooru, with a force of chariots to gather rice from all the kingdoms.

"Sahadeva, you shall also have charge of sending messengers to the kings of Bharatavarsha, inviting them to the yagna; and not just kings, but our own people and any others who care to come.

"The other preparations for the yagna itself will be best left to Muni Vyasa and Krishna, who know about these things. If we agree that we may begin, let us not delay. If anyone has doubts or reservations, let them speak now."

But everyone in Mayaa's marvellous hall was just full of anticipation. The council to discuss the sacrifice was quickly concluded, and the actual preparations got underway.

Nakula arrived in Hastinapura to an affectionate welcome from the elders of that city. Bheeshma, Drona, Kripa, and even blind Dhritarashtra came out to usher him into the Kuru court, where he invited them, formally, to the Rajasuya yagna.

"I have come today not only in love, as a son of Hastinapura, but as my brother's messenger," said Nakula. "Yudhishtira means to perform a Rajasuya yagna in Indraprastha, with the Gods' blessings, and all of yours. He asked me to invite each one of you to the yagna, not only as guests of honour, but as members of our family, and sacrificers yourselves. May I tell my brother that you will come? The yagna will not be complete without your presence."

Dhritarashtra's masklike smile never left his face. "Of course we shall come, now that your brother has sent you to invite us."

Afterwards, Nakula went to every great Kuru, beginning with Bheeshma, then to Vidura, Drona, Kripa, and at last to the younger princes, Duryodhana and his brothers, and Karna. He was humble, respectful; and they were so curious to see Indraprastha they did not hesitate to accept his invitation. They all said how happy they would be to come.

Of course, not all of them were pleased about the yagna; and not Nakula, Yudhishtira or anybody deceived themselves they were. But, as dharma demanded, the Kauravas had been invited to the great sacrifice, and they had accepted their cousins' invitation.

In Indraprastha, preparations were in full swing. The granaries and the treasury did indeed overflow with tribute. This tribute was paid willingly to an emperor whose spirit was immaculate, whose dharma was meticulous and deep, and whose reign was truly blessed, so a time of grace and fortune had come to all Bharatavarsha. The people of the city were full of sweet fervour: they could hardly bear to wait.

Already there was singing and dancing in the streets, and those that had braved a desert for Yudhishtira's sake were amply rewarded now. He made sure that, more than anyone, they shared in his moment of glory. They were appointed to important positions for the sacrifice. Whenever a council met, they sat in places of honour in the Mayaa sabha. They were persons of obvious influence in Indraprastha.

Came spring, the season for the yagna. The very earth, the rivers and hills, the winds and mountains were alive to the news: after an age, an emperor was to be crowned, one sovereign ruler for all the sacred land. In Indraprastha, the royal guests began to arrive. A thousand kings and their legions came to the city, bringing lavish gifts.

The Kuru princes from Hastinapura arrived in some grandeur, their train resplendent. But the Kauravas brought only moderate gifts for their cousins, who had once come out of the jungle like orphans, when Pandu died. That, perhaps, was how the Kauravas always thought of the Pandavas: as poor cousins, upstarts who had taken from them, the king's sons, what was rightfully theirs. Duryodhana and his brothers came expecting to find that every splendid description they had heard of Indraprastha, the Mayaa sabha and the rest, was a huge exaggeration. Indraprastha was more than they had heard or imagined; it was like a city of the Gods.

When the Kauravas arrived, Krishna, who was responsible for the miracle in the wilderness, was there to welcome them with his disturbing smile. How Duryodhana and his brothers flinched from the Blue One's mocking eyes that gazed into their very souls, and the darkness there.

Krishna had said to Yudhishtira, "Make sure your cousins from Hastinapura feel welcome, so they aren't envious of you."

The trusting Yudhishtira had asked, "What shall I do to make them feel welcome?"

"Let them be given vital tasks, like your own brothers. Duryodhana, especially, must have an important charge."

"What charge shall I give him?"

Innocently, Krishna had replied, "Why not charge of the treasury? It will make him feel like one of us."

After the Kurus from Hastinapura were ensconced in stately mansions, Yudhishtira went to meet them. He fell at Bheeshma's feet, Drona's and Kripa's, and sought his elders' blessings. Dhritarashtra himself had cried off from coming, saying being blind would make him unbearably sad on such an occasion. People said this was not the actual reason for his not coming.

With tears of real joy in his eyes, Yudhishtira said, "Treat this city as your own. Bless me so the yagna may be a success; it is your sacrifice as much as mine; it is a Rajasuya of the Kuruvamsa."

He asked Duryodhana if he would take charge of the treasury; and Duryodhana could not refuse the honour. Dusasana was given charge of feeding the guests, Sanjaya of protocol, receiving the visiting kings and assigning mansions for them to stay in, and places to sit at the yagna. Kripa was to distribute gifts to the brahmanas and kshatriyas who came, and the common people.

Every member of the party from Hastinapura found himself with an important charge, and many were pleased to be treated like part of the family. Bheeshma and Drona were given the reverence due to the elders of the clan: they had overall responsibility for the arrangements. Even Shakuni was treated with regard.

But when Duryodhana inspected his charge, and saw the extent of Yudhishtira's wealth, he seethed with an envy that threatened to derange him. Of course, he showed nothing of it, and threw himself into his task. Krishna, who saw into his heart, saw the agony he was in, and smiled to himself. By getting the noble, and at times, naïve Yudhishtira to give Duryodhana charge of Indraprastha's treasury, he had sown a seed that would sprout into a horrific war.

All the kshatriyas had arrived, and the illustrious brahmanas, who would conduct the yagna. Vyasa was to be the chief priest. Narada, Bharadvaja, Sumantu, Gautama, Asita, Vasishta, Chyvana, Kanva, Maitreya, Kavasa, Trita, Viswamitra, Parasara, Kashyapa, Virasena and a hundred others out of Devaloka, not yet sealed from the earth by the darkness of the kali yuga, had also come.

Susharma would chant the hymns of the Sama Veda; Yajnavalkya would recite the slokas and mantras; Paila, Vasu's son, and Dhaumya would pour libation on to the sacred fire. The common people had turned out in crowds. Brahmanas, kshatriyas, vaishyas and sudras, from every walk and station of life, thronged the yagnashala.

With golden ploughs, the immortal brahmanas, among them Brahma's own sons, turned the earth where they would worship the Gods with offerings and slokas. When this was done, Yudhishtira was crowned emperor, and consecrated as the sacrificer.

During the coronation, as he listened to the chanting of hymns, and watched Pandu's son being crowned sovereign of all Bharatavarsha, Narada Muni had a strange and oppressive vision. At first, a pang of panic gripped him, and he turned to look at Krishna, who sat smiling as brightly as ever beside Yudhishtira.

Suddenly, as in a hallucination, Narada saw the smile disappear from the Avatara's face. The muni saw how grim Krishna's expression was, his eyes full of awesome destiny. In a moment, Narada was borne out of himself on a phantasm of the future: of a cataclysmic war, which revolved mysteriously around the Avatara.

Narada saw dismembered corpses piled on a vast battlefield, where the earth was covered with a scarlet patina, a lake of kshatriyas' blood. He saw the kings and princes from Yudhishtira's yagna lay upon that field in the grotesque and passionate postures of death. Some had their heads dissevered, others had arrows and swords protruding from them like organs of horror sprouted from their bodies, and screams frozen on their contorted faces. Narada saw, with terrible prescience, the devastation of kshatriya kind. He saw a new age, of the sudra ruler, risen over the earth: the kali yuga of perpetual night.

In the daze of that chasmal vision, as if he had no will any more, Narada turned to look at the man being crowned emperor today. He saw the goodness on that face, the very quality that would cause the gruesome war.

Narada's eyes wandered from Yudhishtira's face to the face of the unreally beautiful woman who sat beside him. He gazed raptly at Draupadi. With mystic insight, the muni saw the prophecy that attended her birth being fulfilled: that she would be the nemesis of kshatriya kind. How perfect she was, like a dark Goddess who had come where she did not belong. She is too beautiful for this earth, thought Narada; she belongs in a rarer realm, or in the lost past of the world when beauty like hers would have found some comparison. Now, she was alone in her stunning loveliness, like a full moon among dim planets, peerless by a long way: she, the empress of Bharatavarsha.

Sighing, Narada turned his eyes away from Panchali's supernatural beauty. His gaze alighted on Duryodhana. The Kaurava smouldered with the envy in his heart. The rishi wanted to laugh aloud at that prince: his obsession was so absurd. Then, Narada had a powerful premonition of the tragedy in which Duryodhana's envy would result, inevitably, even as night follows day. He glanced at Krishna again, and saw the Dark One was intent once more. The rishi saw Krishna also glance at Duryodhana, watching the Kaurava trying to mask the monstrous hatred that shone so plainly in his pale eyes for a moment.

Narada saw into Duryodhana's heart: Dhritarashtra's violent son imagined himself killing Yudhishtira and, drenched in his cousin's blood, he mounted the emperor's throne. He saw Panchali become his queen; he held her naked in his arms.

Narada looked away from Duryodhana and found himself staring at another face, in which all the darkness of the human soul seemed focused—eyes that mirrored a heart so cold, so malevolent, that even Narada, who had seen plenty of evil men in his time, shivered. He was looking at the crafty and disdainful face of Shakuni. Shakuni saw Narada's regard and favoured him with a sardonic smile; above it, his eyes were like those of a cobra. Narada nodded quickly to Shakuni and turned his gaze away to Karna, who sat not far from Duryodhana's uncle.

Such a contrast: here, if ever, was a noble face, though masked with a studied indifference, a permanent bitterness. Yet, the eyes were honest. Like Yudhishtira's eyes, thought Narada, like Kunti's. If destiny had been less cruel, not Yudhishtira, but Karna would have sat on the emperor's throne today. Then, in a lucid image that only Krishna could have inveigled into his mind, Narada saw Karna also slain. An arrow, shot by a brother who did not know who he was, cut his head from his neck.

The vision of a horrible battlefield engulfed the rishi again. He saw Dhritarashtra's hundred sons being slaughtered, one after the other. He saw all these mighty kshatriyas, who had come to the Rajasuya, laid out on that savage field, their limbs askew in death's final attitudes.

Narada had witnessed the most ancient and legendary battles of the earth. He had seen Siva burn Daksha's sacrifice, in times when the world was a nebulous mystery, an age when the first stars were still being strewn in the sky. Yet, even that muni was filled with horror by what he saw of the war these kshatriyas would fight among them.

Shivering, partly in pity, and partly in fear, Narada turned back to Krishna. Now, the Blue One smiled so knowingly at him, and those fathomless black eyes mocked the rishi tenderly.

ELEVEN

A cousin's anger

THE SACRIFICE OF THE SIX FIRES WAS UNDERWAY. THE GOLDEN VESSELS were the same ones Varuna had used for his Rajasuya yagna, in time out of mind. All the omens in heaven and on earth showed the Gods were pleased. Showers of petals fell from the sky like fragrant dew, so fine they were invisible.

When Yudhishtira was crowned, it was time for him to greet his guests. When all the kings were seated in the yagnashala—not in the Mayaa sabha but another open arena in the palace—Bheeshma rose and said to Yudhishtira, "These kshatriyas and brahmanas have come to Indraprastha to honour you. You must give them arghya, but begin with the foremost among your guests. You must decide who he is, and worship him first of all."

Yudhishtira rose. "My lord, in a sabha like this, it isn't for me to say whom I should worship first. You are my Pitama; you tell me."

Bheeshma was silent for a moment, then, said, "Six men are said to deserve worship: the guru, the priest, the kinsman, he that knows the Veda, the friend and the king. Offer arghya to all these, beginning with the best."

"But, Pitama, who shall have the purodasa?"

Bheeshma said, "Surely, you don't need an old man to tell you only Krishna deserves the purodasa. He is like the sun among the planets; the rest of us only reflect his splendour. Without him, this sabha would be plunged in darkness."

A beaming Yudhishtira called Sahadeva to fetch the arghya. Sahadeva came and sat at Krishna's feet. The Dark One still smiled. There was, perhaps, just a hint of pleasure on his face.

As Sahadeva washed Krishna's feet, tears welled in the Pandava's eyes. It was a sacred moment, an overwhelming one. Sahadeva washed Krishna's dark blue feet as if nothing on earth could give him as much joy.

Flowers of light fell like cool embers out of the spirit realms, and, with the arghya, Krishna had the purodasa at Yudhishtira's historic Rajasuya yagna. There was silence in the yagnashala. You could hear the fragile flowers put themselves out with a thousand sighs. Yet, many of the kshatriyas did not approve of Krishna having this honour. They exchanged hot glances of reproval among themselves, which the Pandavas ignored, if they saw them through their tears.

Suddenly, a sneering laugh rang out, desecrating the sacral silence like a curse. Sishupala was on his feet. Every gaze turned to the pale Bull of Chedi. His eyes on fire, he raged, "What foolishness this is! A bastard asks the son of a river," this was said as the worst insult, "who should have the purodasa in this sabha. The senile river-son says a black cowherd must be offered the first arghya. Another bastard performs the puja, and the heavens bless this touching scene! What can I say?"

He sat down, trembling. Stunned silence for a moment, then, before anyone else could speak, Sishupala jumped up again. He turned on Yudhishtira, "Cousin, either you see more deeply than the rest of us, or you are blind. How can you give this cowherd the purodasa in this sabha? I thought the Pandavas were princes of dharma, and could never set a foot wrong in anything you did. Ah, what have you done today?"

His lips twitched, his voice was somehow bestial. "The cowherd is not even a kshatriya! Look around you, Yudhishtira; can't you see these illustrious munis and these rulers of the earth in your sabha? Yet, you honour this upstart, this nobody, before any of the others? Why, this fellow should not be here at all!

"Do you, perhaps, revere him as an elder? But his father Vasudeva is among us. Shouldn't he have the arghya before his son? Do you think Krishna was a friend in your need? But didn't Drupada give you his daughter when you were exiles? Didn't he keep you in his kingdom? Didn't he agree to let all five of you marry Draupadi?

"Perhaps, you believe the cowherd is your guru? Isn't your acharya here in this sabha, the great Drona?

"Or do you think Krishna is a tapasvin? Surely, he is not a thousandth part the muni that your own grandfather, Vyasa, is."

Froth flecked his lips, and he shook more than ever. "Yudhishtira, we came to your Rajasuya not because we were afraid of you, but because we respected you as a man of dharma. And how do you reward us? By giving this cowherd the purodasa, while the greatest kshatriyas on earth look on like dumb animals! It was to please you that we came; but you seem to have gone mad. If the only purpose of this yagna was to worship Krishna, what was the point in inviting the rest of us?"

Bheema had turned red with fury. Arjuna tried to catch Yudhishtira's eye: so he could silence Sishupala with an arrow through his mouth. Sahadeva and Nakula had their hands on their swords. But the object of Sishupala's tirade was a picture of calm. The smile never left Krishna's lips; his black eyes were still full of good humour.

Helpless to stop himself any more, Sishupala raved on. "If you wanted a kshatriya to honour, Bheeshma was your choice. If not him, there are others here as worthy, a hundred of them. If it was an archer you wanted, Karna is here, a better bowman than your Arjuna. Remember, Karna had the measure of Jarasandha in battle, a feat your cowherd could never match."

Whenever he paused for breath, silence ruled the sabha, and it seemed the other kings were disposed to agree with Sishupala. The Bull of Chedi had not finished. "I am insulted, Yudhishtira, and so are all these lords of men. You have made a mockery of this profound sacrifice. As for Bheeshma, I can only say he has lost his wits with age. Who is this black Krishna, anyway, that you honour him like this? He is not your guru, or your son-in-law. He is just your cousin, as I am. Then why do you worship him? Are you afraid of him?"

His eyes narrowing, Sishupala turned to Krishna. "And you, Yadava; even if the Pandavas give you the purodasa, how can you take it? Did you think for a moment, if you are worthy of it? No. You lapped it up like a dog does the leavings of a feast!"

He turned back to Yudhishtira, "Cousin, you sent your brothers with this cowherd to Girivraja, and you thought Krishna did you a service. The truth, credulous king, was that he did not go there for your sake but his own. Jarasandha was the one man Krishna could never deceive. I tell you, my lords, he was terrified of Jarasandha. He seized the first opportunity he saw to kill him with guile, Bheema, you poor fool, you allowed the cowherd to use you: for his purpose, not your brother's!

"And now he sits here, laughing at us kshatriyas that we accord him the agrapuja in this august sabha. I say to you, Pandava, what you have done is like showing the beauty of a golden dawn to a blind man, or getting a eunuch married. Others may suffer this madness, but not I. The scales have fallen from my eyes. Yudhishtira, now I know you for what you are, and your Bheeshma and your Krishna. I won't stay here a moment longer!"

Like an angry lion, Sishupala stalked out of the enclosure. With a cry, Yudhishtira jumped up and ran after him. He stopped him just outside the yagnashala.

"Lord of men," said Yudhishtira indulgently, as to an erring brother, "don't leave like this. You are overwrought, Sishupala. I did not mean to insult you, or the other kings. To us, Krishna is greater than anyone else is. Shantanu's son Bheeshma said we should give the purodasa to Krishna. Bheeshma is older and wiser than we are; you should not offend him. There are other kshatriyas here, older than you or I; they approved of Krishna being worshipped first. Sishupala, Krishna is more than what you think he is."

Now Bheeshma came there and he was livid. "Yudhishtira, you are an emperor now! How can you plead with this idiot? Not just we, but the three worlds honour Krishna; the very universe does. But this dullard is too blind with arrogance to see who Krishna is. Leave him, Yudhishtira, he is demented with envy."

Sahadeva cried, "Krishna is our guru, he is everything to us. If you have anything more to say about him, I will kill you!"

Sishupala roared in anger, and the other kshatriyas came out to hear him. It seemed many of them agreed with him; his hot words had swayed their minds. But Sahadeva roared louder than the Bull of Chedi. He raised his foot and brought it crashing down. "I will trample on anyone who dares insult Krishna!"

Petals of light streamed down on him.

Bheeshma cried, "The sun, the moon and the planets, all the mandalas, dwell in Krishna. He is the beginning and the end of all things. If Sishupala cannot see this for his vanity, let him leave!"

Crimson-eyed Sishupala howled, "Kshatriyas, we must answer this insult with weapons! Let us defile this unholy yagna. Let us take arms against the cowherd and his cousins, that they dare humiliate us."

There were some shouts of, "Jaya Sishupala! Let us fight the Pandavas!" Many of the kshatriyas seemed inclined to stand with the Chedi Bull. Soon, all the sabha echoed with voices raised on one side or the other. Swords were drawn.

Yudhishtira cried anxiously to Bheeshma, "Pitama, we must do something quickly."

Calmly, Bheeshma said, "It is the dog barking at the lion: nothing to worry about. Let him bark, he seems to like the sound of his own voice."

With a snarl, Sishupala turned on the patriarch. "Old man, you don't fool me with your simpering pretence of being a paragon of dharma. You are a common hypocrite. Let the simple-minded believe in your great vow. We know the real reason for your not taking a wife. You are a eunuch, and the world would have known it if you married!"

Such a hush fell, but Sishupala ranted on. "As for being the son of a river," he sneered, "we all know what a river is. She welcomes anyone who cares to bathe in her, welcomes all comers with equal ardour!"

Bheema cried, "Pitama, how can you stand this?"

But Bheeshma said coolly, "The minds of those whom Krishna has decided to kill become unsettled, like this dog's."

Sishupala screamed, "Krishna! Don't tell me about your Krishna. Bheeshma, you try to frighten these kings with such lies that I am amazed your tongue does not split in a hundred slivers. Your Krishna's fame is because he killed a bull, once, and a horse. Are horses and bulls kshatriyas, that a cowherd becomes a legend because he kills the dumb beasts? Or because he once lifts an anthill called Govardhana? Or perhaps, it is because he killed Kamsa, whose bread he broke, who was his own flesh and blood? Noble Kamsa, who wanted to make Krishna his heir. Or is your Krishna worthy of this lick-spittle worship because he killed Putana, a woman?"

With a roar, Bheema rushed at Sishupala. But Bheeshma seized him in arms still strong enough to restrain the son of the wind. Sishupala cried, "Let him go, old fool! Let him come and perish like a moth in a flame. Let all these kings see on whose side truth lies: with these treacherous Pandavas and their witless grandfather, or with me."

Bheeshma still restrained Bheema, though it was like holding a storm in his arms. The Pitama thundered, "My lords, you have heard all that the king of Chedi has to say, and you have been swayed by him. You have heard the abuse he has heaped on Krishna and the Pandavas, and on me. It is only fair you hear me out, as well. Let us return to the sabha. I don't think even Sishupala will deny me the right to speak."

Sishupala snorted, "Hurry up, old man. Then let us get down to the business of kshatriyas, in which eunuchs have no part."

"Come, friends, come in again; you, too, Sishupala. Listen to what I have to say. It is your life's story I want to tell, and there are parts of it you don't know yourself."

All the agitated kings, their hosts, Bheeshma and Krishna, and Sishupala, also, returned to the yagnashala. Then, at Yudhishtira's Rajasuya yagna, Bheeshma told the story of Sishupala of Chedi.

TWELVE

Dark omens

His deep voice filling the yagnashala, Bheeshma began, "Sishupala, you were not born an ordinary child. You came into the world with three eyes and four arms. You were a freak, and we heard about you in Hastinapura."

Sishupala stiffened where he sat, so full of contempt. He had never heard this before, yet he knew Bheeshma was telling the truth.

Bheeshma continued, "The monstrous child didn't cry like a human baby but brayed like a little donkey, as demons do when they take a human form. Your parents were horrified, and decided to do away with the freak. He couldn't be raised as the heir to the Chedi throne."

"You lie," breathed Sishupala, but his voice lacked conviction. What the Kuru patriarch was saying was irresistible, and light was breaking savagely into the Bull of Chedi's dark spirit.

Bheeshma ignored Sishupala. "When your father Damaghosha thought of killing you, a disembodied voice spoke to him, 'Your son will become a great kshatriya; keep him with you, and raise him. It is not time for him to die, and you are not the one who will kill him. But his killer has also been born.'

"Your mother Srutadevi cried, 'Who will be my son's killer?'

"The asariri replied, 'When you place the child in his lap, your son's third eye and his superfluous arms will vanish.'"

"Strange tales you tell!" scoffed Sishupala, but he was plainly uncertain. "But are they any more than your senile fancies?"

Bheeshma was undeterred. "The kings of the earth heard of the freak born in Chedi, and came to see him. Damaghosha welcomed them, because he wanted to discover who would be his son's killer. Your father brought you in and set you in each king's lap. But your third eye still glared at every kshatriya there, and your four arms remained."

Bheeshma paused; silence held the yagnashala. Slowly, the Kuru patriarch resumed, "One day, his Yadava cousins, Balarama and Krishna, came to Chedi to see Sishupala. He was handed to Balarama first, and the child brayed at him.

"Then Srutadevi placed her son in her younger nephew, Krishna's, lap. There was a flash of light, and the infant's third eye had vanished, and his extra arms. He lay in his cousin's lap, and now cried like any human child. The bestial voice was gone, and Krishna held him, laughing softly.

"Srutadevi is Vasudeva's sister. She knew his own cousin would be her son's killer. She said, 'Krishna, I have a favour to ask you, and you must not refuse me.'

"'Anything for you,' said Krishna.

"'Promise me you will always forgive my Sishupala any offence he gives you.'

"'For your sake, I will forgive him a hundred times!"

"She hugged him and never dreamt that Sishupala could offend Krishna a hundred times. They were cousins, after all, not enemies. But when Damaghosha heard what had happened, he did not believe Krishna's promise to pardon Sishupala a hundred offences.

"When he was still a boy, Damaghosha sent his son to Girivraja to become Jarasandha's pupil. Who else on earth opposed Krishna as boldly as the rakshasi's foster-son?

"Jarasandha had heard about young Sishupala and, when the prince arrived in his sabha, he welcomed him, crying, 'What a handsome fellow you are. I will make you a lion of a kshatriya!'

"In Girivraja, Sishupala met another prince who was Jarasandha's pupil, and who would also become Krishna's inveterate enemy: Rukmi of Vidarbha. Rukmi and Sishupala became great warriors and greater friends. When Sishupala visited Vidarbha with his friend, once, he saw Rukmi's sister, Rukmini, and fell in love with her. When he told Rukmi, his friend promised Sishupala his sister's hand. Sishupala walked on air, thinking he would soon have the most beautiful bride in the world. But Rukmini already loved Krishna of Dwaraka."

None of the kings in the Mayaa sabha stirred. Bheeshma continued unhurriedly, "Meanwhile, Jarasandha had sworn to avenge Kamsa's death. He took eighteen armies to Krishna's gates in Mathura, and in half of them Sishupala fought against his cousin. Every time, Jarasandha was defeated, and each time Krishna spared Sishupala's life.

"Sishupala was certain Krishna would not harm him, no matter what, and his arrogance grew. Whenever a battle was lost, he would abuse Krishna foully. Even if Balarama wanted to kill him, Krishna stopped his brother, saying, 'We must spare him for our aunt's sake.'

"That is why Sishupala behaves as he has today, that he dares abuse even me. He is sure that Krishna will not kill him.

"And Sishupala hates Krishna; it was on the day he was meant to marry Rukmini, that the Dark One carried her away from under the eyes of a hundred kings. He has never forgiven Krishna for that. But when Rukmini loved Krishna, how could Sishupala even dream of having her?

"This, my lords, is why he raves here as if he has lost his mind. I say to the rest of you, it would be reckless to follow a man who is as unhinged with envy as this one."

The patriarch saw the kings now cast dark looks at the Bull of Chedi. Some of them cried, "For shame, Sishupala, you misled us."

"This isn't a kshatriya's way."

Bheeshma said, "Sishupala has exhausted the hundred pardons Krishna promised his mother. His time to die is here."

Sishupala gave the roar of a cornered beast. Turning on Krishna, he cried, "Come cowherd, fight! I am tired of talk. This old fool says you will kill me, but I warn you this won't be like seducing gopis in Vrindavana. It is a fight to the death I want. Dare you fight me?"

Krishna rose. He said to the other kings, "Twice a hundred times I have spared this fool's life for his mother's sake. Today you have all heard him abuse not just me but Bheeshma. You have provoked me repeatedly, Sishupala, and I did nothing to you. Once you set fire to Dwaraka when I was away. You tried to stop my father Vasudeva's Aswamedha yagna. You attacked our king Ugrasena on Raivataka. You were born to a Yadava princess, and you are my cousin. But you have always hated our people.

"As for women, you forced yourself on so many. I should have killed you when you and your friend Karusha molested the Yadava princesses and their sakhis on the highway through Anarta. You ravished Akrura's wife.

"My lords, I have not the time or the patience to recount all this man's crimes. But, worst of all, he wanted my Rukmini for himself…"

Sishupala howled, "I wanted your Rukmini! To whom was she given by her brother and father? Whose bride was she to become when you abducted her? She was mine, cowherd, mine! You stole her from me."

Still calmly, Krishna said, "I have forgiven you as much as you deserve. I will forgive you again, today, for Yudhishtira's sake: because I do not want to desecrate his yagna. But you must ask Bheeshma's pardon, Sishupala," his voice grew softer, "or I will be forced to kill you."

Sishupala laughed in his face. "Ask the pardon of this old eunuch? At a cowherd's command. You forget I am a kshatriya and a king!"

Those were the last words he ever spoke. Suddenly, Krishna had the Sudarshana Chakra burning over his finger. He flicked his wrist forward sinuously, and the blinding disc cut Sisupala's head from his throat in a flash of blood. The huge Bull of Chedi, pale as mist, fell dead in the midst of Yudhishtira's Rajasuya yagna, and his head rolled away by itself. Blood gushed from him, spreading in a dark stain on the ground.

Every kshatriya was on his feet, and Krishna stood there, cool as ever. A pulsing light, like a small sun, issued from Sishupala's neck and flared into the Avatara. He glowed with it briefly, before it was part of him and subsided into his mystery. Krishna laughed softly.

Outside, thunder rent the sky and black clouds, which had gathered unnoticed, began to lash Indraprastha with torrential rain. Strange meteors flared out of the heavens, and the earth shook with deep tremors. Far away, the sea rose in tidal waves and dashed against his shores. It seemed the killing of Sishupala at Yudhishtira's Rajasuya yagna presaged some terrible calamity for the world, most of all, for its kshatriyas.

Yudhishtira ordered his brothers to honourably cremate Sishupala, and crowned his son king of Chedi.

Hardly any of those kings and princes, not even the Pandavas, noticed that Krishna's eyes were full of another joy. None of them knew he had just ended a curse of ages and restored Vishnu's dwarapalaka, Jaya, to eternal life. Narada, who knew all about that curse, smiled.

Once, on another world, some rishis had come to Vaikunta to visit Narayana, who lies upon the waters of eternity. But Vishnu's gatekeepers, Jaya and Vijaya, barred their way because the holy ones came as chattering, mischievous children.

The munis cursed Jaya and Vijaya to three demonic lives on earth. Vishnu promised them that he, too, would be born into the world to deliver them. The first time, in a mythic age, the two had been born as the golden-skinned demons, Hiranyaksha and Hiranyakashyapu, who terrorized creation for a million years. Vishnu came as an awesome Boar and a dreadful Manticore to kill them.

The second time, at the beginning of the dwapara yuga, nine hundred thousand years before Krishna's time, there had been the sinister rakshasa Ravana, and his brother Kumbhakarna. Vishnu came as Rama to rescue the earth from their satanic tyranny; and to release them, as well, from another monstrous incarnation.

Now, as the dwapara yuga ended, Jaya and Vijaya had been born as Sishupala, the Bull of Chedi, and his friend crooked-teeth Dantavakra, king of Kalinga. Krishna had redeemed his dwarapalaka Jaya. Dantavakra waited for the Dark One outside the city, beside the midnight-blue Yamuna. Having received the purodasa, Krishna had to go alone to the river for the avabhruta snana, the closing ablution.

Dantavakra attacked him there. Vishnu's Avatara liberated Vishnu's other gatekeeper with a blow of his mace, shattering his head like a melon. Meanwhile, many of the kshatriyas at the sacrifice were shocked at the calm and brutal slaying of Sishupala. Seeing the omens of the elements after the killing, they may have thought of leaving before the sacrifice was completed; but Krishna stood at the door with the Sudarshana Chakra whispering over his finger. Yudhishtira's Rajasuya yagna was properly concluded in Indraprastha, while sinister omens swept through the world.

THIRTEEN

The green monster

THE RAJASUYA YAGNA WAS COMPLETED AND, ONE BY ONE, THE visiting kings went home. Krishna came to Yudhishtira and said, "I have been here longer than I should. I must return to Dwaraka."

Reluctantly, Yudhishtira drove him to the gates of Indraprastha. Embracing his cousins, Krishna cast a final, lingering look at the city. He had a sure premonition of the evil turn of events that would force the Pandavas out of Indraprastha. In fact, the next time he met them would be in the Kamyaka vana, and they would be without a kingdom.

Forlorn as they always became when Krishna left them, the sons of Pandu returned to their palace. All the other kshatriyas had gone as well, except Duryodhana, Dusasana, Shakuni and Karna, who stayed on to have a look around the fabulous Mayaa sabha. Yudhishtira was pleased; he naively imagined the Kauravas had put their envy behind them.

But first, Vyasa came and said that he, too, must leave. Yudhishtira prostrated himself at his feet. Laying his hand on his grandson's head, the muni said, "This has been a time of joy for me, and your father's spirit will soon rise into Indra's kingdom. The Rajasuya is hardly performed once in a yuga, and I am glad I could be here to see it."

Yudhishtira was troubled. "What did the omens mean, which we saw when Krishna killed Sishupala? Narada says they portend some catastrophe for the world. I am anxious, grandfather, tell me what will happen."

Vyasa looked at his grandson, who was lord of all Bharatavarsha now. The rishi said compassionately, "The ways of fate are inscrutable, my child. The omens can mean only one thing: misfortune, and as I read it, misfortune for fourteen years. But the misfortune is only a part of a deeper destiny that springs in dark Krishna, and uses your brothers and you as its agents. This destiny's ends are beyond my understanding, for it means to destroy the very race of kshatriyas.

"Draupadi shall also be fate's instrument, as prophesied when she came into the world. "Tonight you will dream of blue-throated Siva, wearing a tiger-skin, carrying his trisula. You will see him astride his great bull, gazing south in the direction ruled by the lord of the manes, and drinking blood out of a human skull."

Yudhishtira looked so stricken that Vyasa put his arm around him, and said with a smile, "But don't perplex yourself over fate. There is nothing to be done about what is written in the stars. Yet, Yudhishtira, tell no one, not even your brothers, what I have said to you. Not every man has the serenity to bear the knowledge of what the future contains.

"Misfortune comes only to make stronger souls of those that suffer. In the end, my son, whatever happens in this or any world is for the good of every creature; yet, that is hard to remember when one suffers. As it is hard to imagine how the world will prosper by the death of its kshatriyas.

"But that is what is written for the land of Bharata, and that is what must happen, inevitably. Yudhishtira, when misfortune actually comes, with it come the will and the strength to survive and mould the difficult time to one's advantage. Be forewarned, my son, but not disheartened; I can tell you even now that, finally, all will be well with you and yours. You shall indeed rule the world with your brothers, and fulfil your great destiny."

With these strange revelations, Vyasa left Indraprastha. Yudhishtira was deeply disturbed as he saw his grandfather off. But he was a man of spiritual strength, and, sighing a little to himself, he returned to the Mayaa sabha where Bheema and the other Pandavas were showing Duryodhana, Dusasana, Shakuni and Karna that edifice.

Though outwardly he made every show of being pleased for the Pandavas, Duryodhana was suffocating with envy. He could not bear to see his cousins' glory; every marvel he saw in Mayaa's superb sabha tormented him with a physical pain. Duryodhana kept a look of admiration on his face, words of praise on his lips, and showed nothing of what he really felt.

Mayaa himself had told the Pandavas of a magical quality with which he had imbued his sabha. "If any man comes in here with enmity or jealousy in his heart, the sabha will know him at once."

As Duryodhana mounted the steps, he saw what seemed to be a pool of water at the entrance to the sabha. He remarked to Shakuni, "What a strange place for a pool, as if there are no grounds to set it in. The Asura Mayaa has some vulgar notions of beauty."

But as they climbed the gleaming steps and came nearer, they saw the pool was only an illusion of water. Bheema said, "Look carefully, cousin, is it really a pool?"

Despite himself, Duryodhana gasped. What had seemed like a shimmering pool of water, with lotuses growing in it, was obviously just the polished floor inlaid with marble lotuses. Duryodhana gave a laugh and, with the Pandavas watching him, he stepped forward and fell into that cunning marble pool full of the clearest water and white lotuses. With a cry, he plunged in up to his chest, and Bheema, Arjuna, the twins and Draupadi burst out laughing. Even the guards laughed; they all knew that envy raged in the Kaurava's heart.

Only Yudhishtira was dismayed. Quickly, he ordered fresh clothes fetched for his cousin; but it was not the end of Duryodhana's shame. He passed off his fall into the crystal pool in apparent good humour. He changed his wet clothes and bravely declared he wanted to see more of the sabha's wonders. But it seemed Mayaa's curse followed Dhritarashtra's son. At the next atrium, he was seen walking gingerly across a section of the floor that may just have been water, but was not. Draupadi barely restrained her laughter.

Inside the sabha itself, Duryodhana managed to walk straight into a solid glass wall that he thought was an open door onto a terrace. He struck his head painfully and staggered back. Draupadi lost control, and her laughter rang out in golden peals. She sat down on a chair and, holding her sides, laughed helplessly; while four of her husbands joined her and the fifth, Yudhishtira, did his best to quieten them. But it was too late; Draupadi's laughter entered Duryodhana's ears like smoking oil.

Somehow, the Kaurava managed to keep a straight face, and his eyes turned from Panchali and the younger Pandavas, who by now were convulsed with mirth, tears streaming down their faces. It was sweet revenge for everything he had tried to do to them, and they couldn't resist. Only Yudhishtira suspected it, but this was also destiny at work through a woman's terrible laughter.

Red in the face, but keeping his voice level, Duryodhana managed to bid Yudhistira a stiff farewell, and he stalked out of the Mayaa sabha with Shakuni, Dusasana and Karna. All the way to Hastinapura, Duryodhana did not speak a word. Not a word did he say when they arrived, not to his father, to his brothers or wives, not to Shakuni, or even to Karna, who was closer to him than anyone else. He locked himself in his apartment for a week, and when he asked for a woman to come to him, he would send her out later, bruised, shocked by his dark brutality.

Duryodhana's thoughts burned, round and round, in his mind: 'The Gods are with the Pandavas. When Kunti's bastards went to Varanasi, I was sure I had seen the end of them. But Purochana bungled, and they became stronger than ever. They married Drupada's black daughter, that slut. Then we sent them into the wilderness again, to a desert of thorns. But no sooner did my cousins arrive there, than the desert bloomed.

And now, they are masters of the world. Spineless, simpering Yudhishtira is the emperor of Bharatavarsha!'

Visions of Yudhishtira's coffers haunted the Kaurava. Hastinapura's wealth seemed like the riches of some small tribal kingdom, compared to the treasures of Indraprastha. Duryodhana could not bear it. Again and again, he heard the Pandavas' laughter, most of all, Draupadi's scathing peals. He lay in bed, drunk, trying to drown his pain in wine. It seared him more fiercely; and he lay in a swoon, not knowing sleep from waking, day from night, reality from a nightmare of envy.

Perhaps unfortunately for that prince, unlike his father, Duryodhana was not a coward. Dhritarashtra was as avaricious and as envious as his son was; but fear and caution were his mastering impulses. He would weave a cloak of excuses for not taking the bold course in any matter. He was a chronic coward, adept at deceiving himself. Not Duryodhana: he was always a direct man and a brave one. No one could hope for a truer and more generous friend than him, as Karna had discovered. And neither a worse enemy.

He was a kshatriya. He was strong, he was bold, and he was dashing. He was usually open and exceptionally kind to those he considered his own. Above all, Duryodhana had irresistible charisma. For this quality, eleven teeming aksauhinis would fight for him at the war of Kurukshetra: despite their knowing the Pandavas' cause was just, and Duryodhana's anything but that.

Yet, that prince of charm had one fatal flaw in his character: he was a jealous man past all reason. He could not contain his envy of the Pandavas. It obsessed him, mastered him, and at last, inevitably, it destroyed him. Perhaps, if Duryodhana had not allowed the emerald monster to enslave him, not Yudhishtira but he would have become the Kuru emperor.

But after he returned from the Rajasuya yagna, the Kaurava stayed locked away in his apartment in a long fit of manic dejection. Until Dhritarashtra, who adored his son, sent Shakuni to see if the crafty uncle could talk his suffering nephew out of his black mood.

FOURTEEN

Shakuni's plan

SHAKUNI WAS STARTLED WHEN DURYODHANA OPENED HIS DOOR TO him. His nephew was red-eyed and reeked of wine, and it was not yet noon. He had not bathed in days, and his hair was wild and unkempt, his face unwashed and blotchy, and his clothes the same ones he had worn in Indraprastha. He looked and smelled more like a drunken beggar than a prince. Quickly, Shakuni drew him back into his apartment and locked the door. It would never do to have anyone see the future king like this.

Shakuni sat down, and saw Duryodhana's swollen eyes full of tears. Abruptly, the Kaurava fell at his uncle's feet, and cried, "I can't bear it anymore, Shakuni! You must help me, or I will die of the dreadful thing burning in me. Help me, ah, please help me."

And he sobbed. Shakuni stroked Duryodhana's head and, more to hear it from the Kaurava's lips than because he did not know, he asked, "Are you ill, Duryodhana? Or is it some other sorrow?"

Duryodhana howled, "I am ill with sorrow! Sorrow eats my heart. Shakuni, you say you love me; I beg you, help me." He was fevered and panting. "I will never be well again until I see my cousins destroyed. If you really care for me, Shakuni, make me emperor of the world. Or this ravening envy will devour my life."

Shakuni took Duryodhana's hand, and seemed to be lost in thought. Duryodhana hissed, "No kshatriya worth his name can bear to see his enemies prosper. It is my dharma to fight them, to tear them down. Say you will go with me, Shakuni, and I will take an army to Indraprastha and bring them to my feet."

Shakuni shook his head in alarm. His plump body quivering, he cried, "Oh no, Duryodhana! Didn't you see their legions? And they have Krishna and Drupada with them. They have conquered the earth; they are invincible. Even the Devas would think twice before they attacked the sons of Pandu."

Duryodhana began to pace the room tensely. He gnashed his teeth, and balled his hands into fists. "I would rather die fighting them, than let them be. You don't understand what this means to me: fate has conspired with my cousins to humiliate me."

But now, Shakuni was saying in his silken voice, "I only said it would be foolish to take an army against your cousins. I didn't say there was no way they can be destroyed."

Duryodhana stopped pacing. He saw the smile on his uncle's face, and cried, "You have an idea! I can see you have thought of something." He was at Shakuni's side, grasping his hand. "Tell me what you have thought!"

"The Pandavas are invincible warriors; but there is another weapon we can use against them. They are men of honour: that is their strength; it is also their weakness. We must use their own nobility against them."

"Don't speak in riddles, my heart will stop!"

Shakuni went on dreamily, as if he was talking to himself, "I can make all their wealth and even their kingdom yours, Duryodhana. I can make you emperor of the world. And not an arrow shall be loosed, or a sword drawn, or a drop of blood spilt."

"What is your plan? Some atharva vidya? Black magic?"

"No, Duryodhana, it will be easier than that. Your cousin, the emperor, has a weakness for gambling. And like all men of a noble disposition, he is an execrable gambler. I played him once, for a pittance, and a worse gambler you will not find on earth."

"How does that help us? Stop drivelling, and tell me your plan."

"Duryodhana, in this world there is no dice-player like your uncle Shakuni. I have played against the best, and I have always won. No one throws the ivory dice as I do, and, of course, my dice are loaded." He leaned forward, his snake's eyes gleaming in the folds of his face. "You must invite Yudhishtira to a game of dice, and I will play for you. Your cousin will lose everything to you: his wealth, his army, his kingdom, everything." A feminine hand made the gesture of slitting a throat.

Duryodhana had grown very still. "At dice?" he asked.

Shakuni nodded. "You must convince your father to invite Yudhishtira to Hastinapura for a game. Once the Pandava comes, the rest will be as easy as taking a toy from a child."

Duryodhana thought about this for a moment, then, said, "It will be easier for you to convince the king. He is always afraid. He fears Bheeshma and Drona and, most of all, Vidura, who loves the Pandavas so dearly. You must do this for me, Shakuni, or count me dead. I hear Draupadi laughing at me in my dreams. I cannot live with this shame; I must have revenge."

Shakuni went to the king. Sighing, he said, "Dhritarashtra, if your eyes could see, you would not be able to endure the state your son is in today. He neither eats nor sleeps, but has become like a ghost, pale and worn, as if some terrible anguish consumes him. I fear for his life, my lord. Send for him and comfort him, or I can't say what he may do."

Dhritarashtra doted on his son. Duryodhana was like his very life to him. Showing some emotion, for once, he cried, "Take me to my child, Shakuni!"

In Duryodhana's apartment, the blind king clasped his son in his arms. He stroked his face and felt his hot tears. Dhritarashtra said, "What have you done to yourself, my prince? You are lean and wasted. There is wine on your breath at this hour, and you weep. Tell me what saddens you and I will remove the cause of your sorrow, whatever it may be."

Duryodhana breathed, "I am burning, father! How can I have any peace after what I saw in the treasury of Indraprastha? Gold beyond calculation, beyond imagination! Wealth that Indra would envy. The earth has submitted to Yudhishtira, all its kings bring him tribute: from Kashmir and the Sindhu, from Souvira, Chedi, Avanti, Kerala, Pandya, Chola, Kalinga, even Pragjyotishapura. How can I bear it? Envy devours me; it feeds on my entrails!

"What shall I do? Rejoice in the glory of Yudhishtira, that noble boy, as you call him so dotingly, so hypocritically? When the grandeur of Indraprastha puts Hastinapura to shame, many times over, and makes us seem like an insignificant vassal kingdom! As for the Mayaa sabha, it is even more wonderful than we heard; it is beyond compare. One can hardly believe such a sabha exists in this world of men.*

"No, father, I cannot stand it any longer: not now, that I have seen Indraprastha with my eyes. Do you expect me to be a serf to my cousins, who came out of the jungle one day, and have become the bane of my life ever since? No, Dhritarashtra, I cannot be the hypocrite you are. You are also envious, my lord, but you are too frightened to do anything about it. But not I. I cannot suffer it any more, not after the way that whore laughed at me."

His voice was low, and he was trembling. Slowly, clearly, Duryodhana said, "Father, I want their kingdom and all their wealth for myself, and I want to see the light of Indraprastha extinguished forever. I hate them, do you understand? I hate them so much that I will have no peace until they are destroyed."

And Duryodhana sobbed, while his father stroked his son's head. Dhritarashtra said nothing, though his mind was a whirl.

Smoothly into that silence, Shakuni spoke, "The Pandavas are invincible, and Krishna and Drupada support them. Yet, my lord, there is one way to end this poor child's misery, which neither you nor I can bear to see. Desperate illnesses need desperate cures."

"What do you say we should do, Shakuni?" asked Dhritarashtra cautiously.

"You must invite Yudhishtira for a game of dice in Hastinapura, and allow me to play against him. Yudhishtira is addicted to dice. But like all noble men, he has no skill at the game. I swear he will lose his kingdom and all the gold in it; and Duryodhana will have his peace."

Duryodhana cried, "You must do this for me! It is not much for a son to ask his father."

Dhritarashtra hesitated. "I must consult my ministers and the elders of our court."

"You know Vidura will never agree. And if you don't arrange the game, I swear I will kill myself. Then you can be happy with your nephew Yudhishtira, who is one face of dharma, and your brother Vidura, who is another. You can forget you ever had a son called Duryodhana."

---

* In the original text, there is a detailed, bitter and envious 10 page description of the conquests and wealth of the Pandavas.

Dhritarashtra sighed. He weighed the balance of advantage briefly, and had to decide in his son's favour. If there was anyone on earth for whose sake the king would forsake even his caution, it was Duryodhana.

Dhritarashtra said, "Don't torture yourself any more, my child. We will invite Yudhishtira to Hastinapura to play dice. When your cousin comes, take what you can from him at the game."

Duryodhana gave a sob, and embraced his father. The king said, "Shakuni, arrange for a sabha to be built on the outskirts of our city, at Jayanta. When it is complete, call the Pandavas to come and play dice in it. The rest I leave to you."

"The rest is easy, my lord," murmured Shakuni, and there was a smile on Duryodhana's ashen face.

Work on the sabha at Jayanta got swiftly underway. Duryodhana supervised the construction himself. Inevitably, he had his artisans include various features of the Mayaa sabha in the edifice. Vidura heard a sabha was being built at Jayanta, and learnt its purpose. He came to see his brother.

"I hear you mean to ask the Pandavas to come and play dice in Hastinapura. Dhritarashtra, you sent your nephews away into a wilderness; leave them in peace now. They do not interfere with you or threaten you in any way. I beg you, stop building the gambling-hall at Jayanta."

"You exaggerate, Vidura. Since time immemorial, kshatriyas have played dice. It is a harmless pastime. Besides, the game will be played in my presence and Bheeshma's. What can happen with us there? You are anxious for nothing."

"Listen to me, Dhritarashtra, before it is too late. I am certain that only evil will come out of this game of dice. War, my brother, war with our own blood!"

But Dhritarashtra would not listen to him. "You are always imagining the worst. I tell you, the sabha at Jayanta and the game of dice both have my sanction."

Vidura said, "You are bent on destroying yourself and your son. I beg you, reconsider this folly. It will be the ruin of us all."

But Dhritarashtra was in no mood to listen. Vidura went away, sadly. When he was alone, the king was disturbed by what his brother said. He sent for Duryodhana.

"Vidura is a wise man and he loves us all. He is against the game of dice and, in my heart, I fear he is right. Empires have fallen when enmity broke out among their princes at the gambling table.

"Oh, my son, it is perilous to covet the wealth of others. Only those who are contented with what they have, and keep dharma, live at peace with themselves. Let us forget the sons of Pandu. They are far from us, as Vidura says, and they mean us no harm. Duryodhana, let us abandon this rash plan."

Duryodhana cried, "Father! You cannot betray me now. We have gone too far for that. It is our dharma to ruin our enemies, by fair means or foul. Arrows and swords are not the only weapons a kshatriya may use against an enemy. He may use deceit, and anything that costs his enemy dearly and causes him anguish. Not only the flesh may be pierced, my lord, but the spirit. I seek my enemy's discontent; for his sorrow shall be the root of my prosperity. The supreme statesman is he who achieves his own progress."

But Vidura's certainty that the game of dice boded evil had upset the king. Shaking his head, he said, "I am old enough to know what Vidura says is true. Gambling is a curse. It ends on the battlefield, with weapons flashing and lives lost."

"No! The people of olden times, who began the custom of gambling, were not fools. They knew that gambling did not lead to war or bloodshed. Indeed, it replaced both and still allowed contention between adversaries. And who knows, the game of dice may open the door to heaven, either for us or the Pandavas. One thing is certain: not both will prevail."

Good sense and sage counsel seldom deflect the progress of fate. Finally, Dhritarashtra was ruled by his love for his son. When the gambling-hall at Jayanta was complete, he called Vidura, and said to his half-brother, "I want you to go to Khandavaprastha. Take Yudhishtira this message: 'I have heard about the court that Mayaa built for you in your city. I, too, have built a sabha in Jayantapura, and I want you to come and see it. Come home to Hastinapura, and spend some time with me. We will entertain you with a game of dice.'

"Yudhishtira will come. Bring him as soon as you can, Vidura, I long to have him here with me again."

Vidura pleaded, "My lord, I fear the end of the House of Kuru, if you insist on doing this. I warn you of calamity you cannot dream of.

It is not too late. Let us turn the sabha at Jayanta into a feeding-house for the poor: so heaven's blessings fall on us, instead of heaven's wrath. Dhritarashtra, draw back from the madness you have planned."

His brother said, "I have already decided the Pandavas shall come here to play dice. I am aware of your views on the matter, and have concluded that you exaggerate. Let us have no more argument, Vidura, but go to Yudhishtira. Tell him I wait for him eagerly."

Full of foreboding, Vidura set out for Indraprastha.

FIFTEEN

An anxious messenger

In INDRAPRASTHA, YUDHISHTIRA WELCOMED VIDURA WARMLY. WHEN Vidura's feet had been washed, and madhurparka offered to him, they sat together in a private chamber: the good uncle and his nephews he loved.

Yudhishtira said, "We are delighted to have you here with us, my lord. But you seem anxious. Is the king not in good health? Is there any other cause for concern in Hastinapura? Can we be of help?"

Vidura said, "Your uncle Dhritarashtra is in excellent health, and so are his sons. There is no other cause for concern in Hastinapura, and I have come as a messenger. The king says to you, 'Come home to Hastinapura, Yudhishtira my son, and spend some time with me. We have built a new sabha at Jayantapura, and I want you to come and play dice in it. Don't refuse me.'"

Vidura fell silent, and kept his eyes turned from his nephew's face. Yudhishtira frowned. He knew Dhritarashtra well enough to suspect some treachery.

Slowly, the Pandava said, "Surely, the game of dice is the crux of this invitation. And I fear it will tear the sons of Dhritarashtra and the sons of Pandu further apart."

Vidura said, "I told Dhritarashtra the game of dice will ruin us all. But he would not listen."

Yudhishtira asked shrewdly, "Tell me, who is to play against me?"

"Shakuni."

"The best player! And I am such a poor one. Shakuni is a wizard at dice, and I hear, a cheat as well. No one can beat him. But what can I do? Dhritarashtra knows I can never refuse my elders anything they ask. Whatever God wills must happen in this world and all that happens is for the best. Who am I to resist destiny?"

He fell thoughtful. "I am not obliged to come to Hastinapura. I am no vassal of Dhritarashtra's, and a son need obey his father only if the father treats him as he should. Dhritarashtra has not treated us like his sons. Yet, my blind uncle is canny, and knows my nature well. He knows I will not refuse what he asks, though I know how envious he is of me. He knows I will come, because it is my dharma to obey my elders, however dangerous they are.

"I am also terribly anxious, but I will go with you. I will come to Hastinapura."

Vidura had tears in his eyes.

Thus, Yudhishtira, king in Indraprastha, emperor of all Bharatavarsha, went back to his father's city. He went with his brothers and Draupadi, and other companions besides. The Pandava came bravely to whatever fate held in store for him. But in his mind was the ghastly image from the Rajasuya yagna: of Sishupala's head being struck off by Krishna's Chakra; and the sinister omens that followed the killing.

He heard Vyasa's voice. "The omens portend fourteen years of misfortune; and beyond that, the destruction of the race of kshatriyas."

SIXTEEN

The game of dice

THE RECEPTION THE PANDAVAS HAD IN HASTINAPURA WAS surprisingly warm, not to say effusive. They were welcomed like sons of the city, and every arrangement made for their comfort. Their father's old palace had been prepared for them to stay in, and a host of servants detailed to look after them. Everyone was so cordial, even Duryodhana, the Pandavas were lulled into thinking that this was, after all, just a friendly invitation to spend a few days with their kinsmen.

Most heart-warming was the manner in which the people of Hastinapura flocked into the streets to welcome them. Bheeshma and Drona received them, Kripa and the others, and Dhritarashtra was the fondest, embracing his nephews, kissing each one, saying how proud their Rajasuya yagna had made him. The Pandavas forgot all about the game of dice and no one else mentioned it.

The first night in Hastinapura was a memorable one, and there was a banquet to mark the homecoming. The finest wine flowed, the food was exceptional, and there was not an unfriendly word from any of the Kauravas. Instead, they seemed delighted their cousins had come, and anxious to please them. Duryodhana sat next to Bheema and insisted on filling his glass and heaping his plate with food. But Bheema remembered the day at the river. He only ate when Duryodhana served himself from the same dishes.

It was a grand feast. The singers were in superb voice and the dancers inspired. Yudhishtira thought his prayers were answered and, surely, this was the beginning of a warm new alliance. He slept contentedly that night in the luxurious apartments in Pandu's old palace.

The next day dawned: a golden morning, with no sign that this was to be the most terrible day in the lives of Pandu's sons. They rose early, and were served a sumptuous meal. Then Duryodhana and his brothers arrived to take them to the sabha at Jayanta. The Kaurava put up such a pretense of cordiality his cousins did not suspect his real motives any more.

The Pandavas were shown round the sabha at Jayantapura. It was a crude monument, simplistic and garishly ornate. It strove, quite obviously, to imitate the Mayaa sabha. But the artisans of Hastinapura were inferior spirits, and the result of their labours was an edifice of little originality. The Pandavas, however, wandered through that building making polite noises of approval. They were not to know the Kauravas didn't care a whit about the sabha, but were impatient to get down to the game of dice. They had decided in the night they would play not at Jayanta, as they had first planned, but in the palace in Hastinapura.

Duryodhana brought his cousins back to Dhritarashtra's court. When they all sat, the Pandavas on one side and the Kauravas across from them, and the king, Bheeshma, Drona, Kripa and Vidura on their thrones above, Shakuni produced the long dice, and said smoothly, "Shall we play, Yudhishtira? Let us see the stakes."

Yudhishtira glanced up at the elders. Dhritarashtra's face showed no emotion, only the blind man's smile that hid everything. Bheeshma, Drona and Kripa seemed aloof. Vidura alone sat tensely in his place.

Yudhishtira said slowly, "Dice is a poisonous game; it breeds discord and destroys friendships. It is not a game for kshatriyas, Shakuni, and I would rather not play."

Duryodhana was alarmed; this would defeat the purpose of fetching them here. Shakuni laughed at Yudhishtira. "It's just a game, not war! Dice is as good a way as any to pass the time."

Yudhishtira said earnestly, "A man becomes a fool when he lays his hands on the ivory dice. Gambling is like wine. Worse, it is a fever of the soul; and once the fever seizes a man, nothing can cure him. Let us not play this evil game. It begins lightly enough, but it ruins men."

Shakuni laughed again. He said to the sabha, "I think our Pandava emperor, who performed a Rajasuya yagna, is afraid of losing his wealth.

After all, it is new wealth. Let him keep it. If you are afraid to play, we will not insist. After all, fate decides the outcome of a game of dice, and kings are notoriously wary of fate."

Noble, naïve Yudhishtira cried, "I am not afraid, Shakuni! Not of you, or anyone else. Fate is all-powerful, subtler than the wisdom of men: for, the ends of fate are inscrutable. If you challenge me, I will play. Say who will play against me, and what the stakes are."

Smiling in the friendliest way, Duryodhana said, "I will wager whatever you do. Shakuni will play for me."

"But that is unheard of. The one who wagers must play himself."

Shakuni said, "I see nothing wrong with the arrangement. It does seem you are afraid of playing, Yudhishtira. Why not admit it, and let us find some other way to pass the time."

Meanwhile, the sabha was filling. Every kshatriya in Hastinapura had heard about the game of dice, and no one would miss it. The blind king sat attentive, and Vidura was full of anxiety.

Yudhishtira produced a pearl necklace, set in gold. It was an heirloom, and the jewels on it shone like small moons. The emperor of Bharatavarsha said, "Let us play, and Shakuni can play for you if you insist, Duryodhana. I wager this necklace. Will you match it?"

Duryodhana heaved a sigh. Yudhishtira would play, after all; the rest he could leave to Shakuni. Powerful stars had moved into baleful aspects around the earth. The Pandavas all felt an ominous disturbance in their hearts, a dread. It was to be a more fateful hour than they could have dreamt. But there was no turning away.

Yudhishtira sat grimly across from Shakuni, who twirled his ivory dice in manicured hands.[2] Yudhishtira, also, had dice to throw: innocent dice that rolled true to chance, unlike the loaded ones Shakuni fondled.

It was all Duryodhana could do to remain calm. Unfastening a priceless bracelet from his wrist, he said, "I match your wager."

The Pandava cast his dice first, and scored well. But his eyes bland, Shakuni out-threw him. That first throw was critical; if Yudhishtira had won, he may not have lost control of himself as he did. But then, that is how fate arranged it, and the Pandava's kshatriya blood was roused,

---

2 See Appendix.

when there was little use for it in a game of dice. He was seized by an hour's madness, which would cost him dearly.

"I wager my chariot and horses!" he cried.

His brothers looked at him in alarm. He did not even glance at them any more. He only spun his dice and threw them; and after him, Shakuni, his pale eyes mocking, his plump fingers full of deceit. Again, Shakuni won. A hush fell on the sabha.

Yudhishtira grew more defiant. "I wager my elephants of war."

Duryodhana replied in deadly calm, "I match the wager. Roll."

Yudhishtira threw a fine score. Only a perfect throw by Shakuni, one chance in a hundred, could win. Shakuni spun his dice and produced that throw. The elephants were lost, and so it seemed was Yudhishtira. He had grown very still, his face set taut. Arjuna laid a hand on his arm, and whispered, "Stop this madness before you lose everything we have."

Shakuni tittered, "Had enough already, O Chakravarti? Lost your nerve so soon?"

Like a man in a dream, Yudhishtira shook off Arjuna's hand and, leaning forward, said hoarsely, "I wager all the gold in my treasury, Shakuni. Who speaks of stopping? We have just begun."

Duryodhana looked at Shakuni; this was a strong wager. His uncle nodded imperceptibly, and Duryodhana said, "I match your wager, cousin."

The dice rolled and Shakuni's voice rang again through the sabha, "We have won all your gold!"

His eyes glazed, Yudhishtira was in the grip of the gambling demon. Grown stiff as a corpse, he cried, "I wager my treasury and all the jewels in it."

His brothers sat rooted, nothing they could do any more. It was as if fate had taken Yudhishtira in relentless hands and played him like a puppet, for fathomless reasons.

Shakuni murmured, "An emperor's stakes, surely."

The dice rolled, and again. Shakuni cried, "All the jewels of Indraprastha won, Duryodhana!"

The Kaurava prince sat as still as his cousin across the chasm in which the dice rolled, so facilely, transforming lives. But his was a very different stillness from poor Yudhishtira's. Every cell in the Kaurava's body sang; his eyes shone like malignant stars. If this was Yudhishtira's most wretched moment, it was Duryodhana's most triumphant one.

Yudhishtira was trapped in a nightmare, overwhelmed by evil. He must chase his losses, though he knew he would only lose what he still had. He could not help himself.

"I wager my granary, and all the grain in Indraprastha."

The dice rolled and, inevitably, Shakuni won. Dhritarashtra sat in his throne, knowing everything. Not a muscle moved on his face, but his heart was as alight as his son's was, or Shakuni's.

Dully, Yudhishtira said, "I wager my army."

Shakuni won the army of Indraprastha for his nephew, who sat in unearthly quiet. Duryodhana could hardly believe his fortune; he felt his heart might burst for joy. But when Shakuni, whose fingers were subtle deceivers, won the Pandava army, Vidura came to Dhritarashtra, and said, "My lord, you must stop this game before fate takes us further down the path to doom than we can return from.

We saw evil omens on the night Duryodhana was born: wolves that howled in our streets, bats that covered the face of the moon, a dreadful storm, its rain flecked with blood. You asked me what the omens meant, and I told you they foretold the end of the world." His voice was low, but in the silence which had fallen in that sabha everyone heard what Vidura said. "And that night I said to you, my brother, that you should sacrifice your eldest son to save the world, because he was a monster born to destroy it."

Duryodhana's eyes were terrible, but Vidura continued, "My lord, greed and envy destroy the world. And it is from these that your son uses his uncle's vile skills to cheat his cousins out of everything they own. But you are not young or foolish, Dhritarashtra. Stop this game before it is too late, and the omens come true.

"What you countenance today is robbery, and Shakuni is a prince of cheats. I beg you, stop the game and return what this serpent has won from the Pandavas with his loaded dice."

Not a twitch from Dhritarashtra, nothing. But Duryodhana, who had been growling in his throat like some beast, sprang up and roared, "You ingrate! My father kept you, fed you and gave you authority in Hastinapura. But you always hated me, and favoured Pandu's sons. You wanted Yudhishtira on the throne, though he is not the king's son. And now you dare malign me in this sabha, with some imaginary omens you saw when I was born? Why, you wanted to have me killed, when I was a baby.

"You are the monster, that you tried to make a father murder his son. We do not need you here anymore, Vidura. Shakuni is also my uncle, and he loves me."

Duryodhana was so angry he would have torn Vidura limb from limb. "As for my character, God created me. He decides what will happen in this world, and he has set me sail on this voyage of life. Do you flatter yourself that you can change what God has written, with your moralizing? I have not said this to you before, because you are my uncle and my father loves you. But I will say it today: one must never harbour a man who wishes one harm. Since you dislike us so much, Vidura, why don't you leave Hastinapura? Today!"

That prince stalked back to the game, where Yudhishtira was losing everything he owned. Vidura sighed, "I have always been a well-wisher of Dhritarashtra and his sons," and he sat down. He saw fate must indeed have her way, and nothing he could say would change her course.

Shakuni was mocking Yudhishtira. "You have nothing left to wager, Pandava."

An ashen-faced Yudhishtira sat frozen over the dice. Shakuni made an offer. "Just to show you I am generous, I will wager everything you have lost so far. But do you have anything left, which you can lay down against my stake? I think not, O Emperor."

Yudhishtira did not speak for an age. Then, suddenly, as if he was inspired and had found his way out of staggering misfortune, he cried, "I wager my brother Nakula, who is dark and handsome, and as strong as ten of your best men!"

The court gasped. Yudhishtira's brothers sat motionless and, to his everlasting credit, Nakula showed no flicker of any emotion, let alone protest. Shakuni looked at Duryodhana; his face lit with a fiend's smile, the Kaurava nodded.

The dice rolled and Shakuni cried, "I've won your little brother for our slave, Yudhishtira. What will you wager to win him back?" His restless eyes swept across to Sahadeva.

"I wager Sahadeva. There is no man as intelligent as him."

The dice rolled, and Shakuni murmured, "Today isn't your lucky day."

A dreadful cold gripped Yudhishtira. How swiftly ruin had come to him, in a few rolls of the ivory dice. He hardly knew what he did anymore; someone else, who was determined to destroy him, ruled his head and heart, and spoke from his lips. Yudhishtira, son of Pandu, son of Dharma Deva, would never wager his brothers at a game of dice. But he had done just that.

It was not over yet. Shakuni was saying in his sly lisp, "And now what will you wager, O Emperor? You still have two brothers left, but you do not put them up. Perhaps you don't think your own brothers are as precious as Madri's sons. Or, maybe, they are less dispensable?"

"I wager Arjuna, who has no equal on earth," Yudhishtira choked, "and does not deserve this."

His hands shook as he flung the dice down. It was a perfect score, and Shakuni sat staring at it for a moment. Then he twirled his own dice and matched the Pandava's throw. Yudhishtira threw again, and now his score was low. Leering at his opponent, who was like an innocent child before him, who knew nothing of the sleight of hand and the ruthlessness that make the true gambler, Shakuni asked, "Perhaps you think I will not beat that?"

Then he did, and Arjuna was lost. By now, Duryodhana's brothers crowed and clapped. They shouted Shakuni's name and Duryodhana's; and they mocked the Pandavas, crying the emperor of Bharatavarsha had lost his brothers at a game of dice.

Shakuni said, "And will you wager Bheema next?"

Duryodhana's eyes shone more than ever. This was the finest day of his life. Fate was compensating him for all the torment he had endured, since Pandu's sons first came out of the wilderness. Today was a perfect day, and its crowning sweetness would be if Shakuni won Bheema to be Duryodhana's slave. This would be better than if Bheema had died in the river or the house of lac. Duryodhana stared at his cousin, savouring the moment; and today, for the first time, Bheema looked away.

Yudhishtira said dully, "Bheema is the Senapati of my army, and stronger than all of you put together. I wager him."

Again the dice rolled, and it was a foregone conclusion that Shakuni won. Duryodhana gave a roar of delight, and Bheema sat with his head bowed. Shakuni said, "All your brothers are lost, Yudhishtira. Now who will you wager to retrieve your losses? Or perhaps you have lost enough?"

Yudhishtira replied, "I wager myself."

"For this rarest wager, of the emperor of all Bharatavarsha, I will reverse the order of play so your luck might change. I will throw first, and you beat my throw."

But he threw a perfect score, which could not be beaten only matched; and Yudhishtira could not match it. Now Pandu's eldest son had nothing left to lose. Silence ruled that sabha, but only briefly. Then, Shakuni's reptilian voice was saying, "You think you have lost everything, Yudhishtira? But no, there is still one possession you have which we will accept as a final stake."

"I have nothing left, not even myself."

"But that isn't true!" hissed Shakuni. "You have not yet wagered Draupadi."

Bheema seized his mace, and would have smashed Shakuni's head had Arjuna not stopped him. Yudhishtira trembled. But still in the grip of the demon that whispered there was still hope, he said, "I wager Drupada's daughter, our queen."

Duryodhana's eyes were brighter than when Bheema had been put up. There was a murmur in that hallowed sabha, turned into a gaming-hall. Even the most flinty-hearted in it were saying this was too much, Yudhishtira had no right. But Duryodhana glared around his father's court, and silence fell.

Shakuni sneered, "She is your most precious possession, that you wagered yourself before you wagered her. It is only fair that you have the first throw. Go on, I am sure you will win everything back. How could the Pandavas' fortunes have changed so quickly, so completely?" He turned to Duryodhana and they both laughed.

Yudhishtira cast the dice for the last time, as if he now played with his very life. He raised a fair score and, for the first time, turned his gentle eyes to Shakuni's slitted ones. There was such imploration on the Pandava's face, that even the cold Shakuni turned his gaze away. But when the dice stopped rolling, Duryodhana's yell echoed in the stunned sabha.

"Won!" he roared, hugging his uncle. "Draupadi is ours!"

Yudhishtira sat numb; now he had truly lost everything.

SEVENTEEN

Shame

V IDURA SAT WITH HIS HEAD IN HIS HANDS, SIGHING LIKE A SERPENT. His body was bent, as if to beg the earth's forgiveness for the sin committed upon her. Bheeshma and Drona were shocked; Kripa trembled. But Dhritarashtra was elated. He had asked at every throw of the dice, "And what was won now?" Though he knew.

Duryodhana embraced Shakuni and cried, "This is the most wonderful day of my life, and I owe it to you!"

His eyes glittering, the Kaurava turned to Vidura. "Uncle, rejoice with us! Draupadi is our slave. Go and fetch her, Vidura, so she can enter our harem. She will serve with the other women, sweep the floors and attend to our every pleasure."

The Kaurava panted with excitement. The slut had laughed at him in the Mayaa sabha; he would see how she laughed now. Vidura rose wearily, and said in a voice that had aged years in an hour, "Even now it is not too late, Duryodhana. You don't realize the danger you are in. Only the fool thinks he is in heaven when he hangs over a precipice with a noose round his neck. Punishment for this crime will follow more swiftly than you think. Dreadful nemesis will visit you.

"Relent now, while there is still time. Return everything you have won with Shakuni's deceit. The jackal should not provoke the tiger.

"I know you think I am your enemy; but only your own feeble wit makes you believe this. I am your only friend at this moment, Duryodhana. Listen to me. You must not even think of Draupadi as being your slave. Beware of these sons of Pandu; be as careful with them as with king cobras. Duryodhana, hell already yawns open to receive you and your brothers. Treat this game of dice as a joke, and forget it was ever played."

Vidura fell quiet. For a moment, Duryodhana hesitated; something warned him what Vidura said was true, and he must follow this uncle's advice. Then, he glanced at Shakuni, whose serpent's eyes were fixed on him with distant interest, mocking him coolly. Duryodhana cried, "At such a triumphant moment, this son of a maidservant can think of nothing but doom!"

That prince's eyes roved over the sabha, and alighted on his own charioteer.

"Pratikami, go and fetch Draupadi! Tell her that her master Duryodhana commands her presence in the sabha."

Duryodhana saw fear in Pratikami's eyes. The sarathy looked nervously at the Pandavas, who sat as if they were carved from stone. The Kaurava cried, "Don't be afraid. They are also our slaves, and a slave cannot harm his master. Go, Pratikami, fetch her."

The old sarathy left the court, and went slowly along the passages of the Kuru palace towards the women's day quarters. He knocked gingerly at the door to Draupadi's apartment. Never had he been asked to carry a message like the one he now bore.

When a maid opened the door, Pratikami said, "I must see the queen Draupadi. I have urgent news for her ears only."

Soon, Draupadi stood before him, so regal the poor sarathy grew dumb just to look at her. How could he say what he had come for, when his tongue cleaved to the roof of his mouth?

Panchali said kindly, "Old one, what have you come to tell me, that you couldn't tell my sakhi?"

Pratikami stared down at his feet and, then, somehow whispered, "My lord Duryodhana sent me, Devi. Your husband Yudhishtira has lost everything at a game of dice."

Draupadi sat quickly in a chair, for she would have fallen otherwise. She saw Pratikami still hesitated, but there was obviously more he wanted to say. In a tremulous voice, she asked, "Is there more?"

Never looking at her, he said, "Yudhishtira lost his brothers at the gambling, he lost himself, and..." the next words would not come.

"And?" her pupils dilated with shock.

"Finally, he lost you as well!" cried Pratikami, with the last shred of courage he owned. "Duryodhana is your master now, and he commands you to come to the sabha."

Her world spun, and Draupadi clutched at the arms of the chair. But she was a strong woman, and she asked, "Tell me, messenger, whom did my husband lose first, himself or me?"

"He first lost all his possessions, his wealth, his army, his granary, his kingdom. Then he lost his brothers, one by one, beginning with the youngest; and then he lost himself. Only after that did he lose you, last of all. You were more precious to him than everything else, than himself."

A stab of light in her lovely eyes: a flicker of hope. She said, "Go back to the sabha and say to my husband his wife wants to know if he lost her first, or himself. Ask Yudhishtira only that, and bring his answer to me."

Pratikami bowed, and went back to the crowded court where Duryodhana and his brothers waited impatiently. The old sarathy said, "The queen Draupadi asks if Yudhishtira lost himself first, or her."

Yudhishtira sat graven; not a word did he say. Duryodhana growled, "Let the woman come and ask the question herself. Go back and fetch her, Pratikami."

Unhappily, Pratikami went back through the passages, and stood before Draupadi once more. Her eyes were red, and she shivered as if she had a fever.

The charioteer said, "I took your message to the sabha. Yudhishtira made no reply to your question, but sat like a block of wood. But my prince Duryodhana grew angry, and said you must come and ask the question yourself."

She said nothing yet, but her lips twitched in anger. His heart melting, the sarathy said, "Devi, the end of the Kurus is near that you have been insulted in our sabha. Duryodhana will pay for this with his life."

Taking courage from his words, Draupadi said again, "Go back and ask Yudhishtira what I should do. I will obey him, no one else."

Pratikami returned to the sabha, "Draupadi bids me ask Yudhishtira what she should do. She says she will not obey anyone else."

Yudhishtira sat with his head bent down, down into his chest. Without raising it, he whispered, "Tell Draupadi I want her to come into this court and ask the elders if I have lost her or not, and what she should do from now on."

Duryodhana howled, "Fetch the woman! She is our slave now, won fairly at dice."

Now Pratikami said, "I am afraid to go back to her. Let someone else take this message."

Duryodhana turned to his brother Dusasana, who was if anything more violent than himself. Dusasana stood smirking, in lascivious anticipation of Draupadi's advent. He was a bestial prince, wild of rage and lust, and now his brother said to him, "Dusasana, you fetch our woman."

His eyes lighting up, Dusasana went grinning from the sabha. He arrived at Draupadi's apartment, and his kick flung the heavy door open into the room where she waited.

Dusasana stood leering at her, his hands on his hips, his eyes devouring her slender form, as they would never have dared to in the past. She shuddered.

He began to laugh. "My brother won you fairly. You don't have to fear your husbands any more, you belong to us now. Come boldly to Duryodhana; turn your haughty eyes to the lord of the Kurus."

She moaned. She swayed on her feet at what had overtaken her so suddenly. His voice full of vileness, the fiend continued to torment her.

"Don't pretend to be so modest, you are no virgin. Five men already, and now you will have a hundred more to keep you happy. Ah, you blush! But why, Panchali? We are your husbands' cousins, after all." And his devilish laugh again. Then he came closer, and she thought he was going to touch her; she saw in his eyes how much he wanted to. She drew away from him, shaking. This was a beast with no shred of ruth, and she did not know how to deal with him.

"Come, my dark beauty, let us go to the sabha."

He closed on her, and with a scream, she dodged him and ran towards Gandhari's apartment down the passage. But he was on her in a flash. Dusasana caught Draupadi by her long hair, washed in the holy waters of the Rajasuya yagna. Growling, he began to drag her to the Kuru court—she whom her husbands would hardly allow the wind to touch.

She cried, "Let go of me, devil! Can't you see I am wearing just one cloth? I have my period, I can't come to the sabha like this."

But he had no ears for her pleas, no eyes to see how she wept. He laughed, "You are no queen now, but a slave; and your master calls you! It does not matter if you are clean or not, if you wear one cloth or none."

He hauled her wailing through those corridors, her garment often falling away from her naked shoulders, while she clutched at it for her very life, or for honour more precious than life. Growling still, like a predator with its prey, Dusasana dragged Draupadi into the Kuru sabha by her hair and flung her down on the floor before its kshatriyas, her eyes blazing, her face streaked with tears.

EIGHTEEN

'Am I a free woman?'

AS SOON AS DUSASANA THREW HER DOWN, PANCHALI SCREAMED LONG and loud in primeval rage: a cry from her soul. A wild and cornered thing, she panted, "I curse you, sons of Bharata! I curse you a thousand times! That you allow this outrage in your ancient court of dharma."

Her fury silenced the humming sabha.

"I see the Kuru elders on their thrones. I see Bheeshma, Drona, Vidura and Dhritarashtra before me. Or am I dreaming? For they sit looking on, while a villain, witless with power, tells his brutal brother to drag a chaste woman and a wife into the royal sabha of the Kurus. The fiend drags me through the palace by my hair, washed in the holy water of the Rajasuya yagna, drags me here like some whore. And not a word to stop him from Bheeshma, Drona, Vidura or Dhritarashtra. Surely, this is a monstrous dream from which I will awaken, to find daylight in the world."

She paused, breathless. Then she turned on Yudhishtira, "Here, in this court of righteous men, sits my own husband, who is the Lord Dharma's son; and with him, his brothers, matchless kshatriyas and Devaputras, all of them my husbands." There was such contempt in her voice, and the Pandavas squirmed. "And a messenger from this sabha told me I must come here like a slave because my husband, who is dharma's very image on earth, had lost me at dice.

"I asked for an answer to one question before I came, half-clad and in shame. Instead of a proper reply, Dusasana burst into my apartment and dragged me here like an animal. And none of these great kshatriyas stopped him."

Her eyes raked her husbands. Yudhishtira would have been glad if the earth opened and swallowed him. He never raised his head. She stood like that, her slender shoulders heaving, and no one dared make a sound. You could hear her breathe, as she turned back to the Kuru elders on their thrones.

More quietly, she said, "Dharma has left the Kuru sabha. But I would still like an answer from Pitama Bheeshma, from Acharya Drona, from Kripa, Vidura and Dhritarashtra. My question is a simple one: am I Duryodhana's slave or still a free woman?"

She looked directly at Bheeshma now. "Pitama, they say there is no one nobler than you, nor anyone more learned or wiser. You answer me, am I a slave or am I free?"

Bheeshma said gravely, "It is a fine point of dharma. On one hand, when a man has lost himself already he may no longer wager anyone else. On the other, a man has a right over his wife, whether he is free or not: our meanest servants do. It is hard to say if you are free or a slave, Panchali.

"Yudhishtira knew that Shakuni is a master dice-player. Yet, he chose to play; and though he was losing, he continued until he lost everything, including you."

Draupadi cried, "How can you say Yudhishtira played willingly? In Indraprastha, he told Vidura he did not want to play. Obviously, he was provoked into playing. You were here all the while, Pitama: didn't you know how poor at dice my husband is? That he hasn't the temper for it, that he is too noble, too innocent. Or didn't you, perhaps, know there is no dice-player on earth like Shakuni? But you sat by without a murmur as Yudhishtira gambled away all that he owned.

"O, Pitama, you are the king's uncle; you wield great power in this sabha. How did you allow this? It was like sending a child into battle against a seasoned warrior. And yet, Bheeshma, you speak to me of the finer points of dharma. How do you dare?"

Her delicate form shook, and her wrath was that of an empress. Awesome destiny stood beside Draupadi in that court, and anyone there who had been calm enough would have recalled the prophecy at her birth: that, one day, she would become the nemesis of the race of kshatriyas.

Panchali had not finished. "O Bheeshma, O Drona, O Kuru elders, Yudhishtira lost everything he owned, and then he lost his brothers and himself. When he decided to wager me, at least then couldn't one of you have stopped him?

"Dharma is not merely the details of the law. That is not justice. Is it not clear to your wise old hearts what is just in this matter and what is not? Do you really not know on which side the truth lies? That you, Bheeshma, say to me you cannot decide if I am a slave or free. There is no sabha without its elders. But just being old does not make a man fit to be a patriarch, or deserving of the title of Pitama or Acharya. If the elders don't speak out for dharma when they see it flouted so flagrantly, they are not elders but merely old men, of neither wisdom nor truth."

She still shook with the terror of her plight. Staring at her with unspeakable lewdness, Dusasana taunted, "Who are you to speak of dharma? Your dharma now is to serve Duryodhana, and I dare say your satisfaction lies there as well!"

This coarseness was greeted by laughter from some of the other Kaurava brothers, devils all, spliced once from the misshapen lump of flesh that Gandhari aborted. Draupadi glared at Dusasana as if to burn him up with her gaze.

Bheema, who barely controlled himself all this while, could not bear it any more. He turned on Yudhishtira.

"What have you done? Men who gamble every day have wives, but they do not wager them at dice. But the Pandava emperor does! You are mad. You gambled away all our wealth, our army, our kingdom, everything we had. I said nothing, because you are my older brother. I cared little for what you lost when I set it against my love for you.

"Then, you gambled the five of us away, and still I held my peace. I thought that you are our guru, our king. We all belong to you, and whatever you did would be for the best."

Bheema's face was crimson. Arjuna tried to calm him, but the son of the wind had lost control of himself.

"Everything you did I bore in silence. But now you have gone completely mad. Did you see how that animal dragged Draupadi into this sabha of our fathers? Yudhishtira, I will never forgive you for wagering Panchali!"

His eyes were red, and flecks of froth on his lips. Bheema turned to Sahadeva and cried, "Bring me fire, Sahadeva. I will burn the hands that lost Panchali at a game of dice!"

The man who had been emperor of the world, an hour ago, sat with his head hung low. Arjuna pulled Bheema to a side and hissed, "What has happened to you? You have always treated Yudhishtira like a father. How can you speak to him like this at such a time?"

Bheema was in no mood to relent. "He was like a father till an hour ago, and I respected him. But he has changed: he deserves to have his hands burned! Oh, Arjuna, look at Draupadi. Can you bear this shame?"

Restraining the titan somehow, Arjuna breathed, "Look at Yudhishtira; do you think he feels no shame? How bravely he bears it, and his guilt. His spirit is already broken, Bheema. What will you achieve by burning a broken man's hands?"

Bheema's eyes still blazed, and his great body shook. But he allowed himself to be led away to a corner, where Arjuna said, "There is one thing Duryodhana has not been able to take from us: our unity. Don't complete the Kaurava's joy by gifting him that as well."

Bheema seemed startled. He looked around him and realized he stood on the edge of disaster. With an effort, he calmed himself.

NINETEEN

The miracle and the oaths

Bheema's chest still heaved. Arjuna would have found it impossible to contain his brother, but suddenly another voice spoke, clear and ringing, in the Kuru sabha. It was Duryodhana's brother Vikarna.

He said, "Draupadi is right, dharma has left this sabha. And we will find hell as our punishment if we don't answer her prudently, and make amends for our crime against her."

Duryodhana was taken aback; the elders and the Pandavas were amazed. Draupadi turned wonderingly to Vikarna, who went on, "Why did the Kuru elders not question Yudhishtira when he wagered Draupadi? How do they quibble about the subtleties of dharma, when nothing can be more sinful than their silence when Panchali was put up as a stake? How do these great men still keep silent, when this tormented woman pleads so desperately for some mercy?

"Perhaps, their fear of Duryodhana outweighs their love of dharma. But I will say what I feel. Though I am afraid of my brother, I fear the consequences of our crime more."

Duryodhana was too surprised to speak, and Vikarna continued. "I will answer Draupadi's question. She has not been lost; she is not Duryodhana's slave. She is a free woman as she always was!"

There were astonished murmurs in the sabha. But Vikarna had not done yet. "Yudhishtira wagered Draupadi because he was maddened by the dice. He was not responsible for what he did. Besides, he never thought of wagering her, until Shakuni suggested it.

There are other reasons why the wager is not binding. One is that Yudhishtira had already lost himself when he put up his queen. But there is another, better reason why Draupadi is a free woman. A reason that sets Pitama's argument at naught."

"What is it?" someone asked.

"Draupadi is not only Yudhishtira's wife. She is also the wife of Bheema, Arjuna, Sahadeva and Nakula. They were not asked before she was put up as a gambling stake. They haven't wagered her and she is no one's slave, but free."

There was a small uproar, and everyone seemed convinced by Vikarna's reasoning. It was plain as day, but no one else had thought of it. Dhritarashtra froze on his throne. Bheeshma, Drona and Kripa were quiet, and even Duryodhana seemed at a loss for words.

Then Karna jumped up and cried, "Vikarna, your chivalry is misplaced and your logic specious. How dare you question the wisdom of the king, of Bheeshma and Drona, who have all found that this woman is Duryodhana's slave? How dare you air your callow opinion in front of these elders?

"Do you think the Pandavas would have allowed Panchali to be brought into this sabha, if they were not convinced she had been fairly won? Who was it that sent for her, finally? It was Yudhishtira. Who are you to decide this thing better than he?

"As for all this talk of dharma, I find it absurd. Dharma is not for these Pandavas. Have you ever heard of five brothers sharing the same woman? Is that dharma? Vikarna, you are bewitched by her beauty; but she is no chaste woman, that you should plead her cause so passionately. She is no virgin who has not seen men's beds, that you should feel so pained at her being brought into this sabha, clad in half a cloth or none at all!

"I find your concern laughable. She is a slut, shared already by five men; and now she will have more than five. To have been dragged into this sabha is no outrage to her modesty. You see, Vikarna, she has no modesty to be outraged."

Duryodhana and brothers laughed at this, and cried, "Well said, Karna!"

Karna had never forgotten how, when he took aim at the spinning fish, Draupadi had hissed, 'I will not marry a suta!' Sensing the sabha's mood turning again, he pressed on.

"All six are slaves, and I think that for slaves they stand too haughtily and wear too many fine clothes. Dusasana, strip them of their silks! Let them wear only what slaves should, and let them be made over to their master."

Dusasana licked his lips. He glanced at Duryodhana, who nodded. Grinning, Dusasana went towards the Pandavas. His cousins did not wait for him, but stripped away their upper garments themselves and stood bare-bodied like slaves before their masters.

Draupadi stood turned to stone. She wore just the single cloth of a menstruating woman. If Dusasana stripped that from her, she would stand naked before the Kuru sabha. She looked piteously at Yudhishtira, then, at Bheema, at Arjuna, her heart breaking, and at Sahadeva and Nakula. They all avoided her gaze and she knew they would not help her, because of dharma. They, too, considered her fairly won. She was alone, and Dusasana came leering at her.

Those moments, while the Kaurava covered the distance of a few paces, were an eternity. Panchali willed them to last longer than the stars. She had no one to turn to: this was the end. Then the beast was upon her; his brutal hands seized her cloth. Chuckling, he began to unwind the flimsy garment from her body; hell took the Kuru sabha for this sin committed in it, which would change the destiny of the world.

In a swoon, at that final moment, Draupadi's lips formed a name.

"Krishna!" she breathed, frantically. At once, a tide of faith surged in her, making all that court, and everyone in it, seem so small.

Draupadi stood with her eyes shut, her hands folded like a lotus bud. Her eyelids leaked tears of rapture, for suddenly she knew she was not alone. He whose name she called as her last resort, had not deserted her. Meanwhile, Dusasana was stripping her garment from her, and there was no man in that sabha who did not stare. She was so ravishing: which man could resist looking? It is told that even Bheeshma gazed.

As for Duryodhana, his eyes never left her for an instant, as his rabid brother tore at her cloth, hand over fist, twirling her round. But Dusasana's laughter died in his throat; Duryodhana's mouth was parched for strange oppression. Dusasana pulled on, and the cloth came away easily in his hands, and made a swiftly mounting pile at his feet. Yet, Draupadi was still clothed; she did not stand naked before their hot gazes.

The Kaurava spun her round like a top, unresisting; but there was no end to her uncanny garment. Quickly, there were three piles of shimmering cloth next to Dusasana, and now he tore at it in frenzy, sweating, cursing, maddened by the miracle unfolding in that court. Reams of cloth came away from Panchali's body, in brilliant colours, endlessly.

The others stood transfixed, sweat breaking on them; at last, with a curse, Dusasana gave up and sat on the floor, gasping. Draupadi stood in a trance in the court of the Kurus; tears still streamed down her face. She was lost to that sabha, to the very world. She was far away, borne on Krishna's great mercy, enfolded in it.

An awestruck silence; then, Bheema's voice said quietly, and clearly as a bell, "I swear in the name of everything holy, I will tear Dusasana's heart out from his chest and drink his blood for what he has done today. If I don't, let me never go to my fathers in heaven, but find the naraka meant for the worst sinners."

But seeking to turn the tide again, Karna laughed in his face. Karna said, "Dusasana, take the slave to the harem. She must learn her new duties, whatever they may be!"

With a start, Draupadi emerged from her trance. Terror took her again, and she wailed, "I am no slave! O Elders, tell them I am a free woman."

But no one spoke, until Vidura cried, "Haven't you seen the miracle of the cloth? Heaven protects her! Vikarna is right, Draupadi is no slave."

The cloth of many colours lay there for all to see. The miracle had shaken Duryodhana; but then, Karna had restored his gumption. The Kaurava said to Draupadi, "Stop repeating yourself, woman. The elders have spoken or held their peace, as they saw fit. But your husbands are here in this sabha; let Yudhishtira decide this thing. They say he is a man of honour, and I will abide by what he decides. Let him say if you belong to him now, or to me."

Yudhishtira stood bare-bodied, his head bent, not saying a word. An infinitely sardonic smile curved Duryodhana's mouth. Softly now, he said, "Look, Draupadi, your husbands are silent; but you must have an answer." His eyes were like black flames again, as he stared at her, unwinkingly. Moistening his lips, he said almost gently, "I will answer your question, Panchali."

Duryodhana paused; the sabha held its breath. He continued, "Your husbands have forsaken you in your moment of need, so I will answer you. You were never born to be a slave, but the wife of a great king. Every bit of you cries out as much, and he who cannot see it is blind."

There was another murmur in the sabha: this from Duryodhana was the most unexpected twist of all. Shakuni turned in amazement to his nephew. Karna looked astonished, and Dusasana's mouth fell open. Even Draupadi seemed taken aback. Duryodhana smiled to see the surprise on her face, but he had not finished.

"Panchali, you are a free woman. These five are not your husbands now: they do not belong to themselves, any more, but to me. Look at them, they don't say a word to guarantee your freedom.

"But I, Duryodhana, say to you—you are free! Choose a husband for yourself from this sabha. Choose any kshatriya who is not a slave." His hand swept around the court to show how wide the choice was, and it came to rest finally on his own chest. "Yes, lovely woman, these are not free men any more and must renounce their right over you. Let Yudhishtira declare that he and his brothers are not your husbands, and that you may choose a man from the rest of us."

His very blandness was fearful, and his eyes glittered with lust. Draupadi felt him strip her naked with his demon's gaze, and she shivered. She did not make any reply to Duryodhana, and neither did Yudhishtira. Once more, it was Bheema who exploded, fierce as the tempest his father blows on mountaintops.

"Aaaaaaaah!" he roared, like a wounded lion. "You would all be dead, except that I honour my brother. He stands silent, accepting that he has lost himself at dice. So I also accept it. Otherwise, Dusasana, you would not breathe after you dared touch our queen with your filthy hands. I would have torn you to pieces.

"Look at these arms, Kauravas! I could crush Indra with them. Be thankful for Yudhishtira, and the dharma that binds me to his word."

Some of the Kauravas trembled to see Bheema flex his muscles; the power of his elemental father rippled in them. His bare body filmed in sweat, the son of Vayu shook with the effort of restraining himself. He breathed heavily, and his eyes were bloodshot. Bheema was a terrifying sight.

Ignoring him, Karna said coolly, "Listen to me, Panchali: the plain truth is you are a slave. No slave owns anything, even himself. Since your husbands are slaves, how can they own you? Dhritarashtra's sons are your masters now. Take yourself to their harem, and choose a husband from among them who will not wager you at dice!"

There was more laughter from most of the hundred. Flaming Bheema turned on Yudhishtira again. "Would he dare talk like this except for your foolishness?"

Duryodhana said, "Karna speaks the truth. Yudhishtira, since your brothers will not speak their minds, out of regard for you, I ask you once more: is Draupadi a slave or a free woman? Answer me."

Still, Yudhishtira made no reply. Duryodhana exchanged a knowing grin with Karna. Keeping Bheema in clear view out of the corner of his eye, Duryodhana leaned back in his chair, exposed his thigh upto his manhood, patted the bared flesh and said obscenely, "You are a free woman, my love. Your husbands have lost you at dice. Come, sit here in my lap where you belong!"

Bheema sprang at Duryodhana with a howl, and it was all Arjuna, Sahadeva and Nakula could do to hold him back. Then, all at once, a vision swept Bheema. It was as if his anger had steamed back a veil in his mind, and now he saw through time. In a trance, he said, "I will break that thigh one day with my mace and kill you, Duryodhana. If I don't, may I live in hell forever."

Karna said, "Dusasana, why waste time? Take the woman to the harem. Duryodhana will enjoy her from today."

Draupadi was a deer cornered by hunters; her breath was shallow, her eyes full of panic. She cried, again, to the Kuru elders, "Oh, save me, I am no slave!"

But not Dhritarashtra, Drona or Bheeshma said a word: as if they had lost their wits, their tongues; as if fate addled their hearts so they no longer knew right from wrong. But Vidura was on his feet once more, trying desperately to make his brother see reason.

Meanwhile, Bheema's vision showed him a lucid glimpse of the future. In that court of shame in Hastinapura, speaking more like a prophet than himself, he said in the strangest voice, "I will kill Duryodhana at the great war on the crack of the ages. Arjuna will kill Karna, and Sahadeva will kill Shakuni. I see it all happening before my eyes. Dusasana, I see myself holding your heart in my hands and drinking your blood."

Then, by uncanny osmosis, Arjuna saw part of his brother's vision. He breathed, "The war on the crack of the ages for which we have all been born! The earth will drink the blood of these beasts, Bheema. Duryodhana, Dusasana, Karna and Shakuni will be meat for scavengers on a sacred battlefield, where justice will be done for today's crimes.

"I swear I will kill Karna at the war. Why, we shall slaughter thousands and Yama's gates will yawn open to receive them. Bheema, my brother, Himavan may move from his place, the planets may swerve from their orbits, the sun may lose his fire and the moon his cool lustre, but Arjuna will keep the oath he has sworn today!"

Sahadeva shared their vision through time, and he said, "Shakuni, you are a blot on the House of Gandhara. Your dice will turn into silver arrows and fly to drink your blood. I see myself killing you, Shakuni. I only wonder if you will take the field; if you do, snake, you shall die."

Shakuni blanched; his hands, which still held the fateful dice, were clammy. Nakula, too, was subtly invaded by the vision, and he was saying to Shakuni, "And I will kill your son Uluka for bearing your blood in his veins. Your venomous spawn must not survive you. I, also, see the war upon the edge of the ages. I see all these mocking sons of Dhritarashtra lying dead, with vultures and jackals tearing at their flesh. I see the end of the glory of the House of Kuru, for the crime committed against Panchali today."

Was it a hallucination, or did fine petals, which seemed made of fireflies' lights, rain down on the Pandavas out of the air? An unearthly fragrance blew through that sabha, as if heaven endorsed their ferocious oaths.

Encouraged by the omens, Arjuna breathed, "I can hardly wait for the war, to kill these cowards." His hand gripped the Gandiva that lay beside him. "But for Yudhishtira, I would have revenge now!"

Arjuna half raised his bow and the earth shuddered at his fury; but Yudhishtira grasped his brother's hand. The older Pandava said a strange thing then, softly, so only his brother heard him. "Arjuna, be calm, don't forget dharma. Anger took me also when I heard what Karna said; but I looked down in my misery, and I saw his feet. Suddenly my wrath ebbed from me, because Karna's feet reminded me of our mother Kunti's! His feet are so much like hers, and I felt she came to comfort me, and I grew calm again."

Arjuna stared at his brother. This was the queerest thing he had yet heard. But somehow, what Yudhishtira said quieted Arjuna. Silence had fallen again in the sabha of Hastinapura. A jackal howled on the palace-steps; in unnerving cacophony, its weird cry was answered by harsh-throated birds of carrion: vultures, crows and kites. All round the city, wolves and hyenas added their voices to the infernal din.

When his dead brother Pandu's sons swore their fierce oaths in his sabha, Dhritarashtra shivered on his throne. Now, at the macabre chorus from the creatures of earth and air, the blind king panicked. "Duryodhana," he said, "you have called your death to you. Ah, Draupadi, where are you, my child?"

She stood before him.

Held firm by terror now, Dhritarashtra said, "Panchali, my foolish son has done an unforgivable thing today. To atone for it, I grant you any boon you want. Just ask and it shall be yours."

Duryodhana froze in shock. Karna, Dusasana and the other Kauravas turned to their king and father, hardly believing what they heard. Draupadi also stared incredulously at Dhritarashtra for a moment. Then, realizing he meant what he said, she grew calmer.

She stopped trembling, and asked, "Let Yudhishtira be free."

"I grant you Yudhishtira's freedom. You deserve another boon, chaste queen."

Draupadi said at once, "Let Bheema, Arjuna, Sahadeva and Nakula be free, and their chariots and weapons restored to them."

"So be it," said the king. "But two boons are not enough for a daughter-in-law as virtuous as you. Ask me for another."

With a swift glance at Yudhishtira, Draupadi said, "My lord, it is greed that destroys dharma. I will ask for just two boons. It already means more than the world to me, that my husbands are free men again."

Karna sneered, "These Pandavas are lucky to escape so lightly. Such great kshatriyas can only be saved by a woman!"

Furious that the day was wasted, after all, he stalked out of the sabha, and Duryodhana went with him. Most of the Kauravas followed them in disgust.

Yudhishtira and his brothers gathered their silks from the pile on the floor, and covered themselves: even as if they were born again at that moment. Yudhishtira came and prostrated himself before Dhritarashtra, "My lord, you have always commanded us, and we have obeyed you without question. Tell us what to do now."

Dhritarashtra said shrewdly, "Yudhishtira, noblest kshatriya, sovereign without an enemy, listen to an old man today. The wise never harbour hostility. The good man forgets the faults of others; the best man forgives them, even when he himself has borne their brunt. In the purity of his heart, the virtuous man only sees the virtue in everyone else.

"Yudhishtira, forgive my son his sins today against you and yours. Return to your city in the forest, and rule as before from Khandavaprastha. Try to banish every memory of this day from your mind; think of it all as no more than a bad dream. My son, go home with peace in your heart. This is my fervent wish, and I shall be the happiest man alive if you accede to it.

"Duryodhana and you are cousins; you are older than he is. You are selfless and mature, while he is spoilt and rash. Oh Yudhishtira, forgive my foolish son, or he will perish! I beg this of you as a boon to an old man."

Yudhishtira said, "I will do as you ask, my lord. Bitter as it has been, I will forget what happened here today. But with your leave now, I must return to Indraprastha."

And with Draupadi beside him, and his brothers following him, Yudhishtira set out for home. He was perfectly prepared to put all the shame of the day behind him. But he wondered how Duryodhana would accept having everything he schemed for, all that he had won today— a kingdom, his cousins' shame, their very freedom—snatched from him in a moment, by his father's terrified generosity.

TWENTY

Dhritarashtra's fickleness

DURYODHANA HAD FOLLOWED KARNA AND SHAKUNI OUT OF THE sabha; he did not hear what Dhritarashtra finally said to the Pandavas. He thought his father had restored only their liberty to the sons of Pandu. But when the Pandavas left Hastinapura, Dusasana came running to his brother.

"What is the matter, Dusasana?"

"The king has given back everything you won from them," cried Dusasana.

"The coward!" his brother hissed, and stalked back into the sabha where Dhritarashtra sat with Gandhari beside him.

"Father! What have you done? You swore you would not interfere, and now you have given back everything: their kingdom, their wealth, their freedom, everything. Do you prefer your brother's sons to your own? Perhaps you want me to kill myself!"

Dhritarashtra grew increasingly distressed. Duryodhana was the only one who could tear the blind man's mask away from his father's face; for, the king loved his prince.

"How foolish could you be?" raged Duryodhana. "The Pandavas were more powerful than us, and we decided to ruin them at dice. When that was done, it was safe to humiliate them and their woman. You have given them back their power. They were already dangerous; now they are like cobras spitting venom!

"What madness possessed you, father? Already Arjuna, Bheema and the twins stroke their weapons in anticipation of revenge. Didn't you hear the oaths they swore? Yet, you set them free and gave them back their kingdom, their wealth, their army. Why, my lord? So they can come and kill us?

"Once they reach Indraprastha, do you think they will forget what we did to them today? Even if they do, will Drupada stay quiet when he hears what happened to his precious daughter in Hastinapura? Do you think her brother Dhrishtadyumna will, when he hears how Dusasana dragged her into this sabha and tried to strip her naked?

"Oh Dhritarashtra, you have been so rash. We must fetch them here at once, and take it all back again. Otherwise we are as good as dead."

He grew thoughtful, while his father trembled on his throne. In a moment, Duryodhana cried, "I have it! Call them back, and tell them that in fairness we must play another game of dice. The two kingdoms shall be the stakes. He who loses must go into exile in the forest for twelve years with his brothers; then spend the thirteenth year disguised, so no one knows them. If any of the exiles is discovered, they must spend another twelve years in the forest. Just one roll of the dice to decide this."

A cold smile touched his lips. "It is only fair: after all, anyone can win. Call them back. We know the blemishless Yudhishtira can never refuse his elders anything." Then, softly he added, "In thirteen years, I shall be strong indeed, while they roam the forest wearing deerskin. When they return they will be easy to kill."

A vision of the untold wealth of the Pandavas rose like a dream before that prince's eyes. But now, his mother Gandhari cried to her husband, "My lord, it is perilous to breach a dam built across a great lake. Don't listen to Duryodhana. You must not become the cause of the destruction of the House of Kuru."

Duryodhana gasped. "Mother!"

She continued, "I feel ashamed that you are my son, evil prince. I wish we had listened to Vidura and done away with you when you were born. How the wolves and jackals bayed that night; I can still hear them in my mind. Oh, you are the root of every sin that will bring ruin to this land. You only envied the Pandavas, never tried to understand or know them, or discover what they have suffered. Listen to me today: abandon this monstrous plan. The Gods themselves have given you another chance to save yourself. Seize it with both hands, Duryodhana, not all is lost yet."

"If you relent, the Pandavas may even forget what you did to them. I beg you, my son, and you, my lord: don't invite doom back into this sabha. It has just left us by some miracle of grace. Duryodhana, you know how much your father loves you, and how weak he is because of his blindness. Don't lead him to his death, and yourself with him."

Duryodhana ignored his mother, and said again to the king, "Father, you know the danger. The Pandavas will never forget today's shame. Even now, they must be plotting against us. Before it is too late, call them back for one last game."

Dhritarashtra summoned a court messenger. He said to the man, "Have the Pandavas called back. Tell Yudhishtira I said that in fairness one final game of dice must be played. For, if my son had lost today he would have given up his kingdom."

The messenger rode on the swiftest horse in the king's stables, and soon overtook the Pandavas on their way home. Yudhishtira reined his chariot in, and fear laid its hand on his heart. He had been expecting this rider, and he felt immutable destiny approach him again.

The messenger said, "The king asks you to return to Hastinapura. He says you must play one last game of dice."

Yudhishtira bowed his head briefly. Then, to his brothers' amazement, he turned his chariot around.

Bheema cried, "What are you doing?"

Yudhishtira replied evenly, "God has ordained the fate of every man; there is no escape from what he has written. Good fortune and evil are both beyond our control. We are helpless to resist destiny. We can only remain calm in the face of whatever happens to us. I must obey Dhritarashtra; it is my dharma. He is my uncle, and he gave us our freedom. I must go back," he sighed, "though I am certain the dice will take everything from me again. But I will not be able to live with myself, if I don't return."

His brothers knew, even Bheema, that Yudhishtira was right, and they said nothing. The Pandavas returned to Hastinapura to play another game of dice.

TWENTY-ONE

The second game of dice

In the court of Hastinapura, Duryodhana, his brothers, Shakuni and Karna waited. The dice had been laid out, the same ones. Heralded by the king's messenger, the Pandavas arrived in their uncle's sabha.

Dhritarashtra said, "I knew you would come, Yudhishtira. After you left, Duryodhana said I had no right to give back what you had lost. He said it was like stealing from him. I told him I could not ask for what I had returned. He asked for one more game of dice. I thought it was only dharma."

Duryodhana said, "One game, and our kingdoms the stake. Shakuni plays for me. He who loses goes into the jungle with his brothers, for twelve years, and the winner shall have his kingdom and everything in it. The losers must spend one more year in ajnatavasa, in disguise. If any of the exiles is recognized during the thirteenth year, they must all spend another twelve years in the forest."

Here were high stakes. Duryodhana paused, his eyes boring into Yudhishtira's. The Kaurava said, "Shall we play?"

Yudhishtira's mind churned within him, but he showed no sign of his anxiety. He bowed his head, more to fate than his malevolent cousin, and replied quietly, "Let us play."

He was as calm as a lake on which not a breath of air stirs. Like a tiger that had secured the deer that escaped him once, Shakuni faced Yudhishtira again, twirling the dice in his soft hands.

"Is the wager agreed upon?" he asked suavely.

Yudhishtira nodded. Shakuni said, "You roll first, O Emperor."

Yudhishtira knew the price, but he felt queerly light-hearted. At least, this time his brothers and Draupadi were not put up. What was a kingdom or a thirteen years' exile compared with losing them? He had lived through that; these were small stakes for him now.

Calmly Yudhishtira threw the dice, and had a fair score. But he had no doubt Shakuni would beat it; and that evil one did, smoothly. Duryodhana jumped up in triumph, and embraced his sleek uncle.

"Won!" they cried in one voice.

The Pandavas hung their heads, but now there was no dissent among them. This loss was negligible compared to the last time. The brothers may have even felt the wilderness would do them good, they had grown soft with all the luxury they lived amidst in Indraprastha. They had been raised in a jungle, and part of them always longed for the freedom of the wilds. Most of all, they were together, and Panchali with them. They were unafraid, and quite unattached to comfort or wealth. Fate called them; they were all certain of that now, especially after the visions they saw in the Kuru sabha. They would answer her call.

The Pandavas prepared themselves for exile. They put on garments of tree-bark and deerskin, as the banished must. As they emerged from their apartment, Dusasana and some of his brothers saw them in the passage and burst out laughing.

Dusasana cried, "What is this? Has the palace of Hastinapura become a jungle or a manger that animals roam here? Do my eyes deceive me or is that a fat cow I see waddling towards me?"

Bheema breathed, "You preen and mock today, but you will not laugh during the war. Enjoy our exile, cousin. Because one day I will cut the hand, with which you dragged Draupadi, from your wrist. I will tear your heart out of your chest and drink your blood."

The son of the wind spoke so menacingly Dusasana drew back from him in fear.

The Pandavas came to see Dhritarashtra, Bheeshma, Kripa and Drona. They took leave of the Kuru elders. Other than formal farewells, no word passed between them. Dhritarashtra's face was a mask again, and the others blessed the sons of Pandu quickly, hardly daring to look at them.

But when they came to their uncle Vidura, in private, he embraced them with tears in his eyes. "May God protect you and help you keep your oaths. Dhritarashtra's sons must pay with their lives for this. Bide your time in patience, Yudhishtira. Fate always tests those whom she would exalt; she tries them in the wilderness. The years of exile will flit by, and you will come home in glory."

He paused, overwhelmed. Then, Vidura remembered, "Your mother is too old to go with you. Leave her with me."

Yudhishtira nodded. Vidura drew a deep breath and said, "Ah, my sons, cultivate patience and serenity. It is to acquire these that fate sends you into the jungle. Learn from nature, she has many lessons to teach. Learn to be as calm and generous as water, as forgiving as the earth, as brilliant as the sun, as powerful as the tameless air, and keep compassion for all the living."

He hugged them, and they wept when he finally bid them farewell. Once more, Yudhishtira came to Bheeshma and touched his feet. Bheeshma blessed him distantly, his craggy face inscrutable.

At last, the Pandavas came to their mother from whom they had never yet parted. They stood before her, their hearts too full to speak. Draupadi also stood distrait beside her husbands, her eyes bleary and her hair hanging loose below her waist. She had sworn she would not tie it until Bheema kept his oath and tore Dusasana's heart from his chest, so she could wash her hair in his blood. Now, like a wild vetali's, her black tresses streamed over her face and her shoulders, and her eyes were red with crying.

Kunti, who had just yesterday seen her sons as rulers of the earth, now saw them wearing deerskin and tree-bark, and their ornaments discarded. At first, she was brave; but when she saw Draupadi, she clasped the young queen to her and began to sob.

"My precious child! Forgive my sons. Be kind to them, Panchali, now they have only you to care for them. You could have made them ashes with a look from your eye and all the Kauravas too. Yet, after all that happened, the only boon you asked for was your husbands' freedom. I know most queens would have chosen another path, especially after none of my sons spoke for you. You are a woman of great purity. I bless you, my daughter, and I thank the Gods you are my sons' wife!"

Both women wept, and Draupadi wiped Kunti's tears, saying, "Don't worry, mother, I will look after them."

Kunti said to her, "I leave my Sahadeva, who is still like a child, in your care. Be not only a wife, but a mother to him."

She hugged Sahadeva, and her other sons, crying, "Look after one another, and this jewel of a woman the Gods have blessed you with."

As they touched her feet, Kunti became hysterical. She cried out their names, calling to her husband in heaven to watch over them, calling on God to protect them. How would she live without them for thirteen years? She clasped them to her, one after the other, and would not release them.

Finally, Vidura took her hands and said, "You will have plenty of time to cry when they have gone. Come away now: the sooner you let them go, the sooner they will return to you."

Kunti allowed Vidura to lead her inside. Before she lost control of herself again, her sons left the palace. They walked through the streets, out of the city of their ancestors, and their misfortune. The people of Hastinapura thronged those streets, and followed the Pandavas to the city-gates. They wanted to follow them into exile, even as, an age ago, the people of Ayodhya had wanted to follow Rama when he was banished.

The people always see clearly into the hearts of those who rule them. They said to one another, "Duryodhana wants to be king, with Shakuni, Dusasana and Karna beside him."

"And then not our homes or families shall be safe."

"When demons rule how can anything be safe? Not our heritage, our faith, or our happiness will be secure."

"The world will perish if Duryodhana rules the Kurus."

"Let us leave this accursed city, and follow Pandu's sons wherever they go."

"Let us follow Yudhishtira to the forest!"

The people of Hastinapura cried to the Pandavas, "Princes, you have been banished by treachery. We, the people, are with you. Don't desert us, Yudhishtira; we will be ruined if Duryodhana rules us."

"He will corrupt our children, and plunge us all into darkness."

"But if we stay with you, Pandavas, we will be happy. Your nobility will make our lives fragrant, as lotuses do the water on which they rest."

"We see all the virtues of dharma in you. We are the people; we know what we see. Duryodhana does not deceive us, nor does Shakuni. It is not from pity, but for our own welfare that we want to go with you. We want to save ourselves from these devils."

"We will follow you into exile!"

They set up a great noise, and Yudhishtira spoke gently to them, "My friends, only your affection and loyalty make you see such qualities in us, where they hardly exist."

"You are too modest, Yudhishtira!" someone shouted. The surging crowd took up that cry.

"The Pandavas are too pure!" they said.

"They could kill the Kauravas, and rule both Hastinapura and Indraprastha. If only they weren't so noble."

"We want Yudhishtira for our king, even if it is in the jungle!"

Yudhishtira raised both his hands to quieten them, and when they fell silent, he said, "You must stay behind, my friends. You must think of Bheeshma and Dhritarashtra, Vidura and my mother Kunti. Bheeshma has served you long and devotedly, and so have the king and Vidura. They also share your grief at our exile. You must be of solace to them."

"Dhritarashtra feels no remorse, or he would not have called you back to play a second time!"

"Even if that is true, what about the others? Will you abandon Bheeshma, Vidura and my mother, in their grief?" They were amazed; any other man would have encouraged them to go with him, at least to teach Duryodhana a lesson. But with tears in his eyes, Yudhishtira pleaded, "You must return to your homes, where you belong. Make it easier for us to leave you. In thirteen years, we will come back to claim what is ours."

He folded his hands, and begged them not to follow him any further. At last, the crowd was mollified. The people said, "We must not make their sorrow sharper than it is. Come, we will do as he asks. After all, he is our king. We will be patient and wait for you to return, Yudhishtira."

"Let them go quickly. So they will come back quickly."

Convinced by the justice of what Yudhishtira said, they cried, "Go in peace. We will wait for your return."

Thus, the Pandavas climbed into their chariots and rode away from the city of their defeat. The crowd stayed where it was, gazing after them.

The people hardly saw clearly, for the tears in their eyes. Even when the chariots had driven out of sight, they stood on mutely. Perhaps they hoped the princes would change their minds and come back.

At last, sadly, they did turn back into the city and their homes; dark foreboding for the future lay heavily upon them.

Meanwhile, fear of another kind gripped Dhritarashtra. As he always did, at such times, he sent for Vidura. By the time his brother came, the king was in a panic. When they were alone, he whispered anxiously, "Have they gone, Vidura? What did the people say? And what did the Pandavas say to them? Tell me everything."

For a moment, Vidura stood silent, feeling both pity and revulsion. Then, with a sigh, he said, "Yes, they have gone. They went in their chariots."

"And the people?"

"The people came out of their homes; not a man, woman or child stayed in. They followed the Pandavas like a river, reaching out their hands to comfort them, and there was no one in the crowd who did not cry. They came to the gates, and the leaders of the people approached Yudhishtira and swore they would follow him into the wilderness, because they do not trust your son. They said the kingdom would perish if Duryodhana ruled from Hastinapura."

The king's mask was impenetrable once more. But his brother knew how frightened he was, and today Vidura did not spare Dhritarashtra. The more he could hurt him the better.

"Like Rama of Ayodhya, Yudhishtira left his people, and he had to beg them to stay behind, saying who would look after Dhritarashtra and Bheeshma, Vidura and Kunti, if they went with him. Finally, he convinced them not to follow him. Just as people of Ayodhya wept when Rama went into exile, the people of Hastinapura cried when the Pandavas rode away in their chariots. Some wiped their tears with their cloths, some with their hands; but they all sobbed like children, and stood gazing after the princes long after they were out of sight. Such love can't be bought, not with money, and surely not with fear."

"And how did the Pandavas look when they left? Tell me everything, Vidura, each detail."

"Yudhishtira covered his face with a cloth, leaving only space for him to see ahead, and he kept his eyes turned down to the earth." He paused while the king considered this. "Bheema went grimly and in silence, like a great lion. But he stared at his hands all the time, and his eyes seemed to be on fire."

"And Arjuna?"

"Arjuna followed Bheema, his eyes also turned down. I saw he scattered the dust at his feet, kicking it repeatedly. Sahadeva went, his face darkened with ashes, and his twin Nakula had smeared his whole body with dust and ashes."

"And Draupadi?"

"She had undone her hair, so it covered her face and her shoulders. She wore a single cloth, stained with blood. She went like a vetali, sobbing. Behind the six of them walked their guru Dhaumya: to share their misfortune as he has their glory. As he went, he plucked blades of kusa grass, wherever he saw them growing, and chanted hymns from the Sama Veda, to Rudra and Yama."

"What does it mean, Vidura? Does it mean anything?"

Vidura laughed. His every word the twist of a knife, he said, "Do you doubt that it all has deep meaning? You and your son have left the truth behind you today. But not Yudhishtira; he remembers dharma well."

"Don't speak in riddles, tell me plainly what you mean. What has dharma to do with the way Yudhishtira and his brothers left Hastinapura?"

Vidura said softly, "If Yudhishtira had raised his eyes to look at your city, his wrath would have made ashes of it. Bheema stared at his hands, because he will take revenge on your sons one day with those hands. Arjuna scattered the dust at his feet, as he will the Kauravas. Sahadeva blackened his face for shame, and Nakula, who is the most handsome of the five," now Vidura laughed, "did not want the women of Hastina to be smitten by the sight of his bare body!"

"Why did Draupadi go with her hair undone?" breathed Dhritarashtra, fear taking him completely.

"She showed how the Kaurava widows will walk through the streets of Hastinapura, after the Pandavas kill their husbands and their sons: for what she suffered today in your sabha. Dhaumya walked behind them plucking kusa grasses and chanting the Sama Veda, to say that many funerals shall soon be held in Hastinapura."

The king moaned. Hurtfully, Vidura said, "Remember, these are no empty threats but the oaths of the greatest kshatriyas on earth. What they have sworn, they will do. The omens all foretell just one thing: the end of the Kuru vamsa."

Without offering a word of solace to his brother, whom he had served so loyally and lovingly since they were boys, Vidura walked out of Dhritarashtra's apartment. But when he reached the door, there was a flash of light in the room, and Narada, his body luminous and his face grave, stood between Dhritarashtra and Vidura. The rishi said in a voice like doom, "In thirteen years, Dhritarashtra, all your sons will die for what you have done today."

Dhritarashtra was frantic, "Hah! Who speaks? I heard no one enter the room. Who is it, Vidura?"

"It is Narada Muni."

Narada said, "Till then, enjoy the fruits of evil as best you can. There will be no forgiveness for your sin: it must be washed in blood and the sacral waters of death. In thirteen years, the House of Kuru will be destroyed. Enjoy yourself until then, blind king, if your conscience allows you."

Dhritarashtra jumped up with a cry, and groped before him to try to find the speaker. As suddenly as he had come, the rishi vanished. Dhritarashtra staggered into his brother's arms, his lips working feverishly, though no words came from them.

Vidura said, "He has gone."

Gently as he could, he led the stricken king back to his throne. Now Vidura was moved to pity, and he sat a while holding his terrified brother's hand. When he recovered some composure, Dhritarashtra said quietly, "Leave me now, Vidura. I want to be alone."

The blind king sat plunged in silence, and anxiety plucked remorselessly at his heart. For a week he did not come out from his apartment, and neglected the affairs of the kingdom. One day, his sarathy Sanjaya came to see him. Sanjaya was more than just his charioteer; the king confided in him.

"What ails you, Dhritarashtra? Now you are the undisputed lord of all the Kurus."

The king sobbed. He told the sarathy about the Pandavas' departure, and how Vidura interpreted it. He told him of Narada's brief visitation, and his dire prophecy.

Sanjaya said, "Dhritarashtra, your sin was worse than your son's. How much Vidura begged you that day, speaking in God's very voice to see justice done by the Pandavas. You sat unmoved even when Dusasana tried to strip Panchali naked. Then you seemed to relent, and I rejoiced when you gave the Pandavas back their freedom and their kingdom. I thought, my king's eyes might be blind but not his heart.

"My lord, what possessed you to call them back for another game of dice? What madness seized you again?

"You have sown the wind, Dhritarashtra; no one can do anything for you now. You must live in terror, dreading the day your nephews return to have revenge on you and your sons."

Sanjaya left his master's presence, sadly, knowing there was no help for that fallen king. And peace left Dhritarashtra; he was tormented by fear for the rest of his days.

BOOK THREE

Vana Parva

AUM, I bow down to Narayana, the most exalted Nara, and to the Devi Saraswati, and say *Jaya*!

ONE

The Sun's gift

THE PANDAVAS LEFT THE CITY OF THEIR SHAME. AS IF TO LEAVE ITS very memory far behind, they rode hard and came to the banks of the Ganga, flowing deep and serene. There was an immense banyan tree growing at the water's edge, with a hundred aerial roots, each one thick as a small trunk, spreading down from great branches. It was a copse by itself, and they decided to spend the night under it. They were exhausted, in body and in spirit. They had nothing to eat, and felt they could not cross the river until they had some sleep. That place where they first stopped was known as Pramanavata, after the tree.

Pangs of hunger clutched at them, but they were in no mood to hunt. They drank the river's sweet water, and it refreshed them. The brahmanas, who had insisted on coming with them, lit a fire and chanted hymns from the Vedas late into the night. This comforted Yudhishtira no end. One by one, all the party fell asleep.

They woke with the sun, the next morning, as bird-song trilled in the banyan's canopy. They rose feeling dull and famished. There was nothing to eat, unless they pulled up the stalks of the lotuses floating on the Ganga; and these would hardly satisfy their ravening hunger.

Yudhishtira turned sadly to his brahmanas, "My friends, already you see what exile is like. The forest is worse, infested with danger of every kind, wild beasts and rakshasas, serpents and scorpions. How will we look after you, when we are hard-pressed ourselves to keep body and soul together?

"I am touched that you chose to come into exile with us. But you have made a mistake, and you must go back. Last night I knew you were hungry, but I could not feed you. We will have to hunt game, and when we find none, subsist on roots and fruit."

The brahmanas received this in silence. Then, one of them said quietly, "We did not follow you without knowing you were going into hardship. How could we live with ourselves if we deserted you in your time of trial? We will make ourselves useful. Even in the wilderness, you need someone to perform your pujas. As for food, it will not be the first time a brahmana has survived in a forest!"

Yudhishtira began to protest, but another brahmana said, "Don't turn us away, Pandava. We are devoted to you, and even God does not turn away a good brahmana. We will watch over you in the jungle with prayers, and lighten your spirits with stories from the Puranas. You need us, Yudhishtira, don't send us away."

Yudhishtira said, "How can your company not be a source of joy to my brothers and me? But, friends, how will I feed you? That worries me more than anything else."

Dhaumya had been silent during this exchange. Now he said, "Surya Deva is lord of all the foods of this earth. If you worship him, he will help you feed the brahmanas."

Yudhishtira saw his priest was perfectly serious.[1] So, for two days and nights the Pandava neither ate nor slept, while the others made do with such fruit and roots as they could find. At dawn of the third morning, his body purified by his fast, and his mind calmed by it, Yudhishtira entered the whispering Ganga as the birds on the riverbank sang the rising sun.

Standing waist-deep in the water, his hands folded, Yudhishtira performed Suryanamaskara.

"You are the eye of the universe," he chanted, gazing at the burning star, "you are the soul of all the living." He offered the lotuses his brothers had gathered to the first orange-gold light that spilled over the horizon.

"The Devas follow your chariot across the sky for your blessing. And I worship you today, immortal one who saw the world begin, who

---

[1] Dhaumya enumerates the 108 names of Surya Deva for Yudhishtira. See Appendix.

sustain us. I beg you, incendiary Lord, bless me: that these loving brahmanas and we ourselves do not starve in the wilderness."

Dharma's son Yudhishtira stood with his eyes shut in the Ganga. The sun rose higher, and the world was full of light. Yudhishtira stood motionless.

Then, the light behind his eyelids dazzled him. He sensed another presence in that quiet place, a blazing, awesome presence. He began to tremble, and felt impelled to open his eyes. With a soft cry, Yudhishtira looked: not ten feet from him, poised above the water, was an irradiant Deva. He was the same God who had once appeared to a young Kunti.

Surya, the Sun God, stood before Yudhishtira. His body and his face were light; his eyes shone like other stars, and his locks were tongues of flame that pulsed to some cosmic rhythm, or a transcendent music. Though the Sun's light was cool so the Pandava could bear his presence, Yudhishtira's hair stood on end and he was speechless.

The apparition said, "Dharmaputra, I have something for you."

The Deva held an incandescent disc in his hands. He gave it to Yudhishtira.

A moment ago, when the God plucked it from another realm, the copper platter had blazed as if it were on fire. Now it was cool to Yudhishtira's touch, as he received it reverently. The Sun said, "My platter will feed you all. Whenever you want to eat, it will fill with food and remain full until Panchali has eaten. For thirteen years of your exile, my plate will feed you, Yudhishtira. In the fourteenth, you will have your kingdom back and you shall be lord of the earth again."

Surya Deva vanished like a dream at waking, and Yudhishtira was left holding his precious gift. The Pandava came ashore. He dried himself slowly, chanting mantras in praise of the Sun. He returned from the bend in the river, where he had come alone, to the banyan tree where the others waited.

Yudhishtira brought the gleaming platter to Dhaumya. "It is the Sun's gift to us. The Lord Surya said the platter would never be empty until Draupadi has eaten from it. At least now, we will not starve."

Dhaumya blessed him, and Yudhishtira embraced his brothers. He brought the platter to Draupadi.

"Prepare some food, then serve us from the copper plate."

A few wild roots, half a handful of the grain the brahmanas had brought for their worship: Draupadi cooked these over a fire that Arjuna and the twins kindled. Gingerly, she took what she had made, which was not enough to feed a child, and set it, steaming still, on the Sun's platter. She made the brahmanas sit facing each other, seven in a row, with freshly cut plantain leaves laid before them, to eat out of.

Yudhishtira and his brothers held their breath as she approached Dhaumya, first, to feed him with the morsel that lay on the platter. She had curved a natural ladle with a large, sturdy leaf. As Panchali scooped up the minuscule meal with it, suddenly, quicker than seeing, there was a heap of fragrant food on the magic plate. The brahmanas cried that they were very hungry indeed!

For the first time since Pratikami knocked at her door in Hastinapura with word of the gambling, Draupadi smiled. As she served the brahmanas, the heap of food on her platter never diminished, not by a rice-grain, not though she piled their leaves high.

Soon, Dhaumya said, "Yudhishtira, you were emperor of the world, but I never tasted food like this in your palace!"

The brahmanas agreed fervently, and so did the Pandavas when they began to eat. Bheema was the most delighted of all and, of course, he ate as much as the rest of them together. When they had all finished, there was still some food left on the platter: just enough for herself, thought Draupadi, hungry as she was. She, too, sat down to her meal and relished what she had from the plate of the Sun. When she finished, the platter was clean and bright of itself, without her having to wash it. From habit, she rinsed it with some water from the river.

Knowing their exile was a long one, and feeling calmed by the murmurous Ganga, the Pandavas remained under the banyan Pramana for another day. The food from the Sun's plate stroked their palates and filled their stomachs, and they were at some ease. The princes practised with their weapons, whenever they felt inclined to. Otherwise, they sat with the brahmanas, who regaled them with legends of times when the world was full of miracles, its heroes magnificent, its women ineffable, its battles mythic: times when the Gods came freely among men, when there was a lot of heaven on earth.

The next day, they hardly missed palace life any more; their bodies and spirits grew accustomed to the freedom of nature. Yudhishtira said,

"It is time we entered the deeper jungle, or the terms of our exile won't be fulfilled."

Leaving the shelter of the banyan, they forded the river in rough rafts the Pandavas lashed together, and steered with stalks of elephant-bamboo. They went north, until they arrived on the banks of the midnight-blue Yamuna.* They found a ferryman to take them across and, when they had walked some way, they came to the Saraswati, her currents golden by the setting sun. On her banks, they saw a lush jungle that seemed to call out to them: its presence was so tranquil, deeply inviting.

Arjuna said, "It is the Kamyaka vana. I have hunted here once."

Yudhishtira decided, "I have heard many rishis live in this forest. Let us build an asrama, and spend part of our exile here."

The Pandavas entered the vana, and found a fine glade with an auspicious feeling about it, and another patriarch of the wilds, a mighty nyagrodha tree, growing at its heart. Quickly, the brothers built thatched wooden huts for themselves and the brahmanas; those princes of destiny began living in the Kamyaka vana. Soon enough, the jungle became familiar, its primeval spaces, its wild denizens, and the rishis who lived here in tapasya, praying for the world.

---

* KMG says they went first to Kurukshetra, then bathed in the Saraswati, the Drisadwati, and the Yamuna, before travelling west, from one forest to another, before reaching the Kamyaka vana.

TWO

The king's brother

Meanwhile, back in Hastinapura, Dhritarashtra was suffering. He hardly slept, and when he did terrible nightmares ravaged him. One day, he sent for his brother Vidura.

The blind king said, "The people have no love left for me or my sons, or, indeed, for anyone in the palace. They speak scornfully of us. I know my princes and Pandu's are equal in your eyes. Comfort me, Vidura; give me some counsel that will benefit my sons as much as the Pandavas."

Vidura said, "To my mind it is quite clear what will help both, but I fear you will not like my advice. Bitter medicine heals the ailing system; but are you prepared to drink bitter medicine, Dhritarashtra?"

"Tell me, Vidura, I am listening. Remember it must be good for my sons and Pandu's. It must win back the people's hearts."

"You must send for the Pandavas and restore Indraprastha to them. The world will know you have repented. The Pandavas will forgive you, the people will forgive you; and, in time, their forgiveness will wash away your sin. Everyone will say that Dhritarashtra atoned for the crime Shakuni contrived.

"If you do not do this, prepare for nemesis. I warned you; Narada came to say the same thing. Death stalks you even now, but you can still save yourself. Swallow the bitter medicine of repentance, Dhritarashtra; free yourself from guilt and terror. This is the only remedy for you."

The king sat silent. Encouraged that he had made some impression on his brother, Vidura continued, "The Pandavas are kshatriyas; they are men of their word. They have sworn revenge, and revenge they will wreak on you and your sons. For, the truth is with them. But if you relent now and give back what you took from them by deceit, Yudhishtira will forgive everything. I know him, he is not a vengeful man; and if he forgives you, he will dissuade his brothers from seeking revenge.

"This is the only way, my lord, to avert the retribution that must follow your crime, as night does the day. Otherwise, there will be no escape for Duryodhana and his brothers when the Pandavas return.

"You love your son too much, Dhritarashtra, and that love clouds your reason. If Duryodhana does not agree to return Indraprastha to the Pandavas, then offer Hastinapura also to Yudhishtira."

Still, Dhritarashtra was quiet. Then Vidura saw warning signs on his brother's face: his cheek twitching, the lips working. He saw the king's hands quiver, and next moment, Dhritarashtra cried, "All you want is glory for Pandu's sons, and what matter if mine are ruined? It is easy for you to give such lofty advice. You have no children; or you would not tell me to sacrifice my own son for the sake of my brother's boys.

"I will not do it, Vidura! Duryodhana is more precious to me than Yudhishtira, and nothing in heaven or earth can change that. As for your noble advice, I have had enough of it. It torments me, so your purpose is served. I called you here because I thought you could comfort me in my anguish. For in my way, I also care about Pandu's sons.

"But what do I get from you? Words! Glib, cruel words that multiply my pain a hundred-fold. I cannot bear it any more!"

The king shut his ears with his hands, as if that would keep the words that had entered his heart like fire from burning him. In a rage he cried, "I have no further need of you, Vidura. Leave my city!"

Dhritarashtra rushed out of the room. Vidura sat alone briefly, then, decided he must leave Hastinapura at once. He would find the Pandavas, and spend their exile with them. What could make him happier?

The same day, with a few possessions, and his heart alight, he rode out of the city he had served for so long. Asking villagers, fisher-folk and gypsies which way the Pandavas had gone, he followed them. He came to the great tree beside the Ganga, and forded the river. He rode on and came to the Yamuna, where he met the ferryman who had taken his nephews across. This man took Vidura over as well, and pointed him after the princes. On rode Vidura, a song on his lips and feeling light as the breeze in his face, until he saw the golden Saraswati and, looming on her banks, the deep Kamyaka aranya.

Vidura entered the jungle on foot and, asking directions from rishis who meditated under the old trees, made his way to the clearing where Yudhishtira and his brothers had built their asrama.

The Pandavas sat with their brahmanas, and some forest hermits, in the shade of the spreading nyagrodha. Yudhishtira saw his uncle and rose in excitement. "It is Vidura!"

Then, he was anxious. "Why has he come? Has Shakuni sent him to call us to another game of dice? Do they want to take our weapons from us now? Or has he come with a declaration of war from Duryodhana? That should make you happy, Bheema."

Then, Vidura was near and Yudhishtira ran forward and hugged his uncle. Vidura embraced his nephews. When Draupadi came out of her kutila, he stood stricken to see her: Drupada's daughter, the fire-born princess, the Pandavas' wife, empress of all Bharatavarsha, with her hair loose, no ornaments on her body, and dressed like a hunter's wife.

Vidura wept. When he calmed down and they gave him water to drink, he sat with them under the shady tree, and told them about his last meeting with Dhritarashtra.

"The king is like a sick man who cannot stand the sight of food. He wants no cure for his sickness. He said to me, 'I have no further need of you, Vidura. Leave my city!'"

Vidura sighed. "I was foolish to think he would listen to a voice of sanity. He has gone too far down the path of evil. Perhaps, I shouldn't have tried to make him do the right thing, but just comforted him."

The Pandavas knew Vidura's regret was genuine; he loved his brother, and was protective of him. He had been Dhritarashtra's eyes, and his only support since Pandu left Hastinapura. Yudhishtira consoled his uncle as best he could, and Vidura spent some idyllic days with his nephews in the forest. Yet, his mind always turned back to Hastinapura and its blind king, for whom he felt deep pity.

Meanwhile, when he found he could not live without Vidura, Dhritarashtra bitterly regretted what he had said to him. The king was in agony, and he knew the only person who could comfort him was his brother. Next to Duryodhana, strange to say, it was Vidura that Dhritarashtra loved; and committed though the king was to an evil course, he yearned for his brother's gentle presence. They had grown up together, and despite their divergent natures, or perhaps because of them, Dhritarashtra longed for Vidura, as night longs for day, as darkness does for light.

Just a week after his brother left Hastinapura, Dhritarashtra sent Sanjaya to tell Vidura he was sorry and to bring him back. Sanjaya arrived two days later in the Kamyaka on horseback, while the Pandavas and their uncle sat at their midday meal under the nyagrodha.

Sanjaya was an honourable man and the Pandavas had known him since they first came to Hastinapura. Yudhishtira rose and received him affectionately.

"Welcome, Sanjaya! You are just in time to share our meal. Come, sit down and eat with us."

But Sanjaya was in a hurry. He said to Vidura, "My lord, the king is ailing and asks you to return to Hastinapura. He begs your forgiveness and says he cannot live without you. You are his eyes in this world, and now he truly knows what it is to be blind. Will you go back with me? The king has taken to his bed in grief. I fear for his life, if you do not come at once."

Vidura had been on his guard, the moment he saw Sanjaya. He feared some new treachery from Shakuni or Duryodhana. Sanjaya's manner and his mission were so transparent Vidura quickly had tears in his eyes.

He sighed, and said to Yudhishtira, "My brother is not all evil. Somewhere behind Dhritarashtra's many masks, hides a good man. His blindness has made him weak, or he would be greater than us all. That, and his love for his son. Ah, if he had listened to me on the night that devil was born. If only he had killed Duryodhana before the boy grew up, so dashing, so charming and shrewd: a young man no father's heart could resist."

He shook his head, and admitted wryly, "Well, perhaps Dhritarashtra was right, and Duryodhana too, when they said life was less simple than what I would like it to be. Fate must have other purposes beyond the simple goodness for which I so devoutly wish. There must be deeper designs in the world than the likes of me can fathom."

Sanjaya waited for Vidura's reply. Yudhishtira asked gently, "Will you go back since the king has sent for you?"

Vidura seemed distracted for a moment. "Go back? Yes, of course I must go back. My brother is plunged in darkness, and he begs me to come to him. How can I refuse? We grew up together, and we are still brothers. Come, Sanjaya, let us set out. Happy as I have been with these noble sons of my Pandu, we must leave at once."

Vidura took Yudhishtira aside, and said quietly to him, "He that forgives despite every suffering he endures, surely triumphs and becomes master of the world. For only he who is a master of himself can be the lord of this earth."

Vidura's eyes were moist again as he embraced his nephews, and blessed Draupadi when she knelt before him.

"Look after this queen, she is the rarest treasure!"

He mounted the horse Sanjaya had brought for him, and rode back to Hastinapura where his heart had always been. Now, he went with no hope of convincing Dhritarashtra to return to the path of dharma. He only went home to stand by his brother, during the punishment that must follow the sin the king had encouraged.

When Vidura went back, Dhritarashtra hugged him and sobbed, "Forgive me, Vidura! Forgive me for hurting you."

Vidura put his arms around him, and said, "I am here, my lord. You are my king, and there is nothing to forgive. Your sons are as dear to me as Pandu's; only, the sons of Pandu seemed to be in trouble."

They held each other, with tears streaming down their faces.

THREE

The rishis' warning

BHEESHMA AND DRONA WERE RELIEVED VIDURA HAD RETURNED. BUT Duryodhana was anxious when he saw that, now, his father and his uncle had grown even closer.

One day, when Shakuni, Dusasana and Karna were with him, that prince said, "My high-minded uncle's influence is greater than ever. There is no telling when Vidura will convince my father to bring the Pandavas back. Shakuni, think of some way to stop the king from listening to that interfering son of a maid. I know what it is to sleep at nights again, and I would rather die than have my cousins return."

But Shakuni laughed, "You are forgetting our Pandavas are men of dharma. They are so noble they are scarcely human. The fools are so honourable that, even if Vidura persuades your father to call them back, they will refuse to return. You saw how none of them opened his mouth when Dusasana dragged Draupadi into the sabha. Their reason was that she had been lost fairly at dice!

"Have no fear. They will not come back for thirteen years, not if your father begs them."

Duryodhana looked unconvinced. Shakuni smirked, "Even if they do, we can always have another game of dice, which the perfect Yudhishtira can never refuse."

The others laughed, but Duryodhana looked ill at ease. "No, Shakuni, your reasoning is facile. I have no peace since Vidura returned; he sits whispering in my father's ear all day. We must think of something else, before the king hands Indraprastha back to Pandu's sons."

Karna, the essential warrior, said, "Let us take an army to the forest and finish them off. It will be as easy as killing children, and it will end the division in the Kuru family: only one branch will remain!"

Duryodhana's eyes shone. "And when the earth has drunk my cousins' blood, I will finally have peace. The nightmare, which began when Pandu's sons first arrived in Hastinapura, will be over. They were born in the jungle, let us kill them there."

Karna cried, "Muster a legion, and let us ride today!"

They decided to go without telling Dhritarashtra. As Karna said, "By the time the king finds out, it will be too late. And not even the holy Vidura can call the Pandavas back from the dead."

But before the Kauravas could ride, Vyasa appeared in the court of Hastinapura. He said to the king, "Stop Duryodhana from the madness he is plotting. If your son goes to the Kamyaka vana, he will die. Let him be satisfied with the thirteen years he has won by deceit; and if their kingdom is not given to the Pandavas when they return, the world as we know it will end.

"Listen to me, O king, and you, foolish prince." Duryodhana was astounded Vyasa knew what he meant to do. "Make peace with the sons of Pandu, restore dharma to the kingdom; or such a curse will fall on you that you will rue the day you were born. Duryodhana relent. Beg your cousins' forgiveness; turn away from evil and all will be well again. Otherwise, you will die."

Duryodhana grew pale. But his heart was strong and hard. He said nothing to Vyasa; indeed, his grandfather was one person who inspired some fear in that prince. However, the Kaurava was determined to take an army to the forest, and have done with his cousins. After the wonderful game of dice, Duryodhana was convinced his lucky star was rising, and his time of fortune had come. Even the astrologers in the palace had told him that for thirteen years he would enjoy the best time of his life. What troubled him was what would come after thirteen years; that was what he wanted to settle in the jungle.

But what Vyasa said shook Dhritarashtra. "Father, my mind is swayed by love for my son. I can no longer tell right from wrong. You say what we should do."

Vyasa looked at Duryodhana, and, seeing clearly into his heart, murmured, "I don't believe what I say here will be honoured. Yet, someone else is coming to Hastinapura to speak to you. Rishi Maitreya has been in the Kamyaka aranya with Pandu's sons. Ask his advice, if you think I am prejudiced."

Vyasa left with a searing look at Duryodhana. The prince turned his eyes away; the rishi gazed into the darkness in his soul, and filled him with panic.

After Vyasa left, Dhritarashtra turned to his son to beg him to abandon his mad scheme, when the profound Maitreya was announced. He was a tall muni, with flowing white hair and beard, and great eyebrows chafing each other above his splendid eyes. The sabha rose when he entered, and his presence dwarfed all the rest.

Dhritarashtra touched Maitreya's feet, and sought his blessing. Only Duryodhana did not rise from his place. The muni glared at the prince, but he stared brazenly back at the sage.

When Maitreya was seated, Dhritarashtra said, "Maharishi, we hear you have been in the Kamyaka aranya. We are eager for news of our nephews."

Maitreya made no reply immediately. His brows bristled, his eyes glittered, and his silence was unnerving. The king's palms were damp, though his face betrayed no emotion.

At last, in measured tones Maitreya said, "I have, indeed, been with the Pandavas. I heard about the shameful manner in which they were banished, while this sabha sat by and watched.

"I had not dreamt the House of Kuru would fall so low. Are you a king, Dhritarashtra, or a thief: that you allowed, no, abetted such a crime? Bheeshma, how did you tolerate this sin? I am surprised, and I fear for the future of not just this ancient house, but of Bharatavarsha. I had thought that not the worst kshatriya would stoop to cheating his own blood, out of envy and greed. But I see times have changed."

The muni's eyes flashed at Duryodhana and Shakuni. He went on sadly, "Surely, the kali yuga is near, that such a crime could be committed not just in any kingdom, but in the sabha of Hastinapura. Worst of all, I heard what happened with the chaste Draupadi: sin beyond forgiveness! Oh, Bheeshma, Drona, you watched the Pandavas' queen being dragged in here by her hair, and you did nothing to Dusasana? You watched mutely when he tried to strip her naked. You should have had his head; or banished *him*, at the very least. But you did not say a word."

He shook his head, as if he still could not believe it. "The world is surely coming to an end, and a savage one. Evil days fly swiftly at us, that such a sin was committed in the sabha of the noblest house on earth. Hear me well, Kurus: at the end of thirteen years, terrible retribution will fall on you. Then, who will contain the wrath of the Pandavas?

"Who will stop Arjuna with his Gandiva? Think only of Bheema, and relent from fear. You have all heard how Hidimba died, and Baka and Jarasandha. Now, in the Kamyaka, Bheema has slain Kirmira. Do you know how strong these rakshasas were? Fell masters of the wild earth, until they met the son of the wind.

"Don't let envy lead you to your deaths. It is the Avatara's kin you have made your enemies; sons of the Devas, and Drupada's sons-in-law, besides. Relent, Dhritarashtra, and you, foolish Duryodhana. Go and call the Pandavas back today. Restore their kingdom to them, and beg them to forgive you."

Duryodhana sat tracing an invisible pattern on the floor with his foot, smiling impudently to himself. He did not bother to look up as the rishi spoke. Now, to mock the holy one the Kaurava slapped his thigh with a loud report.

Maitreya turned on him in fury, "Insolent Kshatriya, I curse you! Bheema will break that thigh you are so proud of, and you will die."

His voice was so fierce even Duryodhana was taken aback. He felt a shadow upon his spirit, as of death. Yet, he maintained his laconic expression, of not caring. He still drew on the floor with his foot, and smiled to himself.

Dhritarashtra cried, "Muni, everything my son says and does is from ignorance. I beg you on my knees, take back your curse."

Maitreya replied, "Your son does not believe in a rishi's curse. Otherwise, he would not mock me as he does." But when he looked at Dhritarashtra, who actually knelt before him, his face softened. "Very well. I cannot withdraw my curse, but I will tell you how you can turn it away. Make peace with the Pandavas, and my curse will not come to pass."

With that, Maitreya rose and made to leave. Dhritarashtra said weakly, "Must you go so soon? Won't you tell us how Bheema slew Kirmira, of whom we have heard so much?"

Maitreya did not say another word but walked out of the palace, and that once noble city.

Dhritarashtra's sabha was perfectly quiet when the muni had gone. Duryodhana got up and strode out with Shakuni, Karna and Dusasana. After a while, Dhritarashtra turned plaintively to Vidura. "You met the Pandavas in the Kamyaka. Maitreya Muni said Bheema killed Kirmira. What happened? Why didn't you tell me this before?"

Vidura said, "I did not want to make you more anxious than you were. But I will tell you what happened; our nephews did mention their encounter with Kirmira."

This is the story Vidura told his brother.

Some days after they left the palace, the Pandavas arrived in the Kamyaka vana at nightfall. They entered the jungle by darkness, and all was still around them as they made their way by rushlight and the light of the moon, whenever his beams broke through the trees. They hoped to find a suitable clearing in which they could build an asrama for themselves.

They had walked an hour into the black jungle when they came upon a clearing, and saw two fiery eyes blazing at them from such a height the princes first thought they belonged to an owl. A stench of rotting flesh hung in the air.

Draupadi clung to Yudhishtira. The moon streamed down on the clearing, and they saw an enormous rakshasa before them, carrying a lighted brand. In a soft and awful voice, he said, "Who are you, strangers, whose flesh is so fragrant? Why have you come out from your cosy homes to make me a meal?"

He came near them and Draupadi swooned just to look at him. He was tall as two men, and his skin shone a dull green. His hair was long and tangled, and he was covered from head to foot in slime and filth; otherwise he was quite naked. His head was, like Hidimba's, half a great bat's, and he had wings behind him and fangs like needles in his mouth with which he drank the hot blood of creatures he preyed on. From the look in his ochre eyes, he obviously saw them as his next meal: and a delicious one, because rakshasas prefer sweet human flesh above every other meat.

Vidura paused, and you could have heard the softest sigh in the crowded sabha. Taking his time, perhaps enjoying the court's discomfort, the king's brother took up his story again.

At first, Yudhishtira made no answer to the rakshasa, because Draupadi had fainted in his arms. Kirmira advanced another step and let out a roar that silenced the rest of the jungle. Birds flew from the dreadful baying; wolves and tigers fled in fear.

The Pandavas stood their ground, Arjuna fingering the Gandiva, and Bheema's eyes beginning to shine. The rakshasa growled, "I am Kirmira, king of the jungle. Dare you not answer me, humans? I asked who you are."

Yudhishtira said, "We are the Pandavas. I am Yudhishtira, and these are my brothers Bheema, Arjuna, Sahadeva and Nakula. We have been banished for thirteen years from Indraprastha. This is our queen Panchali. This is Dhaumya, our priest, and these good brahmanas have come into exile with us. Now tell us what you want."

Kirmira gave a start when he heard Bheema's name; his eyes shone brighter. His black wings quivering, Kirmira laughed. He said, "Why, I will drink your blood, of course, what else could I want with you? But tonight I am especially pleased."

Arjuna asked, "Why is that?"

The rakshasa rolled his eyes. He slavered a little more, then, said, "Since someone killed my brother, the peerless Baka, I have tried to find his killer. I ranged the land of Bharata, questioning my brother's people. I first thought some of them had killed him, but the truth was much stranger."

His eyes never left Bheema's face. When he spoke of Baka, his voice, which contained a tiger's roar, a jackal's howl and a rat's chirrup, sounded almost human.

Kirmira went on, "Yes, the truth was strange indeed. I heard that magnificent Baka had not been killed by another rakshasa, but by a human. I doubted this; for which ten men can kill one of us? Any rakshasa is strong as a hundred humans. This man had killed my brother, who was the strongest rakshasa on earth, with his bare hands."

He paused, scratching his jowl thoughtfully with a talon like a dagger, and squinting at Bheema. His breath stank so much when he spoke, the Pandavas drew back from him.

Kirmira continued, "Once, some months before Baka was killed, when we still hunted together, we heard that a human had killed our childhood friend Hidimba. We did not believe what we heard, until my brother died as well; and on my wanderings after he died, I finally learnt the name of his killer. I heard the name of Bheema the Pandava.

"Now, fate has brought you to me in my own jungle. When I drink your blood, Bheema, my revenge will be complete."

Bheema handed his torch to Sahadeva. Arjuna raised the Gandiva, but Bheema stopped him. "This beast comes as a godsend for me to vent my wrath."

With a roar, the son of the wind sprang at Kirmira. Like two tempests, they fought, growling, roaring, hissing, howling, Kirmira pouring out a stream of hot abuse. Their blows shook the earth. When each one saw the other couldn't be felled by punches, they pulled up trees and battered each other. Ten trees each of them smashed, while the others stood at the edge of the clearing, even the Pandavas dazed by the ferocity of the fight. The rakshasa fought to avenge his dead brother, and Bheema to quieten the fire of the shame of Hastinapura.

When he realized tree-trunks were too soft to harm this human, Kirmira hefted a rock. Unfurling his wings, he flew up into the air and hurled it down on the Pandava's head. Instead of crushing Bheema's skull like an egg, the rock broke in bits. The rakshasa hung in the air, stunned.

The son of Vayu glowed with uncanny light; his arms were as strong as typhoons. In his mind, he saw not Kirmira before him, but Dusasana. He leapt up, caught the demon's ankles and pulled him down. Quicker than thinking, he tore off his wings. Kirmira screeched, subliminally, truly like a monstrous bat. Bheema pulled him on to his lap and, with a wrench, broke his back like a twig.

The rakshasa's scream echoed through the night; he lay twitching in death's spasms, until life left him and he grew still. To their amazement, Kirmira's corpse crumbled into a few handfuls of dust before their eyes, and the wind scattered him across the earth.

Bheema's roar echoed through the jungle, as his brothers and Draupadi ran forward to embrace him.

"Thus," said Vidura in the court of Hastinapura, "Bheema killed Kirmira."

Silence deepened on that sabha, and Dhritarashtra sat as if embalmed. Just a muscle on the king's cheek twitched to betray his alarm. But he managed to keep the terror he felt out of his voice, when he said he was tired and would retire to his chambers now.

FOUR

Krishna swears an oath

When Krishna heard what had happened, he went to the Kamyaka vana to meet the Pandavas. With him came Dhrishtadyumna, the new Chedi king Dhrishtaketu, the Kekaya brothers, and a host of Yadavas: Bhoja, Vrishni and Andhaka warriors. Yudhishtira jumped up with a cry of joy when he saw Krishna. Here was the very person he wanted to see: the Dark One who knew the truth of all things, the only one who could comfort him.

When they sat together under the wide tree, Krishna said, "The earth is thirsty, and only the blood of Duryodhana and Karna, Shakuni and Dusasana will quench her thirst. We are all with you, Yudhishtira, we will not stand for this."

There was anger in his black eyes as none of them had seen before. "Why should Draupadi live in the jungle? You need not do this just because they say you must. We all know about Shakuni's dice; he can throw anything he wants with them. I hear you did not win a single throw. You are not bound by the game, not when the dice were loaded.

"I have the Yadava army waiting at the forest's edge. Dhrishtadyumna, Dhrishtaketu and the Kekayas have brought their legions with them. All Bharatavarsha is incensed: you are her emperor. Let us march on Hastinapura, and see how those cowards face us in battle."

But Yudhishtira said, "Krishna, I am not innocent in this thing. I have sinned, and let this exile be my expiation. When we saw evil omens at the Rajasuya, Vyasa told me I would have fourteen years of misfortune. This is that time. How I wish I could call the days back and not have to play the game of dice. But that is not fate's way, and I must pay for my weakness before I am pure again. Forgive me if I don't accept your offer."

Krishna frowned. There was still fire in his eyes, and he seemed to debate whether to go and burn Dhritarashtra and his sons with it. Arjuna laid a hand on his cousin's arm to pacify him. Krishna seemed lost in himself for a while.

At last, he said, "Yudhishtira, your life and mine are one. Your enemies are mine, and mine yours; and so too our friends. No one can come between us. He who harms you becomes my enemy, and he shall perish." A quick smile touched his lips. "But you, my lord, insist on observing the niceties of dharma. So be it. But hear this, cousin, and all you kshatriyas: I swear that retribution is only postponed. One day the earth shall be slick with the Kauravas' blood, and I will crown Yudhishtira king in Hastinapura. Yes I, Krishna, do swear this."

He spoke with uncommon fervour, and Draupadi began to cry. She was already roused when she saw Krishna and Dhrishtadyumna; when she saw how angry the serene Avatara was, she burst into tears.

She came to Krishna, sobbing as if she was being hauled again through the palace in Hastina.

"Oh, look at me, Krishna!" wept Draupadi. "I am the wife of the greatest kshatriyas in the world. I am the Pandavas' queen. I am Drupada's daughter, and Dhrishtadyumna's sister. Best of all, Krishna himself is my guardian. Yet, the beast Dusasana dragged me through the palace of Hastinapura like a whore. He dragged me by my hair, washed in the waters of the Rajasuya yagna. With his vile hands he flung me down in the sabha, where they all agreed I was Duryodhana's slave. Bheeshma was there, Dhritarashtra, Drona and Kripa, too; and none of them said a word to stop Dusasana.

"Krishna, that is not all. My husbands were there."

She choked, and could not speak; this was her worst memory. After a moment, Draupadi resumed, "Bheema is the wind's son; he kills rakshasas with his bare hands. Of what use is his strength if he could not protect me when I most needed him? What is it to me if Arjuna is a greater archer than Indra? Of what concern are Sahadeva and Nakula's conquests of distant kingdoms? Yudhishtira was crowned emperor of all Bharatavarsha; he did nothing to save me from Dusasana when that animal tried to strip me naked!

"What can be more terrible for me, Krishna, than my husbands' silence when I was called a slave in the Kuru sabha? How will I live with the grief of knowing that, except for your grace, I would have stood naked in that court before those slavering devils? Because my husbands would do nothing to save my honour."

Krishna's eyes were like the sea. Draupadi would not be stopped now. "Yudhishtira never tires of talking about dharma. Isn't it a man's dharma to protect his wife? As I have learnt dharma, my husbands should risk their lives to save the honour of any woman. These five raised not a finger to save their own wife from shame. Krishna, dharma is dead in the hearts of men. Either that, or these are not fit to be called men."

And she wept as if her heart was broken. Krishna took her face gently in his hands. His eyes were also full, as he wiped her tears.

The Dark One said with awesome quietness, "Just be patient, Panchali. I swear on everything holy: the Kuru women will cry more than you do now, when they follow their husbands' corpses through the streets of Hastinapura. They shall wear widows' white, their hair will hang loose, and their faces will be black with mud and ashes.

"When Arjuna's arrows spill Karna's blood, they will cry. When Bheema's hands tear out Dusasana's heart, they will sob. When Duryodhana lies dead with his thighs broken by Bheema's mace, they will weep. I swear this to you, Panchali."

His voice did not rise, when he said, "The heavens may fall, the Himalaya may be levelled; the seas may be as dry as dead men's bones, why, the earth herself may burst asunder: but I will keep my oath to you. To avenge the crime against you there will be a war to end all wars. Your eyes, which shed drops of fire today, will see all hundred Kauravas lying dead upon a battlefield. Wipe your tears, revenge will be yours."

He spoke as if he was recounting events he already saw before his eyes. Draupadi grew calm again. She believed Krishna; she knew his were not empty promises. Her tears stanched, she said, "You say this to me, and I believe you, Krishna: for kinship, for honour, for friendship and, above everything else, because you are the Lord. I am content."

Krishna replied, "Be brave, be patient; for you shall, again, be a queen of kings." He turned to Yudhishtira. "If I had been there, the game of dice would never have been played. But Salva attacked us in Dwaraka in a vimana; I had to kill him before I came to you. Even in Dwaraka, I saw the omens for disaster around me, on the earth and in the air. But it was too late, when I heard what had happened." He smiled now, full of gentleness again. "So, perhaps you are right, Yudhishtira, and this vanavasa is part of your destiny."

Then, his eyes mischievous, he said, "But, Pandava, a day of the Devas is a year for mortal men; and you have spent thirteen days in exile. Shall we take the days to be years, then, and march on Hastinapura today? No oath will be broken if we do."

Yudhishtira only smiled, and did not reply. Krishna laughed, "I see you are not to be tempted. Then let it be as you wish. Only remember: just thirteen years, and then I will set the Kuru crown on your head with these hands. But now, there is much to be done in Dwaraka, and I must go back."

The Dark One rose, and embraced his cousins. Dhrishtadyumna bid a tender farewell to his sister, and he too vowed that revenge would be hers. Dhrishtaketu and the Kekayas left, after swearing loyalty and friendship. Krishna and those who had come with him left the Kamyaka aranya, leaving the Pandavas and, especially, Draupadi consoled. But thirteen long years yawned ahead, and despair would often have its way with them. At such times, only Krishna's oath would comfort the sons of Pandu in their exile, and be as a lamp in the dark night.

FIVE

Dwaitavana

AFTER KRISHNA LEFT, THE PANDAVAS WERE DEJECTED. THEY FELT the need to leave the Kamyaka vana themselves. They saw his face everywhere, grave and merry, and they missed him more than they could bear. A week after the Dark One's visit, the brothers sat together under the sage and friendly tree. Yudhishtira said, "The terms of our exile are that we must spend twelve years in a remote and inaccessible place, far from the habitations of men. This vana hardly fulfils those conditions. My own inclination is to find a jungle where rishis live, where we can pass our exile profitably."

Arjuna said, "You must decide where we should spend these twelve years."

Yudhishtira smiled, "Somehow, I think you have a suggestion to make, Arjuna."

"On my tirtha-yatra, I passed through a forest that may be the place you are looking for. It is called the Dwaitavana, and it isn't far from here."

Yudhishtira looked at Bheema, and when he nodded, they decided they would go to the Dwaitavana and spend some of the twelve years there. The Dwaitavana was indeed near the Kamyaka, and they arrived there in a few days.

This was a different kind of forest, lighter, full of open spaces. It was more a vast and untamed garden than a jungle. There seemed to be no fear here, and fine lakes abounded, overgrown with lotuses. The trees, too, were sturdier and grew further apart than those in the Kamyaka, and their branches were homes for koyal, chakravaka and peacock.

There were no rakshasas in this vana, and it fairly bristled with the asramas of rishis. These hermits welcomed the kshatriyas as if they were their own children. In their midst, the Pandavas began living in an asrama of their own, which they built beside a lake on which water birds swarmed, flown here from unknown ends of the earth.

These were blissful days for Yudhishtira; the sylvan Dwaitavana was ideally suited to his ascetic nature. It seemed the zephyrs that blew velvet ripples across the lake, and ruffled the birds' bright plumage, also blew airy balm into the eldest Pandava's spirit. They brought him the distant peace of the mountains, in the lap of which he and his brothers had once been carefree boys.

Most of all, Yudhishtira loved the company of the rishis of the forest. They knew all about the Pandavas, and constantly dropped in on them. These hermits had a fund of arcane lore, handed down the generations from guru to sishya: luminous puranic legends they never tired of recounting. The munis' lore was a sea of fascination on which the Pandavas voyaged. They learnt about the Earth's beginnings, of ages past that were mainly lost to the memories of men. Yudhishtira was perfectly happy: he was always more a sage at heart, than a king.

One day, as they sat on the steps of their hermitage built above the lake, Pandu's sons had an illustrious visitor. He arrived out of the blue, as if he had walked across the azure water. He seemed no more than sixteen summers old, but the rishis who were with the Pandavas prostrated themselves at his feet. One of those hermits whispered the name of the remarkable visitor, "Markandeya."

Yudhishtira rose and prostrated, and his brothers and Draupadi did, as well; the ageless one laid his palm on their heads in blessing. It was by Siva's boon that Markandeya looked so young, for the Lord had blessed the muni with eternal youth. Markandeya sat with them on the asrama's wooden steps. They saw he gazed across the lake's rippling water and a smile lit his fine face, making him seem not sixteen but even thirteen years of age.

Then, Yudhishtira made bold to ask, "Anyone who has come to see us in exile has either been sad or angry at our condition. You alone,

Markandeya, smile so wonderfully! Tell us why you smile, Muni, I am intrigued by your smile."

Markandeya laughed: a child's laugh and an ancient's. The rishi said, "Don't mistake me, Yudhishtira, I also grieve to see you like this. Yet, when I see you here with your wife and your brothers, I am reminded of another great soul. That memory makes me smile.

"You remind me of Rama of Ayodhya: of how Kaikeyi banished him and he went into the deep Dandaka vana, with Lakshmana and Sita. He, too, could easily have stayed behind. His people were with him, and he could have had his father's throne for the asking. Why, Dasaratha begged him to take it. But just like you, Yudhishtira, he would never leave the path of dharma.

"I am much older than I seem, Pandava, and with my own eyes I saw Rama upon the slopes of Rishyamooka, clad in tree-bark and deerskin, with the Kodanda in his hand, Lakshmana beside him, and seeking Sita frantically. Rama, also, was like Indra born into the world: he was so noble, so splendid. His courage was immaculate; his wrath made the earth tremble. He could dry up the ocean, and bring the stars down from the sky. Yet, he would not even think an evil thought, he was so pure."

Yudhishtira realized the remarkable seer's smile had been one of adoration. Markandeya nodded to himself, "Yes, the truly great kings of this world live on in men's memories not because of conquests, power or wealth, but because they walked the path of dharma unswervingly. Why, because of such men, the sun moves in his orbit and his shores contain the sea.

"Think of Bhageeratha or Harishchandra, think of Rama. Yes, I smiled because you remind me so much of Rama. He was also banished to the forest, and fate tried him sorely. But, at last, he returned to Ayodhya and he ruled the world."

The muni paused, then, said softly, "So will you rule the world, Yudhishtira. What is more, you will live for ever in the minds of men."

With that, he grew quiet, and again gazed across the lake, which had now grown still as a mirror. It drew on noon and not a breath of air stirred in the forest.

Markandeya spent a few days with the Pandavas in their asrama, and they would stay up into the small hours, sitting round a fire, listening to that rishi's lore. Of course, what set him apart as a raconteur was the fact that, like Narada, he had seen many of the events he described from the dimmest past with his own eyes. Those days were a joy and a deep education; but at last, promising to return to the asrama beside the lake, the rishi left.

Yudhishtira was more than happy in the Dwaitavana, and with Markandeya's visit, the Pandava's cup was full. The forest was like Brahma's garden: the chanting of the Vedas was always in the air, enlivening it, and tranquility seemed to rise from the lake and enfold him. Of course, nothing made Yudhishtira happier than the company of rishis. Early in the morning, they would arrive from their asramas strewn around the lake, and stay until late into the night, and then come again the next morning. And if they did not, Pandu's eldest son was off, as soon as he had bathed, to seek them out himself.

Truly, Yudhishtira was as happy in the wilderness as he had been in Indraprastha; probably, happier. Yet, he knew that not everyone with him felt as he did.

Bheema did not share his brother's joy, and neither did Draupadi. These two despised the forest, and could not wait for their exile to end. Unlike her husbands, Draupadi had spent no part of her childhood in the wilds. She was unused to life in the forest, and hated every moment of it. Bheema was used to the vana. It made no difference to him where he lived, in a city or a jungle, as long as he was with those he loved. But Bheema couldn't bear to see Draupadi miserable, and he blamed Yudhishtira for her misery.

It seemed some evil planet ruled Bheema's life, and sapped him with sorrow. He neither ate nor slept as he used to. Instead, he barely nibbled at the fine food from the Sun God's platter. He would rise from his bed at all hours of the night, and walk out alone under the moon and the stars. Often, he walked right round the lake because he hated to sleep. For in his dreams, he helplessly relived the day of the gambling in Hastinapura.

Perhaps because of his inordinate physical strength, Bheema was not as strong in his mind as his brothers were. He had little control over his thoughts and, asleep or awake, visions of their humiliation tortured him. Most of all, he saw Dusasana endlessly hauling Draupadi through the corridors of the palace in Hastinapura, while she screamed at him to stop. Bheema saw Duryodhana patting his thigh lewdly and calling Panchali to sit in his lap.

Bheema knew that only when he had torn Dusasana's heart out of his chest and smashed Duryodhana's thigh would he find any peace. He grew particularly depressed after what Draupadi said to Krishna. Whenever he saw her, grim and downcast around the asrama or staring blankly at the lake, he would stalk away by himself, gnashing his teeth.

Bheema seldom spoke to any of his brothers these days. Once, he had been the most cheerful of them, full of jokes and pranks; but since his outburst in Hastinapura, he had not exchanged a word with Yudhishtira. Bheema was wasting away, and Arjuna often tried to mollify him, and explain Yudhishtira's reasons for doing what he had done. But Bheema had no patience for fine logic; and even as Arjuna reasoned with him, Draupadi would come out of her kutila, her face a mask. Bheema would shrug Arjuna off angrily, and stalk away by himself.

If Draupadi had wanted, she could have brought Bheema round, by telling him she was content to wait out the thirteen years, as she had done to Krishna. But she was the unhappiest of them all, and she did not hesitate to show it.

SIX

The trials of Yudhishtira

SIX YEARS WENT BY. ONE WARM EVENING, ONLY THE PANDAVAS WERE in the asrama. No rishis or brahmanas were visiting them today, and Draupadi saw her chance to air her grievance against Yudhishtira. Yudhishtira and the twins sat on the steps of the asrama. Bheema sat a short way off, under a tree, in grim silence. Even Arjuna, who usually kept occupied, seemed lethargic this evening. He sat beyond Bheema and skimmed flat stones across the placid lake.

Suddenly, Draupadi buried her face in her hands and began to sob loudly. Yudhishtira turned to her in concern, "What is it, Panchali? Why are you crying?"

"How long must I bear seeing you like this, Yudhishtira? The lord of the earth living in the forest like a hermit. It breaks my heart, every day, each moment it breaks my heart! And I marvel that you can be so calm. Have you forgotten who you are? Or perhaps you think no misfortune has befallen us? Oh, how do you deceive yourself like this? I cannot stand it any more."

Yudhishtira began to speak; but she was beside herself, and was going to have her say.

"Every day I see our palace in Indraprastha before my eyes. Look where we are living now. I think of the beds of swans-down we slept on; and here we lie on the floor, on mats of straw that bruise the skin if you turn on them.

"In the Mayaa sabha, you were like Indra with the Devas around him. Look at you here, a common hermit surrounded by other munis. At home, I would anoint you with sandal-paste; now, dust and ashes are your liniments. I saw you wearing white silks every morning; now I see you in tree-bark and deerskin. What sort of woman would I be, if I did not cry? Oh, Yudhishtira, I am crying for you!

"And when I see your brothers, I feel my heart will shatter in a thousand pieces. Look at Bheema. He hardly eats or sleeps anymore, and doesn't say a word to any of us. All day, he sits with that hopeless look on his face. His listlessness is despair wearing a mask; bit by bit, it consumes your brother. I fear he will die if he goes on like this.

"Bheema longs to ride into Hastinapura and have revenge on those monsters. And isn't it right, what he feels? Weren't we horribly abused there? But you deny him the revenge that he dreams about, asleep and awake. Every moment he is just waiting, he thinks of nothing else. That is his nature; can you change it?"

Her slender form trembled. Yudhishtira knew it was best for her to vent her sorrow, rather than keep it all darkly within her, choking her life. He did not interrupt.

"Look at Arjuna, my lord. The kshatriya who has no equal in the world sits skimming stones across the lake. For hours, he sits like that. Perhaps you haven't noticed, since you are so busy gleaning wisdom from the rishis.

"Look at our fruit-pickers and water-carriers, Nakula and Sahadeva. Would their mother have wished this for them, when she climbed onto Pandu's pyre? Ah, Madri is lucky she did not live to see her sons today. But not I. I am the most unfortunate woman on earth. Day after day, I see my husbands, who should be masters of the earth, living like beggars in the forest. And for what? For Duryodhana's envy and his malice.

"Yet, Yudhishtira you go about wearing a smile, as if none of this affects you: not the loss of your kingdom, your brothers' sorrow or mine. You are quite content in the jungle, why, you seem happier here than you were in Indraprastha. No thought of revenge moves you, or even of taking back what they stole from us. You are a kshatriya, but this isn't how a kshatriya behaves.

"My body and my soul cry out for revenge. But you are so calm, so patient, even after what we suffered at the hands of those beasts. Is patience a virtue at a time like this? Are tolerance and forgiveness what we need now? No, my lord, a thousand times no!"

The trials of Yudhishtira

Her eyes blazed as if they would dry up the lake.

"It is true, patience and forgiveness are both balm to the spirit. But there is a time for anger as well. Especially for a kshatriya. This is the time for revenge, a time for wrath. A kshatriya must have both rage and mercy in his nature. Even a servant would lose respect for a master who is always forgiving, always patient.

"Perhaps, you have decided to be a brahmana, since you enjoy the company of priests and hermits so much? Is this your true dharma? Is patience alone the need of this desperate hour? Oh, my husband, if not for my sake, at least for your brothers' sakes rouse yourself! A kshatriya does not allow himself and his family to be abused, as we have been, without response. A kshatriya isn't a coward, he is a warrior."

Yudhishtira remained composed. What Draupadi said was nothing new to him; he lived with it, day after day, though more privately than the others. But it was true that Yudhishtira suffered less than his brothers did. He was a master of his emotions, and mainly indifferent to joy or sorrow, a palace or the forest. He was a sannyasin at heart, and full of renunciation. However, Yudhishtira knew his brothers and his wife were not like him and they suffered in exile.

Yet, he could not abandon dharma. It was his dharma, as the eldest, to keep them all on the narrow path of truth, however painful it was. He may have been tempted to attack Hastinapura, especially when Krishna urged him to, perhaps testing him subtly, the Dark One. But Yudhishtira always knew which way the path of dharma led. While circumstances had their way with the others, he remained calm. He saw clearly and far ahead.

But how hard it was to reconcile such opposite temperaments: the son of Dharma and Agni's daughter! Serene as ever, Yudhishtira took his wife's hands. He wiped her warm tears, and said gently, "Precious Panchali, do you really think I don't see how you suffer, and how my brothers suffer? Is that what you think of me: that I am insensitive to your pain, when you are dearer to me than life itself? Do you think I feel no anguish at what happened in Hastinapura? That I feel no anger, no shame. Then, surely, you feel I am heartless: worse than our enemies.

"How little you understand me. But listen to me now, what I have to say is quite simple. You speak of patience and anger, and there being a time for each. My queen, this is not the time for anger; it is the time for patience. It is natural to feel rage at what happened. I feel it, too, as much as any of you. I am not a stone that I am unmoved by what they did to us. But anger blinds the soul, and I will never allow anger to rule me. When the time is ripe, I will use my anger against my enemies; not now, when it is likely to delude me.

"Anger is useful only when the man is master of his rage; and not rage his master, hurrying him to his death. Patience is much harder for us to keep now but patient we must be, if we want to achieve our ends. I see from your face what I say does not please you. Yet, I speak for dharma. I gave my word in Hastinapura: for better or for worse, whether I was cheated at dice or not. Draupadi, to break my word is against my dharma. I will suffer if I do, and those dear to me, no one else.

"Let us both renounce our anger for the time being. I, my wrath against the Kauravas for what they did to us, and you, yours against me for what I am saying to you now."

She was not consoled; instead, she blazed up fiercer than before. She struck her brow with her hand and cried, "Oh, fate is more powerful than anything in the world! Here I am, trying to show you how wretched your wife and brothers are in the jungle, and all you can talk of is dharma.

"Your dharma, my husband, is sitting with the rishis, and listening to their stories of the next world. But we are in this miserable world still! It is true, isn't it, Yudhishtira? I have understood you, haven't I? You are happier with the munis than you are with your family. And you will sacrifice anything for your dharma: yes, your wife, your brothers, anything. No matter whether the dharma is real, or in your imagination.

"Was there dharma in Shakuni's hands when he cast his loaded dice? Or dharma in Dusasana's, when he tried to strip me naked? Or dharma in Duryodhana's heart when he called me to sit in his lap! And for this dharma that rewards you with exile, you will gladly sacrifice Bheema, Arjuna, Sahadeva, Nakula and me. Yes, I know it, Yudhishtira. Your obsession with dharma is stronger than your love for us.

"What is this patience you go on about, my lord? I know nothing of it!" cried Draupadi.

Yudhishtira smiled indulgently. He said with no rancour, "Patience is a Goddess who bestows her favours selectively. You, dearest Panchali, are not one of her chosen. Why, among us all, perhaps patience favours only me. She did not choose Duryodhana to be one of her own, nor Karna or Dusasana; and it seems she hasn't chosen any of my brothers or my wife." He sighed, "Only me. But do you know, I am not disappointed that she has chosen me. I am honoured, and I will do everything in my power to prove worthy of her."

Here was a king speaking, softly yet entirely firmly, as he told his queen what he intended to do, despite her tirade. Draupadi was silenced for the moment. Perhaps she had never wanted to push the argument to a conclusion, but only vent her anguish. She grew quiet.

Suddenly, Bheema, who had sat silently under his tree, rose and came near. Speaking to Yudhishtira directly for the first time since they left Hastinapura, he cried, "Of what use is your great dharma? Where has it brought us? We never strayed from the path, and look where we are today. While those that lie, cheat and would kill to get what they want, live in a palace, without a care in the world.

"Still, you rave about dharma. Did we fight a war of dharma with the Kauravas, that we are banished for thirteen years? Did they vanquish us at a battle or arms? No, Yudhishtira, it was a game of dice, and everyone on earth knows the dice Shakuni throws are loaded. Everyone except my brother. And my brother gambles away a kingdom at a game of loaded dice. Then he talks of dharma!"

After months, Bheema showed some animation. He raged, "When we stood wretchedly in the sabha in Hastinapura, when Draupadi was dragged in like an animal, did Arjuna not have his Gandiva with him? Had Bheema lost the strength of his arms? No! But Arjuna and Bheema forced themselves to remain quiet, and not lift a finger to defend Panchali. Because it was their dharma to obey their older brother, do whatever he decided, go after him on whatever path he chose to tread, even if it led them straight to hell. Yes, for dharma Arjuna and Bheema kept quiet. So later Draupadi would tell Krishna all her five husbands did nothing when Dusasana tried to strip her, when Duryodhana dared call her to sit in his lap.

"And all this for what? For dharma! And where does your dharma get us, but into the jungle for thirteen years? Now think of Duryodhana for a moment. He has lied, he has cheated, and often enough, he has tried to kill us. And what has all that got him? Well, my brother, while your dharma has fetched you exile, our cousin's sins have rewarded him.

He has another kingdom to show for his daring, a kingdom with all its wealth and subjects."

Bheema's chest heaved, his eyes burned in the dying light of the day. Calming himself a little, he went on. "Listen to me for once, Yudhishtira. I beg you, open your heart to what I am saying. It concerns not just you but all of us; not only your life, but ours as well.

"What happened in Hastinapura was not dharma. It was a game of dice. You talk of patience and not breaking your word, and, indeed, that would be just if we were dealing with noble enemies. But they are not noble; they are laughing at what they have done. You had no chance whatever of winning any of the throws of dice: you know as well I that Shakuni cheated. How can you expect your brothers and your wife to give up everything and live like beasts in the jungle, over a game of loaded dice? Is this really dharma? Aren't you carrying things to an insane extreme? Aren't you being negligent towards the rest of us, who hate this forest life as much as you seem to adore it? Aren't you, quite simply, being selfish?

"Yudhishtira, come to your senses. Let your mind be moved to anger to see Draupadi wearing valkala. Let it be moved to seek revenge by the memory of what those devils did to her. Take up your weapons like a kshatriya. You speak of dharma; then, bring dharma back to the House of Kuru. We are five fires, let us go and burn our enemies!"

Bheema stood shaking, his hands clenched as if around Dusasana's throat. Yudhishtira gazed out across the lake on which the last streaks of crimson and gold were dying, after the sun had set. For a long time, he said nothing to answer Bheema, but sat very still.

Bheema and Draupadi exchanged a glance. They thought, for a moment, they had prevailed. The only sound in the asrama was of the water birds roosting on the lake. Arjuna, Nakula and Sahadeva had also turned towards their eldest brother, waiting for him to answer Bheema. Then Yudhishtira spoke, and he spoke with no resentment, but sadness in his voice.

"Bheema, I deserve to have you say all this to me, my brother. Your words are like livid needles in my heart; and for what I did, I deserve worse. It is my fault we are here. It is not as if I did not know I would lose my reason, once I sat at the dice-board. Shakuni knew this, and how to goad me on; but I knew it too. It wasn't the first time I had played dice."

He sighed, and his eyes were moist. "What is done is done, and nothing I can say or do will fetch back time. I am guilty, and I must learn to live with my guilt, finding solace where I may for making all of you suffer. Nothing you say can be worse than my own memories of that day. Over and over again, I see the dice rolling ruin out of Shakuni's smooth hands. I hear myself losing my kingdom, my brothers, myself, Panchali, everything. And it is like dying, worse than dying, for these memories are fraught with such terrible shame. But I must learn to be brave: to accept what I did, to live with it, and to overcome it.

"Draupadi, Bheema, whatever you say to me, your harshest accusations can only be less than my crime deserves."

He fell silent. Bheema was certain he had convinced Yudhishtira. All that remained was for his brother to give the word, and they would swoop down on Hastinapura and set everything right again. Then, lowering his voice, Yudhishtira spoke so softly that he was almost speaking to himself. But the others heard him clearly, and there was no mistaking what he said.

"Yes, Bheema, it is only true, what you say I have done. But there is one other thing. At the end of my folly, when our kingdom was lost at the second game of dice, I gave my word that I would spend twelve years in the jungle in exile, and a thirteenth in disguise. And, hear me well, Bheema, Draupadi, all of you: my word is sacred and I will not break it."

He spoke calmly, but it was clear he meant what he said. It was Yudhishtira, their older brother and husband, who spoke, and now it was Yudhishtira their king. He said, "At the end of thirteen years, if Duryodhana refuses to give us back our kingdom, then, Bheema, I shall indeed become as angry as you want me to. Then I will think of killing our enemies and, at that time, no one will stop me. Just as no one will persuade me today, because I know I have returned to the path of dharma and I will not leave it again.

"At the end of thirteen years, if they do not give back what is ours, we shall have war with them. Then, Bheema, you can strew the field of battle with our enemies' corpses, and you can do it with my blessing. You can dismember Dusasana, and break Duryodhana's thigh. Arjuna, you can kill Karna and his men. Sahadeva can kill Shakuni, and Nakula can kill his son Uluka. And, Panchali, you can feast your eyes on the dead, and wash your hair in Dusasana's blood."

He paused, and it was so strange for the others to hear their pacific brother speak like that of war and killing. They could almost see the jungle turn into a battlefield, and the lake before them into blood. They sat bemused by the visions Yudhishtira conjured for them. He went on as in a dream, still speaking as softly as night fell.

"I will fight beside you then. I will also let my hands and my weapons speak for me. Ah, yes, I will also let loose the fiend, rage, whom I would have shackled for thirteen long years. And no one will say Yudhishtira is the same man who stood silently in the court of Hastinapura while his wife and brothers were humiliated, repeatedly. No one will believe it."

He spoke simply, from his heart, and not Bheema or Draupadi dared talk back to Yudhishtira. It was as if he had been called on to prove he was worthy of being their king: that he could contain them. No one could have proved it so quietly, so effectively.

"Bheema, I swear everything I have said will come to pass if they don't keep their word at the end of thirteen years. But not a day before that. For, in the meanwhile, I must keep my own word. Otherwise, dharma will desert me, and I shall be no better than they are."

Then he paused, before saying, "There is something else. You imagine the Kauravas are perfectly happy now, that they have sent us into exile. You think they are enjoying the fruits of their crime. Bheema, things are not what you imagine. I tell you, Dhritarashtra hasn't a moment of peace. His conscience savages him for what he has done to us, and fear chokes every breath he draws. His life has turned into a hell, and he is in constant dread of the day we return to claim what is ours. Your threats haunt him, and he suffers anguish worse than death. Bheema, our uncle is already paying for what he did.

"And so also, Duryodhana and the others. They are only human, and guilt will not spare them its torments. No man who breaks dharma escapes the consequences. The seat of dharma is not somewhere far from a man, or in heaven, but in his own heart. With all the reasoning in the world, the one person he can never escape is himself. Our enemies already pay for their sin. So let us be masters of ourselves, in the knowledge that, even today, they are punished fiercely by guilt and fear. At the end of thirteen years, if they have not relented, then we shall become the instruments of a final retribution.

"As for the reason I restrained you in the sabha of Hastinapura, it was because rashness never achieves anything. We must reflect before we act. We must act calmly, so we accomplish our purpose. Most often, men do not realize what they do, or why; and they gain nothing by their thoughtlessness."

"So, Bheema," finished Yudhishtira decisively, "we must wait these thirteen years out, patiently. When they are over, if our cousins are still adamant, we will face them in war. That I promise you."

Even as he spoke, it seemed to the others Yudhishtira grew old and wise beyond their understanding. Now Bheema was quiet. What his brother said about the Kauravas already suffering calmed him. Draupadi was quiet; though grudgingly, she, too, saw the sense of what Yudhishtira said. It was only he who saw clearly in this time of darkness, and when he spoke to them like that, with such conviction, the others saw their own immaturity and rashness reflected clear against his quiet wisdom. They realized that he also wanted justice for what they had suffered; perhaps, he wanted it more fervently than they did. Yudhishtira was prepared to wait to see justice done: to be sure it was done properly.

Knowing they had mistaken his deeper concern for indifference, his wife and his brothers fell silent. Just then, a familiar voice hailed them and they saw their grandsire Vyasa walking up the woodland path.

SEVEN

Vyasa's advice

Yudhishtira may have heaved a sigh of relief when he saw Vyasa walking up the path to the asrama. If he had ever needed the support of an elder, it was now; and Vyasa arrived as if he had sure instinct of his grandson's need.

At once, the mood in the asrama changed. The Pandavas and Draupadi lay at the muni's feet for his blessing. Draupadi served a meal, and then, as a golden moon rose over forest and lake, they sat together on the steps of the hermitage.

Vyasa said, "From far away, I saw discord rear its head among you. Bheema you are like a child, impulsive, impatient. It is never wise to follow someone like you. Have you thought how powerful your enemies are, before you want to rush at them without an army? They have strengthened themselves immeasurably since you left. Bhoorisravas and Sala have joined them, and Bheeshma and Drona have sworn to fight for Duryodhana. Regardless of right and wrong, they decided to cast their lot with Hastinapura and its king.

"Have you considered Aswatthama and Karna? Those two by themselves are enough to raze an army. Karna, Drona and Bheeshma all have the same guru. Bhargava has given them astras that can consume the very earth. How will you fight these three without dharma on your side? If you attack them now, every one of you will die. But you did not pause to consider this possibility, did you Bheema? Or you, Draupadi? You were so angry. And you wouldn't have been the first ones to lose your lives because you let anger rule you.

"You are fortunate Yudhishtira is not as rash as you are, but reflective and cautious, as a king should be. Who knows, but for him, all of you might already be dead. And instead of thanking him with all your hearts, you rage at him."

Vyasa paused, and let his words sink in. His eyes were like lamps in the moonlight. He wanted Bheema and Draupadi to understand how dangerous their rashness had been. By the flush on their cheeks and their lowered eyes, Vyasa saw he had achieved his purpose. Yudhishtira showed no pleasure at his small victory; relief was all he felt. He was far more mature than the others, and often saw them as his own children.

And it was Yudhishtira who asked Vyasa, "My lord, if they are so powerful, how can we ever hope to fight them? What if they don't give back our kingdom after thirteen years? From what you say, we shall be helpless."

"The serene mind arrives most quickly at its true destination! Your question is well asked. Do you remember the burning of the Khandava vana? What Indra said when Arjuna asked him for the devastras?"

Arjuna remembered. "He said he would give me all the astras he had, when the time came. But first, Lord Siva must give me his Paasupatastra."

Vyasa said, "The time has come. Send Arjuna to the mountains. He must perform a tapasya to Siva, and receive his Paasupatastra from the Lord. Then, Indra will give him all his astras. You will have need of every one, for the war will be a harder one than you can imagine."

Yudhishtira wondered, "You seem certain there will be war."

Vyasa said grimly, "There will be war, it was written before you were born. There will be a war to end all wars: the Mahabharata yuddha, the war on the crack of the ages. Let Arjuna prepare himself for that war; he will be the key to victory, and Bheema. But Bheema was born with unearthly strength, and he has drunk nagamrita."

Bheema's eyes shone in the silvery night. He for one was delighted to hear that there would be a war. He would have his revenge then; nothing would stop him. They sat in silence, watching the moon float on the lake as a lotus-scented breeze rustled through the forest.

Vyasa said, "You have stayed long enough in the Dwaitavana; this place has grown stale on you. It fills your spirits with melancholy; it fills Draupadi with sadness. The vapours of the lake have this effect. Go back to the Kamyaka now."

Yudhishtira said, "We will leave tomorrow."

Draupadi was glad. She felt her husband spent too much time with the rishis of the Dwaitavana, and neglected her. They sat in silence for some time, then turned in. The next morning, Vyasa was up before the sun, and he shook Yudhishtira awake, and took him down to the lake. He made the Pandava wash in the still dark water, and sit before him under a tree. He made him shut his eyes, and, placing his hand on Yudhishtira's head, the muni chanted a secret mantra. He said, "Receive the pratismriti from me."

A current of energy coursed through Yudhishtira, and if his eyes had been open, he would have seen that light flowed into his body from Vyasa's hand, making him glow uncannily. Vyasa kept his palm on his grandson's head for a while, then, removed it slowly, and the lustre faded. After another moment, the muni said, "You can open your eyes now, the pratismriti is with you. You must teach it to Arjuna."

Yudhishtira felt a deep sense of wellbeing, and he prostrated himself before the maharishi. Vyasa said, "I must leave now, but don't tarry here any more. You have lived six years by this lake, and that is enough. You have been patient, brave and strong, my son, and I am proud of you. But it is time you began to prepare in earnest for the end of your exile and the war you must fight."

Blessing Yudhishtira, Vyasa walked away, promising to see them again soon. The sun rose. The other Pandavas rose with it. When they had bathed and worshipped Surya Deva, they set out for the Kamyaka, retracing their steps of six years ago. By midday, they arrived on the banks of the Saraswati, and fording the river in the same ferry, they were back in the old forest.

They found their way to the clearing where they had built the first asrama of their exile, and saw the hardy wooden huts had withstood the seasons well. A few small repairs to the little kutilas, and the Pandavas, Draupadi and their brahmanas settled back in the Kamyaka. It was remarkable how Bheema and Draupadi, Arjuna and the twins seemed to shed their dejection as soon as they left the Dwaitavana. Perhaps, it was just the change of place, or possibly, they felt restored hearing Vyasa's prophecy that there would be a war: they would have their chance to take revenge on Dhritarashtra's sons.

When they had spent a rather pleasant month in the clearing in the Kamyaka, Yudhishtira took Arjuna aside one day. Taking his brother's hand, he said, "Vyasa is certain there will be a war and, in my heart, so am I. Drona, Bheeshma and Karna will fight against us. You are our main hope against them." He sighed, "Life is cruel, that our Pitama and our Acharya might face us in battle; but we must expect every eventuality. Somehow, I do not believe Duryodhana will return our kingdom to us peacefully; and more than Bheeshma or Drona, even, I fear Karna. You must prepare yourself to face him, Arjuna, and for that you must have the devastras of Indra."

Yudhishtira was loth to part from his brother for even a day. It had been hard for him when Arjuna went away on his tirtha-yatra; but then, their circumstances had been very different. Here in the jungle, the very thought of sending Arjuna away dismayed Yudhishtira. But he must go now; later, there would not be time. Who knew how long he would have to sit in tapasya before Siva gave him his Paasupata? Who knew what trials Mahadeva would subject him to, before he decided he was worthy of having that astra? And only after Arjuna had the Paasupatastra, would Indra give him his weapons.

Still, Yudhishtira hesitated. He did not want to tell Arjuna to go. But eager to be off on his archer's quest, Arjuna said, "It is time I went to the mountains."

With a cry, Yudhishtira embraced him. It was difficult for Arjuna to leave his brothers, and harder still to leave Draupadi who wouldn't stop crying when she heard he was going. Only when Arjuna left did the Pandavas begin to understand the subtle miracle exile had wrought among them: despite their differences, it had brought them closer than ever.

Arjuna hugged his brothers. He embraced Draupadi, and she ran sobbing into her kutila. Yudhishtira insisted on going some way with him. They went quite a distance, silently, until Arjuna turned to his brother, "You must go back now. It will take you a long time to reach the asrama."

Yudhishtira agreed reluctantly, "I suppose you are right. But spend a moment with me. Before he went, Vyasa blessed me with the pratismriti. He told me to give it to you, it will help you on your quest."

Yudhishtira made Arjuna sit before him in the lotus posture, with his eyes shut, and laid his hand on his brother's head. He invoked

Parasara's son, Vyasa Dwaipayana, and at once felt a mysterious energy rise from the depths of his being, from unconscious zones, and flow through his hand into Arjuna. This lasted some moments, and Arjuna's body glowed as he received the pratismriti. Then Yudhishtira withdrew his hand, and they rose.

Once more, with tears in his eyes, Yudhishtira clasped Arjuna tightly. He laid his palm on his brother's head, blessing him, and stood watching while he set off on his mission. Long after he had vanished from sight, Yudhishtira stood gazing after him. Finally, wiping his eyes, he turned back to the asrama.

EIGHT

Arjuna's quest

ARJUNA WALKED SLOWLY, AND THE FIRST HOUR OF HIS JOURNEY WAS a sad one. In his mind, he saw his brothers downcast, and he heard Draupadi crying. But after a while, he was truly on his way and his thoughts turned ahead of him. He wanted to test the pratismriti, which was an occult yogic siddhi. He summoned it, and asked it to help him on his quest.

At first, nothing extraordinary seemed to happen, and for a while, Arjuna thought the siddhi did not work. Then, with a rush of excitement, he realized he was travelling at several times his ordinary speed, as if he slipped in and out of many worlds. For there, already before him, he saw an incredible sight: in a short, magic hour, he had arrived at the foot of Gandhamadana, the fragrant mountain, and gatekeeper to the heavens! This was normally a journey of weeks.

The scents of the wild herbs that grew on Gandhamadana, and gave it its name, wafted down to Arjuna. He felt the mountain greeted him like an old friend. Arjuna folded his hands to the unmoving one, and then, effortlessly, in no time, he crossed Gandhamadana as well, and saw ahead of him Himavan, loftiest of ranges, guardian of the sacred realms. Arjuna lay on his face in the snow and worshipped the mountain-king, the Goddess Parvati's terrestrial father.

On he pressed, through white, breathtaking terrain, through endless snow-drifts, across pristine icescapes where wonderful beings lived—kinnaras and kimpurushas, siddhas, charanas and gandharvas—until he saw a solitary peak before him, thrusting at the sky in splendid isolation:

a mountain apart. It had an aura of being rarer, finer than the others; it was a spiritual mountain, more so than all the rest. Arjuna had never come this far north before. But he knew the name of the massif before him: it was the Indrakila.

A premonition of fortune dawning on him, the Pandava climbed that mountain along a rough trail he found. He still travelled magically, though his destination was only the middle heights, and a suitable place to sit in tapasya. Soon, he saw an ideal-looking cave; but an old rishi, attenuated and bright-bodied, already sat meditating at its mouth.

The sage seemed astonished to see Arjuna. He said, "A strange thing indeed! Who are you, Kshatriya, who climb the Indrakila with a bow and a sword? They are exceptional weapons, surely, but there is no conflict in this place. There never has been, and never shall be." The old one squinted at him. "Rare, indeed, are those who find their way to this mountain. Those who come here do not subdue others with weapons, but only themselves with wisdom!"

He paused, scrutinising the Pandava. His deep eyes twinkled, belying his words: for some reason, the old hermit was overjoyed to see Arjuna. He went on, "This is no place for kshatriyas, but for brahmanas who have left every passion, every vestige of violence, behind them. Never in all time, not since the earth was made, has a battle been fought here. Kshatriya, I cannot imagine how, but you have also arrived in this blessed place. Lay down your weapons now, and seek Devaloka for yourself. For the kingdom of the Gods is close to Indrakila!"

Though he folded his hands reverently to the holy one, Arjuna did not put down his weapons. The shining sannyasi cried, "Ha! You doubt what I say. I do wonder how you found your way here. Didn't you hear me, young man? Cast your weapons down the mountain, you will have no further use for them."

Arjuna stood before the rishi, and made no move to disarm. The hermit's heavy brows bristled in anger, but Arjuna fancied his eyes still twinkled merrily. Uncoiling from padmasana, the rishi sprang to his feet. "Why don't you listen to me, young fool? Don't you know who I am? I command you, throw your weapons down the mountain! You will never have need of them again."

Arjuna stood his ground. He shook his head, refusing to do what the sage asked. The next moment, the muni stood transformed before the

Pandava: his body a flame, clothed in unearthly raiment, wearing ornaments wrought in Devaloka, and a glorious crown on his head. Arjuna cried out. He knelt before that stern and brilliant God, his father Indra.

The Deva blessed his son. He asked, "Tell me, bane of your enemies, what boon do you want from me?"

The Pandava told him about Vyasa's visit, and his gift of the pratismriti.

"Lord, I want the devastras from you."

Indra laughed. "Astras! Do you know where you are? Do you know how near heaven you are? Arjuna, a man who sees me face to face can ask for much more than astras. You can ask for a life of bliss in Devaloka. What do you want with weapons any more?"

Arjuna said, "I have not come seeking the joys of heaven. My brothers and Draupadi wait for me in the forest, and I have come for just one thing: your astras. My mind is full of the war, and revenge. In the Khandava vana, you said you would give me your weapons when the time came. My Lord, the time has come. You must help me, or we shall never vanquish our enemies."

Indra said gently, "You are devoted to your purpose, and I will give you all the astras I have. Yet, as I told you in the Khandava vana, you must first seek Lord Siva, and get his Paasupatastra from him. For, one of your enemies only Siva's astra can kill.

"This is an ideal place for you to sit in tapasya. Worship Siva, my son, and when he gives you his own ayudha, I will see you again."

Indra vanished, leaving Arjuna alone. The Pandava set himself down at the cave-mouth where he had found the macilent rishi. Crossing his legs, he shut his eyes and began to chant the Kotirudra, Siva's thousand names.

"*Siva, Sankara, Sarva, Bhava, Mahesvara, Isana, Rudra, Mahadeva, Pasupati, Sambhu, Lokanatha...*" chanted Arjuna, quickly becoming absorbed. Thus he sat, for a long time, on Indrakila. Then, he grew restless. He felt this was not really the place for him to meditate. He knew Indra always tested a tapasvin, often by misleading him. The Pandava climbed down the Indrakila again, and returned to the forested foothills of the Himalaya. He went on to sacred Mandara.

Donning valkala and the skin of a black antelope, Arjuna found a fine aswattha tree to sit under, and began his tapasya once more. During the first month, he ate just once in three days, and then only roots and leaves. During the second month, when his dhyana grew more intense, he ate only once in six days, and just dry leaves. In the third month, he ate once a fortnight. At last, from the fourth month on, Arjuna did not eat at all any more, but was absorbed in Siva's mantra of five syllables, flowing like his very breath.

"*Namah Sivayah,*" he chanted, silently, interminably, "*Namah Sivayah, Namah Sivayah, Namah Sivayah ...*"

Soon, when he found it too easy to meditate in padmasana, he got up and stood on his toes, with his arms raised to the sky. The devarishis, the vigilant guardians of heaven and earth, saw Arjuna at his penance. Even when the Pandava began his worship, they remarked that in this darkening age such a tapasya was rare and difficult. If the tapasvin's resolve did not break, his worship would compel the God he invoked to grant whatever he wanted.

As Arjuna's tapasya continued, the rishis were hopeful the kshatriya's will would not bear the privation he imposed on himself. But Arjuna showed no sign of weakening. When his dhyana began to affect the natural environs around him, the devarishis grew anxious. Seeing the Pandava worship Siva, they came to Kailasa to meet the Mahayogin, the original ascetic.

Siva said, smiling, "Munis, to what do I owe this privilege? Not one or two, but all of you have come to me together. Surely, something extraordinary brings you to Kailasa."

One of the rishis said, "We are alarmed by Arjuna's tapasya."

Another put in, "We can hardly believe it in these dark times. It seems you will have to grant him any boon he wants."

A third said, "We do not know what Arjuna is praying for; but we dread to think what it may be. He could ask you for the throne of Devaloka, and you would have to give it to him."

The first muni said, "Lord, you must stop Arjuna."

Siva laughed. "Rishis, your anxiety is for nothing. Arjuna is a man of dharma; he does not want heaven, wealth, or even moksha. I know what he wants, and I mean to give it to him. It is in a just cause he asks for his boon. Indeed, when you came I was about to go myself to test this tapasvin. Go back in peace, you have nothing to fear."

Bowing to Siva, and curious to discover what Arjuna the Pandava prayed so fervently for, the rishis returned where they had come from.

NINE

The vetala

A HUNTER CLAD IN TIGER-SKIN, WITH A VETALA'S BOW AND ARROWS, came with his dark and exotic vetali to the forest where Arjuna stood in tapasya. A hush fell on the mountain; even Arjuna at his meditation sensed it. He stood motionless.

The vetala and vetali walked regally towards the copse in which the Pandava stood. Suddenly a commotion broke out. The demon Mooka had seen Arjuna at his dhyana, and he hated the tranquil emanations from the tapasvin. The asura became a savage boar, big as a hillock. Snorting, he came to gore the hermit into a pulp.

Just as the vetala arrived at the copse's edge, Mooka, red-eyed and screaming, charged Arjuna. At speed that defied the eye, Arjuna picked up the Gandiva, fitted it with an arrow and aimed at the boar.

With a squeal the asura stopped in its tracks. Mooka stood pawing the earth, his eyes blazing fear and hatred, equally.

Arjuna cried, "Asura, why do you disturb my dhyana? Are you in a hurry to see Yama's land?"

Then, the vetala cried from the edge of the copse, "Put your bow down, Muni, the beast is mine."

Losing his nerve, Mooka charged Arjuna. In a wink, Arjuna and the hunter both shot their arrows into him, like twin bolts of lightning striking a mountain. They cut him in half. Mooka sank to his knees, dark blood springing from him. As he died, he changed back into his own monstrous form. His truncated body lay twitching for a few moments, and then he was still.

Arjuna turned to the vetala and his woman. Was he imagining it, or did the very mountain glow with the light of the strange pair? Arjuna shook his head to clear it. Even now, his mind chanted, '*Namah Sivayah, Namah Sivayah, Namah Sivayah,*' on and on. He wondered at the hunter's thought-swift archery. A memory of Ekalavya flared through him.

The Pandava said, "Who are you? This jungle is not safe even for men; how are you here with your woman?"

The vetala stood smiling slightly, and again Arjuna thought he saw light all around the hunter. Coolly, the wild man said, "The forest is our home; but what about you? You look as if you have been raised in luxury, in a palace even?"

Arjuna found himself growing angry at the man's shrewdness. "You look like a hunter, but you shot the asura after I killed him." Unaccountable fury surged through Arjuna, a mad urge to fight the vetala. He raged, "How dare you spoil my kill? He lies divided like a father's legacy for two sons. You deserve to die for what you have done, and I will kill you!"

Arjuna raised his bow, and there was ineffable charm in the smile the vetala favoured him with. Despite his anger, the Pandava felt his heart melting. In a hypnotically friendly voice, the hunter said, "I aimed at the boar before you saw him. He was already mine when he charged you, and my arrow killed him. Your shaft struck him after he was dead.

"You are impudent, for a stranger to the jungle. In fact, your life is in danger. I am the king of the vetalas, and you shot my prey after I killed it. What sort of rishi are you, anyway, at tapasya with a bow and arrows?"

Arjuna growled and began to draw back his bowstring. Imperturbably, the hunter bent down and drew out both arrows from the dead demon's carcass. Holding them up, and grinning, he cried, "Look, Muni, both arrows are mine now. Let us see if you are man enough to take yours back from me."

"You don't know who I am that you dare challenge me. Does the jackal challenge the lion, fool?"

"We shall see who the jackal is and who the lion: in battle. Even if you are the lion at words!" replied that suave hunter.

Arjuna loosed a blinding volley at him. Arrows from the Gandiva enveloped the hunter in a shroud of darkness; his woman gave a cry and stepped back. Those shafts would have felled any kshatriya on earth. The rough hunter merely raised his arms and the Pandava's arrows fell away from him. The smile on the fellow's handsome, insolent face was as bright as a slice of the sun. As he may a shroud of silk, the vetala shrugged off Arjuna's deadly mantle.

Arjuna shot another, fiercer salvo, humming from the Gandiva. These were astras, shafts of light and flames, enough to consume a small army. Now some of them struck the vetala, and blossoms of blood sprouted on his body; but the astras' fires were extinguished against his skin.

The hunter still stood before Arjuna with the same maddening smile. Arjuna paused, he thought, 'Who is this hunter? Is he a Deva in disguise? How handsome he is, not at all like a crude vetala.' Arjuna found it a challenge, and a pleasure, to fight him. He was an exceptional warrior; he stood shining against the kshatriya's arrows.

These reflections took just a moment. Arjuna shot at the blithe forester again, while the man stood unresisting before him. Again, the missiles from the Gandiva fell harmlessly around the vetala. It was as if he knew each of them, and they would not harm him. In a storm, the greatest archer on earth shot shafts of white flames at the hunter. He shrugged them off as if they were flowers flung at him by a child. There was blood on him, surely, but his wounds cleared miraculously.

Then Arjuna reached behind him into his twin quivers, and found them empty! These were Varuna's inexhaustible quivers; this was never meant to happen. With a roar, he flew at the hunter and swung the Gandiva at his head.

Instead of splitting his skull, the pristine bow snapped resoundingly in the Pandava's hands. The vetala laughed softly. Arjuna drew his sword and, with both hands, brought the blade down on the hunter's head. That weapon would cut through a stone like butter, but it smashed to dust on the vetala's head.

Panic gripped Arjuna. He howled, "Fight me hand to hand, I will tear you apart!"

He rained a flurry of blows on the hunter. At last, as if he had tired, the hunter struck him back. For Arjuna's ten blows or twenty, the vetala struck him twice, lazily. Pandu's son reeled. The third blow felled him; he slumped to the ground with a sigh, and his world went dark.

When Arjuna came to his senses again, blood flowed down his face and his head pounded. There was no sign of the vetala anywhere. Arjuna pulled himself up groggily, and pain flooded his body. He limped to the forest and gingerly began to gather wildflowers from the trees and bushes. He strung them into a garland. He was anguished that his tapasya had been interrupted, and felt shattered that a mere hunter had beaten him, contemptuously.

Kneeling painfully, the Pandava scooped up some earth and began to fashion a rough parthiva linga with it. When it was complete, Arjuna laid the wildflower garland around it. He lay on his face before the linga, sobbing, "O Siva, a hunter beat me so easily. How will I fight Bheeshma, Drona and Karna? And my brothers depend on me. Lord, only your grace can save me. *Aum Namah Sivayah, Aum Namah Sivayah…*"

Something made the Pandava open his eyes. He saw the earthen Sivalinga had vanished, and the garland he had draped around it. He jumped up with a cry. The vetala stood smiling where the linga had been, and the garland was draped around the topknot of his jata! Arjuna gasped, and next moment, he realized who this hunter was.

"Lord!" cried the Pandava. "Forgive me."

He fell at Siva's feet, his tears flowing. The hunter's smile was the same: serene, dazzling, the smile of Siva. Siva said, "I am pleased with you! Even when you were beaten you never gave up. What shall I forgive? That a kshatriya worshipped me as he knows best? With arrows and blows! There is nothing to forgive. I enjoyed your worship, more than any other in a long time! Arjuna, I have never seen a kshatriya like you. Ask me for anything, and I will give it to you."

Arjuna knelt before Siva, "Lord, I worshipped you for your Paasupatastra, for the war that will be."

Siva the vetala said, "And I came as a hunter to test you, Arjuna. Only a man who is a master of himself should have the Paasupatastra, or he could call an apocalypse down on the earth. I have tried you now, Arjuna, and your heart is pure. You are truly a kshatriya."

The Pandava stood with his head bowed. Siva said, "You will not use the astra unless you have to, and only for dharma. Come, I will teach you the mantra for my weapon."

"Lord, if you think me worthy, there is one other boon I want from you."

"Tell me what it is."

"I would see you as you really are," said Arjuna, with folded hands.

Siva laughed gently, "As I really am, you would not be able to bear seeing me. But I will show you the form of the yogin who sits on Kailasa."

In a flash, the hunter was gone; in his place, stood Mahadeva with Parvati at his side, both of them refulgent. Siva had the crescent moon in his hair, and the Ganga. He was Vyalin: coiling cobras were his ornaments. He wore a deerskin and carried the trisula in his hand. Parvati was so beautiful Arjuna could not look at her for more than a moment. Overwhelmed, the Pandava knelt at their feet. Siva blessed him, Uma did as well, and Arjuna trembled with ecstasy at the touch of their hands.

Plucking them out of thin air, Siva held out Arjuna's Gandiva and his twin quivers: the bow whole again, the quivers full of arrows. "Your weapons, Arjuna, and you shall have the Paasupata as well. Indra, Yama and Kubera know nothing of that astra; it is beyond them.

"But, I warn you, summon it only as a final resort, perhaps against someone who can be killed by no other weapon."

Siva laid his hand of grace on Arjuna's head. Arjuna felt his body fill with tumultuous light. He felt as powerful as a God, and the greatest of all astras was his. With just a thought, Siva taught him the mantras for summoning the weapon, for discharging it at an enemy, and calling it back.

The earth trembled when Arjuna received the Paasupatastra from the Lord. Mysterious conches sounded in the sky. The Devas and Danavas appeared on high in gleaming vimanas to watch the Pandava being given the weapon that would save his life, one day.

Arjuna prostrated himself before Siva once more. He felt Siva's palm on his head again. He heard the Lord saying, "The Paasupata is yours, Kshatriya. It will obey you even as it does me."

The next moment, though it was daylight still on Mandara, it seemed night had fallen. It was only that Siva and Parvati had vanished, taking their radiance with them.

TEN

The Lords of light

For a long moment, Arjuna stood numb with rapture. His mind cried, "Siva appeared before me. We fought! Then he blessed me, he laid his hand on this head of mine."

He felt his head with his fingers. Arjuna exulted, "I have seen the God of Gods with my eyes, he gave me his own astra."

Then, he said, "I must prove worthy of Siva's trust. I must never misuse the Paasupata."

It was at that moment Arjuna heard the first strains of unearthly music. Once more, the mountain Mandara shone supernaturally. Those that came there now did not cloak their splendour; and their bodies were pristine lights.

Arjuna thought he must have fallen into a dream when, suddenly, he heard an ocean roaring on the mountain, the wash of waves. It was no dream: the sound of waves heralded the coming of a God. Varuna walked down from the sky, and the luculence of the Lord of oceans lit up the mountain, his hue of lapis lazuli. Seaweed was his hair, and he wore a crown with a pearl as big as a man's head set in it. The river-goddesses, the daityas and sadhyas who are aquatic, sinuous mermaids and mermen, sirens, sea serpents, all came with Varuna.

A chariot flashed down out of the sky: a vimana swift as thoughts, silent as petals. In it rode Kubera, Lord of treasures, and his skin was like molten gold: the hue of the Jambu river. Around Kubera were the fierce and strange yakshas, whose master he is.

In another vimana, faceted like a diamond, came Surya's son Yama, the Lord of death, who takes all the living; and he was terrible to behold. In his hand, he held his inexorable danda, the staff of retribution. And he came surrounded by the spirits of the dead, the manes.

At last, not in a vimana, but mounted on a white, four-tusked elephant, Airavata who trod air, came the king of the Devas: resplendent Indra, his queen Sachi beside him, lovely as heaven. The other Devas, all glorious Lords of light, flew behind Indra in their flitting vimanas: Agni, Vayu, Dharma and the rest.

Varuna, Kubera, Yama and Indra were the rulers of the quarters: west, north, south and east. Arjuna was numb with awe.

Yama stepped forward, his dark hand raised in blessing. He said in a voice deep as the sky, "We are the Lokapalas, the guardians of the directions, and we bring you gifts. I am Yama."

This exceeded Arjuna's wildest hopes; he stood enchanted.

Yama went on, gravely, "You were Nara in your last life, Mahatman; and all the universe rested in you, because Narayana was with you. But you have forgotten, and it is Brahma's will that you forget: so you can accomplish your mission in this life.

"You must kill Bheeshma, who is a Vasu, and Drona, and my father's son. A hundred Nivatakavachas have been born as Dhritarashtra's princes, to be the terrors of the earth. Them you must kill, and first their brothers in Devaloka. You are wise to come seeking the astras of heaven to fight such enemies."

Yama came forward, and Arjuna knelt at his feet. The Deva of death proffered the danda, his blazing staff, and Pandu's son received it. Yama whispered the mantra for the danda, and when Arjuna repeated it, the weapon was his to command. Yama blessed Arjuna and stepped back from the kneeling kshatriya.

From the west, Varuna came towards Arjuna, and his pale lambency enfolded the Pandava. In a voice in which dim waves echoed, the Lord of the sea said, "I, Varuna, rule the west. I am the master of the ocean and the rivers."

In bright hands, their fingers elegant as wavelets, the Deva held out a mysterious noose to Arjuna. It lay there, a thing alive, made of water, froth and light. It was barely substantial; it was so subtle, so exquisite.

Arjuna knew this was the fabled paasa of the Sea God, a primeval weapon as powerful as Yama's danda.

Varuna said, "Take my paasa. I killed a thousand asuras with it during the war against Taraka, which we fought for Karttikeya in ancient times."

Arjuna received the shimmering, umbilical astra, and Varuna whispered its mantra to him. The fluid noose vanished from sight; but it was with Arjuna from then. Varuna said, "Not Yama could escape my noose of tides if you sent it after him."

Kubera came forward. He was the striking Lord of treasures, Siva's friend. It was for his sake that Siva first came as Rudra to the world. Kubera lives in Alaka, which is next to Kailasa. He came to Arjuna, kneeling with folded hands.

The jewels Kubera wore on his dark body shone hardly less than his satin skin. In a voice full of mountain winds, whistling through gorges whose icy sides are sheer as mirrors, the Lord of the yakshas and guhyakas said, "I am Kubera, master of treasures. I rule the north. I, too, have a weapon for you, Partha. But first, let me bless you that you and your brothers will have all the wealth of this world, after you win the war. Here, take my antardhana."

Kubera held out a weapon of fire to Arjuna, and it was as if a sunflare was trapped inside it. Kubera said, "I burned a million asuras with my antardhana, when my Lord Siva once destroyed the Tripura. Now you burn Duryodhana's evil legions with it!"

He taught Arjuna its mantra, and that astra, also, melted into the Pandava's body. Arjuna fell on his face and cried, "Lords of the worlds, if you will sit in this wild place, I would serve you, my masters: with fruit and flowers, which are all I have to offer."

The Devas seemed glad to sit on the ground, and Arjuna brought them fruit, sweet berries, and water from the nearby stream of the Ganga. And they were pleased by his devotion.

Indra said to Arjuna, "I am proud of you, my son. No mortal man of this yuga has received the astras from the Devas' own hands. And for that, the weapons shall be twice as powerful with you. But you must come to Devaloka with me now. There is something I want you to do there, and there I will give you my astras."

Arjuna bowed acquiescence, though he was a little frightened by the Lokapalas. Indra said, "My sarathy Matali will bring my vimana for you."

One by one, the Guardians blessed Arjuna and vanished like echoing whispers from the mountain, leaving the Pandava alone and dazed. He felt as if his body had turned to water and his heart was a sea of visions. A glint of light higher up the mountain caught his eye. He saw an incredible ship of the sky, a disc even more dazzling than those that had just left him. Softly as flowers, it flew down to the ground.

Wonderful lights flashed on the vimana's smooth body. As Arjuna rose and approached the craft, a door opened at its side and a flight of steps flowed out from it. A small bright being came smiling down those steps. He came right up to the Pandava and embraced him warmly.

"I am Matali!" cried that extraordinary one. "I have come to fetch you to Indra's kingdom."

Arjuna murmured, "I am going to Devaloka without performing any yagna, or even dying. Matali, I must purify myself before I enter your vimana; for your craft is a high way of dharma."

Matali said he would wait for Arjuna, while the Pandava bathed. Arjuna waded into the icy Ganga, and standing in the swirling flow, offered his usual worship. He offered holy water to his ancestors, turned his face to the mountain-king Mandara, and prayed to that unmoving guru.

"Mandara, refuge of rishis, guardian of the earth, by whose grace men achieve their ambitions! I have been so happy in your sanctuary. Like a child in his mother's lap, I had succour from you. I prostrate myself before you, bless me again. I fear the destiny that calls me, and have dire need of your serenity."

Arjuna came out from the river, and prostrated himself. He felt a shiver in the earth under him: the mountain acknowledged his worship. A fresh breeze stirred in the trees as if mighty Mandara sighed that the Pandava must leave his slopes now. Arjuna bowed to the grove where Siva had appeared to him, and, his eyes moist, he turned back to Matali, and Indra's vimana.

Matali said gently, "Shall we go now?"

"You go first, Matali. I am not worthy of going before you into this ship."

Matali mounted the stairway. Bravely, Arjuna climbed after the sarathy. But no degree of courage, none of his long wanderings on earth, not his months of tapasya, nothing at all could have prepared him for what he saw within that supernal skycraft.

It was another world! The light inside the vimana was not of the sun, the moon or fire, but of another order. It just was, of itself, with no source from which it issued. It was everywhere, containing everything. 'The light of time,' thought Arjuna, for no reason he could name.

Matali showed him where to sit, saying, "We will fly in a moment, and we shall go swiftly. But there is nothing to fear, enjoy what you see."

"Are you ready?"

Excited, and eager to be off now, Arjuna nodded. The vimana shuddered, and suddenly Arjuna found himself not in a disc full of unearthly light, but in a white chariot. Matali held golden reins in his hands, and they yoked five green horses whose skins shone like moonlight!*

Then they flashed up steeply into the sky, and in a moment were high above Indrakila and the earth, among the clouds.

"Look how the world seems from here, Arjuna."

Far below him, Arjuna saw the earth dwindle into a blue-green ball, and the loftiest mountain ranges were so small he could hold Mandara and Himavan in the palm of his hand. Already, Matali was pointing up and ahead of them.

"Look."

The sky was no longer a pastel blue. It began to swim with fluorescent colours: purple, violet and mauve, and Arjuna realized dimly that the speed at which they flew had something to do with the spectral hues that appeared around them. The chariot flashed on quicker than ever, and the colours around them grew blinding. Then Arjuna gave a cry, because the sky parted before them like a sea for a prophet! And it seemed a veil had been drawn away from the face of another, grander universe.

Matali laughed softly beside him, and Arjuna was speechless. He wondered if he was dying. They flashed through the cleavage in the sky,

---

* In Ganguli's book, the chariot is described in detail, with great nagas upon its body, as well as masses of white jewels. It is drawn by 'tens of thousands of golden horses.'

and left the dimension of the earth behind them. They were in Devaloka, in what men call heaven.

"My Lord Indra's domain," murmured the sarathy.

A child's delighted smile spread across Arjuna's face. Somehow, the Pandava did not feel this new realm was unfamiliar. He even thought he had been here before, though he could not remember when or how. It was like a fabulous homecoming.

But this world was beautiful beyond description and, most of all, it was made of light. The light inside the vimana was now everywhere. It was always both day and night in Devaloka, bright and dark, dawn and twilight. Arjuna knew that here the spirit dominated everything else. The pervasive light was spiritual, and he saw the stars in the sky of Devaloka were great souls, who flamed on and on with infinite fire.

Devaloka was lit by tapasya; even Matali's chariot flew on faith and little else. Reality here was another thing, a different law from on the earth below. The Pandava felt, queerly, that he was on the 'inside' of the universe, and a little nearer its still centre.

They flew along incandescent skyways, where countless other vimanas, like their own but none quite as big, flitted by, bearing all sorts of celestial folk. Elven gandharvas, Kubera's guhyakas, siddhas, charanas and kinnaras they saw, and apsaras in golden craft; many were flashing discs, and others long, arrow-like ships of the air. Then the Pandava saw some even more incredible voyagers. These had no vimana of any kind, but flew themselves, and some waved in welcome: the rishis of heaven!

Who can describe Devaloka in any tongue of men? Or the glory of Indra's city, Amravati, whose streets are paved with prayers, and slabs of unworldly jewels? And the folk of every immortal race who walk those streets: who can convey their beauty or majesty in words?

Trees whose leaves were full of subtle song lined Indra's brilliant streets: pristine kalpa-vrikshas, the ancestors of all earthly trees. They were alive, and definitely spoke, in an intimate tongue of being and silence.

They flew over great mansions, thousands of them, each one far more magnificent than the finest palaces of the earth. Their walls were made of Devaloka's gold and silver, and set with gemstones cooled from distant stars. Looking at them, Arjuna saw visions of places and times beyond imagination.

When the Pandava happened to glance at his own hands, he saw that he, also, shone strangely here! And he felt weightless, as if he wasn't made of flesh and blood, any more, but only the light of this place, always shifting, yet full of an unchanging peace.

Matali pointed ahead, "Look, Arjuna, your father's palace."

At the heart of Amravati, stood a crystal palace, low, outflung, and set in a garden such as Arjuna had seen only in his dreams.

ELEVEN

Amravati

Softly, Matali flew down into a vast courtyard, outside the palace of the king of the Devas. As Arjuna alighted from the vimana, he saw the sadhyas, the viswas, the maruts, the Aswin twins, and mighty brahmarishis. Indra came slowly down the white steps of his palace. Around his ankles, five white leopards padded. His arms opened wide, and his face wreathed in a smile, Indra came to greet his son.

"Welcome!" cried the Lord of Devaloka. He embraced Arjuna, and sniffed the top of his head like any father.

The others were struck by the likeness between father and son, and how splendid the kshatriya of the earth was. Here, Arjuna seemed every bit a Deva himself. After the Pandava stepped out of the vimana, the world around him seemed less exotic than it had while they flew. Even the luminescence of Devaloka was now a quieter thing, unobtrusive. But he still felt he could float away at any moment, out of himself, on any of the numinous legends that lurked just beneath the surface of this world: the dreams of which all this world was made.

Gandharvas and apsaras had come with Indra, and they went singing up the wide stairway into the palace. This was an exceptional day in Amravati: when Indra's son had come to his father's house for the first time. And what a welcome he had from the immortals of Devaloka.

A little dazed, Arjuna allowed Indra to lead him into the sabha of Amravati, the stunning Sudharma. Arjuna had thought he would come to this place as a humble mortal summoned here by a lofty God. Instead, he found himself feeling at home. Best of all, he was not being treated like an outsider, an inferior, but a prince of heaven, as Indra's son: which, only now Arjuna began to realize, was who he was!

Indra led him to the throne that is worshipped by Devas and rishis, the Lokapalas and all the immortal races: siddhas, gandharvas and apsaras, charanas and kimpurushas. It was carved from a single blood-red ruby, fringed in gold and crystal. Indra sat on that huge throne, the leopards at his feet, and called Arjuna to sit beside him. The Pandava knew Indra would never ask him to sit upon that sacred throne, unless it was his rightful place. Arjuna took his place.

Now the gandharvas set up a song. Arjuna had never heard anything like it before, so hauntingly sad, yet full of joy. The tall gandharvas played on flutes and plucked on sonorous vinas, and their voices were so exquisite he wanted to cry. And since the great Elves sang in a tongue of heaven he did not understand, he whispered to Indra, "What are they singing, what does it mean?"

With a smile, Indra replied, "It is a song about a father and a son who have been separated for many years. The father yearns for the boy, but they cannot meet for reasons of destiny beyond their control. The song tells of how, at last, they meet briefly, and are parted again almost at once."

Something in the Deva's voice brought Arjuna up sharply. When he glanced at his face, he saw tears in Indra's eyes: tears of sorrow and joy just like in the gandharvas' song. The song ended, and everyone in the sabha applauded. The five musicians who had sung and the five who had played with them stood up, solemn and beautiful; they bowed.

Indra made a sign that they should approach his throne, and opening a box of precious trinkets beside him, he rewarded each one, telling them "I was moved by your song."

Those Elves bowed deeply, and one of them said, "Today it seems there are two Indras in Amravati!"

Another song took up in the Sudharma, now entirely festive, and the apsaras of Devaloka, *choros nympharum,* shimmered in on feet light as wishes. Their dance was unutterably graceful, and later, swift past the scope of the eye: so they would appear to be in more places than one or two at the same time. Though only ten apsaras came to dance for their king and his son, at the climactic sections of the performance it seemed they were a hundred.*

Arjuna sat hardly breathing; how would he describe this to his brothers when he returned to them? At times, the Pandava felt he could see the music with his eyes, and at others he felt he strangely 'heard' the dancers' bodies: that their movements actually became the song they danced to.

And those apsaras were so beautiful. Not Draupadi or Subhadra could match these women; their beauty was of another ilk. Indra pointed out Menaka, who once enchanted Viswamitra. Dusky Rambha danced for Arjuna and his father today, peerless Tilottama, and Urvashi, who was perhaps the most seductive of all the nymphs.

When Urvashi saw the kshatriya of the earth, her eyes never left him. Indra did not fail to notice this. He saw that Arjuna, also, stared at this apsara more than at any other dancer. Indra gave no sign that he was aware of the attraction between the two, one of heaven and the other of the earth.

The performance was over, and the apsaras danced their way out of the sabha, anklets murmuring at the hushed end of the gandharva's song. Again, the leader of the musicians, the tall one, came forward to acknowledge the applause of the Deva king.

Indra said, "Arjuna, this is Chitrasena. I think you both shall be friends."

Arjuna rose, and Chitrasena took his hand and then embraced him with a laugh, crying, "We shall!"

Indra said, "Chitrasena, however gifted they may be, human warriors do not learn singing and dancing. It seems they consider it a slur on their manliness."

"The gandharvas are the finest warriors on heaven and earth. Yet, most of all, we are musicians. Song is what we live for!"

Indra said, "Arjuna, I want you to learn music and dancing from Chitrasena. You will not find a better master anywhere. What do you say, Gandharva? Will you teach my son?"

---

* Ganguli's text says thousands of apsaras danced. He names Ghritachi, Menaka, Rambha, Purvachitti, Swayamprabha, Urvashi, Mishrakesi, Dandagauri, Varunthini, Gopali, Sahajanya, Kumbhayoni and Madhuraswana.

"It will be an honour! I watched him while we sang. There is music in him, my Lord, he will make a fine pupil."

A deep gong sounded. Indra rose, and took Arjuna's hand.

"We don't want you going hungry, after your long journey. Come."

The great dining-hall was full of illustrious guests today; the banquet was to welcome Indra's son to Amravati. Dark and bright folk sat at Indra's feast. There were gandharvas, of course, for Devaloka is always full of these blithe ones. Then there were apsaras, kimpurusha centaurs, some of whom had flown here from Earth's lofty mountains, where they love to be, and kinnara fauns. There were serpent lords, nagas with emerald skins; and a host of other extraordinary beings, who put Arjuna in mind that humankind was, indeed, a very small part of creation, whatever men themselves may think. And history was much vaster than we imagine, with our petty concerns and conflicts.

Every face in Indra's dining-hall had deep tales etched on them by time, softening them, making them wise and strong. Arjuna could not begin to think what the experiences of that gathering might have been. Indeed, he could not calculate how old most of those present were. He told himself one could not judge Amravati by the earth's norms, not even remotely. Yet, they were all warm and affectionate.

Arjuna sat beside his father at the head of the high table. The food arrived, and its aromas were divine. It seemed countless courses came, each superbly finished and served up on crystal salvers. They were all, truly, works of art.

Arjuna could not have guessed what many of the delicacies he tasted that day were, nor did he much want to. Suddenly he found he was ravenous. After all, it was the first real meal he was eating since he set off on his quest from the Kamyaka vana. The Pandava did justice, with Indra watching over his son, taking the dishes from the servitors and serving Arjuna himself.

There were succulent fruit, and rice with longer grains than the Pandava had ever seen, and some delectable fish. And, falling to, the kshatriya was reminded of the aphorism of a legendary philosopher, whom Bheema never tired of quoting: that eating was the first of all pleasures!

Wine flowed, poured in tiny goblets that held no more than a mouthful each. Nine or ten different kinds were served, and none more than once.

Arjuna thought he saw flashes of silver or gold dust, or starlight, in some of them. They were heady despite the minute quantities in which they were poured, many times as strong as the wines of the earth. And they were delicious, full of all sorts of fine fires and streams.

The wine focused his mind and, when he had drunk a few glasses, Arjuna felt exhilarated. He was actually here in Amravati, sitting beside his natural father who was the king of the Devas! When the meal was over, a deep languor came over the Pandava. He remembered that he had not slept since his encounter with Siva.

Indra rose, and said gently, "I fear we have worn you out in our excitement at seeing you. You need to sleep. Come, I will show you to your apartment."

Indra led Arjuna out of the dining-hall, down an airy passage, and through a courtyard full of flowers. At the end of that courtyard were the finest apartments in the palace. He kept them for his most special visitors, the ones nearest his heart. The door opened at the Deva's touch, and inside were the most luxurious rooms. When he saw the huge soft bed in the second room from the door, the Pandava said wryly, "I could sleep for a day and a night."

Indra seemed overcome again that his son was with him. He embraced Arjuna, kissed him on both cheeks and the top of his head. The Deva said, "Sleep for as long as you can, my son, and may your dreams be full of peace."

Indra left him, and the Pandava fell on the bed and was asleep at once. His dreams were indeed full of light and peace.

TWELVE

The weapons of Indra

Full, joyful days, Arjuna spent in his father's house in Amravati; and it seemed to the Pandava that the days here were interminable. For, of course, one day and night in Indra's Devaloka are equal to a year on the earth below: the day being as long as a summer, and the night as winter. But day and night in Devaloka were not as sharply divided as on earth. It was never entirely light or dark here, but a mixture of both.

It did not do, in unearthly Amravati, to think too long about the wonders of the place, because these were everywhere. Arjuna spent a lot of time with Chitrasena the gandharva, and mortal man and immortal Elf became close friends. They roamed the lively streets of Amravati together. The gandharva showed the Pandava other parts of Devaloka also in his own sleek disc of the sky. The fields of heaven, where grasses of spirit-fire grew in echoing colours, the two unlikely friends ranged, with the lustrous winds of the outer reaches plucking at their faces.

Chitrasena also became Arjuna's guru. He taught the kshatriya to play on the delicate vina; he taught him singing and dancing. Arjuna learnt all these with talent that made even Indra marvel. The gandharvas are masters of music, and they are masters of teaching music as well. And Chitrasena was among the finest musicians in Amravati.

Indra announced that soon he would have another feast in the palace.

There was a wide field at one end of Indra's palace, and here the Deva gave Arjuna lessons at archery: the final touches to a profound education. Day by day, the God imparted the secrets of the devastras to his mortal son, and he was delighted at how exceptional a pupil Kunti's prince was. Quite simply, he had never seen an archer like the Pandava.

One day, Indra called Arjuna and they walked together to the end of the interminable field. When they arrived under a tall white tree there, Indra stopped.

"I have given you all the astras I have. I have just one more weapon for you."

Arjuna felt his skin tingle. He knew what that final weapon was. Indra said, "I want to give you my Vajra. Once, I sheared the wings from the mountains of the earth with it; with it, I send forth thunder and lightning into clouds, and make the rain fall."

Twilight fell over Amravati, and Indra stood revealed in glory before his son. In his hands, he had a blinding ayudha, a thunderbolt of a thousand joints of adamant, pulsing and elemental. Arjuna knelt before his father.

Indra said in a voice that was the rumbling of the clouds of the pralaya, "Son of Kunti, receive my Vajra!"

Bravely, Arjuna held out his hands. A hush fell over Devaloka, as the father placed the awesome weapon in his son's human palms. Arjuna felt no weight, at all, of the shining Vajra; it might have been made of imagination. Then Indra spoke a mantra more ancient than the earth, and the Vajra entered the kshatriya's body, and his spirit. The thunderbolt of the Lord of Devaloka was Arjuna's: to use in the war he must fight against evil, in the world below, upon the crack of the ages.

The pale and ancestral tree above them, from whose seeds the eldest trees of the earth were once born, was full of deep whispering. A powerful intuition of destiny stirred in Arjuna.

THIRTEEN

The apsara Urvashi

FULL, INDEED, WERE ARJUNA'S DAYS IN AMRAVATI. WHAT HE LEARNT from Indra and Chitrasena was incalculable. Kunti's son not only became a master of weapons, but of music and dance; and he grew in Amravati, by the ethereal tutelage of the spirit.

From here, the concerns of the world below might have seemed distant, even insignificant. But Arjuna yearned for his brothers. He thought of them often, and most of all of Panchali. He also realized from stories of battles fought long ago that Chitrasena would tell him, and from epical songs the gandharva sang, that Amravati was not always full of grace and peace.

Great wars had been fought in Devaloka, against forces of darkness so malignant they were beyond Arjuna's understanding. He knew that here, also, there were times that were good, and others that were evil. There had been times when some invincible Asura or other brought his fell legions to Amravati, routed Indra's army and usurped his throne. Anguished days would follow: the Devas cast out from their home, their women forced to lie for aeons in demons' beds. Deva and gandharva, kinnara, siddha, charana and naga were driven into exile, or, at times, kept as slaves in their own city; while the evil ones who conquered them assumed power over all their dominions, including the earth.

Arjuna heard tales of how Agni, Soma, Surya, Vayu, Varuna, Kubera and Indra himself had to relinquish their lordship of the elements to monstrous Danavas, who then pervaded the three realms with darkness.

and strife. Those were the sinister days, when heaven and earth teemed with devils, and all things of light and love were eclipsed.

When Arjuna lived in Amravati, there was someone in that city smitten by the Pandava prince, since the moment she set eyes on him. She neither ate nor slept, or had a moment's peace for wanting him in her soft bed, her deep arms. Urvashi, the apsara, was stricken with love for the kshatriya from the earth.

She told herself it was an absurd fascination. She had better beware: he was Indra's son; the Deva would be furious with her if she seduced the Pandava. Besides, Arjuna was already married to two women. He was a mortal, and love between a mortal man and a nymph of Devaloka violated the dharma of heaven and earth. But Urvashi was helpless to resist the pang she felt, and it was consuming her. She had to have him for at least a night: no matter if she never saw him again, no matter if he broke her heart. Nothing else counted any more; dark Arjuna haunted her every moment.

One day, when her yearning became intolerable, and she thought of stealing into the Pandava's apartment that night, Indra sent Chitrasena with a message for Urvashi. The Deva king had noticed how the apsara gazed at Arjuna; Indra had seen how his son stared back at Urvashi.

He allowed this passion to simmer for a while: to grow in the denial of what it desired. When he saw that Urvashi was pale with it, he called Chitrasena one morning, shortly after he had given Arjuna the Vajra.

Indra said to the gandharva, "I did not want Arjuna to be distracted until I had given him all the astras. But unless he tastes love in Devaloka, he won't have tasted our kingdom's sweetness."

The canny Elf knew what was coming. "Command me, Lord, to which apsara shall I take your message?"

"Chitrasena, can it be you haven't noticed which apsara's gaze clings to my son, as a rishi's mind does to his dhyana? Can it be, Gandharva, you haven't noticed to which apsara's face Arjuna's eyes turn, as if he has no will to stop them?"

Chitrasena replied with a smile, "What message shall I take to Urvashi?"

"Tell her I said she may go to my son tonight, and let it be a night he will never forget." Indra paused.

Chitrasena asked, "Is there anything else, my Lord?"

Out of a reverie Indra said, "You had better hurry, because she has made up her mind to visit him tonight anyway. Usually, she robs us men of sense and sleep. It is gratifying to see Urvashi bleary-eyed from thinking of my son."

"He is handsome, my Lord, and accomplished beyond what most Devas are," said the gandharva. "And …"

"And?"

"And, as has always been between heaven and earth, he attracts her because he is mortal."

Indra sighed. "Yes, that is true. But hurry now, Chitrasena: tell Urvashi that not only do I approve of her seeing Arjuna tonight, I ask her to."

Chitrasena bowed and began to leave, when his king said in a lighter vein, "And don't tarry with her, you were always susceptible to her charms."

Chitrasena went out with a song on his lips. Musing about how, once he became her lover, the Pandava would tear himself away from Urvashi when the time came for him to return to the earth, Chitrasena arrived at the apsara's palace.

He said to her woman, who opened the door for him, "I must see your mistress at once. I bring her an urgent message from Indra."

He was shown to a private chamber where the apsara received visitors. He waited a short while; then Urvashi came in. Helplessly, the gandharva felt the tremor that unsettled him each time he saw her close. Amravati could boast of many women of exceptional beauty; Rambha, Menaka and Tilottama were among Indra's subjects. But now, to Chitrasena's mind, the apsara Urvashi was the loveliest of them all. There was a fever in her eyes today; a pang of love heightened her complexion, making her more irresistible than ever.

She was not only supremely beautiful. Urvashi's was a strong presence, and she was almost as tall as the gandharva. Only her eyes betrayed the unrest she felt, as she took his hand and said with a bewitching smile, "This is a rare honour. What brings the lord of the gandharvas to my house? You have come yourself, rather than send a messenger."

Enjoying the cool, delicious touch of her fingers, the Elf said, "I come as a messenger myself."

"Whose messenger, Chitrasena?"

"Indra sends you a message."

Distractedly, she said, "Tell me our king's message."

A smile touched Chitrasena's eyes. "Indra asks you to visit his son tonight."

She gasped. "Is it true? Does he really ask this of me?"

"Indeed, he does. He said to me, 'Tell her she has my blessing. Let their love not be darkened with fear, but let them be in complete sweetness and abandon with each other.'

"So, waste no more time. Bathe quickly, make yourself even more beautiful, and go to Arjuna. How I envy him tonight!"

Urvashi squeezed the gandharva's hand gratefully. He bowed and left her. Urvashi ran into her bedroom, crying to her women, "Draw a bath for me."

Some hours later, a burning moon rose into the night. Clad in a gown so sheer the curves of her body were quite plain by the bronze light, which fell on her like a lover, Urvashi made her way to Indra's palace. The pendant at her throat winked back sapphire, emerald and pearl at the moon. She wore wildflowers of Devaloka in her long hair, and their scents were all of desire. Urvashi the apsara, one of the most beautiful women of all time, went forth to love.

Some siddhas and charanas stared at her, helplessly, as she glided through the moon-drenched streets, her hips swaying. She was truly a dream, and she meant to invade Arjuna's sleep.

Her heart in her mouth to think of his mortal's touch, she arrived at his apartment. Her hands were moist with excitement, her golden body covered in a film like dew. She hesitated a moment at the door, and stood there like a breathing idol.

A youth assigned to look after Arjuna came out. The poor boy trembled to see Urvashi, her breast heaving slightly, not from any exertion yet but in anticipation of those to come.

The boy said, "My lady, what brings you here at this hour?"

Regal again at once, with no trace in her voice of the storm within, Urvashi replied, "Tell Arjuna I have come to see him. Tell him his father Indra sent me."

The boy bowed and turned to go, but she called softly after him, "Tell him that I also came because I wanted to."

Asking her in, the youth went off, his eyes knowing. She mopped her face with a gossamer kerchief. In a moment, that seemed a whole night of Amravati to her, the boy came back. "My master is asleep. Will you return tomorrow, or shall I awaken him?"

A flash of annoyance in her haughty eyes, then she softened again. "Show me where he sleeps, I will wake him myself."

The youth hesitated, but only for a moment, after the glare she gave him. He said meekly, "Follow me, my lady."

He led her through three capacious rooms, fragrant with incense, and down a tall passage, until they arrived at a closed door. The boy paused at that door.

Urvashi said to him, "Do you know who I am?"

Blushing, he stammered, "The Devi Urvashi."

She gave him a smile to make his heart sing, and said archly, "Now leave me."

He melted away into the shadows of the passage. Urvashi pushed open the door, and glided into Arjuna's bedroom. Moonlight flowed in through the lofty windows set along the far wall. Between her and the windows was the bed on which Arjuna lay, fast asleep.

For a long moment, Urvashi stood utterly still, and all she heard was her own heart beating. She pulled the door shut behind her, and went towards the sleeping Pandava. The cover he had drawn over himself had fallen away, and she saw he wore no cloth upon his chest. Arjuna slept with his lips parted, breathing evenly. Urvashi felt weak. She could not wait any more, but must touch him at once. She bent down and laid her tremulous hand on the dark skin of his chest; in a swoon, she stroked him with her fingertips.

Arjuna opened his eyes, and sat up with a cry. The moonlight shone through her gown, so no part of her was hidden from him. She heard him catch his breath sharply, and she stood there offering herself in silence.

Arjuna breathed, "Devi, how are you here at this hour?"

He hardly dared look at her for the effect she had on him. He could see her fair breasts, with their long buds. He could see her whirlpool of a navel, above hips flaring out from a waist around which he could join his hands. And below, the shadow nestling between her thighs. Urvashi, the apsara, seemed made of moonlight, desire, and little else; and poor Arjuna's heart lurched wickedly.

Her laugh tinkled through the room, through the moonlight, right through him. She was nervous herself, if not as flustered as the dark archer who stood before her, anxious as a boy.

She said, "I have come to serve you, my prince, your father sent me." A pause, and then, in a voice full of velvet wildness, "And I wanted to come myself."

Fearing the worst by now, Arjuna babbled, "But why, O my mother?"

She had swayed towards him, and she froze as if he had struck her. A spark of rage in her grey eyes, she breathed, "Mother? Did you say mother?"

Solemn Arjuna nodded. His heart and his brother Yudhishtira's voice, deep inside him, pulled him one way; while she, and his own mad flesh pulled in another, so fiercely he felt torn in half. Somehow, Arjuna stopped himself from taking her in his arms.

She said, "Pandava, I have seen you stare at me when we danced for you in your father's halls, and on many other occasions. And now, I come to you for love and you dare call me mother?"

Suddenly she seemed so cold, and her near nakedness a distant thing. But now Arjuna had won his battle with himself. More levelly, he said, "You are the mother of my race, Apsara. That is why I stared at you, thinking, 'That is Urvashi, who was Pururavas' love. She is the mother of the Kurus, and she is far lovelier than I had imagined.' I swear these were my only thoughts. Forgive me if I misled you.

"Great queen, who am I to dare think of you, except as my mother? Can I ever think of myself as being your lover? Oh, not in a thousand lives!"

She remembered that, in a forgotten time, she had loved another kshatriya, of whom this young warrior reminded her. But that had been on earth. So, after a fashion, she was perhaps his 'mother'; that only whetted her desire. She could feel the male in him so aroused he could hardly restrain himself from falling on her. If she was patient, she could seduce him. After all, which man had resisted her? Which Deva or gandharva had? Not Indra, or any of them, ever.

This beautiful mortal was diffident; but she would coax him out of his shyness. Laughing softly again, she said, "Kshatriya, you don't know how it is with the apsaras. We are always young, Arjuna. We never become mothers, but are just for love. I was your ancestor's lover, once, but I never belonged to him or to anyone I loved. We are dancers in Indra's sabha, the courtesans of Amravati. We are here for the pleasure of all, and we are forever free."

He stood mutely before her, his eyes turned down. She went on, frankly, "Don't imagine you are the first of your race to come to Devaloka. Many sons of Puru, and his grandsons and their sons have come to Amravati by their punya. None of them hesitated to make love to me, or to Rambha, Menaka, or Tilottama. We are here to give delight, there is no shame in Indra's realm."

She came towards him again. "The dharma of the earth does not bind the apsaras: time in Devaloka is another river. You will only sin if you spurn me. Aren't you a man, and a kshatriya? Isn't it a warrior's dharma to slake a woman's thirst, when she desires him? I am not your mother, or anyone sacred, Arjuna."

But he stepped back from her in alarm. "Ah, don't say that! You are as much my mother as Kunti is; you are as sacred to me as she. You are the mother of all the Pauravas.

"O, you are beautiful past believing, Urvashi; you are desirable past all reason. But I cannot think of you as my lover, not while I am still Arjuna."

He knelt before her. "Forgive me, mother! Bless me, I am your son."

Love froze in her blood. It shattered there, fragile thing, and turned to wrath. Ravaged by a frustration she had never known, like a demon in her body, she cursed him.

"I thought you were a man. A real man would never scorn me, when I came to you as an offering. Arrogant Arjuna, if you won't have my love let my curse be upon you instead!"

She was as terrible now as she had been soft and desirable a moment ago.

"Since you have behaved like a eunuch tonight, I curse you to become one. You will lose your manhood, Pandava, and spend your days among women, singing and dancing, but incapable of anything else!"

With a sob, she turned and ran out of that room, where he knelt devastated by her curse.

FOURTEEN

The curse

ARJUNA LAY CURLED TIGHTLY IN HIS BED, WITH THE MOON POURING in over him. Abruptly, his visit to Devaloka had turned into a nightmare. It was a fate worse than anything he could have imagined: to never be a man again, never hold a woman in his arms, to never make love to sweet Subhadra or dark Draupadi. Now and then, a fit of sobbing would wrack the Pandava, as he lay waiting for the dawn so he could share his misery with someone. He wondered feverishly when Urvashi's curse would take effect. Would it be with sunrise? Then this was his last night as a man. Tomorrow, he would be…what? Would his body change?

Arjuna rose and paced his room, as the moon set in a final flare of silver beyond his window. An hour of perfect darkness fell on Amravati, night's last yaama. The darkness heightened Arjuna's despair so he picked up one of the quaint lamps that lit up at just a touch, and went to find Chitrasena. Through the night of Amravati the distraught Pandava walked, while the unearthly city slept around him. He came to the gandharva's mansion, its coat of arms engraved with a golden vina and a silver sword.

Since no door in Amravati bears any lock, Arjuna walked straight in. He came to Chitrasena's bedroom. In the silent night, as if to sharpen his agony, he heard noises of lovemaking beyond the door: quick breathing, a woman's moans. But Arjuna was desperate, and he knocked on the door. The sounds stopped at once; there was an annoyed growl. A moment later, the door was flung open and Chitrasena stood there, a cloth round his slim waist, his long hair in disarray, his bright eyes angry.

But when he saw Arjuna, he cried, "Arjuna! What happened? Come in, come in."

Throwing an arm around the Pandava, the gandharva brought him in. A slender gandharvi lay in his bed. Past his bedchamber, Chitrasena led Arjuna into another room beyond it that looked out over a river which flowed through the enchanted garden, Nandana, from the glass mountains beyond.

Chitrasena made Arjuna sit down. He fetched a silver flask from a cabinet, and two tiny glasses. He filled them with a glimmering wine, gave one to the Pandava, and sipped from the other himself. When he arrived at the gandharva's house, Arjuna was so distressed he could hardly speak. But the wine was strong and it swept away some of the anxiety that knotted him. He drained the glass in a swallow, and Chitrasena filled it again.

When Arjuna breathed more easily, the gandharva asked solicitously, "Now tell me, what happened in your father's house to disturb you like this?"

It all came tumbling out of poor Arjuna: how Urvashi came to him, and how he spurned her because she was the mother of his race. Finally, he told the Elf about the apsara's curse.

"My life is over, Chitrasena. How can I live as a eunuch? Any other trial I could face, any hardship, but not this."

He buried his face in his hands, and sobbed. "Chitrasena, how will I look at Draupadi and Subhadra again? Oh, why did I come to Devaloka?"

"Calm yourself, Arjuna. Every curse is a ploy of fate. There must be a reason for it, and it will turn out to your advantage. Let me go and speak to Indra; he will know what it means. You must stay here. It will sadden him to see you like this."

Chitrasena left the flask of wine beside Arjuna. "Keep yourself warm. Everything will turn out for the best. Urvashi loved you; her curse will not harm you."

But these assurances hardly cheered Arjuna, and he sat tensely in Chitrasena's chamber, while the gandharva went to wake Indra.

"What is it Chitrasena, at this hour?" said the king of the Devas, when a servant roused him from sleep and the gandharva was shown into his presence.

"My Lord, you mistook Arjuna when you saw him gazing at Urvashi."

"How is that?"

"He only looked at her because she was the ancestral mother of the Kurus."

"What? Sit down, Chitrasena, tell me everything."

He, too, fetched some wine and poured two goblets for them. Sipping the drink, Chitrasena said, "I took your message to Urvashi, and she went to Arjuna. She woke him, as other men dream of being woken."

"Then what went wrong?"

"My Lord, Urvashi stood before your son and offered herself to him. But he told her he looked upon her as his mother, so he could not have her in his bed. I think she pleaded with him a little, but he knelt at her feet and begged her to forgive him. It was not that she wasn't the most beautiful woman; only, he saw her as a mother."

Indra gave an incredulous laugh. "Are you telling me she offered herself to him, and he refused her? Not you or I, or the greatest rishis ever resisted Urvashi. And you say he didn't lay a hand on her?"

"Not when she stood before him clad in little more than moonlight."

"I cannot believe it!" Indra poured more wine. "What happened then?"

"She coaxed him a while. But he said that for him she was like Kunti."

"She was angry? This has never happened to her before."

"She was beside herself."

"And?"

"She cursed him."

Indra grew still. The Elf went on, "She cursed him that he will be a eunuch and spend his days among women, singing and dancing for them."

To Chitrasena's amazement, Indra smiled. "Well, that is one of them taken care of," he said.

"What do you mean, my Lord?" cried the astonished gandharva.

"It is the best thing that could have happened to him."

"What are you saying? Perhaps you haven't understood me: she has cursed him to lose his manhood."

"Yes, I understand, Chitrasena." Then, as if he thought of it only now, he said, "But the poor boy must be sick with fear. Go and fetch him here quickly, Gandharva. Tell him on the way he need not be afraid, all will be well. Go now, hurry."

When Chitrasena brought an anxious Arjuna to his father, Indra embraced the Pandava. His son stood downcast.

Indra said, "Put aside this mournfulness, Arjuna. You have done what none of the Devas ever could! What the greatest munis and siddhas, the noblest gandharvas and charanas could never do. Ah, you are more than what you seem. You must be who the wise say you are: ancient Nara come again as a man."

Arjuna stood perplexed before his father. "Urvashi has cursed me that I become a eunuch. What have I done, my Lord?"

"How can you ask, my son? You resisted the most irresistible woman in Devaloka! Why, I could never resist her, nor could Chitrasena, or any of the Devas or the munis of heaven or earth. And you ask what you have done?"

Arjuna's head remained bent, "But she was the first mother of my race. Had she been another woman, I wouldn't have resisted her, nor found any cause to." He paused, and a tear glistened in his eye. "And for what I did she cursed me to lose my manhood. My Lord, I am ruined."

Indra said, "I have sent word to Urvashi that her curse must last only for a human year. For that year, it will see you through a time of trial. The apsara is mollified, she regrets having cursed you."

Such a smile broke out on Arjuna's face, when he heard the curse would last for just a year. Chitrasena said, "I don't see how the curse will help him, even if it lasts only a year."

"You forget the conditions of the Pandavas' exile. They must spend twelve years in the jungle, and for the thirteenth, they must go disguised so no man knows them. If they are discovered, they will spend another twelve years in exile."

Chitrasena murmured, "Who would think of looking for Arjuna in a harem, singing and dancing among women?"

Arjuna breathed, "My mother Urvashi has blessed me with a curse!"

His heart was light again, and the Pandava lived at peace in Amravati. He had the devastras he had come for; but now, a new passion seized him, an unlikely one for a kshatriya: Arjuna wanted to excel as a musician and dancer. Chitrasena said he was one of the most gifted pupils he ever taught. The Pandava was dedicated, and tireless at his practice.

The gandharva said to Indra, "He wants to be perfect at everything he does. He already sings as well as most gandharvas in Devaloka. But he isn't satisfied. I have never seen anyone so absorbed in what he learns, or so utterly giving of himself."

Arjuna was quickly almost as fine a musician as he was an archer. The gandharvas are a festive folk, and there is often nightlong revelry in Amravati, in which music and dance have the main part. Soon, the kshatriya from the earth was being asked to sing with the greatest masters of Devaloka. He performed with such inspiration that there was always a cry for another song from him, and then another.

Arjuna began to compose his own songs, and they described life on earth, which to many of the immortals was as exotic as the gandharva ballads of forgotten ages were to Arjuna. Thus, the days in his father's kingdom passed. But the Pandava missed his brothers and Draupadi more than ever. He was sure they pined for him, and often spoke of them to Chitrasena.

But it seemed Indra could not have enough of his son; these days, his life began and ended with Arjuna.

Indra knew his son still had to taste the sweetest fruit Devaloka had to offer. One night, not long after, he sent Tilottama to Arjuna. She stayed with the kshatriya until noon the next day, and was full of blushes, later, when asked about her time with the mortal.

She could hardly wait for night to fall again, to return to his bed. Arjuna confessed to Chitrasena that love with an apsara was more climactic than with any human woman. Yet, he found something lacking in it.

"It is a brief love, Chitrasena, with no bond of any kind as comes from sharing a mortal life together, its joy and grief, its trials, its long, uncertain years." He smiled shyly, "And from Panchali being my brothers' wife, as well. Surely, love on earth is quieter; but it is a deeper, longer thing, touched with more sorrow than ever comes to this place."

Arjuna's days in Amravati were scarcely like hard times of exile. But he constantly thought of his brothers and of Draupadi. One day, when Arjuna sat beside his father, the Rishi Lomasa arrived in the Sudharma.

That muni gaped at the sight that met his eyes: a mortal man, a kshatriya by the looks of him, sat beside Indra on his ruby throne.

Lomasa stood staring at Arjuna. He came forward and paid homage to the king of the Devas, but his eyes strayed to the warrior who sat beside Indra. Indra raised his hand in blessing over Lomasa. With a smile, he said, "You are wondering, O Muni, what tapasya has fetched a mortal to Amravati and set him on my throne."

The sage nodded slowly: the thought had indeed crossed his mind. Indra laughed. "Lomasa, this kshatriya is my son Arjuna. He only sits where he belongs, don't you think?"

Lomasa bowed to Arjuna. Indra had not finished, "He is not just my son. His right to sit upon this throne is more than what it seems."

"Who is he, my Lord?" asked Lomasa. All the sabha was curious to hear who else Arjuna the Pandava was.

Indra said quietly, "He who can resist the charms of Urvashi is no mortal, though he has a man's form for the present. Arjuna has come to learn the devastras from me, and he has come to study music and dance. He will have need of all these when he returns to the world. For he has been born into the world to purify it."

"Who is he, O Indra?" asked the rishi again.

"You have heard the sacred names of Nara and Narayana. They sat in an immortal dhyana, at the mouth of a cave in Badarikasrama. That was when the world was young. More recently, Bhumidevi went to Mahavishnu to tell him of the weight of evil upon her. She said that if he did not lighten her burden soon, she would plunge down into naraka, and the world would be another zone of hell.

"Narayana has sent himself forth as dark Krishna of the House of Vrishni; and Nara has come again as this Arjuna. The earth is full of darkness, Lomasa, full of demons and sin. Arjuna and his brothers have been born to restore the light of dharma to men."

Indra was sombre. "There will be a war, as the dwapara yuga sets and the kali yuga rises over the world, a blood-letting like the earth has not seen in an age. No power of darkness from the dwapara yuga must survive into the lesser age. If even one Asura is left alive, he will be invincible in the age of evil. He will become Lord of the earth, and a terror in the world.

Yes, Muni, there will be an awesome war on the cusp of the ages."

"Won't Krishna be at the war? Then why does Arjuna need the devastras?"

"If Krishna unleashes his power against the evil ones the very earth will be consumed. The task is too small for him. But Arjuna will fight, and he will triumph." He paused, before saying, "Meanwhile, I have a mission for him here in Devalokā."

Arjuna turned to Indra; it was the first he had heard of any mission. Indra said, "The Nivatakavachas have grown too powerful in their city, and they are invincible by the armour they wear. The Devas and gandharvas have failed to drive them back into the deep sky from where they first came. There will be a war in Devaloka soon, and Arjuna will show us his prowess."

The Pandava was radiant at the very mention of battle. But again a shadow crossed his face, and Indra knew the grief that laid its hand on him. He said, "Lomasa, I want to ask a favour from you for my son's sake."

Lomasa said, "For Nara, who has come to rid the earth of evil, ask anything!"

"You see the sorrow on his face. He is anxious about his brothers and his wife who live in exile in the forest. Take word to them in the Kamyaka aranya, Muni. Tell Yudhishtira where his brother is, and that he is well; tell him Arjuna is now a master of every astra."

Arjuna beamed, "Also, Muni, tell my brother that I am learning music from Chitrasena."

Indra said, "Go and comfort Yudhishtira, Lomasa. He is softhearted and grieves too much for his brother. Tell him about the Nivatakavachas, and say Arjuna's mission in Devaloka will be a test for him." He fell silent and thoughtful. After a moment, he mused, "I think Yudhishtira and his brothers should go on a pilgrimage now. They must bathe at all the tirthas.

"Their exile ends; let them purify themselves for the war. They will need every blessing of heaven and earth that they can get. Teeming legions of evil will mass against them, and the fate of the world will hang in the balance. Let the Pandavas go on a yatra to the holiest tirthas on earth; and, good Muni, I would be pleased if you went with them on their pilgrimage. You must watch over Yudhishtira in the wilds, and protect him with your siddhis. For, he must rule the world again, after the war."

Lomasa's face lit up. Even before he came here, he had felt fate urging him to visit Amravati. Now he knew why. He said, "I will go straightaway to Yudhishtira in the Kamyaka aranya."

Indra said, "Let them give generous charity along their yatra. I tell you again they shall have need of every blessing they can have, to turn the tide of evil back from the earth."

Arjuna said, "Give them my love, Muni. Tell them I miss them, and that I will return to them soon."

Smiling fondly at Arjuna, bowing to Indra, Lomasa left Amravati. At speed past believing, he flew along a vivid skyway, one thread of a golden web that links the entire universe. At his wish, this path set him down in the Kamyaka aranya in half the time it had taken Arjuna to fly to Devaloka in Matali's vimana.

FIFTEEN

The Muni Brihadaswa

Back on earth, life in the Kamyaka vana without Arjuna was miserable for his wife and his brothers. Now that he was gone, the days and nights were full of him. The forest seemed desolate without his quiet presence, which had been a middle way between Yudhishtira's position and Bheema's. Most of all, Draupadi missed him; if she loved any of her husbands a shade more than the others, he was Arjuna. Often, she would hide away on her own and cry her heart out.

As the days wore into weeks and months, even Yudhishtira began to feel the bitterness of exile. Not his meetings with the rishis cheered him any more. Bheema and Draupadi did not help matters. One evening, when they all sat together in sombre silence, suddenly Draupadi cried, "All this wretched forest is so forlorn since Arjuna left! Sorrow hangs on every branch, leaf and blade of grass; not even the flowers seem beautiful any more. I can't bear it, I can't bear him being away. Nothing can make me happy until Arjuna returns."

She was near breaking down. This was just the encouragement Bheema needed. He, too, was passionately attached to Arjuna, and felt lost without him. He could always talk to Arjuna, while Yudhishtira was more like a father, someone remote, perfect. He was someone you looked up to, but could not share much with, because he lived in a rarefied world, of dharma and the spirit, in which the earthy Bheema never felt at home.

Now, Bheema cried with feeling, "Not just the forest, Draupadi, but the sky seems to lack the sun without Arjuna, and the night seems empty of the moon and the stars. How I hate this jungle! And everything that is happening to us here."

He began sadly but soon his eyes burned, and yet again, he turned on poor Yudhishtira.

"First you go and lose everything we had at a game of dice. Then you are quite happy living like a sannyasi. You love this life, sitting with hermits from dawn to dusk; and you are determined to make us like it, too. But we are kshatriyas! War is what we are born for, and to rule.

"For a while, this exile over some imaginary dharma of yours was at least bearable, that we were all together. Now, to crown your foolishness, you have sent Arjuna away. Who has heard of a kshatriya doing tapasya? And for what?"

Bheema's voice boomed across the quiet jungle. "Why does Arjuna have to worship Siva? Because you have no faith in him or in me? It would take us just an hour to crush Duryodhana and his brothers. Did you ever think why they didn't challenge us to a battle, but played dice instead? Because they are afraid of us! But though the rest of the world trembles at our names, our brother Yudhishtira doubts Arjuna and Bheema.

"We said we would go to Hastinapura and finish this thing off. You would not listen. It has been so long since Arjuna left. And there is no word from him. Did you think this was a game of dice? That Siva would appear as soon as our brother sat down and called Him? Ah, I don't know what to say to you, except that you have ruined our lives!"

He seized Yudhishtira's arm. "Listen to good sense at least now, Yudhishtira. Let us go and fetch our brother back. Then we will call Krishna here, march on Hastinapura, kill our enemies and have our kingdom back! This forest has become unbearable without Arjuna. It doesn't matter who is older or younger. You must listen to the voice of reason, even if it is I who speak in it. You must listen to me, Yudhishtira: do this for your brothers' sakes, and Draupadi's."

Yudhishtira was to have no respite today. Now Nakula said, "I don't want to live here any more. I see his face in the trees, I hear his voice in the wind, and I want to leave this place until Arjuna returns."

Quietly, Sahadeva agreed, "I, too, would rather leave."

Bheema's tirade hurt Yudhishtira most. Of all his brothers it was Bheema whom Yudhishtira was fondest of, Bheema of whom he felt most protective, for all his bulk and strength. Perhaps this was because Bheema and he were closest to each other in age or, possibly, Yudhishtira felt that, in his way, Bheema was the most vulnerable of them. He knew it was grief that made Bheema speak harshly.

The son of the wind was still in a hurry to wreak revenge on their cousins. He could hardly wait to tear Dusasana's chest open and let Draupadi wash her hair in his blood, or to break Duryodhana's thigh on which the Kaurava had called Panchali to sit. Bheema was obsessed, and Yudhishtira understood him too well to take offence at what he said.

But Yudhishtira loved Bheema very much, and he couldn't bear to see him suffer. To see Draupadi pining for Arjuna also distressed him. Yudhishtira was the most softhearted Pandava, and keeping his wife and brothers calm, until their exile ended, was an unenviable task. Often, time and life itself seemed fearfully short and he was on the verge of giving in, and throwing high dharma to the winds. This was such an evening. Yudhishtira missed Arjuna as much as anyone else did, and he was tempted to let Bheema have his way. And so, when the Rishi Brihadaswa arrived in that asrama, at just this moment, he came Godsent indeed.

Bheema had to stop his tirade, and Yudhishtira's moment of weakness passed. Arghya was fetched for the merry sage, who was a short, plump man with a permanent smile on his round and shining face. The other brahmanas came to meet him. Later, when they had all shared the meal from the Sun's plate, and the night wore on, Yudhishtira and Brihadaswa were left alone together. The others had turned in, the Pandavas obviously upset. Bheema and Draupadi hardly spoke a word all evening.

When the two men had sat in silence for some time, Yudhishtira turned to the muni and sighed, "My lord, I am the unhappiest man on earth!"

"Why do you say that, O king? You are blessed."

It all came pouring out of Yudhishtira: the loneliness he felt since Arjuna left, how the others had turned against him, how difficult exile had become, and how he had been on the point of yielding to Bheema that evening. Tears fell down Yudhishtira's face. "Perhaps I was wrong to send Arjuna away, I feel so alone since he left. It seems none of my other brothers understands the way of dharma, and I have begun to doubt my own wisdom. If only Arjuna were here beside me; he is my strength."

Brihadaswa patted the disconsolate Pandava's hand. "This is not the time to give in to rashness; most of your exile has already passed. This is a trial, and you must be strong. The dark days are almost over, you must not dream of submitting now. Besides, Arjuna will be back with you sooner than you think."

Yudhishtira wiped his eyes. He said warmly, "I thank you for coming, when I most needed to share my burden."

It seemed that just being able to talk about his turmoil relieved Yudhishtira so much that he was actually smiling again. But then, this was Brihadaswa's gift: that his was such a genial presence, and he could make anyone see the brighter side of things.

They sat together late into the night, while a silken moon rose above the forest, in which spirits roamed now as freely as animals did by day. Yudhishtira discovered the plump rishi was a veritable treasurehouse of lore: about legendary kings of the earth, rishis of huge tapasya, divine Devas and gandharvas, powerful and sinister Asuras. Brihadaswa was a font of legends and, awash on his profound and frequently hilarious stories, Yudhishtira soon forgot his troubles, as he badly needed to.

Into the small hours, they sat on the steps of the asrama, Yudhishtira never wanting the night to end or the rishi's grand old tales to stop. Once, Brihadaswa turned solemnly to the Pandava. He said, "Did you know you aren't the first king who lost everything at gambling?"

Somewhat startled, Yudhishtira said, "Was there another as hapless as me, then? Who was he, Muni? Did he regain what he lost or was he ruined forever?"

"You must have heard of him, Yudhishtira, but you have forgotten. He was Nala, king of Nishada.* He, too, lost everything at a game of dice, because he was also tested by time. Would you hear the tale of Nala again? Or is it too late, and time for you to sleep?"

"For me, Muni?" laughed Yudhishtira. "I was worried about keeping you up. These days sleep and I are no longer friends; I lie awake for hours after I have lain down. No, do tell me the story of Nala."

The blithe Brihadaswa told Yudhishtira the story of Nala of old, how he lost his all at a game of dice. Tears filled Yudhishtira's eyes again,

---

* The story of Nala and Damayanti in the Ganguli text is some 50 pages long.

The Muni Brihadaswa

when he heard the trials of that king. How intimately the Pandava felt he knew the long-dead Nala, how well he understood his every misfortune, every dark turn his life took, once he entered his evil time through the very door Yudhishtira had.

The Pandava did not feel so alone any more, knowing his was not the only life that had taken this twisted course. He was eager to discover how Nala's story ended.

"Muni, tell me, what happened to Nala of Nishada finally? Did he take his own life, or did he become a sannyasi in the forest?"

Brihadaswa laughed. "Neither. Once his evil days were over, Nala won back his kingdom. And the lovely Damayanti became his wife."

"He mustered an army in exile?"

"Oh no!" cried Brihadaswa. "It was far simpler than that for Nala. He just learnt to play dice. He won back his kingdom exactly as he had lost it."

Yudhishtira was astonished, "But how?"

"He learnt the arcane akshahridaya, which few people remember any more. Once he knew it, no one in heaven or earth could beat him at dice. He became a master of the very game that had once ruined him!"

Yudhishtira's eyes shone. He was pleased no end for Nala's sake. He said wistfully, "How I wish I could find someone to teach me the akshahridaya."

"You won't have to look far," murmured Brihadaswa.

"You know it! Oh, will you teach me, Muni? Who knows if I will be challenged to another game of dice, and lose my kingdom again, even if we have it back? I beg you, teach me the akshahridaya, Brihadaswa. There is no one on earth that better deserves to learn the secret of gambling."

"You need no dice to learn the akshahridaya. Repeat this mantra three times after me. That will be your first lesson, and then we will sleep; for the mantra must take root in your dreams. Tomorrow I will teach you another mantra. In ten days, you will be a master of the rolling dice. Yudhishtira who lost a kingdom at dice shall be the greatest gambler in the world. Not Shakuni, not anyone, will be your equal."

Yudhishtira had unusual midnight diksha from Brihadaswa, into the occult akshahridaya. That night, the Pandava slept soundly for the first time in months. The jovial muni's arrival in the Kamyaka was like a breath of fresh air blowing through the disconsolate Yudhishtira's life. For just ten days, the little rishi stayed; by the time he left, he had everyone in a more hopeful mood. Even Bheema and Draupadi were smiling at his fabulous stories, which were not only funny but also made them see their own predicament with some detachment. Once their despair was blunted, the world seemed a brighter place, and the flowers and the birds of the forest were no longer forlorn or ominous. Even Bheema realized his mind had been playing tricks on him.

Yudhishtira was a master of gambling, when Brihadaswa left the asrama at Kamyaka and went off into the wide world from which he had appeared so opportunely. As they stood waving to the muni, Draupadi said quietly, "Well, he came just in time, didn't he?" and gave Yudhishtira a wry smile.

He replied, "Arjuna will be back soon. I feel it in my blood."

Hours after Brihadaswa left, they heard the limpid plucking of a vina in the woods, and into the clearing walked Narada, as always with a song of Vishnu brimming on his lips.

The Pandavas, Draupadi and the brahmanas came and touched his feet, and he blessed each of them. When they sat in the shade of the banyan, Narada said, "Yudhishtira, I think it's time you left the Kamyaka. Go on a tirtha-yatra to purify yourselves for the war."

Yudhishtira glanced at his brothers, and he saw their faces light up at the very mention of leaving. He turned to Dhaumya, "I am in favour of a tirtha-yatra. It will lighten our spirits. What do you say, Dhaumya? You are our priest."

Dhaumya was excited at Narada's suggestion. The brahmana cried, "Narada Muni would never suggest a futile pilgrimage. Lord, which tirthas do you have in mind for us to visit?"

Yudhishtira said, "I am curious, Muni. What punya does a man gain by going to the tirthas?"

Narada laughed, "Your grandsire Bheeshma once asked the Rishi Pulastya the same question. I will tell you some of what Pulastya said."

The muni went on to extol the virtue and the power of the great tirthas in the four quarters: of the Gomati in the Naimisa vana; of Prayaga, where the Ganga and Yamuna meet; the Triveni Sangama where the Saraswati joins them; of the Mahanadi, the Nanda and Paramananda, and all the other tirthas, old as the earth, created for her sanctity, and lying upon her as naves of eternal grace where men may wash their sins. He told them some legends of the very first days of the world, when the tirthas were created.*

Even as he spoke, impassionedly, of the miracles that enlivened the tirthas in olden times, another great rishi arrived in their midst. Even Narada rose to greet Lomasa, who had come straight from Amravati. Lomasa's face shone with where he had been, and his eyes with the news he brought.

Narada, who was a trikalagyani, said, "Welcome, Muni. I have been expecting you."

Lomasa bowed to Brahma's wanderer son, greatest of all Vishnu-bhaktas. The Pandavas brought arghya for the illustrious visitor, and had his blessing. When they sat again under the old nyagrodha, Lomasa said, "I have come from Indra's sabha in Devaloka. I met your brother Arjuna there."

He saw the delight on the Pandavas' faces. Draupadi, who couldn't contain herself, cried, "Oh Muni, tell us how he is! Is he happy in Devaloka? What does he do there? Does he miss us at all, does he even remember us?"

Her lips quivered when she thought Arjuna may not remember her. Lomasa said, "He grieves, even in Amravati, because he cannot stop thinking of all of you. But he had to master the astras, which he will have need of during the war that will be. Arjuna sits beside his father on heaven's very throne. Yudhishtira, the Lord Indra asks you to undertake a tirtha-yatra through Aryavarta, to purify yourselves for the war. He wanted me to go with you, and look after you on your pilgrimage."

Yudhishtira asked, "And does Arjuna send us any message?"

"Only that he misses all of you fervently." Then, remembering, "Ah yes, he has a friend and master in Devaloka: Chitrasena the gandharva. Arjuna is not only a master of astras now, but of music and dance as well. Even the Elves of heaven are always keen to have him sing for them!"

The Pandavas and Draupadi began to laugh; they could hardly believe their ears. But Lomasa said, "Indra says that during the thirteenth year

---

* Narada, and then Dhaumya, 'wise as Brihaspati', dwell at some length on the sacred tirthas. Again, some 50 pages in Ganguli's translation.

of your exile Arjuna will find good use for what he has learnt from Chitrasena."

They hardly understood how, and Bheema asked, "Why does Arjuna stay on in Amravati if he has learnt the astras, and music and dancing too?"

"Indra has a task for him. When it is over, your brother will return to the earth."

Narada said, "In the meanwhile, waste no time in setting out on your yatra. I must leave you now, but we shall meet again soon. As always, I have much to do," he smiled, "Narayana's endless work."

Narada blessed them, and went off, plucking on his vina, his voice raised in song to praise the Lord Vishnu, who protects the worlds from evil.

Lomasa said, "I have already bathed twice at all the tirthas. But Indra was keen that I go with you on the pilgrimage Manu himself undertook in the eldest days. What could make a seeker like me happier than visiting the tirthas again?

Precious are the Lord's tirthas on earth, Yudhishtira. They banish fear and doubt from the human heart as no other worship can. And you, noble king, who are true to your word and firm of resolve: every vestige of attachment will leave you if you visit the holy places."

Yudhishtira said humbly, "I am overwhelmed, Muni, that Indra remembers me. I have no words with which to thank you. Choose an auspicious hour for us to set out, and we shall leave."

Lomasa said, "It will be best to travel with a small party, taking only the hardiest of your brahmanas. The journey will be quicker. You must ask Dhaumya who will go and who will stay behind."

Yudhishtira took Dhaumya aside, and the others who had come into exile with the Pandavas, and been such a source of strength and courage to them. He said, "We will leave shortly on the tirtha-yatra. Only those of you must come with us who can bear the rigours of the long journey, the extremes of the seasons, especially the icy mountain winter. But those who cannot endure the hardship that attends any pilgrimage, should remain behind."

The brahmanas' faces lit up at the very mention of a tirtha-yatra. They retired into a little knot of whispered conference among themselves, and then Dhaumya said to Yudhishtira, "We came into exile with you, knowing there would be privations to bear. I don't believe any of us has caused you concern so far?"

He paused, and Yudhishtira glanced at Lomasa and saw he was smiling. Dhaumya seemed to be waiting for an answer to his question. Yudhishtira said slowly, "No, Dhaumya, none of the brahmanas has been a burden in any way. On the contrary, you have all been of great support to us."

Dhaumya cried, "Then take us all with you on your yatra! Without you, we shall never be able to visit the tirthas. Let this be a pilgrimage for everyone."

Yudhishtira turned doubtfully to Lomasa, but that rishi nodded, agreeing with Dhaumya. When Yudhishtira saw the excitement on the faces of the other brahmanas, he did not have the heart to deny them what they asked.

The Pandava said, "Well, then, we will set out at the hour Rishi Lomasa decides on." And there were tears in his own eyes, as those brahmanas embraced him, one after the other.

Lomasa decided they should leave in three days. Bheema and Draupadi could hardly wait, though they were somewhat calmed by the news of Arjuna that Lomasa brought. On the eve of their departure, however, Narada arrived once more in their asrama, and with him came Vyasa and Rishi Parvata, who some said was as old as the earth herself. They had come to bless the Pandavas before they set out on their adventure of the spirit; for, no pilgrimage is any less.

Solemnly, those munis blessed Yudhishtira, his brothers, Draupadi, Dhaumya and his brahmanas. Parvata said in a voice as resonant as his presence, "Let your hearts be pure as you set out. Our blessings go with you, so you will overcome every obstacle on your way."

It seemed to poor Bheema the ancient one gave him a pointed look, and the son of the wind trembled a little. Lying in his bed that night, Bheema prayed that he would become as pure and as patient as his brother Yudhishtira was.

SIXTEEN

Tirtha yatra*

IT WAS THE MORNING AFTER THE NIGHT OF A FULL MOON. THE Pandavas, Lomasa and their party set out at dawn, walking towards the sun. All the yatris wore valkala—tree-bark—or animal-hide. The sons of Pandu carried their weapons on the yatra, because they must pass through jungles full of dangerous animals and rakshasas. The birds were singing the rising sun, singing the end of another fearful night.

Side by side, Lomasa and Yudhishtira walked ahead of the others. The younger Pandavas walked with Draupadi, and she had brightened up marvellously as soon as they set out. Both she and Bheema were almost their old cheerful selves again, full of jokes, teasing each other; and so were Nakula and Sahadeva. Yudhishtira smiled to himself, to think of the harsh things Bheema and Draupadi had said to him in the asrama. It was obvious that, like children, they had forgotten all that.

A little saddened, Yudhishtira turned to Lomasa and said, "Muni, why do I suffer like this? I have always walked the way of dharma, even at some cost to myself. My enemies, Duryodhana and his brothers, care nothing for truth. They will do anything to gratify themselves, with no thought for what is right or wrong. Yet, they live in comfort in a palace, and here I am in the jungle with my unhappy family. I cannot understand this. Why does a man who treads the path of dharma suffer, while those that are steeped in evil come to no harm?"

---

* This, too, is described at much greater length in the original text.

The muni replied, "It is the timeless question that many a good man before you has asked in the wilderness, and countless more will ask it, in despair, along the deep trails of time. The answer is simple: the evil ones do not prosper but only appear to, at that, very briefly. No man prospers by sin. His own conscience gives him no rest, and his crime consumes him from within. Some day, those he has sinned against will recover from the harm he did to them. But the sinner's guilt remains with him, tormenting him until the hour of retribution arrives.

There is no escape for the demonic man. Justice overtakes him, inexorably, despite all his efforts to keep it away; then, he is destroyed. But remember, Yudhishtira, life is not simple, neither is it as short as we think. All this began long ago. You have lived many lives before this one, so have your brothers, and all of us. What you suffer today might well be punishment for some forgotten crime of your own. Of course, that does not justify what has been done to you, but it might explain it."

"The ways of sin and punishment are complicated," murmured Yudhishtira.

"Not really," said Lomasa, "though perhaps they are longer than men realize. But essentially, they are simple and they are universal: the paths of good and evil, of darkness and light.

"Take even the Devas and the Asuras: one race condemned to darkness and misery, and the other blessed with light, glory, and sovereignty over heaven and earth. But it was not always so. Once, they were all spirits of grace, and they all had the choice of which path to take. The Devas chose virtue, while the Asuras disdained it. The Asuras were proud, and pride became vanity; and because they were vain, they were full of anger, which they themselves could not control, but were its slaves. They became shameless, and would do anything to gratify the lusts that were their masters: wrath, greed and the overweening impulse to power.

"Their own sins destroyed the Asuras. The Devas committed to dharma. But at times, they too strayed from the difficult path; and whenever they sinned, they paid for what they did. Often, the forces of darkness routed them in battle; or the Asuras gained influence over the earth, which is a domain of the Devas. And at times, when the Devas grew so proud that they neglected dharma, the demons have even driven them out of Devaloka, and seized all their realms and their power: so both heaven and earth became provinces of hell.

"It was at such times that the Incarnations of Vishnu came to save the world and restore dharma. Though good and evil exist together, in different measures at different times, dharma and adharma, virtue and sin, are primeval and simple. Though theirs is an unending struggle, evil has never triumphed for long over goodness.

"In the most antique days, when the Devas grew vain and lost everything, they purified themselves in these same tirthas we are going to. When you have bathed in them, you also will recover your kingdom and your fortune, as they did."

Yudhishtira walked beside Lomasa in silence. He knew the rishis never speak idly, and what they say is beyond the common wisdom of men. The party of princes and ascetics journeyed on, to purify themselves at the tirthas, which are timeless centres of grace upon the earth. They are beyond men's understanding, but they heal men's souls, wash their sins, and remove the terror that lives in a man's heart after he has sinned.

They travelled through heavy jungle and jade plain, crossing gushy streams and wooded mountains, where forest spirits watched them, unseen. Bheema was surely full of cheer, and so were Draupadi, Nakula and Sahadeva; a heavy burden lifted from the patient Yudhishtira's heart. The journey was so pleasant it seemed the power of the tirthas reached out across the land of Bharata, and touched them with immaterial fingers in blessing.

They came to the sacred forest of Naimisa where, once, in time out of mind, a wheel of light fell, which Brahma cast down into the world and sanctified that vana. The Gomati flowed through the Naimisa, and the Pandavas bathed in her. When they came ashore, they felt lighter than they had in years, as if a turgid darkness had been taken from them.

They went on to Prayaga, where the golden Ganga flows into the midnight-blue Yamuna, and where the Saraswati loses herself in the two greater rivers. Here also they bathed, dipping themselves under the sparkling water with God's name on their lips and in their hearts. Again, they felt cleansed of a darkness that had clung to them, while they hardly realized they had carried such a burden. Draupadi bathed in seclusion, after the Pandavas and the munis; and she would emerge, her eyes and dark skin shining!

The days and nights of pilgrimage passed, but after their first ablutions, they felt no strain whatever from the journey. It was as if a vast strength had risen in their spirits, and it could take them on forever. They came south, following the age-old trail of countless pilgrims before them, to the Mahanadi. Here, too, they bathed, and felt as if they were in a river of light, which washed away the final vestiges of grossness that clung to their spirits.

It was after bathing in the Mahanadi that Bheema and Draupadi came to Yudhishtira. Bheema had tears in his eyes. Red-faced, he blurted, "Forgive me, my brother! I did not realize what I was saying. Oh, forgive me Yudhishtira, I never meant to hurt you."

Yudhishtira embraced his brother. Turning to Draupadi, he saw that she also wept. She fell at his feet, sobbing, "I was wrong to doubt you; my heart was full of sorrow."

Yudhishtira glowed! He raised her up and clasped her to him. He said, "Now I don't feel alone any more. Our hardest battle is already won."

On the banks of the Mahanadi, the Maharishi Agastya had his asrama. Lomasa took the Pandavas to that profound sage for his blessing. Agastya was delighted to receive Yudhishtira and his brothers. He knew who they were, and everything about them.

He said, "The rains are almost upon us. It would be foolish to travel during the monsoon, with these frail munis and a woman. Stay here with us for these four months. You shall be more than welcome, Lord of the earth."

Yudhishtira was happy to accept the invitation; and neither Bheema nor Draupadi made any protest. Four serene months passed swiftly. There was deep blessedness in Agastya's asrama, and time here seemed to flit by. Yudhishtira especially was blissful, because Agastya made it a point to spend time with him, each morning, chatting of this and that. Hardly seeming to, Agastya imparted much wisdom to the man who would be emperor of the earth again one day.

Once, when the maharishi went off mysteriously into the jungle, for a few days, Lomasa told Yudhishtira about Agastya. An age ago, he came down from the mountains when a black night of evil fell upon the earth. The Devas cursed the world, and all the trees in it withered, and a terrible drought seized the land. Agastya came down with the bright seeds of celestial trees in his hands, and scattered them over the sacred country, ending the curse. The rains returned to Bharatavarsha. Lomasa told them other legends about Agastya Muni. He told the story of the demon brothers, Ilvala and Vatapi, who waylaid unsuspecting travellers through this forest, to make a meal of them; until, Agastya disguised himself as a travelling mendicant and ate the rakshasas himself!

Agastya once remarked to Yudhishtira, "How happy I am that you have come to me. Do you know, a yuga ago, another kshatriya came to my asrama in the Dandaka vana? He, also, had his brother with him, and his wife followed him into exile. He too had been banished from his kingdom with treachery."

Agastya stared at Yudhishtira as if to probe his deepest heart. Then he smiled. He seemed to have satisfied himself about the king who sat before him. "Yes, indeed, you do remind me of the prince of Ayodhya. Though that was another yuga, when men lived much longer than they do now. But men's hearts don't change very much, and you are so like that kshatriya. Yudhishtira, though he faced many trials, he survived his exile, went home to Ayodhya and ruled the earth for twelve thousand years. And what a glorious time that was for the world: Ramarajya, the rule of Rama."

He took the Pandava's hand, "Don't worry, my son. You will also rule the earth again one day, soon, and as wisely as Rama did. Destiny will fulfil herself beyond the plotting of evil men. That is what you were born for, Pandava, and that is what will be, inevitably. It is night now for you, a time to look within. Use it well; chasten yourself with this hardship. Suffering also is a blessing, and one must profit from one's trials, and grow by them."

Four months exactly, the monsoon lashed Bharatavarsha. Then one day the sky was clear, with not a straggle of cloud in its cerulean expanse, and Yudhishtira saw it was time to move on. Taking their leave of Agastya, who blessed them with many boons, the Pandavas left the banks of the Mahanadi and journeyed to the rivers Nanda and Paramananda. From there, they walked to the mountain Hemakuta and worshipped its immaculate spirit. Now they turned west, for the last part of their pilgrimage.

All along the tirtha-yatra, Lomasa was full of wonderful legends of the places at which they worshipped. Each tirtha came alive, as it could never have done if the rishi had not been with them. By his inspiration, their worship was pure as stars. Their hearts were full of a sense of being part of God's majestic plan, though they could not begin to fathom its scope. Full of humility, they went from tirtha to tirtha, feeling lighter with every ablution, hope surging in their bodies and hearts.

They bathed in the Godavari and the rivers of the south, then turned west until they came to the ocean. Walking north along the seashore, along a path that Arjuna had once taken, the Pandavas came to Prabhasa. With inscrutable instinct, Krishna sensed their coming, and he was waiting for them with Balarama, Satyaki and some other Yadavas.

When Yudhishtira saw Krishna, he ran across the length of the beach at Prabhasa, with waves lapping at his feet. Crying Krishna's name aloud, Yudhishtira ran into his cousin's arms, feeling his life begin again, miraculously, that he saw the Avatara before him: his dark face, his dazzling smile, his black eyes so full of love! For the first time, Yudhishtira knelt before Krishna, and the Dark One blessed him.

The younger Pandavas came up and Krishna blessed them. He blessed Draupadi, saying, "You look even lovelier. I think the tirtha-yatra has done you all great good."

Then, Dhaumya and the other brahmanas knelt in awe before Krishna, and he laid his palm on their heads.

But Balarama, fair as the kunda flower, the moon, silver, and the white lotus, was shocked when he saw Yudhishtira and his brothers, clad in deerskin and tree-bark, their hair long and matted in hermits' jata. Balarama was seeing his cousins like this for the first time. He clasped Yudhishtira to him, and bellowed, "The eldest son of the House of Kuru wears valkala, with jata down to his shoulders, so I would have never recognised him. Has the world gone mad?"

He turned to Draupadi, "Queen of the earth, my eyes are cursed that they see you like this! Panchali, is this really you? Krishna, how can you bear to see them like this? Ah, how did Bheeshma and Drona allow this? How did Dhritarashtra stand for it?"

Balarama shook his head from side to side, and Krishna had a mischievous gleam in his eye to listen to his brother. Balarama sighed, "How could Duryodhana stoop to this? He banished them for thirteen years, and rules the world from Yudhishtira's throne, while these Pandavas roam the earth like beggars.

"I have seen Yudhishtira in the Mayaa sabha, where every king of Bharatavarsha paid him homage. I am amazed the earth does not yawn open and swallow sinning humankind: that this king of dharma goes like a mendicant upon her.

"Come Krishna, come Satyaki! Let the Yadavas right this wrong. Let us ride on Hastinapura, and restore the Pandavas' kingdom to them."

Satyaki cried, "Let us ride today! We will sweep Dhritarashtra's sons from the face of the earth, and set Yudhishtira on the throne that is his."

Krishna said quietly, "I don't think Yudhishtira will approve of your plan."

To which Satyaki cried, "If Yudhishtira must keep the conditions of his exile, let him. Let us set Arjuna's son Abhimanyu on the throne of Hastinapura, until the exile is over. Don't waste any time, the devils have enjoyed the fruits of their sin for long enough. It is a shame not just for the Pandavas, but for the Yadavas as well, that, while we are lords of the earth, Yudhishtira and his brothers live so miserably!"

Krishna smiled, "Ask Yudhishtira whether he will take the throne of the world, if we win it for him."

When they turned to Yudhishtira, he said gently, "I thank you for your concern, Balarama, and you, Satyaki. But for me dharma is higher than sovereign power, and my dharma is to spend thirteen years in exile, before I ask for my kingdom back. Until then, I must be true to the terms of the exile." He bent his head, "Not only they, but I have also sinned."

Krishna said, "I fear Yudhishtira is right. Moreover, the day is not far when there will indeed be a bloody war, and then the Yadavas shall show their valour. But until then, let Yudhishtira decide his own course; for, as he says, this is his life, and his battle. He must be the best judge of how to conduct both."

Yudhishtira's eyes were moist as he listened to Krishna, as if he heard echoes of a fathomless love in the Dark One's words. He bowed deeply to Krishna, Balarama and Satyaki. "The Lord Balarama's wrath has already begun to destroy my enemies. And when the time comes for war, Krishna will be with us, and so will Satyaki. How will our cousins defend themselves against you? But for the present..."

Krishna finished what he was saying. "We should leave you to your own devices; and, of course, your tirtha-yatra!"

Yudhishtira embraced him. "We know how much you all love us, and that your sympathies lie with us. For the moment, that will more than suffice."

Krishna and Balarama returned to Dwaraka with Satyaki and the Vrishnis. The Pandavas bathed at Prabhasa, and turned north again on their yatra. They came to the banks of the Saraswati, and saw the Ganga before them. Fording the rivers, they arrived at the foothills of the Himalayas.

The great mountains loomed before them, reverberant with the Holy Spirit, the eternal Brahman. Lomasa turned solemnly to the Ganga, which they had been following towards her source. Folding his hands, he prayed, "Ganga, Devi, protect the Pandavas in the Himalayas, which are Indra's domain. Yakshas, rakshasas and gandharvas abound here, and they have little friendship with the race of men."

Yudhishtira was worried. He said to Draupadi, "The way ahead is hard and dangerous. Lomasa and I will climb the mountain, and meet you again in the foothills."

But she cried, "I will also climb the mountain! The muni says Arjuna will meet us on Mandara, and I cannot wait to see him."

When Bheema saw tears in her eyes, he said, "I will carry Draupadi on my back when she grows tired. She is hardly heavier than a flower, and it won't be the first time. I will carry all of you, if need be."

Yudhishtira had to give in. Thus, the Pandavas began their ascent of the white Himalaya.

SEVENTEEN

To Badarikasrama

Dawn was just breaking, and swathed the Himalaya in unworldly violets, pinks and crimsons, edged with startling gold, in a bewitching spectacle, when, after a sound night's sleep at the foot of the mountain, the Pandavas began their long climb. The air was fragrant as if it had wafted down from Devaloka, and the birds in the trees were all alight with song.

They climbed effortlessly during the early part of the day, and Bheema had a tune on his lips. Slowly, the sun crept overhead, the air grew thinner, the slope steeper, and the going became hard. While they had walked together in a cheery knot at first, now they climbed laboriously in single file.

When they had gone like this for a way, and the day ripened into noon, suddenly darkness scudded into the sky. In moments, ominous clouds piled above the mountain, and blue lightning electrified a firmament dim as twilight. Up here, the elements of the air seemed much nearer. The cracks of thunder and the stark gashes of lightning were terrifyingly close, as if the Gods were angry and wanted to drive the climbers down.

An icy gale began to howl through the sheer valleys, in every direction at once. The wind pulled up massive trees on the slope and crashed them down again. Some cedars were torn up like straw-puppets and carried dizzily away.

The wind was deafening, and dust swirled in its giant coils. The climbers couldn't hear each other above it, not if they shouted on top of their voices. Fear gripped them, exposed as they were on the slope, clinging to one another lest they were blown away as well. Lomasa, who led the party, ran forward and crouched in a shallow cave, and the others scuttled in after him. They huddled together in that relative shelter, while the storm raged all around.

The rain came down, whiplashing the mountain. Every drop was like an arrow of fury. Sky and earth were one in that blinding downpour, as if this was already the night of the deluge. The hapless pilgrims crouched in their shelter, numbed by the power of the storm.

For an hour, it poured as if the sea in the sky was inexhaustible, and the rain would not stop until the very mountain was drowned. Streams swelled into cataracts and hurtled down the slopes, sweeping along huge boulders and the biggest trees. Then, as suddenly as it had begun, the storm blew out. The rain dwindled to a drizzle, then stopped. Patches of blue sky appeared above, and the sun broke through them flooding a cleansed earth with light again. The birds in the trees burst into song.

Lomasa crept out of the cave, shaking his head and smiling. The others sat dazed for a while. Then, slowly, kshatriya and brahmana rose, and now the mountain appeared to welcome them. Full of humility, the Pandavas decided to press on.

The ground was wet and often slippery, and their progress was much slower than before. In sombre silence, yet with strange calm come over them, too, as if they had now been formally ushered into the sacred dimension that is the Himalaya, they climbed on.

All at once, Draupadi, who walked between Bheema and Nakula, gave a sharp cry. She lost her footing and tumbled down the slope they were climbing. Fortunately, Nakula was five paces behind her, and stopped her from falling into a gorge they had just skirted. He held her in his arms, and sat on the ground resting his back against a tree that had withstood the storm.

The rest of the party gathered around. Panchali lay in a swoon, with her head in Nakula's lap; and Bheema cursed himself he had not carried her as he had said he would. Sahadeva fetched water from a brook, sprinkled her face and hands with it, and gave her some to drink. They saw how her feet were blistered, and bled from the climb. But she had not complained because she had been afraid she would be left behind, and also, because she did not want to burden Bheema when the going was so steep and slippery. Bheema himself had quite forgotten; he was stunned by the storm. The twins bathed Draupadi's feet in the icy water, and colour thawed back into her face.

But now, someone else confessed he could hardly stand the climb any more. Yudhishtira gasped, "I can't go on. My body burns, my breath heaves, and the mountain swims before my eyes."

Lomasa said, "Nara Narayana's Badarikasrama isn't far from here. We should be able to climb there if Bheema carries Draupadi, and you rouse yourself, Yudhishtira, perhaps with Sahadeva helping you. In Badari we shall find shelter."

So far, not Dhaumya, Lomasa, or any of the other brahmanas seemed in the least tired! For them, this was a sacred journey, the opportunity of a lifetime, and they were not about to let a little discomfort interfere with their pilgrimage. Ruefully, Yudhishtira pulled himself up and climbed on. Now Sahadeva went beside him, to support him if he needed it. Bheema hoisted Draupadi onto his shoulders, and carried her up the mountain as if she were another breath of air.

When they had gone an hour, Lomasa, who strode ahead of the others showing the way he seemed to know well, shouted, "Badarikasrama! There, ahead."

When they looked up to see where he was pointing, they saw the asrama was a speck on the lofty shoulder of another mountain that towered ahead of them, at least ten days' march away! Yudhishtira gave a groan and sat down where he was. "I must rest. I can hardly breathe here, the air is so thin."

Sahadeva and Nakula sat beside him, and even Bheema was red in the face and short of breath. He, too, seemed grateful to set Draupadi down, and to rest himself. But the Rishi Lomasa and Dhaumya's brahmanas were not tired at all. How their eyes shone when they looked where Lomasa pointed; they would gladly have gone on. Yudhishtira smiled to think he had wanted to leave them behind lest they found the journey too arduous.

He said, "I cannot go another step, at least not today. Even if we find something to eat, and resume our journey tomorrow, I can't tell how far I will be able to go."

Sahadeva said, "I can hardly walk."

Nakula added, "Nor I."

Lomasa said with a sigh, "Gandhamadana is snowbound all year round, and the air grows rarer still, as you climb. I can't think how we will reach the Badarikasrama."

Then, Bheema said to Yudhishtira, "I know how we can all reach Badari."

The rest turned to him sceptically. Thinking this was another frivolous idea, Yudhishtira said, "Tell us then, Bheema, how you propose we arrive."

Bheema said, "Ghatotkacha. My son."

The rishi and the brahmanas looked puzzled, they did not know what he meant. But Yudhishtira gave a cry, and hugged Bheema. "Of course! Ghatotkacha can take us to Badari."

How Bheema glowed at his brother's approval, rare as it was. The son of the wind shut his eyes and thought of his rakshasa son, called him silently wherever he might be. In a faraway forest, hidden between two impassable mountains, a vana where no man had ever set foot, a strange being suddenly grew rapt as he ranged that emerald jungle with his companions on a hunt.

He was more than a head taller than the tallest human, and lean muscles glimmered under his velvet skin. When the light caught him at some angles, it seemed he was made of the finest black crystal. At other times, there seemed to be sapphire dust in his pores. To another rakshasa's eye, he was a splendid young warrior in his prime; though it was plain that he bore the blood of two races in his veins, and the rakshasi women could never resist Ghatotkacha.

He was a prince of that secret forest where they lived; a lord of his people, long-eared, fanged and clawed when he fought, beautifully black, and his pate as hairless and smooth as a water-pot. He was a magical being, as many of the high rakshasas of the mountains were. They were a far cry from fiends like Baka and Hidimba, who had devolved to the lowest state their noble race could sink to. Ghatotkacha's rakshasas were not brutish, blood drinking trolls, but charmed beings blessed by Siva and Parvati with supernatural powers; and they lived mysterious lives in hidden forests. They were followers of dharma, knew the Shastras well, and had contact with other uncanny beings from worlds far and near, starry and subtle, realms to which men seldom had access.

However, that day Ghatotkacha on his hunt heard his father's voice in his head, "My son, come to me, I have need of you," as clearly as if Bheema stood before him.

Ghatotkacha called an abrupt halt to his band of rakshasas' careen through the jungle. They were on the trail of a rare golden monkey, whose flesh was a delicacy to them; and especially its brain, because it conferred great virility. But the gilded creature had the power to make itself invisible and, then, it was a dangerous quarry. For it was a killer, which would materialise suddenly behind an unwary rakshasa and strangle him silently, with fingers that were as strong as they were long and fine.

But now Ghatotkacha, who led the hunt, froze with his head cocked and his eyes intent.

"What happened, Ghatotkacha?" cried one of the others in dismay The monkey would have got far away by now.

Ghatotkacha said softly, "My father wants me. Come, we must fly to the Himalaya."

No questions were asked. By instinct, sure as sight, Ghatotkacha knew exactly from where Bheema called him. The rakshasas travelled in a manner that to men would surely be mystic, but for them was commonplace. Quite simply, they vanished from where they stood in the steamy vana; and a golden monkey hiding in the highest branch of a tree heaved a sigh of relief and stopped shaking. In moments, the rakshasas stood before Bheema and the Pandavas with folded hands.

Black, exotic, magnificent Ghatotokacha knelt at his father's feet, and took the padadhuli from them. Bheema hugged his son, kissing his cheeks, sniffing his smooth head, blessing him. Then the rakshasa knelt before Yudhishtira, who doted on him, and whose favourite he was since his childhood.

Hugging his extraordinary nephew, again and again, crying for joy to see him, Yudhishtira said, "Now we shall surely arrive in Badarikasrama."

Sahadeva and Nakula embraced Ghatotkacha; and how radiant he was to see his uncles again. But Draupadi and the brahmanas were afraid of the rakshasas.

Bheema brought Ghatotkacha to Panchali and said, "This is your mother Draupadi, my son. She cannot climb any more, and you must carry her up to Badarikasrama."

Ghatotkacha knelt gravely at her feet, and clasped them in long fingers that seemed to have dark diamonds for nails. Exhausted as she was, and jolted by her fall, she shivered at his touch. Then, she felt how true his spirit was, how loving; and, with a wondering laugh, she placed her hand on his smooth head and blessed him.

Ghatotkacha's solemn eyes saw the cuts and blisters on Draupadi's feet. He made a slight sign to one of his rakshasas, and the wild one loped gracefully away up the mountain. He returned shortly with some dark leaves with a heavy fragrance. Ghatotkacha took the leaves and, crushing them quickly, adding a few drops of moisture he squeezed from some other wet leaves on the ground, he gently applied the paste to the soles of Panchali's feet.

Her feet went numb, and then she felt as if green fingers drew out the pain from them. Not only that, but a thrill of wellbeing spread up through her body. Colour flushed back into her cheeks, and in a moment, she could stand.

She cried, "Look Bheema, the blisters have vanished, and my feet aren't sore any more."

She took Ghatotkacha's hand and, hugging him quickly, cried, "I have heard so much about you. But from today, you are my son also!"

How pleased that rakshasa was. For, truth to tell, he had feared she may resent him, since Bheema had been with his mother before Draupadi entered his life.

"Where is my uncle Arjuna?"

Yudhishtira pointed up at the sky. "He is with his father in Amravati. He will return to us on the Himalaya, we are not sure when. We want to pray at Nara Narayana's asrama, and we are exhausted. Ghatotkacha, you must carry at least Draupadi up the mountain."

Ghatotkacha said softly, "We will take you all up to the Badari, uncle." He smiled, dazzling white against his face. "If the holy ones don't mind being borne there by rakshasas."

Bheema laughed, and Dhaumya said quietly, "We shall be honoured to be borne to the Badari, or anywhere at all, by friends as noble and virtuous as yourselves."

Ghatotkacha bowed to the brahmana. "I will carry my mother Draupadi and my uncle Yudhishtira. My friends will bear the rest. Badarikasrama is not far."

He knelt and scooped Draupadi up, easy as feathers, and set her on one shoulder. He lifted Yudhishtira up and set him beside her. His rakshasas took the other Pandavas, Lomasa, Dhaumya and his brahmanas.

"Hold tight, little mother!" cried Ghatotkacha, but bound Draupadi and Yudhishtira to his back with invisible thongs of his power, so they would never fall.

The next moment they flew up from that mountain, and Draupadi cried out in wonder as they flashed towards distant Badari: an extraordinary flight of demons and pilgrims!

Even through the air, as birds travel, it took a fair part of the day to arrive on Gandhamadana, and the asrama set just below the summit of the scented mountain. They flew over peaks that thrust themselves out of the earth, proud and defiant, as if in memory of the times when mountains had golden wings and flew through the air, roaming the sky at will before Indra sheared their wings with his Vajra. Between towering peaks were valleys and ravines that plunged sheerly away, that none could pass but sure-footed kinnaras, kimpurushas and mountain gandharvas.

Over the Himalaya flew Ghatotkacha and his rakshasas with their unusual burdens, all of them absorbed by what they saw below. Ineffable sunset was upon the white mountain now, and its slopes resonated with colours never seen in the plains. Softly as a breeze the rakshasas descended on lofty Badari, and the hermits who lived on that eagle's perch were astonished by the spectacle of ten demons flying down out of the twilight sky. With a stab of fear in their hearts, especially when they saw shining, black Ghatotkacha, who flew down first, the rishis of Badari rose to receive their visitors.

Then they saw the Pandavas and Draupadi, and the rakshasas who carried Dhaumya and Lomasa landed among them. Lomasa was no stranger to the rishis of Badari, and they came to greet him in some relief. They were still awestruck by the beings that had carried that sage and his yatris to their asrama: these, they saw, were certainly rakshasas. But soon, everything was explained.

Lomasa said, "This is Yudhishtira of the House of Kuru."

He did not have to say more. The rishis of Badari came forward warmly to greet the Pandava. They seemed to know all about Yudhishtira and his brothers, Draupadi, and their exile. They even knew where

Arjuna was. The eldest among them was a muni who looked a thousand years old, if he was a day: a thousand years that had made him more vigorous and full of light for every year he had seen.

That ancient now said, "It draws on time for your brother Arjuna to return to you, and then, time to fight the war at the end of the age." He sighed, "And when the kali yuga sets in, Lomasa, it may be time for us to leave this asrama, and this earth."

He was almost as tall as Ghatotkacha, and he swept the twilight sky and the mountains around them with glowing eyes. "Long years we have lived here, for centuries we have sat in dhyana on the Badari. But, perhaps, in the age of terror there will be no one left to pray for the world, not even on this mountain."

He turned to look curiously at Ghatotkacha and his rakshasas. Bheema said, "Ghatotkacha is my son, Muni. I summoned him to carry us to Badari, for we could not climb here ourselves."

The old one smiled, "I have heard of you, Ghatotkacha, and you are welcome."

Just that night, Ghatotkacha and his silent rakshasas spent in the asrama. The moon rose and, when it was overhead, as they sat up late, talking, Sahadeva pointed down the mountain, "Look!"

The Pandavas saw the moon was not only above them, but seemed also to have fallen to the earth, a long way below them.

"What is it?" whispered Bheema.

The rishis laughed. One of them said, "It is the reflection of the moon on the Bindusaras, where the Ganga has her source."

"Where Siva let her down from his head," murmured Yudhishtira.

"The lake of water-drops," said Lomasa reverently.

The ancient of Badari said, "That is how Sankara let her down, drop by drop, to quell her pride."

The moon lay calmed on the Bindusaras, truly as if he had risen not only in the sky above but also the mountain's heart. He lay there, softly breathtaking.

In the morning the rakshasas rose with the sun and, bidding farewell to the Pandavas, the munis and Draupadi, Ghatotkacha left Badarikasrama, promising to return whenever they wanted him again. Bheema clasped his son tightly, and held him for a long time. When, finally, Ghatotkacha and his friends had flown towards the rising sun, and their forest hidden away in the secret valley, Bheema had tears in his eyes, and so did Draupadi and Yudhishtira.

Already, a fine serenity stole over their spirits. This was the asrama where Nara and Narayana had sat in dhyana once; and their tapasya blessed not only the mountain, but spread through all the earth, and down the ages deeply. This mountain was a chalice of the Holy Spirit, and nowhere else did Yudhishtira, his brothers, Draupadi and the others who travelled with them find such peace as they did in Badarikasrama.

EIGHTEEN

An old monkey

FOR SOME TIME, THE PANDAVAS LIVED IN BADARIKASRAMA ON MOUNT Gandhamadana. Each day they rose with the sun, at dawn so enchanting it dissolved sins, and they thought: today Arjuna will return from Devaloka. But the days grew into weeks, the weeks into months, and there was no sign of him.

Yudhishtira was at perfect peace with himself. He was happy to sit with the rishis of Badarikasrama all day long, specially the ancient one, and listen to their illustrious lore. The mountain was so suffused with the Spirit it was hardly a place of the earth, and Yudhishtira's heart was full with the sanctity of that hermitage. Some nights, he dreamt he saw Nara and Narayana sitting at dhyana at a cave-mouth, and their faces were familiar. When he awoke, he remembered nothing of his dreams.

Bheema and Draupadi were more restless than Yudhishtira, though their impatience of the Kamyaka vana was a thing of the past. The two of them took to going on long walks through the cedar forests of Gandhamadana. Those were fragrant woods, and the very air was like a blessing: and so, indeed, was that mountain named Gandhamadana, for its scented cedar.

But one day, the two of them wandered along a trail that wound its way steeply down the mountain's side, a trail they hadn't explored before. After an hour, the path grew less precipitous and made its way into a thick forest over which an aura of mystery hung. It was darker here than in the forests higher up, because the trees were more tropical and grew closer to one another. Bheema and Draupadi had to walk slowly. They had gone half an hour into the forest, following the trail still, when Draupadi seized Bheema's hand and made him stop.

"Can you smell it?" she breathed, in an ecstasy. "Ah, Bheema, can't you smell that fragrance?"

Bheema sniffed the air, and there was no mistaking it: a scent straight out of heaven was borne on the breeze stirring in that forest.

"What is it?" Draupadi asked. "I have never smelt anything like it in all my life."

They walked deeper into the trees, following the unearthly scent to its source; as they went on, it grew stronger, pervading the forest headily.

Bheema shut his eyes and said, "I feel I am walking into swarga."

The scent was irresistible, and following it blindly, they came into a small clearing. Draupadi stopped.

"Look!" she whispered, pointing.

Growing out of the earth under a punnaga tree was a little flower, scarlet and streaked with gold; and this flower filled the whole forest with the heavenly scent. Gingerly, Bheema and Draupadi crept forward, as if the tiny thing might wilt and die if they set foot too firmly.

When they were near, Draupadi said, "It must be the saugandhika the rishis told us about. No other flower on earth can smell like this."

Bheema sniffed the air again. He walked a few paces beyond where the scarlet flower grew. He said, "The scent grows stronger! There are more of these inside the forest."

Draupadi couldn't help herself any more; she knelt down quickly and plucked the little flower. Sniffing it and sighing, she said, "I must take it for Yudhishtira. The munis said it stays fresh for a year after being plucked. But, Bheema, I want some more for myself. You must get them for me from wherever they grow."

"It's too late today, it will be dark in an hour. Their scent isn't strong; the flowers grow deep in the vana and there may be danger there. Let us go back now, and I will come again tomorrow by myself, and bring you as many as you like."

The bright flower nestled in Draupadi's hand, and it barely covered a tenth of her palm. Reluctantly she said, "Very well; but promise you will come tomorrow. I must have some more of these, they fill me with such delight."

The rishis of the Badarikasrama confirmed that the flower was indeed a saugandhika, and the hermitage was soon awash with its scent. Yudhishtira kept it beside his sleeping-mat, in an earthen vessel filled with spring water, and the next morning it was as fresh as it had been when Draupadi picked it.

The old muni of Badari said, "It is a blessed flower that grows in Kubera's garden. It will not fade for months, its heart is so strong."

The next morning, at crack of dawn, Bheema set out alone for the forest. He went by the same path that Draupadi and he had taken the previous day, and soon reached the punnaga tree where they had found the saugandhika. Through the vana, with invisible fingers, the maddening aroma reached for the son of the wind. Following it, Bheema walked deeper and deeper into that forest.

Soon, the forest was a very different world. Knotted trees with immense boles grew here, their branches so entwined that it was always twilight. Startling flowers that did not grow near the hem of the jungle covered the trees and thickets in gaudy profusion. Birds with livid plumage called in the branches, birds he had never seen before. As he went on, the vana grew stranger and stranger.

Bheema pressed on. The scent of the saugandhika was stronger, but he realized he had a good way to go before he arrived where the flowers grew. The silence of this jungle oppressed him; as if someone or something, perhaps a vana devata, a forest god, watched him with a thousand eyes hidden in stamen and leaf, and did not want him to go any farther. To fight this feeling Bheema raised the conch he carried at his waist, and blew a ringing blast on it. Sleeping lions were roused in their caves. Bheema heard a growl or two, a desultory roar here and there, as he plunged on. The Pandava smiled: this was far better than the intolerable silence.

But lions were not all he roused with his conch. Someone else lay asleep in the forest, someone from another age. He had come here just to meet Bheema, for he had something in common with the Pandava. That being now lifted his tail and crashed it down across the path beside which he sat, leaning against a tree. He was a warrior from another yuga, when everyone was much grander than in Bheema's dwindled time. But Bheema was not to know this, save from stories he had heard, which he hardly took literally. Like men of every age, he, too, thought that all times had been exactly like the one he lived in.

Bheema heard that crash like thunder falling on the earth, and ran towards it. Perhaps some rakshasa had heard his conch and was challenging him? Nothing could be better! How bored he had been, for longer than he cared to think, surrounded by rishis and brahmanas who spoke of nothing but peace and the atman, and moksha. How he longed for a good fight; it would restore his spirits like nothing else.

He loped eagerly through the vana, quickly as the wind. Until he rounded a bend in the trail and saw a wizened old monkey before him, his back turned, his wrinkled head cradled in the crook of his brown arm, and apparently fast asleep. Though the monkey was quite a small creature himself, he had the longest, finest tail Bheema had ever seen. Both tail and its owner lay stretched squarely across the path along which Bheema was rushing to meet whoever had made the earth tremble.

Bheema growled in annoyance. Weakly, the monkey raised his head to see who had disturbed his nap. Bheema towered over him, his brawny hands on his hips. The Pandava saw the monkey was an ancient of his kind. His golden face was covered by fine wrinkles; his eyes, though bright, were so full of age it was impossible to reckon how old he was. He could have been a thousand years; he was so worn and thin. Bheema growled again, hoping to scare the little creature away. But then, the monkey spoke to him in perfect human speech, chaste old language in fact!

In a frail voice, he said, "Young man, why do you make so much noise? I was sleeping peacefully, dreaming fine dreams, and you come blundering through the jungle blasting on your conch."

He regarded the impatient Bheema out of shrewd eyes, with directness the Pandava found disrespectful and somehow unnerving too, though he could not think why. Bheema stood breathing heavily, taken aback. Still using exquisite old language that scholars do, the monkey said again in his rambling way, "Young Kshatriya, for so you may well be, are you a stranger to these parts? I have never met another human being in this forest who makes such a noise. This is no battlefield, young man. Yes, you are surely a stranger here, that you disturb all the jungle-folk with your din."

He paused again, and his shining eyes never left Bheema's face. The Pandava was still speechless with surprise.

"And where are you going deep into the vana? Don't you know this is a dangerous place, and the forest is quite impenetrable not far from here? Don't you know anything at all, young fellow? That you plunge on heedless, blowing your conch."

Bheema was angry by now; but he felt so inexplicably drawn to the little old monkey that he still said nothing. He growled again, trying desperately to collect his wits. The monkey, who seemed to see clearly into everything that went on inside Bheema's head, said, "Come and sit beside me for a while. I picked some fruit for myself."

He uncurled his arm and pushed out an amazing heap of fresh fruit, pear and plum, peach and apple, offering them to the Pandava. "My advice to you, young Kshatriya, is that you sit down and eat a few fruit with me, and then turn back wherever you came from. Though I really cannot imagine where that might be, or who you are, for that matter."

At last, Bheema found his voice. He gave a short roar, and cried, "You are the strangest monkey I ever saw! Talking like a man, and in old language. Who on earth are you?" His eyes narrowed, "Are you a monkey at all? Or a vana devata, who have assumed a monkey's form? Or are you a rakshasa? If it's a fight you want, show me what you really look like and let us begin!"

The monkey laughed. "Rakshasa? Fight? You are certainly a peculiar young man. Can't you see, my fine prince, I am just a tired old monkey, too weak to even move from where I lie? What is all this about vana devatas and rakshasas? And you still haven't told me who you are, or what you are doing in this forest." He gave a groan. "Aah, I feel so ill today, and you won't let me sleep."

Bheema drew himself up and said in his most superior tone, "Monkey, I am Bheema the Pandava. I am the son of Vayu, and I am in a hurry. Let me pass."

The monkey mumbled disapprovingly to himself. "In a hurry? And where are you going in such a hurry? Don't want to take my advice, it seems. Sit down and eat some fruit, young Pandava; and then turn back. It is not safe to go on, I tell you. Ah, but the young never listen, do they? They must learn from their own foolishness."

"I don't want your advice, monkey!" snapped Bheema haughtily. "I want you out of my way, so I can go on."

"Truly, I am in your way, young Kshatriya. But I am so old I cannot move. Otherwise, would I dare lie in the way of Vayu's son? Why, I tremble even to hear that God's name. But I can't move. So just step over me and be on your way, Bheema, if you are determined to go on."

Now Bheema frowned. "You are older than I am. I cannot step over someone older than me." He laughed, mockingly, "But if you insist, I shall really have to make the leap of faith, as Hanuman did over the sea!"

"Hanuman? Who is he? Who is this Hanuman whose very name makes your eyes shine?"

Bheema cried, "I can't believe this. You, a monkey, and you don't know who Hanuman was?"

The old monkey shook his head. Bheema looked down his nose at the creature now. He said, "You deserve to be stepped over; that, being a vanara yourself, you don't know about the greatest vanara there ever was. Immortal Hanuman!"

"Really?" said the monkey softly.

But Bheema had not finished. "Hanuman was the strongest, wisest, most revered monkey that ever lived. He fought at Rama's side on Lanka. Why, it was he who discovered Sita in the asokavana in Ravana's palace, and leapt across the sea to bring her Rama's message. He is a legend not only among monkeys, but among men as well. He has the place of a God; we worship Hanuman. And you have not heard of him.

"Listen monkey. Hanuman is one of the greatest scholars of all time; he is a master of his mind, perfectly devoted to his Rama. Hanuman is a jivanmukta, a liberated soul; he is also a chiranjivi, he lives for ever."

A smug smile spread across Bheema's face. "And just like me, Hanuman is a son of the wind, a Vayuputra. Yes, Hanuman is my brother, as strong as I am, perhaps even slightly stronger."

The little monkey's eyes grew round. But Bheema had finished his eulogy of Hanuman, and he said again, "Let me pass, old monkey, I am in a hurry. I have to find the heart of this jungle, for I must take the saugandhikas back for Draupadi."

"So that's what you're after! Well, as I have told you, I am tired and ill, and really too old to move. If you knew how old I am, you would understand why I cannot move. I fancy I must be as old as your Hanuman."

Bheema growled, "You can't be as old as Hanuman, monkey! You don't know what you are saying."

"Well, anyway, the fact is that I can't move, and, being such a noble young kshatriya, you will not step over me. So, really, there is just one solution to our problem: that you move my tail aside and pass," said the monkey, smiling sweetly.

Grumbling to himself, Bheema crouched down beside the old vanara, and took his fine golden tail in his hand to move it out of his way. The tail would not budge. Growling, Bheema put both his hands to the task. Not an inch could he move the monkey's tail. Great Bheemasena, tameless Vayu's son, slayer of Hidimba, Kirmira and Baka, began to pant with his efforts. Beads of sweat stood on his brow; but he could not shift that wizened old monkey's tail by a hair's breadth.

The monkey cried in his reedy voice, "What is the matter, O Vayuputra, can't you move an old vanara's tail? Or are you making fun of me again?"

Full of quick shame, Bheema strained at the tail, grunting and roaring; but to no avail. Suddenly, he felt a spinning dizziness. He felt every ounce of his vast strength drain out of his arms, all his limbs, and being absorbed uncannily into the monkey. The Pandava keeled over where he knelt. Mighty Bheema fainted on the mud track: vanquished by a monkey's tail!

When he stirred from his faint, he saw the little old monkey had vanished. In its place, a magnificent vanara knelt beside him, smiling, and sprinkled cool water on his face. Ah, this was a different monkey altogether, taller than Bheema, golden-furred, resplendent.

Bheema sat up weakly, shaking his head. He folded his hands and asked, "Who are you, magnificent one?"

The towering creature smiled, and replied, "Just an old monkey whose tail the great Bheema was trying to move."

Bheema bowed his head, "Forgive me for being arrogant, Vanara. I take back everything I said to you. I beg you, tell me who you are."

"But you know who I am, Bheema. You know my name."

Bheema goggled at the splendid one. The monkey said, "Bheema, my brother, I am Hanuman."

A wild cry erupted from Bheema, and next moment they were hugging each other, with tears streaming down their faces. Hanuman cried, "Ah, the same thrill of love courses through me when I embrace you as I felt when I touched my Rama!"

Bheema felt his weakness leave him and a new strength, greater than anything he had before, flooded his body. The Pandava prostrated at his legendary brother's feet. Hanuman raised Bheema up, and then they sat together beside the jungle trail. Bheema was in no hurry, any more, and chewed contentedly on the fruit Hanuman offered him.

The hours flashed by, and nothing the two did not talk about: from the battle of Lanka to the game of dice in Hastinapura. Once during this conversation, Hanuman grew thoughtful and said, "Times have changed indeed. Yet, do you know, Bheema my brother, scratch them a little and there isn't so much difference between those days and these. Good and evil have always existed, side by side, and fallen into conflict even like cats and dogs."

He paused, gazing fondly at the Pandava. Then he patted Bheema's cheek and said, "But it is true, you know, that finally goodness will always prevail. So don't worry: you and your brothers will vanquish the Kauravas, and the Kuru kingdom shall be yours. I, Hanuman, assure you of this!"

Bheema said quietly, "As long as you are with us, we cannot lose. I feel the new strength you have blessed me with."

Hanuman gave a laugh, and cried, "But I will do more! In memory of this meeting with my little brother in the jungle."

"Your blessing is more than enough," said Bheema.

But Hanuman's face had lit up, and he said, "I will sit on your brother Arjuna's banner during the great war! And I promise you, my roars will strike terror in your enemies' hearts, and give courage to your own soldiers."

Bheema hugged him again. Then, he was suddenly embarrassed. Hanuman asked, "What is it, child? There is something you are not telling me."

Bheema blurted, "I want to see you as you were when you leapt across the ocean!"

Hanuman laughed. Then he was still and the forest around them was, also; and he began to grow. In a moment, he was as tall as the tallest tree. The next, he was big as a hill, and then even bigger, big as the Vindhya and he shone like a sun! Overwhelmed, Bheema knelt at his feet. In an instant, stupendous Hanuman, hero of another yuga, was his monkey self again, somewhat Bheema's own size; and he laid a hand in blessing on the Pandava's head.

They ate more fruit together. More news and fabulous tales Hanuman told his brother, both of them excited as boys at meeting. At last, Hanuman looked at Bheema, with his eyes full of love, "I have kept you for long enough. Hurry on, Bheema, and find the saugandhikas you have come for. The way ahead is fraught with danger, for this path leads into the spirit-world. Strange things live in this jungle. It is a forbidden forest, and you must go with some stealth."

Then he laughed. "But my brother is a kshatriya, and no one on earth is as strong as he is. Why should I be anxious for him? It is those who cross his path who should beware!"

Bheema said wryly, "Unless they are old monkeys who are so weak that they cannot move!"

They hugged each other again. Then Hanuman waved Bheema on, and stood looking after him as the Pandava sped up the narrow trail, deeper into the forest. When he was out of sight, Hanuman vanished from that place like a dream.

NINETEEN

Where the saugandhika grows

As BHEEMA LOPED DEEPER INTO THE FOREST, THE FRAGRANCE OF the saugandhika was so strong that he knew he couldn't be far from where the flowers grew. Now, it was not the scent of just one flower that filled the vana, but of a thousand, a million saugandhikas! This must certainly be swarga he had stumbled into, thought Bheema; anyway, not even heaven could smell any sweeter.

Soon the jungle was dense and trackless, and the Pandava ploughed on through it, following just the ravishing scent. As he went, he had to thrust dark, living liana out of his way: vines that grew thick as a man's arm, and coiled themselves around any passing creature. At times, the creepers clung so swiftly and fiercely Bheema had to cut himself free with his sword.

There were the most exceptional monkeys and birds in the branches, peering down curiously at him; some called out in astonishment to see the intruder. The birds were so vividly plumed they were luminous in the twilight forest, and the monkeys had brilliantly coloured faces, like dancers' masks. There were other, more dangerous beasts in that forest; but this was their time for sleep and none of them challenged the Pandava. Though wildflowers of every imaginable kind grew in the jungle he crashed through, only a single fragrance filled the air: the heady scent of the saugandhika. There were bigger flowers than the little scarlet one, there were lovelier ones; but none of these could match the wild and perfect aroma of the tiny flower Bheema had come looking for.

Where the saugandhika grows

When he had gone an hour after he left Hanuman, he heard the swishing flow of water, and next moment, broke into the sunlight of an open glade through which a cobalt river meandered. Its waters were indescribably blue, as if a bit of clear sky had fallen to the earth and turned into a river. But it was not the incredible blueness or sparkling clarity of the river that held Bheema transfixed; it was the riot of minute scarlet flowers that grew on its velvet banks, and upon its shimmering water. From the fragrance which hung over that place they had to be saugandhikas, all thousands and thousands of them!

Had Bheema been a little more observant of his surroundings he might have noticed the river's bank was a carefully tended garden, its shrubs and trees planted with order, its paths neatly laid. The water was gently dammed with earth, so it formed a pool, on which the saugandhikas grew in thick beds. But Bheema was intent on plucking the flowers and taking them back to Draupadi as quickly as he could. He could hardly wait to see her face light up.

Now the Pandava felt very thirsty. The way through the forest had been long, and Hanuman's fruit lay heavy on his stomach. He strode up to the river whose clear water was so inviting, and, without a thought for any danger, knelt to drink.

He did not see the many eyes that watched him from the trees. The moment his lips touched the sweet river-water, angry cries shattered the silence, and in a blink, Bheema found himself surrounded by the weirdest beings he had ever set eyes on, more than a score of them. They were tall and lean; some were even handsome after a fashion; and though they were not rakshasas, they were certainly not human. Their skin shone and their eyes seemed like facetted jewels set in their long faces: some blue as the river, some leaf-green, some wine-red. More bizarrely, some of them had their feet turned back from their ankles, and others had holes in their backs, while still others walked bent almost in two, their hands trailing the ground. All of them wore clothes that seemed woven from bird-feathers, leaves and wildflowers, and some from large patches of butterfly-wing.

Bheema rose slowly, and turned to face the eerie throng crowded hostilely round him. The leader of the beings said grimly, "Who are you, mortal, that dare enter my Lord Kubera's garden?"

Another whispered menacingly, "Don't you know death is the penalty for drinking from Kubera's river?"

Bheema did not flinch, only tightened his grip on his mace. After his encounter with Hanuman, he felt stronger and more unafraid than ever. Gazing back calmly into the glittering insect-eyes of the leader of the motley crowd, Bheema said, "I am Bheemasena the Pandava, Vayu's son and Kunti's. I have come to pick saugandhikas for my Panchali."

"The flowers belong to our king, no one may pick them!" cried the leader of the yakshas and guhyakas. They were Kubera's people, the guardians of the nine treasures. "But if you want flowers for your wife, you must come and ask our Lord Kubera for them. He is generous, and may give you some; but then again, he may not."

Bheema snorted at the idea. "Why should I beg for some flowers that grow on the river? I am a kshatriya. The river flows free on the face of the earth; it does not belong to anyone, and neither do the flowers that grow on its water. I will pick the saugandhikas, and see who stops me."

With shrill cries, the yakshas and guhyakas attacked him. They carried short swords, some produced staffs and javelins, and they set on him from every side except where he had his back to the river. Bheema gave a roar that stopped many of those guardians in their tracks. Then he was at them like a tempest. He was so quick they could hardly see him, and so powerful they fell around him helplessly, heads smashed, bodies shattered by his mace, the clear river stained with blood. In no time, those left alive fled from this fearsome mortal, and back to their king in his palatial cavern: Kubera, Lord of that jungle.

Stepping nonchalantly over the corpses of those he had killed, Bheema waded into the river and began gathering saugandhikas by the armful. As he did so, he sniffed them in delight, his eyes shining when he thought how Draupadi would love them. When he had enough flowers, and much more, since he was never one to do things by halves, he laid them carefully on the mossy bank. He stripped off his clothes and bathed in the cold water, washing off the blood of the yakshas and guhyakas he had killed.

Meanwhile, those who had escaped arrived in some disarray before their king. Kubera was Master of the treasures of the earth, a Lokapala, and Siva's friend. He was a Deva, and his lustre filled his twilight cave-palace. He sat with twelve red hounds at his feet, and surrounded by a colourful array of jungle folk: yakshas, guhyakas, ganas, siddhas, charanas, gandharvas, nagas, kinnaras and rakshasas. Of all the secret sabhas in the world, Kubera's was the most opulent. Precious gemstones of incredible size and fire were embedded in the walls and lofty ceilings of the maze of caves that was his palace.

He himself wore few ornaments on his dark skin, but every ring, bracelet or necklace that adorned him, whether of diamonds, emeralds, huge rubies, or pearls luminous as the moon, was a king's ransom. His throne was carved from a single sapphire, mined and cut in the earth's deepest past; it was the seat of his power. Kubera was a great sovereign of the earth. Now he saw his people run in to him in shock. "What happened to you?"

The yakshas' leader cried, "A terrible warrior appeared at the river. He drank your water, and wanted to pluck saugandhikas to take with him. We tried to stop him, but he killed more than half of us*. Even now, he is picking the flowers as he likes."

Kubera murmured, "One warrior? And he slew half of you? What is he? A gandharva, a Deva, a Daitya or a Danava?"

The tall guhyaka turned his face down, and whispered, "No Lord, he is a mortal."

A murmur of disbelief hummed through the court. Kubera frowned for a moment, then a smile broke out on his face. He rose and said, "I think I know who this mortal is. It is Bheema the Pandava come looking for saugandhikas for his Panchali. He is a friend. Come, we must go and welcome him to our kingdom."

Kubera strode out from his palace, followed by as wild and varied a train of subjects as any king in heaven or earth could hope to have. Many of them wore ashes, jata and rudraksha; for, most of Kubera's people are Sivabhaktas. They were all quite uncanny by any human norm: some were as tall as two men, others short, but bright-bodied, some had more than one head, some were so ugly you couldn't look at them, and others were as beautiful. There were changelings among them, who were wolves or serpents, at times, but at others had almost

---

* A tale is told of an old curse of Agastya Muni's, which is responsible for these yakshas and guhyakas being slain by Bheema. KMG.

human forms, with jewels in their heads. There were centaurs, fauns, and other lively ones, who were spirits at times, and had bodies at others.

Back at the river, Bheema felt very sleepy. The king's water had this effect on those who were unused to it. The Pandava came out of the river and fell asleep on the soft grass beside the flowers he had plucked. He thought he would take a short nap, but he slept longer than he expected to.

In Badarikasrama, the day had worn into evening, and there was no sign of Bheema. Yudhishtira grew anxious, and Draupadi also. She said, "The forest was dark and seemed menacing."

One of the rishis of the asrama added, "Men have never been known to enter that forest. Mysterious creatures are said to live at its heart. But none of us have ventured in there, so we couldn't say if the tales we hear are true or not."

Yudhishtira said, "No creature can harm my brother. But it can't have taken him so long to find the saugandhikas."

Draupadi said, "Let us call Ghatotkacha to take us to look for Bheema."

So they did. In a few moments, Ghatotkacha stood before them, his black hands folded graciously. Yudhishtira said, "Your father is missing since morning. He went into the forest in search of saugandhikas, and hasn't returned."

Ghatotkacha's eyes were worried. "That is Kubera's vana. The saugandhikas grow on the blue river in the heart of the forest, and they belong to the Lord of the yakshas. He does not take kindly to uninvited visitors."

Yudhishtira cried, "We must fly there!"

Draupadi said, "Take me with you. It was I who sent him, I can beg Kubera for his life."

There was no time to argue, and Yudhishtira gave in to her. Ghatotkacha picked them both up, easily, and flashed away from Badarikasrama towards Kubera's darkling vana. The sun was setting over the mountain's shoulder as they flew through the saffron dusk, bathed themselves in its calid colours.

In no time, by fading light they saw a river like a sparkling thread below them, weaving in and out of the sable forest. Like a bird,

Ghatotkacha came gliding down and landed in Kubera's garden, where they saw a most singular gathering. Amidst a crowd of yakshas, guhyakas and others, and seeming to enjoy each other's company hugely, were Bheema and Kubera himself.

Yudhishtira gave a cry of relief when he saw his brother, and ran forward to embrace him. Bheema came to Draupadi with his hands full of saugandhikas, and, when he saw her smile, he clasped her to him, in joy, that he had pleased her. They came before the Lord Kubera, and Yudhishtira and Draupadi paid obeisance to him. He laid a dark palm on their heads, blessing them.

The Deva said, "You must spend at least a week with me here in my Chaitra." That was the name both of his realm and his garden*.

But Yudhishtira hesitated, "Lord, we came to the mountains to wait for Arjuna. Only today I was thinking that perhaps we should go further north, lest he arrive there."

"Stay with me for a week. Then return to Badari, and Arjuna will come to the asrama," replied Kubera.

They spent a charmed week with the Lord of treasures, and there was feasting in Chaitra by day and night, under sun, moon and stars; and the singing never stopped, or the dancing. The wine and the food were fresh, and more delicious than any served in the courts of human kings; and, much to Bheema's delight, there was no end to either.

Ghatotkacha flew to the Badarikasrama, and brought Nakula and Sahadeva back with him to join the others. The Pandavas made many friends in Kubera's garden. Some were exotic and beautiful, some entirely grotesque. But their hearts were true, without exception, and they made Yudhishtira and his family welcome among them; most of all, their mysterious and powerful king did.

---

* The sequence of events that led to the Pandava's meeting with Kubera is told a little differently in the original text. It has been compressed here for convenience.

TWENTY

Arjuna returns

For a magical week, there was uninterrupted festivity in Chaitra: wine, food and song. Draupadi learnt to sing and dance with yakshis, guhyakis and forest gandharvis. But at the week's end, Yudhishtira came to Kubera on his sapphire throne and said, "My lord, we have been overwhelmed by your hospitality. But now we must return to Badarikasrama and wait for Arjuna, for our hearts are full of him."

Kubera gave Panchali precious gifts from his legendary coffers. The jewels she had from him were not of the earth but ornaments of the Devas. There were diamonds, moonstones and rubies, and corals and pearls from the seas of worlds deep in the heavens. They were all stones of great power and fortune. At last, it was time for the Pandavas to return to Badarikasrama.

Kubera had the saugandhikas that Bheema had plucked for Draupadi packed in reed-baskets. They took his blessing before they left because they knew that, for all his geniality, he was one of the masters of the earth: the Dikpala of the north, the Lord of treasures. Yet, not once during their visit did he seem any more than a wise and affable host, if somewhat ageless, since you could not begin to tell how old he was. Not once did he reveal his other, pristine form to them: that of an awesome Lokapala.

Back at Badarikasrama, the days and nights began to seem long as years to Draupadi and the Pandavas. Every morning, they awoke in excitement that Arjuna would return to them today. But each day brought disappointment and, at its end, they would lie in their beds, sleepless, wondering if he would arrive in the dead of night.

Yet the asrama and its surroundings were tranquil and lovely, and did not allow them to remain dejected. The trees of the nearby woods were all in bloom, draped in brilliant cloaks of flowers. They went on long walks together through the cedar groves, and even Draupadi was contented in Badarikasrama. Bheema was always dancing attendance on her, going to absurd lengths to satisfy her every whim. He would climb the tallest tree or up to the most hazardous rock-crevice, to fetch a flower that took her fancy. And, indeed, they were reasonably happy.

But after they returned from Kubera's garden, all their thoughts were full of Arjuna. Five years had passed since he left them, and they could hardly bear the separation any more.

One day, they were out on a rambling walk—the Pandavas, Draupadi and Lomasa, Dhaumya and his brahmanas and some of the rishis—in the pine forest south of Badari, when Nakula, who walked ahead of the others, gave a shout and pointed to the sky. "Look! What is that?"

A light like a piece of the sun come loose hung pulsing in the blue. Most of them had never seen anything like it, but Lomasa smiled. "It is a vimana from Devaloka."

The gleaming ship of the firmament hung perfectly still, as if those inside it were seeking something on the mountain below. The Pandavas and the rishis stood rooted. Next moment, in a silent, thought-swift streak of light, the vimana flashed down to the earth and landed not five hundred hands from where the Pandavas stood. A door at its side slid open, a stairway made of mirrors slipped noiselessly to the ground, and a kshatriya climbed down those steps, smiling from ear to ear.

"Arjuna!" screamed Draupadi, and ran into his arms.

Then Arjuna knelt at Yudhishtira's feet, and Yudhishtira pulled him up and took him in his arms. Soon Bheema, Nakula and Sahadeva were hugging Arjuna, and they were all laughing in absolute joy, tears in their eyes. Arjuna prostrated himself before Dhaumya. He bowed reverently to Lomasa and the rishis of Badari, and embraced the brahmanas of Indraprastha. Such a reunion there was, and Draupadi just stood by, tears flowing from her dark eyes that never left Arjuna's face. It was as if she was seeing him again for the very first time, as she had long ago at her swayamvara.

Meanwhile, the elegant sarathy Matali had come down the stairway that was a threshold between this world and another. Yudhishtira went forward to greet him, with Lomasa and Dhaumya. Matali stood aside at the foot of the glass steps, and they began to throb with light: Indra, king of the Devas, came majestically down them.

One by one, the Pandavas fell at the God's feet; he blessed them all, and the rishis who stood tongue-tied. Indra carried a silver casket in his hands, and he called Draupadi. She knelt before him and he pressed the casket into her hands. "A small gift for my son's lovely wife."

Indra turned to Yudhishtira, "The time draws near when you will sit upon the throne of your ancestors in Hastinapura, and the world will pay homage to her emperor once more. Destiny moves swiftly, and the war on the edge of the ages is near. Another year and some months you still have to spend in exile. I have brought Arjuna back to you, and I thank you for the time he spent with me.

"You will find it was well spent, for your brother is a master of astras now. No warrior on earth, and perhaps none in Devaloka, can match him any more, as my enemies discovered to their cost. But I will leave that tale for him to tell."

Indra clasped Arjuna to him, one last time, and Draupadi thought she saw a tear in the God's stern eye. The Deva said, "I must leave you now, and you must return to the Kamyaka aranya."

He raised a hand over them, and climbed back into his crystal ship. Matali embraced Arjuna, then, with a wave at Yudhishtira and the others, he too climbed back into the vimana.

The stairway of mirrors withdrew without a sound. The vimana began to pulse with light again, until those who stood on the ground had to turn their faces away. In a whisper, the great ship flew up into the sky; quicker than seeing, it was high above the mountain.

Now it seemed Matali was having a little gentle fun. His craft was no longer a disc; instead, a golden chariot had appeared in its place, drawn by six winged horses! Matali himself sat in plain view at its head, reins in one hand, and a silver whip in the other. Behind him sat Indra, entirely glorious now. As those below watched spellbound, the white horses flashed straight up towards the sun, and vanished: they went swifter than light.

For a long moment, the Pandavas stood staring after the Deva; then, the princes linked arms and made their way back to Badarikasrama. None of them spoke much; their hearts were too full at Arjuna's return. Often, in turns, the other Pandavas would go near their brother and hug him or squeeze his hand, as if to make sure he had really come back. Draupadi still walked between Yudhishtira and Arjuna, in a dream, holding both their hands, her gaze never leaving Arjuna's face. At times, she would smile to herself in some quiet bliss, and her eyes were full.

TWENTY-ONE

Arjuna's story

B ACK IN BADARIKASRAMA, THE RISHIS LAID OUT A FEAST TO CELEBRATE Arjuna's return. When they had eaten, Yudhishtira said, "Arjuna, tell us everything that happened to you since you left us in the Kamyaka vana."

Arjuna smiled; there was so much to tell. He himself was full of his most recent exploit in Devaloka, but he began with his journey to Indrakila and his first encounter there with Indra. He told them about his tapasya, and how Siva came as the hunter. He described his duel with the vetala and how, finally, Siva stood revealed before him and gave him the Paasupatastra.

"Soon after the Lord vanished, the sky grew brilliant, and the Lokapalas appeared before me: Varuna, Indra, Kubera and Yama. They all gave me their astras, and the mantras to command them."

Bheema said incredulously, "You have the Lokapalas' astras?"

Arjuna shut his eyes. He made an occult mudra with his fingers, whispered a mantra, and those weapons appeared as golden arrows in his hands. With another mudra, and another mantra, he made the astras vanish again. In fact, he had not truly invoked the ayudhas, just their shadows. If a devastra was summoned frivolously, it would consume the one who calls it, or even the very earth.

Bheema was the most obviously excited at Arjuna's return. He would stroke his brother's face, take his hand, and his eyes would fill as often as Draupadi's. Arjuna told them how Matali arrived on Indrakila in his vimana. He described the inside of that craft, vividly, and the flight to Devaloka.

Like a poet, he described Amravati, and his brothers smiled to hear him. It was so unlike the quiet Arjuna to wax eloquent about anything. But the rishis of Badarikasrama hung on his every word, as if it were amrita to them: specially when he spoke of Indra's throne, which the worlds worship. Arjuna did not mention that the Deva king made him sit on that very throne; he only told his brothers, later, when they were alone.

Arjuna told them about the wine and the food in Amravati, its mountains and forests, Indra's garden, the Nandana, and the lucent river that flows there. He told them about his lessons at archery with Indra, and how he received the Vajra. He spoke warmly of Chitrasena, who became his friend and his master at music and dancing.

Yudhishtira said with interest, "You must show us what you have learned from him."

Now Arjuna said he was tired and would like to rest for a while, but he would continue his story later. The rishis of Badarikasrama politely left the Pandavas and Draupadi together.

When they were alone, Arjuna said, "I did not want to say what happened with the apsara Urvashi, when the holy ones were here."

Panchali looked sharply at him, and he blushed. She said in a tight voice, "And what happened with the apsara Urvashi?"

Arjuna took her hand, "Not what you imagine."

He told them how Urvashi came to him at dead of night. Draupadi's eyes glittered dangerously, when he described how the apsara made a midnight offering of herself. "But she is a mother of the Kurus, and I told her I had only a son's love for her."

"That couldn't have pleased her," murmured Bheema. A smile was back on Draupadi's face, that her husband had spurned an apsara.

"She said many of our ancestors had been to Devaloka as a reward for their punya on earth, and none of them had refused her." Arjuna still shuddered to think of that night. "But I couldn't see her as she wanted me to. I knelt at her feet and begged her to forgive me."

Bheema laughed admiringly, "She must have been angrier than ever!"

"She was," said Arjuna quietly. "She cursed me."

That fetched a gasp from his brothers, and a cry from Draupadi. She whispered, "What was the curse?"

"That I lose my manhood, and live among women, singing and dancing as a eunuch."

Lovely Panchali gave a sigh, and fainted. Bheema sprinkled icy spring water on her face, and she awoke gasping for its coldness. She moaned, "Oh, Arjuna, what will you do? Has Urvashi's curse affected you yet?"

The others stared anxiously at their brother. He said, "Indra had her reduce the curse to one mortal year, the thirteenth year of our exile. And for that time, it will be a blessing: who will dream of looking for me in a harem of women?"

Draupadi breathed again, and his brothers began to laugh. "You might enjoy this curse more than you are meant to," observed Panchali.

Bheema murmured, "Though not as well as he would like to."

Yudhishtira remembered, "Rishi Lomasa told us about a task in Devaloka that Indra had for you."

"That is what kept me so long. There seemed no end to my father's lessons at archery. Then one day, he called me and gave me his Vajra. That was the last astra he had for me. You were always in my thoughts, and I was anxious to return to the earth. But Indra said I must do something for him before I left."

One day, a month after Arjuna had the Vajra from him, Indra called his son to him alone. "You are a master of astras now, and not even the Devas can face you in war, let alone any mortal. But you haven't been tried with battle, and the time has come for you to give me gurudakshina. I told you there is something you must do for me."

"I will do anything for you."

Indra said, "I wonder if you truly understand the power of the astras you have acquired. Do you think you could kill thirty thousand Rakshasas for me as my dakshina?"

Arjuna was startled; but he would have agreed even if he did not have the devastras. The Pandava asked, "Where shall I find the Rakshasas?"

"The Nivatakavachas live in the womb of the ocean of Devaloka," said Indra, and Arjuna saw his eyes misted over, for what reason he could not tell. "They are sorcerers, and very powerful. They were tapasvins once, and they have a boon from Brahma that no Deva can kill them, but only a mortal man. Our enmity is as old as Amravati, and for an age, we have prayed for a kshatriya who would rid us of the Nivatakavachas.

"Their influence reaches down to the earth. Theirs is the power that Kamsa wielded, and Jarasandha; the same power that now supports Duryodhana and his brothers as part of a web of evil spread across a thousand worlds. A malignant disease afflicts creation, and it grows at the very heart of Devaloka.

"Arjuna, for this, too, you were born as my mortal son; and for this task, also, you have come to Amravati. Will you go to their city, and take fire to the Rakshasas?"

Arjuna said, "If it is in my power, I shall."

The thought of his mission excited him, most of all, the idea of using the astras in battle. Arjuna was full of courage, he felt ten times the archer he had been before. Indra had the rishis of his sabha come and say some prayers over the Pandava. This was done with grave solemnity, with all the celestials gathered in the Sudharma: gandharvas, kinnaras, Devas, apsaras, siddhas, charanas, nagas and the others. It dawned on Arjuna that the task ahead was not a simple one.

The Pandava did not sleep well that night. With first light, Matali brought his vimana to the steps of Indra's palace. Indra himself was there to bless his son. Arjuna looked into his face and saw a shadow of anxiety: lest he fail his mission, and Indra lose a son. Arjuna felt chastened. When he saw Matali also wearing silvery mail, and with every auspicious talisman he owned hung around his neck, he realised the terror the demons inspired.

Chitrasena had come to wish him success. Even the gandharva was sombre that morning; he pressed a golden locket of protection into Arjuna's hand, and embraced him.

Matali only said, "Your Gandiva and quivers are in the vimana, and the Vajra lies beside the astras, where you will sit." He paused, before adding, "Where only one mortal man has sat before."

"And who was he?" asked Arjuna.

"A greater kshatriya than anyone before or after him. But his was not a battle in heaven," said Indra.

"Why didn't you ask him to fight the Nivatakavachas?"

Matali laughed, "That was before the Rakshasas came to Devaloka. And that kshatriya's enemy was more terrible than they are, though he lived on earth."

"Tell me who the kshatriya was!" Arjuna cried, though he had heard the legend before and should have guessed.

"Pray for his blessing today, before you set out," said Indra. "It was Rama of Ayodhya for whom I sent the vimana down to Lanka. So he could kill Ravana."

Arjuna knelt before Indra. All at once, the Deva had a golden coronet in his hand, a jewel-studded kirita. Indra set the crown on the Pandava's head. "You shall be called Kiriti from now, O Kshatriya of Amravati!"

He clasped Arjuna, once, tightly. Then, the Pandava climbed into the vimana after Matali. The stairway was drawn up, and the sarathy showed Arjuna another place where he should sit today. It was a high seat, above Matali, which could be thrust out of the body of the crystal ship when the warrior who sat in it did battle.

How proud Arjuna felt, and how humble: sitting where immaculate Rama had once sat. He found that seat swivelled to face every direction, and prayed fervently to Sri Rama of old that he, Arjuna, should not fail today. At the edge of his mind was the nagging certainty that this battle was as important as any he would fight later on earth; and its outcome would decide those of the rest.

Matali passed his hands across the glowing panel that made the vimana fly, and the craft rose from the ground in a whisper, and they flashed away on their mission.

TWENTY-TWO

The wondrous city

Arjuna paused briefly, and Bheema cried, "Don't keep us in suspense!"

His brother took up his story again.

The sun was rising over Devaloka as they flew along. How could he describe the realm of the Gods? He hadn't words for the luminous plains, studded with a thousand cities, in which Matali said a thousand immortal kings ruled; none for the mountains like jagged jewels, the rivers flowing across those fervid landscapes, at times like dreams in turquoise, at others like broken, fluid sunsets. Through visionary cloud-kingdoms they flitted, and a huge excitement took hold of Arjuna.

When they had flown an hour, Matali said, "Look, the sea."

The ocean of Devaloka is a deeper, more vibrant blue than any sea of the earth. It is so profoundly blue you want to plunge into it, drown yourself in it. Plunge into it is exactly what Matali did! Arjuna cried out in alarm as he saw him fly straight down at the waves, without slowing the vimana a bit.

Matali laughed at his anxiety. "How did you think we were going to arrive at the Rakshasas' city? My ship is as easy through water as through air."

Next moment, they had cloven the surface of the sea and were below its waves. It was exactly as the sarathy said; Indra's ship sailed as effortlessly under water as it did through the sky. At first, they could see some of what lay around them by the daylight that penetrated down here. As they dived deeper, they were soon shrouded in a black night.

Matali moved his slender hands over his panel of jewels, and the submarine world was lit by piercing lamps shining out in broad beams on all sides of the vimana. Such a fabulous world those lamps illumined!

This was another universe. If the sights of Devaloka on land were extraordinary to Arjuna's eyes, the translucent world under the ocean of that realm was utterly miraculous. Brilliant fish shone like lights of the soul, in colours that have no names in human tongues. The seaweed and mosses were phosphorescent, the vivid coral breathed, and the very rocks were sculpted into majestic shapes.

As they sank, down and down, the Pandava saw mountains here taller than those on the surface world. Matali's vimana ploughed through the dark water, at his very thought.

Through ravines between towering massifs, that craft flitted like some huge sea-creature, banking and turning as if with eyes of its own, and a will. It flew so swiftly that Arjuna was certain they would dash into one of the mountainsides at any moment. But that did not happen.

He asked Matali, "How does your vimana fly so surely?"

Matali replied gravely, "My ship is alive, Indra's spirit is in him."

Arjuna did not question anything after that, but began to prepare himself for the task ahead. He sat with his eyes shut in dhyana, summoning all the power he had. Even as deep restfulness spread through his body, Matali woke him from his trance, "Look, Arjuna."

The vimana had slowed. They were just emerging from between two mountains that faced each other like titans, both covered in fluorescent mosses, and teeming with fish. Ahead of them, they saw a low plateau rising from a depression in the ocean floor. Arjuna caught his breath to see the city built on that tableland.

It must have been thirty leagues square. All of it seemed made of lucid crystal, of every colour imaginable: some muted, some coruscating. The Pandava saw crystal palaces—there were no homes in that city that were less than palaces—and crystal towers reaching for the surface of the ocean. Blazing lamps lit the city of the Nivatakavachas. They had created their own sun and moon beneath the waves!

The sheer scale of the demons' city astounded the Pandava. It was covered by a transparent dome, and as they drew cautiously near, he saw exotic vimanas flit through the air under this dome. Matali had put out the lamps of their own ship, to approach the Rakshasas' lair unobserved.

For all its grandeur, its loveliness, an aura of evil hung over the submarine city, a darkness of the soul. Matali shivered, and it was all Arjuna could do to keep his hands from shaking. Suddenly, they felt watched by something inconceivably malignant, though they neither saw nor heard anything. Their ship quivered and they could feel it struggling to remain on course, because its every instinct cried out to turn and flee the macabre plateau.

As abruptly as they had sensed it, the feeling of being observed vanished. Matali sighed in relief.

Arjuna strung his bow. He did not trust the lull, and he was not mistaken. The next moment, all the lights of the demons' city went out, leaving them plunged in darkness. As complete as the darkness was the sinister silence that engulfed them. Now it began: the onslaught of the Nivatakavachas on their minds. Arjuna thought he was back in the palace in Indraprastha, and had just woken from a long dream.

So compelling was the hallucination he actually rose from his 'bed', and walked out of his 'bedroom' to wash his face. Matali caught his wrist and pushed him back into his seat.

"It is the demons' maya," the sarathy hissed. But he had a monster's face, bloated and fanged, and his eyes were baleful. Arjuna reached for his sword, when he felt a warmth suffuse his chest, and a burst of light. Someone unseen was fighting the asuras' sorcery. Matali's face was his own again, but worried.

"We mustn't stand still!" he cried. As if in response, the vimana flashed up from where they had lurked in the dark, thinking they were invisible. Lamps on again, they flew directly over the city of the Nivatakavachas, above the dome. Matali passed his hands over his panel; Arjuna's seat was thrust aloft so he was above the rest of the vimana. He was surrounded by a skin of some sheer material, like a large bubble, which kept the water out. Then the seat vanished from under him, and he found he could stand steadily, because the bubble did not sway or shake, but was rock-like.

"The warrior's place," Matali said. "You can shoot your astras through the skin, Arjuna."

The Pandava felt a wave of affection for the little sarathy: he was so calm at this critical time, all his wits about him. As they circled above the eerie city, they saw a flotilla of vimanas spew out from the covering dome, and fly at them. Dark weapons were mounted on these craft; some already spat serpentine narachas.

Burning missiles snaked at them from every side, and Arjuna began to hallucinate once more. Part of him saw the tracers of fire flaring at them; but he thought he was imagining this: because, actually, he was back in the Dwaitavana, sitting beside the lake with Draupadi and Bheema. The first of the narachas rocked the ship, and woke Arjuna from his trance. He should have shot it down, but had stood bemused by the maya of the demons.

Matali cried, "The mohini astra, Arjuna! First, the mohini."

The dazed Arjuna would not have thought of it himself. Even now, it took all his strength to summon the astra. It seemed as if another will held his mind and his limbs in a vice. Strangely, now, he thought not of Indra or any other God, but of Krishna. He saw his cousin's face, smiling at him, just as if he stood before him under that sea. The darkness around them seemed to give a lurch, and dissipate. Arjuna's mind cleared, as if whatever had held him in its power shrank back.

In a flash, he lifted the Gandiva and shot his astra at the city of Rakshasas. They heard the keening song of the mohini. They felt the sea-bed shudder, and then no more illusions troubled them.

But now they were surrounded by the Nivatakavachas in their vimanas. The demons attacked them with all sorts of sorceries, and bizarre astras of their own. It was all Arjuna could do to keep them from blasting their ship in shards. Matali, at his panel, was superb; they flitted here and there, quicker than thinking. The Rakshasas' missiles missed them narrowly, some erupting so close they were rocked.

Arjuna felt no fear or hesitation any more. He invoked the madhavastra, and loosed it at the Rakshasa fleet. Swifter than light, separating in a thousand different astras as soon as it touched water, that weapon blew the demon ships into sand. Those who died never knew what killed them.

And now they saw the strangest sight: some of the Nivatakavachas swam back into their city, swimming as fluently as the fish around them. Their smooth bodies had skins and scales, both. They were humanoid, yet they had fishtails and tentacles, too. Squirting clouds of black ink, so the enemy could not see them any more, they streaked away into the city's fastness before Arjuna could aim at them again. Each one of those monsters was clad in silvery armour, like their skin: their impenetrable kavachas.

Matali below cried, "Look, Arjuna, the dome opens for them. Quick, shoot the Vajra into the city!"

Arjuna cried back, "Be prepared to fly, Matali, or we shall also be consumed."

"I am ready," the sarathy replied. "Quickly Arjuna, before the dome closes."

There was no time for thinking. In a moment, the mantra was on Arjuna's lips and the vimana shook with the summoning of a mahastra. The bubble at the crown of the ship took blinding light. The Pandava looked at his hands and his body, and they were joints of blue-white lightning. The Vajra was upon him, charged with Indra's power. Arjuna drew back his bowstring and loosed the Vajra.

It flew out like a flare from a star, and all the dark water around them turned fulvid. It was daylight, as if the sun had risen from the bed of the sea. The daylight grew luciferous, and they saw the very waves were ablaze. Even as his legs turned weak and Arjuna fell into the soft seat that appeared under him, they flashed away towards the surface. In less time than it takes to think of, they burst out of the water and flew up into the sky.

Below them, the ocean was livid. There was a star erupting under the waves that had turned into tidal flames, reaching for them with white-hot fingers, as they flitted out of reach. As it consumed the city of Nivatakavachas, the explosion of the Vajra shook the vimana high in the air; all Devaloka quaked.

They flew on in silence, both of them overwhelmed, Arjuna trembling. After a while, Matali turned to the Pandava with a smile. Impulsively, he embraced the prince and cried, "You are the greatest kshatriya of all! For an age, no army could do what you have just done by yourself."

But Arjuna's eyes were full of the splendour of the ocean-city they had just destroyed. Sombrely, he said, "Matali, that was the most beautiful city in heaven or earth. I feel more sad than triumphant."

Matali said softly, "That city was not built by the Rakshasas, neither did it belong to them. It was our city, wrought by Viswakarman, once, and great was its glory. We once lived there for yugas; but were driven out by the Nivatakavachas, and we could do nothing to win back our city, because the demons had Brahma's boon that no Deva could kill them." He sighed. "But some days after you had the Vajra from your father, we decided the Rakshasas must die. Even if our ancient home was consumed."

TWENTY-THREE

Hiranyapuri

Matali fell quiet, and they flew in silence again. Arjuna said, "We are not going back the way we came."

"No, there is another task for you. Look."

He pointed ahead, and near the horizon, Arjuna dimly saw an object in the sky that must be another vimana. As they flew nearer, he saw the gleaming thing was no ship of the air, but a golden city. It flew towards them as swiftly as they did towards it.

"Hiranyapuri," said Matali, with no emotion.

"It is splendid!" cried Arjuna.

"Puloma's city of sorcery," the sarathy replied dryly.

"Who is Puloma?"

"The golden witch, and the Kaalakeyas are her sons."

"Who are they, Matali?"

"They are Asuras, changelings who take any form they choose. They go where they like, do as they please. They are strong and cruel; and they, too, are protected by Brahma's boon of old to their mother. For, once, Puloma was not an aabhichari but a tapasvin." He lowered his voice. "She is our queen Sachi's mother."

"What have we to do with them?"

"The Kaalakeyas, also, can only be killed by a mortal man. They mean to invade Amravati for their various pleasures, and it will not be the first time. Indra wants you to torch them from the sky."

They were quite near the exotic city, which flew along like a huge mirage. Suddenly, bees from a golden hive, a swarm of dark vimanas flew out from the portals of Hiranyapuri, and flashed at them. In those sleek battle-ships crouched Puloma's sons.

Some were almost human, and even handsome; others had the slavering faces of beasts. Some had just one head, but many had two, three and more, grimacing or grinning in every direction. Some had hands, but others claws; some, Arjuna saw, were winged. Some were serpents coiled in their vimanas, and some had lions' faces. Many had just one eye, while others had three, and a few, even five, glaring.

Perhaps because they had no natural armour to protect them, all of these were more accomplished warriors than the Nivatakavachas. They hailed Matali and Arjuna in evil voices, some deep, some shrill.

"Devas, you have come back to fight!"

"Weren't you routed the last time, that you dare attack us again?"

"Can you hear us, Indra? You shouldn't have troubled coming here; we were on our way to Amravati."

"Perhaps we can take his head with us!"

Devilish laughter filled the sky. Arjuna could not understand how they cast their voices so far, but there was hardly time to think of that. The Asuras attacked with flaming missiles so Matali's vimana was tossed about like a coracle on a stormy sea. Their ship streaked this way and that; it took all the sarathy's skill to keep them aloft. Often, they vanished before the Asuras, then reappeared in another part of the sky.

But these demons were marksmen, and found their target too often. Arjuna raised the Gandiva and the air was thick with weapons.

He soon cried to Matali, "There are too many of them. I cannot fight them all."

The sarathy cried back, "The Paasupatastra, Arjuna! Use Siva's weapon."

At that moment, darkness fell on the sky, and stark terror. It was inside their vimana, as well, filling Arjuna's eyes, his heart. He felt faint, as if cold hands were on his throat, choking him. The Pandava heard a low gasp below him. He saw Matali's panel was dark, and guessed the sarathy must have slumped across it in a faint. Arjuna called out to him, but there was no response. He was alone, and he did not know how long the vimana would fly itself.

In panic, Arjuna invoked the Paasupata, the final astra. He knew that every time Siva's astra was invoked, it assumed a different guise. By now, a hundred vimanas had flown out from Hiranyapuri. The sky echoed with the roars and howls of a hundred Kaalakeyas. The Paasupatastra filled the vimana with light, like another sun, and Arjuna saw the demons' vimanas veer away. Though they had an answer for every astra the Pandava had loosed at them so far, he saw the light of the Paasupata unnerved them.

The rutilance of Siva's astra engulfed Matali, the ship of the sky and Arjuna.

"*AUM Namah Sivayah*!" Arjuna prayed silently, then shot the arrow that bore the astra from his quivering bow. For a moment, nothing happened, and the archer watched his shaft flare out from the little dome in which he sat. Below him, he heard Matali wake with a cry.

"Are you all right, Arjuna?"

The incandescence of the Paasupata had left their vimana, and now the astra erupted outside, so the Kaalakeyas' fighting craft were blown about like leaves in a storm of light. Even Hiranyapuri in the distance shook.

Arjuna cried to Matali, "Look, the Paasupatastra!"

An incredible spectacle unfolded before their eyes. It seemed the sky, their ship, the Asuras, their vimanas and the golden city of the firmament were all transported to another realm, where time did not move. Like a dreamer, Arjuna could only watch. Where Siva's astra went, a hundred new vimanas filled the sky. In them sat shadowy warriors, with matted dreadlocks and rudraksha beads that glowed like the jewels the great nagas wear in their heads. The warriors were fierce-looking, and covered in ash like rishis.

Arjuna heard Matali breathe, "Ganas. Sivaganas of the Paasupatastra!"

A legion of vimanas and ganas had appeared in the sky, and the rest of the battle was over in a moment. In that moment, the hundred Kaalakeya ships burned, and fell away with their demons already dead. Then, the vimanas of the astra vanished.

Silence had fallen everywhere. Hiranyapuri floated some way ahead. A thousand archers appeared at the portals of the golden city, each one with a bow. Roaring so heaven and earth shuddered with that sound, those Asuras shot a thousand astras at the Matali's vimana. Arjuna could not possibly cut all those missiles down. Matali was helpless, too; they couldn't hope to evade the flaming tide in the sky. They could only wait, and pray for some intercession.

They did not know the Paasupata was not spent. As the wave of a thousand fires came sweeping at them, an awesome figure materialized in the sky: a vast shadow whose feet were planted on the horizon, whose head, which was big as a world, loomed high above Hiranyapuri. He had jata down to his waist: dreadlocks coiled like cobras. White ash covered his naked body from his face to his feet, and great serpents, their forked tongues sliding in and out of their mouths, were his garments. His eyes were like crimson suns; his fangs were massive columns. He wore incredible ornaments upon his bare and black chest: pearls like moons, diamonds like stars, topazes like misty planets. He stood between Hiranyapuri and Matali's vimana like a mountain.

No word did that apparition speak; no sound came from him. He yawned open his mouth, deep as the void, and the thousand astras disappeared into its darkness.

No one had breathed a word, while Arjuna recounted his adventure. Now he paused, still full of awe as he remembered the Shadow of the Paasupata.

Bheema sat holding Arjuna's hand, and his eyes wide. He cried impatiently, "And what happened then? What did the apparition do?"

Arjuna said, "The great shadow glowed for a moment with the astras he had swallowed. A terrible smile lit up his black face. He gave a growl that shook the sky, raised a mountainous hand, plucked golden Hiranyapuri out of the air and swallowed that city as well. All Matali and I heard was an awful scream from a million Asuras' throats, then there was silence."

For a moment, Arjuna was afraid the Spirit of the Paasupata might not be satisfied and turn its attentions to them. As if reading his fear clearly, that Spirit did indeed turn solemnly towards them, but then folded his hands grimly, and bowed: because Arjuna was a master of the Paasupata. With that, the dreadful one vanished as suddenly as he had appeared, and they were alone in an empty blue sky.

Matali hugged Arjuna again and again, crying, "Your father will be proud of you today! I have fought many battles through the ages of Devaloka, but I never fainted before. This was a great battle, my prince, the Kaalakeyas were worthy antagonists."

The Pandava saw the strangest look in that sarathy's eye: one of reverence. Matali said in a low voice, "Arjuna, none among the Devas, even, is your equal."

Arjuna began to protest, but the little sarathy was already back in his place, flying them home to Amravati.

"I am so proud of you!" cried Bheema, hugging his brother.

Yudhishtira asked, "And your father, Indra, was he pleased?"

Indra was waiting for them on the steps of the palace. He came running to the vimana when they landed, and embraced Arjuna; there were surely tears in his eyes.

Later, in his sabha, the Deva king said, "You have more than paid your guru-dakshina to me, my son. Yudhishtira is fortunate to have you for his brother: how will Dhritarashtra's princes contain you when the war on earth begins? Now you are invincible not only against men, but the Devas and the Asuras."

Arjuna was embarrassed, and bent his head. Indra went on, "When you take the field, Bheeshma, Drona, Kripa, Karna, Shakuni, Duryodhana and all his brothers together shall have only a sixteenth part of your prowess. Look what I have for you."

A servant brought a crystal box. Indra opened it, drew out a suit of golden mail and gave it to Arjuna. It was light as the breeze. The Pandava received it in wonder, thinking for a moment that it was an elaborate ornament for a warrior. Indra said, "Not the astras of the Gods can pierce this mail. It is my own kavacha, made before the earth."

He set another crown on his son's head, and then gave him ornaments and silks for Draupadi.

When the brothers opened the casket Arjuna had brought from Devaloka, the light of those gifts filled their cave on Badarikasrama. Arjuna said, "I rested another week in Amravati, then Indra called me. 'I know how anxious you are to be back with Panchali and your brothers. Yudhishtira and the others spend every moment waiting for you. I think the time has come for you to go back.'"

There was a feast that night in Indra's halls, and Chitrasena's gandharvas and Rambha's apsaras sang and danced until daybreak. The sun rose over Amravati and Indra said quietly to Arjuna, "The pushpaka vimana is waiting to take you where your heart is."

Arjuna bid farewell to all his friends in Amravati. His stay there had been so full of wonder he felt he was about to wake from a dream. Chitrasena embraced him, while Arjuna held back his tears. But the gandharva wept openly. "Why are you mortals afraid to show your feelings? Aren't you sad to be parting from me? Then why are you ashamed to cry?"

Indra blessed Arjuna, and said, "I will come to restore you to your brothers."

Matali had brought the vimana to the palace steps again.

"We already knew that you were here, in the Badarikasrama. So here I am," ended Arjuna, radiant to be back.

Yudhishtira rose. He put his arms around his brother, and said, "And we are glad you have returned. The wait was becoming intolerable."

Draupadi murmured, "But you must miss the grandeur of your father's kingdom."

Arjuna said, "Devaloka is glorious, and so is Amravati. But I belong here with all of you, and it is here that my heart is content. For me not the wonders of swarga can match this joy."

They sat in silence for a while. Then Yudhishtira said into the deepening dusk, "I feel as if our enemies are already vanquished and we have our kingdom back. But, Arjuna, curiosity has its way with me: can we see the devastras?"

Bheema cried, "Show them to us!"

Nakula and Sahadeva said, "Show us the astras, Arjuna."

Arjuna rose and went into the crisp evening outside, where the mountains were painted in the fluid colours of sunset. Arjuna folded his hands to the sky, and began to chant some resonant mantras. The rishis gathered round the Pandavas in awe, and Gandhamadana shook below their feet. A sudden darkness obscured the sunset. Above Arjuna, ominous thunder rumbled and gashes of lightning streaked the heavens, though not a cloud was to be seen. A dread fell on the rishis and the Pandavas.

Arjuna's body began to shine, as if lit from within by the fires of the Gods. He stood unmoving, his eyes shut, his hands folded. Draupadi clutched Bheema's hand tightly, and even Bheema shivered at the immense disturbance of the elements. Then it seemed that the very sky parted, and from beyond, from another mandala, unearthly weapons appeared in that darkness, each one a Deva's.

A thunderbolt fell, blinding, before the immobile Arjuna, a shimmering noose, golden arrows, alive and breathing with the elemental forces that filled them, a trident, a burning spear, and a hundred other ayudhas, one after the other, in a refulgent storm. They all waited before the archer who summoned them, for his command; the sky was full of Devas' lustrous shadows, the mountain blazed with light.

The Pandavas stood transfixed, the rishis of the Badarikasrama, too: that hermitage was as bright as day. Then, all at once, the sky was full of vimanas, and the winds were brilliant, as a host of Gods appeared in the sky. They were the guardians of the astras; Indra's Devas, and Rudra's ganas, and with them, brahmarishis seated on clouds, devarishis from Amravati, siddhas, charanas, noble rakshasas and gandharvas. The sky was full of music so sweet it was hard to endure.

A quaint figure draped in a wildflower garland, whose fragrance filled the asrama at Badari, stepped out from thin air before the Pandavas. He plucked lightly on the vina he carried in his hand, and a song brimmed on his lips. Arjuna stood like a stone, his palms folded to the astras.

Narada said mildly to Yudhishtira, "Pandava, when an astra is summoned it must have its prey, or it will consume the very earth."

Yudhishtira prostrated himself before Narada. "I did not know how powerful my brother had become."

Narada said gently, "The Devas themselves have come today to calm these weapons, which are their spirits: of fire, light, water, earth and air. The next time Arjuna invokes the weapons of heaven, let it be only in battle."

"My lord, I was anxious. Now I have no doubt that we will win the war against our cousins," said Yudhishtira, still kneeling.

"They are not just your cousins, but ancient spirits of evil. Do not imagine the war will be easy to win," said Narada softly. The wanderer went up to the unmoving Arjuna. Narada laid a hand on his arm, and the kshatriya shone brighter than the sky for a moment.

Now, Arjuna chanted some other mantras. One by one, the astras rose into the air, circled the one that had summoned them and flashed away into the depths of the sky. As they disappeared, the vimanas above also vanished, each with a God; then, the other celestials, by whose will, too, an apocalypse had been averted.

Finally, Narada melted away as he came. When the mountain did not blaze any more, they saw night had fallen over the world and a full moon was rising over pale peaks, swathing them in cool silver. Everyone in Badarikasrama, the rishis, the brahmanas, the Pandavas and, most of all, Draupadi heaved a sigh of relief. For a while, it had truly seemed as if the end of the world had come.

Even Bheema was unnerved, and stared at his brother Arjuna with new respect in his eyes. Only Arjuna himself was quite calm, as he went back into their cave as if nothing extraordinary had happened.

TWENTY-FOUR

Bheema's adventure

For some weeks more, the Pandavas stayed on in Badarikasrama, and the peace of the mountain where Nara and Narayana once did tapasya filled their hearts. The others showed Arjuna all their favourite places around the asrama. One day Bheema would take him on a long walk, alone; the next day, it would be Yudhishtira or the twins; and the day after that, Draupadi. For the first weeks after Arjuna's return, Panchali saw to it she had him to herself more than any of the others; whether it was out on walks through the cedar forests during the daytime, or in a cave at a slight remove from the asrama at night.

Those were blissful weeks for them all. Then, came a day when Bheema said to Yudhishtira, "The peace of Badari fills my heart, but aren't we escaping from our destiny? Eleven years of exile have passed."

Nakula agreed, "Isn't it time we remembered Duryodhana again?"

Sahadeva murmured, "And our oaths."

Arjuna said nothing, but sat rubbing bee's wax into his bowstring. Draupadi raised her eyes to Yudhishtira; but now there was no acrimony left in her, she only smiled at her husband. As always, Yudhishtira waited for the others to have their say before he spoke himself.

Bheema went on, "This is the twelfth year of our exile, and Arjuna is back with us. Two years more, my brothers, and one of them spent in disguise. Indra asked us to go back to the Kamyaka vana. I think that is what we should do, lest we become unused to the world and its ways."

This was a calm Bheema speaking. He was a dispassionate warrior, considering his battle-plan for the future.

Yudhishtira said encouragingly, "Go on, Bheema. Let us hear all you have to say."

"Our enemies have more peace of mind than they deserve. They may even think we have renounced the world, and taken sannyasa on Badari. Yudhishtira, the rivers and forests have eyes and ears. By now, Duryodhana has heard that Arjuna has been to Devaloka, and we are here on the mountain. Let us return to the Kamyaka, and remind him the Pandavas are still alive. Let him suffer; it will weaken him. Let battle be joined already, in the mind, before we meet our cousins on the field."

Bheema sighed. "We have been more than happy in this place, even I. There is such peace in Badari as there isn't anywhere else on earth. I have seen Draupadi smile here, as she never has since our exile began. But fate calls us back to the plains of Bharatavarsha. Yudhishtira my brother, two years more and we will see you become Lord of the earth again."

Yudhishtira stared at Bheema for a long moment. Finally, he said, "You are right. It is time we went back to the world."

How Bheema glowed, that his brother had conceded he was right! The Pandavas went to the rishis of Badarikasrama, and, bowing before their ancient, Yudhishtira said, "It is time we left you and returned to the plains. We have been happier here than at any other time of our exile, and our debt to you is inestimable. Bless us, Muni, that we may prosper."

The old one said, "It is not only from us that you will part now, Yudhishtira."

Yudhishtira looked puzzled, then he saw the Rishi Lomasa was smiling. Yudhishtira gasped, "My lord, you...?"

Lomasa took the Pandava's hand, and said gently, "Our pilgrimage is over, Yudhishtira. Badarikasrama is the last tirtha in the world, and from here I must return where I came from. My Lord Indra calls me back to Amravati. King of men, the pleasure and the honour of our yatra have been mine!"

That rishi embraced Yudhishtira, and his kindly eyes were damp. Always willing to answer his questions about matters of the spirit, encouraging him to discover more of the hidden world, Lomasa had become as dear as a father to the Pandava. The sage saw Yudhishtira had evolved beyond the condition where he could ever be content with mundane sovereignty. Pandu's eldest son would aspire to enlightenment; and he was fit for it, because few attachments bound him save, perhaps, filial ones. Even with these, he never allowed them to interfere with his commitment to dharma.

Yudhishtira knelt before Lomasa for his blessing, then, the other Pandavas and Draupadi did, as well. At last, after embracing Dhaumya and his brahmanas, and the rishis of Badarikasrama, Lomasa strode away along a trail that led higher up the mountain. The others stood gazing after him, their hearts full; for all his greatness, he was such a gentle, unassuming man. When he was gone a while, they saw a light on the other side of Gandhamadana.

The aged master of Badari pointed, "Look, he goes by rishi-patha."

They saw a bright pathway in the sky that rose beyond the clouds. Along that path, they saw a familiar figure climb swiftly into swarga. Lomasa paused in his breathless ascent, and raised his hand over them in a blessing. The next moment, path and figure both vanished, and the sky was vacant.

Bheema said, "I think we never realized how great Rishi Lomasa is, because he is so humble."

Yudhishtira smiled to hear him. Now the Pandavas took their leave of the munis of Badarikasrama, with whom they had stayed six months. The old one of Badari blessed them, saying, "You shall always be welcome here, Kshatriyas, and may the blessing of the fragrant mountain be upon you forever. May your paths be free of obstacles, and success attend your every endeavour."

Slowly, with sad hearts they made their way down from that most sacred tirtha. Hardest was to bid farewell to the mountain itself, and its airy forests they had roamed so happily, forgetting their troubles. They realized now that the mountain had kept grief away from them. To the Pandavas, Gandhamadana had become a friend and, truly, a master of their spirits: a guru of fathomless peace.

Taking their time, stopping wherever the deep loveliness of a pine grove, or the sparkling spectacle of a waterfall arrested their attention, camping in caves and in the open, under clear skies where the stars hung like waylights revealing secret trails through the universe, they wound their way down Gandhamadana and arrived on Kailasa. On that opalescent mountain, they spent some months with an old friend, the lone hermit Vrishaparva who insisted they must remain with him for a while.

"Kailasa is Lord Siva's home," said he. "You will have his blessing if you spend some time with me."

Loth as they were to leave the mountains, they agreed readily enough.

One day, while they lived with Vrishaparva, Bheema went hunting by himself in the nearby vana. He went a long way, and found no game. He was hungry and pressed on, determined that he would bring back some meat today for his brothers. Yet, not a deer or boar did he see, not even a rabbit or pheasant. Feeling suddenly exhausted he sat under a large flame-of-the-forest decked with a hundred scarlet petal-fires.

Bheema mumbled to himself, "Vrishaparva said there was plenty of game in this jungle, but I have not seen a single beast. I feel tired and I'll sleep a while before I hunt any more."

He stretched himself out at the foot of the tree, and was soon asleep. It was extraordinary that he felt so tired, and he should have been warned that something strange was afoot. Bheema fell into a comfortless slumber. He dreamt lucidly, so he stood apart from his body and watched himself sleeping. He was amazed that the same forest he had hunted so vainly in now teemed with game. In his dream, Bheema wondered if some magic had made him blind and lured him to the place where he slept.

A prescience of evil darkened his slumber. He felt an indescribably sinister creature watched him with greedy interest. Bheema tossed in his sleep, but he could not wake up though every cell in his body cried danger! He was aware that whatever the malevolent creature was, it watched him exactly as a hunter does his prey; that it had lured him here with bewitchment, and meant to kill him. He felt no fear, because fear was alien to his nature. But he could not wake up, and neither could he see what it was that stalked him.

Then Bheema stopped dreaming. He was back in his sleeping body, and he felt something awful and cold wrap itself around him, slowly, at its ease, something that made his flesh crawl. Suffocating, he awoke with a cry. He found his arms pinned to his sides, and he was engulfed from head to foot in a clammy clasp, so he could not move a muscle.

He stared down in horror, and saw moist, mottled, yellow and green coils. A gigantic serpent held him fast.

The cold dampness and the purulence of those coils were more than he could bear. Bheema roared. He flexed himself against the huge python that held him as helpless as it might a wild boar, or a chital stag the great snakes hunt. But he was Bheema, son of the wind, and no snake was going to hold him for long; the Pandava strained against the shiny coils. They held him with more than unearthly strength; they held him fast with sorcery.

The forest rang with Bheema's roars. He struggled with all his untold strength against the snake's embrace, but he could not loosen it a bit. Indeed, he quickly found that the more he tried to get free the more strength drained out of his own body, like water from a hole in a pitcher. Bheema stopped struggling. He lay helpless as a baby in the constrictor's clasp.

He heard a sibilant swishing above him. When he raised his eyes up to the branches of the tree he lay under, he cried out in astonishment. The python was bigger than he had thought. It was stupendous, twice as big as the very tree. The monstrous serpent had coiled itself around the flame-of-the-forest many times, and held Bheema easily with just a part of its gargantuan body. A snake's head, ten times as big as his own, peered down at him from the branch around which its interminable neck was draped. Lidless eyes regarded him as a tiger may a deer, a cat a mouse, or a common python a little pig it has firmly in its coils.

A forked lightning-streak of a tongue flickered at the lipless mouth from which two fangs protruded like sharpened pillars. A pervasive hissing filled the clearing where the flame-of-the-forest grew.

In a strangled whisper, Bheema asked, "Who are you, great Naga? Why do you hold me with your sorcery?"

An evil smile stirred in the depths of those green, pool-like eyes. In the weirdest voice, half an aggressive hiss, and half human, the snake said, "I am hungry. You will make a fine meal, for there is more meat on you than on the fattest chital stag in this forest. Besides, the wild creatures know me well and they are difficult to hunt these days. That is why I am hungry. Indeed, once I have eaten you and grown a little stronger, I mean to go away to another forest where I am less well known. Hunger is a terrible thing, isn't it?"

The python grew thoughtful, and, bringing his enormous head lower, stared hard at Bheema. "But who are you, human, who wander where you should not?"

"I am Bheemasena the Pandava," said Bheema with dignity, "and I wander where I please. I am Vayu's son, and Yudhishtira's brother. Lions and tigers I have slain, hardly noticing I did; rakshasas like Hidimba and Baka I have dispatched. Who are you, great worm, that you have robbed me of my strength with your wizardry? For I am the strongest man in the world."

The snake laughed, a dreadful sound; but then, its eyes were alive with interest at what Bheema said. It peered more closely at him. It slithered its coils up and down his body, making him cry out in disgust. The python hissed contentedly to itself, as it stroked Bheema: fondling a choice morsel before it ate him.

"I am lucky today. Weeks have passed since I ate anything worthwhile. I say again, human: you are a well-fleshed creature; you will make a fair meal."

"But tell me who you are, O Serpent. At least tell me that before you eat me!" Bheema cried.

The naga's eyes clouded briefly in some dim and unpleasant memory. It spoke again, and it seemed to Bheema that now its voice was more human than before. "Mine is a long story, and an old one. I was once a king, I cannot recall how many ages ago it was, and I was king of Devaloka. Then I was cursed, and here I am in this snake's body. My name was Nahusha; perhaps you have heard my name before? Ah, great was the majesty of King Nahusha, son of Ayu, deep was his learning; but with them came arrogance. I was mad with the power I wielded, and vain with the wisdom I had. Once, fate brought the Rishi Agastya to my palace in Amravati, and in my wretched pride, I insulted that profound one.

"He cursed me, mortal. He cast me down from heaven, and as I fell to the earth, I saw a hideous change had come over me. I had become a python. Gone was my body of light, vanished all my glory. Instead, I had a serpent's coils, and this serpent's head. As I lay sobbing on the ground, I heard Agastya's voice say to me, 'Now your swollen pride has found its true shape. This is what you really are, that you have become a slave to your conceit. Remain in the world as a snake, Nahusha. You are not fit to be a king any more.'

"I gnashed my teeth and wept, but there was no cure for me. I cried to Agastya, 'My lord, forgive me! I am penitent already, release me from your curse.'

"He answered grimly, 'You are so bloated with vanity you do not know what penitence is. The curse has just begun. You have an age to live as a serpent, before the one who releases you from my curse comes along.'

'Who will my saviour be?' cried I, desperately.

'A king of the race of the Moon. An exile from his kingdom, like you are, Nahusha,' he answered.

"'How will I know him?' I wailed.

"'He will come to you when you hold the strongest man in the world in your coils, and he will answer any question you ask him. He will be wiser than you are, and he will teach you a deep lesson about wisdom.'

"He told me the name of the king who would set me free, but I have forgotten it. Ah, mortal, I have lived many centuries in the world in this worm's body. The most wretched food has passed my lips: fresh flesh and blood. Pigs and rats I have eaten, deer, elephant and tiger. At first, I used to feel horror at where I was, and what I had become. Often, I tried to kill myself by starving. But I could not, and by the power of the curse, bestial greed would overcome me again. I would hunt a pig or a buffalo, or another serpent, and gorge myself as if I had no control over what I did.

"Ages have passed. I remember so little of my days in Devaloka. I am no longer certain if I was ever a king called Nahusha, or if all that is just a dream."

The snake sighed and twitched his coils. But he held Bheema firmly, so the Pandava could not move. Nahusha the python looked down at his captive again, and said, "Such a pity. Young Kshatriya, somehow I like you; or perhaps, it is Nahusha, whose spirit still dwells in this python's body, who likes you. But, alas, it is the python that lives on this earth, and he who must devour you. A pity, such a pity, for I do feel a strong fondness for you."

Bheema thought he glimpsed such a human flicker in the snake's slitted eyes. The creature went on, "Do you know, that just now when you said you were the strongest man on earth I felt a stab of hope, as I have not for centuries? I thought to myself, here I am with a mortal in my coils who says he is the strongest man on earth. Perhaps, the day of my salvation has come at last; perhaps I shall not have to eat this fine young human. But no, that is not to be, or our saviour should have appeared by now. I beg you, believe me, young Bheema, when I say that it would please me no end if I did not have to eat you. What can I do? Already, the serpent juices in my belly begin to burn and compel me."

TWENTY-FIVE

The riddles of Nahusha

Somehow, the serpent sounded entirely sincere. Bheema was certain he even saw a tear shining in the cursed creature's eye. Despite his own plight, the soft-hearted Pandava was moved by the python's story.

Quite calmly he said, "Nahusha, I feel no enmity towards you, I feel sorry to hear about your long suffering. Yet, I am sad I have to die, and leave my brothers when they still need me. Perhaps you do not know this, but they depend on me to win the war on the crack of the ages. The war on which the future of the world hangs."

Bheema considered that war. He smiled wryly and said, "Of course, now things are different that Arjuna has the astras. Very likely, he can win the war by himself. Perhaps that is why he went to Devaloka in the first place. Because it was fated that you would eat me before the war began, and he would have to win it by himself.

"Possibly, it is no great matter death has come for me. I have no fear. I have lived a full and joyful life, in palaces and in jungles. What man could hope to have better parents than I did, or more noble and loving brothers? As for our wife! Ah, Nahusha, my friend, you should just see our Panchali. There is no woman in heaven or earth to compare with her."

Bheema called the python his friend quite sincerely. He felt a bond with Nahusha, even because the great constrictor was going to devour him. Bheema felt nothing strange about this, either: for there was no escaping fate.

He went on, while the python listened in perfect silence, his eyes, now, definitely trickling tears. A pang of sadness flitted across Bheema's face. "My brothers will rule the world again, even without my help. Arjuna will win all our battles, but I shall not have the revenge I swore against Dusasana and Duryodhana. Friend Nahusha, my mother Kunti and my Panchali will grieve for me when I am dead. I am also sad to die without fulfilling the oaths I swore to my queen: that I would drink Dusasana's blood for tormenting her, and that I would break Duryodhana's thigh, on which he dared call her to sit.

"But fate is all knowing, and decides everything for our own good. If we were to choose ourselves what course our lives should take, or when we should die, the world would be a difficult place to live in!"

Bheema fetched as deep a sigh as he could, with the python's coils around him. Nahusha, meanwhile, was fighting a battle with himself. The king in him was so taken up with Bheema, especially his courage in death's very jaws, that he was loth to harm the Pandava. But the hungry serpent, with the long chasm of a belly where greedy juices stirred, was determined that Bheema was, first and last, a succulent meal. It was a difficult battle, and Nahusha fought it bravely.

In the meantime, back in Vrishaparva's asrama, Yudhishtira saw evil omens everywhere. Jackals stood to the right of the hermitage and howled mournfully. An arid wind flew, and hideous vartikas, one-winged, one-eyed, and with one leg, stared at the sun and vomitted blood. Draupadi felt ill, as if someone was squeezing her life from her. Yudhistira's right arm twitched and his left leg trembled. Sudden, unreasonable fear gripped the other Pandavas. Draupadi cried, "Something terrible has happened to Bheema. Go and look for him, Arjuna. Quickly, before it is too late!"

But Yudhishtira said "I will go," and he was off before anyone could protest.

He set out in the direction he had seen Bheema take earlier. Hours had passed since his brother left, but Yudhishtira had been raised in the forest, and his father Pandu had taught him how to follow the subtlest trail. Now, he easily picked out Bheema's passage. On soft earth, he saw his brother's footmarks. He saw trampled bushes, and branches torn off from trees: Bheema did not travel without leaving signs of where he went.

On strode Yudhishtira, his anxiety growing with each moment. He was on the verge of panicking and running headlong through the trees, when he broke into a little glade with a flame-of-the-forest growing at its heart. What he saw there made him feel faint. Bheema lay in the clasp of a leviathan out of forgotten times, a serpent that was surely a great Asura, a survivor of the last deluge perhaps. Its pale coils were thicker than the bole of the tree. Its sleek, flat head was bigger than an elephant's.

But Yudhishtira knew how strong his brother was, and he cried, "Bheema, we have been anxious for you! Stop your game now, it is late. Kill him, if you must, and come back with me. Draupadi is sick with worry."

Bheema replied, "I can't move, he is much stronger than I am."

Yudhishtira looked at the python in amazement. "Who are you that can contain my brother, who is the strongest man on earth? I am Yudhishtira, and I beg you, let my Bheema go. He is my strength; I will be lost without him. O magnificent one, he is my favourite brother and I have never shown him how much I love him. Whoever you are, mighty Spirit, let him go and I will bring you whatever food you want: anything from the three worlds; for all my brothers are kshatriyas and they obey me.

"I know you are no ordinary serpent. Release my Bheema, take me in his place."

A new light glimmered in the python's eyes, when it heard Yudhishtira's name. In its voice like sibilant thunder, it repeated that name, as if it stirred some long-buried memory. Then the serpent gave an uncanny shout making the forest quake.

"Yudhishtira!" cried the python. "That is the name of he who will come when I hold the strongest man on earth in my coils. Agastya said Yudhishtira would answer my questions, and set me free. Come near, let me tell you who I am."

"Who are you, great one?" asked Yudhishtira, even more amazed.

"I am Nahusha."

Bheema was astonished to see his brother prostrating himself before the python. He cried, "What are you doing? Run away, or he will eat us both!"

Yudhishtira said, "Have you never heard the name of Nahusha, Bheema? He was our ancestor, the Kuru king who became Lord of Devaloka for his dharma."

Nahusha murmured, "Now I know why I found it so hard to eat you, young Bheema. You are my own flesh and blood."

He turned his head to Yudhishtira. "Yes, I was indeed king in Devaloka, when Indra was cursed after he killed Vritrasura. Then I grew arrogant, and here I am, a serpent ekeing out his curse. But Agastya told me that Yudhishtira would release me from my long torment."

Nahusha's eyes glittered, "I hold your brother in my coils, and I will eat him if you don't answer my questions on dharma, which no man, no Deva, no gandharva, no one at all has ever been able to. I think the danger to Bheema will sharpen your wits, because I see that you love your brother more than your own life. Let us test you, Yudhishtira. Let us see if your knowledge of dharma is as deep as Agastya Muni thought it would be. Come closer."

Yudhishtira came forward. Bheema lay bemused in the python's coils. This was taking on the quality of a bizarre dream, and Bheema wanted to laugh.

Nahusha rolled his eyes, and asked the first question. "What is a brahmana?"

Yudhishtira thought for just a moment, then, said, "To me, a brahmana is anyone who is truthful, generous, compassionate, and capable of sacrifice."

The serpent stared at him. Slowly, it nodded its head. "What is the supreme knowledge?"

"I would say the Brahmam," said Yudhishtira, without a moment's pause.

"Which is superior along the way to liberation, sorrow or happiness? Which makes the way clear?"

"I have heard that, to the enlightened, what we call sorrow and joy are not different from each other."

And so the questions came, and Yudhishtira answered them all, easily. Yet, he never answered assertively, or with arrogance. He always said either, 'I think', 'I have heard', 'I have been told', or 'in my opinion', and Nahusha marvelled that a man of such knowledge was as humble, as gentle as the mortal king before him was. He felt deep affection for Yudhishtira, and admiration, as well.

As for the Pandava, he grew so absorbed in the python's questions he forgot all about Bheema, whose life hung by the thread of his answers. Yudhishtira was enjoying himself, and Bheema blessed every rishi with whom his brother had spent time in the Kamyaka, the Dwaitavana, and the mountains. Though he had scoffed at him then, now his own life depended on what his brother had gleaned from the sages.

Fortunately for Bheema, Yudhishtira had learned with love, and he had learned well. The exchange between Nahusha and the eldest Pandava was animated and profound. The questions ranged far and wide: the ordering of society, the nature of the soul, of time, varnasrama, poverty and wealth, old age and youth, death, liberation, sorrow and joy, wisdom and power, dharma, and again dharma.

It was an enforced education for Bheema, and he would never forget any of Nahusha's questions, or Yudhishtira's answers, not as long as he lived. Often, later, Bheema would repeat the lively exchange, word for word, for his brothers and Draupadi; and some rishis who heard him said that whatever he was reciting was scripture.

Suddenly, Nahusha declared, "Yudhishtira, I have no question for which you do not have the answer! You are the wisest man I ever met; but more important, you are the humblest one as well. That is the lesson I have learnt from you, the lesson I will never forget. I have met many learned men during my years, on earth and in heaven. Some, I have even eaten," the serpent smiled. "None of them were gentle like you, but arrogant of their knowledge. You are different, O Rajarishi; for you, your life and your knowledge are not separate things."

The python said, "I am not hungry anymore. How can I think of eating Bheema, when I know he is your brother, O Yudhishtira Muni?"

He loosened his coils, and Bheema fell out of them gratefully. Yudhishtira ran to embrace him. With unusual tears in his eyes, Bheema said, "Your knowledge of dharma has saved my life today. Forgive me for mocking your wisdom once."

But Yudhishtira held him close, and whispered, "Ah, child, there is nothing to forgive. And if all my knowledge was lost today, that I have you back alive, I would not care."

But now, there were a hundred questions of his own that Yudhishtira had for Nahusha, and the python was happy to answer them for the Pandava. Time flew by in the heart of the forest, while Bheema, an unlikely new convert to the discourse of wisdom, listened raptly. At last, Nahusha slithered down from the tree. He said in a voice full of wonder, "I feel a transformation come over me. Yudhishtira, the curse ends!"

A golden lustre lit the twilight sky above them. In a swirling of winds, a vimana flew down into that clearing. Yudhishtira and Bheema stood dazzled by the craft; but in front of them, the python was also refulgent. As they watched, his serpentine elements dissolved, and a king of vast majesty stood where the snake had been. He was glorious past describing; the crown on his head sparkled with jewels from other worlds.

Nahusha embraced Yudhishtira and Bheema. "My friends, I will never forget you both. I owe my new life to you. O Yudhishtira, Mahatma, you are even wiser than Agastya said. May your lesson of humility always remain with me, for it is the most precious wisdom of all."

The brothers stood a little awed. Nahusha said gently, "But now, I must leave you. For an age my people have waited for me, and the streets of our city hum with the news of my return!"

He embraced them again, then crossed to the vimana and climbed in. Without a murmur, that ship lifted straight up into the darkening sky, and flashed away quicker than the eye could see. Yudhishtira and Bheema stood staring after it for a long time. Then, arm in arm, they turned back to the asrama.

Almost a year, the Pandavas spent in Vrishaparva's asrama, and on the slopes of the Prasravana. Until one day, reluctantly, they bid their final farewell to that muni and to the mountains, and made their way down onto the plains of Bharatavarsha. They went quickly now, putting the Himalayas, where they had found some peace, behind them. They arrived on the banks of the Saraswati and, crossing her, made their way once more into the Dwaitavana, and their old asrama beside the lake of lotuses. Now they were all calmer, Bheema and Draupadi, too. Knowing it drew near, they looked forward to the end of their exile.

One year more they must live in the forest; and then the last year, the ajnatavasa, when they must be disguised and remain undiscovered. Just one thought absorbed all of them: the war that loomed ahead.

TWENTY-SIX

Markandeya's lore*

WHEN THEY HAD NOT BEEN LONG IN THE DWAITAVANA, MONSOON winds began to sweep across the land, and dark clouds gathered heavily above Bharatavarsha. The rains came, lashing forest and earth with healing showers. The Saraswati swelled in her banks, a turbulent Goddess, and the lake of lotuses spilt over. The scent of those flowers, and of wet earth, filled the Pandavas with hope. Each day the end of their exile drew nearer.

When the monsoon passed, Yudhishtira said, "Indra said we should go back to the Kamyaka vana, and I have this persistent feeling someone wants to visit us there."

They returned to the first asrama of their exile. It was strange, settling down in the old clearing, where little had changed. The big nyagrodha still stood there, with green shoots of the latest rain sprouting on its branches. It was like returning to the fringes of another life, which still excluded them: for less than two years more.

Yudhishtira was worried that the Kamyaka might evoke the old impatience in Bheema. Instead, Bheema took to visiting the rishis of the forest with him! The son of the wind would sit entirely absorbed in whatever conversation Yudhishtira had with the hermits, and not a word out of him.

Then, one day, Krishna arrived with Satyabhama. There was such a reunion. They hugged one another, repeatedly, and when Krishna clasped Arjuna to him, it seemed he would never let the Pandava go.

---

* The discourse and stories of Markandeya are some 110 pages long in the KMG text.

He whispered in Arjuna's ear, "I have heard all about your stay in Amravati. I am so proud of you!"

Their lives made perfect sense again to the sons of Pandu, as it did every time dark Krishna was with them. Joy was upon them, and he, the uncanny Blue One, was as cheerful as ever.

When they sat under the banyan tree, Krishna said, "Subhadra and Abhimanyu are with us in Dwaraka now. He is a splendid kshatriya, and a better archer than you, Arjuna!

"Draupadi, your sons have also come to Dwaraka to study archery with me. Dhrishtadyumna brought them from Kampilya, and each one is an image of his father. Sometimes I feel you five are with me in my city, but grown younger!"

Tears rolled down Draupadi's face for her sons she had not seen for eleven years. Seeing her cry, Satyabhama took her hand and they went off into the asrama; and Draupadi was grateful for the company of another woman.

When they had gone Krishna leaned forward, and, a glint in his eye, whispered, "Yudhishtira, you have served eleven years of exile; if you ask me, eleven years too many. Why wait any longer? The army of Dwaraka is prepared; Drupada and Dhrishtadyumna are ready with their legions; the Kekaya brothers strain as if at a leash, to attack Hastinapura. Let us ride now! We will take them by surprise, and crush them before they realize that retribution has arrived. Why must you torment yourselves any more? Why suffer another year of this indignity, and then one more of going like beggars in disguise? Let us go and kill Dhritarashtra and his sons today!"

He sounded earnest. But Yudhishtira smiled and said quietly, "I thank you for your kind thought, Krishna, but you know how I feel about this. We must see out another two years somehow, and then ride on Hastinapura armed with dharma. As you say, it will be hard, especially for my poor Bheema. But I must wait."

Then, incredibly, Bheema said, "I agree with Yudhishtira. We should wait another two years. Time flits by in the jungle, anyway, and the weeks are like days: specially with the helpful visitors we have."

There was a twinkle in Bheema's eye, and Krishna flung an arm around him and burst out laughing. "Yes, Bheema! Just two years more, and we shall let you loose on the enemy like a tempest of your father.

But now, Arjuna, I am agog to hear about your stay in Devaloka. I have heard so many versions of it, and each one so different, that one would hardly think they were the same story. So tell me yourself, all of it."

Krishna stayed with his cousins in the Kamyaka for some weeks, and it was a happy time. The wildest beasts of the jungle would come to the hermitage and stand gazing at the Dark One. Deer would walk right up to him, nuzzle their faces in his hand, as he stroked them, and spoke to them just as if they were human children.

A few days after Krishna's arrival the Pandavas had another visitor, whose fund of lore was always a source of delight. The ever-youthful Markandeya was a masterly pauranika, and Krishna was the most eager of them all to hear the maharishi's tales.

When the sage, who arrived at nightfall, had been with them for an hour, and a simmering moon rose above the forest, Krishna said, "Muni, they say you have no equal in the world as a pauranika. When I was a boy, my mother Yasodha would tell me a story every night, when she put me to bed. How well she told them! I felt I was part of the Purana she was recounting; I could see its spaces before my eyes. I could smell its forests and flowers, and the characters would appear before me, real enough to touch.

"Muni, I don't believe there is any story-teller to match my mother. But we shall give you a chance to prove yourself her equal."

Bheema, who loved a good story, cried, "Come, Muni, give us a legend or two. The night is perfect for it."

Markandeya did not need much persuading, but launched into some shining tales of the eldest days.

"At the end of the last kalpa, the three worlds were plunged in a solitary, undistinguished night," began that rishi. "There was nothing but a single dark sea everywhere: Ekarnava. There were no Devas, no rishis, nothing but the black sea. Upon that desolate and awesome sea, the Lord Vishnu Narayana slept on the interminable serpent Ananta Sesha. A thousand heads Vishnu had, a thousand arms and feet, and a thousand eyes.

"He wore a fulvid yellow robe." Markandeya glanced at Krishna's electric garment, and continued, "Narayana's eyes were like suns, and his body was immeasurable, an infinite sky the hue of blue clouds. As he slept, out of his navel a white lotus sprouted, its corolla blue, its stalk golden and endless. It was the heart of the worlds, that primal lotus, and its divine scent spread everywhere.

"Within that first sacred flower Brahma was born: the Creator, four-faced and irradiant. The lotus-born Pitama, grandsire of all beings, poured forth creation. First, he gave out the waters, fire, air, the sky, the wind and the earth, the rivers and oceans, mountains, and the ancestral trees. Then the moments, the hours, the days, the weeks, the fortnights, the months, the half-years, the years, the yugas, the manvantaras and the kalpas flowed from him.

¹"He made the Sapta rishi, sons born immaculately from his mind: Marichi, Daksha, Bhrigu, Angiras, Pulastya, Pulaha and Kratu. From his breath came Daksha, Marichi from his eye, Angiras from his head, and the rest from other parts of Brahma's body. And with the advent of the seven sages, dharma had a human form."

Markandeya paused to be sure they were listening. None of them stirred; his Purana was hypnotic. He continued, "Then, Brahma made the other living beings. Tamas was the quality that first arose in that Prajapati. He extruded the Asuras from his hind-parts, and they were his firstborn, from his body. Brahma abandoned his creative body, and at that moment, from the castaway form, night was born, full of darkness and sleep. And the demons, the Asuras, worship the night, and are strongest during the hours of darkness.

"Brahma assumed another body, and this had the essence of sattva. From it he made the Devas, beings of light, exuded them from his face. He abandoned the body of sattva, and, because it was made of light, day was born from it. Thus, the Devas worship the day. Brahma took yet another form of sattva, and from this, the Pitrs, the manes, were born. When he cast off this body it became the twilight, sandhya, which all beings, of both darkness and light, worship."

Now Krishna murmured, "Ah Markandeya, you are a sublime pauranika."

They all glanced at the Dark One, and saw by the streaming moon that his eyes brimmed with yawning visions. It was as if Krishna gazed directly into the times and events Markandeya described. They waited impatiently for the rishi to continue. These were not tales that any of them had not heard before; but they had never heard them told like this: so they came alive and the silver sky was filled with a primeval sea, an interminable Serpent, a shadowy Blue God, a shining Lotus, and all the rest.

Markandeya resumed, "Now Brahma assumed a body of rajas, and from that form of his, his passionate sons, men, were born. When he abandoned that body, it became the dawn.

"He assumed yet another material body, made of sattva, tamas and rajas, all three, and from it sprang the rakshasas who roam the night, and are creatures of both darkness and passion. From that body of mixed gunas, also came the yakshas and gandharvas, the nagas, the kinnaras and charanas, and other divine beings.

"Then he created the birds of the air and the beasts of the wilds; trees, herbs and plants were born from Brahma's hair. From his eastern mouth, the Gayatri mantra issued, and the Rig Veda, and the melody of the Saman, and the Agnistoma yagna; from his southern mouth, the Yajur Veda, the Brihatsaman melody, the Trishtubh mantra; from his western mouth, the Sama Veda and Jagati mantra, the Vairupa and the Atiratha yagna; and from his northern mouth, the Atharva Veda, the Aptoryaman yagna, the Anushtup mantra and the Vairaja saman.

"From all his limbs, he emitted the various creatures."

The muni, who now sang his Purana softly, paused, and Yudhishtira said, "Rishi, tell us about the yugas."

Markandeya said, "Fifteen nimeshas, instants, is a kaastha. Thirty kaasthas is a kaala, and thirty kaalas is a muhurta. Thirty muhurtas long are a day and a night. Three hundred and sixty-five days and nights make a human year: one day and night of the Gods.

"Four are the ages called the yugas: the krita, the treta, the dwapara and the kali. Twelve thousand divine years long are the four ages together. The pristine krita yuga lasts for four thousand years of the Devas, and for eight hundred years more, its twilights. The second yuga, the treta, lasts for three thousand years of the Devas, and for six hundred years its dawn and dusk. The dwapara yuga, the third age, lasts for two thousand years of the Devas, and four hundred cosmic years its cusps. The final yuga, the kali, the age of evil, is for one thousand celestial years, and two hundred years its twilights; and then another krita yuga begins.

"A thousand yuga chakras, wheels of twelve thousand years each, is a day and a night of Brahma. Fourteen manvantaras are a day of Brahma, called a kalpa. Each manvantara is eight hundred and fifty-two thousand divine years, and three hundred and sixty-seven million human years. At the end of each day of the Creator, the worlds, the stars and galaxies are all recalled into dissolution, while Brahma sleeps through his night, which lasts as long as his day. When he awakens again, he pours forth the worlds once more.

"One year of Brahma lasts for three hundred and sixty-five such days and nights, with all their creations and dissolutions. Brahma's life lasts for a hundred years of such days and nights. At present, O Kshatriyas, half Brahma's life is over. This is the first kalpa of the second half of Brahma's life, his fifty-first year. It is the kalpa called Varaha."

Markandeya's eyes glowed in the moonlight, and soft excitement gripped his listeners at his account of time. How small and insignificant all their trials and concerns seemed against the immensity he conjured. Krishna cried, "But tell us the nature of the yugas, O perfect Markandeya! I have heard everything that happens in time is determined, first and last, by the nature of the age in which it occurs." He flashed a smile, "Even the lives of the Avataras, I am told."

Markandeya bowed to Krishna. "Knower of all things, it is true, indeed, that the age determines everything that happens within its span. All that are born during each yuga are influenced by the spirit of the yuga: how long they shall live, what course their lives will take, how great or worthless they shall be. Because all beings are subject to their own natures, and their natures to the primary nature of the yuga.

"As for the Avataras, O Krishna, they are not influenced by the yuga, but only seem to be. But yes, they also assume the outward raiment of nature in their lives and their deeds, and these surely belong to the yuga into which each Avatara is born."

TWENTY-SEVEN

The four yugas

KRISHNA LAUGHED HAPPILY. HE SAID, "HOW SIMPLY YOU ILLUMINE the most profound mysteries, Muni! Now tell us about the different natures of the yugas."

Markandeya said, "The krita is the immaculate age, when there is no trace of evil on earth. Eternal dharma is four-footed in the krita yuga, but only three-footed in the treta, because evil enters the world during the second age. Dharma stands on just two feet in the dwapara, and in the kali yuga, princes, dharma barely survives, hobbling on just one foot.

"In the pristine krita yuga, dhyana is said to be the highest virtue, gyana in the treta yuga, yagna in the dwapara, and bhakti in the kali of vice and darkness.

"Brahma is the Lord of the krita, Surya of the treta, Vishnu of the dwapara, and Rudra of the kali. Brahma, Vishnu and Surya are all worshipped in the kali yuga; and Siva, who bears the Pinaka, in all the four yugas.

"In the krita yuga, every creature is perfectly contented. They live at peace with themselves and in harmony with the divine Brahman. Their livelihood arises in spontaneity, from their pleasure in it. In the krita, there is no distinction between the best and worst of men; they are all equally gifted, in wisdom, in longevity, and in beauty. They are free from sorrow, and given to seeking solitude. They are tapasvins, and their goal is Mahadeva Siva. They live without selfishness of any kind, and are full of natural joy, welling endlessly in their hearts. They have no permanent homes, but live either beside the ocean or upon mountains.

"In the krita yuga, also, children are born from sexual intercourse. But the ecstasy of lovemaking is much more profound and prolonged than it is in the lesser ages."

Krishna sighed, "Ah, indeed. But then, the men and women of those times were more like Gods, weren't they, Muni? They lived for thousands of years, if I remember what my mother Yasodha told me."

Markandeya went on, "At the end of the krita yuga, the natural font of joy in the hearts of the people of the earth dried up; but another blessing arose, as if in its place. When the eternal wellsprings ran dry in the hearts of men, those waters appeared materially in the sky, as clouds: sacral rain fell upon the world, life-giving and full of bliss.

"When that precious deluge covered the surface of the earth, lustrous trees sprang up. These trees were called homes, O Pandavas, and they were the ancestors of our trees of today. The people of the world got their food from the trees, as they did anything else they wished for; and they, too, were as happy as the men and women of the krita yuga. The trees were full of visions, which moved the spirits of those who sat near them to rapture.

"But then, evil came to the earth. It came first into men's hearts, where there was a void left by the cessation of the waters of joy, which were sukshma, subtle, spiritual: of God.

"When the evil seed sprouted in the hearts of the men of the treta yuga, they grew passionate and greedy. And the wishing trees, which they had called their homes, vanished from the world. The men and women of the earth were repentant, and returned to the path of dharma. They still craved all that the trees had given them, but they knew their greed had made the trees disappear.

"Once more, the trees called homes reappeared across the earth, and now they gave the people clothing, fruit and ornaments. Cavities in the trees were full of divine honey, which no bees or birds fed on. The men of the earth lived on that ambrosial honey, and were content. Joy returned to them, for many years; but the evil, which had sprung once in their hearts, did not die. After a while, the people of the treta yuga turned to greed and violence again. For the first time, they seized the wishing trees for themselves, making possessions of them, and attacking one another to own them.

"The trees vanished again from the world, as suddenly as they had first appeared. Bitter days fell on the people of the treta yuga. The elements turned against them in wrath; savage extremes of heat and cold beset them. Burning rains fell on them, and they built shelters for themselves against the fury of nature. Many perished for their crimes in those days of retribution, and the people of the earth turned back to meditation: to seek their souls in dhyana, so some peace may return to the world.

"The rains turned mild over the earth again. They flowed down mountains and valleys as the first rivers, flowing always into the ocean. Now, the first herbs of the earth sprouted from the alchemy between the new rain and the soil. As if to answer the prayers of the people, fourteen great trees reappeared in the world, with flowers and fruit.

"A brief time of peace came to the earth. But evil had taken root in men's hearts, and it diminished the people of the treta yuga, as the age wore on inexorably to fulfil its destiny. Avarice and passion rose again, and men seized field and tree, village and shelter for themselves. They seized their brothers' women. The lust for possessions overcame them, and perhaps it was because they were afraid of losing all these again.

"The life-giving herbs disappeared back into the ground. Desolation stalked the world again. It was then, at the command of the manes, that Prithu milked the earth. Again, violence swept the land, as rapacity mastered the dwindled men of the treta yuga. It was in those fateful days that Brahma created the kshatriyas to rule the earth, to curtail the anarchy that had seized her, and to bring peace to the brahmanas. It was in the treta yuga that the classes of men were ordained and each varna was given his own dharma by God, by which they could aspire to nirvana.

"Those times are inscrutable, for great wonders and various blessings were still upon the earth. After the first agonies of transformation, men lived in harmony again, with themselves and all the mysterious and divine forces in the world. Thus the treta yuga wore on, and then the dwapara yuga dawned.

"The evil in men's hearts took many forms by now, some subtle and some openly sinister. The dwapara was an age of conflict, and men doubted the very nature of truth. While the Veda had been single and sacred in the treta, in the dwapara it was divided in four by the son of Parasara and the river-girl. Anxiety arose among men, suspicion, and an abhorrence for life itself. They could no longer distinguish between truth and illusion. For the first time, disease swept the world as monstrous plagues. Drought came to the earth, and terrible suffering, because of which men began to think about liberation from birth and death, to think of moksha. They thought of the futility of life, the emptiness of desire; they meditated upon their own deepest natures.

"Rajas and tamas arose to dominate half the dwapara yuga, in war, doubt and strange knowledge born from brutal conflict. Man's very mind divided against him. He became a power and a law unto himself, divorced from the natural world. He sought to control his suffering, and was alienated from the natural earth. Yet, all these dark tendencies were tempered, curbed by the profound virtue that men had inherited from the krita yuga, and the treta, as well.

"But in the kali, the age of wrath and darkness, the earth becomes a realm of night, and the sattva guna is all but lost in dominating sinfulness. It is in the spiritual apostasies of the brahmanas that the evil of kali yuga is rooted; for, the holy ones are corrupted in that age, and forgetting dharma, they turn to unthinkable sins. Why, in the kali yuga, the twice-born themselves are ignorant of the Veda."

Markandeya sighed as if he could hardly bear the thought. The Pandavas shuddered at the mention of the kali, the fell yuga that lay in wait around the corner of time. Krishna, alone, was as serene as ever. He said with a laugh, "But the kali is the age into which every spirit of all the other ages prays to be born. For it is the easiest age in which to have moksha." Softly he said, "They say that in the kali yuga a man need not perform any great deed or sacrifice; he need not even be pure. Let him but take the name of God, and he shall be liberated. Is this true, O Markandeya?"

There were fathomless mysteries beneath the surface of his words. Did his tone gently mock the rishi? Was there so much the sage had left out of what he said, which, indeed, he did not begin to suspect? Great truths that dark Krishna knew. Other worlds stirred in the heart of the earth: unknown, unknowable, legendary dimensions, all of them uncannily part of Krishna's mystery. The Pandavas saw their cousin transformed. It was not a physical change; but for that instant, he seemed to encompass the very universe within himself.

The moment passed. Krishna smiled at them. He looked at Markandeya, who seemed to have turned to stone in the Avatara's mystic moment. The Blue One said, "Muni, you have not answered my question about the kali yuga. Is it true, what they say, that it is the simplest age for a man to attain moksha in? Is it enough for a man to chant the name of God in the evil yuga, for him to find nirvana?"

And now, here was another mystery: Krishna was full of earnest inquiry; he was an anxious seeker. Truly, as if he sought liberation for himself, or as if he could liberate all mankind, if he only found moksha first; as if all Time was just Krishna's quest for his own freedom. Markandeya and the Pandavas sat absorbed in the Dark One's mystery. Somehow, they had never thought of him as a seeker. They realized now, especially the Pandavas, that they had never thought of him as having any needs of his own.

Krishna flashed his smile again, breaking the trance. He urged Markandeya, once more, "Tell us, Muni, about the kali yuga. Forgive my foolish interruptions; I only wondered about moksha, and how it was to be had most easily."

Markandeya said in a low voice, "Krishna, there is nothing on heaven or earth that you do not know. But it is, indeed, as you say: the kali is the simplest age in which a man may find moksha, and he can find it by just saying the name of God. Yet, the reason for this is not simple. For a man suffers horribly merely by being born into the age of wrath.

"He suffers undreamt-of terror, constantly, from within himself and from the world, as well. He lives shrouded in evil; every breath he draws is in fear. In the kali yuga, the kings who sit upon the thrones of the earth will have neither tranquillity nor dharma. They will be men mainly of tamas, full of rage, vanity and lust, full of lies. They will find their pleasure in inflicting torment and death on their subjects, even women and children. And they rise to power just briefly, and then fall away. The kings of the kali will be short-lived, greedy and rapacious.

"The people will be contaminated by the customs of others. Kings will employ wild barbarians and murderers, and these will have their say in the violent affairs of state. And with the people living in perversion, far from dharma, ruin will come to all the land.

"Wealth alone will confer nobility, regardless of a man's birth or his character; power alone will define virtue. Pleasure will be the only reason for marriage, seductiveness the quintessence of womanhood. In disputes of justice, the ability to distort the truth will determine who prevails. Just wearing a thread will determine who is a brahmana; for the twice-born will lose their dharma and be steeped in sin themselves. They will not have dhyana, gyana, yagna or bhakti, in the age of night.

"All the world will be plunged in a turbid darkness of the spirit, and the earth will be full of deceit and passion, greed and wrath. The precious waters of the soil will dry up at the fearsome ways of men. A man's worth will be decided not by his truthfulness, by his wisdom or goodness, but only by the wealth he has amassed, by even the vilest means.

"Arrogance and sin will pass for wisdom and righteousness, brashness and a loud voice for scholarship. Only the poor will have any honesty or virtue left, and the powerful will make life so miserable for them, that they, too, will become corrupt. Feebleness will be the only reason for not being employed. Just a bath in water will come to signify purification, and charity will be the only surviving virtue.

"Unimaginable evil will engulf the sons of men. Abduction will be equal to marriage, and wearing costly clothes and ornaments to dharma. The very affectation of being great will pass for greatness, and boastfulness for heroism.

"Men of power, men of great faults within themselves, and kings with the hearts of monsters, will rule the earth. Oppressed beyond endurance by their rulers, the good people of the world will flee the macabre cities of kings to hide in secret valleys between mountains, where they will turn to nature for succour, living off wild honey, roots and fruit, birds and flowers. Violence and perversions will rot the cities, and all the land. Terrible wars and demonic diseases will decimate the human race, and savage cold and scathing heat, scorching droughts and sweeping floods will terrorize the people of the kali yuga. Until, the earth will be a hell in creation, where souls are born for no pleasure at all, but only searing expiation."

Yudhishtira said quietly, "Already, there are omens of what is to come."

"It is not far from us," said Markandeya. "Why, it is prophesied that with your war against the sons of Dhritarashtra, the kali yuga will begin." He paused, and said in a low voice, "And it will truly set in when Krishna leaves the world."

Krishna murmured thoughtfully, "Yes, it will be rare for men to even say the name of God in the age of evil."

"And so they will indeed find moksha, if they do, with a devout heart," put in the rishi.

Bheema said, "I pray I will not see much of that wretched time! But tell us, O Markandeya, does the world itself end with the kali yuga?"

"At the end of the kali yuga, when the earth has been ravaged and laid waste by men's sins, a drought arises that lasts for a hundred years, with not a day's rain. Every creature in the world will perish, all the species. And Siva comes as Rudra for the dissolution.

"In an awesome form, he comes. He enters the seven rays of the sun as transcendent fire, and subsumes the myriad waters of the earth, draining them into himself. Oceans and rivers he absorbs, lakes, mountain-springs and streams; he dries up the darkling waters of patala. Then, those seven rays he has entered become seven separate suns blazing in the sky. They set alight the three worlds as cotton balls dipped in ghee. Mountains, sea-beds, green valleys, islands, the continents, are all ignited, and burn like dry grass in that firestorm.

"When Rudra has consumed the worlds, he stands upon the cosmic ether, and from his chasmal mouth banks of clouds issue, greater than galaxies: clouds like vast elephant herds in fathomless space, thunder-roaring clouds, gashed with immense lightning to blind the terrified Devas in heaven.

"Some clouds are dark like the twilight lotus, which bloomed once in jungle-hearts; some are yellow, others amber. Some have the colour and texture of chrysoberyl, others of sparkling sapphire and yet others are like red lacquer. Some clouds have the shapes of sea-conches, some of jasmine flowers of crystal in the sky; these are white as goose-feathers, but streaked with lightning black as kohl.

"But others are menacing, themselves dark as night; still others are bright as blue jays' wings and peacock-feathers. Swiftly, there are towns of clouds in the sky, mountain ranges of them; there are unimaginable palaces in the firmament, and the strangest faces, some calm, some demented, staring with eyes of fire, latticed with veins of lightning.

"The cloudbanks roar to deafen even the Devas' dimensions, which are not material. Then they open in the sky, and a sheet-rain falls over the inferno that rages upon the three worlds below. In a day and a night, the rain has extinguished the conflagration of God, which consumed his creation. At the end of each kali yuga, the destruction stops with this deluge; but at the end of a kalpa, a thousand cycles of yugas, the pralaya does not stop.

"It rains on, endlessly, torrents pouring down by night and day in the unnatural light; until, the worlds dissolve in those tidal waters and the seven suns are extinguished in the sky. The loftiest world, Bhuvarloka on high, is flooded, and a watery night falls over all of creation. Still those rains do not stop; they pour on for a hundred years without pause.

"At last, the precious waters have swollen into the realm of the Sapta rishi, and the ocean covers everything. It is upon this infinite sea that a pipal leaf floats, my princes, and the Lord of the kalpa, the Blue Infant who sucks on his toe, lies on that singular, resplendent leaf. From his mouth, issue great winds to blow away the clouds of the pralaya. For a hundred years, these winds blow before the clouds are all scattered.

"Then, Hari is Narayana, lying upon his eternal serpent-bed, Anantasayanam, as both Vishnu, and Brahma who lies in the golden lotus that sprouts from Vishnu's navel. Both sleep for as long as Brahma's night lasts, out on that ocean of hardly a ripple. At the end of a thousand chaturyugas, Brahma stirs again. Once more, he pours forth Creation."

Krishna fetched a contented sigh when Markandeya finished. He breathed, "Ah, good Rishi, you are indeed a wonderful pauranika. Why, I would even say you are my mother Yasodha's equal!"

Sahadeva said, "Tell us more, Muni. Your Purana enchants us."

"Yes, do," Krishna said. "How I love these old stories." His tone was fathomless.

They stayed up almost until dawn, while the Rishi Markandeya told them a score of tales of the oldest times. About all the yugas he told them, of Dundhumara, of Kuvalaswa, and of the Rishi Angirasa. About Agni, Markandeya told them, and the Fire God's love for Svaha. Of the first war in heaven, he spoke: when Soma the Moon abducted Brihaspati's wife, Tara, and the Devas and the Asuras fought. He described other wars also, vividly, the churning of the sea for amrita, and the Incarnations of the Lord Vishnu.

He told them about the Asura Taraka, and the strange boon he had from Brahma: that only a son born to ascetic Siva, the Mahayogin, could kill him. He described the birth of Parvati, who was once Sati, who killed herself; how she grew in her father Himavan's palace; how Siva came to a nearby tapovana, and was deceived by Kama into love. How Siva made Kama ashes. Of the wedding of Siva and Parvati, Markandeya told, and the birth of Karttikeya, child of wonder, in the bank of sara grasses; and how that child slew Tarakasura on a fateful seashore.

That was on the first night. Finally, Markandeya yawned. "I think we should stop for tonight. Let us resume tomorrow, when the storyteller and his listeners are fresh."

So they turned in, their minds alight with visions. Such dreams they dreamt that night, the Pandava princes, dreams they would remember nothing of, except that they were splendourous.

TWENTY-EIGHT

The foolish brahmana

For a month, Markandeya remained in the asrama at Kamyaka. Every night, after the evening meal, Krishna and the Pandavas sat eagerly around the muni, and voyaged with him on luminous adventures in the magic ship of his Purana. The days and nights flowed swiftly by, like the waters of a river, unnoticed.

Then, Markandeya left them, saying he must return to his tapasya. After just a few days more, Krishna also said it was time he went back to Dwaraka. Sadly, Yudhishtira and his brothers bade farewell to their dark cousin. Satyabhama and Draupadi had grown as close as sisters, with Satyabhama telling Draupadi about life in exotic Dwaraka, and the exploits of the blue master of the ocean-city. And Panchali told Satyabhama about the mountains, about Badarikasrama and Arjuna's journey to Devaloka.

Finally, the moment of parting came. Embracing Krishna, Yudhishtira whispered, "When you are with us it seems as if our exile is heaven. But when you leave, we can hardly bear it."

Krishna took his cousin's hand and said gently, "Great events are near, Yudhishtira, we must prepare for them. Anyway, I never leave but only seem to, because my heart is always here with you."

He turned and left them quickly, before he, too, was overcome.

Legion were the brahmanas that came and went from the Pandavas' asrama. They came in concern for the future of the world. Already, in the hearts of distant forests, rishis sensitive to the spirit felt the effects of Duryodhana's sinister rule. It was they, in their dhyana, who first grew aware of any influence that arose in the world, whether of darkness or light.

Now they had clear sense of the rising tide of evil in Hastinapura, where Duryodhana, who was king in all but name, had inveigled his own trusted courtiers into every position of power. These were ruthless men, most often chosen by Shakuni: a very different breed from the men of dharma who had ruled the Kuru kingdom in the past. Duryodhana's murderous coterie wielded increasing power, and the only virtue their master expected from them was unquestioning, sycophantic loyalty, which he bought with lavish gifts of land, wealth and position, and with fear.

Most of the rishis and brahmanas who came to visit Yudhishtira in the Kamyaka vana were wise men, and genuinely concerned about the future. But not all the fingers on a hand are the same, and inevitably, some fools came with the sages.

One foolish brahmana, who had enjoyed the Pandavas' hospitality for a week, arrived in Dhritarashtra's sabha. He hoped to turn what he had seen and heard there to his advantage, and elicit some reward from the Kuru king for the information he had to offer. This brahmana was a garrulous man, fond of his own voice, and of embellishing the truth with his fancies.

When Dhritarashtra heard of his arrival in Hastinapura, he sent for him. When the brahmana came to the sabha, the blind king said, "We hear you visited our nephews in the Kamyaka vana. Tell us about them, my friend."

The man needed no urging. "Lord of the earth, I have just come from the Kamyaka aranya, where the sons of Pandu made me welcome. But those princes and their Draupadi are in a pitiful condition: royal kshatriyas, and living in a hut! I fear they are full of bitterness."

The brahmana held forth on how miserable the Pandavas were, how they burned for revenge. Lowering his voice, he said, "But they have not been in the Kamyaka vana all this while."

Dhritarashtra had already heard about his nephews' tirtha-yatra: a muted account from a wiser person than this man. The king wanted to encourage the foolish brahmana into telling him all he knew. He said,

"Really, O Muni? Have they been to Indraprastha, perhaps? And broken the conditions of their exile?"

"My lord, they have not broken the conditions of their exile. But they have been on a pilgrimage to the holiest tirthas in the land: to purify themselves for war!"

Dhritarashtra showed no emotion, but waited for him to continue. The man, who had never before had the chance to address a royal sabha, was happy to do so. He described the Pandavas' tirta-yatra at length, and told how they arrived at Badarikasrama. He spoke as if he had been with them on their pilgrimage, whereas, in fact, whatever he knew was gleaned from the munis that had actually gone with Yudhishtira.

After describing the tirtha-yatra in detail, many of which were out of his imagination, he paused and looked grandly around him. Then, he said in a whisper, "But, my lord, Arjuna was not with his brothers on their pilgrimage."

Pretending to be mystified, Dhritarashtra asked, "Where was he then?"

The brahmana began to fairly babble. "Didn't you know about Arjuna's journey into the mountains?"

Dhritarashtra leaned forward in his throne and breathed, "No, most knowing one. Tell us."

The man launched into an account of Arjuna's tapasya in the mountains: how Siva came to him as a hunter, and gave him the Paasupatastra; confirming what Dhritarashtra had already heard from his spies. Warming to his tale, the brahmana moved on to an excited description of how the Lokapalas had given the Pandava their astras, and how Indra sent his vimana to fetch his son to Amravati.

The truth was that, while this witless fellow had been in the Kamyaka vana, a certain Dark One was there as well. Krishna had fed the brahmana every tidbit he knew about Arjuna's encounter with Siva, and those of his stay in Amravati. Krishna had sworn the brahmana to secrecy, knowing he would take his tale to Hastinapura, as soon as he could.

Now, in the court of the blind king, Arjuna's adventures in Devaloka were vividly recounted, with many trimmings. Of course, Krishna had said nothing about the curse of Urvashi; he had warned the Pandavas, also, that was best kept to themselves. Dhritarashtra heard everything he would have least wanted to: how Arjuna received the Vajra from Indra, how he killed the Nivatakavachas and the Kaalakeyas; and nothing that might prove useful to him.

Finally, Dhritarashtra rewarded the brahmana with a purse of gold, somewhat less generous than the man had hoped for, and had him shown out of the palace. The king was panicstricken. "Nemesis flies nearer every day. My brother's sons, who slept on beds of down, spend their nights lying on bare earth. We shall not escape punishment for what we have done."

He fell silent, then said as if to himself, "Now Arjuna is a master of the devastras, and he watches his brothers suffer, and Draupadi suffer. How will he forget what Dusasana and Duryodhana did to her in this sabha? While we sat by and let it happen. Ah, we shall not escape with our lives; not I, not my sons."

Again, he fell quiet, chewing his lip. Then he said, "It is foolish to think they will forget even a moment of what happened. It is they who have suffered, not we, and they will have revenge. How Bheema must smoulder. He will blow like a storm when he comes to kill us. How will we resist them, when they have dharma on their side? Oh, I was so foolish, when I gave in to Duryodhana. Now we will pay for my weakness."

Shakuni was in the court, and heard all this. Slipping out, he took word of it to Duryodhana. That prince cried, "My own father! And this is how he speaks in the open sabha. Ah, he is such a coward."

Shakuni said, "You are Lord of the earth. The kings of the world are all loyal to you. May your cousins never come back."

Karna was there. He said, "Indeed, you are Lord of the earth now. Your enemies live in the jungle like wild beasts, with as much honour as animals!"

Duryodhana was still tense. Then Karna cried, "I have an idea, my prince. Would you hear it?"

Duryodhana paused his restless pacing, and said dully, "Tell me."

"Let us go to the Kamyaka vana and feast our eyes on the Pandavas. Who is a happier man than he who can gloat over his enemies' adversity, while he himself prospers? Won't it make you glad to see Yudhishtira, his brothers and the arrogant Draupadi shorn of their pride? They, who were masters of the world, are beggars in the jungle now.

"You will see the anguish on their faces. You will see them try to hide what they feel, but they will not be able to. Come, Duryodhana, seeing your cousins will restore your spirits."

A dark smile touched Duryodhana's lips. Shakuni was beaming in approval of Karna's plan. He said, "Surely, nothing is sweeter than seeing one's enemy in his worst moment. The experience is as delectable as the birth of a son, or finding a treasure."

Karna said, "Make your wives put on their finery. Let them deck themselves in their costliest ornaments, and take them to the Kamyaka, where Draupadi wears valkala. She is no sannyasin. Let every diamond on your women's bodies send a shaft of fire into Panchali's proud heart. Let her rue the day she mocked you."

Duryodhana said, "I would love nothing better than to see Bheema and Arjuna clad in the barks of trees, and the haughty empress of the Mayaa sabha as queen of a hut of logs. I long to see the look in her eyes, when she sees my wives wearing silks and ornaments, while she herself is as poor as a beast of the jungle."

"What stops you then, Duryodhana?" cried Karna.

"My father would never permit it. You heard what he said in the sabha. He is full of fear; he will not allow us the pleasure of gloating. Besides, Bheeshma must be persuaded as well."

Karna said, "Give me this night to devise a plan. By tomorrow morning, I will come to you with a way to convince the king."

But Karna came back the same night. Shakuni and a man who seemed to be a cowherd were with him. Karna said, "I have a plan, and it is so simple we should have thought of it at once."

"Tell me," said Duryodhana, bringing them into his apartment and pouring some wine.

Shakuni said, "This is our friend Samanga, the cowherd. He will persuade your father to let us go to the Dwaitavana, from where the Kamyaka is near enough."

Duryodhana looked at them, unbelievingly. "Is this a joke, Karna?"

"Not at all," replied his friend.

The next morning, in court, Samanga presented himself before the king. He was careful to arrive on his own. Shakuni, Karna and Duryodhana were already in the sabha, and showed no sign they knew the cowherd. Came the hour for petitions, and Samanga rose and said, "My lord, the time has come for branding the cattle in Dwaitavana. You must send someone you trust, so the counting can be done quickly."

Now Shakuni said, "The hunting season is upon us, my lord. Let the Kuru princes go to the forest to help count the cattle, and to hunt deer as well."

Dhritarashtra turned his blind face to where he knew Duryodhana was sitting. His son said, "The weather is perfect, and I am ready to go on a ghosha-yatra."

Dhritarashtra was thoughtful for a moment. Slowly, he said, "It is a good idea; but I have heard the Pandavas have their asrama close to our cattle in Dwaitavana. I am afraid to let you anywhere near them. They live in poverty and sorrow; there is no telling what might happen, if you encounter them in the jungle." He lowered his voice. "Arjuna is a master of the devastras now. No, it is better we send someone else."

Shakuni said, "My lord, the sons of Pandu are noble; they will never break their word. Otherwise, they would have already attacked us here in Hastinapura. Besides, we will stay clear of them, so there can be no danger."

Duryodhana said, "We will take an army with us if you are anxious. But I feel the need to get away from the city, to be out in the wilds, to hunt and relax myself."

Reluctantly, Dhritarashtra gave them permission to go to the Dwaitavana.

TWENTY-NINE

Duryodhana's ghosha-yatra

With an army of a thousand men, Duryodhana, Dusasana, Shakuni and Karna set out for the Dwaitavana. With them went their wives, richly clad and adorned, travelling in golden palanquins. Musicians, pauranikas, dancers and other court entertainers went, as well, in a colourful troupe; and they made their way to the forest in fine chariots.

A yojana outside the Dwaitavana, was a lake of sweet water, with a feast of lotuses on it. In some woods, a short way from the banks of this lake, the Kauravas set up an elaborate camp. They pitched tents, and furnished them with comforts hardly less than those of a palace. They had brought the finest cooks with them, and a surfeit of provisions. First, Duryodhana went dutifully to inspect the cattle. When the heads were counted, and recounted for good measure, all of which took three days, the Kaurava returned to his luxurious camp. The lake was not far from where the Pandavas had their asrama. But Duryodhana decided he would wait for his cousins to discover him; no blame would attach to him if they came to meet him of their own accord. Only if they did not, would he seek them out.

The first few days after the counting of the cattle were spent in an orgy of hunting. Strangely, or fatefully, the Pandavas, who were not far from all that savagery, heard nothing of their cousins' arrival in the forest. Then one day, Duryodhana decided he would like to swim in the lake with his wives. He sent some of his men through the woods to inspect the water. The lake was near enough his camp, and three Kaurava soldiers arrived quickly at its side.

As these scouts knelt beside the water, suddenly melodious voices hailed them from all around. From the trees stepped tall figures, clad in silvery mail that no smith of the world had forged. Their brightness filled the dim woods; their faces were at once solemn and blithe; when they spoke, it was as if there was always a song in their throats.

One said in a ringing voice, "Mortals, who are you?"

"Don't you know our king is bathing in the lake with his women?" asked another.

A third cried, "Dare you creep upon our king at his pleasure? As long as we are here, this lake is forbidden to humans."

Their voices were musical, but full of menace. Duryodhana's men stood rooted, they had never seen such wonderful beings before. The bravest of them mumbled, "Who shall I tell my prince says the lake is already taken?"

Laughing, the first tall one said, "Don't you know the gandharvas of Devaloka?"

Another had a bow in his hand and an arrow that shone like a band of the moon. "Begone mortals!"

When they sensed the woods were full of shadowy presences, the Kaurava soldiers quickly turned back to their camp. They came nervously before Duryodhana.

"Well?" said the Kaurava. "Is the lake fit to bathe in?"

"My lord," said one of his soldiers, "there are gandharvas in the woods. They say their king bathes in the lake with his women, and no mortal may approach the water."

Duryodhana frowned. "Did you tell them who I am?"

"No, my lord. They hardly gave us the chance."

"Go back and say that Duryodhana of the Kurus wants to bathe in the lake with his queens. Tell them to leave at once, or I will send my army to remove them."

The three soldiers took another ten men with them, and went back to the woods. They walked under the trees for a while, and saw nothing of the Elves. They hoped that, perhaps, the gandharva king had decided to leave the lake anyway, since he had been disturbed. They had not arrived at the water when, again, the dimness was full of tall figures materialized as if out of the very air.

"Didn't we warn you off from here, humans? Didn't we say our king bathes in the lake with his women?"

The Kaurava soldiers trembled just to see the gandharvas. Their presences were of untold age, yet it did not show on their bright faces or forms.

Mustering his courage, one of the soldiers declared, "The Kuru prince Duryodhana wants to swim in the lake with his wives. He orders you and your king out of here at once."

The gandharvas' laughter was like a terrible song among the trees. Their eyes glittered more fiercely still, so the soldiers longed to flee.

Another Kuru soldier managed to blurt, "Duryodhana warns you to obey him, or he will come here with his army."

Again the musical, ferocious laughter: so old and so young. "Dare a mortal command the gandharvas of heaven, as if they are his servants? The least among us is far beyond your puny prince. Go back and tell him to be grateful we haven't sent him your corpses as our reply to his insolence."

"Go!" cried the other Elves, and the soldiers obeyed with alacrity, for there was grave danger in their voices.

They came shamefaced before Duryodhana, who demanded, "Well? Have the gandharvas gone?"

"There were many of them, and we ten couldn't drive them away."

"Did you tell them what I said?"

"We did, my lord; but they laughed, and said they took no orders from any mortal. They said if we went back to the lake again, they would kill us."

"Dare they! Gather the army. Tell Karna, Dusasana and Shakuni there is better sport about than hunting deer. We will show these singing celestials the might of the Kuru legions."

Two gandharva sentinels in their tree-perches at the edge of the woods saw the Kuru army approach, with Duryodhana, Dusasana and Karna at its head. They flew back to their king at the lake.

"Chitrasena, the army of mortals approaches."

"How many are they?" asked Arjuna's friend and master.

"Some hundreds, my lord."

"We are fifty. It will be a fair encounter," smiled the gandharva, wiping his body with a cloth of tender leaves. "We will fight them."

The Kuru force arrived at the edge of the trees, when, all at once, strange cries erupted among the trees. There seemed to be a thousand Elves in the darkling wood; so thickly and furiously did their arrows fly out to greet the soldiers of Hastinapura. And they were no common shafts but full of light and fear, each becoming ten, and every one deadly.

The first wave of Kuru soldiers, those that did not fall, turned and fled. Karna blew a blast on his hunting-horn and plunged his chariot forward. Arrows as wizardly as the gandharvas' shafts streamed from his bow and each one found its mark. Karna brought the Elves tumbling from their trees, shot through their arms and chests, crying out in their sweet voices.

Duryodhana, Shakuni and Dusasana came to join the fray and, though they were deathless folk, the gandharvas were driven back. The Elves realized these were no ordinary soldiers, but kshatriyas, and masters of astras.

In a wink, the woods emptied, the immortals vanished like the breeze. Duryodhana's army surged forward, roaring in triumph; and behind the fighting men, came the Kaurava women, borne in their golden litters: so assured was the Kuru prince. Meanwhile, the gandharvas were back at the water, under the spreading tree where their king lay among his women.

Breathless came his fifty to Chitrasena, and cried, "They have at least three masters of astras with them; one, especially, fights like no kshatriya of the earth. He wears golden mail, as if it is his very skin, and earrings of gold that gleam as if the Sun himself dwells in them! We cannot turn them back, Chitrasena; you must come yourself to fight."

Chitrasena said thoughtfully, "The golden warrior must be Karna. He is, indeed, the blood of Surya Deva. Yet, he is only a mortal."

Slowly Chitrasena rose, and he was taller than the rest of his people. His face shone, and, now that he prepared for battle, his eyes were like drops of star-fire. One of his lovely women strapped on his quiver for him, and it was light as a breath. Chitrasena picked up his slender bow; but he did not go to fight Duryodhana's force on foot. He took his women and climbed into the vimana that waited for him, not touching the ground.

Flitting through the trees like some weird spirit of the future, that disk flew at the Kuru army. At an open panel, sat Chitrasena: fierce and brilliant. From his silver bow, a storm of arrows hummed. They were shafts of sorcery and assailed the Kuru army with dark phantasms.

Terrifying spectres beset Karna and Shakuni, Duryodhana and Dusasana, and all their soldiers. Nightmares stalked the trees. Monsters out of dreams howled at them. A hundred vimanas flew at them, shining and smooth, every one full of fear. As a man, Duryodhana's men turned and ran.

Bemused by the flashing armada in the air and on the ground, and by the hallucinations in the woods, Karna reined in his chariot. But the gandharva king's arrows brought not only dreams and illusions; other shafts brought death, very real and final. In moments, hundreds of fleeing Kuru soldiers were cut down. Chitrasena's fifty warriors fought from the trees. They were angry at their earlier rout, and irresistible now that their king led them.

Chitrasena's vimana was everywhere. Five blinding arrows incinerated Karna's chariot. Roaring, he leapt into a fresh ratha and fought on. But Chitrasena had seen that he was the greatest threat: he pursued Karna in the flitting vimana, and consumed his new chariot as well. Karna could not possibly fight the gandharvas from the ground. Most unnerving were their musical cries; they were so haunting you wanted to throw down your bow and run away.

Karna fled the battle, and then no one else could even remotely stand up to Chitrasena. The Kuru soldiers ran any way they could. Shakuni, too, quickly decided flight was better than valour.

Yet, there was one Kuru made of sterner stuff: Duryodhana stood his ground, roaring, a tide of fire flowing from his bow. But he was almost alone; only Dusasana and a few of his brothers stood with him. Chitrasena fought them from the air, from the trees and open ground, flying circles around them.

When all the other kshatriyas had fled, fifty gandharvas turned just on Duryodhana, Dusasana and their brothers. Duryodhana's chariot was smashed under him. In a flash, a score of the immortals surrounded him and brought him captive to Chitrasena, who seized him by his hair and flung him into a metallic net, like an animal. Dusasana and all his brothers who stayed to fight were taken.

The palanquin-bearers of the Kuru princesses were neither kshatriyas nor heroes. They had panicked at Chitrasena's first attack and, dropping their precious burdens, fled. In all their finery, dripping jewels, Duryodhana's wives were seized by Chitrasena's gandharvas and flung tardily into the wide net. The desperate litter-bearers, and some panicstricken soldiers with them, came flying through the forest to the Pandavas' asrama. Yudhishtira sat before a sacramental fire at his daily worship, with his brothers around him.

The Kaurava soldiers came and fell on their faces before the Pandavas. Those men cried, "Yudhishtira, save us! A gandharva has captured Duryodhana and his queens. You must help us or they will die."

Bheema began to laugh. He clapped his hands and cried, "Well done, Gandharvas! I am happy to know we have some friends left in the world. Fate has caught up with our cousin. He came here to gloat, and he has the payment he deserves. Those who wish evil upon others find it for themselves!"

And he laughed again loudly. But Yudhishtira laid a hand on his brother's arm. "This is no time to gloat, Bheema. The Kauravas are our cousins, and between cousins, there will be misunderstandings. But they are our blood, our family, and no outsider should harm them. The gandharvas have taken not only Duryodhana and his brothers, but their women. The women of our Kuru clan."

Bheema began to speak, but Yudhishtira held his hand up and silenced him. "The Kauravas are our enemies, certainly, but our own honour is at stake here. Arm yourself Bheema; take Arjuna, Nakula and Sahadeva with you. Go and free our cousins."

Bheema was livid. He cried, "What are you saying, Yudhishtira? You may be able to forget everything they have done to us; yes, with your yagnas and your dhyana, you may forget. But not I! They are paying for their sins, and they have brought this punishment on themselves. You cannot ask me to fight the gandharva. Why, I consider him my dearest friend, and I am in his debt forever!"

But with the anger of a patient man, potent because it is so rare, Yudhishtira flashed at his brother, "Aren't you ashamed of yourself? You sit here and let someone you don't even know steal sacred revenge from you. Are you a coward, a weakling, or both, that you allow a stranger take what is yours? Go and rescue them, Bheema. Only then will you be able to keep your oath, when the time comes."

Bheema looked startled; he had not thought of it like that. Yudhishtira took him aside and, lowering his voice, said, "Knowing our cousin, I am sure Duryodhana wronged the gandharva. Yet, the Elf has taken not only him, but his wives. We can't stand for that. The Kauravas are our enemies; they are a hundred against our five. But when an outsider attacks our kin, we must always be a hundred and five.

"Bheema, receiving a boon from a God, inheriting a kingdom or having a son are fortunes indeed. But saving an enemy's life is a pleasure equal to all those three put together!"

Bheema bowed, "You are right again, Yudhishtira. I will fight the gandharvas."

Yudhishtira hugged him, "Try talking to the celestial first. Only if he doesn't listen, speak with weapons. Jaya vijayi bhava!"

THIRTY

The shaming of Duryodhana

THE FOUR YOUNGER PANDAVAS SET OUT, TAKING DURYODHANA'S men with them. When they were still some way from the lake, they saw gandharvas in the trees, moving with the ease of wild animals. With them were the Kauravas they had taken captive, Duryodhana, Dusasana, their brothers and wives. Arjuna shot a clutch of arrows over the Elves' heads. They stopped and turned angrily, weapons appearing in their hands as if by magic.

Arjuna cried, "Release my brother Duryodhana, prince of the Kurus!"

The gandharvas laughed at him. One cried back, "Mortal, haven't you learnt your lesson yet? I told you, we take no orders from anyone but our king."

Duryodhana's face was a picture when he saw the Pandavas. Arjuna cried, "Gandharvas, you have taken my cousins' women captive. Release them, or the earth will drink your unearthly blood."

"Brave words, mortal!" said the gandharva, laughing melodiously. "And strangely, I think I have seen you somewhere before. But, Kshatriya, we have just routed an army of a thousand men, and you four want battle with us?"

Arjuna raised his bow. "We four are four armies. Release them or fight!"

"Then fight!" cried the gandharva, and the fifty Elves stood against the four Pandavas, with weapons raised.

Battle ensued, swift and fierce. The dark woods lit up with shafts of fire and light. What Yudhishtira said about strangers depriving them of their revenge had touched his brothers deeply; they fought as if their lives depended on this battle. The gandharvas filled those woods with illusions again.

But ranged against them now was Arjuna the Pandava, himself a master of the weapons of maya. He shot a golden shaft from his Gandiva. It exploded in stardust, and the hallucinations vanished.

After this, there was no containing the Pandavas. Vimanas appeared like mirages among the trees, and the gandharvas bundled their captives into these, clambered in themselves and flashed away. But Arjuna was not about to let them escape. He filled the sky with a cloud of arrows, which lashed the elven ships with molten showers. The quicksilver discs flew down again, prisoners and all.

And now the biggest gandharva vimana took to the air under Arjuna's cloak of fire. At a clear panel in that craft stood Chitrasena. From his silver bow, a storm of light beset the Pandavas, who stood chariotless on the ground. Those shafts brought new illusions, not of fear, but delight. The Pandavas saw naked apsaras beckoning from the thickets. The fragrances of Devaloka filled the twilight woods, so the brothers wanted to fling their weapons down. Who wanted to fight, when heaven had come to the earth around them? Delicious languor filled their limbs.

But Arjuna had learnt all about these weapons of enchantment in Amravati, from Chitrasena himself. He did not know yet who the gandharva in the vimana was, but he knew the astra to dispel his visions. When this was done, in a moment, he covered the vimana with a volley of arrows that locked together in a shroud around the disc, and drew it down inescapably to earth.

Arjuna was surprised the Elf gave in so easily. The brothers stood with their bows raised, as the vimana descended. But when the tall gandharva king stepped out of his craft, and Arjuna saw his face by the dying light, he gave a shout. "Chitrasena!"

He threw down his bow and ran to embrace the unearthly warrior with starlight in his hair. Arjuna brought Chitrasena to Bheema and the twins, and said, "This is Chitrasena, my master of music and dance. And these are my brothers, Bheema, Nakula and Sahadeva."

They bowed to one another; Chitrasena greeted them in old speech, he blessed them in the starry tongue of the gandharvas. Around them now the other Elves appeared with their prisoners. Looking at

Duryodhana, who stood between two of his captors, his hands tied behind his back with green vine, his head hung, Arjuna said to Chitrasena, "Why have you taken our cousin and his women? They came to Dwaitavana to count their cattle. What harm have they done you?"

The gandharva took Arjuna aside. "His heart is black, the one you call your cousin. He is a devil, full of malice and conceit. He did not come to count cattle but to gloat. He brought his wives with him to make Panchali suffer. Indra knew what Duryodhana was plotting.

"Indra said to me, 'Go and protect your friend.' Arjuna, these are my prisoners, fairly taken in battle. They are so full of arrogance they don't deserve to be free. I will release them only to Yudhishtira. After I tell him why the Kauravas came to the jungle, let your brother decide what he will do with them."

So all of them went into the Kamyaka, to the asrama where Yudhishtira had just finished his worship. Chitrasena dragged Duryodhana along, his head bent low and not a word from him. Yudhishtira received the gandharva graciously.

Chitrasena said, "He came to gloat over your privation. Say a word, and he will die."

But Yudhishtira looked alarmed. "I thank God you did not kill them, Chitrasena. Ah, my cousin is miserable. Let him and his brothers and women be free."

Chitrasena said, "So be it then." He nodded to his people, and they cut Duryodhana and the others loose.

Chitrasena embraced Arjuna, and bowed to the other Pandavas. The chariots of the sky had followed him here. He climbed into his vimana, and so did the rest of the gandharvas. Noiselessly those craft lifted into the air, a shining squadron, and flashed away quicker than time.

When the sky was clear, Yudhishtira turned to Duryodhana. He laid a hand on his shoulder and said, "Being spiteful never brought anyone joy. Go back to Hastinapura, and don't be so rash again. Go in peace, I wish you well."

All that while, ever since he was taken by the gandharvas, Duryodhana stood with his head bent down into his chest, so no one saw the shame in his eyes. Without a word, for he had no voice to speak with, and his face and heart burning, he stalked out of the Pandavas' asrama with his brothers and his wives.

When the Kauravas had gone, the asrama echoed with laughter. It was Bheema laughing, and Draupadi with him.

"Did you see his face?" Panchali cried.

"Ah, that was sweet!" roared Bheema.

But Yudhishtira looked at them so sternly that they stopped.

THIRTY-ONE

Despair

IN A DAZE, DURYODHANA STUMBLED OUT OF THE PANDAVAS' ASRAMA. He didn't say a word to his brothers or his wives. His retinue followed him in silence, fearing his wrath if they dared speak. Night had fallen, and a burnished moon rose above the Kaurava party. They came to a small river that flowed beside the path on which they walked. Duryodhana stopped, and signalled that they should make camp for the night.

Tents were pitched, fires lit and food cooked. But Duryodhana sat apart from the others, staring across the river. Dusasana came to call him to eat, but his brother waved him away. The night wore on and, exhausted by the day's adventure, the other Kuru princes fell asleep. Their women slept, as well, and the soldiers. Only Duryodhana sat on the riverbank, gazing dully at the moon riding on the water, his eyes seeing nothing.

Early the next morning, they heard horses' hooves and shouts approaching the camp. It was Karna. He rode up like a storm, leapt down from his chariot and embraced Duryodhana.

"O Kshatriya!" cried Karna. "You vanquished the gandharva. I did my best, but he was invincible: an archer from Devaloka, his weapons unearthly. How did you beat him, Duryodhana? I am amazed."

Duryodhana had not uttered a word. Now he turned his face up to Karna, and tears flowed down his cheeks.

Karna was taken aback. "What is this? Why are you crying?"

With a sob, Duryodhana confessed, "It was not I, but Arjuna who beat the gandharva."

"Arjuna?"

"We were routed by the Elves. They took us all. Then, Bheema, Arjuna, Nakula and Sahadeva arrived and gave them battle. Arjuna filled the sky with fire, so the gandharva king Chitrasena had to fly down to the ground. When he got out of his vimana Arjuna ran to embrace him, because they are friends. Chitrasena knew why we came to the forest, and he told the Pandavas everything. Arjuna asked him to free us. The gandharva said he would not, unless Yudhishtira wanted it.

"So we went to the asrama in the Kamyaka, after all; ah, Karna, not as we intended, but in shame! Bound hand and foot like some thief, I stood before my cousin, praying the earth would open and swallow me. The gandharva said to Yudhishtira, 'You decide their fate. They came to gloat over your privation.' Of course, the noble Yudhishtira told Chitrasena to set us free. Can you imagine what I felt then, Karna? Death could not be so terrible.

"When we were free, and Chitrasena had flown off in his vimana, Yudhishtira turns to me in his gentle, maddening way, and says, 'Being spiteful never brought anyone joy. Go back to Hastinapura, and don't be so rash again. Go in peace, I wish you well.'

"He wished me well! I stood there, wishing I was dead. How much better it would have been for me to have died fighting the gandharvas than have the Pandavas save my wretched life. Karna, what is my life worth now, that I owe it to my cousins? I do not want to live any more. As I left their asrama, I heard Bheema laughing and that slut as well. I can't bear to go back to Hastinapura. I have decided to stay here, and not eat or drink until my miserable spirit has left my body. And then, perhaps, some honour will be salvaged from this shame."

Duryodhana turned emotionally to Dusasana, "My brother, go back to Hastinapura and become king in my place. Rule wisely, with Karna and Shakuni beside you. Always be a sanctuary to your friends, and generous to your brahmanas. Mix justice with mercy when you judge a crime. There is no one better to teach you discernment than our uncle Vidura."

Dusasana began to cry. Duryodhana turned back to Karna, "My friend, I thought you and I would rule the world together. All that is just a dream now; this is the end for me. But you must always be at Dusasana's side, and make him a better king than I was."

With a wail, Dusasana fell at his feet, "What are you saying? How can you even think of dying, when we all depend on you? And you are asking me to be king in your place, while you die? The earth will split in two before that happens. The sky will fall into the sea and the sun spin loose from his orbit, before I rule in my brother's place!

"How dare you say this to me? Is this how much you love me? Do you wish all our brothers dead, that you speak of killing yourself? Don't ever say such things, you are my very life!"

Duryodhana raised him up and they both sobbed like boys. Karna said, "What is this crying and moaning over nothing, Kuru princes? It was just a childish prank we came on, and we were caught out. Let me tell you, the Pandavas did not help you out of any love, only for their precious dharma. They would have done the same for anyone.

"Besides, do you think they did not realize what a humiliation it would be for you, that it was they who saved you lives? And you talk of killing yourself. You are doing exactly what they want. Who will be happier than Pandu's sons if Duryodhana kills himself? Think with your head, my friend, and not your grief. Come back to Hastinapura. If you kill yourself, you will be the laughing-stock of the kshatriyas of the earth."

"I agree with Karna!" cried another voice. Shakuni had arrived, unnoticed. "You talk of killing yourself over such a petty thing? I am amazed at you, Duryodhana. This is unmanly. It shows an immature nature: too used to comfort, unfamiliar with pain.

"If you are so concerned that you have wronged your cousins, why not go and make up with them, since they saved your life? If you think your reputation is ruined, restore it by returning their kingdom to Pandu's sons. Repay their noble gesture by being even nobler. Yudhishtira did certainly treat you like his brother. You do the same: return Indraprastha to them, if you dare, instead of killing yourself like a coward."

Then, Shakuni's voice was a familiar hiss again. "Remember, you can only kill your enemies if you are alive yourself!"

But for once, Duryodhana was unmoved by even his suave uncle. That prince said sadly, "Shakuni, I have nothing more to do with any of that. I care nothing for wealth, kingdom, honour, friendship or pleasure. I beg you, leave me alone! I have decided to die, and no power on earth will stop me. All of you go back to Hastinapura, and let me die in peace."

He rose and walked away from the others, down the riverbank by himself. When he found a secluded spot, hidden by a screen of thornbushes, Duryodhana cast off his royal robes. He put on a simple cloth he had brought with him, a rag he had taken from a common soldier. He gathered an armful of kusa grass, spread it on the ground, and sat on it facing west in the posture of the lotus. He began to pray, fully intending to die.

The day wore on, and Duryodhana sat with his breath controlled, and his eyes shut. Twilight came, and then night fell. There was no semblance of peace in the Kuru prince's heart. Turbulent thoughts, frenzied anxieties, hunted one another through his mind. He heard Bheema's scornful laughter. He heard Yudhishtira's gentle voice, 'Go in peace, I wish you well.' He saw the handsome face of Chitrasena, his eyes bright and mocking.

And soon, his life began to play itself out in chaotic pictures in Duryodhana's mind: his childhood, his adolescent cruelties, and the day the Pandavas first came to Hastinapura. His loves flashed before his eyes; then, the day of the gambling, when he had his cousins banished. Ah, that was such a sweet day. He sighed to think of that day's triumph, when he won a kingdom at a game of dice!

Then he thought of death and he shivered. He knew his time to die had not come. There was so much he still wanted to achieve, most of all ... yes, he wanted to see Yudhishtira and his brothers dead. Only that would put out the fire in his soul.

The night wore on. The Kaurava did not stir, though pangs of hunger began to roil him.

THIRTY-TWO

The powers of darkness

ALL CREATION IS RULED, IN TURNS, BY THE FORCES OF DARKNESS AND light: the earth as well. Both forces have their own creatures in the world, ordinary men and those with great power. The Kauravas and the Pandavas served opposite causes.

On another world, the Daityas and Danavas, who are the masters of evil in the universe, had recently suffered some reversals at the hands of the Devas. They were cast out of the higher realms, and back down to the patalas and narakas, where they belonged. The two sides fought bitterly for sovereignty over the middle region, the earth: most of all, since Krishna was born.

These were the days of a yugasandhi, a cusp of ages between a dwapara and a kali yuga. Krishna's mission was to ensure that no power of evil survived into the coming, lesser age, to dominate it.

The powers of darkness were losing what was, just years ago, a stranglehold over the earth and its affairs. Krishna had killed Kamsa, Jarasandha, and thousands of other incarnate demons. Now an ancient mantle of evil had fallen on the shoulders of Duryodhana of Hastinapura. He was the last hope of the forces of tyranny and violence on earth, for Krishna had swept the other evil ones before him in a tide of light.

And now Duryodhana sat beside the river, having decided to kill himself.

In grim patala, under world, domain of perpetual twilight, some of the most powerful Demons sat in conclave. Many of them were as old as the earth herself. Some had great saurian forms. Some were humanoid, but huge, their eyes dreadful; and still others were unquiet vapours. They saw what Duryodhana meant to do, and their persuasions within his mind seemed to have no effect on the Kuru prince. He had grown numb, and seemed determined to die.

Those Asuras lit a fire of yagna and sat around it chanting eerie mantras. The fire blazed dark and high; as the incantations grew more resonant, a kritya, a naked female spirit, appeared among the flames. She was tall as a palm tree, her eyes burning, her hair flames, and her body a cool fire.

She stood before the monsters that had summoned her, and said in a hollow voice, "Command me, masters of the night. Why have I been called from the pit?"

In fell voices, the Demons said, "Fly up to the earth and fetch the Kuru prince Duryodhana to us."

Duryodhana, who sat with his eyes shut beside the river, fell into a dream. He dreamt a fierce and naked woman flew down out of the air and plucked him up in her arms. Before he could ask who she was, in the way of dreams she was bearing him far away, to a remote land. All was dim in that country. They flew at breathless speed over mysterious continents and seas, and she brought him to a hidden island and a crystal cave that was a palace.

In a secret chamber within that palace an emerald fire burned, and around it sat a group of the strangest old men Duryodhana had ever seen. They were fair and dark, big and small. They were somehow unreal: as if their present forms were appearances assumed for Duryodhana's eyes, and they looked very different when they were truly themselves. Duryodhana was inexplicably comforted in their presence; he felt a deep sense of belonging. He felt he knew these strange men from another life, and knew them well.

The smallest, but the eldest, Demon said to Duryodhana in an echoing voice, "King of men, how can you think of killing yourself, when there is so much you must still accomplish? The very purpose of your birth!"

Another, a graybeard, said, "Kshatriya, you are no ordinary mortal. We worshipped Siva and the Devi with a thousand yagnas, so you would be born. Above the waist, your body was made by Mahadeva out of impenetrable vajras. Below the waist, the Devi herself made your form from the flowers of heaven, to please the women of earth. You were created by Siva and Uma."

Another said in a woman's voice, "You must rule the earth. Narakasura's spirit has entered Karna: you have nothing to fear from Arjuna, Karna will kill him. Millions of Danavas and Daityas have been born into the world of men, to be your legions. The Pandavas cannot stand against you, Duryodhana!"

"Don't let a petty defeat deflect you from your true purpose, Kaurava," said the first one who had spoken. "Yours and ours is a great destiny. We shall rule the earth for a thousand years of the Devas. It is an older war than you think that you fight. It is almost the dawning of the kali yuga. We must win the war on the crack of the ages, and win it we shall. You are never alone, Duryodhana; we are always with you, proud spirit!"

Those Demons blessed him with bizarre mantras, and laid their ashen hands on his head. The woman of fire picked him up in her cool arms again, and flew back into the world. When she set him down, she stroked his face briefly and vanished. Duryodhana awoke with a start. He saw it was dawn, and Karna sat before him on the riverbank, gazing curiously at his face.

Gently, Karna stroked his friend's cheek. "Duryodhana, do you think the Pandavas have forgiven you for everything, just because they rescued you from the gandharva? No, they kept you alive only so they could have the satisfaction of killing you themselves. Oh my friend, does Arjuna's archery fill you with dread? I swear I will kill him for you. Drona, Dusasana, all your brothers, Bheeshma and Aswatthama are with you. What force on earth can stand against us?"

Karna grasped Duryodhana's hand, and cried, "I will kill Arjuna! You shall kill Bheema! As for the other three, any of our warriors can finish them. You must never think of killing yourself, vast power and kingdom are written for you. But is that a smile on your face? Tell me you have abandoned your madness!"

With a cry, Duryodhana embraced Karna. He said, "Let us return to Hastinapura! I am resolved to fight. Either I will kill the Pandavas and rule the earth, or killed by them in war, I will find heaven for myself. Let there be no more cowards' talk among us. My life's purpose is clear to me now."

Karna noticed the change in his friend. There was a new maturity and determination about Duryodhana, as if he had undergone some profound experience in the night. The Kuru prince did not tell Karna what it was; in fact, he hardly remembered it himself. Arm in arm, they walked to Karna's chariot. The rest of the Kuru force had gone back in dismay to Hastinapura, Duryodhana's queens in panic. As soon as they arrived, the news spread like fire through the city.

Duryodhana returned to Hastinapura with Karna and made his appearance in court, as casually as ever. Dhritarashtra clasped his son to him, choking, for he had feared the worst. Even as he held Duryodhana in his arms, his blind father sensed a new cold resolve in the prince: as if he had grown up suddenly. A little frightened by him, the king returned to his throne.

But Bheeshma spoke his mind that day. He said, "I told you, my child, not to go to the forest. You could not face the gandharva, could you? Not you or your Karna, in whom you place all your faith. But Arjuna and his brothers had Chitrasena's measure. Do you know why? Because they have dharma with them. On this earth, there is no force equal to the power of dharma.

"It is as if the Gods themselves have spoken to you, Duryodhana, and they have warned you. Go back to the forest, make peace with your cousins. You have seen how powerful they are. Beg their forgiveness, and bring them home in honour. Do it today, my son: if not for the Pandavas' sake, then for your own."

Bheeshma was hopeful that, after the rout in the forest, he could persuade Duryodhana to see the light of sanity. The Kuru patriarch could not have been more mistaken. Duryodhana stood there in that sabha, staring blankly at Bheeshma for a moment. Then the prince threw back his head and, as he had never done yet, laughed in his grandsire's face. With that, he nodded to Shakuni who also rose from his place. Both walked out of the Kuru sabha, in contempt, while Bheeshma's face was scarlet with the insult.

Duryodhana and his inner circle sat in council. There was surely a new sense of purpose about the Kaurava. He said, "Ever since Yudhishtira performed a Rajasuya in Indraprastha, I, too, have longed to undertake one here in Hastinapura. To show the world that we are no less than our cousins." He turned to Karna, "Only you, my friend, can realize this dream for me."

Karna said, "This is what I love to hear from you! Old Bheeshma always extols the sons of Pandu, as if you are less than they are in some way. He looks down on me also, and his condescension scathes me. It took five Pandavas to subdue Bharatavarsha, and to hold a Rajasuya yagna in Indraprastha. For you, Duryodhana, I will conquer the earth on my own, and bring its kings in fealty to your sacrifice. Gather your brahmanas for the yagna. I am ready to ride today."

Duryodhana had the brahmanas fetched. They demurred, "You cannot think of a Rajasuya yagna while Yudhishtira lives."

But Duryodhana growled at them, "Can a hermit in exile, who has no kingdom, no army, no wealth, who wears deerskin and tree-bark, be considered the Lord of the earth? The very idea is absurd. The throne of Bharatavarsha is empty, and I have decided to be the emperor that sits on it."

The brahmanas saw a new Duryodhana before them: a mature man who knew his time was limited. They said, "So be it, then; only the greatest kshatriyas are given the ambition of a Rajasuya yagna. Choose the auspicious ground where you will perform the yagna, turn the earth with your own hands, and have a sabha built for the sacrifice. But first, you must subdue all the kings of the world; most of all, those who are your enemies."

"Find the auspicious ground, then," said Duryodhana. "And find an auspicious day for the Kuru army to ride under Karna's command!"

So, while in Hastinapura feverish preparations got underway for the yagna, Karna rode out at the head of a Kuru army to conquer the kingdoms of the earth. He quelled Drupada first, in single combat, just as Arjuna once had. News of this victory went before Karna, and hearing it, hardly any other king dared fight him. Those that welcomed him, acknowledging Duryodhana's sovereignty, he invited graciously to the Rajasuya. Those who gave battle to the Kuru army, he swiftly quelled. Karna was like a thousand kshatriyas in battle; he was prodigious and irresistible.

When he rode back in triumph to Hastinapura, a spectacular, if garish, sabha had been raised for the royal yagna. Duryodhana came to the gates to welcome his conquering Senapati. Embracing him, the Kaurava prince cried, "As long as you are with me, I will definitely rule the earth!"

Karna replied, "That is your destiny, my friend!"

But when some of the older brahmanas learnt that Duryodhana would perform the Rajasuya yagna, they raised an objection. "Dhritarashtra lives, and he is king of the Kurus. How can you perform the Rajasuya in your own name, while your father is alive? The world will scoff at you."

Duryodhana roared, "Have all Karna's conquests have been in vain? Does the glory he won for me amount to nothing?"

They saw his mood was dangerous. Quickly, the brahmanas said, "There is another yagna you can perform, as great as the Rajasuya. Indeed, only Mahavishnu himself has ever performed that sacrifice, in the most ancient days."

"Which yagna is this?"

"The Vaishnava yagna."

"Let it be the Vaishnava yagna then. Let the holiest brahmanas be invited to it, and let every king who owes us allegiance be present. It must be the greatest sacrifice of these times." Duryodhana was thoughtful for a moment. "Let us not be accused of not inviting the sons of Pandu. Dusasana, send someone to the Kamyaka vana to ask Yudhishtira and his brothers to attend our Vaishnava yagna."

"Let us see if they will come as easily in your time of glory, as they did when you were in trouble," said Karna.

The same day, a messenger rode to the asrama in the Kamyaka vana. The man came before Yudhishtira and, bowing, said, "My lord, the Kuru prince Duryodhana is to perform a Vaishnava yagna in Hastinapura. King Dhritarashtra and my lords Duryodhana and Dusasana have sent me to invite you and your brothers to the sacrifice."

The man stood waiting for an answer. Yudhishtira said pleasantly, "So Duryodhana means to perform Vishnu's own sacrifice. My brothers and I would have been delighted to come, but we have sworn not to enter Hastinapura until we have served thirteen years in exile."

For good measure, Bheema growled, "And when the thirteen years are served, we will return to Hastinapura. Tell Duryodhana we shall come for another sacrifice then, and he and his brothers will be the sacrificial goats!"

Yudhishtira said, "Hush, Bheema. What has this poor man done to offend you? He is only his master's messenger, come to invite us to a sacrifice."

But of course, along with Yudhishtra's, Bheema's message was borne back to Duryodhana. However, preparations for the yagna were underway, and all Duryodhana said was, "They are afraid our yagna will be greater than theirs."

And there were many in Hastinapura, most of whom had not attended Yudhishtira's Rajasuya in Indraprastha, who said Duryodhana's Vaishnava yagna was the greatest sacrifice in living memory. There is no denying that, largely, the people of Hastina felt proud. But there were others, albeit a few, who whispered, "Duryodhana's Vaishnava yagna is not a tenth the sacrifice that Yudhishtira's Rajasuya was."

"Whatever you say, a Rajasuya is a Rajasuya."

"This yagnashala does not compare with the one outside the Mayaa sabha. Nor are the priests as holy."

"The truly great brahmanas would not come, because they know Duryodhana is an evil prince."

Yet, mainly, the people of Hastinapura were overjoyed, and they thought this was the most magnificent yagna they had seen. They came and blessed their blind king and his son, who was now an emperor in his own right. At the end of the sacrifice, Duryodhana came before his elders, Bheeshma, Dhritarashtra, Vidura, Drona, Kripa and the others, and paid homage to them. And on that day, even Bheeshma and Vidura were full of nothing but praise for him.

In the public sabha, Duryodhana embraced Karna and cried, "Here is the greatest warrior of this age! Without him my yagna would never have been possible."

The people roared their approval. Later, in private, an exultant Duryodhana said to Karna, "With you at my side, we shall soon rule the earth without a rival. And then I will perform not the Vaishnava, but the Rajasuya yagna."

Karna cried, "You will, Duryodhana! I have said this often enough, but today I swear a solemn oath." He flung down the goblet of wine in his hand, shattering it on the floor. "I will neither drink wine nor eat any meat until I have killed Arjuna!"

His pale eyes shining, Duryodhana said, "The Pandavas are dead men."

THIRTY-THREE

The Rishi Durvasa

THE KAMYAKA FOREST ABOUNDED IN GAME, AND HERE, IN THEIR BY now familiar asrama, the Pandavas spent the twelfth year of their exile. Again, Vyasa appeared unexpectedly, and spent some days with his grandsons. The muni was full of old lore and wisdom, and Yudhishtira would always press him to share some of what he knew.

Once, when they sat together under the nyagrodha tree, Vyasa said with a sigh, "Life is never purely dark or bright, but always a mixture of both. When good fortune comes, one must know how to enjoy it without losing one's wits. And when misfortune is one's lot, one must know how to bear it with fortitude, to survive, and, yes, to learn wisdom from it. For suffering is a greater teacher than any other in the world."

They sat in silence for a while, and the silence of the Rishi Vyasa was an eloquent thing. Of all his ancestors, Yudhishtira was happiest to trace his lineage back to this seer; as frequently happens with eldest grandsons and their grandfathers.

That day, Yudhishtira asked, "Which gives a man more punya, charity or asceticism?"

Vyasa said with no hesitation, "Charity is hard, my son. At the best of times, it is difficult to give away what one has earned with toil. Always give charity to those that are needy. One may deceive oneself that asceticism is more difficult than charity, but this is not true."

Thus the twelfth year of their exile passed. Many illustrious sages came and went from the asrama. Some were contemplative men, of resonant quietness, who spoke more with silence than words; others were flamboyant munis full of brilliant conversation and fabulous stories. And it was never a problem to feed the visitors: Draupadi depended on the copper plate of the Sun, which never let her down. Of course, she always ate last, after the others had finished, since once she had eaten the platter became empty.

Inevitably, word of the Sun's platter travelled to Hastinapura, and to Duryodhana, whose vanity had swollen considerably after the Vaishnava yagna, now that he was a king himself. But the Kaurava knew, in some niggling way, that his Vaishnava yagna had not been equal to Yudhishtira's Rajasuya. This knowledge lay in his heart like a live ember.

More than ever, Duryodhana was obsessed by the thought of his cousins in the vana, and their return, which drew nearer each day. When he heard how they entertained the munis of the wide world, how the humble asrama in the forest had become as much a focus of wisdom as Indraprastha had been, Duryodhana was livid with envy.

He dare not attack the Pandavas in the forest, but he spent all his days thinking of how to harm them. Then, as if in response to his wishes, one day Durvasa arrived in Hastinapura with a hundred followers.

Duryodhana rushed out to meet the rishi, who was as much a legend for his swift temper as his spiritual power. Why, Durvasa once cursed the Devas to become mortal: and the amrita was churned up from the Kshirasagara. That was in the earliest days of the first krita yuga. No one knew how old Durvasa Muni was. Many believed him to be an incarnation of Rudra, and this accounted for his temper.

Sensing a heavensent opportunity, Duryodhana came to the gates of Hastinapura to welcome Durvasa, as he had never been welcomed to any city before. The Kaurava himself washed the rishi's feet, then, with every show of honour, showed him to an opulent apartment in his palace. One could see at a glance why people feared Durvasa so much. He was full of a restless energy, as if he was already on his way to another place, when he had barely been received in this one. He was a towering figure, with a leonine head: a sage from a nobler time; his flashing eyes missed nothing around him.

The moment he was seated, Durvasa cried imperiously, "Fetch me food, quickly! Have my munis eaten? We don't have all day to waste here."

His tone would have been intolerable in another guest. Wherever he went, it was his way of provoking his hosts; and heaven help them if they dared answer him back in similar vein. It was said Durvasa always had a curse ready on the tip of his tongue. Discretion was invariably the wiser course when one dealt with this muni, and Duryodhana was the very soul of that virtue now. The usually arrogant Kaurava fawned over his guest.

At last, Durvasa finished eating, and he had only nibbled at the delicacies set before him. He sat back, and suddenly his face softened into a smile that creased his face in kindly wrinkles.

The muni said, "Duryodhana, you are not at all like what the world says you are. You are kind and considerate. You have honoured me, as I have not been for a long time. Why, you served me with your own hands like a kitchen boy. I don't care what the world says; I judge you as I find you myself. Noble king, I want to grant you a boon. Ask me for anything, and you shall have it."

Duryodhana said at once, "My cousin Yudhishtira lives in the Kamyaka vana. Let it please my lord to visit him in the forest, and seek his legendary hospitality. Only, holy one, arrive in his asrama when Panchali has finished eating."

Durvasa was a little startled at the strange boon the Kaurava wanted; but he was bound to grant Duryodhana whatever he asked. So it was that, when he left Hastinapura, Durvasa and his party of a hundred made straight for the Kamyaka aranya, and Yudhishtira's asrama. They arrived late in the afternoon when Durvasa knew, clairvoyantly, that Draupadi had finished eating.

Yudhishtira came out to welcome the sage and his party. Reverently, the eldest Pandava washed Durvasa's feet. The rishi cried, "We are starving, Yudhishtira. And we have heard about the unworldly fare Draupadi serves in this asrama."

Behind the door of the wooden hut, Draupadi gave a groan. Innocent of her plight, Yudhishtira said, "My lord, there is a river nearby where you can wash. I will show you the way, and we will have a meal served for you when you return."

Yudhishtira called Draupadi, "Panchali, we are going to the river. Have food ready for our guests when we return."

He and his brothers walked away into the forest with their visitors. Draupadi felt faint. She had just eaten and had washed the platter clean. Where would she find food for Durvasa and his disciples? Like everyone else, Draupadi had heard of the rishi's temper.

She sat on the floor with her head in her hands, and whispered in despair, "Krishna, help me!"

Hardly had she said this, when a bright voice hailed her from the door. "I am starving, Panchali! Give me something to eat, quickly."

She jumped up with a cry. There he was, the Dark One, wearing a pitambara robe, the peacock-feather gleaming above his head. Draupadi wailed, "Krishna, there is nothing to eat here! I have just eaten myself, and washed the Sun's platter clean. Durvasa and a hundred of his munis have arrived, and they are hungry. Yudhishtira took them to the river, and they will return any moment. When Durvasa finds there is nothing to eat, he will curse us. Oh Krishna, I am terrified. I don't know what to do."

"Is there nothing in the copper plate, Draupadi?" asked the Dark One. "Come, let us take a look at your wonderful platter."

"I just washed it, Krishna. There is nothing in it."

"But show me, just in case you left something. Anything you serve will do for me, even a grain of rice."

"There's nothing in the platter. I'll fetch it, look for yourself."

Krishna took the platter from Draupadi. As he looked at it, a smile touched his lips. He said, "You say there is nothing in this plate? I tell you, Draupadi, if you have faith there is enough here to feed every creature in the world!"

Draupadi came near and stared at the plate she had just washed. Krishna pointed with his finger: nestling at the very rim of the platter was a particle of vegetable, barely visible. Despite her anxiety, Draupadi giggled, "You are going to satisfy your hunger with that?"

Krishna said serenely, "Not only mine, Panchali, but the hunger of your untimely guests."

With his finger, Krishna scraped the green shred from the plate. He said softly, "Let the hunger of every creature on earth be sated with what I eat," and licked the bit of green off his finger. "Aaah!" cried Krishna, as Draupadi stood watching him in disbelief. "That was the best meal I've had in years. You must invite me to eat with you more often!"

Just then, Sahadeva called from outside, "Panchali, is the food ready? You know what a temper Durvasa has, you mustn't keep him waiting."

But it was Krishna who strode out of the kutila. Sahadeva gasped to see him. Before Draupadi could say anything, Krishna cried, "Yes! Food is served, and I have just finished eating. And a curse on anyone who does not do justice to such a meal. Go to the river, Sahadeva, and tell them to hurry back. Say Draupadi has laid on a feast, but it will get cold if they don't come quickly."

Yudhishtira, Bheema, Arjuna and Nakula appeared.

"Krishna!" cried Yudhishtira. "How are you here?"

"I will tell you. But first, Sahadeva, go and call your guests for lunch. And mind you don't tell Durvasa I am here."

Sahadeva went off down the path. Yudhishtira had not let go of Krishna's hand. He said again, "How are you here, Krishna?"

The Dark One smiled quizzically, "You should ask your wife that, cousin. I heard her calling me, and here I am."

Yudhishtira knew nothing of Draupadi's panic. "What happened, Panchali?"

"I had eaten," she said. "How were we going to feed Durvasa and his munis?"

Yudhishtira cried, "How are we going to feed them now?"

Krishna said softly, "Somehow, I don't think they are as hungry as they were. In fact, I don't think they want to eat any more."

The Pandavas stared at him. Meanwhile, Sahadeva had run back to the river. To his surprise, he found its bank deserted. He saw the munis' footprints on wet sand, leading not towards the asrama but away from it.

Earlier, even as the Pandavas were on their way back to the asrama to see if lunch was served—this was when Krishna ate the green scrap he found in Draupadi's plate—Durvasa and his party, bathing luxuriantly in the river, abruptly felt as if they had eaten three feasts. In a moment, they found their bellies bloated and even belched helplessly.

One of them cried, "I feel gorged, though no food has passed my lips!"

Another said, "So do I. How will we eat Draupadi's meal?"

Durvasa himself looked worried. "I couldn't eat another grain of rice, if my life depended on it. I feel as if I have eaten all the food in the world."

"But how can we not eat, when we go back?"

Because it is in every man's nature to think that other men share his traits, Durvasa said anxiously, "What if the Pandavas curse us? We told Draupadi to serve us food, and if we go back and say we are not hungry, it will seem we mocked them in the most arrogant way. If anyone did that to me I wouldn't spare him."

"A fine mess we are in. What shall we do?"

Durvasa thought for no more than a moment. "There is only one sensible thing to do. We must not go back to the asrama."

"Then let us leave before one of them comes to call us!"

They beat a hasty retreat through the forest, some of them without even drying themselves. When Sahadeva arrived at the river, he found Durvasa and his munis gone.

Back at the asrama, Krishna smiled, "I think your guests have been called away suddenly. I don't think they were hungry, after all."

Sahadeva came and announced, "Yudhishtira, they left without eating."

Krishna said quietly, "Durvasa was sent here by someone who knew the platter would be empty after Draupadi ate. That person wanted him to curse you."

Bheema breathed, "Duryodhana!"

Krishna rose from under the tree, and stretched languidly. "Well, I must go back to Dwaraka now. I came in a hurry to hear Draupadi call."

Yudhishtira said, "How did you come, Krishna?"

The Dark One smiled. "Perhaps I never left at all, Yudhishtira."

Then, with a wave, he walked off into the forest and was gone.

THIRTY-FOUR

Jayadratha

T HE PANDAVAS MOVED BACK TO DWAITAVANA, AND THE ASRAMA beside the lake. The twelfth year of exile seemed as long as the other eleven together; especially to Yudhishtira, who each day cursed his folly, which made his brothers and his wife suffer as they did. He would lie awake at night haunted by guilt. Often he would walk out into the mooned nights, and sit on the steps of the asrama, staring across the bright lake, crying.

Though he never showed the others how badly he felt, he, more than any of them, recalled every cruel word said in Hastinapura on the day of the gambling. Repeatedly, he saw the obscene Dusasana trying to strip Draupadi in the Kuru sabha. He saw Duryodhana grin, and bare his thigh. He heard his cousin calling Panchali to sit in his lap. Every night those images, those echoes tormented poor Yudhishtira. And being the eldest, he had no one he could turn to for solace, particularly since that would weaken his obstinate position that they must serve out their exile. But when the others saw his drawn face in the mornings, they knew that he suffered. Out of respect, they said nothing, though it saddened them to see him like that.

In Hastinapura, there were still those loyal to Yudhishtira and his brothers. They brought word of Karna's oath: that he would neither eat meat nor drink wine, until he had killed Arjuna. Indeed, since the unforgettable day when Karna had appeared like a dark sun at the princes' tournament in Hastina, and Duryodhana befriended him, Yudhishtira had been anxious. Since that day, the Pandava had known there was another archer in the world who was not merely Arjuna's equal, but better than him. Karna disquieted Yudhishtira; there was something uncannily familiar about the golden warrior, as if he knew him from another life.

When Yudhishtira heard about Karna's oath to kill Arjuna, he insisted they move again to the Kamyaka from Dwaitavana, where they had been hardly a month. Scarcely two weeks after this move, one day, persuaded by the restless Bheema, all the Pandavas went hunting together into the deeper forest. That day, Jayadratha, the king of Sindhu, happened to pass through the Kamyaka on his way from his capital to the kingdom of a friend. From his chariot, Jayadratha saw the Pandavas' asrama, and he did not know whose hermitage it was. Then he saw Draupadi standing at the door of her hut. Jayadratha did not know who she was, either, but her beauty struck him like an astra. He wanted that dark woman more than he had ever wanted anything.

He sent one of his companions to find out who she was. The man came back and said, "It is the Pandavas' wife Draupadi, she is more dangerous than a cobra. Let us not stop here, my lord; turn your heart away from peril."

Jayadratha gazed raptly at Draupadi. As if he did not hear what his man had said, he climbed down from his chariot and walked towards her.

The lord of Sindhu said, "Do you know me? I am Jayadratha."

"Oh!" she cried happily. "Little Dussala's husband. I am so glad you came. You must wait for my kshatriyas. They have gone hunting, and they will be back soon."

Dussala was Duryodhana's sister, and Draupadi fetched a pitcher of water for Jayadratha to wash his hands and feet. He washed clumsily, since he did not take his eyes off her. He set the pitcher down and said, "You are the most beautiful woman I have ever seen. Come with me, Panchali, and be my queen!"

She gasped, but he went on, "This forest is no place for you. Is this the life your husbands should give a woman like you? I will keep you as you should be kept, as a queen."

Her eyes flashed at him. She cried like fire, "Aren't you ashamed? You should be like a brother to me. You come from a noble house, but there is no dharma in you. Don't you fear for your life when the Pandavas hear about this? They will not spare you, Jayadratha."

He grinned like a beast in rut. "Your husbands don't scare me, woman. I want you, and I intend to have you."

He seized her, flung her easily across his shoulder and strode back to his chariot. Draupadi's cries rang through the silent forest. "Wretch! Dare you defile me? Let me down! Let me go!"

Dhaumya came running to hear her. He cried in horror at Jayadratha, "What are you doing, O king?"

"Out of my way, priest! This is the kshatriya way, honoured through the ages."

"By kshatriya dharma you may not carry her away without facing her husbands in battle! This is a sin, and you will taste the fruit of your madness. Let her go, Jayadratha, there is still time to save yourself."

Jayadratha pushed Dhaumya out of his way, and climbed into his chariot. "Ride!" he cried. "Today, I have the finest prize in the world."

They rode away through the forest, Draupadi screaming, and Jayadratha deaf to her cries. Dhaumya picked himself up, and ran along beside the footsoldiers of that force, who laughed at him, but did not turn him away.

Meanwhile, on the hunt, Yudhishtira suddenly said, "Look how the animals wheel to the left. Look at the flights of the birds."

Arjuna breathed, "There is some danger in the asrama."

They came running back, to find Draupadi's sakhi, Dhatreyika, in tears and Dhaumya's brahmanas panicstricken.

"What happened?" cried Yudhishtira.

The woman only sobbed hysterically, pointing where Jayadratha had gone.

"Where is Panchali?" Bheema roared, and the forest trembled.

The terrified sakhi cried, "Jayadratha carried her off, and Dhaumya followed them. That way!" and she fainted.

All five Pandavas went after Jayadratha. Running through the forest they knew well by now, flying along secret trails, they quickly caught up with the Sindhu king, who went along rather nonchalantly with his soldiers. All at once, a rage of arrows flared out from the trees, from the sky, from everywhere. In moments, Jayadratha's legion lay dead around him. Leaving Draupadi, he leapt out of his chariot and fled.

Dhaumya roared like any kshatriya, and ran forward to embrace the Pandavas.

Sahadeva cut away the ropes with which Jayadratha had bound Draupadi. She clung to him fervently, then came to her other husbands, sobbing in relief.

Yudhishtira said, "We were fortunate. Our boyhood lessons in reading omens were not wasted, after all."

Arjuna murmured, "More than a hundred men dead."

Bheema's eyes blazed. "I will go after that wretch. He won't live after what he did!"

Yudhishtira said, "I will not allow you to kill him. He is Dussala's husband, and mother Gandhari will be heartbroken if you make a widow of her only daughter."

But Draupadi cried, "If you love me at all, you will kill the beast!"

That was enough for Bheema. He said, "Yudhishtira, go back to the asrama with Draupadi. Sahadeva, Nakula, go with him. Arjuna, come with me!"

He plunged into the forest after Jayadratha. The jungle held no mystery for Bheema and Arjuna, while Jayadratha kept slipping on soft earth, or tripping over roots sprung from nowhere in his path. He fell so often the two Pandavas soon caught up with him. Jayadratha ran for his very life, but Arjuna and Bheema taunted him, crying, "Is this the valour of the Sindhus?"

"What kshatriya are you, that you run so swiftly from a fight?"

"Or do you only fight women, coward?"

Jayadratha had to turn and face them. In a blur, Arjuna shot his bow out of his hands, and then, with a chilling roar, Bheema was on him. Bheema caught Jayadratha by his hair and flung him down to the ground. He stamped on that king's face and head until Jayadratha fainted. Still, Bheema kicked him. Arjuna pulled him away, crying, "You will kill him!"

But Bheema was beside himself. He pulled a crescent-headed arrow from Arjuna's quiver and began to shave the Sindhu king's head. Half his hair and moustaches Bheema shaved, and left half of them—in fact, five tufts—so his victim could not have looked more ludicrous. Jayadratha awoke, whimpering.

Bheema said, "So you are still alive, wretch. But not for long, unless you cry out that you are the Pandavas' slave. Go on, shout it for the world to hear!"

Without hesitating, Jayadratha yelled, "I am the Pandavas' slave! I am the Pandavas' slave!" so the forest rang with his cry.

Bheema growled, "Who is to hear you in this jungle? I would kill you anyway, except that Arjuna never kills a beaten enemy. I have no such compunction, but my brother Yudhishtira says it will break little Dussala's heart, and mother Gandhari's heart, if we kill you. But, oh, how my hands itch to wring your neck!"

Jayadratha whimpered louder, when he saw the look in Bheema's eyes. Arjuna said, "You have punished him enough. Let us take him back to the asrama before you change your mind."

They bound Jayadratha's hands, tied a rope round his neck and led him back to the asrama like a dog. Flinging him down at Yudhishtira's feet, Bheema cried, "Tell Panchali that this cur has declared himself our slave!"

Bheema kicked the kneeling Jayadratha down flat on his face at Draupadi's feet. She said, "That will do, Bheema; you have humiliated him, and I am satisfied. Spare his life."

Yudhishtira pulled Jayadratha up and said, "I set you free. Go now, but never repeat what you did today."

Reluctantly, Bheema cut Jayadratha's bonds. That king prostrated himself at Yudhishtira's feet and then, getting up, ran into the jungle without a word. The Pandavas went back to their daily chores, the routine of the asrama, but Jayadratha ran blindly through the trees, his eyes streaming. He could not return to his kingdom, for the world would soon know of his shame. He flew through the jungle as if trying to escape from himself; until, exhausted, he came to the banks of the Ganga, and flung himself down on the moss beside the river.

In that place, he sat in tapasya. For a year he sat, his heart on fire, worshipping Siva. At last, Siva appeared before him in a mass of light. The Lord said, "What boon do you want, that you worship me like this?"

Jayadratha prostrated himself at the feet of the vision. He said, "Lord, grant me that I defeat all the Pandavas in battle one day."

Siva said, "Not a lifetime's tapasya would be enough for you to have that boon from me. The Pandavas' dharma is great; their valour is greater. They are invincible and dark Krishna protects Arjuna. But this much I will grant you: if you meet the other four Pandavas in battle, you shall hold them up by yourself. More than that, I cannot do."

Somewhat mollified that, at least, he would have his moment of triumph, Jayadratha returned to his kingdom.

A few days after Jayadratha tried to kidnap Draupadi, Markandeya returned to the Pandavas' asrama. It was a time when they were all disturbed by what had happened, and the rishi's coming was like balm to them. As always, he was full of lustrous stories; the brothers forgot their troubles, as they sat late into the nights listening to him.

Yudhishtira was deeply shaken by the incident with Jayadratha; it hurt him most because Jayadratha was Dussala's husband. On his last visit, Markandeya had told Yudhishtira about Nala, the king of Nishada, whose exile had not been unlike Yudhishtira's own. Now, the muni told them about Rama of Ayodhya, whose trials were harder than his. He told the story of Savitri, who turned Yama, Death himself, away with her wisdom and devotion.

Indeed, Markandeya came to the sons of Pandu as if the Gods sent him, at a time when Yudhishtira, particularly, was so full of guilt: a time when there was no telling what the eldest Pandava might have done, because his will was almost broken. More than anyone, in those trying days, the Rishi Markandeya gave Yudhishtira the strength to carry on along the narrow path of dharma.

But the Pandava suffered torments of self-reproach in that twelfth year. He blamed himself endlessly for what had happened to his family, his conscience gave him no peace. Long after the night's stories were told, long after the moon had set, Yudhishtira would lie awake or sit out under the tree in the clearing by himself under a sky full of stars, ravaged by the enormity of all that happened to them because of his weakness. In those days, another face haunted him with terror: the strong, rebellious face of the enemy whom Yudhishtira was obsessed with, for no reason he could name, the man he feared most. The remarkable face of Karna haunted Yudhishtira relentlessly.

Over and over, he saw Karna urging Duryodhana to strip Draupadi in the Kuru sabha on the day of the gambling. Again and again, he heard Karna's arrogant voice, 'She is a slut shared by five men, and now she will have more than five!'

In that twelfth year of their exile, Yudhishtira, who had been the most restrained of his brothers, who had always advocated dharma and restraint, found that, when he was awake at nights and all the others slept, bloody visions of revenge possessed him. Every cell in his body felt as if it were on fire. All these years, he had been accused of being too patient and forgiving, of not being a true kshatriya. His brother Bheema, who had most accused Yudhishtira of all this, would have been shocked if he had seen into his older brother's heart, during their last year in the jungle.

But Yudhishtira was different from Bheema. He was a master of his emotions—perhaps, even because they were so strong—while Bheema followed his like a child. Pandu's eldest son could hardly resist the anxiety and impatience that raged in him during that twelfth year. There were nights when he was tempted to awaken Bheema and give the order to march on Hastinapura in the morning: because he could no longer contain the fury he felt. But somehow, Yudhishtira proved equal to the trial of those days and nights. All he did was to move, again, from the Kamyaka back to Dwaitavana.

His brothers saw how drawn and uneasy he was. They saw the dark rings around his eyes, his distracted manner, and, knowing he was tried by fire, they grieved for him. But there was little else they could do.

THIRTY-FIVE

The lake of death

It was the last month of their exile in the jungle. The Pandavas were back in the asrama at Dwaitavana. One clear morning, a distraught old brahmana arrived there. Breathless from having run through the forest, he cried to Yudhishtira, "Help me, O king! You must help me or my puja will be ruined."

"What happened, Muni, to disturb your puja?"

"I had hung the arani sticks I use to kindle my sacred fire on the branch of a tree in my asrama. I went into my hut to fetch some ghee for the fire, when I saw a stag run under the tree. The string of the aranis got entangled in the stag's antlers. They were the same aranis my father and grandfather used, and I cannot perform my puja without them. Kshatriyas, you must find the stag, and retrieve my kindling-sticks!"

He was so upset he sat down and cried. Yudhishtira and his brothers set out at once in the direction the brahmana pointed, where the stag had gone. Their eyes peeled and their bows in their hands, the Pandavas ran through the familiar jungle. Scraping their bodies against trees, scratching themselves against thorn-bushes until they bled, they combed the forest. They saw no sign of the stag.

After two hours, they came to a part of the jungle they did not know, and they were exhausted. Panting, they flung themselves down at the foot of a fine pipal tree. They were as distraught as the brahmana; for it is a kshatriya's inviolable dharma to help anyone who comes to him in need, specially, a rishi.

Nakula said in despair, "Yudhishtira, why are we cursed like this?"

Parched with thirst, Yudhishtira replied, "My child, in times of misfortune, troubles never come singly. It is to be a trial that they come, and we hardly know why: whether for any fault of ours or not. All we can do is bear them resolutely. Those that are enlightened say that whatever we experience in this life, good and bad, are the fruit of our own karma of the past, of our punya and paapa."

Bheema was quick to seize his chance. "Suffering is always punishment for past sins. And I know what my sin is: I should have never left Dusasana and Duryodhana alive after what they did to Draupadi!"

Arjuna agreed quietly, "You are right, Bheema. I should have never spared Karna after what he said to her that day. But I let him live, and I am paying for my sin."

The mood infected Sahadeva; he cried, "I longed to kill Shakuni, but I stayed my hand. That is why we are suffering like this. Now we shall have the brahmana's curse as well."

Yudhishtira smiled at them. "This is no time to reproach ourselves. Thirst churns our minds; we must find some water. Nakula, my brother, climb this tree and see if there is any water nearby."

Nakula already regretted his innocent query. He shinned up the tall pipal, to its crown. The view of the forest was spectacular, a thousand virescent shades of green, and, away to the left, he saw the blue sparkle of water.

He called down, "I see a lake through the trees, not far from here."

Yudhishtira said, "I am too tired to go another step. Come down, Nakula, and fetch us some water in these quivers."

As Nakula ran through the forest with the quivers strapped to his back, he had the eerie feeling of entering a charmed zone of the jungle. The trees were all unfamiliar, and the birds in them sang songs he had never heard. But he pressed on, and arrived at the water he had seen from the treetop. It was indeed a calm, blue lake, so inviting that he rushed to it and knelt to quench his searing thirst.

As he raised the cool water in cupped palms, a voice spoke in that place like a crack of thunder. "You may not drink the water from my lake until you have answered my riddles!"

Startled, Nakula looked around; but he saw no one. He bent his face, and drank thirstily. Hardly had the sweet, fresh water passed his lips, when the Pandava keeled over, his face turning blue. He fell into a deep swoon, like death.

Meanwhile, back under the pipal tree, the others waited impatiently for Nakula. When there was no sign of him for an hour, Yudhishtira said to Sahadeva, "The lake was not so far that he should be this long. Go and see what has happened to him."

Sahadeva arrived at the lake, and saw Nakula lying dead.

Sahadeva cried, "You have died of thirst, my brother! I had better drink quickly."

He knelt beside the water, and made to fill his cupped hands. Again, the voice spoke crisply out of the very air. "You may not drink from my lake until you have answered my riddles!"

But Sahadeva thought it was a hallucination of his thirst. He drank a mouthful of water, and he also fell in the deathlike swoon beside Nakula. Another half-hour went by, then Arjuna said, "I fear they are in some trouble. Shall I go and find them?"

Yudhishtira nodded. By now, the breath rasped in their fevered bodies. Arjuna arrived at the lake. He saw his brothers lay dead, their skin turning blue.

"Ah, who has murdered you, my little brothers? I won't spare them!" cried Arjuna.

So parched was his throat, only a hollow whisper came from him. Realizing he would be easy prey for whoever had killed Nakula and Sahadeva, Arjuna knelt at the edge of the lake, cupped his palms and scooped up some water. Again, the mysterious voice spoke, "Kshatriya! Answer the riddles I have for you before you drink. Or you will also die."

Arjuna whirled around and, in a blur, shot twenty arrows where he thought the voice spoke. A soft laugh mocked him. "You will kill innocent jungle creatures, Kshatriya, and you will sin. Answer my riddles, and drink freely from my lake."

Arjuna thought this was some playful woodland spirit, and he could not bear his thirst any more. Ignoring the voice, he knelt and drank a deep draught of the cool water. Arjuna also keeled over, as if dead.

In a while, Bheema followed Arjuna to the lake. When he saw his brothers, he thought this was the work of some forest yakshas, such as live in trees, have holes in their backs, and whose feet point behind them.

"Aaaahh!" roared Bheema weakly. "The yakshas will die for this. But first let me drink, or they may kill me too."

Again, the voice spoke, "Don't drink the water from my lake, until you have answered my riddles. Or you die."

Bheema cried hoarsely, "I will drink. And then, you will die for what you have done to my brothers!"

He knelt, drank, and fell beside the others.

Yudhishtira waited another half-hour. By now, he was so weak and thirsty he was certain he could never reach the lake. But when Bheema also did not return, he rose with an effort, and stumbled through the trees after his brothers. He had no idea how far the water was, and, often almost falling, he staggered along with thirst savaging him.

The world was misting over before Yudhishtira's eyes, when he arrived at the lake and saw his brothers lying dead. Yudhishtira was too weak to cry out. He tottered forward and collapsed on to his knees beside Bheema.

"Who has done this to my invincible brothers?" whispered Yudhishtira incredulously. "But no blood or struggle marks the place. They haven't fought, yet they lie dead."

He passed his hands over their faces. "There has been treachery here, and Duryodhana's dearest wish has come true without a blow being struck in war. Has he done this thing? But by what sorcery? What will I tell Panchali? And Kunti? And to die now, when our exile is almost over."

He took Bheema's cold hand and cried, "Bheema, forgive me! I should have listened to you. We should have marched on Hastinapura years ago. How could I have been so blind? I caused you all so much grief, and now I have caused your deaths. Oh, my sweet brothers! You may forgive me for this, the Devas and Pitrs may forgive me; but I will never forgive myself."

Then, he had another thought. "My brothers lie dead before me, their lives' purposes, all their talents betrayed, the reason for their noble births unfulfilled. Yet, I cannot shed a tear. My mind is bewildered, but my heart is strangely calm ... as if nothing has happened. As if they are not dead!"

A pang of thirst convulsed him. He looked at his brothers and wondered if the water was poisoned. But they lay serene, no sign of pain twisted their features. Yudhishtira approached the lake to drink.

The voice spoke again, "The lake is mine. He that drinks from it without answering my riddles dies. I caused your brothers' deaths. If you drink my water, you will die as well."

Yudhishtira rose away from the lake. Folding his hands, the Pandava said, "Who are you, great one, who could kill my brothers?"

The voice laughed softly, making Yudhishtira's skin crawl. It said, "I am a crane, and the lake is mine."

Yudhishtira said hoarsely, "What crane are you, that killed my mighty brothers with no injury upon them?"

The velvet laugh again, "I am no crane, Kshatriya."

"Who are you then, O Spirit? Are you the lord of the maruts? Are you a rudra, or an airy vasu? Who are you, that slew my brothers, whom not the Devas or gandharvas, not the Asuras or rakshasas could harm?"

"If you must know, Yudhishtira, I am a yaksha."

"You know my name!"

"There are many things I know, son of Pandu. But our concern is not what I know, but if you can answer my riddles."

Despite his dead brothers, despite his wild thirst, Yudhishtira's curiosity was aroused. "I would see you, great one, if you would honour me with that vision."

Another low laugh, then, a dark mist rose above the water. Within it, Yudhishtira saw a spirit-form stretched right across the lake, huge jewels on its fingers and upon its monstrous breast, and its ghastly, ten-eyed face in the very sky, big as a moon. Yudhishtira was not sure whether that twilight being was male or female; he fancied it might have been both. The vision lasted but a moment, and the mist faded. Yudhishtira folded his hands to the yaksha, who was invisible again.

The Pandava said, "I am honoured that you let me see you, magnificent one."

The yaksha seemed pleased with Yudhishtira. It spoke to him reasonably, in its clear, androgynous voice. "When they knelt at the water, I told each of your brothers they must answer my riddles before they drank. But they would not listen to me, even when they saw the others lying dead. To you also I say, you may not drink unless you answer my riddles first."

Yudhishtira bowed to the yaksha. He said, "Awesome one, you say the lake belongs to you. How can I drink its fragrant water without your leave? But I am thirsty, and I would be grateful if you ask me whatever riddles you have quickly."

THIRTY-SIX

Yaksha prasna: the yaksha's riddles

THE YAKSHA SAID, "YOUR BROTHER ARJUNA SHOT ARROWS AT ME, BUT they did not harm me. I said to him, 'Answer my riddles'. He would not, and he drank the water and perished. But you are different; you are humble. I am pleased with you, and if you are ready I will ask my riddles."

Yudhishtira bowed to indicate he was ready. The yaksha allowed the Pandava no time between riddles to collect himself, and Yudhishtira answered as quickly as the questions flashed at him. Only occasionally, when the yaksha was pleased with an answer, he would laugh.

"What makes the sun rise?"

"Brahma."

"Who are the sun's companions?"

"The Devas."

"Why does the sun set?"

"Dharma makes him set."

"In whom does the sun dwell?"

"In the Truth."

"What makes one learned?"

"The study of the Srutis."

"How does a man achieve greatness?"

"By tapasya."

"Does a man always have a friend?"

"Yes. His intelligence."

"How is intelligence acquired?"

"By serving one's elders."
"Where does the brahmana's divinity lie?"
"In his knowledge of the Vedas."
"What diminishes a brahmana's divinity?"
"He is mortal."
"What confers divinity on a kshatriya?"
"His weapons."
"What diminishes him?"
"Fear."
"Tell me about yagnas. What is Sama? And Yajus? And what is the refuge of a yagna?"
"Life is Sama, the mind is Yajus. Rik is the sanctuary of the yagna."
"A man breathes, he enjoys every sensual pleasure, and the world holds him in esteem. Yet, he is not truly alive. Why?"
"Because he makes no offerings to the Devas or the Pitrs."
"What is more important than the earth itself?"
"One's mother."
"What is higher than heaven?"
"One's father."
"What is swifter than the wind?"
"The mind."
"More numerous than blades of grass?"
"The thoughts in the mind."
"What is the highest sanctuary of dharma?"
"Liberality."
"Of fame?"
"A gift."
"Of heaven?"
"The truth."
"What is a man's soul?"
"His son."
"Who is the friend the Gods give a man?"
"His wife."
"His support?"
"The clouds."
"What is the most praiseworthy thing of all?"
"Skill."

"The most valuable possession?"
"Knowledge."
"The greatest treasure?"
"Health."
"The greatest happiness?"
"Contentment."

The riddles came breathlessly now, and Yudhishtira hardly paused before answering.

"What is the highest dharma?"
"To injure none of the living."
"What must be controlled?"
"The mind."
"What renounced, to make a man agreeable?"
"Pride."
"And what renounced to make a man wealthy?"
"Desire."
"And what can be renounced with no regret?"
"Anger."
"And what may be relinquished to gain happiness?"
"Greed."
"What makes the way?"
"The good make the way, indeed, they are the way."
"Who is the ascetic?"
"He who remains faithful."
"What is true restraint?"
"That of the mind."
"And what, true forgiveness?"
"He who endures enmity, truly forgives."
"What is real knowledge?"
"The knowledge of God."
"What is tranquillity?"
"When the heart is still."
"Mercy?"
"When one desires the happiness of all creatures."
"Simplicity?"
"When the heart is tranquil."
"Who is the invincible enemy?"

"Anger."
"What disease has no cure?"
"Covetousness."
"Who is the honest man?"
"He who desires the happiness of all the living."
"And the dishonest one?"
"The one who has no mercy."
"What is ignorance?"
"Not knowing one's dharma."
"And pride?"
"When a man thinks that he is the one who is the doer in life."

By now, Yudhishtira was so engrossed he had quite forgotten his predicament. He was enjoying himself, answering the yaksha's profound riddles.

"What is grief?"
"Only ignorance."
"How does a man become patient?"
"By subduing his senses."
"Which is the true ablution?"
"When the heart is washed clean."
"What is charity?"
"Protecting all creatures."
"Wickedness?"
"Speaking ill of others."
"Who is a brahmana? One who studies the Veda, or one who is born a brahmana?"
"Neither. The true brahmana is he whose life is pure."
"How is a man agreeable?"
"When he speaks agreeably."
"How does he get what he wants?"
"When he acts with discernment."
"How is he happy?"
"When he has many friends."
"And how does he find bliss in the next world?"
"By being virtuous in this one."
"What is truly amazing in this world?"

Yudhishtira thought for just a moment. Then he said, smiling, "Every day, countless lives enter into the temple of death. Yet, those who remain in this world think themselves immortal. What could be more amazing?"

The yaksha laughed appreciatively. He asked, "Which is the path?"

"Debate and philosophy lead to no conclusions. The Srutis all differ about the nature of Truth. There is not a rishi, whose opinion is infallible. Yet, the path is within us: the way of dharma, the golden trail the great have trodden through all time."

"What is the news?"

"This world of ignorance is like a cook's pan. The sun is the fire. The days and nights are the fuel, the seasons are the ladle. Time is the cook, who stirs us all in the pan. That is the news, what else?"

"Who is a real man?"

"Word of one's good deeds reach heaven, and are spread from there across the earth. As long as that word lasts, one is called a man."

"Who is he, Yudhishtira, who has every kind of wealth?"

"Only he to whom joy and sorrow, fortune and misfortune, past and future, are all the same."

The yaksha's delighted laughter rang across the lake. He said, "I am pleased with your answers! Yudhishtira, you are the wisest man in the world, and the most righteous one too. I grant you a boon: ask me for the life of any one of your brothers."

Unhesitatingly, Yudhishtira said, "Let my dark and handsome Nakula live."

"I am surprised. I know Bheema is dearest to you among all your brothers. You depend on Arjuna to win the coming war. Yet, you choose Nakula's life over theirs. Why?"

"I would rather sacrifice my life than dharma. O Yaksha, my father had two wives, Kunti and Madri. One of Kunti's sons already lives: I. It is dharma that one of Madri's sons should also live. So I chose Nakula."

Again the yaksha laughed. "Ah, you are a great soul indeed, Yudhishtira. I will never look upon another like you in all time. I grant you not just Nakula's life, but the lives of all your brothers!"

Yudhishtira saw Bheema, Arjuna, Nakula and Sahadeva open their eyes and sit up groggily. He ran to them, and hugged them. Arjuna said in wonder, "I am not thirsty any more."

Bheema said, "My tiredness has left me."

The yaksha materialized again over the lake, covering it from shore to shore. Yudhishtira gazed at the dark form; then he prostrated himself on the ground. The Pandava cried, "My Lord! You are no yaksha. No yaksha knows the subtleties of dharma as you do. No, you are a Deva, or at least someone who loves us dearly. I feel powerful kin with you. Are you perhaps our father Pandu? Show me your true form, whoever you are!"

There was a flash of light above the lake. The monstrous yaksha vanished, and in its place stood a God, bright as the sun. His presence transformed the sylvan lake into a realm of wonder. The trees breathed, the very air seemed made of many colours, floating, and of subtle music.

The splendent one smiled at Yudhishtira, and spoke in a deep and beautiful voice. "I am indeed your father, Yudhishtira my son. I am not Pandu, but Dharma. I wanted to meet you and these heroic brothers of yours, so I came."

Yudhishtira breathed, "My Lord!"

The radiant one continued, "I am more pleased with you, my child, than I had ever hoped. You are as righteous as I had heard, more so. You and your brothers will conquer the world, and you shall sit upon the throne of all Bharatavarsha. But, Yudhishtira, you have already conquered a far greater kingdom. You have conquered the kingdom of dharma: you have conquered yourself! What are worldly conquests, or the thrones they bring, beside this immortal one?

"Your fame will live forever, not just on earth but in Devaloka. In the kali yuga, let a man but say your name and he shall be dear to me. Just four names will be so precious: the name of Nala of Nishada, of Rama's wife Sita, your name, Yudhishtira, and the name of the Dark One whom you love so dearly, Krishna of Dwaraka."

Yudhishtira stood glowing before his natural father. The Lord Dharma said, "My just son, I want to give you another boon. Ask me for anything."

Yudhishtira did not hesitate. "Lord, we came into the jungle to find a brahmana's arani sticks. Grant that we may find them, or we will fail in our kshatriya dharma."

Dharma smiled, "I was the stag in whose antlers the brahmana's aranis were entangled. Here they are. But that is no boon, ask me for something else."

Yudhishtira asked wisely, "Grant, my Lord, that we are not discovered during the thirteenth year of our exile, which will soon begin."

Dharma Deva said, "Which has begun even today. I grant you that boon: go safely back into the world, disguised. No one will see through your disguises. Yet, ask me for something else."

Yudhishtira knelt before the Lord Dharma. He kissed the Deva's feet. The Pandava said, "I am the happiest man on earth today that, at last, I have met my father face to face. I want no other material boon from you, for I know we have to struggle in this life, and suffer, before we achieve. But if you grant me another wish, let it be that I conquer my six deadly enemies one day."

The knowing Dharma asked, "And who are they?"

His son said, "The enemies that lurk in my heart: lust, anger, greed, possessiveness, arrogance and envy. Grant me, father, that my mind always leads me towards the Truth. I want nothing else in the world."

And his father, the great Dharma, said, "You ask for what you already have, Yudhishtira. You have long since conquered these enemies, O prince of dharma. As for the Truth, you will surely come to it in time."

Dharma Deva blessed them all. At last, he said, "Go, my sons, and be joyful. I am with you, and you shall be victorious. And remember, wherever dark Krishna is, there I am as well."

With that, and his hand still raised over them in a blessing, he vanished. Their hearts full of fresh hope, the Pandavas walked slowly back to their asrama with the arani sticks. It was time to now seriously consider the disguises they were going to adopt for the thirteenth year of their exile, the ajnatavasa. Duryodhana's spies would be everywhere, eager to find them, and send them back to another twelve years in the wilderness.

They were anxious, but Dharma Deva's assurance had put new heart in them.

BOOK FOUR

Virata Parva

AUM, I bow down to Narayana, the most exalted Nara, and to the Devi Saraswati, and say *Jaya*!

ONE

The thirteenth year

YUDHISHTIRA GATHERED DHAUMYA AND HIS BRAHMANAS TOGETHER in the asrama on the banks of the lake at Dwaitavana. He said, "Our twelve years in the jungle are over. Holy ones, but for the solace of your company we would have found these years an intolerable burden. Now the hardest part of our exile begins. For this last, thirteenth, year we must live among men again, in disguise. And the price of being discovered will be another twelve years in the wilderness."

His voice choked, "I have no words to tell you how beholden we are to you, none to say how much we love you, and how much we shall miss you. But our ways must part now, for this final year; the time has come to say farewell. We must disguise ourselves, and no one must know where we are, lest our whereabouts are inadvertently betrayed. At the end of this year I will have my kingdom back: in peace, if the Gods will, or with war if fate so decides. And we shall meet again."

Now he sobbed like a boy. Dhaumya put an arm around him, and said, "This thirteenth year is the last yaama of the night, before dawn breaks. When it ends, you will shine over the earth again like the sun. You must be brave until then."

Bheema was visibly upset to see his brother crying. He took Yudhishtira's hand and began to speak flippantly to him, as one would to distract a child. Touched by this, Yudhishtira smiled and wiped his eyes.

Most of them in tears, the brahmanas blessed the Pandavas, and went back to Hastinapura and Indraprastha, to the homes they had left twelve years ago. Some of them remained in the forest. The Pandavas went to bid farewell to the other rishis of the vana. Again, Yudhishtira was in tears, for those hermits had become like kin to him.

When all the other brahmanas had gone, the Pandavas, Draupadi and Dhaumya sat beside the lake in Dwaitavana. Yudhishtira said sombrely, "We have to choose a kingdom in which to spend the next year, and we must choose wisely. Arjuna, you have ranged these lands as none of us has. Tell us where to find a home for a year."

Arjuna said, "Seven kingdoms surround the Kuru country: Panchala, Matsya, Salva, Videha, Dwaraka, Kalinga and Magadha. For myself I have heard that Virata in the Matsya kingdom is a fine city; and we must live in a city, where people abound and we can pass unnoticed. But you must decide, Yudhishtira."

Yudhishtira agreed at once. "We shall go to Virata. I would have gladly chosen Dwaraka or Panchala; but those are where Duryodhana's spies will first look for us. As for the other kingdoms you named, I know little about their kings. Virata I know about. He is a man of dharma. He is powerful, charitable and our wellwisher, as I have heard. Moreover, he is not a young man, or a fickle one. Let us decide on the Matsya kingdom, and the city of Virata."

Bheema said, "Shall we go as ourselves?"

"We must go in disguise, and never be recognized."

Arjuna asked, "Yudhishtira, how will you go to Virata?" His voice tremulous, he said, "Oh, my brother, how can we think of you in another king's sabha? Even these twelve years in the jungle you have been our lord. King of the earth, how can I bear to see you serving another man?"

Arjuna's eyes filled at the thought. Yudhishtira wiped his brother's tears; gently he said, "I will be no king's courtier, Arjuna. Listen to what I propose for myself. I will go as a brahmana, calling myself Kanka. I shall wear tulasi and rudraksha, and I do know something of the Vedas and the Vedanta. I will also show the king that I am a master of dice."

Bheema stiffened. Yudhishtira glanced at him and both of them laughed. Yudhishtira said, "You must not forget, Bheema, that the Muni Brihadaswa taught me the akshahridaya. I think the Matsya king will take me for a companion, especially when he realizes that I want no wealth or favours from him."

A sense of adventure was rising in place of the anxiety they had first felt at the prospect of leaving the jungle. Arjuna was mollified. "The Matsya king is sure to treat you with honour. I am content."

"And being an old man, he may have some use for such small wisdom as I have gleaned in the forest from the rishis. But my disguise is the least of our worries. Bheema, how will you contain your strength and your temper for twelve months? For a few flowers Draupadi wanted, you slaughtered a hundred of Kubera's people." Yudhishtira took his brother's hand fondly, "The slightest provocation, little one, and your eyes blaze. How will you last a year, obeying someone's orders?"

Bheema said, "Nothing will induce me to lose my temper. After these twelve years, no provocation will make me risk another exile."

Arjuna asked, "How do you intend to appear in the Matsya king's court?"

Bheema grinned. "You know that I love cooking almost as much as eating. I have spent a lot of time in kitchens, both in Hastinapura and Indraprastha, and there is little I don't know about them.

"I will go to Virata as Ballava, a great cook, and ask him to let me have charge of his palace kitchen. I will tell him I am a wrestler, as well, and offer to train the young men of his city. I am sure he will employ me."

Yudhishtira said, "Suppose he asks where you worked before?"

Bheema laughed. "I was the emperor Yudhishtira's cook in Indraprastha! I can furnish him with convincing details. I will say that since my lord Yudhishtira went into exile, I have been seeking another master as noble as him. And I heard the king of the Matsyas is such a man."

His brothers and Draupadi laughed at his ingenuity. Yudhishtira turned to Arjuna, "And how will you, tameless Kshatriya, live as a servant yourself, when you were so anxious at the thought of seeing me as one?"*

Arjuna turned his eyes down. He spoke in a strange new voice. "Yudhishtira, twelve years of our exile have ended. But I did not realize this because Dharma Deva said so."

---

* In Ganguli's translation, Yudhishtira says here that Arjuna is 'the tenth Rudra, the thirteenth Aditya, the ninth Vasu, and the tenth Graha.'

He was silent again, and it seemed to the others that the lines of his face had softened. Puzzled, Yudhishtira asked, "How did you know twelve years had passed?"

Arjuna flushed. "The curse of Urvashi is taking effect. My body has changed, I am not a man any more."

His brothers stared at him. Yudhishtira said, "What do you mean to do, Arjuna?"

"I will also enter the Matsya king's employ. What better disguise for me than a beardless face and a eunuch's body? I will wear my hair in a plait, and offer my services in the king's harem. Chitrasena taught me to sing, dance and to play on the vina. I will teach the king's women these. Besides, after the usual inspection, the king will have no anxiety about letting me into his harem, as a member of the third sex."

The others were so taken aback they said nothing. A small moan came from Draupadi and Bheema's eyes bulged. Yudhishtira turned to Nakula, "And you, little brother? How will you hide your beauty? And you are so sensitive, how will you tolerate a year of servitude?"

Nakula was also prepared. "I shall be Damagranthi, the man who has power over horses: which, as you know, I do, for I can speak to them. When he sees me with his horses, the king will not refuse to give me charge of his stables. I can remain at a remove from the court," he blushed, "and its women, too."

"Well done!" said Yudhishtira. His eyes still worried, he turned to Sahadeva. "My child, what have you planned? You are the wisest of us, as knowing as Brihaspati. When we left her, all our mother could think of was, would her Sahadeva be looked after? How can I let you serve another king, when you are such a child still?"

Sahadeva laughed disarmingly. "I am not a child any more, Yudhishtira! I also have a plan for myself. I am as good with cows as Nakula is with horses. When the Matsya king sees me cajole his cows into yielding more milk than ever before, he will give me charge of his herd. Moreover, his cattle are his main wealth and he will be happy to have me look after them. I shall be Tantripala, the gifted cowherd. Best of all, I do love being with the gentle ones."

Then, the most anxious, most miserable part: Yudhishtira turned to Draupadi. "You must endure another twelve months, Panchali. Have you thought how you will go to Virata, delicate queen?"

Draupadi smiled bravely. "When you, emperor of the earth, can enter the service of another king; when Bheema, who has never obeyed another soul except you, can become a cook; when Arjuna can go as a eunuch in a harem; when the beautiful Nakula can be a groom and the brilliant Sahadeva a cowherd, what does it matter what Panchali does? You five are my life, my soul. My burden will be as nothing these remaining twelve months."

"But what have you decided to disguise yourself as?" asked Bheema anxiously.

"I will dress myself as a sairandhri and be the Matsya queen's sakhi. I know how to do a woman's hair in a hundred ways; to string fine garlands with flowers of every kind; and to distil perfumes for a queen that will make her husband mad with desire. The queen of the Matsyas will not refuse to have me as her companion."

Yudhishtira said quietly, "We are ready for the last year of our exile."

The Pandavas left Dwaitavana and went back to the Kamyaka. They walked on from there to the southern bank of the Yamuna. On they went, through the lovely wild places, tangled with exotic plants and fruit trees. At last, they reached the frontiers of the Matsya kingdom.

Now Yudhishtira embraced Dhaumya, and said, "Go to Drupada's court and keep our fire of agnihotra lit there. Take Draupadi's sakhis with you. If anyone, even Drupada himself, asks where the Pandavas have gone, say we left you in the Dwaitavana and walked away without telling you where we went."

Solemnly, Dhaumya performed some sacred rites for the safety and wellbeing of the Pandavas. Then, blessing them, embracing them all, the brahmana turned towards the Panchala country.

The sons of Pandu and Draupadi were alone, and, with a prayer in their hearts, they set out for the city of Virata, and the final year of their exile. When they had gone some way, Draupadi sat on a tree-root and said, "I am tired, and Virata is nowhere to be seen. Let us sleep here tonight, and go on tomorrow."

Nakula and Sahadeva were tired, as well, but Bheema had wandered some way ahead. It fell to Arjuna to carry Draupadi. How well they looked together, like a dark cloud bearing a streak of lightning through the jungle.

TWO

Kanka, the gambler

THEY TRUDGED ON THROUGH THE DIM JUNGLE, AS AFTERNOON BEGAN to wear into dusk. At last, through the trees ahead they saw that the forest ended, and beyond a stretch of fields, silhouetted against the sinking sun, was the city of Virata.

Yudhishtira said, "There it is, our destination."

Gently, Arjuna set Draupadi down. He asked, "Shall we enter the city now?"

Yudhishtira replied, "Can you imagine the attention we will draw if we go in together, carrying our weapons? Just the Gandiva would give us away, and remember, Duryodhana's spies must be everywhere. The quest for us will not be less than a war for our cousin. If we are found, we must spend another twelve years in the wilderness, and that should certainly be the end of us."

"What shall we do then?"

"We must leave our weapons somewhere in this forest, and come back for them at the end of the year."

Arjuna said, "I have been here before. If I remember correctly, there is a cremation-ground not far from here, a much feared place full of snakes and wild animals. No one will dare search it too closely, nor stay there a moment longer than they need to."

"Let us find the burning-ground."

It was not far. One pyre still smouldered among the trees, and there were other dead bodies, unburnt, mouldering. Arjuna pointed to a tree, a giant that grew at the very heart of the grove of death. "The sami would be an ideal hiding-place for our weapons."

"Our bows have jewels that might catch the light of the sun."

"We will wrap them in a sheet of hide, as if they were a corpse, and tie them to a high branch. No one will climb a tree as tall as this to inspect a corpse."

The Pandavas made a bundle of their weapons. And they were a curious sight to see, those kshatriyas: their eyes full of tears as they gave up their bows and quivers, their swords and daggers, and Bheema his mace. It was as if they were parting from their lovers! Arjuna tied the bundle up just in time.

Some men from a nearby village were passing that way, travelling to the city of Virata. They saw five splendid young strangers and an exquisite woman with them, crying as they made fast a corpse in its sheet. The giant among them was the most distressed, and the eldest was consoling him as one would a child.

The villagers approached the Pandavas and one of them asked, "Whose corpse are you tying up, friends? Who have you lost, that you cry so bitterly?"

At which, Bheema turned on them, his eyes bleary and terrible, and spoke in a voice that made the poor villagers quail. "It is our mother who died, who else? She was a hundred and eighty." He added threateningly, "And we want to be left in peace to hang her up."

The villagers knew only sorcerers and demons hang their dead from trees, and when red-eyed Bheema took a step towards them, all seven bolted through the forest.

The Pandavas wrapped their weapons in the hide of a dead cow to protect them from wind, sun and rain. Yudhishtira himself climbed the sami and lashed the 'corpse' to the upper side of one of the thickest branches, so it could not be seen from the ground. When he climbed down again, he invoked the Goddess, the Devi.

"Mother Durga, I leave these weapons as precious as our lives in your care. At the end of our ajnatavasa, let them be returned only to Arjuna or to me. I worship you, Devi Bhagavati, hear me in the hour of my need."

A breeze stirred in the darkening forest. Unearthly fragrance filled the trees and a light grew lucid before the Pandavas. Within that lustre was She, mounted on her mythic beast, the tiger. She was eight-armed, fabled weapons in every hand, beautiful past imagining. Her grace seemed to pervade the earth.

The Devi said, "No one will know you this next year, and your ayudhas will be safe when you return."

"Bless us, Mother!" cried Yudhishtira fervently, and Draupadi and the Pandavas prostrated themselves before her.

"You will rule the earth again, Yudhishtira, and you will prosper. But why do ask that the weapons be returned only to Arjuna or yourself?"

"My brother Bheema is quick-tempered. He may decide to seek his own revenge against Dhritarashtra's sons, before the year is over. He may order Sahadeva or Nakula to fetch the weapons for him, and they may feel they must obey him."

The Goddess laughed softly. She said, "So be it, then. Only Arjuna or Yudhishtira shall have these weapons back at the end of the year."

She blessed them, and vanished.

Yudhishtira said, "Let us sleep in the forest tonight, and from tomorrow, enter the city, separately."

They lay down on some thick grass. Bheema asked, "We must go separately? Does that mean we should seem not to know each other in Virata?"

"We shall be strangers, unless we happen to meet when no one else is about. And even then, we must be careful. Let us give ourselves some names to know each other by, if any messages have to be passed between us."

Yudhishtira said, "I will call myself Jaya. Bheema, what name will you have?"

Sleepily, the son of the wind said, "Jayesha."

Arjuna said, "I will be Vijaya."

Nakula said, "Jayatsena."

And Sahadeva, "Jayadbala."

At dawn, they bathed in the river, worshipped the Gods, and hugged each other tearfully. Then, dressed as Kanka the brahmana, carrying his ivory* dice in a square of plain cloth, wearing rudraksha and chanting Siva's many names, Yudhishtira set out towards Virata's city and the

---

* KMG says 'golden dice set with lapis lazuli'.

king's palace. The others must wait and follow him, one at a time, with some days' interval between them so no suspicions were aroused.

It was the public hour in the court of the aging Matsya king, when the brahmana stranger presented himself in his sabha, and stood without bowing, his head held high. King Virata of the Matsyas was a little taken aback, not only at the brahmana's hauteur but his altogether noble appearance. It was a critical moment, and Yudhishtira trembled a little.

Virata thought, 'Who is this? He stands before me as if he were the king and I his subject. He does not bow, and yet, strangely, I don't feel offended. It is uncanny, but I feel he is my superior, and I should rise and bow to him. He wears a brahmana's cloth, but his gait and bearing are those of a kshatriya. Look at him, like a tiger! As if he ruled all the world.'

Virata inclined his head to the brahmana to say he should approach the throne. The brahmana came forward a few steps, and then, incredibly, Virata rose and went to him!

That king said, "I am honoured you have come to my sabha, Brahmana. To my eyes, you seem more like a mighty kshatriya, but you are welcome in my city. Tell me, what can I do for you?"

Yudhishtira said, "I am Kanka, O king. I belong to the Vaiyaghra family. I am a master of dice, and I once lived in the palace of Yudhishtira of Indraprastha. He and I were so close, my lord, that you might say I was his very soul, and he mine. Alas, he lost everything he owned, and went away to the forest.

"I hear that you are as noble as Yudhishtira, and hope to find solace in your company, and sanctuary in your palace. I have no one I can call my own, and today joy and sorrow are the same to me. I have no desires left, Virata, but I am tired of wandering. I have come to you seeking rest and peace. Shall I find refuge in your city?"

Deeply moved by the presence and dignity of the brahmana, the Matsya king said without hesitation, "You honour me that you choose to come to my house for refuge. I am as fond of the rolling dice as Yudhishtira was, and I will be happy if you teach me every secret you know of the game. You say you are a master of dice, and I am old enough to know that you are not a boastful man."

Virata turned to his amazed court and said loudly, "From this day, Kanka is as much king here as I am. All my wealth is his, to dispose as he chooses. He shall ride with me, sit beside me, and rule even as I do. Let no man dare displease Kanka in this kingdom."

But Kanka, the brahmana, said, "My lord, you are too kind. I have no need for wealth. But may I be allowed to keep what I win at dice? As for the kingdom, I will advise you on the affairs of state, of which I have some little knowledge since I was as close to the emperor Yudhishtira as he was himself. As to other things, my lord, I have sworn an oath that I will eat only one meal a day, at night, and that I will touch no leavings. Grant me so much, and I will gladly stay with you."

Virata embraced Kanka in welcome.

THREE

Ajnatavasa

THREE DAYS LATER, BHEEMA ENTERED VIRATA WITH A LADLE IN HIS hand. The people of the city stopped to stare at the titan. No one dared accost him as he walked into the palace.

The extraordinary Bheema came and stood before the Matsya king. Virata said, "Welcome, splendid stranger! Which country do you rule? Tell us what we can do for you."

Bheema said, "I am Ballava, my lord, and I am one of the world's great cooks. I seek work in your kitchen."

Old Virata gazed shrewdly at the young giant before him. The king said, "Ballava, you seem to be far above the profession you claim for yourself. You look more like a prince of the earth to me, than a cook."

"I can cook you a thousand dishes, and every one a delicacy. I once cooked in the kitchens of Yudhishtira, in Indraprastha. But now that king has fallen on hard times, and I am out of work. I will not work for just any master. But I have heard how generous you are, and how kind."

Virata said slowly, "Your physique is not a cook's, Ballava. You are more suited to commanding an army from an elephant's back, than plying a ladle in a kitchen."

Bheema smiled. "That is because I am a wrestler, as well, my lord. It has always been my hobby, and people tell me I am as good at wrestling as I am at my fires. If you let me, I will also train the young men of your court in the craft of kushti."

"Very well," cried Virata, beaming. "You shall be in charge of my kitchens from now, and also my wrestling-pits. And welcome, noble stranger!" He paused, then, asked, "Tell me, are you sure you are not a kshatriya?"

Bheema laughed, "I am a cook, sire!"

He was shown to the kitchens. Two days later, King Virata was out in the morning to inspect the royal stables, and the horses he loved as if they were his own children. As he made his round alone—he had come early and unannounced—he came upon a curious sight. Virata saw a dark young man, who was so handsome he took one's breath away, speaking to the finest of the king's horses, in the most intimate voice.

Virata paused in the shadows to watch. The young man was handsome enough to make another man wish he were a woman! Most amazing was the way the horses responded to him. Those haughty thoroughbreds, who would bite and lash out with their hooves if a stranger came anywhere near them, now nuzzled their pedigreed faces in the young man's hands, as he stroked them and whispered to them. The horses spoke back to the dark stranger!

For a while, the king stood absorbed by the spectacle in the dawn light. Then he stepped out from the shadows and asked, "Who are you, young man?"

When the stranger turned to face him fully, even old Virata felt a pang. Nakula, every fibre of him regal, beautiful, answered the king, "My lord, I am a groom and I know horses well. I have come seeking work in your stables."

"Truly, you know horses and they seem to love you. But to my old eyes you seem more like a kshatriya than a stable-hand. You don't look used to rough work."

"I am Damagranthi, my lord. It is horses I love, and with them that I am happiest to be. As for knowing this work, I know it well. For once, my brother owned a great stable. I have heard you are a noble master, and that you love your horses like your own children."

Virata thought the young stranger, handsomer than any man he had even seen, spoke more like a prince than a groom. The king said, "I shall be honoured if you look after my horses. Unless, of course..."

"What, my lord?"

"You would rather have command of my army," said Virata shrewdly.

But Nakula only smiled and said, "I will be content in your stables."

After another few days, Arjuna came to the court of the Matsya king. With this last week in the forest, his transformation was complete. The third Pandava was a eunuch now, and rather a lovely one, though his shoulders were broad, and his arms and chest too muscled for him to pass as a woman.

Wearing a woman's clothes, his face painted like one's, wearing necklaces of pearl and coral he had from Draupadi, and a hairpiece he bought with jasmine strings threaded cleverly into it so it might have been his own hair, wearing bangles and perfume, his hips swaying when he walked: Arjuna came and stood before the Matsya king in his court.

In a deep woman's voice, he said to Virata, "I am Brihannala the dancer, my lord. I can sing and play the vina too. No one on earth can sing and dance like me, for I learnt from a gandharva."

"What can we do for you, Brihannala?" asked the king, and his canny old eyes roved over Arjuna's arms and shoulders. "Stay with us, and rule the kingdom with me. Your arms make me think you are more an archer than a dancer. Tell me truthfully, are you really a eunuch?"

Arjuna laughed like the most seductive woman. In his soft new voice, he said, "My lord, the only string I play on is a vina's. The only art I am a mistress of is dancing. Look, I will show you."

Chitrasena's gifted pupil sang and danced briefly before the Matsya king. So delectably did he do both, the king said at once, "You shall teach my daughter, the princess Uttaraa, how to dance."

Arjuna replied, "I will make her the finest dancer on earth."

Virata sent for Uttaraa and said to her, "This is Brihannala, who dances and sings better than anyone I have seen. She will teach you, but be sure you treat her with the respect you would show a queen."

As sweet a young princess as one would find anywhere, Uttaraa led the eunuch away to her apartment. She and her companions became Brihannala's sishyaas and her friends as well. Soon, Arjuna enjoyed his ajnatavasa more than he had thought he would. Though, with all that nubile young womanhood around him, he often wished he were himself again, and a whole man.

A few days after the arrival of Brihannala in Virata's court, Draupadi entered the city of that king. Wearing old and torn clothes, she came as a sairandhri. But the people in the streets stopped to stare at her, for she could not hide her dark beauty.

Queen Sudeshna, who was once a princess of Kekaya, was out on her balcony, looking up the main city thoroughfare that led to her palace. She saw the striking young woman, dark as dusk; some townspeople crowded round the young woman. One of them asked rudely, "Who are you, stranger?"

"I am a queen's sairandhri. I have come seeking work," Draupadi answered.

The men in the crowd looked her over frankly. Perhaps out of jealousy, seeing how beautiful she was, the women began to taunt her. They mimicked her royal accents, "I am a queen's sairandhri," and laughed. The jeering crowd followed the young woman down the road. Soon, some of them prodded and pinched her viciously. She cried out, and quickened her stride; but the crowd was merciless.

Sudeshna saw all this from her balcony, and the queen sent her maids out to the terrified Panchali. "Tell my guards to scatter the crowd, and fetch that young woman here."

The maids ran out into the street with the guards, and the jostling crowd was quickly sent on its way. Draupadi stood trembling before the queen's sakhis. They gasped when they saw her at close quarters: she was stunning. Those women took the frightened sairandhri's hand, "Come, Queen Sudeshna wants to see you."

Her heart still fluttering from her encounter in the streets, Draupadi arrived before the queen. Her hands entwined nervously and her eyes turned down, she stood before Sudeshna. Sudeshna drew a sharp breath when she saw Panchali near. She made Draupadi sit beside her.

Stroking Panchali's face, almost disbelievingly, the queen breathed, "You are so beautiful, my child, as if you belong to another world! Who are you, dark one? How are you alone? How does your husband dare let you out by yourself? Tell me why you have come to Virata. You look like a queen, at the very least."

Slowly, Draupadi stopped shaking. But she said nothing yet, and Sudeshna urged her again, "Your face, your eyes, your body, are all so perfect; yet you are out on your own. Who are you? Are you a yakshi or a gandharvi, an apsara or a devi? You are as lovely as Lakshmi herself."

Now Draupadi answered, "I am Malini, my Queen, and I am a sairandhri in search of work. Once, I used to make up the Queen Draupadi's face, and weave blue lilies and jasmine flowers into her hair. But, alas, she has gone away into the forest and has no use for my gifts anymore. Queen Sudeshna, I have heard how kind you are, and I have come seeking work with you."

The queen looked at her thoughtfully for a moment, then, said, "You are the most beautiful woman I ever saw. Yet, your face and your eyes tell me that you have suffered deeply. Tell me your misfortunes, Malini."

There were tears in Draupadi's eyes, and she clasped Sudeshna's hand tightly. She said in a low voice, which only the queen heard, "I am married to five gandharvas. But they were cursed to leave me for a year, and I have never been apart from my husbands before." She gazed imploringly into the other woman's face, "I beg you, O queen, keep me with you for a year. I dare not think what will become of me otherwise. I will do your face and hair every day. You are so kind, I already feel like a daughter to you," and she wept.

Sudeshna stroked her hand and said, "My poor child, such privilege you must have enjoyed when you were with Panchali. Use this palace as your own from now. You will be my sakhi, and you may use my private garden whenever you want to be alone."

The queen paused, before she said slowly, "Malini, you shall live with me in my palace, and the thought delights me. Yet it troubles me, as well."

"Why is that, my queen?"

"Like all men, my husband is fond of a beautiful woman. If he sees you, he will not be able to resist you; nor, for that matter, would any man. Why, you make me wish I were a man! I am afraid if the king sees you he will fall in love with you, old as he is. And he would leave me then, wouldn't he? Is it wise for me to keep you here?"

Draupadi said, "My lady, I may not see them for this year, but my gandharva husbands watch over me. No man will come near me, not your king or any other. Besides, how could I betray your kindness, if you kept me here? I will always remain in your inner rooms and your garden, and never show my face outside. Trust me, I won't cause you any grief."

Sudeshna kissed her and cried, "You are such a ravishing child! How can I refuse you?"

Draupadi turned her eyes down and said, "But I, too, have some small conditions I must keep."

"What are they?"

"My husbands would not tolerate it if I were to eat any leavings. And they would be angry if I had to press anyone's feet."

Sudeshna smiled, "You will never have to do either in this palace."

Thus, Yudhishtira's Queen Draupadi, once empress of all Bharatavarsha, joined the service of Queen Sudeshna of the Matsya kingdom, as her flower girl. A week after she was ensconced in the palace, Sahadeva, the most intelligent Pandava, arrived quietly in Virata's court dressed as a cowherd, carrying a staff in his hand. He said to that king in chaste language, and a voice as deep as the rumbling of clouds, "My lord, give me work in your cattle-sheds. I have a way with cows, and when I tend them, they give twice the milk they would otherwise. If you like, I can prove it to you before you take me in."

The king gazed at the self-effacing young man. He said slowly, "Stranger, somehow it seems to me that you haven't always been a cowherd."

Sahadeva smiled, "My lord, cows are all I know. I can cure any disease your cattle may catch. My name is Tantripala, and your herds will be contented and beautiful when I look after them."

"We never refuse any good soul who comes to us. From now on, Tantripala, you shall be our chief cowherd. And I have lived long enough in this world to know I will not regret employing you. Indeed, you honour me by joining my service."

He looked so acutely at Sahadeva, the youngest Pandava felt certain that Virata saw though his disguise.

The Pandavas, who were born to rule the earth, settled into the palace in the Matsya capital. Soon the king was happy only when he was in the company of his new courtier Kanka. He found the man even wiser than he had judged at first; and at gambling, the brahmana was peerless. After he had received the occult siddhi from the Rishi Brihadaswa, Yudhishtira was an invincible master of the rolling dice. He beat the best players in the Matsya court, easily, and entrenched himself in the king's favour. Besides, Virata soon began to consult Kanka on complex and delicate matters of state, and found in the brahmana an exceptionally sagacious counsellor.

Bheema was as pleased as he could possibly be in the king's kitchens. He slept on a cook's bed, but on a wonderfully full stomach. Besides, he did enjoy cooking almost as much as eating what he cooked, and the mighty Bheema was blessed with a spectacular culinary talent: he was, quite simply, a magnificent cook. Then, he wrestled. He taught the young kshatriyas of Virata, but he was careful never to reveal his true strength. The king saw that Ballava was as good a wrestler as he was a cook. Well pleased, he rewarded him with gold and jewels.

The horses of the royal stables were in finer fettle than Virata had ever seen them. Their coats were sleek and glossy, and their fierce spirits contended. Virata rewarded Damagranthi, his new groom, generously. The cows of the Matsya king yielded more milk than ever before and they, too, shone with a quiet joy at being in the care of the new herdsman. Sahadeva was happy with the herd, and the king was pleased with him.

Under the watchful eye of her guru, the eunuch Brihannala, the gifted princess Uttaraa began to blossom into a rare dancer. Very often, Virata would spend an hour or two watching his daughter at her lessons. The old king would gaze at Brihannala out of the corner of his eye, marvelling at the eunuch's powerful shoulders and her muscled arms. But there was no doubt that Brihannala was indeed a eunuch, for the king had him examined. Still, a persistent suspicion troubled Virata: that Brihannala was more than what he seemed to be; that some mystery lurked behind the eunuch.

The Pandavas spent three happy months in Virata's court, hidden as if they were back in their mother's womb. Even Draupadi, the sairandhri, was satisfied enough with her lot; though, when she thought of her husbands as courtier, cook, stable-hand, eunuch and cowherd, her eyes would fill.

FOUR

The cook and the wrestler

THE PANDAVAS HAD IMAGINED THE THIRTEENTH YEAR OF EXILE would be the hardest. They found themselves happy and occupied in the kindly Virata's court. Bheema was delighted to be back in a city; somehow, from here Hastinapura and Indraprastha did not seem so far.

Virata was already very fond of the strangers he had taken into his service, and by some miracle, he never thought of connecting them to one another. In the fourth month of their ajnatavasa, there occurred an incident in the Matsya capital that made Ballava the cook a greater favourite than ever with the king.

It was a festival day, when Siva was worshipped in the city. There was a tournament of wrestling, and contestants came from all over Bharatavarsha to show their prowess. Virata's wrestlers were renowned for their skill and strength, and one of them had never failed to take the prize. This year things were not going well for them.

On the very morning of the wrestling, a sullen giant of a wrestler arrived in the city, from a distant land whose name no one had heard. The judges asked him, "Who are you, stranger?"

Grinning insolently, he replied, "I am Jimuta, and know that I am the greatest wrestler in the world, and none of your puny fighters can face me. I am as strong as ten lions, so let every wrestler in Virata* beware!"

---

* Virata is both the King and the city.

He declared all this standing in the middle of the arena, and never bowing to the king. Some of Virata's courtiers said among themselves, "A great braggart, anyway. We shall see if his wrestling matches his boasting."

But it did. No one could face the huge stranger for more than a few moments. His strength was hardly human, and he crushed Virata's best wrestlers. He was savage in victory, always breaking an arm or a leg of all his opponents, needlessly, after he had beaten them. Soon no one dared fight him, and the rough fellow stood unchallenged in the ring.

Virata was beside himself. The wrestler's conceit was intolerable, but he seemed invincible too. The king turned to Kanka, the ascetic gambler who sat at his right hand. "Is there no one in all this kingdom who can beat this arrogant man?" the king whispered, his kindly eyes glittering in anger.

Kanka said quietly, "But there is, my lord; in your very kitchen. When both he and I were in Yudhishtira's court at Indraprastha, I had occasion to see the friendly fellow wrestle. This lout is no match for your cook Ballava."

Bheema had said earlier to the king, "My lord, I shall have a busy day in the kitchen preparing the feast. You must not ask me to come to wrestle, or the food will not be as it should."

Though he longed to fight, Bheema was anxious lest he was recognised. Virata was disappointed; but he thought of Bheema more as a cook than a wrestler, and made no point of it.

But now he said to Kanka, "Let Ballava be fetched from his kitchen. This is a matter of honour. I would hate to see the foreigner win our tournament."

Bheema was brought to Virata's enclosure, and the king said, "Ballava, Kanka tells me you can teach this braggart a lesson. Fight for the honour of the Matsyas today."

Though he would have loved nothing better, Bheema hesitated. With a glance at the swaggering wrestler in the ring, he knew he could beat him, but he had learnt a lesson of caution from twelve years of exile.

Then, Kanka said, "You mustn't refuse the king today, Ballava. He has been so kind to you that no price should be too high to pay in return."

A flicker in the cook's eyes at this; Ballava bowed and said, "I will fight for the honour of the Matsyas today, and may Siva bless me."

The king had it announced that a challenger would wrestle with the brute in the ring. The giant laughed. Jimuta called out, "Have you found another fool to risk himself for you? I am the greatest wrestler on earth. I have my strength from a rishi's blessing, and no one in the world can fight me. I have torn tigers limb from limb, and brought a bull-elephant to his knees with a blow of my fist. What man can stand against me? I am the mightiest!"

He smote his chest, across which he wore a tiger-skin, and roared like a tiger himself.

The king said, "Stranger, we don't dispute your strength. But we have a man in our court who will beat you."

The wrestler growled, "The world acknowledges that I am the greatest wrestler of these times. No champion has lasted more than a few moments against me. I say to you, your challenger will not leave the arena alive. So make your choice: either give me the reward, or have your wrestler's death on your conscience!"

He strutted around the ring again, roaring from time to time. The king was very fond of his cook Ballava. He blanched to hear the wrestler's threat, and turned to Kanka in some alarm. Kanka laid a hand on Virata's arm and said, "Have no fear. Your cook is more than this braggart's equal."

"Where does your challenger come from, Virata?" cried the wrestler.

"From my kitchen. My cook is more of a wrestler than you are!" answered Virata warmly.

The arena echoed with the lout's laughter. Then, clad in a black singlet, his body oiled and shining, Ballava stepped into the ring like a lion. He wore a crimson mask over his face. The crowd stood up to cheer him.

The king also rose and cried, "This is my cook Ballava, and he will teach you a lesson, O greatest wrestler in the world!"

Jimuta gave a start when he saw Bheema. He knew this was no common cook that came to fight him. The foreigner could tell at a glance that he was no common wrestler either. And why did his heart flutter as if death had stepped into the arena with him? But, repressing the stab of fear, the champion roared at Bheema, "Fool, go back to your pots and pans or I will break your neck for you!"

Bheema said nothing. He bowed to the king, and approached the smouldering wrestler. Their gazes met and locked. It was as if they already strained together, limb against mighty limb. The crowd fell hushed, and you could hear the breeze in the leaves of the palace trees. Both at once, the outsider and Bheema bent at the waist and began to circle each other.

Never touching they circled; their arms were extended before them and every muscle in their bodies was taut. To the crowd, it seemed as if they were dancers in a weird play. They circled ten or, perhaps, twenty times, and then the foreigner's courage faltered. He cried, "Stop circling, cook! Let us have done with it."

Jimuta lowered his head like a bison and charged Bheema. Later, those who watched remembered vividly what happened next. For, though it happened so swiftly that it was all over in a moment, it seemed time dilated herself so every detail was engraved on the people's memories.

The wild charge was a technique the wrestler had used against his other adversaries. He had knocked them down, and battered them into submission before they got their breath back.

But when he struck Bheema, with awesome force, it was as if he struck a rock. The cook did not so much as sway at the impact; instead, the wrestler staggered back stunned. In a flash, Bheema seized him and lifted him over his head. He whirled the giant around thrice, and flung him down, head first, like a thunderbolt, driving his neck into his thick body, crushing his skull, killing him instantly.

There was a moment's awed silence; then the crowd was on its feet, running into the arena to embrace Ballava. The people yelled his name, and carried him aloft on a sea of shoulders. Finally, he managed to free himself and cried, "Let me go, friends. I have fifty dishes on the fire, and they will all burn!"

Ballava bowed to King Virata, who was also on his feet, applauding, and Kanka the gambler was beside him, his eyes shining. His task accomplished, the cook ran back to his fires. Through it all, even when he received the new champion's generous purse, he kept his crimson mask in place.

From then on, Ballava became a favourite not just with King Virata but the people of his city. And the feast he produced that day did not suffer a bit from the short while he was away from his kitchen.

FIVE

Karna's dream

WHEN INDRA SENT LOMASA TO THE PANDAVAS, THE MUNI ALSO brought a secret message from the Deva, just for Yudhishtira.

Indra said, "I know the dread in your heart, Yudhishtira. You fear Karna because you think he is a greater archer than Arjuna. Do not be afraid, I will take some of Karna's power away from him."

Yudhishtira kept Indra's message close, and it consoled him. And one dark night of a new moon, Indra decided to keep his promise to Yudhishtira. The Pandavas' exile neared its end, and the great war drew near; it would not do to leave Karna as invincible as he was. But Karna's father, Surya Deva, divined Indra's intention.

That night, as Karna lay asleep, the Sun God came to him in a dream. He came as an illustrious brahmana. He said to the warrior, "Listen to what I have to say, Karna. I have come to save your life."

The brahmana seemed strangely familiar, and Karna said, "Tell me what you have come to say, Brahmana."

The brahmana said, "You worship the Sun God at noon, and never turn away anyone who comes to you for alms at that hour. Your charity sets you apart from other men.

"But tomorrow, Karna, a mortal enemy will come to you for alms. Indra himself will come to you as a brahmana, and he will ask for your kavacha and kundala. He is Arjuna's father, and the alms he will ask for are the two things that are your very life."

In the dream, Karna stood amazed before the brahmana whose eyes were flames. He stood passive, in the way of dreams, and listened avidly.

The brahmana continued, "Your golden earrings belong to Aditi, the mother of the Devas, and the armour you wear was dipped in amrita. Part with the kundalas, Karna, and you will part with half your life. Give away your kavacha, and you will not live long after. The mail you wear is protection not merely against enemies' weapons but time itself.

"I wish you well, Karna. When Indra asks for your kavacha and kundala, offer him anything else in their place. Offer him your army, your kingdom, but tell him he cannot have the earrings and the armour."

Karna was moved. "How fond you are of me, stranger! And you are no ordinary brahmana, who know what will happen tomorrow. Why, you know the mind of Devendra himself.

"Then, Brahmana, you are even more extraordinary in that you seem to love me. I have lived many years in this sad world, and only two people have truly cared about me. My mother Radha loves me, and Duryodhana loves me like his own brother. Now you seem to be a third. Brahmana, tell me who you really are."

The brahmana shone brighter than ever in Karna's dream. He said, "I am Surya whom you worship every day, and I bear you great love!"

Karna saw the brahmana's body was iridescent now, and he fell at the Deva's feet. He cried in a fervour, "My Lord! You are my Ishta Devata, the only God I worship. I am blessed a thousand times tonight, that you have come to me yourself."

Karna clasped the brahmana's feet in his hands and wept for joy. Surya Bhagawan said, "Karna, there is more truth in you than any other man alive. I have not come lightly, but to warn you of dire peril, and to save your life. When he comes begging tomorrow, do not give your kavacha and kundala to Indra."

Karna raised his eyes to look into the face of the God, who was his father, though the son did not know it. He said, "My Lord, I have sworn my oath for you. Every day, after I worship you, I wait for someone to come to me for alms. The alms I give are in your name, and I give anything I am asked.

"All these years, I have never wavered in this ritual. The oath I swore was in anguish, that the world shunned me because I was a sutaputra. My own guru cursed me when he discovered what I was. It was after Bhargava cursed me that I swore my oath, and since that day, some peace entered my life. This charity is what sustains me; it calms my unquiet heart.

"The dearer what I give away is to me, the greater the peace I find. Lord, if someone asks me for my very life, I pray I have the wisdom and the courage to give it without a thought. For that shall be my salvation, and bring me honour."

The splendid Sun stood over his child, listening to him absorbed, in deeper love than Karna guessed, anxiety and pride. Karna went on, "I have never loved this life of mine much, anyway. I have never belonged anywhere, or to anyone. Not even to my mother Radha, since I am not her flesh and blood, though she loves me more than her life.

"Above everything else, I crave honour. Honour is the only balm that soothes my pain, and I have won honor for myself in the hardest way any man ever has. If tomorrow Indra asks me for my kavacha and kundala, and I refuse to give them to him, my honour will die in a moment. It is true that I might live longer then, but my shame will outlive me.

"If the Lord of heaven himself, who slew Vritrasura, comes to me as a beggar, why, it will be with pride that I give him my very life. And that final charity must bring me eternal fame."

A shadow crossed Karna's proud, ravaged face. He smiled wryly, "Fate has never been my ally, not since my natural mother abandoned me. It seems I have a harder road to walk than any other man. I have no doubt that, like Indra, fate is also on the side of the Pandavas. In my heart, I know that even if I am the better archer, Arjuna will kill me. I have never told this to anyone before, but I know when he and I face each other in battle, finally, as we were born to, I will die by Arjuna's hand.

"I am certain of this, and not a day passes without my thinking of it. Yet, even if Arjuna takes my life, there is one thing he shall never have: my honour. I love my honour more than my life. Long ago, I chose honour for my bride, and I will cling to her even in death. Only she imbues my life with meaning, invests it with purity. Without honour, life is meaningless. Why should I seek to prolong my life after I abandon its meaning, its very soul?

"I care nothing if Indra takes my kavacha and kundala, when, by doing this, he shall bless me with the everlasting life of the spirit.

"I swear in your name, Surya Deva, my only Lord, I will not refuse Indra what he wants. Why, most of all, because he asks for no less than my life!"

Karna's dream

The Sun God said, "Ah Karna, don't do this foolish thing. Life is as precious as honour. And what about your wife and your sons? And Duryodhana, who you say loves you as his brother? Give away your kavacha and kundala, and you will give away the war that is coming; for only you can stand between the Pandavas and victory.

"What use, Karna, will honour be to you when you are dead? My bhakta, even as you have worshipped me every day, I too have loved you. In the name of that love, I implore you, don't do this senseless thing! Turn Indra away when he comes tomorrow to beg for your life."

With tears in his eyes, Karna said, "It is only you I have ever worshipped, and my heart is full today seeing how you love me. Yet, I cannot do as you ask. I am not afraid of death, but the very thought of dishonour terrifies me. I have sworn an oath. I must not betray myself by breaking it, not for the sake of victory, or of all our lives.

"Ah, my Lord, what greater joy can I wish for than your coming to me like this? Bless me, Surya Deva. Lay your hands on my head, and grant me undying fame."

Surya, the brahmana, said, "Your dharma is greater than even Yudhishtira's: almost as if you both were brothers, and you the elder one! I am proud of you, Karna. When Indra comes tomorrow and takes your kavacha and kundala, ask him for his Shakti in return. That Shakti will protect you, in some measure, when your golden armour is gone."

The Sun God laid his nitid palms on Karna's head, and vanished from the warrior's dream. Karna awoke with a start in the darkness of night. Over and over, he relived his dream, until dawn lit the world outside.

SIX

The brahmana at noon

At dawn, it seemed the sun rose slowly, as if to postpone the hour of Karna's worship. But rise above the world he must, and he did so, inevitably. Karna was in a fever, impatient for the star to climb to midheaven. He was full of an urgent sense of destiny.

At last, the time for his worship came and Karna stood bare-bodied at noon, with his hands folded over his head, staring at the sun above and chanting the Surya mantra. At the end of an hour, just as he lowered his face, he heard a thin voice beside him, begging weakly, "Alms, O king, alms for a poor brahmana."

Karna turned and saw an aged and emaciated brahmana, with both shaking hands outstretched. "Alms, alms. I have come to you for alms. I have heard you never send anyone away empty-handed at this hour."

His heart beating wildly, Karna stared at the old brahmana, incredulous that this was the king of the Devas who stood before him. After a long moment, Karna said, "What are the alms you want, old one?"

"I want no cows, no jewels, no gold, Karna," the brahmana replied. "I don't want what other brahmanas ask for."

"Then what can I give you?"

The brahmana's eyes lighted lovingly on, first, Karna's kundala in his ears, then strayed down to the golden mail on his chest, which was like his skin. The mendicant whispered, "Those! Your kavacha and your kundala."

Karna laughed. He had decided to make Indra beg a little. He said slowly, "Strange alms for a brahmana! What will you do with these?"

"I have heard you are the greatest alms-giver in the world, Karna," said the brahmana.

"I will give you other kavacha and kundala, brahmana, as many as you want, as priceless as you please. But these are part of my body, they cannot be removed."

"It is your kavacha and kundala I have come for. They are all I want."

"I will give you vast wealth, I will give you my very kingdom. But not these."

"I have come only for your golden kavacha and kundala. Cut them from your body and give them to me. I have heard you never refuse anything you are asked at this hour. Have I heard wrongly?"

Delighted that he could tantalize the Deva king, Karna said, "Brahmana, perhaps you don't know what you are asking for. The sheen of my kavacha and kundala attract you; but when you hear what they mean to me, I am sure you will not want them.

"Muni, these are no common armour and earrings. They are the guardians of my life, for they have been dipped in the amrita the Devas drink. I was born with these, my lord, to be an invincible warrior. I have sworn to my friend Duryodhana that I will kill Arjuna, and win the war of the age for him.

"So, ask me for something else, anything at all. But leave me my kavacha and kundala."

The brahmana repeated, "It is for your kavacha and kundala that I have come a long way. It is these I want from you, and nothing else."

Karna saw the anxiety on his face, and began to laugh. "Why do you laugh?" cried the brahmana.

Folding his hands, Karna said, "Because I know who you are, my Lord! I am blessed, O Indra, that you, the greatest Deva, the most munificent of all alms-givers, have come for alms to a mortal. I know why you want my kavacha and kundala; I know for whose sake you have come. And though it is my life you have come begging for, I am proud to give you even that at this sacred hour."

Karna drew his sword and severed the armour from his chest, cutting golden links, and the kundala from his ears, drawing more blood*. Smiling, he set them down at the astonished God's feet. "Here, my Lord,

---

* KMG's text says he is called Karna for this severing of his earrings.

the alms of Karna's life. For I never refuse anyone at this hour, be it anything they come to beg for."

Karna's face shone in the grace of this ultimate charity: when he gave away his own life. He was so ecstatic he wept. Flowers of light fell on him out of heaven, and Indra stood revealed before him, the Deva's eyes also full.

Indra said, "You are the noblest man I ever saw. Ask me for any boon, and I will give it to you. You can have anything except my Vajra."

Karna said, "For me, to ask a gift in return is not to give at all. My charity would lose honour if I took something from you. Yet now, I will indeed ask you for a gift, and I will tell you why.

"My Lord, out of your love for Arjuna and his brothers, you asked me for my life, at a time when I would dishonour myself if I refused you. Indra, the world shall speak ill of you for this. Give me your Shakti for the kavacha and the kundala, so men will say Indra gave Karna his own ayudha in return for what he took from him. The Shakti will not save my life; that is doomed, anyway. But I feel strange love for you, and I want to protect your reputation."

Indra could hardly believe the warrior before him, whom he had come to betray to his death, was a mortal man. He breathed, "Today you have conquered the king of the Devas. There shall be no scar on your body where you cut away the kavacha and kundala."

Indra raised his hand, and those wounds vanished. The God said, "May your body be brighter than it was when you wore your armour," and Karna was radiant. "As for the Shakti, I will give it to you. You may use it only once, and it will destroy the one at whom you cast it. Then it will return to me and you will never see it again.

Karna smiled, "I need to use it only once. I have only one enemy."

Indra grew very still. "Krishna protects my son. You cannot kill Arjuna even with my Shakti."

Karna said, "We shall see, my Lord. At least, I can try to win the war for Duryodhana."

"Win or lose the war, it is a small matter. Today you have won immortal fame with the alms you have given me. I name you Vaikartana for cutting your kavacha from your flesh; and men will say, ever after, that the greatest of all alms-givers was not Indra, but Karna. As long as the world lives, Karna, your fame shall live in it.

"But now, it is time I left you."

Indra picked up the golden kavacha and kundala that lay at his feet. They shone more brilliantly than ever at his touch. But Karna knelt before the Deva, and said, "Ah, my Lord, I feel I have made a friend of you today, and that you have some affection for me. I have another gift to ask of you, incalculably dearer than the one I asked for before."

"What is it, O prince among men?"

"Cast your light upon my deepest sorrow, O Indra. Tell me who my natural father is, and my mother."

Indra's eyes were full of pity. He said gently, "It is not fated you know that secret yet, and I cannot change fate. But, one day, you will surely know," he added thoughtfully, "and he who tells you shall be a greater one than me."

Karna smiled in resignation, and, wiping his tears, said, "No matter, then. I will carry my grief until the time comes for me to know the truth." He laughed, "Besides, I am lighter now since I gave away my kavacha. Lighter than I have ever been, lighter by my very life!"

Indra laid his hand on Karna's head. "May your name be a sweet fragrance through time. And those who merely hear about this deed of yours, even in the vilest days of the kali yuga, they shall not stray from the path of truth."

The day was dark now, because the sun hid his face behind some clouds in sorrow. A breeze stirred around Karna and Indra; a thin drizzle fell upon them; the earth was full of soft joy. Taking the kavacha and kundala, Indra vanished before Karna's eyes.

Karna was happy. Though he had possibly lost his life, the Deva had given him something far more precious. Indra had blessed him with immortal fame.

SEVEN

The queen's sairandhri

In the city of Virata, Queen Sudeshna grew very fond of her exquisite flower girl, and Panchali was well cared for in the palace. Malini the sairandhri was quite above the jealousies and intrigues that haunt every harem, and despite her beauty, all the queen's women liked her.

Eleven peaceful, comfortable months passed. Only once, when he arrived unannounced in his wife's apartment, did King Virata catch a glimpse of Malini. He said breathlessly to his wife, "Who is that sakhi of yours? Send her to me tonight."

"My lord, not her! She is a strange creature, cursed to be apart from her gandharva husbands for a year. But they watch over her, invisibly. If you seduce Malini you will invite your death to you."

Virata was wise enough never to pursue Draupadi, or even ask after her again. But Sudeshna had a brother called Keechaka. He was a fierce kshatriya, the Senapati of Virata's army. When the Pandavas came to the Matsya kingdom, Keechaka, an insatiable conqueror, was away on a campaign. The sons of Pandu had been in Virata for eleven months, when one day Keechaka came home with his legions, and ample treasures, the spoils of war.

There was singing and dancing in the streets, a procession, and then a banquet in the king's halls. It was early evening when Keechaka managed to tear himself away from the festivity, and visit his sister in her apartment. He was much younger than Sudeshna, almost like a son to her, and she received him excitedly. They sat together for an hour, while she fed him all the dainties he had loved since he was a boy. Whenever they were together, it was as if they were children again.

It was getting late, time for Keechaka to return to his own palace. He paused at Sudeshna's window, and said wistfully, "Your garden is in bloom. How lovely it is and how peaceful, after all the killing I have seen and done this past year."

Sudeshna said, "Why don't you walk back through my garden? There is a small gate below it, you can go that way."

Sniffing the breeze outside, and the scents of flowers, Keechaka kissed his sister and went out through the window. It was as if fate called him. He strolled along the garden-paths, alone, stroking soft petals with his warrior's hands. He was pensive, an unusual mood for him. Turning a final corner, he saw the little pavilion at the bottom of Sudeshna's garden, tucked away in a stand of trees. The sun was setting, and, framed starkly against its last light, Keechaka saw the most beautiful woman he had ever set eyes on. She stood in the small cloister, her dark face turned towards the sinking sun. She was far away, in a world of her own.

Keechaka looked at her and knew his life would never be the same again. He stood transfixed, staring at the vision before him, knowing himself lost. Sudeshna had given Draupadi freedom of this garden; she came here to be alone with her sorrows, and her yearnings. Today, from her window, she had watched Keechaka's triumphal entry into the city. It had stirred memories in her: of how Bheema, Arjuna, Nakula and Sahadeva had ridden into Indraprastha during the days of the Rajasuya yagna. Full of nostalgia, she had come here to cry alone.

As she stood watching the sunset, a man's deep voice hailed her, "Who are you?"

Draupadi whirled around to find Keechaka standing at the foot of the steps to the little arbour. His eyes roved over her body in naked adoration. Seeing him look like that, Draupadi ran down the steps on the far side of the pavilion, but Keechaka caught up with her.

He seized her arm and said hoarsely, "Who are you? This is not the first time I have come to my sister's palace, but I have never seen you before. For if I had, my life would have changed forever."

He devoured her with his gaze. Slowly, he whispered, "I never knew any woman could be so beautiful. You are a human woman, aren't you?

Or are you a Goddess? Why are you by yourself, without a man? What a terrible waste! Tell me who you are, I want to be your slave."

Draupadi shivered at his touch. She cried, "I am your sister's flower girl Malini. I am a servant here, please let me go. It is not right that a man of your nobility speaks to a mere maid."

"Maid!" he roared. "I will make you my wife. My only wife from now, and all the others your slaves. I am Keechaka, the real master of this land. There is no man on earth as strong as I am Malini, though now your beauty makes me dizzy, and I feel as weak as a young bird in spring!

"Come with me, be my wife. Your slightest whim shall be my command. The king is no king at all; he dare not raise his voice against me. Keechaka rules and you shall be as a queen beside him. I am in love with you, Malini, and I realize now that I have never known love before. All my time, all my strength and power shall be as incense at the altar of this love. You are my life from now. I beg you, come with me."

She trembled when she saw he was serious. She wrested her arm from his grasp. She saw his eyes fill, and he knelt before her!

Draupadi said, "It is not proper for a kshatriya to speak to a maidservant. You could have any woman in this city. You must have many lovely wives already. My lord, a man should say such things only to his wife.

"Besides, you mistake me, Keechaka: I am not a single woman. I have five gandharva husbands, who let me live in Queen Sudeshna's palace, saying I would be safe here. They are dangerous and would kill you, if they knew you spoke to me as you have done. I beg you, leave me alone."

She turned to go, but with a cry, he seized her ankle. She said, "You are tying a noose around your neck, mistaking it for a garland of flowers. I warn you, don't play with your life; my husbands are immortals. You are a powerful man in this kingdom. You have a family, wives and children you love, and who love you. Don't throw all that away for the sake of this brief madness. I warn you again, Keechaka, if you pursue me my husbands will kill you."

His grip was numb on her foot; Keechaka was like a dreaming man. Draupadi freed herself and fled from the garden. He still knelt there, dazed. Then, slowly, he pulled himself up and walked back to Sudeshna's palace.

She rose in surprise when she saw him. When she saw how he looked, Sudeshna cried, "What happened, Keechaka? Why are you back?"

Keechaka covered his face with his hands, and fell on her bed. Anxiously, she cried again, "Has something happened to you, my child? Tell me what it is. You were well when you left here, just moments ago."

Keechaka said nothing for a while; then he sat up. His eyes burning, he asked, "Who is she, Sudeshna? Who is your sairandhri? I have never seen anyone like her before. I must have her for myself, or I will die.

"I confessed my love. I offered to marry her, but she ran from me. Ah, my body is on fire, and my heart is trying to break out of my chest. Sudeshna, I will die if I don't hold her in my arms!"

Alarmed, Sudeshna sat beside him. She stroked his face, and said, "Malini came to me eleven months ago, asking for a year's sanctuary. She is a wonderful young woman, charming and honest as she is beautiful. Yet she is full of some deep sorrow, and keeps much to herself, though she serves me well as a flower girl. But Keechaka, she is more than what she seems. She is married to five gandharvas; they have been cursed to be apart from her for a year.

"One day, Virata saw her and he also wanted her. But when I warned him about the gandharvas, he was wise enough to leave her alone. You must also forget about Malini. She is mysterious, and ominous powers lurk near her.

"I have a hundred lovely sakhis. Choose any of them but Malini, and I will send her to you tonight. For your very life, Keechaka, forget about the sairandhri."

Keechaka laughed grimly. "How can you ask me to think of another woman after I have seen Malini? My old life is behind me, now that I have seen her; I feel I have been born again. And if I could hold her in my arms, I shall have the kingdom of the Gods! She is a sacred flame, and her eyes are like sparks leaping from it. Oh Sudeshna, I don't think you realize what seeing your sairandhri has done to me.

"As for the gandharva husbands, you forget I am not an old man like Virata. I am Keechaka! For her I would kill a hundred gandharvas; how can five keep me from having her?

"And it seems you know little about women, though you are one yourself. Haven't you seen her eyes, her flaming eyes? She is the kind of woman who cannot bear to be apart from her husband for even a day. I have known many women, and she is surely the most exquisite one I ever saw. But I am sure she is the most passionate, as well.

"You say she has five husbands, and she has been away from them for eleven months. Can you imagine how she yearns for a strong man's embrace? She will be easy to seduce. I must have her, Sudeshna; my life is worthless unless I have Malini. I see her in my arms, already. I hear her sighs, her cries of love."

His sister saw how lost he was. Sudeshna was full of foreboding. But she saw that, if she did not help him, he would pursue Malini on his own. It was a choice between the word of protection she had given the sairandhri and her love for her brother. The queen thought, suppose he is right: perhaps the flower girl will give in to him, and eagerly. Who was she, Sudeshna, to stand in his way, when he was so ardent for her?

She said, "I am full of fear for you, but I know you will not rest until you have seduced Malini. Go from here now, Keechaka, and I will send her to you soon, for some wine perhaps. Woo her gently, and I will be happy if you win her. But oh, my brother, if you fail and she is angry, I tremble for you. I fear her gandharvas, Keechaka, somehow I fear them terribly."

Keechaka jumped up and hugged his sister. "No one loves me like you do! Just send her to me, the rest will be easy."

He ran impatiently from her apartment, already imagining the moment when Malini would be in his bed. No woman he wanted had ever refused Keechaka before. He did not think the flower girl would be an exception. He imagined her very refusal to give in immediately was a sign that she desired him. Keechaka was borne away by a dangerous dream.

EIGHT

The besotted Keechaka

SUDESHNA DID NOT SEND DRAUPADI TO HER BROTHER AT ONCE. SHE waited two weeks in the hope that good sense would dawn on him. She thought that, perhaps, he had been so lonely during his long campaign that he had lost control of himself. She prayed that a few nights in his palace with his wives would cool some of his ardour.

Instead, daily, a messenger came from Keechaka asking why she delayed keeping her word. On the seventh day, a servant came and told Sudeshna her brother had taken to his bed. He neither ate nor drank, or saw any of his wives or children. He did not go to the court, but seemed ill for his very life. The queen sent a message back that this very day, at noon, he should wait for the flower girl.

Sudeshna sent for Draupadi. Just a fortnight remained of the Pandavas' exile. The Matsya queen had even hoped she could see the year through, and then Malini would leave Virata. It was not to be, and Sudeshna loved Keechaka too much to let him languish as he did.

When Draupadi came into her room, she found Sudeshna in bed. The queen said, "I am feeling unwell, Malini. I hear Keechaka has brought some herbal wine from his campaign. Take this carafe to his palace and fetch me some." She did not look at her flower girl directly.

Draupadi said, "Just two weeks remain for me to leave your palace. I beg you, don't send me to your brother for the wine."

"And why is that?"

"He made advances to me in the garden. I did not tell you because I thought you would be upset. If you send me to his palace, he will take advantage of me. All these months you have looked after me as your own daughter. Just fourteen days remain before I vanish from your life. Don't send me to Keechaka now."

Guilty, but determined, Sudeshna said furiously, "How dare you? My brother is a kshatriya, he would never stoop to making advances to a maid. You have become arrogant, Malini, and lazy. This is just an excuse to avoid a chore. Go and fetch me the wine at once. Keechaka will hardly notice you, let alone lay a finger on you. It is your vanity that makes you think every man who sees you must desire you."

Draupadi opened her mouth to speak, but Sudeshna held up an imperious hand and cried, "I don't want to hear another word. Go and fetch the wine. I am thirsty!"

Tears in her eyes, Draupadi took the silver carafe from the queen. Neither woman looked at the other, and the sairandhri walked out without another word. Trembling in every limb Draupadi came out into the day. The Sun was overhead and, in despair, she prayed, "Surya Deva, I beg you by my chastity, protect me from Keechaka."

The Sun heard her, and sent an invisible rakshasa to watch over Panchali.

Keechaka was at his window, waiting. When he saw the flower girl making her way through Sudeshna's garden towards his palace, he ran down his stairway. He flung open his front door and stood beaming at her.

"Come in! Come in!" cried Keechaka, and Draupadi quailed when she saw the look in his eyes.

She said, "My lord, I have come to fetch some wine for your sister, the queen."

He winked at her. "You have even brought a carafe to fill! I will send the wine with someone else. You come with me, let me show you my bed of swan's-down. Since the day we met, I have had it made up for you, and covered with mallika flowers. Cruel one, how long you have made me wait, how much you have made me pine for you. It has been worth the anguish. Just look at you, how perfect you are! Oh, my love, you are the most beautiful woman on earth. Give me that carafe and let me feast my eyes on you."

She stood frozen before him, and said again, "I have come for wine for the queen, and not for your pleasure, my lord Keechaka. I beg you, fill the carafe and let me go back."

A spasm of darkness twitched on his face. Keechaka's voice grew hard, "Fill the carafe and let you go? You must be mad to think I would let you go just like that!"

Soft as a hunting cat, he moved between her and the door. He shut it behind his back. He loomed over her for a moment, then seized her wrist and pulled her to him. Draupadi screamed, and flailed out at him. At that moment, it was not just she who struck him but the Surya rakshasa who had come in with her, invisibly. Keechaka staggered back and fell. Momentarily, Draupadi stood astonished, then she wrenched the door open and fled.

She knew she could not run back to Sudeshna, she would find no refuge with the queen. Her hair streaming behind her like a black cloud, her clothes slipping off her dark body, Draupadi ran towards King Virata's palace.

With a roar, Keechaka sprang up and went after her. He caught her again as she flew through his garden, and flung his arms around her. He meant to ravish her out in the open, as he had done countless women in far-flung cities he had plundered. Draupadi's screams rang through the afternoon, and again the Surya rakshasa struck Keechaka, knocking him down.

Draupadi's screams brought Bheema running out of his kitchen. He saw Keechaka flung down and Panchali fleeing from him towards Virata's court. Bheema rushed to pull up a tree in the king's yard, to smash Keechaka down. Then Kanka the gambler was at his side, hissing, "Everything will be lost if you do this!"

There were others called out by Draupadi's screams. Yudhishtira said aloud, "This tree is still green, you can't use it for firewood."

Somehow, Bheema controlled himself. But now Keechaka was up and flying after Draupadi, and Yudhishtira and Bheema went after him.

Panting, weeping, her clothes awry and her hair dishevelled, Draupadi ran into Virata's sabha with Keechaka hot on her heels. When she was near the throne, he caught up with her. He kicked her down at the Matsya king's feet, and stood raging over her.

Panchali wailed, "Virata, look what happens to one who has sought refuge in your kingdom! I am a married woman, and this animal means to ruin me. I have come to you for sanctuary, for though I have five husbands they won't help me today."

Yudhishtira was at the king's side, and Bheema was in the court, his eyes on fire. It was a moment when anything could happen. Yudhishtira contained Bheema with a look. But what was he going to do about Draupadi, who was beside herself?

She cried again at Virata, "You saw him kick me, O king. I ask you for justice!"

But Keechaka was the Senapati of the king's army; he was Sudeshna's brother and Virata dare not cross him. Mildly, Virata said, "Young woman, I only saw what happened here in the sabha. I did not see what happened outside, or how you provoked Keechaka. Surely, he is not so angry without reason. Moreover, Keechaka is our Senapati and I suggest you leave our sabha, Sairandhri."

Yudhishtira still had to restrain not only his own anger, but his wild brother with a warning look.

But there were others in that sabha who knew Keechaka well and were less afraid of him than the king was. Some of them spoke up.

"The young woman is noble."

"We know Keechaka, he must have tried to molest her."

"Whatever the provocation, he should not kick a woman."

Yudhishtira saw Draupadi's eyes fill again; he also saw the rage in them. He was terrified that, just two weeks before their exile ended, she would give everything away and tell Virata who she was.

Kanka said, "Sairandhri, you heard the king. Go back to the queen's apartment. Your gandharva husbands will know the injustice done to you, and see it punished. Perhaps the time is not right, and they don't care to be cursed again, after their long penance. Only fifteen days more and you will be free. Wait until then before you seek justice. Go now, go back to your rooms."

The sairandhri did not move. Her jaw was set and Yudhishtira saw the stubbornness in her eyes. Malini said, "King of the Matsyas, you have no dharma."

Kanka the gambler cried, "Sairandhri, Virata is the most righteous of men! And look at you, young woman, with your clothes in disarray, your hair loose, crying immodestly in a court full of men: you look like an actress. Go back to your apartment!"

With a moan, Draupadi straightened her hair. She set her clothes right, and wiped her tears. Her eyes flashing, she said to Yudhishtira,

"You are right, O wise man, to call me an actress here. But it is only because my first husband is a gambler that my other husbands have to be cowards today!"

With a scowl at the sabha in general, she stalked out. Ballava, the king's cook, had already left. It seemed twelve years in the forest had taught him a sound lesson in patience. Even he would not risk another exile, when only fourteen days remained for their ajnatavasa to end. With a sigh of relief, Yudhishtira settled down beside the king, to a game of dice. But his heart raged within him.

With a sneer on his lips, Keechaka also walked out of the court, more determined than ever to have the sairandhri.

NINE

Ballava's night visitor

Back in her apartment in Sudeshna's palace, Draupadi locked herself in and wept. She felt defiled. Tearing off her clothes, she made a pile of them and set them on fire. She went and bathed, long and sorrowfully. At last, feeling somewhat cleansed, though not in her mind, she came out and dressed. There was a knock at the door and, not bothering to wipe her tears, she went to open it. Sudeshna stood there.

The queen saw her sairandhri red-eyed, and still crying. She took Draupadi's hands and said, "What happened, my child? Why are you crying?"

With a sob, Draupadi pulled free and flashed at her, "How can you pretend to be so innocent? You sent me to your brother, and you knew what he wanted. How can you ask me now why I am crying?"

She saw Sudeshna also had tears in her eyes. The queen sat down on the sairandhri's bed, and said in a low voice, "Tell me what happened, Malini. I swear I did not mean to hurt you. Only that my brother was frantic to meet you."

Sobbing, Draupadi described everything that happened. Sudeshna, who was terrified for Keechaka, tried her best to console her sairandhri. But the young woman ended viciously, "My gandharva husbands have heard what happened, and your brother won't live long."

Sudeshna rose and ran from the room. The sun set on the world outside. Still, Draupadi sat on her bed, staring glassily out of her window while shame and rage had their way with her. She must see Keechaka dead, nothing short of that would do. He dare lay his filthy hands on her, he dare kick her. He did not know her: she was a flame; she would consume him.

She did not eat. She did not sleep, or even lie down. She sat there like a fierce statue, plotting Keechaka's death. Slowly, a plan formed in her mind. Near midnight, she rose and walked out of her apartment. Around her the palace slept. Like an avenging spirit on the prowl, she moved through the deserted passages, out into the mooned night, and into the king's palace through a back door. Grimly she headed for the kitchens and the room behind them where Ballava, the king's cook, slept.

She glided into that room; seductive as moonlight, she went and lay beside him. With petal hands, she aroused him in his sleep. Smiling in his dream, Bheema reached for her. Then he opened his eyes. He gave a cry and sat bolt upright. "Panchali! You must be mad to come here. What if someone saw you?"

She stopped his mouth with a kiss. She stripped away his clothes, and made such tender love to him. When it was over, and he lay in a fine swoon, she said, "How can you sleep when your Panchali is in torment? Have you also become as hard-hearted as your brother? I cannot believe it of you. Of the others, yes, but not of my Bheema. How can you sleep after seeing how that devil kicked me down in the sabha? After you heard how he tried to violate me?"

Bheema said, "You should never have come here. Suppose we are found together? It will be the end of everything. What would Yudhishtira say?"

"Yudhishtira! How can you say his name after you heard him in the sabha today? 'You look like an actress, Sairandri. Go back to your apartment. It is immodest to cry in front of so many men.' And was what Keechaka did modest?"

She was trembling next to him now, naked and wounded, and Bheema couldn't stand it much longer. Sensing victory, she pressed on, "Yudhishtira has no honour left, or would he let Keechaka live after what he did to me? You were also there, Bheema, you did nothing either."

Poor Bheema cried, "I would have killed him. I would have razed this city! But Yudhishtira stopped me with his eyes."

"Yudhishtira has no feelings for me, all he wants to do is gamble. He is so happy after he learnt that mantra. Now he thinks he is the greatest dice-player on earth. What does he care that Keechaka tried to rape me? What does he care if his wife was kicked in a king's sabha? I want Keechaka dead!

"I cannot hope for revenge from Yudhishtira. Because they are loyal to him, Arjuna, Nakula and Sahadeva will not help me either. Oh, my Bheema, I can turn only to you. Only you are man enough to stand up to Yudhishtira. You have always loved me the most. You have always done anything I asked you to, even if your brothers would not.

"Ah Bheema, look at your Panchali's hands today!"

She held out her hands to him and there were tears in Bheema's eyes, when he felt they were calloused. Draupadi sighed, "From grinding perfumes for Virata and his queen, and they both betrayed me today. Oh, I am a cursed woman, that no one loves me!" She sobbed.

Bheema wiped her tears; he kissed her again and again. "Panchali, ah Panchali, don't say that. You know how much I love you, more than my life. But Yudhishtira was right to stop me today. If we are discovered now it is another twelve years in the jungle: not you or I, nor any of us could stand that. Keechaka is as good as dead, my love, only wait two weeks."

She drew away from him, and sat up. Her eyes glittered, and she said harshly, "I couldn't have dreamt you would be so heartless. You were my last hope. But if you won't kill Keechaka, I must drink poison and die. For I know he will ravish me before your two weeks pass."

She covered her face with her hands and sobbed more than ever. Bheema melted. How could he resist her? He had a child's heart. For her sake, he would risk anything, even another twelve years of exile, worse than dying.

"Aah, don't cry, don't cry!" He put his arms around her. "My queen, don't cry; his life is not worth a single tear of yours. I will kill him for you tomorrow. But we must do it in secret, so no one knows."

She wiped her tears at once; her woman's need satisfied, she smiled. Kissing him feverishly, her eyes shining, she said, "Have you a plan, Bheema?"

He held her close, and whispered, "I knew you would come tonight, so I thought of a plan earlier."

She laughed delightedly. "Tell me your plan, Bheema!"

"Send a message to Keechaka. Tell him you only pretended to spurn him, to inflame him more."

She gasped. He went on, "Tell him to meet you at midnight in the dance hall. Tell him there is a silk couch there, perfect for making love!"

"And then?"

"Tell him to come to you secretly. When he comes he will find me in the dark, and I will kill him."

"Bheema, my love! I knew I could count on you. And we shall not even be discovered. I am grateful to God that you are my husband. You are the only one who is not a coward, the only one who really loves me".

With a last lingering kiss, Draupadi floated out of Bheema's room, leaving him happy in the dark. In a short while, he slept again, snoring softly, drifting into dreams of her.

TEN

The long day

THE NEXT MORNING, DRAUPADI WENT OUT TO THE LITTLE PAVILION in the garden to plan how she would entice Keechaka to the dance hall that night. She stood there, wondering if she should send a messenger or go to him herself. Suddenly the man appeared, startling her.

He wore a smile on his face, and said, "Malini, you saw the king is afraid of me. There is no one in Virata to stop me from having you. Won't it be wise for you to come to me yourself?"

She smiled sweetly at him; she let her hand brush his arm. He quivered at the fleeting touch, and thought his heart would burst for joy when she said in her husky voice, "My lord, I refused you only from fear of my husbands. Which woman would spurn a man like you? Your strength makes me faint with desire. I have found a way for us to be together. Late at night, my gandharvas do not watch me, believing I am asleep. Meet me at the king's dance hall at midnight. There is a couch of silk there."

The blood roared in his body; he was speechless. She whispered, "I will wait for you at midnight, come to me in the dark. But remember, don't tell a soul about our tryst. For my husbands can read men's minds."

Keechaka said hoarsely, "I am mad for you, Malini! I could pluck the sun out of the sky, for midnight to come at once."

She said, "Go now, my lord, lest we are seen together. I will meet you in the night."

Keechaka went off with a song on his lips. Draupadi came to find Bheema in his kitchen, before the other cooks arrived. Flushed with excitement, she said to him, "He will come to the dance hall at midnight. Don't fail me, Bheema."

"He will not live to see the dawn."

Malini went back happily to her tasks of the day. Sudeshna was surprised to see her flower girl so completely recovered. She marvelled that those lovely eyes, which had wept such tears, now shone with some mysterious joy. The queen did not mention the previous day, and neither did her sairandhri.

It was a long day for three souls in the palaces of Virata. To Keechaka, the hours seemed like weeks, to Draupadi and Bheema, also. At last, the sun sank in the west, and twilight fell on the city of the Matsyas. It was the hour for drink and food. The king remarked that the dishes Ballava had conjured today were exceptional, even by his own lofty standards. He summoned the cook to commend him.

Then, the day wound down and the city turned in for the night. Lamps were put out, as the people turned to love and sleep. But Keechaka was awake. It was ten, then eleven, and at last, almost midnight. A slim moon had risen into the sky. Shrouded in a long cloak, so no one recognized him—if anyone was about in the forbidden hour, when the souls of the dead roam the earth—Keechaka crept out to his secret assignation, like an unquiet spirit himself. He stalked into the garden, and down its central pathway, towards the dance hall where Brihannala the eunuch gave her lessons by day.

ELEVEN

The angry gandharvas

An hour before Keechaka set out for the dance hall Bheema stole out of his kitchen, wrapped in a length of silk. As he crept through the dark passages of the palace, a soft hand reached out of the night and startled him. It was Draupadi. Like two ghosts, they made their way to the dance hall. They pushed the tall doors open and went in.

Silence reigned over the night. The sickle moon peered in through the windows and they could dimly see the couch at the heart of the hall. Bheema went and lay on it, and pulled the silk cloth over his head. Draupadi hid herself behind a pillar that rose to the ceiling nearby. They spoke in whispers, for a while, and her excitement was palpable in the darkness. Tonight's revenge would be the beginning of a long redress that time owed her.

Bheema said, "It's nearly midnight, we must be quiet now."

The moon rose above the palace, and now only the stars shone into the dance hall. In the stillness, Bheema could hear his own breathing, like a sea, and Draupadi felt her heart pounding.

At last, they heard the door ease open; Keechaka had arrived. He glowed in the dark. He was like the dying flare of a flame just before it goes out. Draupadi was as still as the pillar she stood behind. Bheema's stillness was of a beast of prey, before it springs.

Keechaka shut the door softly behind him. He called into the dim hall, "Are you there, my love?"

There was no answer. Then Bheema stirred where he lay, and Keechaka caught his breath. In a moment, he crossed to the couch by starlight.

He stood there gazing down at the silk-covered form he thought was the woman he was mad for. Hoarsely he said, "This has been the longest day of my life, Malini. Ah, my love, my love, you don't know how happy you have made me!"

He went on in a fever, "When my women saw me, they said, 'How radiant you look today!' I only smiled."

He could not wait any more, and, with a sigh, knelt beside the couch. Blindly he reached for his love in the dark. "Come to me, Malini."

Two immense hands seized Keechaka, and a terrible form rose from the couch. A deep voice growled, "So you are radiant today! And so you should be, since you have come to meet the woman who loves you. Long she has courted you, Keechaka, and tonight she asked me to deliver you to her. She is death, Senapati, and she is impatient to have you in her arms."

The shocked Keechaka breathed, "Who are you?"

That veteran of a hundred wars had no time to recover, but Bheema flung him down on his back, planted mighty knees across his arms and chest, and fastened inhumanly strong hands on his throat. Keechaka threshed about, his legs kicking the air. But the rage of thirteen years was in his assailant's grip; it was inexorable. Keechaka's tongue lolled from his mouth, his eyes rolled up in his head. Panchali appeared ethereally from behind her pillar. In his final moment, the Matsya general saw her standing above him, joy on her dark face, ineffable triumph. With a sigh Keechaka subsided, his limbs twitched no more.

But killing Keechaka tapped a spring of savagery in Bheema; he was like a beast unleashed. While Draupadi stood watching, he mutilated the dead body. He kicked the corpse, again and again. In frenzy he broke its arms and legs, and thrust them into the torso. So, also, the staring, blue head: Bheema shoved it down into the chest. As if in some exact ritual, he reduced the lifeless Keechaka to a bloody lump of flesh.

It seemed he was having revenge for what he, his brothers and Draupadi had suffered for thirteen years: his revenge on Duryodhana and Dusasana, on Karna, on all the Kauravas. Until at last, panting and dripping sweat, his hands and feet bloody, he stopped, and the frenzy left him. He lit the torch again, and turned to Draupadi, "There, my queen, are you satisfied now?"

She was a flame of fulfillment. Moaning, she came to him and flung her arms around his neck, kissing him searingly. She was like death pressed against him, soft and terrible. A little taken aback, he freed himself from her embrace. He said, "We mustn't be found here together. I will leave. But you stay, so the world will beware of you from now."

Bheema slipped out of the dance hall, leaving her alone with the mangled Keechaka. A current of joy in her blood, a great hope like she had not felt for thirteen years, Panchali ran out into the passage and shouted for the palace guards. She brought them into the dance hall, and showed them Keechaka on the floor. "He wouldn't believe me when I told him about my gandharva husbands. Look at your Senapati now."

The guards ran out crying, "Keechaka is dead! The sairandhri's gandharvas have killed Keechaka!"

In no time, the dance hall was full of people, terror stroking them when they saw their invincible general's corpse. Keechaka's one hundred and five half-brothers arrived there, the dazed Upakeechakas. King Virata and Queen Sudeshna came there and wept.

The Upakeechakas sat up mourning, the rest of the night. They set their brother's body on a bier and chanted grim mantras over it until dawn. At sunrise, they lashed the bloody corpse to the pall, to take it to the burning ground in the forest. One of them saw Draupadi lounging against a carved pillar, and cried, "He died for her; let him have her at least in death."

His brothers took up the cry, "Bind her to his litter, let us burn the sairandhri with Keechaka!"

"It will please his soul."

Some of them went off to the king. They said to Virata, "We want to burn the sairandhri with our brother. He loved her, and we want to send her to him."

Virata could hardly refuse what the powerful Upakeechakas asked today. Those kshatriyas wasted no time in laying hold of Draupadi. They bound her hands and lashed her to Keechaka's litter.

"Our brother was your lover. Let death not separate you."

She began to scream, so the palace rang with her cries. "My husbands, save me! O Jaya, Jayesha, Vijaya, Jayatsena! Jayadbala, save me!"

Only Bheema in his kitchen heard her. The others had made sure they were far away from the dance hall, from where the funeral procession set out. Bheema heard her, but it was daylight now. He could not attack the Upakeechakas in the palace or the streets. He panicked, but only briefly. Then he ran out of his kitchen, away from the pallbearers, towards the high wall behind the palace. He scaled it easily and ran like his father Vayu to the forest.

He took the shortest way, and arrived at the cremation ground well before the Upakeechakas. Certain that none of her husbands had heard her, Draupadi screamed all along the march through the streets of Virata, lined with the people, out through the city-gates, and down the road that led into the forest. She was bound firmly to the litter, her head at Keechaka's feet. She screamed to the sky, the wind, to anyone who would hear her, to please save her life, there was so much she had yet to live for! The Upakeechakas chuckled among themselves.

In the forest, Bheema gnashed his teeth to hear Panchali's screams. He dare not go to her rescue yet; there was no telling how many Upakeechakas might escape him in the open. He pulled up a young sala tree by its roots, and waited, seething in the gloom. Solemnly, Keechaka's brothers arrived in the forest. Without a word to one another, or even to stop Draupadi's screams, those hundred and five stalked towards the burning zone.

The sun had risen above the trees, but this part of the forest was a dim place. From the dimness, with no warning, all hell broke loose over the funeral party. They hardly saw who attacked them. It had to be a hundred spirits from naraka, roaring horribly, with trees for weapons: a demon phalanx. Forms of wind, warriors of air: not a hundred but a thousand of them swirled at Keechaka's brothers, bludgeoning their heads off, or driving them bodily into the ground with terrific hammer-blows, striking from every side, and from death's awning that was the canopy.

Even their screams were lost in that whirlwind. In moments, a hundred warriors were battered to death. Draupadi, who could not move from where they had dropped her, still lashed to Keechaka's litter, screamed louder than ever. She did not know what was happening, and it was terrifying. Five Upakeechakas fled, but they did not escape. Bheema came howling after them, and cut them off brutally in the open.

The cremation ground in that forest was like a gory battlefield. Splashed with blood, Draupadi lay whimpering among the Upakeechakas' corpses, hardly daring to hope it was her Bheema who had waylaid them, like Yama himself. But then, it was indeed Bheema who ran up and knelt beside her, a kitchen knife flashing in his hand as he cut her loose. She rose, sobbing in relief. He wiped her tears with his great hands, so terrible a moment ago and so gentle now, and held her until she was quiet again.

Bheema said, "How brave you were! You did not call our real names even when you were frightened for your life. We must go back separately, and hurry. God willing, no one will suspect anything."

The guards at the city-gates waited for the Upakeechakas to return after burning their brother and the flower girl. They were astounded to see the sairandhri walking up the king's road alone. Without a glance at them she swept into the city, her dark head held high, her gaze fixed straight ahead of her. Word spread; the people ran out of their homes and lined the street along which Malini walked to the palace, her clothes bloody, every inch of her exuding defiance. No one dared come near, terror walked beside her.

Word flew to Virata and Sudeshna that the sairandhri's gandharvas had also killed Keechaka's hundred and five brothers in the forest; she was unharmed and returning to the palace.

Virata was petrified. He told his queen, "This woman's beauty is a deadly thing. She is irresistible; but if any man falls in love with her, her gandharvas come and kill him. Sudeshna, your sairandhri is too dangerous to keep. Tell her she must leave today."

Meanwhile, Draupadi arrived back in her chambers, exhausted, and flung herself down on her bed. She was blissful, and a delicious languor was upon her. She shut her eyes and drifted off into bright dreams. But she did not dream long, before a sharp knock on her door woke her. It was Sudeshna, her eyes red from crying, and fear in her voice.

"You must leave at once!" that queen breathed. "I gave you a home, I gave you freedom of my palace. I treated you not like a flower girl, but my own sister. This is how you have repaid me: my brother Keechaka murdered at dead of night, and my stepbrothers slaughtered like rabbits on a hunt. You are a terrible woman, Sairandhri. Go back to your gandharvas, you are not welcome here for another moment."

Malini faced her coolly; the flower girl was more regal than Sudeshna. The sairandhri told the queen, "I warned you, time and again, of what would happen if your brother pursued me. He would not listen, and neither would you. As for your stepbrothers, they wanted to burn me alive. Would my husbands stand for that? I am a chaste woman, O queen, I have not sinned in thought or deed."

Sudeshna said, "I want you out of here within the hour."

Her voice firm, Malini replied, "You have kept me like your sister, these eleven months. The curse on my husbands will end in thirteen days. Bear with me till then, and you shall find my husbands grateful."

The queen said nothing, only stared dully at her flower girl. Draupadi sighed, "I know how much you must hate me at this moment. But tolerate me for just thirteen days more, and I swear you will be glad you did."

The sairandhri spoke humbly, but the queen realized she did not leave her any choice. Numbly, Sudeshna said, "I cannot refuse what you ask, I am afraid of you. But, I beg you, don't let your husbands harm the king or me."

Malini inclined her head, promising. Sudeshna said, "Stay for thirteen days, but I don't want to see you during that time."

The queen walked out of the flower girl's room.

TWELVE

Duryodhana's spies

MEANWHILE, DURYODHANA'S SPIES COMBED BHARATAVARSHA, ALL the kingdoms, all the sabhas, whispering questions among the people, but found no trace of the sons of Pandu. One by one, they came home to Hastinapura. One morning, when all his agents had returned, Duryodhana called them into his court where he sat among his brothers with Karna, Drona, Bheeshma and the Trigartas.

The chief spy was an old and attenuated man, who had looked as he did now ever since Duryodhana knew him. He said, "My lord, we have scoured the world for the Pandavas, but nowhere are they to be found: in no king's court, upon no mountain, nor hidden in any valley or forest. We went to Dwaraka, but they were not there. We went to Panchala, disguised, and no one had seen or heard of them in Drupada's kingdom. We went among the people, everywhere, but there was no sign of your cousins."

Duryodhana sat perfectly still on this throne, watching his agent with unwinking eyes. Another spy, a man as old as the first, said, "My lord, we believe the Pandavas are dead. We went across the earth like the breeze; we went among the people like their very breath. If they all conspired to hide the sons of Pandu, at least their thoughts would betray them: and we are experts at reading men's minds. Duryodhana, it is as if the earth yawned open and swallowed your cousins."

A third spy, a young fellow, was emboldened to cry, "Rule the world without a rival, Duryodhana! The Pandavas are not alive any more."

Duryodhana greeted all this with silence. His hooded gaze moved from one spy's face to the next. They shivered at his scrutiny. Then, apparently satisfied, he said, "Have you anything else of interest to report?"

The oldest spy now said, "The world talks of the death of the Matsya Senapati Keechaka." The man looked quickly at the Trigartas, and they shifted uncomfortably in their places. "I think the Trigartas remember Keechaka well; he defeated them often in battle."

"How was Keechaka killed?"

"He was strangled in a dance hall in the middle of the night, and no one saw the killer. They say a beautiful woman was the cause of his death. They say she has a gandharva husband who watches over her. Keechaka tried to molest the woman, and he died."

Another spy said, "I was in the Matsya country myself, the day after Keechaka was killed. His brothers tied the woman to his litter, to burn her with him in the forest. But her gandharva killed them all, and set her free."

Duryodhana said, "The death of Keechaka and his brothers is of passing interest to me. Give me news of the Pandavas. The time of the ajnatavasa is almost over, and you have brought no word of them."

The chief spy replied, "We have told you, my lord, the sons of Pandu have vanished as if into death's clasp. No trace remains of them, that we should presume they are alive."

Duryodhana gave his spies gold, and dismissed them. Silence ruled the court, and the Kaurava said, "The ajnatavasa draws to an end. If we do not find them quickly, they will come asking for their kingdom. Let some cleverer agents be sent forth. Let them bring word of our cousins, or let them also confirm that Yudhishtira and his brothers are not to be found anywhere. Perhaps it is true the Pandavas are dead; they may have been eaten by wild animals in the forest."

He savoured the thought. Drona rose and said, "Yudhishtira and his brothers are men of destiny. They were not born into this world to be killed before their time by wolves or tigers. Duryodhana, listen to me, I am your guru. For thirteen years, you have enjoyed what belongs to the sons of Pandu. At least now, relent. When your cousins return give them back their kingdom graciously; beg their forgiveness, and even you might find salvation. If you dare make peace with the Pandavas, you will certainly find great fame."

Bheeshma said, "The Acharya speaks truly. The Pandavas are alive, wherever they may be. Would my blood not cry out in my body if they died? Duryodhana, my son, it is later than you imagine. Retribution is not far, and I am full of fear for you." He sighed. "Ah, I see in your eyes that you have no patience to hear what I have to say. I will be brief; why, I will say all I have to in one word: dharma!

"Duryodhana, where dharma is, victory shall also be. No man in this ancient world, however powerful or wealthy, has ever escaped that truth. Relent, my child, give back what is not yours to keep. Seek Yudhishtira's forgiveness. He is noble, and loves you still."

Duryodhana ignored what they said and asked instead, "But where have the Pandavas hidden themselves?"

He rose and began to pace the floor. Bheeshma laughed. "You have not found the Pandavas because you don't know where to look for them."

Duryodhana stopped pacing. He turned to his grandfather. "Do you know where to look, Pitama?"

"Where Yudhishtira is the land will be more fruitful than it has ever been before. The granary and the treasury will spill over in plenitude. The rain will come at its appointed time, and the harvest will be bounteous. The grace of God shall be upon the people of that land, and fear, anger and envy will melt from their hearts.

Yudhishtira's presence in that kingdom shall be as a God's. For him, the birds of the sky will sing more joyfully, and the flowers of the field will bloom more brightly. The fruit on the trees will be sweeter than they have ever been. If he lives in a city, there will be music in the air, as if invisible gandharvas played by day and night. The milk the cows of that land yield will taste like amrita.

"So, Duryodhana, now you know where to look for the Pandavas. Send your spies to discover a kingdom in which there is a sudden surfeit of prosperity, and you will find Yudhishtira Dharmaputra and his brothers there."

Duryodhana stared at his grandfather. He began to speak, but Bheeshma had not finished. "Hear me out, I have something more to say to you. So far, I spoke as a loyal Kuru and as a courtier to his king. Now listen to what a grandfather says to his favourite grandson. I must tell you what my heart feels, as well.

"Since you were a child, I was partial to you, even when I knew you were wrong. I always felt you were sensitive and vulnerable. Of all the princes in your generation, none is as generous as you are to those whom you love. You are brave and truly a kshatriya. Today, a doting grandfather implores you, Duryodhana: repent!

"The Pandavas have suffered too long, and for no fault of theirs. You are not a young man any more. Time has flown, and what you are today is not what you were thirteen years ago. For thirteen years, you have enjoyed this kingdom by yourself. You must have learned much during these years, and fulfilled yourself in many ways you could not have before. Now it is time to take account of yourself. Give back what is theirs to your cousins, and rule the world with Yudhishtira as your ally. If you are united, no force on earth can stand against you both.

"Leave your childishness behind you, Duryodhana, be a mature king. Age softens the mind; it must have softened yours. Let the end of the thirteen years mark the end of your enmity with the sons of Pandu; spend your last years in the world at peace with them." Bheeshma's old eyes were bright with tears. "Ah, my child, don't destroy yourself!"

Duryodhana's mouth was a thin line, as he retorted, "I can never do what you ask, Pitama. The Pandavas are my enemies. I hate them, and my hatred rules my very life. I will never give them back their kingdom. I will move heaven and earth, and I will find them, wherever they are. Then they must go back into the forest for another twelve years. Let those twelve years also pass, and perhaps I will be old and soft enough to return their kingdom."

Now Kripa said, "No one can stop a man when he has decided to seek his own death. Duryodhana, you have chosen the path to doom. All of us see this clearly, and the astrologers say that the eclipse of the Pandavas' fortunes is almost over. Still, you choose war. So I say to you as a warrior, since you have chosen an indomitable enemy, at least be prepared! Begin to collect an army such as the world has never seen. Send messengers to all the kings who came to your Vaishnava yagna. Tell them about the war that will be, and make sure they will stand with you.

"Duryodhana, the Pandavas are invincible; it is folly to fight them. If fight them you must, to be well prepared is your only hope."

Duryodhana sat pensively through what Kripacharya said, nodding now and again, to show he agreed. His thoughts were elsewhere. When Kripa finished the Kaurava clapped his hands to summon a guard.

"Call back my spies who just left the sabha."

When the spies stood nervously before him again, he said, "Recount the death of Keechaka to us once more. Leave no detail out."

When the spy who was in the Matsya kingdom repeated his story, Duryodhana's eyes shone, and he cried, "I should have known at once! It is so obvious."

The others stared at him, puzzled. Only Bheeshma smiled. Dusasana asked, "What is obvious?"

Duryodhana said, "I know where the Pandavas are! Just four men on earth were as strong as Indra himself: Balarama, Bheema, Shalya, and Keechaka was the fourth. Keechaka is dead. Only one of the other three could have killed him with bare hands. Which was it? It could not have been Balarama or Shalya, or we would have known. Now consider the woman who was the cause of Keechaka's death: the queen's sairandhri. Eleven months ago, she arrives mysteriously in the Matsya kingdom, and tells Sudeshna about her gandharva husbands, cursed to be apart from her for a year.

"She is dark, this sairandhri, and beautiful; Keechaka could never resist a beautiful woman, and fell in love with her. The way you describe her, she is no ordinary beauty. Who is she, the flower girl for whom Keechaka is willing to sacrifice his very life? Who is she, with the gandharva husbands?"

He paused, and looked around the sabha. Karna and Dusasana breathed together, "Draupadi!"

Duryodhana said, "And it was Bheema who killed Keechaka. Don't you recognize our cousin's style? The head and the arms thrust into the torso, the body mutilated. Then, there is the midnight assignation in the dance hall, the secrecy that shrouds the killing.

"Surely, the Pandavas also live disguised in the Matsya king's palace; perhaps they serve Virata in some menial capacity. Bheema could not kill Keechaka openly, since he would risk being discovered. I would not be surprised if Yudhishtira and the others did not know about the plan. They may have thought it too dangerous, but not Draupadi or Bheema.

Think how Keechaka's brothers died in the forest: bludgeoned with a tree. If that is not my cousin Bheema's work ..."

He was up and pacing the sabha again, a predator who had scented his prey. He went on breathlessly, "The spies say the Matsya kingdom has never known a harvest like the one they have this year. The king's coffers flow over, and, if you think about it, Virata is just the kind of old fool whose hospitality our cousins would seek."

Dusasana was on his feet. "We must attack the Matsya kingdom!"

Duryodhana said, "The Matsyas' cattle is their wealth. If we lift their herd, with Keechaka dead, the noble Pandavas will come to their hosts' defence. And back to the forest with them for another twelve years. Gather an army, we ride at once."

Susharma, king of the Trigartas, jumped up. "I will ride with you, Duryodhana. The Matsyas humiliated me repeatedly when Keechaka lived; now that he is dead I want revenge. I will attack Virata from the south, and take the Matsya herd. That will fetch Virata's forces out. Without Keechaka there, I will crush them. The day after I attack, you ride at them from the north. The Pandavas will have no choice but to show themselves, and, Duryodhana my friend, we will achieve both our ends."

Karna cried, "We welcome Susharma's plan! Two armies are always better than one."

Duryodhana was already on his way out of the sabha, "Susharma, you ride ahead and attack Virata tomorrow. The day after, a Kuru army, with Bheeshma, Kripa, Drona and Aswatthama, Karna, Shakuni and Duryodhana will ride at Virata from the north. Tomorrow is the eighth day after amavasya, and, the day after, navami, the ninth. Victory will be mine!"

With that, he was gone. The sabha emptied itself; only Drona, Bheeshma and Kripa remained in it. Drona said to Bheeshma, "Is this just? Shall we ride with Duryodhana to send the Pandavas back into exile?"

Bheeshma smiled, and answered cryptically, "We ride tomorrow. But it will be less easy than Duryodhana imagines to send Yudhishtira into exile again."

Meanwhile, Susharma already flew towards his capital to collect his army for the next day's exploit.

THIRTEEN

Virata's battle

Like a storm in spring, the Trigartas blew at Virata's cattle-sheds, south of his city. The cowherds could hardly resist Susharma's soldiers, and, abandoning their herd, they fled to Virata. The Trigartas drove away a hundred thousand cows.

The cowherds ran into the king's court and cried, "Enemies are upon us! Our herd is gone! Save us, Virata!"

The old king was on his feet, crying out orders to muster his army. In moments, his brothers were at his side, battle-hardened kshatriyas: Sataneeka, Madiraswa and Suryadatta. Virata's eldest son was with them too, Veeresankha. Within the hour, the Matsya army gathered at the city-gates, footsoldiers, horsemen, chariots and elephants. The king took his place in the leading chariot, at the head of his own army after so long; for it was always Keechaka who led the Matsyas to war. A miracle beginning in his spirit, the years seemed to fall away from Virata. He felt he was a young man again, a virile kshatriya full of courage.

Kanka the gambler appeared at his elbow, and said quietly, "My lord, I know how to fight, from horseback or a chariot. I can wield a bow and a sword. Let me ride with you."

The king cried, "Sataneeka, give Kanka a chariot, armour and weapons!"

The gambler said, "Your cook Ballava and Damagranthi and Tantripala, too, are fine warriors. They will be glad of this chance to repay your kindness to them."

Virata said, "Let them be given weapons and chariots. With these four around me I am sure to win the day!"

Kanka was pleased. As they rode out, Yudhishtira told his brothers, "Susharma is a great kshatriya, and Virata may well need our help. But stay behind, and remember who you are meant to be. Use no astras unless there is dire need and I tell you to."

The Matsya force overtook the Trigarta army quickly, since the enemy was slow because of the cattle they had lifted. Moreover, Susharma was eager to avenge himself on Virata, and went at his ease. Battle was joined and men fell in thousands. Susharma was surprised. With Keechaka dead, he had not expected such resistance from the Matsyas. The fray was fiercer than either Virata or Kanka had thought.

Then Kanka took charge of the Matsya legion. Expertly he formed Virata's warriors into fighting formation: a Garuda vyuha, an eagle phalanx of which only the greatest Senapatis are masters. Kanka had studied the secrets of the vyuhas of battle with Bheeshma and Drona.

Kanka himself was at the head of the bird of war. Tantripala and Damagranthi were stormy at the wing tips, and the tremendous Ballava, mace in hand, was its tail. Inspired by Kanka's fluent command, the fighting eagle of fifty thousand men swooped on the Trigarta force, with death at its beak and talons, wings and tail. A thousand of the enemy Kanka accounted for, himself; twice that number, Ballava the cook killed, once his brother allowed him freedom in battle. Fiercest of all were the twins at the eagle's wings. Damagranthi's victims were thrice what Kanka's were and Tantripala's, four times as many. Soon, the field was a sludge of blood and corpses, and Susharma was beaten back.

Evening fell, and then darkness over the clash of swords, warriors' roars and screams of the dying. A ghostly moon rose over the earth, but neither army fought any less fiercely. Battle raged on, and the Matsya king was the most tireless kshatriya. He was everywhere in his wheeling chariot, shouting encouragement to his soldiers. Virata was rediscovering his old prowess, his courage, finding himself again. His roars rang louder than all the others', he killed as many of the enemy as Kanka did.

With nightfall, the Trigartas grew stronger, and the Garuda vyuha seemed dissipated. Susharma rode out from the rear of his army and confronted Virata. He came in a swirl of chariot-dust and darkness. It seemed sorcery drove his horses, and the Matsya king aimed his arrows in vain at Susharma in the moonlight. Suddenly, the Trigarta fell on Virata from behind. Virata's charioteer died in a scarlet flash; his horses reared in panic. Out of the night Susharma swooped on the Matsya king, set a blade to his throat and dragged him from his chariot.

Susharma and two of his brothers seized Virata, flung him into a Trigarta ratha, and rode from the field, roaring in triumph. Seeing their king taken, the Matsya soldiers fled in every direction; the Trigartas pursued them, cutting them down easily.

Kanka the gambler cried out to Ballava, the kings' cook. Ballava rode up beside him under the gibbous moon, and Kanka said, "You must rescue the king. Be as quiet as you can. Go on, fly!"

Ballava, splattered in enemies' blood, roared, "I ride to save our king!"

A few yards on he stopped his chariot and leapt down. Nearby stood a sala tree, and he wanted to use it as his cudgel! Kanka caught up with him as he strode towards the sala.

"What are you doing, Bheema? Pull up that tree and Susharma will have no doubt who you are. Use a bow and arrows, and a sword. Let Nakula and Sahadeva ride with you to watch your flanks."

Ballava laughed aloud. The exhilaration of battle had restored him wonderfully: this was what he was born for! The three brothers rode after Susharma, a storm of arrows flying before them, mowing down the Trigarta soldiers in waves. The Matsyas saw this and turned back to battle, following the chariots of the cook, the cowherder and the stable-hand. The Trigarta legion could not stand before the Matsyas swarming to free their king.

Bheema killed Susharma's sarathy with an arrow that plucked him from his seat and nailed him to a nearby tree. Virata sprang up and fought Susharma hand to hand.

Seeing his fortunes rudely reversed, Susharma leapt down and tried to run. Ballava was on him in a flash. He seized the Trigarta by his long hair. Roaring, Bheema lifted Susharma into the air and flung him down on the ground.

"Dare you invade us? Dare you take our king captive? Die for your daring!"

Susharma fainted in terror of the dreadful cook. Ballava tied him up and hauled him before Kanka and a glowing Virata. The herd had been retrieved, and the Trigarta army put to flight. Once more Ballava threw Susharma down, now at Virata's feet, and began to kick the hapless Trigarta savagely.

Kanka cried, "Stop, Ballava! Why do you want to kill him? Victory is ours, and the cattle have gone back to their sheds."

The glowering cook replied, "If the wretch wants to live, let him declare he is Virata's slave. Or I must kill him." He gave Susharma another kick.

Kanka smiled. "He is already Virata's slave, whether he says so or not. He is a vanquished king, and that is shame enough. Let him go, Ballava."

Reluctantly, Bheema cut Susharma free. The Trigarta stood red-faced before them. Virata laughed at him, and Kanka said, "Go, Susharma, you are free. But never return to Matsya lands."

Burning with shame Susharma stumbled from there. Tears in his eyes, Virata embraced Kanka, Ballava, Tantripala and Damagranthi.

"My friends, you saved my life. Everthing I own is yours. Kanka, I should crown you king beside me!"

The gambler said, "It was the least we could do to repay your generosity. Think no more of it, my lord."

Virata embraced him once more, and said, "Best of all, I feel like a young man again! For too long I sat on my throne or in my harem and did not taste battle, because Keechaka was always there to fight for me. Today I feel I have my life back; I have not felt so alive in years! Let us pitch our tents here, and spend what remains of the night under the moon and the stars. Ballava, tonight we shall dine together. I owe you my life, my friend, and there is nothing I can ever do to repay that debt."

The king sent word of their victory back to his palace. He ordered musicians and dancing-girls brought out, and food and wine for all his soldiers. The next day, with the sun, he would re-enter his city in triumph.

Soon the drinking, singing and dancing were underway, and the feasting, as well, for they all had a great appetite after the day's battle. Cooks' fires blazed up all over the camp and the mighty Ballava, when he was not seated at Virata's side, flitted from fire to fire, to ensure the king's meat was done to a turn.

FOURTEEN

The prince and the eunuch

WHEN DAWN BROKE THE NEXT MORNING, VIRATA AND HIS SOLDIERS, Kanka, Ballava, Damagranthi and Tantripala were all fast asleep outside the city after nightlong revelry. With dawn, Duryodhana's army attacked the Matsya capital from the north, and made off with sixty thousand cattle.

Once more, the cowherds ran to the palace. The king and all his men were away at the camp, which was some yojanas beyond the southern gates. Only Virata's youngest son, the prince Bhoominjaya, also called Uttara Kumara, was there, playing his vina for the women of the royal harem. The prince was a handsome youth of sixteen.

The cowherds came to him, and their leader cried, "The Kuru army invaded us! They lifted sixty thousand cattle. Your father always says what a fine kshatriya you are; this is your chance to prove him right. Hurry, Uttara Kumara, rescue our herd!"

Another cowherd said, "You play sweetly on the vina, my prince. But fetch your bow now, and let the music you play on it strike terror in our enemies' hearts!"

Uttara Kumara put aside his vina. He rose solemnly, and he was truly a fine-looking young man. Glancing into a mirror on the wall as he spoke, he said grandly, "I will come to rout the Kuru host!" He paused. "But how shall I ride without a sarathy?"

He let imagination carry him away for a moment. "I lost my sarathy in a twenty-eight day war I fought recently. Just find me a sarathy and watch Bheeshma, Drona, Kripa, Karna and Aswatthama die. As they fall, or flee, they will cry, 'Is this Arjuna? For no other man can fight like this!' Cowherds, only find me a sarathy, and you shall have your cattle back."

Malini was there among the other women. She blanched to listen to the prince compare himself to Arjuna. Her eyes flashed, she bit her lip and then she heard Brihannala the eunuch calling her into the passage outside.

Taking her hand, Brihannala said, "I thank you for your anger, my queen! But there is no time to lose. Tell the princess Uttaraa that when the Khandava vana burned, Brihannala was Arjuna's sarathy. Tell the princess that Brihannala is a superb sarathy. Let her brother take me into battle."

Draupadi looked doubtfully at him. The eunuch said, "Hurry!"

Malini took princess Uttaraa aside, "The Matsya herd can be saved. I have a sarathy for your brother."

"A sarathy, here?"

"Yes. Brihannala was Arjuna's sarathy when the Khandava vana burned. I have heard there is hardly another charioteer like the eunuch."

Uttaraa stared at the sairandhri. Malini said, "Tell the prince to take Brihannala into battle, and I swear the Kurus won't stand before them. Why, the Devas and gandharvas would run from the eunuch's chariot."

The princess looked at the flower girl again, to see if she was joking. Malini was entirely serious. Uttaraa ran to her brother and cried, "Put on your armour, pick up your bow! I have found you a sarathy."

He turned to her, amazed, "Who is the man?"

His sister said, "The sairandhri tells me Brihannala was Arjuna's sarathy in the Khandava vana. He says there is no sarathy on earth like Brihannala."

The prince called Malini. "Is it true that Brihannala is a sarathy?"

Draupadi said, "The best there is."

Uttara Kumara could hardly extricate himself honourably now. All the women had heard his boast. He mumbled, "But I am a kshatriya. How can I go into battle with a woman for a sarathy? Not even a woman, but someone who is neither a man nor a woman. Besides, will Brihannala agree?"

Malini said, "In a crisis, my prince, you shouldn't think too much of such trivia. Just a moment ago, you were saying how you would fight like Arjuna. Now you have Arjuna's sarathy to drive your horses, Uttara Kumara, show us you are a kshatriya! As for Brihannala, let your sister ask him and he will not refuse."

The prince was cornered. The women and the cowherds all cried to him to ride after the Kurus. Helpless, and with a young man's bravado, he told Uttaraa, "Ask Brihannala if she will be my sarathy."

Uttaraa summoned the eunuch. Brihannala came into the women's chamber with mincing steps. Uttara Kumara said, "The sairandhri tells me you were Arjuna's sarathy in the Khandava prastha. She says that not Indra's Matali, Krishna's Daruka, or Dasaratha's Sumantra is your equal. The Kurus have stolen our herd and I must ride after them. Will you be my sarathy, Brihannala?"

The eunuch tittered, "Ah, prince, what do I know about fighting? All I know is music and dancing. How can I be your sarathy, O Kshatriya? Won't your enemies laugh if they see me at your chariot-head?"

Uttara Kumara said, "Brihannala, put on armour and be ready to ride."

His sister Uttaraa appeared with a coat of mail, light as the wind, bright as the sun. She pressed it into her dance-teacher's hands. Giggling, Brihannala received the burnished armour.

"I am supposed to wear this? But I don't know how to put it on."

The eunuch struggled with the coat of mail; first putting it on back to front, then dropping it clumsily. The women laughed. Uttara Kumara came forward in exasperation and helped her into the armour, securing it at her back. This was exactly as Arjuna intended; he never put on his own kavacha when he went into battle. At last, Brihannala was ready in the coat of mail. Now the princess and her women looked at the eunuch strangely, for it seemed her femininity fell away from her when she donned the kavacha. Brihannala stood among them, quite splendid, and the sairandhri had such a gleam in her eye.

Brihannala said, "Come, my prince, I can't wait to see you raze the Kuru host!"

The prince's chariot was at the palace steps. Carried away by now with his own heroic image of himself, Uttara Kumara climbed into the chariot: a great kshatriya at least in the eyes of the women. Still tripping daintily along, the eunuch climbed up to the sarathy's place and took the reins.

Princess Uttaraa cried, "Brihannala, when my brother has beaten the Kurus, bring me their capes to make clothes for my dolls!"

Brihannala called back, "You shall have the Kurus' silks!"

She flicked the reins expertly over the horses and they were off, the eunuch and the young prince, to fight the Kuru army on their own.

FIFTEEN

Uttara Kumara

"FLY BRIHANNALA!" CRIED UTTARA KUMARA, AS THEY RODE OUT through the city-gates. "The Kurus thought no kshatriyas remained in our city, but they shall be surprised, friend eunuch."

The way they rode led towards the forest and the burning-ground. They had not gone a half-hour before a vast noise fell on their ears: like the sea makes on a night when the moon is full. Brihannala smiled to herself, but Uttara Kumara cried anxiously, "What is that sound?"

"Only the Kuru army that you mean to burn."

The eunuch lashed the horses so they flew on. Then, ahead of them they saw Duryodhana's legions: a sea of soldiers, elephants, horses and chariots, their armour and weapons gleaming in the sun, with kshatriyas among them who looked like Gods. Brihannala urged her horses on, but the prince behind him had fallen very quiet. Uttara Kumara's mouth was parched, his hands shook and he was short of breath.

He gave a long whimper and sat petrified. The truth was this was his first battle and terror gripped him. He tried to speak, but no words would come. Brihannala, calm as ever, drew up the chariot where they could clearly see the enemy.

Her eyes twinkling, the eunuch said, "There, my prince, is the Kuru army. Look at its kshatriyas carefully before you decimate them. Riding the white stallion is Duryodhana, their king. He is fierce and majestic, isn't he? Beside him is his brother Dusasana, on the grey charger. Do you see the warrior riding up on the other side of Duryodhana? That is the matchless Karna, dearer than a brother to the Kaurava. He is the greatest archer they have, and Duryodhana pins his faith on him to win the war against the Pandavas. Karna has sworn he will kill Arjuna."

Uttara Kumara stared numbly at the Kuru host. He had broken out in a sweat, and not a sound did he make. Brihannala went on, "Turn your eyes to the left of Duryodhana, across the army. Do you see the sparkle of a crown that seems to capture the sun in its brilliant noose? Do you see the face below it, which seems to belong to another age of the earth? That is the Kuru Pitama, Bheeshma."

Brihannala allowed herself a small sigh. "It was Bheeshma's oath that turned the fate of the Kurus down a dark way. For years, he was virtual king of the ancient House, but then a change came over its destiny. Beside him, you can see another figure in white, like a flame. That is Drona, acharya to the Kauravas and the Pandavas, the greatest master on earth. The young man beside him, with the scarlet jewel at his throat, is his son Aswatthama. There are those who say that he is a better archer than Arjuna."

Not a sound came still from poor prince Uttara Kumara. He felt there was a sea raging inside his chest, in which he was also drowning. Brihannala said, "You will be the first man ever to fight all these heroes together, single-handedly. Shall we ride at them, Kshatriya?"

The prince wailed, "I am terrified, Brihannala! I have never seen warriors like these before. I thought my uncle Keechaka was the greatest kshatriya alive. Each of these Kurus is twice as great as he was, and there are so many of them! Indra himself would be afraid of these men; how will I fight them by myself? Eunuch, my body burns, my head spins, and I feel faint. Can't you see I am just a boy, sarathy? I cannot fight these awesome men. Turn the chariot round, Brihannala, ride back to our city like the wind!"

The eunuch laughed, "You are afraid? Just a short while ago you dragged me out of the palace, crying, 'Hurry, Brihannala! Take me to the Kurus, I can't wait to fight them.' If you turn back now, Uttara Kumara, your women will laugh at you and every kshatriya on earth will hold you in contempt.

"My prince, these Kurus do not tread the path of dharma. They come as thieves, and they are not as powerful as they seem. I swear your chariot shall flit through them like a wasp, and their arrows will never find a mark on us. You can shame these Kurus today, and become a hero. Your father is a noble kshatriya, your uncle was the mighty Keechaka. You must have some of their courage in your blood.

"Even I do not feel afraid, then how can a prince like you turn away from battle? The sairandhri sang my praises to your sister, saying I was the finest sarathy on earth. After that, even a eunuch cannot go back without recovering the herd. Be bold. Face your enemies one by one, and I swear the day will be ours!"

The prince moaned, "I don't care if the women laugh at me, or if all the world does. Let the Kurus take whatever they want: our cattle, our wealth, our kingdom. I will not fight them; my kshatriya blood turns to water at just the sight of this enemy. No Brihannala, this is no place for a boy like me. If you won't turn the chariot back, I will run from here on my own!"

Uttara Kumara flung down his bow, leapt out of the chariot and began to run back towards the city. Brihannala shouted after him, "Don't disgrace your noble birth! It is better to die in battle than run from it."

But the prince was going as quickly as he could. Now, in plain sight of the astonished Kauravas, Brihannala also leapt down from the chariot, a strange figure in a crimson mantle, her long hair flying behind her, and ran after the fleeing prince. The Kaurava soldiers laughed. In a moment, the longhaired one caught up with the boy and seized him.

Uttara Kumara cried, "Let me go, Brihannala! I will give you a hundred gold coins. I will give you jewels beyond your dreams, a chariot and ten thousand elephants. But let me go!"

Meanwhile, the Kaurava soldiers said among themselves, "Who is this fantastic pair? A boy and the queerest creature I have ever seen."

"The odd one is dressed like a woman, but he is a man."

"Or a eunuch! But he resembles someone I know."

Drona said, "The boy ran because he is scared. The eunuch is trying to bring him back to fight us. I know this eunuch's noble head; I know those long arms. Who would run after a stripling to force him back to fight the Kuru army by himself? It is Arjuna!"

Karna scoffed, "You see Arjuna everywhere, Drona. Now even as a eunuch! Virata and the rest of his warriors have gone after Susharma, leaving this little prince behind. He must have been the only man left in the Matsya king's palace. No sarathy remained, either, so he brought a eunuch! Now the youngster who set out so bravely comes face to face with our army. Panic grips him, and he runs. The eunuch, left alone, is even more terrified, and runs after the prince. Why bring Arjuna into it?"

Acharya Kripa said, "Drona is right. Arjuna has caught up with the boy; he will bring him back to fight. But when they return, the boy will be the sarathy and Arjuna the archer."

Drona said, "Feel the dry wind around us. Look at the clouds that blow into the sky out of nowhere. Look how our horses tremble. We are in danger, none of us shall stand before Arjuna today."

Karna cried, "All you ever think of is Arjuna! Brahmana, your Arjuna is not a sixteenth part the archer I am. Even if it is him, why are we afraid?"

Duryodhana said in annoyance, "Let the eunuch be Arjuna or Krishna himself. Let him be Bhargava dressed as a woman. What can he do by himself? And if it is Arjuna, we have achieved what we came for. If we find even one Pandava during the ajnatavasa, all of them must go back to the forest. That is what we came for, not to kill them in battle. I pray this peculiar creature is indeed our cousin."

Meanwhile, Brihannala held Uttara Kumara firmly and the youth could not escape him. The eunuch said, "I will not let you run away and bring shame upon yourself. If you are afraid, be my sarathy, and I will fight the Kauravas. Nothing will harm you, and we shall win the day. This isn't a time for cowardice, but glory."

Something in the eunuch's voice, in his eyes, made Uttara Kumara believe him completely. All at once, as if Brihannala had taken the boy's fear from him bodily, he felt no urge to run any more. Uttara Kumara said meekly, "I will drive the horses, Brihannala, if you will fight."

Amazed at himself, Uttara Kumara climbed up to the sarathy's place and took the reins. Brihannala climbed in behind him. But when the prince was about to drive his horses forward, the eunuch said, "Take us to the forest where the dead are burned."

In a daze, the prince obeyed. The chariot drove away from the Kaurava army. Drona said to Bheeshma in an old dialect, which just they two understood, "My lord, I am certain that is Arjuna and he will be back to fight. What will happen when he shows himself?"

Bheeshma answered in the same tongue, "There is no cause for anxiety, the ajnatavasa is over. I knew this before we set out, but I want to teach Duryodhana a lesson. Arjuna is full of anger. When he routs us all, Duryodhana may think twice before he declares war on the Pandavas. Also, Arjuna will fight fiercely today, but not to kill."

Tears springing in his eyes, to know it was his favourite sishya he had seen, Drona cried to Duryodhana, "That is Arjuna. Mark my words we will not stand before him today. There is no archer on earth like Arjuna!"

Karna's face grew dark, but Duryodhana said, "Acharya, I haven't come here to fight Arjuna, but to find him. If I do, he and his brothers must go back to the jungle for twelve more years. And even if the eunuch is a Deva in disguise, my arrows shall drink his blood."

Bheeshma and Drona exchanged a glance; they had to admire the Kaurava's assurance. It was true: Duryodhana feared no one, not even Arjuna.

SIXTEEN

Unearthly weapons

As THEY RODE, BRIHANNALA FELT URVASHI'S CURSE LEAVE HIS BODY. He was a man again. He was Arjuna. All that remained of the eunuch were his clothes and long hair.

They arrived at a lofty sami tree in the forest. Brihannala made Uttara Kumara stop the chariot. He pointed into the branches, "There is a bundle tied there, wrapped in a winding-sheet. Climb up and fetch it down."

"A corpse!" cried the prince. "I am a kshatriya, eunuch. How can I touch a corpse? I will be defiled."

Brihannala laughed. "Surely, you belong to one of the great royal houses of the earth. I would never make you do anything that might pollute you. Trust me, wrapped in that cerement is something with which I can face the Kuru army. Your bow and arrows are not quite enough to fight such enemies. Climb the tree and cut the rope that secures the bundle."

Uttara Kumara brought down the corpse-like bundle. Brihannala said, "Open it, my prince."

The prince undid the twin knots on the winding-sheet. He peeled away the cloth from whatever it covered. Within, there was another covering of cowhide. Uttara Kumara undid the thongs that bound this layer. When he drew back the flaps, he cried out in awe: it was as if a rainbow had been captive in that hide, and now burst forth.

The Matsya prince breathed, "Unearthly weapons! What are they, eunuch?" He knelt beside the dazzling ayudhas, gingerly he reached out to stroke them with his fingertips. "They are so beautiful, and they seem to be alive. Even as you and I are, Brihannala."

Then he grew afraid, and backed away once more from the gleaming weapons. He turned to Brihannala, and saw the eunuch standing very still, a hint of tears in his eyes.

Uttara Kumara said, "What are these weapons? I have never seen any like them before. They seem to be made of starlight and gandharva jewels. Which is this bow, eunuch, like a serpent of light? The arrows beside it burn like the sun and fire. Ah, they are so lovely and so terrible as well. Whose are they?"

Brihannala said, "These are the Pandavas' weapons. The bow you touched is the Gandiva; it belongs to Arjuna. There is only one of its kind that remains in the world, and it brings undying fame to one who owns it. In olden times, the Gandiva belonged to Brahma, for a thousand years. Then Indra had it for five thousand. Soma, the Moon, owned the bow after Indra, and he gave it to the Lord of the sea. Agni had it from Varuna, and recently, for the first time since it was wrought, the bow passed into the hands of a mortal man. When Arjuna helped the Fire God burn the Khandava vana, Agni gave him the Gandiva."

Uttara Kumara stood bewitched. He whispered, "And this other bow, set with turquoise and blue sapphires?"

"That is Bheema's. The son of the wind subdued the kings of Bharatavarsha with it, before his brother's Rajasuya yagna."

"And the one that burns red for the rubies embedded in it?"

"That is Madri's son, Nakula's, bow, and the one green as leaves is his twin Sahadeva's. The emeralds upon it are not of this earth. And the most slender bow, with golden bells that tinkle in the breeze, belongs to their eldest brother and their lord, Yudhishtira."

"And these silver quivers that seem to be made of moonlight?"

"One for each Pandava, and look, each arrow in them has one brother's name engraved upon it. They are magical quivers, and they are never empty. When the Pandavas disguised themselves for the thirteenth year of their exile, they tied their weapons to this tree. After the ajnatavasa is over, the sons of Pandu will return for them."

Like one who had walked into a dream, Uttara Kumara asked, "Where have the Pandavas gone, leaving these weapons here? Where is Draupadi? We heard, a year ago, that they had left the Kamyaka and the Dwaitavana; no one has seen them since. You seem to know so much about them. You even know where they hid their weapons. Brihannala, do you know where Yudhishtira and his brothers are?"

Then, it seemed to the prince that the eunuch was taller than he had been before. Brihannala smiled at him, "Why, my prince, the Pandavas have been very near you. Indeed, they have been your father's guests in Virata, this past year."

Astonishment on Uttara Kumara's face, and disbelief; Brihannala went on, "Kanka the dice-player is Yudhishtira. Your father's cook, Ballava, is Bheema. Damagranthi the stable-hand is Nakula, and your cowherd Tantripala is Sahadeva."

The prince breathed, "And Draupadi?"

"Your mother's sairandhri, Malini, is Panchali."

"And Arjuna?"

And now, it seemed to him he did not know the eunuch at all, his sister's dance-teacher. Brihannala was transformed into a mythic hero about whom Uttara Kumara had heard glowing legends since he was a child. The one before him said simply, "Why, my prince, I am Arjuna."

He saw excitement erupt softly on the prince's face. The next moment, Uttara Kumara was full of doubt. "If you are Arjuna, tell me the ten names you are called, and how you had each one."

"So, it is hard to believe that a eunuch is a kshatriya! My names are Arjuna, Phalguna, Jishnu, Kiriti, Swetavahana, Bhibhatsu, Vijaya, Partha, Savyasachi and Dhananjaya."

The joy in Uttara Kumara's eyes grew and grew. On the point of belief, he whispered, "And what do they mean?"

"I was Dhananjaya when I conquered the kings of Bharatavarsha during the Rajasuya yagna, and won wealth from them. I am Vijaya because I have never been defeated in battle. The horses the Lord of Fire gave me are white, so I am Swetavahana. My father Indra set a crown on my head in Devaloka, so I am Kiriti. I fight fairly, so am I Bhibhatsu; Savyasachi, being ambidextrous; Arjuna, since my skin has the colour of that tree; Phalguna, since I was born under the Uttara Phalguni nakshatra. I am Jishnu because I am fierce when roused, and because of my solemn oath: that if anyone spills even a drop of my brother Yudhishtira's blood on to the ground, I will kill that man and all his clan. Finally, I am Partha because I am my mother Pritha's son."

Uttara Kumara knew it was Indra's son Arjuna, who stood before him. The Matsya prince thought back on the Pandavas' lives in his father's palace. In terror, he fell at Arjuna's feet.

"My lord, I announce myself! I am King Virata's youngest son Bhoominjaya, also known as Uttara Kumara. I am the first one to whom Arjuna revealed himself after his ajnatavasa: long shall my fame last because of this.

"O Kshatriya, I tremble when I think of the menial tasks that you, your brothers and your queen performed in my father's palace. Humbly, and on my father's behalf, also, I beg you to forgive us if we disrespected you in any way."

He said all this lying on his face at the Pandava's feet, and his tears falling on the ground. With a laugh, Arjuna raised the youth up and embraced him. Gently he said, "Why should you be afraid or ask my forgiveness? We have all been happy in Virata, and your father has been generous to a fault. But come now, prince, the Kauravas are waiting for us. Fear nothing, I swear no harm will come to you."

The prince smiled radiantly, and said, "I swear I shall never be afraid again in my life."

Arjuna turned to the weapons in the winding-sheet. He folded his hands to them, and picked up the Gandiva and his silver quivers. It seemed to Uttara Kumara that both the warrior and the bow shone brighter with each other's touch. Arjuna took a folded banner from the bundle. He took down the Matsya lion from the chariot and hoisted his own flag in its place. It bore an image of magnificent Hanuman, and Viswakarman, who wrought that flag, had placed many powerful spirits upon it. Those superhuman ones, too, took their places again. Arjuna removed the eunuch's bracelets and bangles from his arms, and put on an archer's golden gloves. He tied his long hair in a white silk scarf, strapped the silver quivers to his back; and now, before an enthralled Uttara Kumara stood Arjuna, the Pandava, ready for battle! No trace of the eunuch Brihannala remained.

In awe, the young prince helped Arjuna into his chariot. Then he climbed into the sarathy's place and took the reins. Urvashi's curse ended finally when Pandu's son took up the Gandiva once more; Arjuna said in a deep man's voice, "Let us ride."

The prince flicked his reins over his horses and they flashed forward.

SEVENTEEN

Dissension

As the chariot sped towards the Kaurava army, Arjuna raised Mayaa's sea-conch, the Devadatta, and blew a deep bass on it. As they drew nearer he pulled on the bowstring of the Gandiva, and sent a wave of fear through the Kaurava footsoldiers. They saw him transformed; they saw the flag of Hanuman above the youth that had changed places with Arjuna.

Drona cried excitedly, "The eunuch has vanished, here comes Arjuna! Prepare to surrender their herd to the Matsyas, none of us will stand before Indra's son today."

Duryodhana snapped, "Acharya, you forget yourself! You are disheartening our men. Anyway, we did not come here to seek battle, only to unmask the Pandavas. We have seen Arjuna before the end of the ajnatavasa. If they are men of honour, they must go back to the forest for another twelve years.

"And why does Arjuna's very name strike such terror in the hearts of the Kurus? Bheeshma, Drona, Kripa and Aswatthama stand petrified in their chariots. I say what if it is Arjuna? Won't the Kuru army face Indra or Yama, if they came to challenge us?"

Karna rode up, and said in disgust, "Not a man in our army wants to fight because of what Drona said. But, Duryodhana, to Karna it does not matter who the enemy is. Let it be Bhargava or Indra, Arjuna by himself or with Krishna beside him: for you, I will fight them all, by myself if need be!

"I pray that is Arjuna; for thirteen years, I have dreamt of this encounter. I will cover him with arrows, till he is like a mountain mantled in the crimson flowers of spring. Then, as Garuda does a serpent in his talons, I will pluck him out of his chariot.

"I know the thought of Arjuna has been a thorn in your heart, Duryodhana. Today I will remove it forever. As for the rest of you: stand by, if you dare not fight, and watch me!"

He spoke with such contempt that Kripa cried, "Do you never think of anything but war and killing? A kshatriya only fights when he cannot avoid battle, but you are always eager to cover yourself in blood. Why must you try to prove you are Arjuna's equal? We all know how much better than you he is.

"But why bother to make you see sense? You are so stubborn, Karna, you would reach your hand into a cobra's mouth to show how brave you are. Instead of boasting, let us stand together. Let Bheeshma, Drona, Aswatthama, Kripa, Karna and Duryodhana unite to contain Arjuna today. He has waited thirteen years to be at us, and even together, I fear we will not hold him. To speak of facing him alone is foolishness; Karna, you don't know what you are saying."

Karna swore at this. "Kripa has lost his manhood seeing Arjuna, but I don't need him or any of you to face the Pandava. I, alone, am enough. Duryodhana, today your friend will discharge a part of his debt to you. My lord, a brahmana's advice should be sought only when a yagna is to be performed, a feast held, or the poor fed. Since they tremble at Arjuna's name, let Kripa and Drona ride back to Hastinapura. I will fight by myself."

Aswatthama cried in rage, "Duryodhana, the Matsya herd is still in Matsya lands. Your friend talks as if the battle is over, and Arjuna has already been defeated. As for brahmanas, they are not given to bragging. They are like the elements.

"Does fire boast it can consume all it touches? Does the sun sing that he lights up the earth? And the earth, our mother, does she say, 'Look at me, how wonderful I am: how heavy the burden I bear, how marvellous my fortitude!'

"No, for the truly great have no need to boast: their deeds speak for them. Only the ineffectual and the impotent are full of talk, and little else."

Aswatthama turned on Duryodhana. "Brahmanas don't win kingdoms by cheating at dice. A vaishya may earn his livelihood by buying and selling, even by cheating; it is in his blood. But who has seen a kshatriya doing these things?

"Karna talks so glibly of brahmanas being afraid. Duryodhana, did you conquer Indraprastha with arms? Did you send your cousins into exile after beating them in battle? Why, you did not play dice yourself against Yudhishtira, but had a cheat play for you.

"Do you remember what Vidura said then? 'All creatures inherit the patience of the earth to varying degrees, even the ants and little insects. And the greatest men are the most forbearing of all.' But you went too far, when you and your brother humiliated Draupadi in the Kuru sabha. Your nemesis rides at you in that chariot. Arjuna has not forgotten that day, it is burnt in fire on his heart. He has no use for patience today, and none of us will escape his wrath.

"This fool dares call my father and my uncle cowards. They spoke knowing Arjuna's worth, as I do. This braggart is no archer compared to Arjuna. He is just consumed by envy, alas, the same envy that has been your ruin. You could have been such a great king, Duryodhana, if only you hadn't let your envy of the Pandavas rule your life."

Aswatthama said, "Duryodhana, let Virata take the field today and I will fight for you. But I will not fight Arjuna. He is as dear to me as my father, and Karna has wronged them both."

He flung down his bow and quiver.

EIGHTEEN

The Kuru army

Bheeshma said to Duryodhana, "Karna had no right to insult Drona and Kripa. Pacify the Acharyas, Duryodhana. How will we face the enemy if we are already at war amongst ourselves?"

To Aswatthama, the patriarch said, "Don't be offended by Karna, he only wanted to put heart in our soldiers. Wise men's memories are short, Aswatthama, and we must stand together against Arjuna."

Aswatthama said, "Let Drona forgive him, and Kripa; and I will as well. But why should this man be so envious of Arjuna?"

Sensing a crisis on his hands, Duryodhana cried, "Acharyas, forgive me! I meant no offence, and I beg your pardon."

He told his friend, "Karna, you should ask the Acharyas' pardon, too."

Immediately, Karna flashed an ambiguous smile. He said, "Forgive me, O masters. I meant no harm."

Drona said, "I have already put my anger behind me, let us forget that sharp words passed between us. I have something else to say; Duryodhana must not meet Arjuna in battle today. There is no telling what the Pandava might do if he sees you. I am also certain Arjuna has not shown himself like this before the ajnatavasa has ended. Let Bheeshma say if I am wrong."

Duryodhana turned pale. "Pitama, it isn't true! The year of the ajnatavasa is not over. I have counted the days."

But Bheeshma said, "Drona is right, my child. I consulted the astrologers before we left Hastinapura, and their calculations are immaculate. They said to me, every five years that pass see two months of real time added to them. In thirteen years of the sun, five months and twelve days more than those years elapse: by the moon's orbit. The Pandavas have already spent five months more than they need have in exile. But Yudhishtira did not want to leave room for any doubt, so he waited until thirteen years of the sun passed."

Duryodhana's face seemed to crumble. He cried, "And by the count of the sun?"

"By the count of the sun, the ajnatavasa ended six days ago. If you do not believe me, ask Yudhishtira; even you know your cousin would never lie."

Bheeshma paused for a moment, looking at Duryodhana in some pity. He said, "Look at Arjuna, he won't be stopped today. And how much more terrible the Pandavas will be when five of them fight us together. Remember who they are, Duryodhana, besides being your cousins. They are Devaputras, men of destiny born to rule the earth. Make peace with them, my child, you cannot send them back into exile. Time does not obey one man's will; her wheel of fortune has come round, inexorably. Return their kingdom to the Pandavas, and spare the earth such slaughter that you can't even dream of."

Duryodhana's face was grim. Tightly he said, "You say the Pandavas are Devaputras, Pitama. They may be; but they are no blood of mine, and I will not give them what was never theirs in the first place. Let us have no more talk of peace, but of bloody war. I mean to fight today, and later, as well. If I cannot banish them to the forest peaceably, I will kill them on the field. They came out of nowhere, like a plague into my life. They ruined my youth, and stole my birthright from me. I have suffered them for too long. Let them either stay in the wilderness where they were born, or let them die. Pitama, don't talk to me anymore of peace with the Pandavas."

Bheeshma's eyes were moist, as he turned away to watch Arjuna's chariot paused in the distance.

Drona said, "Let our army be divided in three. Duryodhana, take a fourth part and ride back to Hastinapura. Let another fourth of our men drive the cattle after you. Half of us shall remain here to face Arjuna; Pitama, you command those that stay to fight. Hurry, Arjuna is tired of waiting: here he comes!"

Though his eyes flashed with disappointment, Duryodhana saw the wisdom of what Drona said. He took half the army and turned back towards Hastinapura. Bheeshma began to form the rest of his soldiers in battle array.

"Drona, keep yourself at the heart of our vyuha. Aswatthama, guard the left flank, and Kripa, the right. Karna, your place is at the front of our army. You will have what you want, and be the first to meet Arjuna. I will be at the rear."

The Kaurava force deployed itself. Across the open space separating them, Arjuna saw the Kuru army manoeuvre. He smiled and said to Uttara Kumara, "Look, the chandrakala: the phalanx of the crescent moon! Bheeshma is in command of the Kaurava army; he is a master of the vyuhas. Ride a little to the left, that is the weakest part of this formation."

As they forged ahead, Arjuna shaded his eyes, and beyond the crescent, at its curve, he saw a crimson banner fluttering over a fine chariot: a banner that bore the emblem of a golden palm-tree. It was great Bheeshma's banner, which struck fear in his enemies' hearts.

NINETEEN

Arjuna

Like bright thoughts, two arrows flew down at Drona's feet, two more at Bheeshma's, and another two at Kripa's. Arjuna was still too far for them to see him clearly, but a grandson and a pupil greeted his elders! An inspired Uttara Kumara flicked his reins over his horses. As Arjuna's chariot flew nearer, another arrow hummed past Drona's ear, and one more. Both spumed up into the sky. Then two shafts whistled past Bheeshma's face, almost brushing his cheek, and two past Kripa's: Arjuna was announcing his intention to fight. The Kuru elders picked up their bows.

As the lone chariot skimmed along, Uttara Kumara was a superb sarathy, and he hardly knew how himself. Arjuna cried, "I see Drona and Kripa. I see Karna at the head of the Kuru legion. I see my Pitama behind the crescent moon, but nowhere do I see Duryodhana."

His charioteer cried back into the wind that swept their faces like a river, "I see another force riding away to the west. Look, Arjuna, a banner in the wind!"

It was a golden banner, with a menacing black serpent upon it. Arjuna said with a smile, "They have decided Duryodhana must not meet me today. But I mean to fight him. Veer to the west; we must pass the crescent and follow my cousin. He has your father's herd with him, and we are here to free the cattle."

Uttara Kumara swung his horses to the right. But by now they were too near the Kaurava phalanx to avoid it entirely. As the chariot stormed at them, some Kaurava warriors rushed forward to challenge Arjuna.

The Pandava cried to his sarathy, "Go after the serpent banner, Uttara Kumara, go like the wind!"

The Matsya prince turned the chariot sharply, but some of Duryodhana's brothers were too close to evade. A tide of arrows rose from the Gandiva, driving them back, while Uttara Kumara's chariot flitted past one tip of the crescent moon.

Bheeshma cried, "He is after Duryodhana! Catch him quickly, or he will kill our prince."

Bheeshma turned his own chariot, and went after Arjuna as hard as he could. Meanwhile Arjuna neared the Matsya herd. He said to Uttara Kumara, "Slow the chariot, let us free the cattle first."

Another fire-tide from the Gandiva, and, in moments, a thousand men guarding the Matysa herd died. The rest fled. Exultant Arjuna roared to his charioteer, "Indra's Matali cannot match you today! After the serpent-banner again, Kumara."

As if he had been a sarathy all his life, Uttara Kumara went furiously after the fleeing Duryodhana. When the Kuru horsemen herding them fled, Virata's cattle turned and stampeded back home to their cowherds. Prince Uttara weaved through the milling herd, and stayed on Duryodhana's trail. Bheeshma, Karna and the other Kurus barred his way.

As a mind does its thoughts, the Gandiva streamed arrows.

Karna peeled away from the main Kaurava force and plunged at Arjuna. As he went, Aswatthama cried at him, "If you lose, you can always ask Shakuni what to do next!"

Arjuna said to Uttara Kumara, "Ride into them, I will fight them all together. Look! Duryodhana has turned around. He is no coward that he would run from a battle."

Karna roared at Aswatthama, "Taunter, today you will see my arrows speak for me!"

Quickly Arjuna was in the thick of the Kurus, just as they wanted. He fought those awesome kshatriyas as disdainfully a lion does a jackal-pack. All together, they rained arrows on him; but Arjuna's archery was hardly a thing of the earth, so, too, the Matsya prince's skill with his horses! Arjuna's chariot was so quick it was impossible to aim at it, yet the Pandava's arrows were everywhere, finding chinks in Kuru mail.

Inevitably, Karna and Arjuna faced each other. Laughing easily, the shafts radiating from his bow like rays from the sun, Arjuna cried, "Here we are at last, face to face! I hear you brag there is no archer like you on earth. Words are cheap, prove yourself with arrows. I won't spare you today Karna, for everything you have said and done."

Karna's reply was to strike Arjuna's horses and sarathy with shafts like fire. The Matsya prince was imperturbable. Calmly, he plucked out Karna's barbs with one hand, while the other guided his horses as brilliantly as before.

When Arjuna saw Uttara Kumara bleeding, with a roar he lifted his own archery. Karna had his bow cracked in his hands. Wave upon wave of arrows flew at him from every side, from the sky, and it seemed, up from the very earth. He could not face Arjuna. His horses killed, and he himself bleeding, Karna leapt out of his shattered chariot and ran. Arjuna's arrows chased him from the field, in mockery, one for every step he went. Of course, Arjuna would never kill an enemy in flight, but this revenge was sweet enough.

Drona rode up to challenge the Pandava. The master could not match his pupil today. Arjuna was no longer just the bowman his acharya had made him; he was much more. Yet, he never broke his guru's skin, but beat Drona back with a luminous tirade, and then plucked the bow out of his hand with a shaft as subtle as prana, as breath.

Aswatthama came to help his beleaguered father. Arjuna shone in Uttara Kumara's chariot: his body as bright as a God's, his arrow-storm coruscating. Bheeshma and Kripa came to engage him, and Arjuna beat them back effortlessly, and cried to his young sarathy, "Ride at the serpent-banner, my prince! Duryodhana is the one I want."

Horses and elephants perished around Arjuna, footsoldiers and horsemen in incredible thousands, in moments. Duryodhana, mortified, saw his dreams of victory scattered like straws in a gale, all his heroes' valour consumed by the majestic Pandava. His cousin's blinding archery cut down his serpent-banner, and shrouded him in swift fear. He, too, turned his chariot and fled.

Exhilarant Arjuna cried after him, "Duryodhana, come back and fight like a kshatriya! Do you love your life so much that you abandon your honour for it?"

It seemed Arjuna's taunt was sharper than his arrows, and Duryodhana turned his chariot around. Karna also rode back at his friend's right hand. Drona, Bheeshma, Kripa and Aswatthama surrounded Arjuna again, but the son of Pandu, Indra's son, was implacable. He was a fire, and they could not contain him.

So far, no astra had been invoked. Now the Kauravas pressed Arjuna all together, and he would have to kill some of them if they fought on. He also feared for his sarathy, the Matsya prince's, life.

Arjuna invoked an astra, no apocalyptic weapon, but one that would quell the enemy. Drona and Kripa, Aswatthama, Duryodhana, Bheeshma and Karna saw the Pandava turn his bow over their heads. A silver shaft floated languidly at them. They turned their eyes up at it, for it shone so hypnotically on its strange, slow flight. From that arrow what seemed to be a shower of fireflies fell on the Kaurava army, like snow.

Bheeshma laughed, "The sammohanastra!"

Next moment, the Kuru heroes, their footsoldiers and horsemen were all covered in the rain of stardust, and enchanted by that weapon of sleep, they fell on the ground or in their chariots. The army of Hastinapura lay like a sea quieted, not a man moving.

A delighted Arjuna said to Uttara Kumara, "My prince, you were perfect! We beat them as much by your chariotry as with my arrows. Do you remember what your sister asked for? Go and fetch the mantles of the Kurus for her dolls. And when they wake up, let Duryodhana and the others know they were beaten."

Uttara Kumara leapt down from the chariot-head. He took Acharya Kripa's glistening cape of white silk, Karna's fulvid yellow one. Arjuna cried to him, "Don't leave Duryodhana's blue cloak, or Aswatthama's crimson one."

But when the prince approached the supine Bheeshma, Arjuna said, "Don't go near the Pitama. The sammohana will not hold him for long; he knows its mantra. Come away, we have enough souvenirs."

Even as Uttara Kumara, his arms full of silks and jewels, climbed back into the chariot, Bheeshma awoke with a roar and gave them battle. After a short, fierce fight, Arjuna's arrow plucked his bow from the ancient warrior's hands. Arjuna folded his palms reverently to his Pitama, and told prince Uttara, "Ride home now, our mission is accomplished."

In a while, the other Kauravas awoke from the astra's slumber. Karna roared, "After him! Arjuna won't escape me today."

Bheeshma laughed at him. "Haven't you had enough shame for one day? Arjuna has stripped you of your mantles and jewels. He has taken your honour. He could have had your lives; but he is too noble to kill sleeping men, even if they are his enemies. Let us admit defeat and ride back to Hastina."

As he spoke, a conch sounded at the shoulder of an undulation in the earth. They looked up and saw Arjuna's chariot framed against the sky. Shimmering, dreamlike arrows appeared again, seemingly out of nowhere. They flashed down at the feet of Drona, Bheeshma and Kripa, in salutation and farewell. Another shaft streaked at Duryodhana, and knocked the crown from his head! Then, they saw the Pandava's chariot no more.

Duryodhana howled, "Back! Back to Hastinapura! And never speak of this black day."

The Kuru army turned home, leaving its dead on the field of its humiliation. Some way off, on the road back to Virata, Arjuna asked Uttara Kumara to stop the chariot. The Pandava said, "Your cattle have gone home. Now send word back to the city that you vanquished the Kuru army by yourself. As for me, I must be Brihannala again."

"I can't do that! You beat the Kurus. How can I even dream of telling such a lie?"

"Do it for my sake. Your father must not yet learn that the Pandavas are in his city. When the time comes, in a day or two, he will know everything. Until then you must keep up the pretence."

Reluctantly, Uttara Kumara agreed. They drove back to the cremation-ground in the forest. Arjuna returned the Gandiva to the winding-sheet; he took down Hanuman's banner and folded it away; the great vanara and the other spirits flew out from it and vanished into the air. Arjuna peeled off his archer's gloves, and put them back with his silver quivers. He tied the bundle up, so it resembled a corpse once more, and hoisted it back into the tree.

The Pandava untied his hair and put on Brihannala's silks again. He walked round the great tree in pradakshina, climbed into the sarathy's place, took the reins, and with Uttara Kumara back in the archer's seat, they drove towards the city of Virata.*

---

* The KMG translation describes the battle between Arjuna and the Kurus in great detail, and some thirty pages.

TWENTY

A gambler's blood

LATER THAT DAY, VIRATA ENTERED HIS CITY. SURROUNDED BY FOUR Pandavas, he rode up to his palace. Queen Sudeshna and the princess Uttaraa received him on the palace steps with arghya, and marked his brow with the crimson tilaka of victory. The king did not see his favourite son. "Where is Uttara Kumara? Why isn't he here to receive me?"

Sudeshna had tears in her eyes. Virata cried, "Tell me! Where is my son?"

Princess Uttaraa said, "The Kurus attacked us from the north when you were away. They also drove away our herd. There was no other man left in the city, so Uttara Kumara rode after them. Brihannala has gone with him as his sarathy."

Her father was aghast. "My little son has ridden alone against Bheeshma and Drona, Kripa, Karna and Duryodhana? With a eunuch for his sarathy! We must go after him at once."

Kanka said, "If Brihannala has gone with the prince we have nothing to fear."

The king frowned. But he trusted his gambler implicitly, especially after the victory against the Trigartas. Virata sat waiting in his apartment with his queen and his daughter; the hours dragged by. Then they heard cowherds' voices outside asking to see the king.

Virata cried, "Let them in! They may have news of my boy."

The cowherds, their faces flushed, were shown in. Their chieftain said, "My lord, we come from near the field of battle. We followed the herd, and we saw prince Bhoominjaya's chariot. Brihannala was driving the chariot and she stopped when she saw us."

"The news, man, tell us what news!"

The cowherds began to speak all together, repeating themselves.

"The herd has been rescued!" cried one.

"The prince defeated the Kaurava army by himself."

"Uttara Kumara crushed the Kurus."

"Brihannala said to us, 'Run back to the king and tell him the prince has triumphed. Let the city prepare to receive him.'"

Virata was on his feet. He roared, "Let our city be set out in flowers and arches to receive my son! There is no kshatriya on earth like Bhoominjaya. Did you hear, Sudeshna? Our prince has beaten the Kuru army by himself!" Kanka the gambler smiled to himself, and murmured, "I am not surprised when Brihannala was his sarathy."

The king frowned again, but he was so delighted at the news he made no reply to Kanka. Virata said, "Let our musicians and dancers take to the streets to welcome the hero!" He turned to the cowherds, "How long before they arrive?"

"An hour, my lord."

"I can hardly wait!" Virata saw the sairandhri in the passage, "Malini, fetch the dice-board. I am in the mood for a game, Kanka. Come friend, let us play, I am sure I will beat you today."

"My lord, our minds are excited, and one should never gamble when one is not calm."

"Absurd! We are not playing for money, only to pass the time until my son returns."

"It is a dangerous game at the best of times. It cost Yudhishtira everything he had. It robbed him of his reason, and he lost his kingdom, his brothers, his wife and even himself. Wine is as nothing compared to dice, to make a man mad. We will play later, my lord, or tomorrow when we are both calmer."

But the king must have his way, and the board was set up and the game began.

As they played, Virata said, "Kanka, you have no idea how proud I feel. Not all of us together could have done what my boy did today. I always knew he would be a great kshatriya some day, but he has exceeded my fondest dreams."

Kanka said quietly, "My lord, Brihannala won the day."

Virata's face turned crimson. He cried, "This is the third time I have heard you praise Brihannala for Bhoominjaya's victory. You forget yourself, gambler. My son is a kshatriya prince and your Brihannala a eunuch. How dare you compare them?"

Through clenched teeth Virata said, "I forgive you this time, Kanka, but don't insult my boy again!"

The gambler smiled, and said serenely, "My lord, truth is not always pleasant, yet truth must be told. Let me tell you what must have really happened. Your son was Brihannala's sarathy, while the eunuch fought. How could Uttara Kumara face the Kuru army that the Devas themselves would fear?"

The king exploded in anger. "Brahmana wretch! Dare you?" He flung the dice in his hand at Kanka. The heavy thing struck the gambler's forehead. He cried out and clasped his brow. The sharp corner of the ivory had drawn blood, and Kanka cupped his palms under the wound, collecting every drop of his blood, not letting a single one spill on to the ground.

With a cry, Malini ran forward with a bowl of water. She mopped Kanka's brow with the sari she wore, stanching the blood. Gently she bathed the wound, and Kanka washed his hands in the bowl she held for him. Together they managed to stop the bleeding and no drop of the gambler's blood fell on the ground.

Virata watched this contemptuously. But when the sairandhri used the hem of the silk she wore to wipe the gambler's face, the Matsya king cried, "What are you doing, Malini? The fool deserves what he got!"

The flower girl replied angrily, "For every drop of this man's blood that falls on the ground, your kingdom will go without rain for a year! And there is he who has sworn to kill anyone who spills Kanka's blood. If he sees the gambler bleeding, you shall not live, Virata. I have just saved your kingdom and your life."

The king hardly believed her; he was still furious with Kanka. Just then, a messenger ran in. "My lord, prince Uttara Kumara has returned. I left him at the palace steps. He is on his way here, and Brihannala is with him."

Kanka sprang up, and before the king could say a word, he drew the messenger aside. "Quick, fellow! Brihannala must not come here. Make sure only the prince comes in first; tell the eunuch that Kanka said so. Run now!"

Not ten paces down the passage outside, the messenger met the prince and Brihannala. He plucked Brihannala by his sleeve, "An urgent message for you from Kanka."

The eunuch stopped at once. "You go on to your father, my prince. Remember to keep our secret!"

When Uttara Kumara had gone, the messenger said, "Kanka says you must not go into the king's chambers yet. He will send for you."

Brihannala nodded, and waited outside. Uttara Kumara walked into his father's apartment, and Virata embraced him with a cry. "O Kshatriya!"

But the prince had eyes only for Kanka the gambler, and the dark sairandhri who wiped the blood from his face. Uttara Kumara whispered, "Who did this to you, noble one?"

Kanka only smiled. Virata said, "The brahmana dared compare you to the eunuch, and I threw the dice in his face."

Uttara Kumara gasped. "Father! Beg his pardon at once, lest the Gods curse you for injuring a brahmana."

Virata looked puzzled. But he was so happy to see his son that his rage had left him. He went up to Kanka, took his hand, and said gently, "Forgive me, my friend. I owe you a great deal, and would not have you angry with me."

Calmly, the gambler said, "It was nothing, my lord. I was only anxious lest my blood fell on the ground."

Virata still looked perplexed. Then, the joy of his son's deed was upon him again, and he began to press the prince for every detail of the battle. Kanka signalled to the guard at the door to call Brihannala in.

The eunuch came in, glowing. He bowed to the king. Kanka stood with the side of his face where the dice drew blood turned away from Brihannala. Virata said, "Brihannala, I thank you for being my son's sarathy. I always knew he would be a great kshatriya; today he has surpassed all my expectations."

Brihannala smiled. Uttara Kumara blushed and said quickly, "But, father, it wasn't I who defeated the Kurus!"

The eunuch looked warningly at the prince. Uttara Kumara said, "It was a Devaputra."

The king whispered, "A Devaputra?"

"A Deva's son. He was at the enemy like a host of light."

"Who was he? I want to offer him my kingdom. And my daughter Uttaraa!"

The prince said, "He vanished after the battle, but he has promised to see us very soon."

As the prince spoke Brihannala turned his gaze to Kanka, but the gambler kept his face turned away. Virata said again to Brihannala, and now more humbly, "I thank you for bringing my son back to me safely."

Brihannala bowed to the king and to Kanka, and left the royal apartment. He went to the princess Uttaraa with the silks and jewels from the battlefield. She hugged him, and cried, "Now my dolls will wear Kuru warriors' silks! And one day my sons will wear their jewels."

Brihannala patted her cheek and left her. But he was troubled: he could not fathom why Yudhishtira kept his face turned from him in Virata's apartment. Was he displeased that he had shown himself to the Kauravas?

Brihannala took his anxiety to Ballava. Bheema gave a shout to see his brother, and embraced him. "So you routed them! How sweet revenge must have felt. And I am glad you didn't kill any of them, but left that for when I could be there as well."

Arjuna said, "Bheema, why did Yudhishtira turn his face from me in the king's chambers? Is he angry at what I did?"

"I have no idea. He should be as delighted as I am. Let us go and ask him."

When Yudhishtira saw Arjuna in his rooms, the eldest Pandava jumped up with a cry and clasped his brother. "How proud I am of you! Oh Arjuna, our evil days are over."

But Arjuna had seen brother's wound. "What is this?" he cried. Bheema was glowering at it, as well.

"Ah, it's nothing," said Yudhishtira. "I said you must have fought the Kauravas, and the king thought I was insulting his son. He threw the dice at me."

"So that was why you kept your face turned from me."

Bheema's eyes were already ablaze. He hissed, "If you hadn't stopped us this Virata would have been dead long ago."

Arjuna said, "Enough of your patience, Yudhishtira. I am going to kill Virata."

He spoke so quietly it was plain he meant every word. Bheema cried, "Let us be lords of Matsya first. Then we can conquer the world from here."

They rose to go, but Yudhishtira said, "Bheema, Virata does not know who I am. Besides, he has been very kind to us this past year. We have been his guests and eaten his food. We must not be ungrateful."

Bheema and Arjuna began to protest, but their brother stopped them. "Hear me out. All I say is that he deserves another chance. Tomorrow we will show Virata who we are: I will go and sit on his throne. If he is still defiant, you can kill him. But if he honours us, we must forgive him."

Arjuna and Bheema exchanged a glance, and nodded.

TWENTY-ONE

The Pandavas

THE NEXT MORNING*, THE PANDAVAS ROSE BEFORE THE SUN. AS THEY used to, when they were masters of the earth, and for the first time since they were exiled, they bathed in scented water. They dressed themselves like kings, in silks, and put on the royal ornaments the sairandhri had kept secretly for them. Before the Matsya king came to his court, the five brothers and Draupadi entered that sabha. The flower girl also wore finery now, and she was every bit a queen of queens.

Yudhishtira climbed up to Virata's throne, and sat in it. Draupadi sat beside him in Sudeshna's place, and Bheema, Arjuna, Nakula and Sahadeva stood around them. That sabha had never been so resplendent.

Shortly, Virata arrived with his courtiers. He saw the Pandavas and cried, "Kanka, how dare you! Explain yourself, gambler, if you value your life."

But the spectacle before his eyes was so regal, he could not be as angry as he might. He was confused, more than angry. Yudhishtira did not answer, only smiled mysteriously at the Matsya king. His confusion mounting, Virata drew his sword. He said, "Explain yourself, Kanka!"

Arjuna replied quietly, "Virata, be careful how you speak to this man. Your throne is blessed that he sits on it, for he is fit to sit upon the throne of the king of the Devas. This man, my lord, is the greatest soul born in this age. He is an embodiment of dharma."

A tumult in his chest, Virata said, "Who is he?"

---

* KMG has it as the third day after Arjuna's battle.

"Yudhishtira, whose fame will last in the world as long as the sun rises over it."

Virata gasped, "Yudhishtira?"

Arjuna said, "Do you still think he should not sit on your throne?"

Gaping at them, the Matsya king breathed, "If he is Yudhishtira, where are the other Pandavas? Where is Draupadi?" knowing what the answer would be, the truth dawning on him. But he must hear it from them.

"Your cook Ballava is Bheema, the wind's son. Your daughter's dance-teacher Brihannala is Arjuna. Your equerry Damagranthi is Nakula, and Tantripala, the cowherd, is Sahadeva."

His heart pounding, Virata turned his gaze to Draupadi, her skin like night, softened with moonbeams. Arjuna said, "Your queen's sairandhri is Drupada's daughter Panchali."

Virata was speechless. Just then, Uttara Kumara came in. He took his father's hand and said, "My lord, this is Arjuna. He is the Devaputra who humbled the Kauravas yesterday. I was his sarathy."

With a moan, Virata fell at Yudhishtira's feet. "God has blessed me! You lived in my palace for a whole year. No wonder such fortune has come to my kingdom. Noble Yudhishtira, forgive me, forgive me a thousand times! Forgive every offence of mine. Have mercy, O Pandava; I never knew who you were. My kingdom is yours to rule, and I am your servant. Only, forgive me for all the indignity you have endured in my palace."

Yudhishtira took Virata's hand, "My lord, I am not angry. No, I am grateful to you. This last year of our exile was the hardest to think of, since we had to hide ourselves behind disguises. Your kindness made this the happiest year. Let me thank you with all my heart, there is nothing to forgive."

Yudhishtira embraced Virata. Uttara Kumara said, "Father, yesterday you said you would give Uttaraa to the Devaputra who routed the Kurus. Shall I fetch my sister? What greater honour for us than Arjuna marrying her?"

Without waiting for Virata's reply, the prince ran off and brought Uttaraa back with him. She was startled at the spectacle that greeted her in her father's court. Then she was overjoyed, and amused, as well, to learn who her dance-teacher was!

Virata brought his daughter to Yudhishtira, and, kneeling before him, said, "I beg you again to forgive us if we wronged you in any way. And to show that you do, I ask you to take this child of mine to be your brother Arjuna's wife." He turned to Arjuna, "Greatest of kshatriyas, she has been your pupil for a year, and she loves you. Now take her to be your bride, and with her take my kingdom for your own."

Arjuna said, "My lord, the Pandavas do not want your kingdom, but we must have your support when the war begins. As for Uttaraa, I thank you for the love that prompts you to offer her to me. But she has been my sishyaa for a year, and like a daughter to me. How can I marry her now?"

He saw the disappointment on Virata's face, on Uttara Kumara's, and the princess', too. Arjuna took Uttaraa's hand, and said, "She has been my daughter all these months, and let her always be. I accept your princess, Virata, to be my son Abhimanyu's wife! He is Subhadra's son, and Krishna's nephew, and he has grown in Dwaraka. He will make the perfect husband for my favourite pupil."

Arjuna kissed Uttaraa's cheek, and said, "From now on, sweet child, you are truly my daughter."

Then they heard voices raised in the passage outside, and the guard announced a messenger from Hastinapura. A dark-faced, shifty-eyed man entered. Squinting at the sabha, he delivered his message. "My lord Duryodhana sends this message through me. He says to the Pandavas, 'We saw Arjuna before the ajnatavasa had ended. You must go into exile for another twelve years.' So says my master Duryodhana."

Now Yudhishtira laughed at his cousin's audacity. He told the messenger, "Take my reply to your master. Tell him his cousin Yudhishtira says let our Pitama Bheeshma decide if Arjuna showed himself before or after the ajnatavasa ended. Tell Duryodhana, also, that I will send my own messenger to him in a few days with a question. Let him be prepared to give me an answer. Until then, let him send no more messages, but leave us in peace."

TWENTY-TWO

A wedding in Upaplavya

Across the green world flashed the news that the Pandavas had returned. In every kingdom, north and south, east and west, kings and commoners alike spoke of nothing else. A current of excitement surged through the holy land, and everyone speculated, what would Duryodhana do next? Would he return their kingdom to his cousins?

Meanwhile, the Matsya king gave the Pandavas another city within his borders in which to live, to be their home for the time: excellent Upaplavya. Once they settled in Upaplavya, in relief that their exile was over, Yudhishtira sent messengers to all those he loved. The first ones he sent word to were Krishna and Drupada. He said to them that the ajnatavasa had ended, and Abhimanyu would marry the princess Uttaraa in the Matsya kingdom.

The Yadavas were the first to arrive in Upaplavya. Yudhishtira and his brothers, Virata and his sons and brothers, all went out to the city-gates to receive them. Balarama alighted from his chariot, and Virata and Yudhishtira came forward to embrace him. The other Pandavas and Virata's family greeted Balarama. The second chariot from Dwaraka drew up, and in it rode he whom they had all been waiting for: Krishna arrived with Subhadra and Abhimanyu.

As always, Yudhishtira was overwhelmed when he saw Krishna, and he wept. They embraced, and the Pandava said, "The exile is over, and now that you have come, I leave everything else in your hands. Krishna, I bless our exile for one reason: it has made me more certain than ever that our fate always rests in your hands, and our future depends on what you decide. My Lord, I submit to you, do whatever you will."

Krishna's eyes were not dry, as he hugged his cousins one by one, Arjuna clinging to him. At last, Draupadi came and stood before him. She only said, "Krishna."

Then she knelt before him, her tears flowed, and neither of them could speak for a while. Krishna took her hands and raised her up. Softly, he said, "Dry your eyes, O queen, the time for tears is past. Let me see you smile. You have such a lovely smile, to light up the very world. Do you remember what I promised you, thirteen years ago in the Kamyaka vana, when you had just been banished? I always keep my word, Panchali. I intend to cure your sorrow, whatever saddens you."

Even as they spoke Drupada arrived, and with him, Dhrishtadyumna and Shikhandi. Drupada had also brought the other Pandava-putras with him. Draupadi had not seen her sons for thirteen years, and they were all young men now. With a cry, she clasped them to her. She sobbed for joy, and bitterly, as well, for the thirteen years of motherhood of which Duryodhana had robbed her.

Virata said, "Let us not stand here for ever, the city has been waiting to receive all of you. Come, let me welcome you to Upaplavya."

Once they were in the city, their hearts turned to the wedding, and for the moment, the past was forgotten. There were many arrangements to be seen to still, for a host of friendly kings would soon begin to arrive with their armies. Everything was perfect on the day of Abhimanyu's wedding to the princess Uttaraa. Like a flame, himself, was that young lion as he sat before the sacred fire, and another flame was his bride.

Dhaumya was there as chief priest for the occasion, grave and radiant, as he intoned the mantras that joined two lives as one, forever. The wedding of Abhimanyu and Uttaraa was like a dream, almost too good to be true. Krishna and Arjuna sat next to each other. All that day had a wonderful auspiciousness about it, as if the sun of fortune rose again on the Pandavas, after the long night of their trials. They cherished the solemn ceremony deeply, as they perhaps could not have, had they not tasted privation and shame these thirteen years.

Yet, even while the wedding was underway there was a certain tension among the other kings who had come here at Yudhishtira's invitation. All of them knew the very future of Bharatavarsha must soon be decided. What would Yudhishtira do now? And Duryodhana?

None of the royal guests breathed a word of those momentous matters today. This was the day when Arjuna's son Abhimanyu married Virata's delectable daughter Uttaraa. And how splendid the kalyana mantapa was: with Balarama and Krishna there, like the Sun and the Moon, and the others like stars around them. Upaplavya was like Indra's Amravati; Draupadi and Subhadra were queens of the palace, and Sudeshna their sakhi. Enchantment was in the air, and bright, whispering petals fell out of the Devas' realms, to bless the young couple.

Abhimanyu looked into his bride's eyes, and saw a love there so strong it startled him. When the last mantras had been chanted, and they were man and wife, singing and dancing broke out in the palace and in the streets, and never paused for a week.

Glossary

Abhichara – sorcery. Also a spirit raised by an occult ritual.
Abhichari – sorcerer.
Abhisheka – investiture.
Acharya – a brahmana master.
Achyuta – immortal; a name of Vishnu's, and Krishna's.
Adharma – evil.
Adi kavya – first Poem. The Ramayana.
Adisehsa – great Serpent, Vishnu's rest.
Aditi – mother of the Devas.
Aditya – son of Aditi. Being of light, also son of the Sun God.
Adityahridaya – lit. heart of the sun.
Agni – Fire God
Agni – fire.
Agnihotra – fire ritual.
Agni kunda – fire pit.
Agneyastra – fire weapon, missile.
Agneyi – self-immolation by invoking inner fire.
Aindastra – Indra's astra.
Airavata – Indra's four-tusked white, flying elephant.
Akasa – sky, cosmic ether, fifth element.
Akhanda – universe.
Aksauhini – a legion. One version of its size is 21,000 chariots, as many elephants, 65,000 horse and 110,000 footsoldiers. (But this count does not tally with the total number of men killed during the Mahabharata yuddha, in 11 aksauhinis.)
Alakananda – a name of the Ganga.

Alidha – archer's stance.
Amavasya – new moon.
Amravati – Indra's heavenly city.
Amrita – nectar of immortality.
Amsa – essence, part.
Ananta – Sesha cosmic Serpent on which Vishnu rests.
Anarta – Krishna's kingdom.
Anarya – ignoble.
Andhaka – a Yadava tribe.
Angaraka – Mars.
Anima – the occult power to make oneself small.
Aniruddha – Krishna's grandson.
Anjali – offering.
Antapura – harem.
Apsara – nymph.
Arani – a twig from a sami tree. A fire kindeld with these is always sacred.
Aranya – jungle.
Arati – worship with lamps.
Ardha – half.
Arghya – offering of welcome.
Arya – noble.
Aryavarta – land of the noble. India. Bharatavarsha.
Aryaman – ancestor, the first man. Also, the Sun. Lord of the manes.
Asariri – disembodied voice.
Asrama – hermitage.
Asramas, the 4 asramas of life – brahmachari, grihasta, vanaprastha, sannyasi. Celibate, householder, renunciate, hermit.
Astra – unearthly weapon.
Asura – demon.
Aswamedha yagna – horse sacrifice.
Aswattha – pipal tree.
Aswins – heavenly twins, known for their beauty.
Atharva – the fourth Veda, concerned with sorcery, spells, etc.
Atman – the individual Soul.
AUM/OM – holy syllable, represents the Ultimate Reality.
Avatara – Incarnation.

Ayudha – weapon.
Bala/atibala – strength, extreme strength.
Bhajan – devotional song.
Bhakti – devotion, worship.
Bhakta devotee.
Bharatavarsha – India. The land of Bharata.
Bhasha – language.
Bhasma – holy ash.
Bhiksha – alms, begging.
Bhoja – a Yadava tribe.
Bhumi – the earth.
Bhumidevi – Earth Goddess.
Bhuta – ghost, spirit.
Bindu – point; mystic singularity.
Brahma – God of the Hindu Trinity. The Creator.
Brahmachari – a celibate.
Brahmacharya – celibacy.
Brahmahatya – murder of a brahmana.
Brahman – Ultimate Godhead; Holy Sopirit; different from Brahma.
Brahmana – priestly caste, also 'Brahma's people'.
Brahmarishi – sage of Brahman.
Brahmavadi – knower of Brahman.
Brahmavidya – knowledge of Brahman.
Brighu – an ancient rishi.
Brihaspati – guru of the Devas. Also the planet Jupiter.
Budha – Mercury.

Chaitra – an auspicious lunar month.
Chaitra – Kubera's garden.
Chakra – a wheel. In the body, a subtle centre of energy along the spinal column and in the brain.
Chakravaka – a water bird.
Chakravarti – emperor.
Chamara – silken whisk.
Chandala – an untouchable.
Chandra – Moon.
Charana – unearthly being.

Chiranjivi – long-lived, almost immortal.
Chital – a kind of deer.
Chitraratha – king of the gandharvas.

Daksha – Brahma's son, Sati's father. A prajapati.
Danava – demon, son of Danu.
Danda – a staff, also punishment.
Daitya – demon, son of Diti.
Dakshina – south.
Dakshinayana – the sun's southern migration.
Darbha – a kind of grass.
Darbhasana – seat made of darbha grass
Deva – a celestial, elemental, being. A God. Also 'Being of Light.' 'Divya' is light.
Devaloka – heavenly realm of the Devas.
Devaputra – son of a Deva.
Devi – Goddess.
Dharma – truth, justice.
Dhanu – Sagittarius.
Dhanusha – bow.
Dhanvantari – the original physician, who rose from the sea of milk with the amrita.
Dharma – truth, justice, duty, righteousness.
Dhruva – North Star.
Dhyana – meditation.
Dikpala – lord of a direction.
Diksha – gift/offering for a brahmana.
Dvividha – a vanara.
Dwapara – yuga third great age.
Dwaraka – Krishna's ocean city, raised for him by the Devas.
Dwarapalaka – gatekeeper.

Ekarnava – the original sea of life.

Gada – mace, club.
Gana – servitor, companion of Siva.
Gandharva – heavenly warrior minstrels. Elf.

Gandharva – vivaha marriage by abduction, elopement.
Garuda – Vishnu's Eagle.
Gayatri – the mother of all mantras.
Ghee – clarified butter.
Gochara – planetary transit.
Gopa – cowherd. Krishna was raised by gypsy cowherds.
Gopi/gopika – cowherdess.
Gotra – family, clan, lineage.
Graha pravesha – formal entry into a new home.
Grihastha – householder.
Guna – essence in nature. Sattva, rajas and tamas.
Guru – preceptor, master.
Guru dakshina – a formal fee or gift given to a master by his pupil, when tutelage is complete.
Gurukula – stage of life as a student, under a guru.
Gyana – knowledge.
Gyani – a wise man.

Halahala – original poison, which Siva drank.
Hari – Vishnu.
Hatya – murder.
Havis – the burnt offering from a sacrifice.
Himavan – Himalaya.
Hiranyagarbha – pregnant with the Golden Egg of the Cosmos.
Homa – ritual worship.

Ikshvaku – Ancestor. A race of the Sun is named after him.
Indra – king of the Devas.
Indradhanush – rainbow.
Ishta devata – personal God.

Jatakarma – caste ritual.
Jambavan – king of bears.
Jambavati – Jambavabn's daughter. Krishna's wife.
Janaki – Janaka's daughter, Sita.
Janardhana – Vishnu.
Janmanakshatra – lunar birth star.

Japam – chant of God's names.
Jata – dreadlocks like rishis wear.
Jaya – victory.
Jaya vijayi bhava! – Be victorious!
Jitendriya – one who has conquered his senses.
Jivatma – embodied soul.

Kaala – time.
Kadamba – a tree.
Kalakuta/Halahala – Poison churned up from the kshirasagara.
Kali yuga – the fourth, and the most evil, of the ages. Not the black Goddess, Kaali.
Kalpa – cosmic tract of time. 1000 yugas.
Kalyana – marriage.
Kalyanamantapa – marriage hall, enclosure.
Kama – God of Love. Also pleasure, enjoyment.
Kamadhenu – first, sacred, cow of wishes.
Kamandalu – brahmana's water-pot.
Kama shastra – sacred arts of loving.
Kanchana – golden.
Kanya – virgin, maiden, young woman.
Kapila – great sage. Vishnu's incarnation.
Karma – action, duty, also the fruit of past deeds.
Karttikeya – Siva's son.
Kavacha – armour.
Kirita – crown.
Kiriti – Arjuna, after he wore the crown ndra gave him.
Kirtana – devotional song.
Kohl – black substance used to line the eyes.
Koyal – cuckoo.
Krita yuga – first of the four ages; the purest, most pristine yuga.
Krodhagraha – chamber of anger.
Krosa – about 2 miles, a fourth of a yojana.
Kshatriya – warrior.
Kshetra – field; also, field of experience, knowledge etc.
Kshirasagara – mythical sea of milk.
Kubera – Lord of treasures. A Deva.

Kula – clan.
Kulaguru – the teacher of a royal family.
Kulapati – head of a clan.
Kundala – earrings, ear-studs.
Kurma – tortoise: Vishnu's second Avatara.
Kushti – wrestling.
Kutila – hut.

Lagna – ascendant, rising sign.
Lakshmi – Goddess of fortune. Vishnu's consort.
Linga – phallus, phallic emblem, Siva's.

Madhurpaka – sweet offering to a guest: usualy, honey and milk.
Maha – great or powerful.
Maharathika – great warrior.
Mahavishnu – second God of the Hindu Trinity. The Preserver.
Mahima/anima – the occult siddhis to grow big and small.
Mahodadi – great sea.
Mahodara – consumption
Malaya – of a mala, a mountain.
Manasa sarovara – holy lake on the Himalaya that Brahma made from his mind.
Mandala – dimension, galaxy.
Mangala – Mars.
Mantapa – pavilion.
Mantra, mantram – sacred incantation.
Manu – ancestor, law-giver.
Margasirsa/Mrigasirsa – an auspicious Hindu lunar month.
Maricha – demon who turned himself into a golden deer in the Ramayana.
Marma – a vulnerable place in the body.
Marut – divine companion of Vayu, the Wind God. There are 49 Mauts.
Mathura – city of the Yadavas.
Matrihatya – matricide.
Matsya – fish: Vishnu's first Avatara.
Matsya yantra – a fish device.
Maya – illusion, cosmic illusion; as different from the Reality of God. Also, sorcery.

Maya – Goddess of illusion.
Mayaa – great demon builder and king.
Mayavi – sorcerer.
Meru/Sumeru – sacred, golden mountain north of the Himalayas, from which the continents are said to have unfurled. Heart of the world.
Mlechcha – alien, untouchable.
Mohini – enchantress: Vishnu as a woman.
Moksha – liberation, salvation.
Mowna – silence.
Mrityu – death.
Mrityunjaya homa – a ritual to keep death away.
Mudra – hand-sign, gesture of occult power.
Muhurta – a small measure of time, esp. an auspicious moment to begin a new enterprise.
Muni – seer, rishi. Silent one, knower of minds.
Musth – elephant's season/rut.

Naga – great serpent; also magical, serpentine beings.
Nakshatra – asterism in lunar Hindu astrology. They are 27 stellar goddesses, wives of the Moon.
Nandana – Indra's garden.
Naracha – fiery missile.
Narada – a great rishi. Brahma's son, born from his mind. A devotee of Vishnu.
Naraka – hell.
Narasimha – manticore incarnation of Vishnu's.
Narayana – the Sleeper on eternity's waters, which are called the Naara. Vishnu.
Nilakanta – blue-throated One: Siva.
Nilgai – a species of deer.
Nirvana – moksha, liberation.
Nishada – untouchable.
Nritya – dance.

OM, Omkara – the primal, holy syllable, which represents Godhead. AUM. Pranava.
Oshadhi – healing herb.

Paapa – sin.
Paasa – noose.
Paativratya – fidelity.
Padadhuli – lit. 'dust from feet'. A spiritual emanation from a holy person or elder's feet.
Padma – lotus.
Padmanabha – lotus-navelled. Vishnu. Brahma is born in the lotus that sprouts from Vishnu's navel.
Padmasana – lotus-posture.
Padya – water for washing the feet.
Panchabhuta – the five elements.
Parabrahman – Brahman. The ultimate, undifferentiated Godhead.
Paramatman – Supreme Soul, God.
Parasurama – brahmana incarnation of Vishnu. Axe-bearer.
Parivrajaka – mendicant, holy man.
Parthiva linga – an earthen phallic symbol.
Parvati – Siva's wife, lit. mountain-daughter.
Pasupati – lord of animals: Siva.
Patala – under-world, nether world.
Pativrata – a devoted wife.
Paurnima/Purnima – full moon.
Payasa – a liquid sweet.
Phalasruti – a description of the fruit, results to be had from listening to or reading a holy text.
Pipal – holy tree.
Pisacha – evil spirit.
Pitama/Pitamaha – grandfather.
Pitr – ancestor. Lit. father.
Pitriloka – realm of the manes.
Pradakshina – circumambulation, in worship, respect.
Pradyumna – Krishna's son.
Prahlada – son of the Asura Hiranyakashyipu, but Prahalada was a great Vishnu bhakta.
Prajapati – a lord of the first races of men.
Prakriti – nature. Ying. Feminine principle.
Pralaya – the Deluge.
Prana – life breath.

Pranava – AUM.
Prayatna – difficult endeavour.
Prayaschitta – penance.
Prayopavesha – fasting for a cause, or a boon.
Preta – a spirit.
Prithvi – the Earth.
Puja/Pooja – ritual worship.
Punnaga – a tree.
Punya – virtue, merit.
Purana – ancient legend, revelation. Also, collections of such legends about the Gods and their lives and deeds.
Puranika/Pauranika – a raconteur, expert on the puranas.
Purohit – priest.
Purusha – the masculine principle. Yang. Also, soul as opposed to the feminine prakriti, or nature.
Purushottama – 'best among men', Vishnu.
Pushkara – lake sacred to Brahma.
Pushpaka vimana – sky chariot. UFO!
Putrakama yagna – sacrifice for the birth of a son.
Putrasneha – attachment/love for one's children.

Raga, raaga – special combination of musical notes.
Raghuvamsa – the clan of Raghu, an ancient king.
Rahu – dragon's head, a demon.
Rajarishi – a king who is a sage.
Rajas – the second guna: active, energetic.
Rajasuya – an imperial sacrifice.
Raksha – protection, amulet of protection.
Rakshasa – demon.
Rakshasi – demoness.
Ratha – chariot.
Rathika – expert charioteer.
Rekha – line of power.
Rik/Rig Veda – the first Veda.
Rishabha – the second note of the scale. Re.
Rishi – sage.
Ritvik – priest.

Rohini – asterism, goddess, the Moon's favourite wife.
Rudra/Siva – also a class of fierce beings associated with Siva.
Rudraksha – holy beads; lit. Siva's tears/eyes.
Rukmini – Krishna's wife.

Sabha – court, hall.
Sachi – Indra's queen.
Sairandhri – flower girl to a queen.
Sakhi – female companion.
Sama – a Veda.
Samadhi – absorption in the Soul/God. Mystical trance.
Sambur – a species of deer.
Samsara – the world of illusion. This life of appearances.
Sanatkumara – one of four original sages, born from Brahma's mind.
Sandhi – conjunction, cusp.
Sandhya – twilight.
Sankara – Siva.
Sannyasa – asceticism, renunciation.
Sannyasi – hermit.
Saptarishi – seven sages, born from Brahma's mind.
Sarabha – great mythical bird.
Saras – lake.
Sarasa – water bird.
Saraswati – Goddess of learning. Brahma's consort.
Sarathy – charioteer.
Saringa – Krishna's Bow.
Sati – Daksha' daughter. Siva's first wife, who immolated herself, and was then born as Parvati.
Sati – when a widowed woman kills herself by sitting on her husband's pyre.
Sattva – the first, pure guna.
Satyabhama – Krishna's wife.
Senapati – general; lit., lord of an army.
Shastra – scripture.
Shimshupa – a tree.
Siddha – a self-realized being.
Siddhi – occult power.

Sirasasana – yogic posture, headstand.
Sishya – pupil, disciple.
Siva – third God of Hindu Trinity. The Destroyer.
Shavasana – corpse-like yogic posture.
Skanda – Siva's son, Karttikeya.
Sloka – sacred verse.
Soma – the Moon God. Also, lunar nectar.
Srarddha – death ceremony.
Sruti – tone, sacred recitation, text.
Sruva – ladle.
Stamba – post, pole.
Sudarshana Chakra – Vishnu's weapon, a blazing disc.
Sudharma – Indra's court in Amravati.
Sudra – fourth Hindu caste, the servitors.
Sukra – Venus, guru to the Asuras.
Sukshma/sthula – Subtle/gross. Incorporeal/corporeal.
Surya – Sun God.
Suryanamaskara – yogic ritual for worshipping the sun at dawn.
Suta – bard, charioteer.
Sutaputra – son of a suta.
Swamini – female of swami, saint.
Swapna – dream.
Swarga – heaven.
Swayamvara – the ceremony at which a princess chooses her own husband.

Taala – rhythm, beat.
Tamas – the third and grossest guna in Nature.
Tandava – Siva's dance of dissolution.
Tapasya – penance, long meditation or austerity.
Tapasvin – one performs tapasya.
Tapovana – grove of worship.
Tarpana – offering of water for the dead.
Tilaka – auspicious mark made on forehead.
Timmingala – mythical whale-eater, possibly giant squid.
Tirtha – holy place of pilgrimage.
Tirtha yatra – pilgrimage.
Treta yuga – the second great age.
Trikalagyani – one who knows the 3 times.

Trimurti – trinity: Brahma, Vishnu and Siva.
Tripathaga – of three paths.
Tripura – three sky cities, built by Mayaa, which Siva brought down with a missile of fire.
Trisula – trident.

Ucchaisravas – horse of the Sun.
Upanishad – holy book, dealing with the Brahman, the formless God.
Usanas – Sukra. A male God, guru to the Asuras, as Brihaspati, Jupiter is to the Devas. Greatest of poets.
Uttara Phalguni – a nakshatram.
Uttarayana – the northern migration of the sun.

Vaastu – land, property, house etc. also, the sacred science of these and building. Ancient Indian feng shui.
Vaastu shanti – rite for peace in a new dwelling.
Vaikunta – Vishnu's celestial city.
Vairagya – detachment, relinquishment.
Vaisya – third Hindu caste; the traders.
Vajra – Indra's thunderbolt.
Valkala – fabric made of tree-bark, worn by hermits.
Vamana – dwarf: Vishnu's fifth Avatara.
Vana – jungle, forest.
Vana devata – forest god.
Vanara – ancient, magical race of monkeys. Lit. dwellers in the vana.
Vanavasa – living in the forest as a renunciate.
Vandana – worship.
Varaha – boar: Vishnu's third incarnation.
Varanasi – city sacred to Siva.
Varsha – continent. Also, rain.
Varuna – God of seas.
Vasantha – Spring.
Vasuki – king of the nagas.
Vayavyastra – wind weapon.
Veda – ancient book of sacred hymns.
Vedanta – lit. the end of the Vedas. Includes the Upanishads. Discourses on the Brahman.
Vedi/vedika – altar.

Vetala/i – hunter, huntress
Vidya – an art.
Vidyadhara – magical being.
Vimana – sky ship.
Vina – Indian stringed instrument, like a lute.
Vina nadam – the sound of a vina.
Viswakarman – divine artisan.
Viswarupa – Cosmic Form.
Vivasat – ancestor: the Sun.
Vrata – vow.
Vrishni – a Yadava tribe, to which Krishna belongs.
Vyuha – battle formation.

Yaama – a measure/hour of the night.
Yadava – Krishna's clan.
Yaga, yagna – sacrifice.
Yagnapashu – sacrificial beast.
Yagnashala – enclosure for a sacrifice.
Yajaka – one who undertakes a yagna.
Yajus, Yajur Veda – a Veda.
Yaksha – a forest spirit.
Yama – God of Death.
Yamala – a tree.
Yamaduta – death's messenger, servitor.
Yantra – occult symbol. A device.
Yatra – journey, often with religious significance.
Yoga – 'union'; union with the Self, with God.
Yogi, yogin – one who is united with his higher Self, with God.
Yogini – female yogi.
Yojana – 8/9 miles approximately.
Yoni – vagina. Vaginal symbol at the base of a linga.
Yuddha – war.
Yuga – an age.
Yuganta/Yugantara – conjunction of two ages; a time of great change.
Yuga sandhi – the cusp between two yugas.
Yuvaraja – crown prince, heir apparent.

Appendix

Book 1. Adi Parva

1 a. Vyasa originally composed the Mahabharata in 24,000 slokas, and the wise call just this number the great Bharata. However, later, the Poet composed another Mahabharata, 600,000 verses long. Of these, 300,000 slokas the Devas know, 150,000 the Pitrs know, the gandharvas know 140,000, and 100,000 are known in the world of men. The present retelling is based on the version of 100,000 verses, but probably amounts roughly to the core of 24,000 slokas.

Vyasa divided the 100,000 slokas into 18 major Parvas.

1. Adi Parva: This is divided into 227 sections, and contains 8,884 slokas.
2. Sabha Parva: This has 78 sections, and 2,507 slokas.
3. Aranyaka Parva: 269 sections, 11,664 verses.
4. Virata Parva: 67 sections, 2,050 slokas.
5. Udyoga Parva: 186 sections, 6,698 slokas.
6. Bheeshma Parva: 117 sections, 5,884 slokas.
7. Drona Parva: 170 sections, 8,909 verses.
8. Karna Parva: 69 sections, 4,964 slokas.
9. Salya Parva: 59 sections, 3,270 slokas.
10. Sauptika Parva: 18 sections, 870 slokas.
11. Stree Parva: 27 sections, 775 slokas.
12. Shanti Parva: 339 sections, 14,732 slokas.
13. Anushasana Parva: 146 sections, 8,000 slokas.

14. Aswamedhika Parva: 103 sections, 3,320 slokas.
15. Asramavasika Parva: 42 sections, 1,506 slokas.
16. Mausala Parva: 8 sections, 320 slokas.
17. Mahaprasthanika Parva: 3 sections, 320 slokas.
18. Swargarohanika Parva: 6 sections, 209 slokas.
   (The totals given by KMG do not add up exactly to 100,000!)

1 b. The Adi Parva. This abridged Mahabharata begins with the latter part of the Sambhava section of the Adi Parva. The Anukramanika, Sangraha, Paushya, Pauloma, and Astika sections, with which the original text actually opens, have been left out; so, also, have several other chapters/sections throughout the book, for the sake of reducing it to a readable length.

2. We begin our story with the story of King Shantanu of the Kurus. The original text begins with a detailed description of the Mahabharata and its parvas, and several other legends: of creation, the birth of the Devas and Asuras, of the nagas, and Garuda and the amrita, various sages, Utanka, Bhrigu, Chyvana and Astika; of a battle between the Devas and the Danavas; of Rishi Kashyapa and the Naga Takshaka; of Shakuntala and King Dushyanta; of a snake sacrifice; the birth of countlesss demons into the world as human kshatriyas and kings; of Nahusha and Yayati; the lineage of Puru, of which family tree the Kurus of Hastinapura were a branch. Until, we come to the time when Shantanu was king. This fascinating preamble is some 200 pages long. These pages are between 525 & 550 words long.

3. The names of Dhritarashtra's son, in the order of their birth are:

Duryodhana, (Yuyutsu*, who was not Gandhari's son, but a Vaishya woman's, and wasn't one of the pot-born hundred), Dusasana, Duhsaha, Duhsala, Jalasandha, Sama, Saha, Vinda, Anuvinda, Durdarsha, Subahu, Dushpradarshana, Durmarshana, Durmukha, Dushkarna, Vivimsati, Vikarna, Sala, Satwa, Sulochana, Chitra, Upachitra, Chitraksha, Charuchitra, Sarasana, Durmada, Durvigaha, Vivitsu, Vikatanana, Urnanabha, Sunabha, Nandaka, Upanandaka, Chitravana, Chitravarman, Suvarman, Durvimochana, Ayobahu, Mahabahu, Chitranga,

Chitrakundala, Bhimavega, Bhimabala, Balaki, Balavardhana, Ugrayudha, Bhima, Karnaka, Karnakaya, Dridayudha, Dridavarman, Dridakshatra, Somakirti, Anudara, Dridasandha, Jarasandha, Satyasandha, Sada, Suvak, Ugrasravas, Ugrasena, Senani, Dushparajaya, Aparajita, Kundasayin, Visalaksha, Duradhara, Dridahasta, Suhasta, Vatavega, Suvarchas, Adityaketu, Vahvashin, Nagadatta, Agrayayin, Kavachin, Krathana, Kunda, Kundadhara, Dhanumudra, Ugra, Bhimaratha, Virabahu, Alolupa, Abhaya, Raudrakarman, Dridaratha, Anadhrishya, Kundalabhedin, Viravi, Dhirgalochana, Pramatha, Pramathi, Dirgharoma, Dirghabahu, Mahabahu, Vyudhoru, Kanakadhvaja, Kundasi and Virajas. Besides, these 100 sons, Dhritarashtra and Gandhari had a daughter, Dussala.

(Some names here—these are from Kisari Mohan Ganguli's full-length prose translation, using both the Bombay and Bengal Sanskrit texts—seem to be repeated. Also, more than one name is shared by other kings and princes who appear during the Great War. It is hard to say if they refer to the same person or persons.)

4. Some of the kings at Draupadi's swayamvara, apart from Dhritarashtra's sons are: Dandadhara, Sahadeva (Jarasandha's son), Jayatsena, Meghasandhi, Virata and his sons Sankha and Uttara, Vardhakshemi, Susharma, Senabindu, Suketu and his sons Sunama and Suvarcha, Suchitra, Sukumara, Vrika, Satyahridi, Suryadhwaja, Rochamana, Nila, Chitrayudha, Agsuman, Chekitana, Sreniman, Samudrasena's son Chandrasena, Vidanda, Dana, Paundraka, Vasudeva, Kalinga, Tamralipta, Pattana, Shalya's sons Rukmangada, Rukmaratha, the Kuru Somadatta and his three sons Bhrui, Bhurisrava and Sala, Sudakshina, Kamboja of the Purus, Brihadbala, Susheana, Sivi son of Usinara, Patcharanihanta, the king of Karusha, Balarama, Krishna, Samba, Charudeshana, Pradyumna, Gada, Akrura, Satyaki, Uddhava, Kritavarman, Prithu, Viprithu, Viduratha, Kanka, Shanku, Gavehsana, Asvaha, Aniruddha, Samika, Sarimejaya, Vatapi, Jhilli, Pindaraka, Usinara, Bhagiratha, Brihadkshatra, Bahlika, Srutayus, Uluka, Kaitava, Chitrangada, Suvangada, Vatsaraja, the king of Kosala, Sishupala, and many more.

5. Janamejaya asks Vaisampayana why Agni wanted to consume the Khandava vana. This is the story that Vaisampayana tells.

Once, in ancient times, there was a king called Swetaki, whose power rivalled Indra's own. On earth, there was none to match his strength, intelligence, and his generosity. Swetaki performed the five great yagnas, and gave munificent gifts to the brahmanas of the world. Indeed, that king's heart was always set upon sacrifices and charity—so much so, that his priests grew weak from performing his ceaseless yagnas, their eyes were afflicted by the smoke issuing constantly from the yagna kunda, and they left.

However, they sent other ritviks to him, so he could complete the sacrfice that he had already begun. Hardly a few days passed, when Swetaki decided to undertake yet another yagna, one that would last a hundred years. But he could find no priest who would conduct the sacrifice for him.

Swetaki, his family, and friends began to assiduously court the brahmanas in his kingdom, with fulsome praise and priceless gifts. Yet, they refused to perform the yagna that king of measureless energy wanted. Now Swetaki lost his temper and cried, 'Brahmanas, if I were a sinner, or lacked reverence for you, you would be justified to refuse to perform my yagna. I wait on you even as a slave, I give you the most generous gifts, and still you refuse to do as I ask. If you persist in this enmity, I shall be forced to seek out other brahmanas who will undertake my sacrifice.'

The wornout brahmanas replied in some annoyance, 'Rajan, your yagnas are interminable. We are exhausted, officiating at your sacrifices, and we beg you not to pester us to sit over this one. We advise you to seek Rudra's help to fulfil the sacrifce you plan. Only he can help you!'

Hearing the censure in the voices of his priests, the king grew angry, and decided that he would seek Rudra's help. He went to Mount Kailasa and began an intense tapasya there. He kept the most severe vratas, mainly living on just fruit and roots, and often never eating at all. For six months, Swetaki stood with his arms raised heavenward, unmoving, even like a tree or a stone column planted in the ground.

Siva appeared before that tiger among kings, in a mass of glory. Gravely, calmly, the God said, 'I am pleased with your tapasya. Ask me for any boon.'

Swetaki prostrated before Siva and replied, 'Most illustrious Lord, whom the three worlds worship, help me complete my yagna. Help me yourself, O God of gods!'

Siva smiled, 'We Gods do not help at sacrifices. Yet, since your have sat in such austere tapasya, I will make an exception for you—but on one condition.'

'Anything, Lord,' said Swetaki.

'King of kings, if for twelve years, observing brahmacharya and perfect dhyana, you pour libations of ghee into a sacred fire, without a moment's interruption, I will do what you ask.'

Swetaki went back to his kingdom, and did as Siva asked. Twelve years later, he returned to Kailasa, and stood before Maheswara again. Siva glowed to see the king. He said, 'I am pleased with your devotion. Yet, only a brahmana may fruitfully assist you at your yagna. In the world, there is such a brahmana, who is my own amsa. His name is Durvasa, and he will help you perform your sacrifice. Go back to your city, and make all the preparations for your great yagna.'

Swetaki did as he was asked, collecting everything needed for the yagna, and then he went back to Rudra. The king said, 'Mahadeva, all is ready for the yagna. I beg you, let me be installed as yajaka tomorrow.'

Rudra summoned Durvasa Muni. He said to the sage, 'Durvasa, this is Swetaki, best of kings. Best of brahmanas, I command you to help him complete his sacrifice.'

Durvasa said to the Lord, 'So be it.'

The sacrifice began at the proper time, and was duly completed. Receiving their bounteous gifts from the king, the brahmanas left, as did the other guests. Now, Swetaki entered his palace again.

However, during the first vow Swetaki kept in Siva's name, Agni Deva had drunk clarified butter, without a moment's interruption, for twelve years. Sated, Agni dare not drink any more ghee from any other yagna. He grew pale, lost his brilliant colour, and did not shine as he did before. The Fire God had no appetite from the excess of those twelve years. He wasted away, and fell sick.

As he felt his energy wane dreadfully, Agni Deva sought Brahma's counsel. He went to Brahmaloka that the worlds worship, and stood weakly before the Creator upon his splendorous throne.

The Fire God said, 'Pitamaha, I drank too much ghee during Swetaki's twelve year vrata to Lord Rudra. I still feel glutted, and cannot imbibe a drop more. Lord, look how I have waned in strength and splendour. Only you can help me regain my natural power and glory.'

Brahma replied, smiling, 'For twelve years you fed on a river of ghee being poured down your throat. Anyone would fall sick after such excess. Do not despair, O Agni, you will regain your former light and strength. The time has come, and you shall feed again, and be well again.'

'How is that, Sire?' Agni Deva asked.

'Do you remember how, once, you consumed the Khandava vana on earth at the behest of the Devas? The forest has grown again, and teems with fell plants, trees, and creatures. When you have consumed all of them, and drunk the fat and blood of every vile species, you will have your old splendour back. Fly, Agni, and devour the Khandava vana, and your sickness will vanish, and you shall be yourself again.'

Agni Deva, also called Hutasana, flew to the Khandava prastha. There he blazed forth in wrath, and, helped by Vayu, the Wind, began to consume the dark forest. The denizens of the jungle did their best to put out Agni's conflagration—hundreds of thousand of elephants fetched water from the rivers, lakes and streams, and sprayed it copiously over the flames. Great hooded serpents, also in thousands, spat water over Agni's fire, from their many mouths. Every creature of the forest joined the effort and soon the fire was extinguished.

Seven times, Agni attempted to consume the Khandava vana, and each time the creatures of the jungle foiled him. Most of all, Indra helped them, sending down lashing showers to quench Agni's fiercest flames. In frustration, and his sickness uncured, Agni flew back to Brahma, and told the Pitamaha what had transpired.

Brahma thought for a moment, then said, 'The ancient ones, Nara and Narayana, have been born into the world to serve a great mission of the Devas, and to purify the earth. Go and seek their help. For, if they are with you, even Indra shall not prevent you from devouring the Khandava vana today. Look: they are in the evil forest today. Agni, fly!'

Thus, the Fire God came to Krishna and Arjuna.

Book 2. Sabha Parva

1. Abhimanyu, scourge of his enemies, had his name because he was fearless and fierce. Arjuna begot him on Subhadra as fire by rubbing a sami twig, during a yagna. When Abhimanyu was born, Yudhishtira gave ten thousand cows and countless gold to worthy brahmanas. Quickly,

the radiant child became a favourite of his uncle Krishna, and the other Pandavas, too.

Krishna himself performed the rituals of infancy, and Abhimanyu grew like the moon waxing during the bright fortnight. He learnt the Vedas, and Arjuna taught him archery and the use of weapons, both mundane and celestial, which comprise four branches and ten divisions.

Exceptionally powerful, he also learnt the art of repelling the astras of enemies. Rapidly, he was Arjuna's equal, and his fleetness of hand at the longbow was exceptional. Arjuna would look at his son and be as glad as Indra when he looked at Arjuna.

Upon his handsome body, Abhimanyu bore every auspicious mark and sign. His shoulders were wide as a bull's, his face was like 'the hood of a snake', and bright as a full moon. He was proud as a lion, and mighty as an elephant in rut when he wielded his bow. His voice was deep as a bass drum or the rumbling of thunderheads.

Yudhishtira's son by Draupadi was called Prativindhya because he could withstand the weapons of an enemy even like the Vindhya mountains.

Bheema's son Sutasoma was born after Bheema performed a thousand yagnas to Soma Deva.

Arjuna's son by Panchali was called Srutakarman because he was born when Arjuna returned from his exile, during which he performed many remarkable feats.

Nakula's son Satanika was named after a Rajarishi of old in the Kuru line.

Sahadeva's son was named Srutasena because he was born under the constellation of Kartikeya, who is the Senapati of the devas.

2. When Gandhari comes to Hastinapura to marry Dhritarashtra, several of her brothers come with her, including Shakuni. There is some sort of altercation with the Kuru hosts, and Bheeshma and others have the Gandhara princes incarcerated. They are given just enough food to keep them alive, and all of them will soon die of starvation.

They decide among themselves to give all their portions of food to just one brother, Shakuni, so he will live, and perhaps take revenge one day on the Kurus.

This is what happens. His brothers die of starvation, Shakuni survives, and returns to his father's kingdom, with his brothers' ashes and bones.

Later, he comes back to Hastinapura and ingratiates himself with Duryodhana, who was not born when the tragedy occurred. But all the while, Shakuni plots revenge, stoking Duryodhana's envy and hatred for the Pandavas at every opportunity.

Most important, when the game of dice takes places between Yudhishtira and Duryodhana, the dice Shakuni uses are made not of ivory but his dead brothers' bones! They have occult powers, and his brothers' spirits influence the way they roll.

Book 3. Vana Parva

1. The 108 names of the Sun are:

Surya, Aryaman, Bhaga, Twashtri, Pusha, Arka, Savitri, Ravi, Gabhastimat, Aja, Kala, Mrityu, Dhatri, Prabhakara, Prithibhi, Apa, Teja, Kha, Vayu, Soma, Brihaspati, Sukra, Budha, Angaraka, Indra, Vivaswat, Diptanshu, Suchi, Sauri, Sanaischara, Brahma, Vishnu, Rudra, Skanda, Vaisrava, Yama, Vaidyutagni, Jatharagni, Aindhna, Tejasampati, Dharmadhwaja, Vedakarttri, Vedanga, Vedavahana, Krita, Treta, Dwapara, Kali, Kala, Kastha, Muhurta, Kshapa, Kshana, Samvatsarakara, Aswattha, Kalachakra, Vibhavasu, Purusha, Saswata, Yogin, Vyaktavyakta, Sanatana, Kaladhyaksha, Prajadhyaksha, Viswakarma, Tamounda, Varuna, Sagara, Ansu, Jimuta, Jivana, Arihan, Bhutasraya, Bhutapati, Srasti, Samvartaka, Vanhi, Sarvadi, Alolupa, Ananta, Kapila, Bhanu, Kamada, Sarvatomukha, Jaya, Visakha, Varada, Manas, Suparna, Bhutadi, Sighraga, Prandharana, Dhanwantari, Dhumaketu, Adideva, Aditisuta, Dwadasatman, Aravindaksha, Pitri, Matri, Pitamaha, Swargadwara, Prajadwara, Mokshadwara, Tripistapa, Dehakarti, Prasanatman, Viswatman, Viswatomukha, Characharatman, Sukshmatman, and Maitreya, the merciful.

(The list in Ganguli's translation contains 112 names! Obviously, some of these names refer to other Gods and heavenly bodies, as well. In some manner, we might suppose, at their root, they are also names of the Sun. Often, Siva and Vishnu share names in the Puranas.)

Yudhishtira's prayer to the Sun is given in some detail, as well:
'You are, O Sun, the eye of the universe, the soul of all corporeal life, the origin of all things, the embodiment of all the punya of the sages.

You are the refuge of the samkhyas, the support of the yogins, a door without bolts, the sanctuary of those that seek moksha. From compassion, you illumine and sustain the earth. Brahmanas that know the Veda adore you with the proper hymns. The rishis worship you. Wanting boons from you, siddhas, charanas, gandharvas, yakshas, guhyakas and nagas follow your blazing chariot through the sky. The thirty-three devas, Upendra, Mahendra, and the Vaimanikas all found grace by worshipping you. Offering you garlands of mandara flowers, the vidyadharas had their desires fulfilled. The guhyas and the seven orders of the Pitrs, human and divine, all adored you before they became superior beings, as did the vasus, maruts, rudras, sadhyas, marichipas, valikhilyas, and the siddhas. Nothing in the seven realms, including Brahma's, is past your understanding. No other being owns your lustre and energy. All light exists in you, indeed you are the lord of light. The five elements dwell in you, as do all intelligence, knowledge, asceticism, and the occult siddhis. Viswakarman fashioned the nave of Vishnu's Sudarshana Chakra using your energy.

'In summer you draw out the moisture from the earth along your searing rays and from all her beings, and return this as rain during the monsoon. Not fire, homes, or warm clothes keep away the cold as your rays do. Your rays light the thirteen mahadwipas of the earth. If you did not rise, the world would be blind and virtue would die. Then, none could pursue dharma, artha, kama, and moksha. Your grace enables the four varnas to perform their dharma.

'Those that know cosmic time, say that you are the beginning and the end of each day of Brahma—every one a thousand yugas. You are the lord of the manus and their sons, of man and the universe, of the manvantaras and their sovereigns. When the time of the apocalypse arrives, your wrath ignites the fire Samvartaka, which consumes the three worlds. The many-hued clouds that then fetch the pralaya, the deluge, are born from your mystic rays, from Airavata and the vajra. Making yourself twelve suns, you again drain the twelve seas.

'You are Indra, Vishnu, Brahma and Prajapati. You are Agni and the subtle mind. You are the Lord and the eternal Brahman. You are Hamsa, Savitri, Bhanu, Ansumalin, and Vrikshapi. You are Vivaswan, Mihira, Pusha, Mitra, and Dharma. Thousand-rayed, you are Aditya, Tapana, Martanda, Arka, Ravi, Surya, Saranya, Divakara, Suptasaspti, Dhumakesin, and Virochana.

'You are swift as thought, the dispeller of darkness, who owns the golden steeds. He that worships you humbly on the sixth or seventh day of the moon receives the grace of the Devi Lakshmi. All your bhaktas are delivered from every danger, sufferings, and sickness.

'Lord of all food, grant me an abundance of food to feed my brahmanas, and my guests, with reverence. I also bow to those that have taken refuge at your feet—Mathra, Arna, Danda, Asani, Kshuva, and the rest. I bow to Kshuva, Maitri, and the other mothers of all beings. Let them deliver me from my predicament.'

(This roughly was Yudhishtira's prayer to Surya Deva.)

THE MAHABHARATA

THE MAHABHARATA
A MODERN RENDERING

Volume II

RAMESH MENON

RUPA

Published by
Rupa Publications India Pvt. Ltd 2004
161-B/4, Gulmohar House,
Yusuf Sarai Community Centre,
New Delhi 110049

Sales centres:
Bengaluru Chennai
Hyderabad Kolkata Mumbai

Copyright © Ramesh Menon 2004

All rights reserved.
No part of this publication may be reproduced, transmitted,
or stored in a retrieval system, in any form or by any means, electronic,
mechanical, photocopying, recording or otherwise, without the prior
permission of the publisher.

ISBN: 978-81-291-1492-1

Seventeenth impression 2025

20 19 18 17

The moral right of the author has been asserted.

Typeset by Mindways Design, New Delhi

Printed in India

This book is sold subject to the condition that it shall not,
by way of trade or otherwise, be lent, resold, hired out, or otherwise
circulated, without the publisher's prior consent, in any form of binding or
cover other than that in which it is published.

Contents

BOOK FIVE: Udyoga Parva   1
The council in Upaplavya   3
A choice for two kshatriyas   10
'Everyone seems to know me'   16
The two armies   20
The messengers   25
The Pandavas' reply   36
A blind king's terror   42
Sanjaya delivers a message   52
'Not land to cover the point of a needle'   59
A second council in Upaplavya   66
Krishna arrives in Hastinapura   74
In Vidura's house   79
In the court of Hastinapura   83
Duryodhana and Krishna   88
'I am not alone'   96
Krishna and Karna   102
The Pandava Senapati   110
The Kaurava Senapati   115
On the banks of Yamuna   118
'Come away to your brothers'   122
For love of his friend   124
Balarama and Rukmi   128
Uluka's embassy   132

BOOK SIX*: Bheeshma Parva   137
Sanjaya's gift   139

Kurukshetra	144
A moment of crisis	149
The Bhagavad Gita	155
The Song of God	161
The Bhagavad Gita	165
The Bhagavad Gita	170
The Song of God	174
The Bhagavad Gita	178
The ghastly war	184
The second day: two krraunchas	189
The third day: the eagle and the crescent	196
The fourth day: Bheema and his son	202
The fifth and sixth days	209
The seventh day: many duels	216
The eighth day: the field of death	223
Duryodhana's despair	230
The ninth day: the terrible patriarch	234
The last night of an age	242
The tenth morning	251
The bed of arrows	256
'I never hated you'	263
BOOK SEVEN: Drona Parva	**269**
Drona, Senapati	271
The eleventh day	275
Susharma	279
Bhagadatta's elephant	282
An ancient and his beast	289
Drona's vow	293
The chakra vyuha	297
Jayadratha's moment	300
Abhimanyu	304
Arjuna's vow	309
Jayadratha's terror	317
Arjuna's dream	323
The three vyuhas	327
Arjuna the magnificent	331

At the rim of the red lotus	336
Deep into the enemy's army	341
The sound of Krishna's conch	347
Terrible Satyaki	352
Yudhishtira's anxiety	355
Bheema arrives	360
Karna and Bheema	365
Satyaki and Bhoorisravas	370
The setting sun	374
The war at night	378
Karna, Kripa and Aswatthama	386
Awesome Karna	389
Ghatotkacha rules the night	397
Indra's Shakti	403
Drona	410
One white lie	416
Recriminations	427
Narayanastra	433
BOOK EIGHT: Karna Parva	**439**
Senapati Karna	441
Many duels	446
The lucid night	449
Shalya	453
The two brothers	457
In Yudhishtira's tent	463
The tastiest drink	467
Karna and Arjuna	471
The mired wheel	476
The sorrowing sun	483
Out under the moon	487
BOOK NINE: Shalya Parva	**491**
Kripa and his sishya	493
Tameless Shalya	497
The last men	502
The Dwaipayana lake	505

Magnificent Duryodhana	509
The two cousins	513
At Samantapanchaka	517
The clarity of Krishna	522
BOOK TEN: Sauptika Parva	**529**
In Hastinapura	531
The white owl's lesson	536
The savage camp	542
Aswatthama's jewel	549
BOOK ELEVEN: Stree Parva	**555**
With Dhritarashtra and Gandhari	557
Gandhari's curse	562
Tarpana for a kshatriya	567
BOOKS TWELVE and THIRTEEN:	
Shanti Parva and Anusasana Parva*	**573**
Yudhishtira's grief	575
A new king in Hastinapura	581
The dying patriarch	585
Bheeshma's wisdom*	589
Dharma	599
The passing of a patriarch	607
BOOK FOURTEEN: Aswamedha Parva	**611**
Krishna says farewell	613
The Aswamedha yagna	616
BOOK FIFTEEN: Asramavasika Parva	**629**
The passing of the elders	631
BOOK SIXTEEN: Mausala Parva	**643**
Ritual at Prabhasa	645
Krishna	653
Arjuna's anguish	655

BOOK SEVENTEEN: Mahaprasthanika Parva   659
The final journey   661

BOOK EIGHTEEN: Swargarohanika Parva   667
The law of heaven   669

Phalasruti   674

Glossary   675

Appendix   689

BOOK FIVE

Udyoga Parva

AUM, I bow down to Narayana, the most exalted Nara, and to the Devi Saraswati, and say *Jaya*!

ONE

The council in Upaplavya

THE MORNING AFTER THE WEDDING, ALL THE KSHATRIYAS GATHERED in Virata's sabha to discuss their other purpose. Being elders Drupada and Virata sat at the head of that council; beside Drupada sat Balarama and Satyaki. Yudhishtira and Krishna sat next to Virata. Draupadi's sons were there, five young lions, with their fathers and uncles: Bheema, Arjuna, Nakula and Sahadeva. Krishna's sons were there, too, Pradyumna and Samba. Abhimanyu sat between Arjuna and Krishna.

The sabha got underway. At first, there was some polite chat, mainly about the wedding. When everyone had taken his place, Krishna rose to speak and silence fell.

The Dark One said, "There is no one here who does not know that perfidy sent the Pandavas into exile; we all know about the game of dice, and how Shakuni cheated Yudhishtira. Yudhishtira lost his kingdom, his wealth, his army, everything he owned, not on the field of battle but at a low game where he never stood any chance of winning. Thirteen years the Pandavas and Draupadi spent in the wilderness like beggars.

"Though Yudhishtira could have crushed Duryodhana in war and taken back what was his, he never did so. Though many of us urged him to take arms against his cousin, and promised him our support. As kings yourselves, you might imagine the ordeal of the Pandavas and their queen in the wilderness. Now their exile is over, and the sons of Pandu are back with us. We have met here today to decide what they should do next.

"For myself, I urged Yudhishtira thirteen years ago to kill the Kauravas, and take the entire Kuru kingdom. Duryodhana and his brothers deserve to die for what they did. Yudhishtira is a man of dharma; not for me would he abandon what he thought was just. Even now, after all that he and his family have endured, this saintly man speaks only of peace. He speaks of dharma still."

Krishna paused, and you could hear the morning breeze murmuring in the trees outside, for the silence in that sabha. He resumed, "We know nothing of what Duryodhana intends. I, for one, feel he will never give anything back to his cousins: that, already, he is preparing for war. But Yudhishtira insists we must ask him formally if he will return half the Kuru kingdom; half only, though to my mind the whole kingdom belongs to the Pandavas, since Pandu conquered most of the lands the Kurus rule today. Yudhishtira does not want war. He does not want bloodshed, but peace.

"I think we should send a messenger to Hastinapura, and ask for half the kingdom. But first, let us hear what the rest of us have to say."

Krishna sat down, unaccustomedly solemn today, and for once, unsmiling. After a moment's pause, Balarama rose. Wearing resonant blue silk, he towered over the sabha. "My brother has spoken impartially. He spoke of Yudhishtira's dharma and, I am happy to note, said little that disparaged Duryodhana."

Krishna had some idea of what was coming. His brother could hardly resist taking a different position from him, if for no other reason than that it was different.

Ponderously, Balarama continued, "Krishna says the Pandavas want only half the Kuru kingdom. Now this is noble of them, and I think Dhritarashtra's sons should be grateful. It is just the course to take to avoid a war. I agree that we should send an honourable messenger to Hastinapura to ask for half the kingdom."

Krishna was a little perplexed; his brother seemed to be endorsing every word he himself had said. Balarama was only warming up. "The messenger should go to Hastinapura with his mission clear in his mind: to pacify Duryodhana. He must greet Bheeshma, Dhritarashtra, Drona, Aswatthama, Vidura and Kripa decorously."

There was some murmuring at this. However, Balarama went on, impervious, "He must speak respectfully to Shakuni and Karna, and be the soul of courtesy to Duryodhana and his brothers. He must submit Yudhishtira's plea humbly in Hastinapura."

By now, there were loud noises of dissent in the sabha, and Krishna glanced at Arjuna with a twinkle in his eye. Balarama held up his hands to silence the protests. He said, "Duryodhana must not be provoked or antagonized, or all hope of peace will be lost! For, let me tell you, Duryodhana was not solely to blame for what happened. What about Yudhishtira's part in the gambling? Should an emperor gamble away everything he owns, his brothers and his wife? There is no excuse for what Yudhishtira did. He was foolish.

"I have heard the Kauravas repeatedly tried to persuade him not to play. But he would not listen to them."

A shocked silence had fallen. No one spoke out of respect for Krishna and for Balarama himself. Balarama mistook the silence for approval, while his brother sat smiling openly now.

Balarama ploughed on. "Yudhishtira is a notoriously bad dice-player. Yet, he must play. There were a hundred players in Hastinapura as bad as himself. Why did he choose to play Shakuni, who is the best player on earth? Yudhishtira is obstinate. Repeatedly, Shakuni beat him, but he would not stop. Again and again, Shakuni asked him if he hadn't lost enough. Yudhishtira would not accept defeat. He played on, until he had lost even himself.

"But how can Duryodhana or Shakuni be blamed if Yudhishtira insisted on losing everything he had to them?" He paused. He was not a natural speaker, and fumbled for words. Yudhishtira had grown tense, but managed a rueful smile from time to time. Most of the sabha realized why Balarama was speaking like this: he had certainly heard a very special version of the game of dice from Duryodhana, whom he still doted on.

Quite oblivious of the effect his words were having, Balarama continued, "And since Duryodhana cannot be blamed for what Yudhishtira brought upon himself, we must be careful that our messenger speaks in a conciliatory manner to the Kauravas. I say we must prevent war at all costs. Our messenger must be a soft-spoken man, a master of diplomacy."

Yudhishtira still said nothing, but the line of his jaw was tight and there was hurt in his eyes. Balarama had not finished, but before he could say any more Satyaki jumped up in rage, "A man's words mirror his heart! There have always been both brave men and cowards in this world, and all men are one or the other. Why, both types are found in the same family. From the same tree, grow branches that are either fruitful or barren. Yet, O Balarama, I am not as upset by what you say as by the silence of these others that let you speak without protest. Your foolish words are like arrows in the Pandavas' hearts, and you still haven't finished!"

Satyaki had a powerful voice, and he was an orator when roused. "I don't see how anyone can think for a moment that Yudhishtira is to blame for what happened in Hastinapura thirteen years ago. And I cannot bear to listen to you accuse this saint among men, as casually as you do. How, my lord, do you say Yudhishtira had any choice in the game of dice? As a kshatriya could he refuse to play? Did they play in Indraprastha, where the game might have been fair? Isn't it clear the game of dice was a plot hatched by Duryodhana and Shakuni?"

Satyaki was shaking, and drew a breath to calm himself. "And now, hasn't Yudhishtira served every last day of his exile, and some more besides, from what I hear? Why should he send a humble messenger or a conciliatory message to that monster? Isn't this the Kuru kingdom we are talking of, most of which Yudhishtira's father conquered, and his brothers much of the rest? Why should Yudhishtira beg for it? Why should he be anxious about annoying Duryodhana?

"Balarama, even if Yudhishtira were in the wrong, there is no need for him to placate Duryodhana; and Yudhishtira is far from being in the wrong. To keep his word he has spent thirteen years in the jungle. You will not find another man like him on this earth; he is as noble as Rama was.

"Since you exonerate Duryodhana so completely, I ask you to consider the message Dhritarashtra's son sent from Hastinapura. 'We have seen Arjuna before the ajnatavasa was over. You must go back into exile for another twelve years.' Do you say, Balarama, this is what a loving cousin does?

"You have a unique picture of what happened in Hastinapura on the day of the gambling: one so far removed from the truth that it is laughable. You never mentioned how Vidura begged Duryodhana to relent, and return the Pandavas' kingdom to them. But your favourite sishya would not! Was it part of Duryodhana's dharma, also, that Draupadi was dragged into the Kuru sabha and Dusasana tried to strip her naked? My lord, there must be some limit to your fatuousness!"

Satyaki turned to Yudhishtira, "Send me as your messenger to Hastinapura. I will speak to that devil in the only language he will understand: the tongue of burning arrows. I will bring him to your feet, Yudhishtira, or I will kill them all, the cowards!"

He paused, as if a more attractive idea struck him. "And if it is war they want, why should we be afraid of them? Who in this world can stand against Arjuna and Krishna, or this Satyaki? Who will face Bheema? When Nakula and Sahadeva take the field, which Kaurava will ride against them? Who will fight Shikhandi and Dhrishtadyumna? How will they contain Gada, Samba and Pradyumna? Which of them will face Abhimanyu?

"Our enemies are rotted soft with the sins mouldering in their hearts. How will they stand against the forces of dharma? We all know Duryodhana. He will never give back the kingdom, and I think gentle Yudhishtira knows this as well as any man here. Why should our emperor, for whom we are all ready to die, demean himself with an obsequious message to a serpent who has always done his best to destroy him and his family?

"No! Yudhishtira should send word to Duryodhana that he must return what no longer belongs to him, at once, or prepare to meet death on the field of battle."

Satyaki sat down with a final glower at Balarama. The sabha burst into loud applause. Yudhishtira smiled gratefully at the young Yadava. Krishna had an inscrutable and, now, rather faraway look in his eyes. The time had come for an elder to speak, and Drupada rose. "What Satyaki says has the ring of truth. Duryodhana will never give back the kingdom without war; most likely, he already prepares for it. Dhritarashtra will stand with his son. Shakuni and Karna are with him. Bheeshma and Drona will be foolish if they take his part, but it is not impossible we find they do.

"I differ with Balarama today. We must not send a humble message to Duryodhana; he must not think we are afraid of him. If there is any hope of his returning the kingdom without war, it is if he fears us. An animal like him does not understand gentleness or dharma, only violence and fear. We must send a messenger to Hastinapura; but he must carry our word in strength, not weakness."

There were noises of approval from the council. Drupada went on, "But, to my mind, sending an ambassador to Hastinapura is not our most pressing concern. In all likelihood, our enemies already prepare themselves for war and so must we. Let word go out to all the kings of the earth who will ally themselves to us. I am an old man, and I have some instinct for history. I sense a horrible war, formed like a foetus, growing in the womb of time, and its birth drawn very near. A war such as this earth has never seen: a war between dharma and adharma, good and evil, for the right to rule the world. Let us not deceive ourselves with foolish hopes, but be well prepared.

"There is an old saying that a kshatriya always agrees to support the man who goes to him first. We must not lose any allies because Duryodhana sent word to them before we did. Yudhishtira, this very day, let your messengers ride to the courts of Shalya, Dhrishtaketu and Jayatsena. Let the loyal Kekaya brothers not feel we have left them out of our deliberations. Let Bhagadatta be told of our plans, and the hundred other kings we know[1]. We must not underestimate Duryodhana. He is so charming he can turn our best friends against us, if we don't make sure they are firmly on our side before he reaches them."

Drupada glanced pointedly at Balarama. Drupada's daughter had been humiliated in Hastinapura; she had been exiled. The Panchala king loved Draupadi more than his life. He would not rest until Duryodhana was dead. "Let me send my family priest as our messenger to Hastinapura. He is a wise and distinguished man, and used to dealing with kings. He will not be cowed by the opulence of Duryodhana's court, or cringe before the Kurus. Tell him what message to carry to Dhritarashtra, Bheeshma, Drona, Duryodhana and the others, and he will deliver it without dishonouring the sender."

Smiling, Krishna rose again. "Drupada speaks wisely, though he speaks on the part of the Pandavas; and that is natural, since his daughter is their wife. I agree with what he says. But I must make one thing clear: the Yadavas are keen to see Yudhishtira's kingdom restored peacefully to him. Strange though it may sound, I see the Pandavas and the

---

1 See Appendix for some of those kings' names.

Kauravas with equal eyes. I have no doubt that Bheeshma and Dhritarashtra, Drona, Kripa and Vidura will listen attentively to Drupada's messenger.

"We came here for Abhimanyu's wedding. We are grateful to Virata that he has honoured us by giving his lovely daughter to our nephew. The wedding is over and it is time we went back to Dwaraka. We hope Drupada's wisdom will prevail upon Duryodhana and his elders, and there will be peace again between the Kuru cousins."

Balarama, who sat crushed by what Satyaki and Drupada had said, breathed a sigh of relief. Unpredictable as ever, Krishna had not turned against his brother in public, whatever he might have felt about his views.

Krishna turned to Yudhishtira, "If Duryodhana doesn't see reason, if he is determined to have war, send for us and we will come to fight for you. We shall see how they face Arjuna and Bheema away from the dice-board!"

On that note, the sabha in Upaplavya concluded. Virata bid farewell to his guests, sending them home with many precious gifts. Krishna and Balarama left with the Yadava army, and went back to Dwaraka, Balarama rather chastened, and Krishna with a growing instinct of the war that plunged ever closer along the maze of time. The Dark One also had a premonition of a piquant choice that would soon confront him in his ocean-city, the prospect of which he quite relished.

Yudhishtira and Virata began to prepare in earnest for war. They sent messengers abroad, to kingdoms far and near, to warn their allies of the impending war and enlist their support. News of this travelled swiftly to Duryodhana, and he, too, sent his own envoys to powerful kings who were his friends.

Soon, armies on the move covered the earth. Some went to the Matsya kingdom to join the Pandavas, while others marched to Hastinapura to be part of Duryodhana's legions. And surely, the greater number went to the Kuru capital; for in those days, Duryodhana was at the height of his influence and power.

TWO

A choice for two kshatriyas

DRUPADA SENT HIS ERUDITE AND EXPERIENCED PRIEST TO THE Kaurava court. This man was a highborn brahmana, and presented himself with dignity before the blind king, Bheeshma, Drona, Vidura and the other Kauravas.

Earlier, before he left the Panchala capital, Drupada had said to him, "You know the gravity of the mission on which I am sending you. You are aware of all the circumstances, the injustice the Pandavas and my child have endured. You know Duryodhana's character. Vidura was the only one in the Kuru sabha who spoke for dharma on the day the Pandavas were banished. But Dhritarashtra paid him no heed.

"Shakuni is a malignant creature; he is the heart of all evil in Hastinapura. Duryodhana and the others have gone too far down the path of darkness to turn back now; there is no point talking to them. Address yourself directly to Dhritarashtra. He is old enough to fear death, and wise enough, at least by his infirmity, to acknowledge his fear. Yet, he dotes on his son, and you might not persuade him. However, though you address the blind king, what you say can influence those wiser than him: Bheeshma, Drona and Kripa. And I am sure the good Vidura will support you.

"If you speak of dharma in Hastinapura, at least you will sow some doubt in the minds of Duryodhana's followers. If you speak of how much their deeds are at variance with the ways of the Kuru sires, the Kaurava may well have to spend some time winning back their hearts. That will be time won for us, and we can strengthen our forces. This is the real purpose of your embassy to Hastinapura, a subtle and vital one. Set out under the Pushyami nakshatra, at the time of day called Jaya."

In Upaplavya, Yudhishtira and Virata called Arjuna. Yudhishtira said, "Krishna hasn't committed himself to our cause. He even said the Kauravas and Pandavas are the same to him, and Balarama seems to be against us. More than anything else, this worries me. I want you to ride to Dwaraka, and ask Krishna for which side he will fight. He is always mysterious, and I will have no peace until I know what he means to do."

Arjuna set out alone for the city in the sea. He had not gone far, when Duryodhana's spies learnt of his mission and word reached the Kaurava. Duryodhana burst in on his uncle, and main advisor, Shakuni.

"Arjuna is on his way to Dwaraka! What shall I do?"

Shakuni's serpent eyes flickered for a moment. He said with rare urgency, "You must reach Dwaraka before Arjuna does, and ask Krishna to support you in the war. Take your swiftest horses, go now!"

Within the hour, Duryodhana swept towards the ocean-city. Meanwhile, Arjuna went along with no doubt in his mind that Krishna would join the Pandavas. How would the love the Blue God bore his cousins allow him to fight for the Kauravas? Arjuna did not hurry, but went in faith and arrived in fabulous Dwaraka only after Duryodhana did.

It was early morning. The city of dreams lay languid on a sea tinted with the colours of a new day. Arjuna took his chariot across the bridge that led into Dwaraka; the city was just beginning to bestir itself. Still rubbing the sleep from their eyes, some Yadavas came out of their homes to worship the sun. They saw Arjuna, shouted his name in surprise, and waved. He arrived in Krishna's palace, and a guard brought him to a waiting room. He saw Duryodhana sat there already, grinning smugly at him.

"Greetings, cousin! Whatever brings you to Dwaraka, young Arjuna? Could it be the same thing I have come for? But I came before you and I will speak to Krishna first."

Arjuna sat as far away from Duryodhana as he could, and said calmly, "What does it matter who came first or last? He who decides all things, for his own reasons, will decide this as well."

"We shall see."

Satyaki came into the room. He seemed agitated, and flashed Arjuna a dark look as if to say, 'Why didn't you come before him?'

He greeted them both perfunctorily, and said, "Krishna is still asleep, but you can come in and wait beside his bed. He will speak to you when he wakes up."

Duryodhana jumped up to follow Satyaki, and Arjuna went after them at his ease. In his chamber, Krishna lay asleep. At the head of his bed stood an exquisite chair carved from dark rosewood. Duryodhana crossed to it and sat down. Arjuna went slowly to the foot of the Dark One's bed, and stood there, his eyes shut and his hands folded to the sleeper. Duryodhana fidgeted in his chair. He looked scornfully at his cousin; Arjuna stood motionless at Krishna's feet, in prayer.

Satyaki had barely left the room, when Krishna opened his eyes, yawned, and saw Arjuna at the foot of his bed.

"Arjuna!" he cried. "When did you come?"

"Just now, my Lord."

Krishna was all smiles. As he rose, there was a cough behind him. He turned to see Duryodhana, sitting stiffly in his chair. The Kaurava said, "Krishna, I came before Arjuna and it is only just that you hear me first."

Krishna said softly, "How nice to see you, Duryodhana. And I am glad to hear you speaking of justice today!" He scratched his cheek thoughtfully. "Yet, when I awoke, it was Arjuna I saw first. Well, I must be fair to both of you, since you have come so far to seek my advice or help, or…what is it you have come for?"

Duryodhana said, "Krishna, we mean to have war between us. There is no point pretending otherwise, since both of us are mustering armies. I have come to ask you, Krishna, to fight for the Kauravas. And I came before he did."

Krishna turned questioningly to Arjuna, who inclined his head to say that he, also, had come for the same reason. Duryodhana went on smoothly, "Krishna, they say you favour neither the Pandavas nor the Kauravas. It is only dharma you join the one that came to you first. The rishis all say you are the greatest man in the world. You must not violate dharma."

Krishna nodded gravely at Duryodhana, and the Kaurava smiled as if he already had what he wanted; and if Krishna joined him, the Pandavas would be finished! He would have won the war before it began. He would not be surprised if Yudhishtira abandoned the thought of fighting and went back into the jungle for another twelve years. Sending him here was a masterstroke of Shakuni's.

Krishna said gently, "Duryodhana, I don't doubt you came before Arjuna; but when I opened my eyes, I saw Arjuna first. To be fair, I cannot turn either of you away. So I will offer you a choice."

Duryodhana began to protest, but now Krishna's tone brooked no argument, "Moreover, Arjuna is younger than you are, Duryodhana, and he must have the first choice."

Again, Duryodhana wanted to speak, and again Krishna would not let him. "Listen to the choice I offer before you protest. I feel you will both be pleased with my offer. Can you agree to trust me? For once the choice is made, it will bind all three of us. I promise it will be fair to both of you: a choice after your own hearts, and neither of you shall be disappointed. Will you trust me?"

Arjuna nodded at once, and, after some hesitation, Duryodhana did as well. "Make your offer, Krishna."

Krishna said, "On one hand, I offer myself, just me mind you, and I will carry no weapons during your war, nor strike a blow regardless of who wins or loses. On the other hand, I offer an aksauhini of Yadava warriors*, and they shall bear arms and fight for one of you. Arjuna, you choose first."

Arjuna did not hesitate. "This is the easiest choice I ever had to make. I choose you, Krishna! Who else do I need in this world, or the next?"

Duryodhana had to restrain himself, so he did not laugh aloud. On one hand, an unarmed Krishna who would not strike a blow, and a formidable legion of Vrishni heroes on the other: if he had the first choice, he would certainly have chosen the Yadava warriors. What could Krishna do if he did not fight? It was a laughable choice, and what was more, the fool of a Pandava had made it for him.

"Krishna, are you sure you will not fight?"

"I swear it, Duryodhana."

"Arjuna has chosen, and I am content," said the Kaurava.

---

* Another variation is that he offers a great force of warlike cowherds, called the Narayanas.

He could not keep the glee out of his eyes, and Krishna smiled to see it. Duryodhana thanked Krishna quickly and hurried away, thinking his war as good as won, since the Pandavas' most dangerous ally would not carry a weapon or fight for them. He was so overjoyed he ran straight to his master Balarama.

"My lord!" cried Duryodhana, kneeling before his old guru.

Balarama raised him up. "Duryodhana, I am glad to see you. Have you heard how I defended your cause at Upaplavya?"

"I have heard, my lord, and I thank you! I have come to tell you how much what you said there has helped me."

"How is that? Krishna and Satyaki are against you."

"Arjuna and I saw Krishna together. He said he would be fair to both of us. He offered us a choice, and asked Arjuna to choose first."

"I told you he favours the Pandavas."

"Oh no, my lord! In this instance, he has been entirely fair. In fact, Arjuna made a foolish choice, and Krishna smiled at me as if to say, 'Now you have what you want, Duryodhana!'"

"What was the choice he offered?"

Duryodhana laughed, "On one hand, himself, and he will bear no arms, nor strike a blow during the war, whatever its outcome. And on the other, a legion of Vrishni warriors who will fight!"

A knowing look had crept into Balarama's eye. He said softly, "And Arjuna chose Krishna?"

Duryodhana cried, "I would have chosen the aksauhini, even if I had chosen first."

"I feared as much," said Balarama with a sigh. "It was no choice he offered you."

But Duryodhana was too excited to notice his master was not enthused. The Kaurava was already saying, "So, will you fight for me, my lord, as part of the Yadava legion? Then the Pandavas' fate will be sealed."

Balarama shook his head. "How can I fight against my brother? I have already told Krishna I will take no part in this war. If you and your cousins do fight, I shall go away on a pilgrimage to pray for all of you. And for Krishna." He sighed again, and put his arm around his pupil's shoulders. Kindly, he said, "Duryodhana, among all my sishyas, you were always my favourite. You are a brave man, born in a noble house.

Fight your war like the proud kshatriya you are. You are a jewel of your line, don't bring shame on yourself."

There was such pity in Balarama's voice, which Duryodhana in his jubilation did not notice. The Kaurava embraced his guru, and strode out to his chariot to ride back to Hastinapura with his wonderful news*. How pleased Shakuni would be! When Duryodhana had gone, Balarama sat very still for a long time, and a tear glistened in his eye. He rose and poured himself a bowl of wine.

There was no doubt now that there would indeed be war, and blood would flow in scarlet streams. It would be Krishna's great yagna, the one he had been born for, and he would cleanse the earth with it. Balarama drained the bowl and set it down.

He whispered, "Oh, my brother, how savage are your ways. Choice! What choice did you offer? You knew both their hearts. The only choice you offered Duryodhana was his death."

---

* Before leaving, he meets Kritavarman, lord of the Bhojas, who promises him an asksauhini.

'Everyone seems to know me'

WHEN DURYODHANA HAD GONE, KRISHNA TURNED TO ARJUNA WITH reproach in his eyes.

"You made such a foolish choice! Didn't you hear what I said, that I would carry no weapon during the war? Did you think the Sudarshana Chakra would be yours to cast at the enemy? I will not strike a blow, Arjuna. You had the first choice, and you chose wrongly. Did you see the delight in Duryodhana's eyes? Ah, what have you done, Pandava?"

Arjuna began to laugh. Krishna cried, "And laughing now? After being so rash."

Arjuna said, "Don't make fun of me, my Lord. I have what I came for, though I came slowly and arrived after my clever cousin. Krishna, I will raze the Kaurava army by myself. But will you be my sarathy? So I can fight in your name, and in the name of dharma, and rid the earth of the evil that chokes her. And if you will, my own name shall become immortal: for they will call you Parthasarathy!"

Krishna's accusing look evaporated. He took Arjuna's hand and said, "I will be your sarathy, Partha. But are you certain you have made the right choice?"

"I know you, Krishna! Where you are, victory shall be. Life is a storm, and you are our only shelter. You have come to the world to till this ancient land, and let kshatriya blood in a sea to renew her. I will be your priest for that ritual, Krishna.

"Spring will be greener, when we have finished our sacrifice. Rainclouds will be darker, and the colours of autumn more resonant. Winter will be purer, and the summer more true because your blue feet walked the earth! My heart knows all this, why do you try to make me think it is otherwise? When Arjuna fights, Krishna's will shall be done through him, not his own. Win or lose, no matter, for posterity will know that Krishna fought on the side of the Pandavas. Not I, or any of my brothers would have it otherwise."

Krishna embraced Arjuna. Then he led him into another room in his palace, where Satyaki was pacing the floor. Krishna said, "Look, Satyaki, at what this Arjuna has done."

Satyaki cried anxiously, "What did he do?"

"He chose to take my hand, even if it meant losing the war."

Satyaki gave a shrill laugh. "I thank God! I was terrified Arjuna would make the wrong choice." A shadow crossed his face. "But Duryodhana has gone to meet Balarama, to ask him to fight on his side. Kritavarman says your brother is already with him."

Krishna said, "My brother will take no part in the war. He did his best to keep me out of it as well. But that would not do, would it?" He smiled, mysteriously as ever. "Balarama isn't happy with his Krishna, but that can be set right later. The vital thing is, he will not fight."

He took a grape from a silver bowl, and chewed thoughtfully on its purple flesh. "It was surely Shakuni that sent his nephew to me in such haste, and he will be overjoyed at the news Duryodhana takes back to him. That is the pity with people like Shakuni: they are satisfied with the skin of the fruit. But in the end, it is Arjuna and his brothers who will taste the flesh. This is always the way of time: that the righteous shall have lasting victory, while evil only appears to win, and for a short while."

He spat some seeds through a window, from the grape he had just eaten. "Anyway, I am thankful I did not have to turn Duryodhana down when he came to me. Now no one can say Krishna was not just. Though heaven knows what I would have done if I had not seen Arjuna standing at the foot of my bed when I awoke, while the Kaurava sat haughtily where I could not see him. I really wonder what I would have done."

Satyaki said quietly, "Shall I tell you what you would have done? You would have told Duryodhana that you had already decided to join the Pandavas. That is what you would have done. I know you, Krishna!"

"Do you really, Satyaki? Everyone seems to know me, these days, better than I do myself. A short while ago, when I questioned the wisdom of the choice he made, Arjuna said to me, 'I know you, Krishna!' Just yesterday, Balarama said the same thing. Shall I tell you what my brother said?

"'I know you, Krishna,' he said to me. 'You will not rest until you see this war fought. You are determined that Duryodhana and Karna must die, and I will not fight against you. I don't much care what happens, either; I don't care who wins or loses, lives or dies. But I feel sorry for Duryodhana. Time will remember him as the man who sent the Pandavas into exile, the kshatriya who cheated at dice. But what about his other qualities, Krishna? His generosity, his charm, his intelligence, his courage: who will say Duryodhana was a respectful pupil, a softhearted and loyal friend? He will be remembered only for one folly, and not for his kindness towards Karna, whom he treats like his own brother. I ask you, would any of the Pandavas have been so generous to a man who is not their own blood, but a sutaputra. Would anyone?'

"He sighed. 'I wish I had gone to Hastinapura to negotiate with Duryodhana; he would never refuse anything I asked him. But that was not what you wanted, was it? I know you, Krishna. Only what you have decided will happen. The others are all your puppets, and they don't even realize it. Once Shakuni twirled loaded ivory dice; now you twirl the dice of fate in your hands, my brother. And they are loaded, too, with the deaths of Duryodhana and Karna, both of whom have never been given a fair chance in this life.'

"He said again, 'I know you, Krishna. I want no part in this war,' and he stalked out."

"Krishna sighed, "My brother is very unhappy, Satyaki. I suppose it is true, what he says, that one fault has eclipsed all Duryodhana's undeniable qualities. It is sad, but then this is a sad world, isn't it? And should Yudhishtira, who is the noblest of men, suffer endlessly for no fault of his? Why should he? Because he is truthful and patient, and because he never leaves the path of dharma? No, he has suffered enough for being righteous. The hour of reckoning has come, now Duryodhana must pay for his sins.

"Shall Bheema not keep his oath, which he swore when Dusasana tried to strip Draupadi in the sabha of Hastinapura? Shan't Draupadi have the revenge for which she has waited thirteen years? They shall! Or dharma has no meaning. But, Satyaki, my brother doesn't really know me. If there was any way at all, I, as much as Yudhishtira, would prevent this war. But I do know Duryodhana. His hatred rules him, and he will not relent. And I fear the war on the crack of the ages must be fought." Softly he added, "As it was always meant to be."

For a moment, he was plunged in some thought too deep to share. Then Krishna smiled brightly again at Arjuna and Satyaki. He put his hands on their shoulders, and said, "But now we must hurry to Upaplavya. As Balarama says, the die is cast, and Yudhishtira waits anxiously for us."

FOUR

The two armies

MADRI'S BROTHER, AND NAKULA AND SAHADEVA'S UNCLE, THE MIGHTY Shalya, heard that the Pandavas' exile was over. He was thinking of visiting them in Upaplavya, when Yudhishtira's messenger arrived in his court.

"My lord Yudhishtira wants you to know there may be war between the Pandavas and the Kauravas. He sends word to ask you to fight for him."

"Tell my nephews I will come at once to Upaplavya."

Shalya set out the next day with one aksauhini. It was some way from his kingdom to the Matsya city, and the going was hard. Duryodhana heard of Shalya's march. He decided he wanted to win the powerful kshatriya to his side, and strike the first blow off the field of battle.

Duryodhana arranged for luxurious camps for Shalya's army along its tedious progress. Wine flowed, the food was fit for kings, the music was sweet and the dancing-girls were seductive. Duryodhana even had his agents lead Shalya some way from his true route, and feted him lavishly in mansions built within Kuru lands. Duryodhana's arrangements quite overwhelmed Shalya, who thought Yudhishtira was his host. Duryodhana had instructed his men not to reveal for whom they worked.

One day, in the fourth or fifth haven, Shalya was awash on his secret host's hospitality, particularly on the heady wine. He said to the servants, "Call your masters who serve my nephew Yudhishtira. I want to thank them."

A little puzzled, the servants bowed and withdrew. Duryodhana himself was waiting in that mansion. The servants came to him and told him what Shalya said. With a smile, the Kaurava walked into his unsuspecting guest's presence.

Duryodhana bowed, and said, "I hear you wanted to see me, my lord."

"Duryodhana! But I thought..."

"I am pleased to be of service to such a great kshatriya."

Shalya got up and embraced him. "You have looked after me and my men with unforgettable affection. I must reward you! Ask me for anything, and it shall be yours."

Duryodhana knelt before Shalya, "My lord, I want just one boon from you: that you fight the war for me."

Having given his word, Shalya could hardly refuse. "I will fight my nephews for you, Duryodhana. But I was on my way to meet Yudhishtira. You go back to Hastinapura, and I will come there after visiting Pandu's sons. You have my word."

Duryodhana said, "I trust a kshatriya will not forget his word?"

"No, Duryodhana, my word is sacred. I will fight on your side."

Duryodhana embraced Shalya. "Then hurry to Upaplavya and meet your nephews. So you can join me quickly in Hastinapura."

And Duryodhana was gone. Shalya was left wondering if he had not been more than a little rash under the influence of the excellent wine with which the Kaurava's men had plied him. He pushed the thought aside, and gave orders for his army to march within the hour to Upaplavya.

Shalya was quite sober when he arrived in that city. When he saw his nephews and they welcomed him so warmly, he regretted having agreed to fight for Duryodhana. He embraced each of them, crying, "My poor children, what an ordeal you have been through. I am so pleased it is over now, and you are back among us. Draupadi, my child, how good to see you again. And just as beautiful as you always were!"

When they sat together in the palace, Yudhishtira said, "Our trials are not yet over, uncle. It seems we must still have war with our cousins."

He saw Shalya flush. Yudhishtira looked at him curiously. Shalya took a deep breath and said, "Yudhishtira, I have promised Duryodhana I will fight the war on his side." He told Yudhishtira how he had been enticed into making that promise.

As he spoke, he saw Yudhishtira's eyes fill. When Shalya finished, and lapsed into a sorry silence, the Pandava said gently, "I understand how it happened, my lord. Duryodhana planned the whole thing. But it pains me that we will have to fight our own uncle in this terrible war."

Red-faced, Shalya mumbled, "Yudhishtira, you know how much I love you. Especially when I think of your exile, I could cut my tongue out for giving my word to Duryodhana. But having given it, I must keep it."

Yudhishtira was thoughtful. Suddenly, he said, "I think I have a way in which we can turn this defeat into a victory. As a kshatriya, you must not break the word you gave Duryodhana. But you must make me also a promise."

"I will do anything except break my word."

"It is not an honourable thing I am going to ask you, but it is something that must be done. When I think of all the enemies ranged against us, I truly fear only one of them: Karna. Only he can kill Arjuna, the rest are no match for my brother. Perhaps Karna is not his equal either, but my heart tells me to beware of him.

"Krishna will be Arjuna's sarathy during the war, and Karna will want a sarathy who is as good as Krishna. We all know you are the finest sarathy on earth, my lord. At some time, Duryodhana will ask you to drive Karna's chariot. I am certain Arjuna and Karna will come face to face on the field, and the duel between them shall decide the outcome of the war. Dharma is with us but, somehow, I fear that against Karna dharma alone won't suffice."

"What would you have me do?"

Now Yudhishtira spoke as if he was another man. He whispered, "Talk to Karna when he rides into battle. Dishearten him! Compare him to Arjuna. Extol my brother to the sky, and make Karna believe he is inferior to him. Fill his heart with doubt. Tell him a sutaputra can never be the equal of a kshatriya and a Devaputra. I know it is base; but I fear the earth shall be lost to us, if Karna fights as he can. His inconfidence is his only weakness, we must take advantage of it."

A grim smile touched Shalya's face. "Perhaps it was a Godsend, after all, the rashness which made me commit myself to Duryodhana. It may be that I shall be a deadlier foe when I am near him. As you say, it is hardly what a kshatriya should do; but when I think of the thirteen years you spent in the wilderness, and of Draupadi's shame, my blood cries out for revenge. Yes, at the critical time, I will whisper doubt and fear into Karna's soul. I bless you, Pandava. Victory shall be yours, and you will rule the earth as you deserve to."

More than a little ashamed, Yudhishtira said, "Of all of them it is only Karna I fear. I am not sure why."

It was as if some part of his mind murmured to him, insistently, that Karna was not what he seemed. Yudhishtira could never quieten the niggling fear he had of that warrior, not though Arjuna had beaten him convincingly outside Virata. When it came to a duel to the death, Yudhishtira was afraid Karna would prove invincible.

Shalya left Upaplavya, and marched to Hastinapura with his legion. Duryodhana welcomed him like a brother.

The first of Yudhishtira's allies to arrive in Upaplavya was Satyaki, with his one aksauhini. Then, Dhrishtaketu, king of the Chedis, came with another aksauhini. Jarasandha's son Jayatsena came from Magadha with a glittering legion, and the five Kekaya brothers, with theirs. Drupada arrived with his army, with the brilliant Shikhandi, whose roots were deep and strange, the fire-born Dhrishtadyumna, and with Draupadi's sons, the young tigers chafing to prove themselves worthy of their fathers in battle. Virata brought one aksauhini, as well, from his capital, and came to Upaplavya with his sons and brothers, and Uttara Kumara who was a celebrated kshatriya now! The Pandya king, and Neela, king of Mahishmati, came with their legions.

Seven oceanic aksauhinis flowed across the earth, a tide of fighting men, and swarmed around Upaplavya; and they were the Pandavas' to command.

But if immense legions came together at Upaplavya, the legions that swelled the ranks of Duryodhana's army in Hastinapura were vaster. Bhagadatta was the first to answer the Kaurava's call, and he brought an aksauhini. Then Shalya arrived with his army, as did Bhoorisravas. Kritavarman came from Dwaraka with the promised Yadava force. Jayadratha of Sindhu, Sudakshina of Kambhoja, Vinda and Anuvinda of Avanti, all brought an aksauhini each. And there was a host of other, lesser kings of the earth, loyal to Duryodhana, who answered his summons to war, and their combined forces amounted to another three aksauhinis.

The Pandava army numbered seven aksauhinis, and Dhritarashtra's son had eleven to call his own. Duryodhana kept his legions on the banks of the Ganga, and employed another army of servants to cater to the soldiers' every need. The Kaurava was lord of the earth. After the years of the Pandavas' exile, his coffers overflowed with their wealth and his own. Duryodhana's army camped outside Hastinapura was well cared for.

FIVE

The messengers

MEANWHILE, THE BRAHMANA FROM DRUPADA'S COURT ARRIVED IN Hastinapura, and was shown into Dhritarashtra's palace. He was an imposing figure, with clear, sage eyes. When Bheeshma, Dhritarashtra and Vidura heard the Pandavas had sent him, they received him with honour. When the brahmana's comfort had been seen to, the blind king called a council to hear what he had come to say.

When all the royal and powerful in Hastinapura filled the Kuru sabha, Dhritarashtra said, "The Pandavas have sent this good brahmana from Drupada's court as their emissary. Let us hear what he has to say."

The brahmana had been well looked after, and perhaps they hoped to hear words of conciliation from him. He rose and a bright and imposing figure he was, that old man. He began, "This is an ancient house in which I am honoured to speak today. My lord, yours is a noble line, and all your ancestors who sat before you on the Kuru throne were men of dharma. Which is why the House of Kuru has lasted so long upon the face of the earth, and its glory did not diminish."

The brahmana looked around him leisurely; he was at his ease.

"Yes, this is an august sabha into which I am privileged to bear my message. You all know, far better than I, the dharma that a kshatriya is sworn to. Dhritarashtra and Pandu are sons of the same father; no one doubts that. The world knows that Pandu conquered most of the present Kuru kingdom. Thus that kingdom belongs equally to the sons of Dhritarashtra and the sons of Pandu."

The brahmana lowered his voice, to make his point better. "The sons of Dhritarashtra have a kingdom to rule today. Why is it the sons of Pandu do not? The kingdom you bequeathed to them, Dhritarashtra, the wilderness that flowered when Yudhishtira sat on his throne in Indraprastha. In this house of dharma, time and again, Dhritarashtra's sons have tried to be rid of their cousins; even to kill them. Force was of no avail and Duryodhana and his uncle Shakuni resorted to deceit.

"They took Yudhishtira's kingdom from him at a game of dice. The world knows that Shakuni is not only a master player, but also a master of cheating. It was not as if the elders of this sabha did not know Shakuni was using loaded dice when he played Yudhishtira. Yet, the Kuru elders sat and watched, as Shakuni took everything Yudhishtira owned from him. Was this the dharma of one of the noblest houses on earth? Was this how Pandu's sons should have been treated in Pandu's brother's court?"

He paused, and a hush had fallen on the council in Hastinapura. From the brahmana's tone, it was abundantly clear the Pandavas were not offering any compromises.

"But the Pandavas do not want revenge for all they have suffered. They only want back what is theirs by right. They want half the Kuru kingdom, which Dhritarashtra himself once gave them. I have come here to ask the Kuru elders to give back what belongs to Yudhishtira, what was to be returned to him once his exile had been served. Yudhishtira is a man of peace. He does not want a war in which kshatriya kind itself will be destroyed.

"But if his kingdom is not returned honourably, he will have no choice left except to fight. Let this august sabha know that the sons of Pandu are far from helpless. Seven aksauhinis have gathered at Upaplavya. If Duryodhana does not put his greed behind him, and relent, there will be a war like the world has never seen. Kshatriya blood will fall upon the earth like crimson rain!

"When Satyaki, Bheema, Nakula, Sahadeva and Yudhishtira take arms against you, how will you resist them? When Indra's son Arjuna, with Krishna as his sarathy, blows at you like a gale of death, how will you contain him? O Bheeshma, Dhritarashtra, Vidura, you are all wise and experienced men. Kuru elders, I have come to ask you to persuade

Duryodhana to relent. Do as I ask, I beg you; or the House of Kuru will be destroyed, and with it, the very race of kings."

Having delivered his message, the brahmana sat down.

Bheeshma responded to him. "I am pleased to hear the Pandavas are well, that Krishna is with them, and they have no wish to leave the path of dharma, though they have an army of seven aksauhinis. Yet you bring a haughty message from my grandsons, Brahmana, and your tongue is sharp.

"However, what you have said is not false, and I honour your words. It is true the Pandavas have suffered as kings of the earth hardly do. They and their queen were forced to live like hermits in the prime of their lives. It is true that they, too, have an equal right to this kingdom of their fathers. And it also true there is no kshatriya in the world like Arjuna, and any army will find it hard to contain him. Yes, all of us here know these things well."

Bheeshma had not finished, when Karna jumped up and cried, "Is there no end to this? We hear the same things repeated in this sabha. Brahmana, you have said nothing new or very wise. Yes, we all know Yudhishtira lost a game of dice to Shakuni, and he gambled away everything he owned, including his freedom. We know that without your telling us, messenger. But now Yudhishtira dares send you here to threaten the Kuru sovereign! Because he has Drupada's support? And old Virata's? Has Yudhishtira lost his wits in the forest, that he thinks he can threaten Duryodhana? Listen to me, Brahmana, Duryodhana will not give Yudhishtira a foot of land out of fear. But if it is for dharma, he will give away his entire kingdom! Have the Pandavas forgotten the real conditions of their exile? That if any of them was seen during the ajnatavasa, they would all go back to the forest for another twelve years. Yudhishtira himself agreed to this condition.

"All of us here, why, the Kuru army saw Arjuna in the Matsya kingdom. Dharma demands the Pandavas live in the jungle for another twelve years. But the noble Duryodhana does not insist they do so. He is prepared to receive them here, and have them live among us as his cousins and dependents.

"It is not Duryodhana, but Yudhishtira who must leave the path he treads, which leads straight to disaster."

Duryodhana smiled to hear his fierce, loyal Karna. The Kaurava nodded to agree with what his friend said, and in appreciation of the manner in which he chose to say it.

Bheeshma was outraged. "Enough! I have heard enough of your brashness in this court, Karna. You speak too loudly for one who fled the field when you faced Arjuna in battle. Six renowned warriors from this sabha, I among them, could not contain Arjuna though he fought alone, with just a boy for his sarathy. Can you imagine what a force he will be with Krishna at his chariot-head? Just as surely as Karna ran for his life a few days ago, Duryodhana and all of us will die, if we are foolish enough to fight a war against the Pandavas.

"It is not only that they are greater kshatriyas than we are, and Bheema and Arjuna are a match for ten Duryodhanas and Karnas. No, eternal dharma is on their side, and Krishna is Arjuna's sarathy! Many of you may be too young to realize what this means. But I have no doubt in my mind that, if we don't give back what is theirs to the sons of Pandu, we will lose everything, our lives as well. Doom is what awaits us, and all kshatriya kind, if we don't stop this careen into madness on which Duryodhana leads us!"

Shaking, livid at Karna, Bheeshma sat down. Now Dhritarashtra said, "I agree with Pitama Bheeshma. He speaks for the good of both the Kauravas and the Pandavas, and from his love for us all. When this good brahmana brings a message of peace, Karna, how dare you speak arrogantly to him? We must not have this war, at any cost, or there will be bloodshed as not the eldest among us can imagine.

"Brahmana, go back to my brother's sons. Tell them I will consider every aspect of this grave and perilous circumstance in which we find ourselves, and I will send Sanjaya shortly to Upaplavya to tell Yudhishtira what we have decided. I must sit in careful consultation with my sabha before we arrive at a conclusion. Tell my son Yudhishtira he will hear from me soon. And I thank you, good Brahmana, for coming here on a mission of peace."

The brahmana bowed, and went back to Upaplavya, where he conveyed all that had transpired in the Kuru sabha to Yudhishtira and his brothers, to Krishna and Drupada, and the Pandavas' other allies. Now began the anxious wait for Sanjaya.

In Hastinapura, the king called for Sanjaya. This courtier, who was also the king's sarathy, was one of the few men alive with whom Dhritarashtra shared any of his true feelings. Since he heard how Arjuna routed the Kurus in the Matsya kingdom, Dhritarashtra had been terrified.

Now he said to Sanjaya, "Old friend, go as my ambassador to the Pandavas. Say I asked after their wellbeing, not only now, but also through their thirteen years of exile. Tell them I was never their enemy, and I am pleased their ordeal is over. I have watched Yudhishtira since the day he first came to Hastinapura, when he was just a boy. I have never known a character so lofty and pure. I doubt the earth has seen many men to equal him in all her ages."

Sanjaya thought his king was on the point of breaking down and crying. Dhritarashtra said, "They are true and honourable, Sanjaya. My nephews are blameless; they walk the way of dharma. Who can hate them except my envious Duryodhana, and that wild and thoughtless Karna of his? The world loves the sons of Pandu, all the Kurus love Yudhishtira."

The king trembled. "Sanjaya, I am alone and afraid. How can my son think he can rob the Pandavas of their kingdom? But, alas, he will not listen to anyone."

The king struggled against a darkness that engulfed him, choking his life. "Duryodhana is so foolish he does not see beyond his own vanity, or realize with whom he is dealing. They are not just his cousins; they are Devaputras! Why, if he wanted to, Arjuna could burn up the earth with his Gandiva. But Duryodhana does not understand this. Bheema could scatter the Kuru army as the wind does a pile of grass. Nakula and Sahadeva are hardly less than Arjuna; they will hunt our men like eagles do sparrows."

Another thought struck the king, and he groaned. "Sanjaya, with Krishna on their side, what army of heaven or earth can withstand the Pandavas? Doesn't Duryodhana know who Krishna is? That he dares fight against him. Ah, my son's heart is as blind as his father's eyes are.

"Duryodhana thinks he has eleven aksauhinis against the Pandavas' seven. His friend Karna assures him that greater numbers will win the war. But I know better, and Bheeshma and Drona know better. Go to Yudhishtira, my good Sanjaya, and tell him his uncle wants peace. Tell Krishna, also, that Dhritarashtra sues abjectly for peace. Tell Krishna to ask Yudhishtira to accept the peace I offer him. Yudhishtira will always listen to what he says. Old friend, this is the most critical mission of your life. God go with you."

And the king gave Sanjaya a message to take to his nephews.

Sanjaya arrived in Upaplavya, and Yudhishtira received him affectionately. When all the kings gathered in the sabha of that city to hear the message Sanjaya brought from Dhritarashtra, Yudhishtira said, "What news of our elders in Hastinapura, Sanjaya? Does our uncle remember us? And our Pitama? Do our cousins think kindly of us? Sanjaya, do you bring good news?"

Sanjaya said solemnly, "In Hastinapura, they do, all, surely remember you, Yudhishtira. My lord Dhritarashtra asks kindly after your welfare, your brothers' and your wife's. Your virtue has not been forgotten, or Arjuna's prowess, and Bheema's strength. Nakula and Sahadeva are not forgotten, either, or their valour."

Yudhishtira said, "Does Duryodhana remember Chitrasena, and how my brother Arjuna rescued him from the gandharva?" Then, suddenly, his eyes were moist. "But, Sanjaya, I know that one good turn is hardly enough to achieve love between our cousins and ourselves. My friend, what effort have I spared to make peace with Duryodhana? How easy it would have been for me to attack Hastinapura, long ago, or to allow Chitrasena to kill my cousin. Alas, Duryodhana will not think of it like that, he is so deranged with greed and envy."

Sanjaya said, "My lord, in the court of Hastinapura there are both good and evil men who surround Duryodhana, and he is our virtual king after the Vaishnava yagna. But Dhritarashtra would be a fool if he were against you. He grieves for you, and he has not forgotten your strength. During all the years of your exile, unknown to you, Dhritarashtra asked constantly after your whereabouts and your wellbeing. He grieved deeply over what happened.

"None of us can say what the future holds. Who would have thought the great Yudhishtira, who performed the Rajasuya yagna, would spend thirteen years in the forest like a rishi? Dhritarashtra says you are a man of perfect dharma. He depends on you to find a solution to the crisis between yourself and your cousins. He prays there will be no war between the sons of Dhritarashtra and the sons of Pandu. The king has conferred with his sabha, and he sends you this message through me. Shall I repeat the words of my king?"

Yudhishtira asked him to, in that crowded court. Sanjaya began, "'I, Dhritarashtra, king of the Kurus, send my greetings to my sons Yudhishtira, Bheema, Arjuna, Nakula and Sahadeva. I greet my dear Krishna, Satyaki, Chekitana, Virata and Drupada. I hope that Drishtadyumna and Draupadi will also hear a message I send through Sanjaya.'"

All those addressed were present, and many more, besides. Sanjaya went on, "'I have known you since you were a boy, Yudhishtira, and I know you will never walk the way of evil. You are the most honest and steadfast man on earth, and you are born into a great house. You know that the noblest thing a man can do is to give up his life for the sake of his kin. Yudhishtira, I implore you, abandon the shameful thought that has entered your heart, of having war with your cousins. If you spill the blood that unites you, that sin will ruin your taintless dharma forever. It will be a stain upon your character that can never be erased. Yudhishtira, it seems you have decided to destroy the very world, as we know it! What matter, then, who wins or loses the war you want to fight?

"I concede that you, your brothers and your allies might well prove stronger than my sons. Even if you succeed, how will you ever have peace of mind after killing your cousins? Just think, my child, however powerful the kshatriyas you have with you may be, the Kuru army is not a force you can trifle with. Bheeshma, Drona, Kripa, Aswatthama, Karna and a host of others, who are like Gods upon the earth, will face you in battle. Blood will flow, as we have not dreamt. Yudhishtira, by your dharma, isn't that a sin?

"What good can come of this dreadful war? Win or lose, it will be the same. There are no victors in such a war, only the vanquished and the dead. The Pandavas have been righteous all these years; they have walked the path of truth unflinchingly. You must not ruin your fame with such a terrible crime. O Krishna, O Drupada, I pray you listen to me and advise Yudhishtira against the calamity he is plotting. I speak not just for the good of the House of Kuru, but of kshatriya kind, why, of the very earth.

"Bheeshma and I both beg you, think only of peace!"

Surprisingly, now Yudhishtira lost his composure. He cried, "This is intolerable! My uncle is accusing me of wanting this war, of the enormous sin of wishing millions dead. Why does he speak as if I need to be persuaded to peace? Our messenger came to Hastinapura to offer peace. If I wanted war, I could have waged it thirteen years ago. The sons of Kunti have always walked the way of dharma, and the world knows this.

"Why does Dhritarashtra accuse me of being a warmonger, when it is to his own son he should look for the cause of the war that will be? Duryodhana's heart is a dark fire; feed a fire, and it wants more and more fuel. Perhaps my mistake was to feed it in the first place, with our exile. Now he wants more, because his greed is insatiable. He wants everything, all that is ours, as well.

"As for my uncle, he is not innocent. Didn't he stand with his son when the Pandavas were exiled? Did he raise his voice to stop the shame Panchali suffered in his sabha? Did Bheeshma, for that matter? No, Dhritarashtra does not care for me or mine, but now he is afraid. He sent us to Varanavrata, and then gave us a wilderness in Khandavaprastha to be our patrimony. He is as guilty as Duryodhana."

None of them had seen Yudhishtira like this before. Bheema and Draupadi had feared he might accept any beggarly terms Dhritarashtra offered, but they saw another Yudhishtira today. This was no longer the infinitely patient Yudhishtira of their exile; and he had not finished what he had to say.

"Our uncle Vidura was the only one who told Duryodhana the truth, that he was wrong. Vidura was the only friend we had, and the Kauravas had. Even on the day of the dice, the most evil day of my life, Vidura warned them of the consequences of what Duryodhana was doing. Did Dhritarashtra listen to him then? Did Drona or Bheeshma?

"When it comes to his son, Dhritarashtra is blind in not only his eyes, but also his spirit. No price is too high for him to pay to secure whatever Duryodhana wants, even if it is the suffering or the kingdom of his brother's sons. And Duryodhana has no thought for dharma. He is wanton and selfish, and his tongue is as vicious as his heart is evil. Does he give the elders of the most ancient sabha on earth the respect they deserve? No, he merely uses them for his convenience; and Dhritarashtra encourages him.

"On the day of the dice, we heard Vidura beg Dhritarashtra to stop the game. But the king only asked, 'Who won?' I will never forget that. I saw the excitement on his face. For once, he did not bother to hide his feelings behind his blind man's mask. At every throw he cried, 'Who won?' and I thought, who is more anxious to have my kingdom, the son or the father?

"At least Duryodhana does not disguise his hatred for us with pretences or sweet words. With him, we know where we stand. But my uncle, whom we revered like our own father, his heart is darker than his son's. Yet, he is a coward and dare not show what he feels. Ah, this king is more devious than Shakuni. He is trying to say I am the one who wants war, and he is for peace! On the day of the gambling, when I saw how Dhritarashtra refused to listen to what Vidura was saying, I knew the end of the House of Kuru was at hand."

His voice full of sorrow, Yudhishtira said, "Who are the law-makers in Hastinapura today? Who are they who wield influence, Sanjaya? Are they men of dharma, or are they the opposite: greedy, villainous men? Duryodhana is the real king in Hastinapura, and we know what he is. Naturally, only those who are close to Duryodhana have real power in his city. And who are these? Shakuni, Dusasana and the sutaputra Karna! It is not hard to imagine the nature of the kingship, and the course it is set on.

"Sanjaya, Yudhishtira may be a man of dharma. He may follow the path of truth to the point where he appears foolish. But Yudhishtira is not entirely a fool. Even before you complete the message he sends, I know what Dhritarashtra wants. He wants to keep the whole kingdom. I say to you, good messenger, go back to Hastinapura and tell your king that Yudhishtira does not want war. But if he isn't given back what is his by right, half the Kuru kingdom, there will be war between the Pandavas and the Kauravas."

Sanjaya said quickly, "My lord, you haven't heard all of the message I bring. The king says to you, 'Man's life is brief, Yudhishtira. Why let it end in shame? Why allow yourself to be remembered as the Kuru who spilt the blood of his own kinsmen? Don't lead your life into this war; that will be the end of you, regardless of whether you win or lose.

"I fear the Kauravas will not give up their kingdom now; they have ruled it for thirteen years in your absence. What does an earthly kingdom count for anyway, Yudhishtira? For a man of dharma like you, it would be better to live on the kindness of the Vrishnis and Andhakas, than fight this war against your own blood. The first course would establish you as the noblest man who ever lived, and assure you immortal fame.

"Yes, this human life is a short one, and full of sin, suffering and sorrow. Dharma is more important than wealth or possessions. Only honour is permanent in this unstable world. The desire for material possessions is what steals a man's judgement from him. A man like you, a seeker after truth, should burn every vestige of desire from his heart. The longing for wealth and power is a shackle on the spirit, an obstacle on the path to salvation. Few men can renounce it. You are one of the few, Yudhishtira, prince of dharma!

"I have heard about all the time you spent in the company of the rishis of the forest. Have you learnt something from them, nephew? Haven't you learnt, as I can tell you being an old man today, that wealth counts for nothing in life? It is only a burden to the soul. Honour and freedom mean everything. Be free of the desire for kingdom and wealth, Yudhishtira. Think of dharma, which is wealth in the next world. Even if you do win the terrible war you plan, what will you achieve? You will have to atone for the sin of having killed your kinsmen. Guilt is all you will gain for yourself. How will you enjoy a kingdom won by spilling your cousins' blood?

"I say to you, again, as one who has lived longer than you have: life is shorter than you think. It is full of grief and sickness, and it ends quickly in death. You may win back your kingdom; you may perform the Aswamedha and the Rajasuya yagnas. But when you die, and that will be all too soon, my son, this dark deed of yours will cover your glory with shame and sin.

"Thirteen years ago, you suffered what you now perceive as an injustice. Why didn't you fight my sons then? Krishna, Balarama, Drupada, the Kekayas and Satyaki were all with you. Your friends and your brothers begged you to declare war. But you would not; you were stubborn and steadfast. Now, suddenly, after thirteen years, you decide to fight. Why, Yudhishtira? You have been patient for so long. If you continue to be patient until you die, the world will remember you as a saint.

"Anger is a demon that cripples the mind. Munis say that a man who swallows his anger comes to peace. What will you get, even if you can kill Bheeshma, Drona, Kripa, Shalya, Duryodhana, his brothers, and Karna? What will your final reward be? This vast earth bounded by the sea? But you will not escape old age and death. Once you have actually killed those you now set out to kill, you will mourn them. You will bitterly regret what you have done. Heed what I say, Yudhishtira my son. One must never betray one's own nature. I know your nature, you are a gentle man.

"My last word to you is, give up your anger. Forget everything that happened, and return to the forest. Spend the rest of your life in quest of nirvana, and win undying fame and joy for yourself. Or else, live with Krishna in Dwaraka; live off the alms of the Vrishnis, they will see to your every need and comfort. You have walked the high road of dharma for so long, why leave it now for the alleyways of sin? I beg you, forget the bloodshed you are planning. Live in peace.'

"So said my King Dhritarashtra to you," said Sanjaya in Upaplavya. Having delivered his message in full, he sat down and was silent, waiting for Yudhishtira's response.

SIX

The Pandavas' reply

A<small>T FIRST, DHRITARASHTRA'S MESSAGE STUNNED THE SABHA OF KINGS</small> in Upaplavya, and no one spoke. For a moment, it even seemed the Pandavas were the ones who wanted war, and a festival of bloodshed; while, the blind king in Hastinapura and his sons were men of dharma, praying for peace. Then the cold evil of the whole thing struck that court.

Bheema jumped up and, his eyes turning crimson, began to pace the floor like a great tiger, growling from time to time. Sahadeva's face was dark, his chest heaved as if his rage would erupt from him in fire. Arjuna, his mouth a grim line, glanced at Krishna. Krishna read his impulse clearly: to stop this negotiation with evil, to ride to Hastinapura and burn its malignant king.

Drupada sat stricken, hardly able to believe what he heard. Draupadi trembled where she sat. For a moment, perfect silence held the sabha. Yudhishtira also was too shocked to speak. He had not dreamt his uncle would go to this insane extent. The Pandava's mind flashed back to all the years when he had obeyed Dhritarashtra implicitly, loved him like a father, trusted him absolutely. Coldness gripped his heart; he felt invisible hands were strangling him.

Then he realized that his brothers and all the kings were waiting for him to answer Dhritarashtra. Panic swept over Pandu's son; for the thing that held him in a vice would not allow him to breathe, let alone speak. At that moment, he turned to Krishna. In the Dark One's eyes he saw complete understanding of what he felt, and a wave of relief flooded him. At Krishna's look, the evil that seized Yudhishtira faltered and released him.

His heart still pounding, but fury driving fear from his body, the Pandava found the courage to speak. In a steady voice, he said warningly, "Sanjaya, you are only a messenger so I will not show you my anger. But from now, be careful what you say in this sabha. Don't forget I am not a brahmana, but a kshatriya. Perhaps, Dhritarashtra believes some of what he accuses me of, before all these, my dearest ones on earth. It is not my place to answer an elder in an open sabha. It is his privilege to believe whatever he wants, and my dharma to keep what I think to myself.

"As for the reply, which my uncle obviously expects from me, I leave that to Krishna. He has heard everything you said. Let him decide if we should desist from war because of the message Dhritarashtra sends," his voice sank, "or whether we should have war just because of his message. Whatever I have done so far has been with Krishna's blessing. Today, I relinquish my will and my future to him. Let him decide what we must do, I will abide by his decision."

Only the Dark One saw, in his clear heart, how more subtle pieces of fate fell in place for a bloody war. He had come to remove a burden of evil from the earth, and his brilliant life had not been a peaceful one. But this final war between the forces of darkness and light would be an unprecedented purification. The war on the brink of the ages would shed more blood than any previous one, and the grateful earth would be lighter by millions of arrogant lives. Then she could cross easily into the age to come, the diminished kali yuga, with no power left upon her that might dominate the coming night.

The true reasons for Krishna's birth into the world at the age's end were as mysterious as life itself, as inscrutable as he was. But he had come to cleanse the earth, and the Kuru war was to be the climax of that ceremony. Knowing how inexorable destiny is, Krishna smiled to himself at these courtly messages and deliberations.

But in the council in Upaplavya, he said, "Sanjaya, I am moved that my cousin relinquishes his very fate to me, the welfare of the Pandavas is my first concern. Yet, I would also like Dhritarashtra's sons to have long lives. Your king's message is strange indeed. It seems to me, he seeks to blame Yudhishtira for Duryodhana's crimes.

"After the game of dice, we all urged Yudhishtira to take back with force what he had been deprived of by low deceit. But he said he was also to blame for what had happened, and the path of dharma led surely through thirteen years of exile. Now the blind one in Hastinapura dares fault him for his rectitude, for his majestic patience. Sanjaya, a thief must be punished. Even a king who takes what is not his, is just a thief. To my mind, Yudhishtira should punish Duryodhana; it is his kshatriya dharma.

"There will be no peace, as long as Duryodhana holds what rightfully belongs to Yudhishtira. I say, not only is Duryodhana a thief, but his father Dhritarashtra is also one. Didn't he encourage his son to take what did not belong to him? Didn't he enjoy the fruits of Duryodhana's sin? Even now Dhritarashtra does not want to give back what is not his to keep: what he gave away, long ago, though it was only a desert then. And Dhritarashtra dares preach peace to Yudhishtira, who is an image of dharma on earth? I would laugh at his temerity, were it not so heartless and so tragic.

"I still say to you, Yudhishtira does not want this war. And neither do I. We do not wish to stain the earth with the blood of eleven aksauhinis, or even to kill Dhritarashtra's sons. Let them return Indraprastha to Yudhishtira, and there will be no war. Only Yudhishtira's selfless nature makes this solution possible. A lesser man would have extracted terrible revenge for the shame he and his brothers, and, most of all, Draupadi suffered in Hastinapura, and for thirteen bitter years of exile. Can Duryodhana even imagine what these lords of the earth endured when they were deprived, in a day, of everything they had?"

This was not the genial Krishna, whom everyone knew and loved; it was another Krishna, grave and fearsome. He spoke softly, slowly, and there was no laughter in him at all. "Yes, return to your king and tell him what I say to you now. Tell every man in that sabha Krishna said each one of them deserves to die for what they did to Panchali on the day of the game of dice. I except no one: not the elders, who sat by and watched what happened without stirring to stop it. All of them, save Vidura, deserve to die. Sanjaya, tell Karna that Arjuna has never forgotten what he said to Draupadi on that day. Tell him my cousin does not sleep at nights because he hears those words murmuring in his head, relentlessly.

"Tell Dusasana, Bheema has not forgotten what he tried to do to the precious Panchali. Remind him of Bheema's oath. Tell Dusasana that Draupadi has not yet tied her hair; she is waiting to wash it in his blood before she does. Tell Duryodhana that, awake and asleep, Bheema sees the thigh on which he dared call Panchali to sit. Ah, Sanjaya, you know everything that happened. I am surprised that you bring this message to us from your king. Go back and tell them Sahadeva has not forgotten the oath he swore to kill Shakuni. Every day he thinks of the smile on Shakuni's face, when he told Yudhishtira across the dice-board, 'You still have Draupadi to wager.'

"Every morning, at his prayers, Nakula renews his oath to kill Uluka. I need say no more. Dhritarashtra has not sent you here because he truly wants peace or to give up his greed, but only because he is afraid. We want peace not because we are afraid, but because we do not want to see kshatriya kind destroyed by the war; because Yudhishtira still cares for the lives not only of his brothers, but of his cousins. That is a great difference, Sanjaya. I know Yudhishtira; he does not want to make widows of the Kauravas' wives. But Duryodhana is full of darkness and obstinacy.

"Go back to your king, and say all this to him. Say I will come myself to Hastinapura, soon, to try to make them see reason. I do not think I will succeed, but I will surely come and try. In the meanwhile, tell Dhritarashtra he did not choose his words wisely when he sent his message through you. He does Yudhishtira an injustice; and if Duryodhana does not relent, this foolish message will be answered with arrows.

"There are two trees in this generation of the Kuru House. One is a sinister tree that grows in Hastinapura, a tree of evil. Its name is Duryodhana. Its trunk is Karna, its branches are Shakuni, its flower is Dusasana, and its deep roots from where it truly springs, is your blind king, with his secretive heart: cowardly, dangerous, cold-blooded Dhritarashtra.

"Look here, at the other Kuru tree, fair and lustrous: a tree of dharma and wisdom called Yudhishtira. Arjuna is its trunk, Bheema its branches, Nakula and Sahadeva are its fruit and flowers." Krishna smiled suddenly, "And I am the root of this tree of light. A storm will sweep the earth, a savage storm of war. Think carefully, Sanjaya, which of these trees shall withstand that storm?

"Go now, you have reply enough from us to take back to your king. Tell him everything we said to you. Say the Pandavas wish fervently for peace, and peace there will be if Yudhishtira's kingdom is returned to him. Otherwise, there will be war, and the war will be the end of the Kauravas."

Sanjaya said sadly, "Yudhishtira, the message I brought was not my own, nor does it express what I feel. I am only my king's voice, when I come as his messenger. I have known you and your brothers since you were boys, and you know how fond I am of you. You must not think harshly of me, and you must not either, Krishna. I have always wished the sons of Pandu well, and I still do. Now give me a message for the king."

Yudhishtira had regained his composure. Gently he said, "I did not mean to hurt you, Sanjaya, but I was stung by my uncle's message. You have always loved us as much as Vidura has, and I am aware of it. You were there on the day of the game of dice, and I know you warned the king against what he did. Good Sanjaya, a golden bowl does not change to a base metal because poison is poured into it.

"As for the message I send back through you: wish them all well in Hastinapura; greet the elders for me, and the others. Then tell Duryodhana I said to him, 'Cousin, the only music in your heart is of your desires. Sometimes you must listen to other sweeter songs. We want peace with you, Duryodhana. You are a great king; give back what is mine, and be a greater king than ever. Either return Indraprastha, or fight me. I pray you will listen to reason, and there may be lasting peace between us.'

"Give this message to my cousin, Sanjaya."

Arjuna did not like the softness of his brother's message. He rose and said in anger, "Indraprastha is like a bondwoman to Duryodhana, while Yudhishtira is her true master. Tell Duryodhana to release our city and our kingdom, or he will face the Pandavas in battle. We have Krishna, Satyaki, Drupada, Drishtadyumna and Shikhandi with us. Duryodhana made my brother sleep on a rough bed for twelve years. In return, we will make him sleep forever on a bloody field. Yudhishtira has kept his anger to himself, these long, hard years. If he unleashes it, his rage will consume Duryodhana and his army as fire does a dry forest in summer.

"Yama wields a mace. Duryodhana will see Bheema wield his mace among the Kaurava host, and I swear my brother's wrath shall not be less than Death's. Let Duryodhana remember the other sons of Pandu. Let him think of Abhimanyu, who is Arjuna's son and Krishna's nephew. Let him think well how he will stop my boy on the field of war. Abhimanyu will blow like a tempest at the Kauravas!"

It was rare, indeed, for the quiet Arjuna to say so much. Obviously, he was moved and they all listened to him in silence, because he was eloquent today.

"Remind Duryodhana we have the indomitable Drupada and Virata with us. Surely, he has not forgotten Shikhandi and Dhrishtadyumna. Tell your king the fire-born Dhrishtadyumna shall be the Senapati of our legions. Tell Duryodhana again that Satyaki is with us. I am certain he has forgotten Satyaki's valour, or he would not even dream of war.

"More than any of these, remind my foolish cousin that Krishna will be my sarathy. Tell him, Sanjaya, that the Pandavas plan a yagna. Krishna will be the priest for our sacrifice, the song of the Gandiva will be the sound of the Vedas, and the havis, the burnt offering, will be the Kaurava host. Take my message back to our cousin."

Arjuna sat down, red-eyed, and Bheema, who stood some way off at the back of the court, cried, "Tell that fool what Arjuna says! Say Bheema says the same thing."

When the sabha was quiet again, Yudhishtira said, "Sanjaya, you see how angry my brothers are. You must persuade Duryodhana to give me back my kingdom. I have no wish to be the occasion for this war. If everything else fails, I will accept just five towns to make peace. Let him give me Indraprastha, Vrikaprastha, Jayanta and Varanavrata. These hold memories for us. The fifth town, why, let it be a village, can be of his choice."

Bheema and Arjuna exchanged a glance at this madness, and Krishna smiled. Yudhishtira went on, "This is my offer to show Duryodhana I do not want war. Let him give me these five towns, and I will be content. How can I want my cousins dead? No, I want peace."

Sanjaya bowed. He left the court in Upaplavya with tears in his eyes, that Yudhishtira should suffer as he did. Anxiety went with that good messenger, as he rode back to Hastinapura.

SEVEN

A blind king's terror

It was late in the evening, when Sanjaya arrived back in Dhritarashtra's palace. He was deeply troubled, and decided to see the king straightaway. But he would deliver the message from Upaplavya only the next day, in court.

Sanjaya said to the guards, "I want to see the king if he is not asleep. Announce me to him."

Dhritarashtra had been waiting for his messenger's return. He took Sanjaya's hand, and made him sit beside him. "What happened, Sanjaya? What did the Pandavas say?"

Sanjaya heaved a sigh. "Yudhishtira prostrates himself before you, and asks after your health." Now he paused, as if hesitating to say what was on his mind.

"Is that all, Sanjaya? I can feel you have more to tell me."

"How I hated being your messenger on this vile mission! I felt at peace in Upaplavya. I felt I was in a pure and unsullied land again. Hastinapura rots at its very soul, and though you are such an intelligent king, you choose to do nothing about it. I have known you for many years, my lord, and this is not the time for me to lie to you, or say only what you want to hear.

"How could you have been so cruel to your brother's sons? And having been so cruel, how can you dream you will escape retribution? Have you lost your reason, Dhritarashtra? You stand at the edge of a precipice and insist you must walk forward, you and your arrogant son. Listen to me, my lord, this is your last chance to turn back from the chasm. Everything you have done so far is adharma. You abandoned wisdom, and encouraged your son to walk an evil path; and now you want to convince the Pandavas to give up the kingdom you yourself gave them. But Yudhishtira says you must return Indraprastha to him, or there will be war."

Dhritarashtra released his messenger's hand. Sanjaya said, "I have travelled a long way, and I am tired. I want to rest now. I will deliver Yudhishtira's message in your sabha tomorrow."

Without waiting for his king's leave, Sanjaya rose and walked out. Dhritarashtra was left alone in the darkness. The blind king knew there would be no escape now. Slowly, he rose and crossed to his bed. He curled up on it, his arms raised above his head, as if to ward off the punishment that must fall on him. Sleep would not come to Dhritarashtra, only visions of nemesis. In terror, he called his guard.

"Send for Vidura, I must see him at once."

Woken from sleep, Vidura came immediately. Dhritarashtra was shaking. The king clasped his brother's hand tightly, and led him to a couch. He said in a voice full of fear, "Sanjaya has come back from Upaplavya. He spoke roughly to me, Vidura, and went away without giving me Yudhishtira's message. But he said the Pandavas will have war with us if their kingdom is not returned. Sanjaya was harsher than I have ever known him to be.

"I cannot sleep Vidura. Stay with me, I am afraid. I have no one except you. You are the only one who loves me as I am, with all my faults. Help me sleep my brother. I must sleep, I must."

Vidura withdrew his hand. He said, "I have heard there are five kinds of men who cannot sleep. A man who lusts after another man's wife, a thief, a man who has lost his wealth, a failure, and a weak man threatened by a strong one. I hope you are none of these men, my lord. You are not a greedy man are you, Dhritarashtra?"

The king repeated dully, "Help me find sleep, Vidura, I must sleep."

Vidura looked at his half-brother pityingly. "It is nothing new, my lord. You haven't been able to sleep for years now. Why, you have not slept since the rishis of Satasringa brought Pandu's sons to Hastinapura. Perhaps you could not sleep even before that, though you told no one of it. I remember the night Duryodhana was born. You called me and said, 'I hear Pandu already has a son. Which of them shall sit on the throne, my boy or his?'

"No, Dhritarashtra, your insomnia and your jealousy are not new. Your heart is full of evil, and your nephews have suffered because of you. The root of the sin that will destroy your own sons lies in you. There is no escaping that. You tell me you cannot sleep; how can someone like you sleep? Yudhishtira loved and honoured you. He obeyed you as if you were his father, and you repaid his love with treachery. And now, you want me to tell you how you can sleep."

Vidura paused. He rose and paced the room while his brother followed his movements with his unseeing face. Taking his time, Vidura came back and said more softly than ever, "Do you want to sleep, my lord? I will tell you the only way you can sleep."

The king grasped his brother's hand again. He whispered, "Tell me, Vidura! You still love me."

"If only you were a wise king, and a master of your greed, my lord! You would know yourself what you should do, just as you would have known what you should not do. Do you want to sleep my brother? Give Yudhishtira's kingdom back to him, and you will sleep like a baby."

Dhritarashtra stiffened, he let go Vidura's hand. His face worked in anguish, then, he said, "Vidura, tell me about a wise man and a foolish one. What are their qualities?"

Vidura sighed. This was an old ploy of his brother's: to skirt round and round an issue, never facing it. Vidura said, "A wise man aspires not for riches or kingdom, but the higher things of life, for the evolution and salvation of his soul. He knows himself. His virtue is steady; he is diligent and hard working, patient and understanding. Not anger, joy, pride or grief can distract him from his purpose. He acts, and always thinks he serves not merely this world, but the next one as well. Desire does not taint what he does. Honest deeds delight him, and he is indifferent to slight or acclaim. He is as serene as a lake along the Ganga."

Vidura waited, and Dhritarashtra whispered, "And the fool?"

"The scriptures are a book he never opens. He is vain, thinking himself the wisest of all, when truly he knows little. The fool must have what he wants, and does not hesitate to use evil means to acquire it, though they destroy him. He is envious and covetous."

Vidura paused again, and his eyes glowed in the dimness of that chamber. Slowly, he continued, "And I will tell you a strange thing about sin, my lord. One man commits a sin, and a hundred others enjoy its brief fruits. But in the end, when the time of reckoning comes, it is only the first man who pays."

Perhaps Vidura still clutched at straws, hoping wildly that he could frighten his brother into giving back the Pandavas their kingdom. "A wise king should be discriminating, or he brings ruin not only upon himself and his family, but the earth. He must know right from wrong. He must constantly strive to walk the way of dharma. It is his daily struggle, from which he shall have no respite. How can he be a master of the world, if he cannot first master himself? A wise king must know who his friends are, and who are his enemies.

"Poison or an arrow will kill one man, but evil counsel will destroy a kingdom. Dharma is the highest good; the supreme peace is forgiveness. In the knowledge of truth lies the only stability and contentment, and joy only in benevolence. It is not hard for a king to be great. He need but refrain from harsh speech, and ignore those who give him evil counsel.

"You know what the mortal sins are. Theft of another man's property, lying with another man's wife and disloyalty to friends. Lust, anger and greed destroy the soul. A wise king always gives sanctuary to those who come to him in need; equally, he avoids those who are of small sense, and near-sighted. He avoids men who procrastinate, men who flatter him and those that are lazy."

Vidura paused. "Would you hear more from me, my lord? Or do my words hurt you?"

Dhritarashtra said, "Don't stop, Vidura. I grow strangely calm listening to you. Your words are like fire, yet they soothe me. Don't stop, go on."

"Five are those that a man must worship: his father, his mother, the fire, his guru and his soul. A king should cling to truth, charity, benevolence, forgiveness and patience, as if for his life. His high birth, his wisdom, restraint, learning, prowess, moderation, gifts and gratitude give glory to a king. The body is a house of nine doors, three pillars and five witnesses. The soul sits over them all.

"The wise king knows there are ten kinds of men, who have no knowledge of what virtue is. The drunk, the inattentive man, the man who raves, the tired man, the angry one, the starving one, the despondent one, the covetous one, the frightened and the lustful one.

"He who does not grieve when calamity strikes him, he who has controlled his senses: he is the best of all men, no other. He who bears no malice to anyone, who does not speak arrogantly, who is forgiving; he is the noblest man.

"The good king does not tax his people more than they can bear. The bee that sips honey never takes so much that he destroys the flower. The gardener plucks flowers, but he does not uproot his plants. A wise man gleans goodness from whomever he can, from every side, and the whole world is his school. He preserves his virtue by honesty, his learning by application, and his beauty by purifying his body. He preserves his high lineage by living a life of faultless character. A well-born man, whose character is loose, can never command respect.

"And a king who suffers from envy, whether it is envy of another's wealth, beauty, power, lineage, joy, fortune or honour, suffers from an incurable disease. A man must know how to behave himself, and the man who is drunk with wealth is more dangerously intoxicated than the one who is drunk with wine. He who is drunk with prosperity will only come to his senses after a fall.

"Dhritarashtra, even as the moon waxes during the bright fortnight so do the calamities of the man who is a servant to his senses. The foolish king wants to subdue his court before subduing himself. He wants to subdue his enemy before his court; only failure and death await him. But the king who first conquers himself shall conquer the earth. For the hardest battle is against oneself, and the finest victory.

"This body is the vehicle, the chariot, the sarathy is the soul within, and the senses are the horses yoked. When the senses are restrained, like horses well trained and obedient, the chariot goes safely and pleasantly through life. But if the horses are not properly broken, and the charioteer is not skilled, you can imagine the fate of the chariot. Lust and greed have plunged many a king into ruin.

"The sages say that for a man to control his own tongue is the hardest thing. Pure speech, full of meaning, can save the very world; just as evil talk can bring doom. They say that a forest cut down with axes can grow again. But the heart wounded with cruel words may never recover. Arrows you can pull out of the flesh, but a word that pierces the heart: who will ever fetch it out? The savage words a man speaks defile him.

The wise man never causes injury by speaking harshly; he knows how grievous this is.

"He whom the Gods want to destroy, they first make foolish. When the light of the intellect is dimmed, evil begins to seem like dharma, and that man's end is near."

Dhritarashtra leaned back. His body swayed as he listened raptly to his brother. Vidura went on, "Bathing in the tirthas and compassion to all beings, these are said to be equal in punya. Many say that living compassion is the greater sacrament. For as long as a man's kindness is extolled in this world, he has glory in heaven.

"The Gods do not protect us with weapons. Those whom they wish success, they bless with intelligence. The intelligent man knows what dharma is; only he who is righteous is wise, for there is no other cleverness in this world. Reciting the Vedas does not save a deceitful man. As fire does gold, a man's birth is tested by his character, his honesty by his conduct and his courage in a time of panic. Poverty tests a man's self-control, and his friends are tested in times of danger and adversity.

"Eight are the paths of dharma: sacrifice, study, asceticism, charity, truth, mercy, forgiveness and contentment. The first four may exist from vanity; the last four are found only in the truly great man. When you act during the day, think of the night, which will surely come. Do nothing by the sun that will rob you of sleep or visit you with nightmares, when darkness falls. Let your youth be as the day; use it to make your old age calm and joyful. Let your whole life be as a bright day, live it so your hereafter is blessed.

"Those dark knots in your heart, Dhritarashtra, undo them with serenity. Quiet your passions; observe true dharma. Look upon both the pleasant and the unpleasant as your own self. Be silent if someone slanders you. It is not the one who is slandered who is destroyed, but the slanderer himself. And if the slanderer has any virtues, they find a home in the man he sought to slander.

"Never fall out with your true friends, O king, though they do not say what you want to hear. Avoid flatterers, they are cunning and base. Do not desert your nobility, and never be arrogant; arrogance is what causes a man to fall. Let anger never master you so you speak harshly. Cruel words are the most terrible weapons. They scorch the very entrails, the bones, and the marrow of men.

"Silence is holier than speech. If you must speak, speak the truth, and speak it agreeably.

"Not just birth makes a noble man, but asceticism, restraint, knowledge, sacrifice, a pure marriage and charity. Men die and are born again; and again, they ripen and wither. Often, they stop their careen through endless time, and ask, 'Who am I, where am I going?' Often grief strikes them along the long way. Joy comes, as well, in its turn, as do all the opposites of life: gain and loss, pleasure and pain, plenitude and penury. The wise man does not grieve when he is unfortunate, nor does he exult when fortune smiles on him. His equanimity is founded in his wisdom, his soul, in God his refuge, and in dharma. He rises above the opposites; he is free.

"Excess kills men: the excess of pride, of speech, in eating, anger and desire.

"Kings, my lord, are meant to have strength of five sorts. Of these, the strength of arms is the least. The king who has good advisors is strong, as is he who has wealth, and a noble birth, which confers the strength of his sires. But the primal strength, by which the rest are acquired, is of the intellect, of the spirit.

"The man for whom the clod of earth and the bar of gold have the same value, who is above joy and sorrow, who is withdrawn from the world, he is the true yogi. If prosperity is a flame, its fuels are seven: intelligence, tranquillity, restraint, purity, sweet speech, and kindness to friends. Pleasure and pain are evanescent, but virtue lasts forever. Birth, death, and the phases of life are transitory, but beyond these is the truth, which never changes or fades. Yoke yourself to that truth; and you shall find peace.

"Kings of awesome power and wealth have ruled this earth, since the eldest days. Which of them escaped death? What wealth, power or enjoyment did they take with them to the next world? Nothing, except their good deeds and their sins; and others enjoyed what once belonged to these kings, while fire consumed their bodies. Not their sons, friends or wives followed them into the next world, only their karma. Men should be careful, most of all, of what they do.

"The rishis have likened life to a river, and the soul, as well. The waters of the river of life are the senses; lust and rage are its crocodiles. Let restraint be the raft on which you cross over the waves of births and rebirths, to the shore of salvation.

"As for the soul's river, virtue is its holy ablution, purifying it; truth is the water of virtue, self-control and relinquishment are its banks, and compassion its currents. The man of dharma purifies himself in this river, washing away his desires; because the atman, the soul, is sacred."

The night was alive with gentle Vidura's wisdom. Visibly moved, Dhritarashtra said in a hush, "Vidura, tell me more of the atman. Tell me how, with this body, I can still meet the Eternal One. Tell me about death."

Vidura said, "I am born a sudra, my lord. My knowledge is limited by my birth, and I may not say more about these profound things. Yet, if you truly want answers, there is someone I can summon who will enlighten you."

"Someone in Hastinapura?"

Vidura laughed softly. "No, my lord, someone from another world. Sanat-sujata, a mukta, a liberated muni."

"You can summon him?"

"With bhakti all things are possible."

Dhritarashtra pursed his lips; he breathed, "Call the holy one; tonight, I would be enlightened."

Vidura sat on the floor in the posture of the lotus. He shut his eyes, and spoke a quiet mantra. In a moment, the room filled with an exceptional light. Dhritarashtra could not see it, but he felt its subtle vibration. The light grew blinding, at its heart a tall figure materialised, whose white hair flowed down to his shoulders, whose eyes were pools of lambency.

Vidura prostrated himself at the apparition's feet. Dhritarashtra was also intensely aware of his presence. The king rose and, helped by Vidura, knelt before Sanat-sujata. The rishi laid his hands on their heads, blessing them. Vidura said, "Swami, Dhritarashtra wanted to know about death, and I could not answer him."

The rishi asked, "What do you want to know, O king?"

"My lord, I have heard that the rishis say there is no death. Yet, even the Devas and Asuras take vows of celibacy to keep death away."

"The wisest ones, who are truly free, say death is only ignorance. They say that where there is no ignorance, there is no death either. Death is not a beast that devours men. If a man's heart is clear, death will not approach him. If desire and anger do not sway a man, he does not die. Death is a form of ignorance. If a man kills desire at its first stirring, he need not fear death. Death is a materialisation of the wrath and greed that possess an embodied soul. The man of wisdom will not meet this demon.

"Even as the body is destroyed when it dies, death itself is destroyed when faced with the light of knowledge."

Dhritarashtra said, "What is the aim of tapasya, of mowna? How does one attain to mowna?"

"With quietude you reach the Brahman that is beyond language and its trammels. True mowna is the quiescence not only of speech, but of the senses and the mind. It is the consciousness of the Absolute. *AUM* is the Brahman: the gross, the subtle and the original. Mowna is when a soul gradually merges the gross in the subtle; and the subtle in the causal. And beyond the Bindu of the *AUM*, is the immaculate Brahman, eternal, unchanging.

"Brahman is the ultimate attainment, after which there is no other. Brahman cannot be attained in a day, or a life, but through many, many lifetimes. Brahman cannot be attained without brahmacharya. By continence, a man becomes like a child, pure and free of passion. He triumphs over death. By good deeds, men attain only to the transient realms of Devaloka. When the punya of his deeds is exhausted, the man is born again into the mortal world. But the punya of ultimate knowledge is imperishable; with this, a man attains the everlasting Brahman."

Dhritarashtra said, "They say that a wise man finds the Brahman in his own soul. What is the Brahman like, what is its colour, its form?"

"Not on earth, or in the sky, not in the waters of the ocean is there anything like it. Not among the fathomless stars, in lightning, the clouds, or rain: nowhere is its form seen. You cannot see it in the akasa, not among the Devas, not in the sun or the moon. Not in the Rik, among the Yajus, the Atharvas or, even, in the taintless Sama will you find it.

"It cannot be fathomed, or known with the intellect. Why, even the cosmic Destroyer is destroyed by it, after the dissolution. It is smaller than atoms, invisible. It is everywhere, and the basis of everything that exists. It is changeless, actless; yet, it is also all this visible, tangible universe. It is vast; it is full of bliss. All beings spring from it, and to it they return. It is not twain, yet it is manifest as the universe. It is immanent, pervasive. Those who know say it never changes, but only the languages that describe it.

"Ah, those who know That in which the universe is established, they are blessed indeed!" said Sanat-sujata. With a smile, the sage added, "So renounce your greed, O king. Follow the straight path of dharma, and knowledge and freedom shall be yours."

His palm raised in blessing over the brothers, the enlightened one vanished from Dhritarashtra's chamber.

EIGHT

Sanjaya delivers a message

The next morning, the Kauravas filed into the court of Hastinapura. Bheeshma and Dhritarashtra entered first and sat on their thrones. The blind king was haggard after the long night, already defeated before the first arrow was loosed or the first blade drew blood. When all the others were in their places, Sanjaya came in. The sabha settled quickly, and Dhritarashtra asked, "Sanjaya, what message do you bring from my nephews in Upaplavya?"

Sanjaya rose, "Yudhishtira sends his greetings to you all. Listen to what transpired in the sabha into which I took your message. Hear what Krishna said, and what Yudhishtira and Arjuna said after him."

Sanjaya had been sent as a messenger also for a special gift he had: his prodigious memory. He launched into a vivid description of the council in Upaplavya, and he remembered details that no other man would have. He described the clothes the different kings wore, and, even, who was grim or who smiled, and when. Not a word had he forgotten, not an inflection of tone or a flicker of expression in a speaker's eye. The sabha in Hastinapura sat riveted while he spoke.

Sanjaya was fierce, when he came to what Arjuna said. "'Tell Dhritarashtra's son if he does not give up half the kingdom, he will see Bheema hunt his soldiers like Yama. Tell the foul-tongued sutaputra that he will die, when I meet him again on the battlefield. Tell him I cannot wait to cut his arrogant life short. Tell Duryodhana he will repent when he sees Satyaki take the field against him. Tell him Krishna will be my sarathy, and no Kaurava will escape death.'"

Sanjaya concluded, "And Yudhishtira said finally that if Duryodhana will not give him back his kingdom, let him give just five towns. Let him return Indraprastha, Vrikaprastha, Jayanta, Varanavrata and any other village of his choice, and Yudhishtira will disband his legions."

Having finished, Sanjaya sat down amidst silence in that sabha. No one spoke for a time, then Bheeshma said in his deep, slow way, "Ah Duryodhana, are you intent on courting death? Don't you see whom you have chosen to be your enemies? Arjuna and Krishna. The rishis all say they are Nara Narayana of old come to wash the earth in blood. They are invincible, my son. Listen to an old man; give up your obstinacy. Give back their kingdom to the Pandavas, and be grateful that they won't seek revenge."

Duryodhana sat stiffly in his place, not a muscle moving. Bheeshma looked at his favourite grandson, with untold tenderness and anxiety in his old eyes. And he spoke not because he thought there was any hope of Duryodhana doing as he asked, but he felt it was his sacred duty to say, again, what was obvious.

The Pitama resumed, "They have dharma with them, and if that is not enough, they have Krishna as well. Duryodhana, you will decide if there will be war. All the rest, Dhritarashtra, Dusasana, Karna, even Shakuni, will do as you say. I beg you, my child, even now it is not too late: return their kingdom to your cousins and let us have peace."

Duryodhana was impassive. In despair, his grandsire cried, "Do you hope the vile, scheming Shakuni will win the war for you? Or your brother Dusasana, steeped in every vice known to man? No, you rely on Karna. How blind can you be? You hope a sutaputra can win a war against the noblest kshatriyas in the world. Have you forgotten he was cursed by his own guru for lying to him? How will he turn away Bhargava's curse? And the brahmana on the seashore, whose cow he killed, cursed him. Your friend has already set himself on a course to death. Must you follow him, Duryodhana?

"Or haven't you heard that he has given away his kavacha and kundala to Indra? Without them, how will he stand before Indra's son in battle? Duryodhana, as I love you, listen to me. You cannot win this war."

Karna sprang to feet and cried, "Bheeshma, you cannot speak to me like this whenever you care to! Have I been disloyal to Duryodhana that you rebuke me? I may not be born one, but I am more of a kshatriya than most of you. My birth is not as important as my loyalty. And for you, Duryodhana, I will kill all the Pandavas by myself!"

Bheeshma would not deign to address Karna directly. He turned to Dhritarashtra and said, "For so many years, I have been listening to this fool bragging about how he will kill the Pandavas single-handedly. Yet, so far, it has only been great words, never deeds. Dhritarashtra, the sutaputra is not a sixteenth part the archer Arjuna is, and I lay the blame squarely on him for the plight we are in today. He incited Duryodhana to humiliate the Pandavas in this sabha.

"Duryodhana, depending on this braggart, you made enemies of your mighty cousins. What could Karna do against the gandharva in Dwaitavana? What did he do against Arjuna in Virata, even when we were all with him? Both times he was routed, and he fled. But I see reproach in your eyes because I censure your friend. I feel so sorry for you, my child, but I fear you are past my help."

Before his Pitama had finished, Duryodhana insultingly turned his face away from the patriarch; and that was always his way with anyone who said a word against Karna. The love between Duryodhana and Karna was not something that Bheeshma or anyone in Hastinapura understood. It was a thing of the soul, much like the love between Krishna and Arjuna: a sacred covenant, a relationship that transcended every other.

Lately, there was a lot of ill will against Karna in the Kuru sabha. The elders felt the suta's son wielded too much influence in the kingdom. Bheeshma was the only one who spoke out openly against him. Duryodhana drifted farther and farther from his grandfather, assuming a remote, barely civil formality towards the old man who loved him so dearly.

Except for Duryodhana and his brothers, hardly anyone in Hastinapura cared for Karna. Dhritarashtra was careful to keep on his right side, but only because the king did not want to estrange his son. As for the rest, they disliked the brash sutaputra, and resented the power he had. But they dare not cross him, for fear; and if anyone slighted Karna, it seemed that Duryodhana's love for him only grew. He was as protective as a mother. Duryodhana felt the anguish Karna endured set him not only apart from, but also above the rest of mankind. He saw Karna as a suffering God. If there was anyone Duryodhana loved as dearly as he did himself, it was his brilliant, tormented friend.

An abrasive silence or an eyebrow sardonically arched were weapons the Kaurava used to effect. Now, with a sneer, he turned his face away from Bheeshma, as if everything the patriarch said was nonsense.

Drona rose to speak. "What Bheeshma says is true. The messages Krishna and Arjuna sent are not empty threats. If they say they will kill the Kauravas, they do not speak for the pleasure of hearing themselves brag. Arjuna is my sishya, I know what an archer he is. Then he was only a boy; now he is a man, and a master of the devastras. He has Siva's Paasupata. When I am told there is no kshatriya on earth like him, I believe what I hear.

"The first lesson any warrior must learn is never to underestimate his enemy; there is nothing more foolish. Yet, this sabha is doing just that. Duryodhana, Karna, you are like children that have no notion of who they are going to war against. Make peace with the Pandavas. If there is a war, I, Drona, tell you that you will not win."

Dhritarashtra grew more restive than ever. When nobody else spoke after Drona sat down, the king turned his face towards Sanjaya and said, "Sanjaya, tell us about the army the Pandavas have gathered in Upaplavya."

Sanjaya rose again, and he let his mind wander back to the force he had seen outside that city. Suddenly, with eerie intensity, he saw multitudinous legions around him. He felt he was back in Upaplavya. He heard the awesome noise of a million voices speaking at once. He saw the glitter of weapons, the gleam of mail. He smelt the living bodies of a million fierce men. He saw the grim faces of the kshatriyas who led them. All this swept over Sanjaya in a moment, and as if fate laid its hand on him, his eyes rolled up and he fainted.

A commotion broke out. Some courtiers sprang forward to revive the sarathy, and the king asked in alarm, "What happened? Why doesn't Sanjaya speak?"

Bheeshma said dryly, "He swooned at the memory of the Pandava army."

Dhritarashtra's hands were cold again. Sanjaya was revived with sharp salts, and as he began to describe the army at Upaplavya in a low, clear voice, Dhritarashtra's terror grew.

"My lord, besides the Pandavas and Satyaki, Virata will fight against us; and with them, Drupada, Shikhandi and Dhrishtadyumna, Yuyudhana, Jarasandha's son Jayatsena, Dhrishtaketu, the Chedi king, and many others as unconquerable. Their armies teem with kshatriyas whose names I do not know. But I saw them, and they are hardly less formidable than their kings."

Dhritarashtra whispered, "Listening to you, Sanjaya, I fear for my sons' lives. And more than any of the kshatriyas you have named, I fear Bheema! I see him at nights, red-eyed and terrible. I hear the oath he swore that he would kill Duryodhana and Dusasana. I feel certain that, truly like Yama himself, he will raze our army and kill all my sons. Ah, Duryodhana, I see you with your thigh broken, dying slowly, in agony. Dusasana, my child, I see you with your chest torn open by Vayu's son, and his lips stained with your blood.

"I see Bheema sweep over our legions like a scarlet Ganga in spate. I am blind, I know, but I see all this with ghastly clarity, even as sighted men see the world. Listen to me, my sons, I have never spoken to you like this before. I don't sleep at night, but lie awake watching these visions of death. I see Yudhishtira's angry eyes turned to glare at my children. They are terrible eyes, Duryodhana, and I cry out when he looks at me.

"Oh, my friends, I am helpless; my son will not listen to me. He has sinned, but it is not too late to turn back from his sin. If only he would relent."

Unexpectedly Sanjaya cried, "My lord, it is you who are to blame not Duryodhana! The sin is yours. For years, Vidura tried to bring you back to dharma. Tirelessly, he sought to show you the way to light. But you were greedy and envious, my lord, you would never listen to him.

"I was in this sabha when the game of dice was played. How much Vidura begged you to stop it. Did you listen? Your ears were keened to the roll of the ivory dice, and you would turn to me to whisper, 'Who won? Who won?' My lord, a father is the best friend a man can have in this life. You have denied your son the fortune of having a wise father's advice and firmness, when he most needed it. You were not a wise father, but a selfish one. You thought only of your own material benefit, not of the harm you were doing to your son's character. Dhritarashtra, you led your boy to his ruin.

"You were the king. A word from you would have been enough: you could have stopped the game of dice. Your brother Pandu served you loyally when he was alive. His conquests make up most of this kingdom. But when his sons came home to Hastinapura, you did not treat them justly. This kingdom and this city rightfully belong to Yudhishtira, but you gave him a desert. And he made it bloom. Then your son took that away from his cousin, as well, with deceit.

"When the Pandavas were banished, you felt no grief for them, Dhritarashtra, but only fear because they left swearing revenge. Do you remember you called me that day, my lord?"

The king had nothing to say. Sanjaya went on, relentlessly, "And I say to you today, O king, the sons of Pandu shall fulfil their oaths. They will kill your sons. And your princes will die not so much for their sins, as for yours, Dhritarashtra; that you did not stop them when you should have, but, instead, abetted their folly from your own avarice.

"At least Duryodhana has those that love him in this world; for his sake, eleven aksauhinis have come to Hastinapura. All these kshatriyas are ready to die for him. They have not come for you, Dhritarashtra, or for the Kurus, but for your son. This prince would have been an emperor in his own right, except that you led him down an evil path. Once I thought you were more clear-sighted than men that saw the world with their eyes; you have proved you are truly blind.

"My lord, your sons will die on the battlefield, but they will not die cowards. They will die such deaths that the world will remember them. All their sins shall be forgiven, and they will find the heaven meant for kshatriyas killed in battle.

"Duryodhana's selfishness will be forgiven, because he will die a resplendent death at Bheema's hands. And this Karna, this most generous man on earth, will die for his Duryodhana. What greater gift is there than to give one's life for one's friend? He will be remembered as the noblest of men. But you, my poor lord, will find no such release. You will outlive all your sons in dreadful grief. You will live to see ruin, to gaze into the face of doom. And then you will curse yourself that you did not relent earlier, and prevent this war. You will not escape retribution, Dhritarashtra, there is no salvation for you."

Dhritarashtra had turned pale on his throne. His lips worked feverishly, and he could not hide the terror he felt. Now and then, a moan would escape him, as he sat huddled within his blindness; but he was so transparent and pathetic today.

NINE

'Not land to cover the point of a needle'

Duryodhana saw his father terrified, and he rose in sorrow. "Why are you so afraid, my lord? The news Sanjaya brings about the Pandava army is nothing new to me. I am aware they have a vast and powerful host. But our cousins have been in exile for thirteen years, while we have prepared for this war. Father, do you think me a fool that I am not aware of what we are going into?

"No, I remember my own anxiety of thirteen years ago, when dark Krishna, Satyaki, Drupada and Dhrishtadyumna went to meet Yudhishtira in the Kamyaka vana. They had mustered an army for him. They saw the Pandavas wearing deerskin and tree-bark, and they told Yudhishtira to march on Hastinapura straightaway, and take back his kingdom. If he had listened to them, we would have been finished. For then, all the kings of the earth were against us; only this loyal Karna was on my side.

"I heard an army had gathered near the Kamyaka aranya, and I was afraid. I went to Acharya Drona and I said, 'What will we do if they attack us now?'

"Drona said, 'Don't be afraid, Duryodhana. Any one of us, Bheeshma, Kripa or I, can defeat them. When he took the princesses of Kasi, your Pitama vanquished an army by himself. With Bheeshma on your side, you need never fear.'

"My lord, even when the Pandavas had all the kings of Bharatavarsha with them and we had none, Drona said we would beat them. Today I have more friends than they do, and I have nurtured my friendships. Our cousins have been in the wilderness for thirteen years, and they have been all but forgotten. They are like some dim memory now, their power barely real any more. If they have seven aksauhinis, I command eleven. Moreover, most of those who will fight for them are their own blood: which is seldom any guarantee for having the best warriors."

He paused, and his lip curled. "As for Bheema, father, I am the better mace-fighter. I have spent hours, every day, perfecting my skills. Even when we were students, our guru Balarama would always say, 'Duryodhana is my best sishya. He is my equal, none of you others can touch him.' Bheema knows I am better than he is, and so do Krishna and Arjuna.

"As with everything else, my cousin is a crude mace-fighter. He has brute strength but few finer skills. I long to meet him on the field! I have loathed Bheema since we were boys. He always thought he and his brothers were superior to everyone else. I look forward to the moment when we come face to face, and I smash his soft head like a melon. After Bheema is dead, even I will be able to kill Arjuna. The Pandavas' spirit will break, and we will rip through them."

As he spoke, Duryodhana paced the sabha like a lion in his prime. Honour and morale were at stake here; this was as crucial a moment as the hour of battle. It was here, in this sabha, that he would win the hearts of his own kshatriyas; here that he would exorcise the spectre of fear that Sanjaya, Drona and Bheeshma had raised among the Kurus. Hearing his son so assured, Dhritarashtra stopped trembling.

Duryodhana had not finished. "And then how can you be afraid, when you think of our own army? Only a coward would predict defeat for us after he has seen my legions."

The Kaurava's voice rose, "My lord, Bheeshma is with me! Bheeshma of the awesome vow, Bheeshma of the boon that death will come to him only when he summons it. Is Bheeshma just any man, that these Pandavas dare challenge us? He, by himself, can raze our cousins and their army. But we also have Drona! Was Drona born like an ordinary man? He is the Acharya of us all, and he fights on our side. No sishya is greater than his guru, not even Arjuna.

"Shall Aswatthama, born by Siva's grace, whom many say is an amsa of the Lord, be conquered in battle? Can Acharya Kripa be defeated? No! These men could oppose the legions of Devaloka. Yet, even having such heroes with us, we seek to set fear among ourselves. I say to you, the Pandava army will not defeat us; but we will vanquish ourselves, before battle is even joined."

Briefly, his face was dark. "Then, I have Karna with me. I know there are those in this sabha who differ, but Parasurama Bhargava said that Karna is his equal. My Pitama says Karna is not powerful, any more, because Indra came to him like a beggar and Karna gave the Deva his kavacha and kundala. But what Bheeshma does not know is that Karna had something from Indra in return; something he would not have taken, except for his love for me. Karna has Indra's Shakti."

A murmur arose in the sabha. Duryodhana cried, "And yet, like women, we let fear rule us? Listen to me, all of you, my loving friends. Let me name some of the warriors who will fight on our side, and then decide if your hearts still quail at the thought of the Pandavas.

"Hear their names: Bheeshma, who by himself would do for the enemy, Drona, Kripa, Aswatthama, peerless Karna, Baahlika, Brihadratha, Bhagadatta, Shalya, Sala, Vinda, Anuvinda, Jayadratha, my hundred brothers led by my ferocious Dusasana, Shakuni, and I myself. I have eleven aksauhinis against their seven. I ask you, should I spend sleepless nights, as Sanjaya wants, in terror that we shall be defeated, when my reason cries out that victory will be ours? No! I am no coward. I will not give in to the Pandavas. We will fight, and I will win!"

There was some applause in the Kuru sabha, especially from those close to Duryodhana. Dhritarashtra sat much straighter in his throne, and there was a proud smile on his lips as he listened to his masterful son. Sensing the tide of opinion turn in his favour, Duryodhana pressed on.

"Why should I tremble at the decrepit Virata's name, when the tameless Trigartas are with me? Susharma smashed Virata's chariot and seized him. Susharma will crush the old Matsya again for me. Will Arjuna fight all the Trigartas by himself? Ah, my father, be at peace. Listen to your own counsel, as you always have, because you are wiser than those who presume to advise you. I tell you, I will win the war!"

Duryodhana went back to his place and sat down, amidst loud cheering from all the Kuru sabha, except Bheeshma, Drona, Sanjaya and a few others. Dhritarashtra's fear had not left him entirely, and the king said, "I have a last question for you, Sanjaya. Tell me, are the sons of Pandu as confident as my son? Are they prepared for war? Do they also feel that victory will be theirs?"

Sanjaya laughed. "They are better prepared than we are. Yet, they are not eager for bloodshed as your son is. Yudhishtira begged me to prevent the war if I could. Shall I tell you what the Pandava said?

"'Sanjaya, go back and say to Duryodhana, "Because of you, cousin, we have suffered in exile beyond what you can imagine. More than anything, it is what you did to Panchali that we cannot forgive. But you are our blood and we do not want war with you; I only want my kingdom back. Why, Duryodhana, even if you don't give me back my kingdom, I still do not want this war. I shall be content with just five towns.

"'Give me Indraprastha, Vrikaprastha, Jayanta, Varanavrata, and a fifth of your choosing, and I will be satisfied. Why should we make war on each other? Let brothers live as brothers, and fathers not be riven from their sons. The Kauravas and the Pandavas are one blood; let us live in peace. Cousin, for the sake of peace I will give up my kingdom. I have no wish to be the cause for eighteen aksauhinis slaughtering one another. But these five towns you must give me.'"

"'Sanjaya, I have no secrets. Look over our forces if you wish, and see what they are. But then, go back to Hastinapura and tell Bheeshma and Dhritarashtra that, if it is fought, this war shall be the end of the rule of the kshatriyas on earth, regardless of who wins or loses.'

"So I went among those legions, I spoke to kshatriyas and common soldiers. I asked them who would be their Senapati, and I learnt that it would most likely be Dhrishtadyumna. However, they have not decided yet, and there is to be a council to make the choice.

But I did learn that their plans for war are carefully laid. They have even agreed among themselves which of them will kill which of us."

Sinking swiftly back into fear, Dhritarashtra whispered, "How is that?"

"Shikhandi has chosen Bheeshma for himself." The Pitama felt a tremor, as of fate. He saw Amba's face before his eyes. Sanjaya knew the Pandavas' plans well. "To keep his vow, Bheema will hunt Duryodhana and his brothers. Arjuna has marked Karna, Aswatthama and Jayadratha. The Kekaya brothers say they will kill their cousins who have joined Duryodhana. The Malavas and Salvas will confront the Trigartas. Abhimanyu, who bears both Arjuna's and Krishna's blood in his veins, has chosen the Kosala king Brihadbala and Duryodhana's sons to be his prey. Dhrishtadyumna will stalk Drona, with the Pandavas' sons to help him. The fire-born prince swears he will kill the Acharya, and fulfil his destiny. Satyaki is furious with Kritavarman for joining Duryodhana, and swears to kill him. Sahadeva means to keep his oath, and have Shakuni's life, and Nakula Uluka's.

"My lord, they are well prepared for war. The thirteen years of exile have strengthened their bodies and spirits, while your sons have lived in luxury's soft lap. The Pandavas have no doubt that, since dharma and Krishna are both with them, victory also shall be theirs."

Once more, cold terror gripped Dhritarashtra. His voice unsteady, he said, "You are right, Sanjaya. We shall all die if we don't give Yudhishtira back his kingdom."

Duryodhana cried angrily, "My lord, how can you let fear move you so easily? It is the only way we can lose this war, and that is exactly what the Pandavas intend: to frighten you with their cunning talk of peace and dharma. Can't you see they are afraid? Here they are, agreeing to settle for just five towns, and you speak of us losing the war to them!"

But after last night's encounter with Vidura and Sanat-sujata, Dhritarashtra was not convinced by his son. Weak with fear, he said, "War is a great evil, as Yudhishtira says. How can we think of sacrificing so many lives for our selfishness, our greed? It is not dharma that we keep a kingdom that belongs to Pandu's sons. Duryodhana, listen to me, I speak from love. Neither you nor I will profit from keeping what is not ours. Turn away from evil, it is still not too late. The world will praise us, and we shall have our honour back.

"It is harder to seek peace at this stage, I know. But just think, Duryodhana, all these kings gathered here, who have come with their armies because they love you: in their hearts, they would much rather not fight this war. If you make peace with the sons of Pandu, every one of these kshatriyas will bless you."

Duryodhana sprang up and cried furiously, "Very well! None of these kings need stay and fight for me. Let them all leave, and take their legions with them. No one here need fight for me. I have Dusasana, and I have Karna. The three of us are enough to demolish the Pandava army!

"Hear me clearly, my lord, all of you: I will never return their kingdom to the Pandavas, not all of it, not five towns, not five villages. *Why, I will not give them land to cover the point of a needle!* I have heard enough craven talk of peace. I want no peace with them. I want war. I have always wanted war with my cousins. I want to see them dead!"

Silence fell on the sabha. In a lower voice, Duryodhana went on, "Of course, Yudhishtira wants peace, but not for any reason of dharma, as he makes out; he wants peace because he is afraid. He begs me for just five towns. I can easily give him what he asks. But if I give him even a speck of earth, I would be admitting that he is right and I am wrong.

"Once, I used to admire Yudhishtira. I thought he was wise, that he was brave and noble. Now he sends word begging five towns to escape fighting a war. Yudhishtira, who was lord of the earth! Exile has broken his spirit, if he ever had any. These Pandavas are cowards, and I do not respect them any more. They are not fit to rule one village, let alone five towns, or a kingdom. I will give them nothing, except battle!"

Vidura rose and said, "Do you believe Yudhishtira is a fool, because he is gentle? Haven't you noticed for which towns he has asked? He doesn't for a moment believe you will give him what he asks. He knows you will refuse, and there will be war. But by naming just these towns, he is reminding you, and the wise men of this sabha, of the trail of the Pandavas' suffering.

"Vrikaprastha, first: Pramanakoti where, Duryodhana, you poisoned Bheema and pushed him into the river. Varanavrata, where you had Purochana build the house of lac. Indraprastha, the wasteland you gave them, Dhritarashtra, as their patrimony. Jayanta: Duryodhana, you have not forgotten the sabha you built in envy of the Mayaa sabha, after you came home from the Rajasuya; the sabha that was your pretext for calling the Pandavas to Hastinapura for the game of dice.

"The trail that led to exile; are you so dull that you can't see what Yudhishtira is saying to you? He says, 'After all you have made us suffer, you say I must be patient. Who is there as patient as I am? But now, the fifth town I leave to your choice. If you do not give me Indraprastha, I shall take Hastinapura. If you don't give me back my kingdom, we will have war.'"

Dhritarashtra breathed, "He is not afraid, but angry! Arjuna befriended Agni Deva when the Khandava vana burned. The God of fire will help the Pandavas against us. Arjuna fought his father Indra for Agni's sake, and now Agni will burn the Kauravas to repay his debt.

"Have we all lost our wits that we forget who these sons of my brother Pandu truly are? They are no blood of ours, but Devaputras! Won't Dharma, Indra, Vayu and the Aswins help their natural sons? They are Gods; how will we resist them? Why, Varuna has already given Arjuna the Gandiva."

Dhritarashtra was beside himself, almost raving. "When Bheema met his brother on the mountain, Hanuman swore he would sit on Arjuna's banner. The Gods are with the Pandavas, and we are on the side of darkness. We have no hope of winning this war; my sons will all die. No! We do not want this war with the Pandavas. We must give back his kingdom to Yudhishtira."

Duryodhana was on his feet, roaring, "Father! How can you be so sure the Devas are with the Pandavas? The Gods are indifferent to our petty quarrels. They have no attachments or enmities in earthly affairs; we are too far beneath them. If Indra, Vayu, Dharma and the Aswins were concerned about their sons, would they have waited before avenging them? Thirteen years is a long time.

"Perhaps, as you say, they have dharma with them. But shall we fear them just for that? Dharma is with me, as well. I have been a good king, our people will tell you as much. The rains fall in season over our kingdom, and my subjects are not poor or unhappy. Ask my friends, they will tell you I am loyal and loving. How can the Gods judge a king like me harshly? No Deva is against us, be certain that we shall win this war."

With that, and sudden tears stinging his eyes, Duryodhana walked out of his father's court. The next moment, Karna was up and had followed his friend. Then, in a show of solidarity, the other kings and princes all stood up, as a man, and went after the Kaurava. Slowly, Bheeshma and Drona also left. Dhritarashtra was left alone with Sanjaya. The king sat in his throne, sobbing.

TEN

A second council in Upaplavya

Meanwhile, some days after Sanjaya left, Yudhishtira called another council in Upaplavya. He said to Krishna in that sabha, "You heard Dhritarashtra's message, my Lord. My uncle does not intend to return my kingdom to me. The man who should be as a father to us is like a thief instead. I fear there will be war. How else do two kshatriyas resolve their enmity? Will you go to Hastinapura, Krishna? To sue, one last time, for peace."

Krishna said quietly, "I will. And if I can achieve the impossible, and make peace between the Pandavas and the Kauravas, why, my fame will live forever. No one shall be more pleased than I if the kings of the earth give up their hubris and save themselves from death."

Yudhishtira had a second thought, "Duryodhana cannot be trusted, there is no telling what he may do. And if anything were to happen to you, Krishna…"

Krishna smiled. "Yes, they may try to harm me: Duryodhana, his brothers, and their uncle Shakuni. Men like these will stoop to anything. And if they do, Yudhishtira, I will save you the trouble of a war. I will kill them all."

He said this so simply, and somehow no one doubted he would do as he said. Krishna continued, "Don't fear for me, I am in no danger; though I feel sure my mission will be in vain. We all heard Dhritarashtra's message; he does not want peace, perhaps because Duryodhana gives him no choice in the matter. Dhritarashtra is a coward, left to himself he would not fight; but his son would rather die than see you back on the throne of Indraprastha.

"But you are a kshatriya, Yudhishtira. How can you ask for peace after you heard Dhritarashtra's message? How can you still have feelings for these monsters? Or think of them as your relatives? They have never requited the love you have for them. They are not your blood, who treat you with such hatred and contempt. A kshatriya has no kinsmen, Yudhishtira, only friends and enemies. These are your enemies. Not for a moment have they thought of you as a nephew or a cousin, not the elders of Hastinapura. I say they deserve death for what they have done.

"The court of Hastinapura is a nest of serpents. It needs to be burned with fire. In that city today you have just the hollow name of Kuru; the rest is an illusion. The one you so fondly call your grandfather, Bheeshma, won't he be the first to face you in war? What Pitama is he to you? He will fight for Duryodhana."

Krishna saw the sadness in his cousin's face, and he shook his head and sighed. "Ah, Yudhishtira, I can't fathom you. What weakness or strength makes you reach out again to these sinners with an offer of peace? For myself, I will tell you why I am going to Hastinapura. It is not that I believe there is any possibility of peace. No. I am going to tell the people of that city, and the kings who have allied themselves to Duryodhana, about you. I want the world to realize how noble you are, and how vile Duryodhana and his blind father.

"Let the people know that you will accept peace, if they give you even five towns. Let them know how arrogant Duryodhana is that he will not give you even these. I am going to Hastinapura so the truth may be preserved in the hearts of common men. Dhritarashtra and Duryodhana will never tell their people the truth of what happened between the Kauravas and the Pandavas. Already the blind one seeks to make a villain of you with the message he sent through Sanjaya.

"While I am away, cousin, prepare for war. And let war begin as soon as I return."

Yudhishtira bent his head and said, "I leave our lives in your hands, Krishna. You always know what is best for us."

"I see omens of war everywhere I turn. The birds of night are awake all day, as if in terror, and those of day sing at midnight. Wolves come out of their forests and howl at the cities of men. Elephants and horses run from jungle to jungle, in strange panic, as if seeking a sanctuary that exists nowhere on earth any more. Let us not deceive ourselves. There will surely be war, and we must be prepared for it."

There was a brief silence, while every king in that sabha was so absorbed in his own thoughts that no one noticed Bheema squirming in his place. Suddenly, the son of the wind said, "Krishna, I will be happy if you can make peace between the Pandavas and the Kauravas. We do not want the sin of killing our cousins on our conscience. Don't try and frighten Duryodhana by saying how powerful we are. He is proud and obstinate; he will not be intimidated. But gentler persuasion may succeed.

"I agree with Yudhishtira that we must do everything in our power to have peace. Otherwise, a hundred kings will die, thousands of kshatriyas and countless common soldiers. Think of their wives and children; war is a calamity that we must avert if we possibly can. Arjuna, I am sure you understand what I mean and you agree with me."

All that council, especially Bheema's brothers, stared at him in amazement. Then, Krishna began to laugh, golden laughter ringing through the morning. He cried, "Bheema! Are you really saying this? You want peace? Until last night, we heard of nothing but the war from you, how long you had waited for it. You told us how you would tear out Dusasana's heart and smash Duryodhana's thigh. You said you had not slept properly these last thirteen years, for the shame you had to swallow. Some of us have seen you wriggling like an angry serpent in Yudhishtira's grasp. We have seen you sit apart from your brothers in the jungle, as if you carried an insupportable burden.

"I heard people say that Bheema had gone mad in his frustration. You sat alone, smouldering like a fire covered with ashes, your brow knit, talking to yourself, your hands sweating as you clenched and unclenched them. Then you would jump up with a growl, pull up a tree, dash it on the ground, and begin to cry and laugh at once. You would shout, 'The lotus may bloom on the peak of ice, the sun may rise in the west; but I will keep my vow. I will break Duryodhana's thigh where he dared call Panchali to sit!'

"You would brandish your mace, and roar so the forest echoed with your wrath. Is this the same Bheema, who is faint-hearted as a woman today at the very thought of war? Who begs me to go and sue the Kauravas for peace, because he balks at the thought of blood? Ah,

Bheema, you are the raft on which your brothers will cross over the sea of misfortune. But if you turn coward, I dread to think what will become of the others."

Krishna saw his words went home. He saw Bheema's eyes become red as plums at the word coward. It was as Krishna intended; it would never do if Bheema became soft at this time.

The Dark One continued, "Think back, Bheema! Remember the shame of the game of dice; remember the long anguish of exile. Remember you are a kshatriya, and the men you have sworn to kill are sinners. Put aside this womanliness; harden your heart against these affections.

"Peace! You talk of peace, you whom peace does not suit at all. You are a kshatriya, Bheema, every fibre of you. What peace can be yours, until you kill them all? What has happened to you that you are afraid now?"

Bheema sprang up and cried, "You wrong me, Krishna! How can you accuse me of being a coward? When the war begins you will see if Bheema is afraid. Not Indra himself will save Duryodhana and his brothers, when these hands lay hold of them. Look at my hands, Krishna! Aren't they made just for war? Look at this body!"

He was trembling. "Wild elephants shall not stand before Bheema when he takes the field with his mace! I only pitied those who would face me in battle, their families whom I will bereave. And you call me a coward?" He smote his chest and roared, so the sabha shook. "Bheema is no coward, Krishna! Never! Never!"

Krishna took his hand. "That is the Bheema we know! This is no time for softness. We are on the brink of war, and you are the greatest force we have, our strongest warrior. More than any of the others, we rely on you. If you turn to fine feelings now, what will become of the rest? Who doesn't know that Bheema is no coward, but the bravest kshatriya on earth? I only said what I did because I want Bheema to be himself."

He embraced his cousin. "Never fear, there will be a war. No one will stop it, and you will have your revenge. I swear you will wash your shame and your anger in streams of blood. Don't speak of peace any more. There will be no peace, but war!"

Bheema gave a growl of satisfaction, and sat down. Now, Krishna turned to the third Pandava, and Arjuna said, "I agree with you, Krishna.

Duryodhana will never accept peace. He has gone too far down the way of sin. I feel we should not compromise Yudhishtira's dignity while suing for peace."

Then he smiled. "But, finally, only what you want will come to pass, my Lord. All this is just your maya! If you are determined there shall be peace between us cousins, then peace there will be; and even Duryodhana will do what you ask. But if you decide there should be war, and the earth's burden removed—as the rishis say you have—so it shall be. Whatever it is, we will walk the path you choose for us, happily."

Krishna laughed. "Arjuna, I wish it were as simple as that. I will do my best to convince Duryodhana that we should have peace, not war; and I will not bargain with Yudhishtira's dignity. But there is no other miracle I can work. Like you, I fear Duryodhana has gone too far down the way of evil to turn back willingly. He is hardly master of himself or his own fate, any more. He is an instrument of other sinister forces; they will not relent, even if Duryodhana wants to. But I will go to Hastinapura to clear Yudhishtira's name with the people, because he is the noblest man alive."

Krishna turned to Nakula, who said in his soft voice, "The thoughts of men are like the shapes of clouds in the sky, always changing. When we were in the jungle, or on our tirtha-yatra, we did not think much of a kingdom. When we first came to Virata for the ajnatavasa, we thought only of not being recognised, and of our exile's end. Now the thirteen years are over and we are thinking of nothing but the kingdom, how we can win it back.

"Krishna, I think we should sue for peace. Speak gently to Duryodhana at first; if he does not listen, use strong words, threaten him. Tell him about the kshatriyas who are with us. Duryodhana is just a man, like any other; he can be frightened into accepting peace on our terms. And when you are the messenger, Krishna, there is nothing that cannot be achieved."

Krishna smiled, and did not have time to turn to Sahadeva, before the youngest Pandava sprang up and cried, "We must have war, Krishna! You must make certain we do. Let the Kauravas beg for peace, if they like; but we must have war, and only war, with them! What else can we want after what they did to Panchali in their sabha? How can we think of peace for even a moment? I don't agree with my brothers. If Yudhishtira, Bheema, Arjuna and Nakula want peace, let them make shameful peace with those animals. I mean to fight, if I have to fight alone, and to see Duryodhana dead. Tell him from me, Krishna, that Sahadeva says he will die.

If my brothers decide that virtue lies in seeking peace with Duryodhana, let them keep such virtue for themselves. I will fight, and kill that devil!"

Satyaki jumped up and cried, "I am with you, Sahadeva! We shall have no peace with the Kauravas. Death is what Duryodhana deserves, and death he shall find. Krishna, you saw these Pandavas in the forest, wearing valkala, like beggars. How can you make peace with the men who reduced them to that? The Kauravas must die, every one of them!"

The sabha resounded with the approval of the kings in it. Suddenly, Krishna turned his face to where the most beautiful woman on earth sat. Krishna asked gently, "Panchali, what have you to say?"

Her lovely eyes were full of tears, and she rose without wiping them, so they fell down her face. Draupadi said fiercely, "I bless Sahadeva and Satyaki! Who, it seems, are the only kshatriyas in this sabha. Krishna, you know everything that happened. I beg you, if you care at all for my honour, use no soft words with Duryodhana. Gentleness wins only good men, not fiends of hell. Hastinapura is a nest of demons; it must burn!

"I wonder that you can even ask me what I have to say. I want war, Krishna, a bloody war to avenge what I suffered on that terrible day, and for thirteen years after. I want every Kaurava killed. The elders who sat by, not lifting a finger to help me when I begged them to, I want to see them dead! I know Yudhishtira was always for peace, at whatever cost to himself and his family. But when I hear Bheema, Arjuna and Nakula talking of peace today, I can hardly stand it. I want neither peace nor friendship with the Kauravas. If you love me at all, Krishna, if you ever felt sorry for what happened to me, make sure there is war between the Pandavas and the Kauravas. I must see my enemies lying dead on the field, as carrion for jackals and vultures."

"She lost control of herself. Convulsed with sobs, she took her hair, hanging behind her like a dark serpent, and brandished it at that court. "I have not tied my hair since the day Dusasana dragged me by it! Look at my hair, all you kings. I carry it like a stain on my very soul, that the beast defiled it with his filthy hands.

"In the forest, Yudhishtira said to me that I must be patient for thirteen years. I have waited thirteen years, and only I know how long the wait has been. And now what do I hear from Yudhishtira? Not a word of war or revenge, but again words of peace. And today I am amazed to hear Bheema talking of peace! Duryodhana was not mistaken when he called them cowards. How lofty it is to talk peace. But who will bring peace to my heart?

"For thirteen years, every night I was awake thinking of just one thing: the day I would see Dusasana's jewelled hand cut off, and lying on the ground streaming blood. I will have no rest until I see that sight before my eyes. Krishna, think of me when you are in Hastinapura. For it was I who was dragged like a whore through the palace there, I who was shamed in front of all the Kuru sabha. And I say to you, *there is a fire burning in my heart, and the only cure for it is war.* I beg you, Krishna, don't come back from that evil city without declaring war!"

And she stood trembling, while her tears flowed. Krishna said to her, "As you cry today, Panchali, I swear the wives of the Kauravas shall weep very soon. But there will be no cure for their tears, because they will have lost everything. Not one Kaurava shall live. I have not forgotten what I promised you in the Kamyaka vana. I have come into the world for this war." His voice was wistful, "The earth must be rid of her burden of kings, and so she shall. Dry your eyes, Panchali, let me see you smile. The thirteen years of exile are over. I promise you, Yudhishtira will be lord of the earth again."

Draupadi wiped her tears, and smiled wanly at Krishna. He said, "It is decided then, I will leave for Hastinapura tomorrow."

Thus, the second council at Upaplavya ended.

The next morning dawned, bright and auspicious, and Krishna was up early. The Dark One bathed. He worshipped the sun and the fire, and then called Satyaki.

"Prepare my chariot, Satyaki. See to it yourself that my weapons are in it. Duryodhana and his brothers are not to be trusted, and I must not let them find me unprepared."

Now Yudhishtira came there, and said, "Satyaki, you must go with Krishna. I am reluctant to send him at all on this pointless mission, and I will not let him go alone."

The chariot was ready, and all the Pandavas came to see Krishna and Satyaki on their way. Yudhishtira's last words to him were, "Give our mother our love, and tell her we shall soon be with her."

Krishna embraced them all, and, cheerful as ever, set out for the Kuru capital.

ELEVEN

Krishna arrives in Hastinapura

THE MORNING KRISHNA SET OUT ON HIS MISSION TO HASTINAPURA, the strangest omens were seen. There was not a cloud in the sky, yet suddenly, in diverse parts of the land, thunder and lightning erupted in the vacant azure, and uncanny rains lashed the earth. On that day, rivers turned around and flowed back to their sources; deep and quiet wells gushed forth in geysers.

On his way, Krishna saw none of these omens, but only nature's bounty: trees laden with flowers and fruit, and birds singing in their branches to mark the saviour's passage. In every town and village he rode through, the people came out in crowds to greet the Avatara, and they stood enchanted by the sight of him, blue and ineffable. At Vrikasthala, beside a pool of lotuses, Krishna stopped his chariot.

"Night grows on us, let us rest here tonight."

Meanwhile, in Hastinapura, his spies came to Dhritarashtra in his sabha and said, "My lord, Krishna is on his way here, bringing an embassy of peace from the Pandavas."

Dhritarashtra sent for Bheeshma, Vidura and Sanjaya. Drona and Duryodhana were already in the court. When the Pitama and the king's brother had joined them, Dhritarashtra said in some excitement, "I have wonderful news. Krishna is coming to Hastinapura! Vidura, let no effort be spared to give him a grand welcome. All the munis say no one on earth is as worthy of worship as Krishna. Besides, we need his blessings more than ever, and his good offices."

"Open our wayside retreats for him, along his journey; and when he arrives, we must receive him with gifts of chariots, elephants and jewels. Krishna honours us by coming to Hastinapura. I will go out myself to welcome him. Vidura, you must arrange the reception; overlook no detail. He will spend tonight at Kusasthala, and be with us by midday tomorrow."

There was a brief silence in his court, and the king turned his face this way and that. He asked, "Vidura, don't you approve? Don't you think Krishna deserves the gifts I mean to offer him? Why are you so quiet?"

His brother laughed. "Of course, my lord, he deserves your gifts. Why, no man who was ever born into the world, or ever shall be, is as great as Krishna. Not just your gifts, he deserves the very earth.

"Yet, that is not what makes you so generous; nor is it any love for Krishna. You want to bribe the incomparable one. You mean to try to buy him to your side, to drive a wedge between him and the Pandavas with your gifts. You will not part with five towns to your nephews, and now you speak of giving horses and elephants, chariots and jewels to their messenger.

"I beg you, my lord, do not be foolish; don't insult Krishna with such a barbaric gesture. He will not take what you give him, but scoff at you. His very life is bound to Arjuna's. How can you hope to part him from Arjuna and his brothers with your paltry gifts?

"If you really want to honour the Dark One, accept the terms he brings for peace. He comes in the hope that you and your sons will see reason. He comes in a last effort to make peace in the House of Kuru, and save the world from war.

"Dhritarashtra, remember the Pandavas have no father. At least for Pandu's sake, think that you should be like a father to them. There is still hope, my brother; if you turn back to dharma, Krishna will heal the bitterness between the Kauravas and Pandavas. He will even persuade Draupadi to forgive your sons for what they did to her. But you must take the first step towards peace yourself; no one can do that for you. The fate of the world as we know it is in your hands. I pray that you make the just choice, though I fear you will not."

Duryodhana rose and, surprisingly, said, "I agree with Vidura. It is foolish to think we can estrange Krishna from the Pandavas. He will laugh at you if you try to bribe him; worse, he will think we are afraid of him. No, we must not insult Krishna by trying to buy him to our side. We must receive him with dignity, or we shall be the laughing-stock of the world."

Bheeshma said, "It will make no difference to Krishna if you honour him or not; he is above your honouring or insulting him. Nor will you sway him with foolish gifts, because he is a man of truth. He comes not to seek some petty wealth for himself, but genuinely to secure peace. He comes to see you acknowledge the injustice done to the Pandavas. He comes with the faint hope that dharma may be restored to the House of Kuru without bloodshed. The only way you can honour Krishna is to give the Pandavas back their kingdom."

Duryodhana jumped up and cried, "Pitama! You always take our cousins' side, but I will not give in to them or to you. I will never share what belongs to me. Why should I? After the Vaishnava yagna the kingdom is mine, and I mean to keep it."

Bheeshma said in despair, "Dhritarashtra, this son of yours is so full of evil that he has lost his reason. I fear his time has come to die, and he will not listen to anything that might save him. And I cannot stand any more raving."

Bheeshma rose and walked out of the sabha, and that was an end to the day's deliberations. Late next morning, Krishna arrived with Satyaki, and Dhritarashtra went to the city-gates with Bheeshma, Drona and Kripa to receive him. Duryodhana went, as well, and his brothers. The people of Hastinapura milled in the streets of the city of elephants to welcome the Avatara. They reached out loving hands and chanted his name, as he rode through them. The women flung flowers down on him from their balconies.

Krishna came to Dhritarashtra's palace, and was ushered into the sabha of Hastinapura. The king had asked for a jewelled throne to be set beside his own, and Krishna was shown to that seat. When he had greeted the Kuru elders, the Dark One sat chatting to the Kaurava princes, and he was full of smiles. It seemed this was another day like any other, and he had come to the city for a friendly visit. Then, Krishna said, "If you allow me, my lords, I want to meet Vidura in his palace, and pay my respects to my aunt Kunti."

Dhritarashtra gave orders for Krishna to be taken to Vidura's home. He sent word to his brother, and Vidura came in excitement to his door to receive him with arghya. He, at least, was entirely aware who it was that honoured him with a visit.

When they sat together inside, Vidura asked, "How are Pandu's sons, Krishna? I fear there will be a war between them and the Kauravas. Duryodhana is determined to fight, rather than return a foot of land to his cousins."

Krishna told him about the sabha in Upaplavya, and all that was said on the last day, before he set out for Hastinapura. "I have little hope that Duryodhana will turn back to dharma now. But I thought I must come here to clear Yudhishtira's name, so the people know that he still wants peace."

Vidura bowed his head, and Krishna saw his eyes were full. He laid a hand on Vidura's arm, and said, "Be consoled, Vidura. None of us can change fate, and everything that happens is for the best. Now take me to my aunt Kunti. I am sure she is waiting to see me, and have news of her sons."

When Vidura brought Krishna into Kunti's chambers, she rose with a cry and embraced her nephew. "Oh, Krishna! I am so happy you have come."

She made him sit next to her, and held his hand tightly. She wept now, and said, "I feel so much stronger, that you are here. Tell me about my sons. How are Yudhishtira, and my Bheema? You know Bheema was always his older brother's favourite. How did my boys spend their years in the forest, with all the danger that lurks there? How did Bheema control himself for so long, after the way Dhritarashtra's sons abused him? Ah, forgive me, Krishna, I know I am not waiting for you to answer my questions. I have waited so long to ask them, that they will not come singly, but all together!

"How is my Arjuna, your friend? How did he conceal himself during the final year of the ajnatavasa? I am surprised no one discovered my flame-like son. And Sahadeva, who is so delicate and sensitive? He looks like a grown man, but he is just a child at heart. And my youngest, my Nakula, my most handsome son at whom women always gazed? How did he hide his dark beauty during the final year? Krishna, how is Draupadi? I cannot think how she endured the hardship thrust upon her.

"Time and again, I see Dusasana dragging proud Panchali through the palace of Hastinapura. I see my sons standing with their heads hung in the sabha, while Dhritarashtra's princes reviled their queen. Only your grace saved her from utter shame."

Kunti wiped her eyes, and sighed, "Krishna, though I have known great joy in this life, I have also suffered as few women do. First, I became a widow, and we came here to Hastinapura to live on the charity of those who did not truly love us. Then they tried to kill us. When, at last, we settled in Indraprastha I thought our troubles were over. They were just beginning, and fate separated me from my sons.

"We have suffered enough! We also deserve some happiness, after so many years of anguish. Tell my sons the time has come for them to show they are kshatriyas. Tell them their mother says it is their dharma to fight. And if they don't, they are no sons of mine!"

She sobbed again. Krishna took her hands, "Don't cry. Your sons have become great men by their long penance, and no force on earth can resist them now. Their night is ending; day is at hand, and victory. I promise you, Yudhishtira shall soon be lord of the earth."

TWELVE

In Vidura's house

Krishna walked into Duryodhana's palace, and it was more opulent than Dhritarashtra's. In his garish sabha, Duryodhana sat on a golden throne, with Shakuni, Karna and Dusasana around him. They all rose when Krishna entered, and Duryodhana came forward, smiling, to welcome the Blue One. There was a place, lower than Duryodhana's throne, set apart for Krishna, a silk-covered chair inlaid with ivory and precious stones. Krishna allowed himself to be led to it.

Duryodhana said, "Welcome to our palace, Krishna. Honour me by sharing a meal with us."

Krishna replied, "I must decline your invitation for the moment, Duryodhana."

The Kaurava's eyes flashed. "You wound me, Krishna. Why won't you eat with us? We have arranged music and dancing for you, as you love. Our cooks prepared a feast, but you went straight to Vidura's home. Why?"

"A messenger may not eat until the task he has come for is fulfilled."

"That hardly matters! I have heard you say you are impartial in the dispute between the Pandavas and ourselves. We are fond of you, Krishna; there is no enmity between you and me. When you go to Upaplavya you stay with the Pandavas, don't you?"

There was an inscrutable look in Krishna's eyes. He said, "I fear you will make me say things I never meant to, Duryodhana. One eats in another man's house out of friendship, goodwill, or necessity; none of these applies between us. I do not care for the feast you have made for me; I never eat in a thief's home because his food is polluted. And I am not starving that I need your hospitality."

Duryodhana's eyes blazed. Krishna would not be interrupted, though he spoke equably still, "As for the Pandavas, I do not hold you and them in equal regard. The truth is, Duryodhana, I am the soul of the sons of Pandu. They are mine in a very special way, because they are men of truth. You have shown, repeatedly, that you detest them; often enough, you have tried to have them killed. You banished them by deceit, humiliated them in your sabha, and now you refuse to give back what is theirs. You are my enemy, Duryodhana, and I will not eat in an enemy's house. I will eat in Vidura's home, because he is a friend who loves me."

Krishna's voice and his presence were suddenly so awesome that even Duryodhana was tongue-tied. Smiling still, Krishna got up and walked out of that palace.

He strolled down the open street and the people ran to him, to greet him, to clasp his hand or offer him a flower. Bheeshma and Kripa came out, and said, "Krishna, we have a palace ready for you to stay in."

He answered them, "You are too kind, my lords, but I am going to stay with Vidura."

They stared at him; but he waved to them and walked on to Vidura's home. Vidura washed Krishna's feet himself, in some ecstasy that the Avatara had chosen his home to stay in. It was late afternoon. They ate together, and then Krishna said, "I am a little tired. I would like to rest for an hour."

"Your rooms are ready, Krishna, I will show you to them."

When Krishna had slept, he rose and bathed, and now night had fallen. He went out to join Vidura. When they sat together, sipping wine in an open courtyard, with fateful stars shining down on them, Vidura said slowly, "I think your coming here was a mistake, Krishna. Perhaps you don't realize how far down the road to ruin Duryodhana has gone. He is bent on having war, and nothing will stop him. He thinks he will win with superior numbers. He says he has Bheeshma, Drona, Kripa, Aswatthama, Karna and Jayadratha with him, besides his brothers and the other kshatriyas of the eleven aksauhinis. How can he lose? Most of all, he depends on Karna.

"Ah, Krishna, how much I have tried to tell him that his sins are ranged against him, and they will drag him down to his death. How often

I have begged him to relent. Not just I, but the other elders of the court. But he won't listen, and Karna, Shakuni and Dusasana tell him to fight. They are so certain they will win the war. It is no use your trying to make peace; Duryodhana is in no mood to listen to wisdom.

"I beg you, my Lord, don't go to Dhritarashtra's sabha. It is not a court of dharma any more. I fear they will insult you, and the thought distresses me."

Krishna said, "Vidura, I am touched by your concern. I have nothing to hide from you, so listen to why I have come. I have not come with much hope that my mission will succeed. Yet, it is my dharma to try to save the lives of these men, who seem so eager to die. If I do succeed, Vidura, I shall have glory; and even if I fail, no blame will attach to me. At least, I will be satisfied that I spared no effort in a good cause.

"Every man can be redeemed. If a man has sinful thoughts, but does not translate them into evil deeds, no sin clings to him. So I pray it might be with the Kauravas. I read their hearts clearly, and see the darkness in them. But there is always hope. Suppose, by a miracle, they decide to give back the Pandavas' kingdom because of my embassy? All men deserve every chance to save themselves; Dhritarashtra and his son do, as well. Most of all, the House of Kuru deserves a final chance to save itself. If I did not do everything I can to stop this war, I would fail in my dharma.

"So here I am, to try to drag Duryodhana and his brothers back from the edge of a chasm. As for Yudhishtira, he still says he wants peace. Vidura, I know you will understand me when I tell you that Yudhishtira is the greatest man born into this age. Most of all, I have come here for his sake. To clear his name of any taint, so the world will remember his greatness forever.

"Let the people know that it is not just anyone whom Duryodhana has sinned against, but the truest, most compassionate man on earth. Let the kings who have flocked to Duryodhana's serpent-banner know against whom they are going to war. Let them realize they mean to fight on the side of evil, and let their arrogant hearts tremble a little.

"Yes, this is why I have come: to let Bheeshma know, and Drona and Kripa know, and the others, that they clasped danger to their souls when they chose to fight against the sons of Pandu. They cannot escape this truth, let them see it clearly."

Now Krishna sighed. "Ah, Vidura, how I wish this war could be avoided. I don't think even Yudhishtira or you, or any of the others realize how terrible it will be. But I fear that not all our prayers can prevent it. I have come to make it clear on which side dharma lies, and on which, adharma. That is my real mission. Gentle Vidura, you are the only Kuru in Hastinpaura on the side of truth. That is why I am staying in your home. But let us speak of other things, because tomorrow I must be fresh for what I have come to say, in Dhritarashtra's sabha."

Late into the night, they sat talking of many things: of Dwaraka, of awesome kings of the past, and how rapidly the times diminished. Until they turned in to sleep, they spoke of anything but the war.

THIRTEEN

In the court of Hastinapura

THE NEXT MORNING, DURYODHANA AND KARNA CAME WITH RETINUE to take Krishna to Dhritarashtra's sabha. Krishna went in his chariot with Satyaki. Duryodhana and Karna followed in Duryodhana's chariot, and Kritavarman, who was also in the city, came after them. A legion of elephant and horse followed the chariots through the streets of Hastinapura, choked with the people turned out to catch a glimpse of the blue saviour.

The Dark One was radiant, as he alighted at the palace steps, and climbed them with Vidura and Satyaki on either side. Karna and Duryodhana went before Krishna, leading him solemnly into Dhritarashtra's court. Kritavarman walked behind them. When Krishna entered the Kuru sabha, all the elders, including the blind king, Bheeshma and Drona rose. Once more Krishna was shown to the place of honour, and just as he was about to sit, he saw Narada at the door to the sabha, with some other rishis. Bheeshma rose to welcome the sages.

Krishna waited for them to be seated, and only then sat. Dusasana showed Satyaki to a majestic chair, and his brother Vivimsati brought Kritavarman to another.

Next to Krishna sat Vidura; not far from them, to their left, Karna and Duryodhana shared a wide seat for two, and Shakuni sat beside them. Every gaze in the sabha was riveted to the Avatara's face. They gazed at him, helplessly, and could not have their fill. He was more God than man today, but gentle, and handsome. It was as if the Kuru sabha was elevated into a finer realm, because Krishna graced it. In his xanthic robe, he was like a blue mountain with the sun rising over it; and the kaustubha ruby on his breast was a gleaming secret.

The sabha sat staring raptly at him, and he sat smiling at them. For a long moment, there was silence in that court; then, Krishna addressed Dhritarashtra.

"My lord, I have come to Hastinapura to prevent the deaths of all these kshatriyas. I have come to make peace between the Pandavas and the Kauravas. I am glad I have come at a time when most of what needs to be said has already been debated in this sabha. Everything is known, and there is not much I have to add to the words of the wise."

They listened to him entranced; there was that quality in his voice. "Since the most ancient days, the House of Kuru is a legend upon the earth. The world knows that yours is the oldest house in Bharatavarsha. Generations of Kuru kings have ruled vast kingdoms, and they have all been renowned for their justice and their mercy." He paused, and looked around him; a slight smile still played on his face. "Dhritarashtra, it does not become you that you are the first king in your line to be so different from your sires."

Dhritarashtra shivered in his throne. Krishna continued, "Your sons plunge down a blind alley of sin. They think nothing of fighting a murderous war in which millions shall die. It is for you to stop them. You are the king of the Kurus, my lord, and not your son. You must stop this madness.

"This is not the time for weakness and vacillation. You must assert yourself, as you should have done long ago. Having left it so long, it will be harder for you now. But it can still be done, if you assume the firmness that every king should have. The first step is to think kindly of your brother's sons. Think of them not as enemies to be feared, but as your own children, your own soldiers who will make you lord of the earth. Unite this house again, Dhritarashtra, as it should have always been.

"Already, there is no kingdom to rival this one. For Bheeshma protects it, Drona and Kripa, Karna, Vivimsati, Aswatthama, Jayadratha, Somadatta and Duryodhana. But just think what the glory of the House of Kuru would be if you added the names of the Pandavas and their sons to those: as it has never been before! If you can bring the Pandavas and the Kauravas together, your fame will be sung in heaven as well as the earth.

"Yet, it seems you prefer to court shame and ruin, rather than glory. Tell me, Dhritarashtra, what will this war bring you except the death of your sons?" Now his voice was stern. "And the death of some millions of fighting men, and of all these kshatriyas gathered here to perpetrate the madness your son has planned. You have everything to lose by this war, and nothing to gain. Look at this court of dharma, defiled by this council met to plot a war between brother and brother, while its elders sit here, and do nothing to stop the enormous sin. Never since the Kuru kingdom was founded, in time out of mind, has this sabha seen such shame. This is no sabha anymore, my lord, but a den of vice.

"Do not take what I say lightly, because I speak with love. I say to you, return what is his to Yudhishtira. Bring back dharma to your kingdom, which yearns for it. If you don't make the just choice, this land will be ruined past redemption, and with it the world."

He spoke so gravely that no one dared interrupt him. His words struck all of them deeply, and what he said frightened them. At last, Dhritarashtra broke the silence, "Krishna, don't you realize how helpless I am? I do not rule this land, and what I say is of little consequence. My sons are the masters here, and they have no regard for my wishes any more. If you can persuade Duryodhana and his brothers, and Karna and Shakuni, who wield more power than I do, I will be grateful to you forever.

"But I fear your task is hopeless. We have all tried to reason with Duryodhana, to no avail. Bheeshma has tried, Vidura, and even Gandhari; and I have, too. He is stubborn, and determined to sacrifice us all. Still, if you can succeed where the rest of us failed, no one will be more in your debt than I."

Duryodhana sat sullen and fierce. Krishna turned to him kindly, "Listen to me, Duryodhana. You are a son of the noblest house in all Bharatavarsha. Why do you behave as if you were born in the streets? Why has your mind turned to such pettiness? What you mean to do will not cover you in honour, as you imagine; it will fetch you eternal infamy. Turn away from this folly, Kshatriya; resume your true nature. Forsake the hatred that consumes you from within. Be the good Duryodhana again, whom the world loves! Perhaps you think it is too late for you to turn back. No man ever falls so low that he is past redemption, and least of all a prince with as generous a heart as you have.

"This is the hour of an historic decision, Duryodhana. Do you want to be remembered as the man who destroyed the world, or the one who had the courage to save it? For it will take more courage to turn your face away from sin, than it will for you to be obstinate. Choose wisely, Duryodhana, and be the bravest kshatriya of the Kuru line. Make your father and your grandfather happy, your gurus and your mother proud. Change the course of destiny; you still can."

Duryodhana had grown pale, and he sat stiller than ever. Krishna went on, his power deeply upon the sabha. "There are three kinds of men in this world, Duryodhana. There are the selfless ones, who seldom leave the path of dharma. Then there are those who seek their own benefit in whatever they do. Even if that is your nature, you should think wisely, of what will profit you. Death surely will not.

"If you want to be king in Hastinapura, won't it be better if you have the Pandavas' support, rather than their enmity? If you make peace with him, Yudhishtira will crown you yuvaraja of this city; and after your father's time, you will be king of the Kurus. The Pandavas will be content with Indraprastha, and never be a threat to you. And with your cousins on your side, who else will dare challenge you?"

Duryodhana's face twitched in contempt; he exchanged a scornful smile with Karna. Krishna paused, then, his voice softer, said, "There is also the third kind of man. He lives to sin, because nothing else pleases him; his unnatural thirst is satisfied only with blood. Duryodhana, you are not that kind of man, are you? Cast off your old life as a snake does his skin. Emerge anew as a king of truth, and make this age the brightest one in history. You hold the future of the world in your palm; only you can save it."

Bheeshma cried, "Listen to him, Duryodhana, make a new beginning. I beg you! Do it in your mother's name, for her sake."

Drona urged, "Krishna speaks the truth, Duryodhana, this can be your moment of greatness. You can do this, my prince; your heart is big enough. Only the first step is hard, the rest will come easily."

Vidura said, "If you don't listen to wisdom, it is not yourself you will hurt most, but your mother and father. I pity them, that they will have to survive their eldest son, and most likely, all their sons. Who will look after them in their dotage?"

Bheeshma begged him again, and Drona as well. Duryodhana had not spoken a word, but only listened grimly to their united entreaty. Vidura said, "Duryodhana, the choice is so simple: between death and life. Why do you hesitate?"

FOURTEEN

Duryodhana and Krishna

Though his eyes were restless, Duryodhana had listened patiently to everything Krishna said. Now he rose, and addressed Krishna quietly, reasonably. "You spoke eloquently, Krishna, and all that you said was for me: all the blame. My father and my grandfather, also, point their fingers at me, as do my Acharyas and my uncle Vidura. I have tried to see your point of view; but I am afraid I cannot, because this is not nearly as simple as you make it out to be.

"Let me tell you my version of whatever has happened so far. We asked Yudhishtira to play dice, and he agreed readily enough. He enjoys the game, more than I do anyway. We did not force him to play, and it was not as if he did not know, from the start, that he was to play against Shakuni.

"Yudhishtira lost his kingdom at dice. How do you blame me for that? I did not decide what the stakes would be. I did not sit in my cousin's place, and play rashly for him. It is easy to accuse me; but if you think about it, how am I responsible? Yudhishtira was foolhardy and he was unlucky. How is Duryodhana to blame for that?

"This court knows I returned everything he lost to me. But you say it was my fault he came back to play a second time, and lost it all once more. How am I responsible for his stupidity that he thought he could play an acknowledged master of dice like Shakuni? And does my cousin wager some thousand gold coins as other kings do? No. He wagers his entire treasury, then his army, then his kingdom, and finally, his brothers, himself and his queen! Wasn't this an emperor's arrogance? How am

I to blame for it? Didn't I return his brothers and his wife to him? Didn't I set him free, though he had lost himself to me? Yet, I am to blame."

Krishna sat smiling faintly, none of the others spoke. The Kaurava continued, "And not only all of you, but my cousins, also, have decided that I am to blame for their misfortunes. Do I control the motions of the planets that I decide what happens to every man on this earth?

"They have joined forces with the Panchala king, whom these same Pandavas once attacked for Acharya Drona's revenge. Now they mean to fight us together. For what? For something they imagine I did to them. I did nothing. Their troubles were of their own making, and I am not afraid of Pandu's sons." His voice rose, "As long as my conscience is clear, I will never fear them, or anyone else. Why, I would not fear Indra himself. We will not bow to their threats. We have Bheeshma and Drona with us; Kripa, Karna and Aswatthama are with me. No power on earth can stand against these men. And, as for me, when I accept the Pandavas' challenge I only honour the way of the kshatriya. My dharma is to fight.

"If I must, I will die fighting. Otherwise, I will make a bed of arrows for my enemies to sleep on forever. Isn't that kshatriya dharma? To fight, and either die or be killed. The warrior that dies without bowing his head to his enemy goes straight to heaven. Then why do you ask me to humiliate myself so I can save my life? What will my miserable life be worth if I save it like that? I prefer to die without having submitted in spirit, than to live as less than a king. This is the law every kshatriya is born into, and it is the only dharma I acknowledge. I mean to live or die by it, as fate decides."

He paused, and looked around him. Silence still greeted his bold words, and the smile still played on Krishna's lips. Duryodhana drew a breath, and resumed, "As for Indraprastha, I know my father gave it to the sons of Pandu, when the Kuru kingdom was divided. I was against what he did then, but I could not say anything. Today, I rule an undivided kingdom; Indraprastha and Hastinapura are mine. And as long as there is life in this body, I will not part with any of my lands."

Now Duryodhana loomed over the sabha, dominating it darkly. He looked straight at Krishna and said, "Mark my words, Krishna, lodge them in your heart: I will not give the Pandavas a mote of my kingdom, not even what would cover the point of a needle!"

Duryodhana remained staring defiantly at Krishna after he had spoken, and it was as if a shadow fell over them all. Then Krishna laughed. It was a terrible laugh, as none of them had heard from him before: at once, a mocking laugh, a sad and wrathful laugh, and the Kurus trembled to hear it. Krishna rose, still smiling, but now his eyes were crimson. Somehow, Duryodhana faced the Avatara as he was then. It seemed primeval forces of darkness and light tested each other, as the Yadava and the Kaurava stood with gazes locked across that sabha.

Calmly, Krishna said, "If you really want a bed on a battlefield to lie on forever, you shall have one. You have always got whatever you wanted, haven't you Duryodhana? So be it then; as you say, let fate take her course. Be strong, O prince, be firm. For in just some days, there will be a slaughter that you cannot dream of. And in its bloody midst, you will meet the death you long for. You and all those that are with you."

Krishna had not raised his voice. He spoke almost sadly, or at least, only with anger born of grief. "You dare tell me you have caused the Pandavas no suffering, that you are not to blame at all for what they endured these thirteen years. You dare. And in this sabha of wise men, who know you since your infancy, *who know every sin you have ever committed*. Well, let them decide whether any guilt attaches to you or not. I knew how fiercely you would argue today, Duryodhana, how glibly. That is why I came here, and not because I had any real hope of convincing you to return to dharma. I am sure all these wise men have heard your clever arguments often enough. Now let them hear another point of view, and decide which one is true.

"You were consumed by envy when Yudhishtira performed the Rajasuya yagna. Already, you had tried to kill your cousins more than once, because you hated them from the moment they came home out of the wilds. When you saw the wealth of Indraprastha and the splendour of the Mayaa sabha, you could not bear your envy any longer. I am not sure whether it was you or your uncle Shakuni who decided to conquer the Pandavas at a game of dice. Probably Shakuni thought of it; it sounds like what he would prefer, a battle he could not lose. You would have gone to war if the choice were yours, that is more your nature.

"Even if the plan was Shakuni's at first, you embraced it readily enough. You did not protest that it was a perfidious way to quench your envy of the sons of Pandu: to humiliate them, to destroy them if you could. The plan worked well. Yudhishtira accepted your challenge, poor, high-minded king. Exactly as you had calculated, he lost his reason at this game that did not suit him at all. Don't tell me, Duryodhana, that you believed Yudhishtira stood a chance of winning at dice against Shakuni. Don't tell me the game was played in friendly spirit with no harm intended. You could have stopped the game, any time you chose; but it was not to stop that you had begun. You did not stop until Yudhishtira had lost everything, and his very honour, that day. And you say you are guilty of no crime? Do you take everyone in this sabha for a fool?

"As if the game of dice was not enough, you had your brother haul Panchali into this court. He dragged her in by her hair, and all these great men heard what you said to her then, your cousins' wife, how you called her to sit in your lap. And then, your brother, this grinning Dusasana, tried to strip that queen naked in this hallowed sabha." Krishna's voice was almost a whisper now, what he said was reverberant. "And you tell me no blame attaches to you, and you are an innocent man? Well, I have come here to learn how such a paragon of dharma like you, Duryodhana, chooses to fight a war in which millions shall die, brutally, when Yudhishtira still offers you peace."

Krishna's eyes blazed again, "You are no innocent, Duryodhana. You are the most evil man that draws breath in this world. Why do you try to deceive us, or is it yourself you need to deceive? Or do your sins weigh on you so heavily that you no longer know what dharma is? That you no longer see right from wrong, good from evil, darkness from light?"

They all shifted uneasily in their places to hear him; no conscience in that sabha, save Vidura's, was clear. Krishna said, "Duryodhana, you are beneath contempt," and fell silent.

Dusasana sprang up, and cried angrily, "Duryodhana, you will be forced to make cowardly peace with Yudhishtira. It is clear that Bheeshma, Drona and our own father mean to bind us hand and foot, you, Karna and me, and deliver us into this wily Krishna's hands. Why should you tolerate their speaking to you like this in your own court? Who is Krishna that we must listen to his lofty judgements here? The world knows he is partial to the sons of Kunti. After all, they are his blood and not we!"

Duryodhana was on his feet. He glared at Krishna for a moment, then, contemptuously, at the others. Without another word, but a hiss like an angry cobra's, he stalked out of the court. In a moment, all his brothers, advisors, and the kings who were his allies also left. The sabha was almost empty.

Bheeshma watched his grandson's arrogant exit, sadly, knowing its full significance. However, he also felt a sense of relief, as if a long and heavy burden had been taken from him. The worst he had feared, the unthinkable, had happened; now there was no looking back. Bheeshma, who had served the House of Kuru for so long, felt his own end drawn near. At last, he felt perfectly helpless, and almost glad of it.

He turned to Krishna with a sigh, "I have done everything I could to prevent this, but I see that I have outlived my usefulness. The hour of reckoning is here. Duryodhana is past saving. Doom has finally come to the House of Kuru; ah, Krishna, a sea of blood will flow. In all my life, I have never had such prescience of tragedy as I do now. Not just the Kurus but kshatriya kind will perish in the war that is upon us."

He stared quizzically at dark Krishna, sensing the Avatara knew immeasurably more of what he, Bheeshma, prophesied than he did himself. Yes, Krishna knew all about why the apocalyptic war must be fought; he had come to the earth to wash it with just this enormous bloodletting. Krishna stared gravely back at the tired old kshatriya.

Bheeshma sighed again, and murmured, "Yes, the time is ripe, I can feel it in every cell of my body. The war will be the end of the world, as we have known it, and the beginning of an inconceivably different age. Am I right, O Krishna who know all things?"

Krishna said, "I blame all of you for what will happen. You could have nipped this evil bloom in its bud. Instead, you nurtured it carefully, and helped it grow until it chokes us all. If you could not kill him, why didn't you lock Duryodhana away in the darkest dungeon? Are you so blinded by filial love that you still do not see who this prince is? He is a monster, a demon born into the world for its destruction. But there is one final hope I offer you, O elders of Hastinapura. Listen to me, I do not speak idly.

"When my uncle Kamsa was a tyrant in Mathura, I killed him though he was my own blood. Since the world was young, the wise have said that one man may be sacrificed if he threatens the welfare of the family; one family, if it threatens the village; one village, if it threatens the kingdom; and the very kingdom if one's immortal soul is imperilled.

"I ask you to undo the evil you have nourished in this sabha. The method is simple, if drastic; but consider how much less drastic than the war you plan. Four men stand between the very earth and peace; you must sacrifice them. Bind Duryodhana, Dusasana, Karna and Shakuni, and make them over to the Pandavas. Listen to me, O elders, and save kshatriya kind."

It was as if the Avatara tried fate. He still doubted the savage mission for which he had been born, and sought any means to avoid the war he knew must, ineluctably, be fought. Dhritarashtra grew very still at what Krishna said. He turned to Vidura, "Go and fetch Gandhari. She is the only one who might still turn our son back to dharma."

Poised and regal, her eyes bound as always, Gandhari came into the sabha. She allowed Vidura to lead her by the hand before the king. The Kuru queen said, "My lord, you have summoned me to the sabha today. What is the matter?"

"Duryodhana walked out of this sabha, insulting Krishna and all the elders. He will not listen to anyone, but is determined to have war with the Pandavas. He wants to ruin us all."

For a moment, Gandhari stood silent before her husband. Then she said, "My lord Vidura, fetch Duryodhana back; say his mother calls him here."

When Vidura had gone, she turned to Dhritarashtra again. "I prayed the day would never come when I had to say this to you: this kingdom does not deserve to be ruled by an evil prince like my son. It breaks my heart to say it, but he has plunged us all into the depths of hell. And you, my lord, are most to blame. I begged you not to give such absolute power into Duryodhana's hands; but you are a doting father, and you would not listen to me. You have made him king in your place, while you still live. More, you have walked down the path of sin with him, willingly. Even now, only your fear turns you back.

"Dhritarashtra, you are the king of such a great kingdom. If he cares for them at all, does a good king make a prince like Duryodhana a virtual ruler of his people? Just think, wouldn't they rather have Yudhishtira as their sovereign? Wouldn't they have profited richly from it, wouldn't we all? Instead…" she broke off, as they heard Duryodhana's angry tread in the sabha. Gandhari turned, "Duryodhana, is that you?"

"Yes, mother, it is I. What do you want from me?" His voice was stiff with annoyance.

"I am your mother and all I can ever want is for you to be safe and happy. My son, it is neither easy nor pleasant to be the king of a great country. A man must first be a master of himself, before he can rule a kingdom. Otherwise, he will drag both his people and himself into ruin. How can anyone who has not conquered himself dream of conquering his enemies? Duryodhana, a man's worst enemies are within himself: his weaknesses. They derange his mind, and he sees enemies all around him; while, in truth, he himself is his only enemy."

The mother held her hands out to her son. She said, "Don't you trust me, Duryodhana? This is I who speak, that love you most. But I will not lie to you or encourage you, when you rush towards your death."

Duryodhana made no move to take her outstretched hands. She sighed, let her arms fall to her sides again, and said with deep sorrow, "My son, it is time you heard what I am about to tell you. On the night you were born, omens of evil besieged this city in warning. The feral creatures of darkness flocked into our streets. Jackals and wolves howled at us, and vultures and swarms of bats wheeled across the face of the moon. Peals of thunder shook heaven and earth, and gashes of lightning flared not from the sky to the earth, but from the earth up into the heavens. In many places, it rained blood.

"That night Vidura said the child born to us would cause the end of the world, as we knew it. But I could not imagine my son would be evil. How could he, when I had always kept dharma? Alas, I was wrong and the omens were true."

Her son stood before her, made of ice. As she described that longago night, a smile flickered on his lips. He said nothing.

Gandhari begged him, "My child, abandon the thought of war. You have no right to put the lives of millions in jeopardy for the sake of your greed and your hatred. I know you think that Pitama Bheeshma, Acharya Drona and your Karna will vanquish the Pandavas. But your cousins have an ally who is greater than all these men, greater than the Gods, even. Dharma is with them.

"Then, Krishna is with the Pandavas, and Arjuna is one of them. These two, alone, can subdue Indra's Devas and all the Asuras in patala. Don't you know who they are? They are Nara Narayana. But how would you know that? You are so full of yourself and your own darkness. Duryodhana, if you won't listen to anyone else, at least you will not ignore what I am saying to you. You cannot fight dharma, my son. Dharma is eternal. You, your brothers, and everyone who fights for you will die." A sob shook her. Her voice dropping to a whisper, she said, "And the earth shall be made pure again."

Gandhari broke down and wept. Her son still stood with the same mocking smile on his lips. When his mother had finished, he did not say a word to answer her. He turned on his heel, and, without a glance at anyone in the sabha, Duryodhana walked out again.

FIFTEEN

'I am not alone'

Duryodhana stormed back to his apartment, where Dusasana, Shakuni and Karna waited for him. He was shaking with anger.

"They will do anything, Dusasana. They brought Gandhari into the sabha to tell me to mend my ways! Can you imagine how I felt? Like a small boy being scolded by his mother in the Kuru court. And Krishna sat there with that maddening smile on his face."

He swept a priceless crystal decanter of wine off a table. It smashed into shimmering dust on the black marble floor. Now he raged aloud, "Enough sanctimonious counsel! From Pitama, from my father, from Drona, from Vidura, from Krishna, and now from my mother. I want to be left alone! Is any man perfect, that he lives his life just by dharma? What about Krishna? Is he so perfect? The world knows how many women he keeps in Dwaraka. He never hesitated to kill anyone who stood in his way, by any means he could, with weapons or guile.

"He knows that life is not black or white; and neither are we. Men have never been like that. They have never done what they should, but what they wanted to. That is life! That is destiny. Always, there have been those too afraid to act, who tried to stop those who were bold enough to take what they wanted: to stop them with talk of dharma! You should hear my father now, and, of all men, Krishna preaches to me. The hypocrite! I have had enough of the lot of them."

Dusasana looked anxious. "If they brought our mother to speak to you, they will stop at nothing. Next thing, they will bind the four of us and hand us over to Yudhishtira. And the king will not stop them, any more. It would be the simplest solution; it is only we four who oppose their cowardly peace."

Duryodhana was startled at the thought. Then, a slow smile spread on his face. "Krishna is as dear to our cousins as their breath; without him, they are nothing. And we, also, have much to learn from this dark lion Krishna."

"What do you mean?"

"Krishna tells our elders to deliver us to the Pandavas, so there might be peace. What if we follow his advice? Take Krishna captive before anyone moves against us! And keep him here in Hastinapura as our hostage. I know how much the Pandavas love this black cowherd, whom the world calls the Avatara. If we take him hostage, it will break their spirits. If we hold Krishna, they will agree to anything, even to the peace everyone wants. They will agree to peace on my terms."

Dusasana said, "We must strike first, and victory shall be ours!"

But just they four could not hope to hold Krishna. Some others were taken into confidence, and a conspiracy hatched. Inevitably, word of the plot leaked out. Satyaki heard of it, and stormed into the Kuru sabha where Krishna sat with the elders of Hastinapura.

"Duryodhana plans to take Krishna hostage! Dhritarashtra, your son has lost his mind."

Vidura jumped up in shock. "Now we are doomed! Krishna, you must leave at once. We don't know who all are with Duryodhana in this treachery."

Krishna was not surprised or agitated. Mildly, he said, "It will not be easy to take me."

Dhritarashtra was panicstricken. "Fetch Duryodhana here at once."

Duryodhana stalked tensely back into the court. "Father, you sent for me."

"Sinful child!" wailed Dhritarashtra. "Evil as you are, I didn't dream you would stoop to this."

"What do you mean, my lord?"

"You dare even think of taking Krishna a hostage? This greatest of men, the Avatara? Duryodhana, I knew you were vain and foolish, but I never realized you were mad. The Devas and all the rishis in heaven, together, could not do what you are planning to. Idiot child, can you hold the wind in the palm of your hand? Can you take the sun a prisoner, or carry the earth in your arms? Why, these things are easier than making this man your prisoner. "

Duryodhana stood defiantly before his father. Krishna said softly, "Duryodhana, you think I am here by myself. But look, I am not alone."

As he spoke, the sabha filled with a thousand presences. Krishna said again, "Look, Duryodhana, I am not alone."

Duryodhana saw the hosts of heaven and earth crowding his father's court at dark Krishna's word. He saw the Pandavas in armour, their weapons in their hands. He saw the brilliant Vrishnis of Dwaraka and Mathura. The Andhakas he saw, and all the Yadava warriors, while Krishna said, "Yes, they are all here with me."

They saw the iridescent Adityas in that sabha, and the eight Vasus. Then, Krishna began to shine like lightning, so they could not bear the effulgence of him. From his blinding body emerged the Devas, one by one, and they were lucific, but pale beside the one they had issued from. They were dull beside the Cosmic Person Krishna had become, and as small as his thumb.

The court in Hastinapura, dwindled to nothingness, saw Brahma, four-faced, on Krishna's brow. On his chest, spanning infinite space, they saw the eleven terrific Rudras, masters of ages and galaxies. On the Avatara's shoulders, they saw the guardians of the quarters, the Kshetrapalas Indra, Varuna, Kubera and Yama. Agni blazed from his fanged mouth. The Adityas, the Vasus, the Maruts and Devas were all contained in him, and his tremendous laughter rang through the sabha of Hastinapura, through heaven and earth, and all the yawning kalpas. Duryodhana fell on his knees, his eyes shut and his hands clamped over his ears. Still, he saw and heard everything, helplessly.

Krishna laughed. Now, in the palm of his left hand, bright as the first light from which the universe was made, stood the Yadava army with Balarama at its head. On the Blue One's right palm stood Arjuna, the Gandiva in his hand, the Pandava legions behind him, and Bheema, Yudhishtira, Nakula and Sahadeva at his side.

But these were just two hands of a thousand arms. Others held starry weapons, ayudhas that could extinguish constellations. He wielded the mace Kaumodaki, the sword Nandana, both spewing fires like sunflares, the legendary bow Saringa; and, above another forefinger, wheeling silent and nitid, a sun compressed: the Sudarshana Chakra!

This was his cosmic form, and his tusked mouth spewed tongues of flame as long as nebulae. Flames leapt from his eyes and nostrils. He was too terrible to look at, and, like Duryodhana, most of the Kuru sabha shut its eyes; but not Bheeshma, Drona or Vidura, nor the rishis who had come to that court. They did not blink, but gazed raptly, in adoration, at the spectacle of spectacles. And he, the Lord, gave them the power to gaze on him, impervious; otherwise, a moment of this vision would have destroyed them. Those wise ones drank him into their very souls through staring eyes.

Then, a miracle: Krishna gave blind Dhritarashtra, who had never seen the world, sight, and this vision of God to behold. Tears coursing down his face, speechless, the king gazed at immortal Krishna, so dreadful and so ineffably sweet. Even those whose eyes were shut tight in fear heard celestial music in that sabha; even they felt the barely material flowers that rained on them out of heaven, and smelt their unearthly fragrance.

Overwhelmed, sobbing, laughing like a child, Dhritarashtra fell on his knees and cried in an ecstasy to Krishna, "My eyes see! Oh, you are the Lord of heaven and earth, Dark One! I am blessed that you sat in my sabha, and showed yourself to me like this. Yet, O Krishna, I have a boon to beg of you, king of kings. Having seen you like this, I do not want my eyes to see anything else. Take back the sight you have given me, let my only memory of vision be of you."

Krishna granted him that. But now, the Avatara had assumed his Viswa Rupa for longer than the earth could bear. The planet began to quake. Tempests swept the oceans, and the seven seas began to evaporate in boiling tides. It seemed that time was ending, and the world would burst asunder at any moment. Terrified birds flew in wheeling alarm, and wild beasts dashed frenziedly everywhere. People of the earth came running out of their homes, screaming. The palace of Hastinapura shuddered, and would have crumbled in a moment; then Krishna reverted to his human form. He was God no more, but just the mysterious master of Dwaraka again.

Duryodhana was still on his knees, with his head buried in his arms. All the others had their gazes riveted to the Dark One. Krishna rose. He took Satyaki and Vidura's hands and walked out of the sabha. Like a deep blue flame he went, and all the kings and all the munis rose and followed him, as smoke does a fire. He neither turned his face to them, nor spoke a word. Kritavarman had seen Krishna emerge from the sabha, and brought his chariot to the palace steps. Krishna went down those steps with Vidura and Satyaki; Kritavarman saw measureless sorrow in his black eyes that glistened with tears.

From the top of those steps, Krishna heard Dhritarashtra's anxious voice, "Krishna, you have seen how powerless I am. What can I do when my son will not listen to me?"

Krishna had one foot on the board of his chariot; the people had collected in the street. He paused, and said loudly, "I have done everything I could to bring peace to the Kurus. Duryodhana will have none of it; he says he will not give his cousins even land to cover a point of a needle. Now the king admits he is powerless to stop his son from having his way. There is nothing more I can say. I must go back to Yudhishtira."

He climbed into the chariot. "Go quickly, Satyaki. I must say farewell to Kunti before we return."

At Vidura's home, Krishna told Kunti what had happened in the Kuru sabha. He said grimly, "This nest of evil will soon burn with a conflagration called the Pandavas." He took her hands, "But I must leave you now, and fly back to Yudhishtira. Do you want to send any message for your sons?"

Kunti's eyes were full of grief, full of fire. Quietly, she said, "Tell my sons that they are all kshatriyas, and heavenly voices spoke when they were born. Their mother expects them to do what kshatriyas should. Krishna, tell Draupadi that no mother was ever prouder than I am to have her as my daughter."

A smile broke out on her gracious face, lined with the years. She said, "As for a mother's anxiety, I have none, Krishna, because I know you watch over my sons. Go in peace, my child."

She embraced him. He touched her feet and went to his waiting chariot. Krishna set out for Upaplavya with Satyaki.

In the Kuru court, Duryodhana uncoiled himself off the floor like a hamadryad. He roared, "Prepare for war! We shall have war at once! I will not sleep or eat until battle is joined."

Bheeshma cried, "Duryodhana, listen…"

Dhritarashtra cried, "My son!"

Vidura and Drona tried to stop him, but Duryodhana strode away from them. Soon, eleven aksauhinis prepared to march to the field of Kurukshetra for the war on the crack of the ages.

SIXTEEN

Krishna and Karna

As KRISHNA RODE OUT OF HASTINAPURA, HE SAW KARNA STANDING alone on the palace steps, gazing at the horizon. Krishna told Satyaki, "Stop the horses."

The Dark One called out, "Karna! I must talk to you."

Karna stood for a moment, looking doubtfully at Krishna. Then he came down the steps.

Krishna said, "Come for a short ride with me."

Without a backward glance, Karna climbed into the chariot, and they drove out of the city-gates and to some nearby woods.

"Stop, Satyaki, this will do. Karna let us take a walk together."

When they had walked some way, Krishna turned abruptly and laid a hand on Karna's shoulder. Karna raised an eyebrow in surprise. Krishna said urgently, "I know you well, Karna, I have watched you carefully. You are a man of truth, a man of your word, and one of great courage. All your life you have fought against impossible odds, and you have often prevailed. You are hard, but you are not evil. I know you are a master of the Vedas and the Vedangas. Behind the callous mask you wear is a learned man, who knows the subtle shades of dharma."

When Karna laughed, Krishna held up a hand. "Let me finish, before you mock. You don't deceive me, Karna, I know the man behind the mask. You are not what you pretend to be, and shall never be. You are not like Duryodhana, Dusasana or Shakuni. You have a noble heart as few men possess; you have great character. You have ample wit, and you know your friend sets himself and all those with him on a course to death. He walks the way of sin, and you, who know better, walk with him. Why, Karna?"

Karna smiled, as he seldom did, and his severe face softened. He met Krishna's gaze evenly, "Why do you flatter me today, Krishna? I have not heard such praise from you, of all people. What do you want from me? Surely, it is what you can never have."

Krishna murmured, "Perhaps not."

Grave again in a moment, Karna said in his intense way, "If you really want to know why I walk with Duryodhana, I will tell you. What you say is true, about the path he has chosen for himself. He treads the dark way of sin: perhaps, the short way of sin?

"But I say to you, Krishna, *there is no man on earth as noble as Duryodhana.* I will never judge him as you or the others do, and my reason is simple: *I love him too much.* The world spurned me because I was a sutaputra; but not once has Duryodhana even thought of me like that. To him I am never Karna the sutaputra, but Karna his friend. And I am as dear to him as his brothers, dearer.

"Once I came to this city in search of a livelihood. I was finally an archer, and I heard there was to be a tournament. The Kuru princes were to show the skills they had learnt from Drona, who refused to take me as his sishya, because I was a suta's son. Do you know the story of my life, Krishna? It has not been an easy life."

Krishna said nothing, only listened. Karna resumed, "I studied archery with Bhargava. Yet, I did not leave his asrama with his blessings, but his curse: because I was a sutaputra. When I came to the tournament in Hastinapura, I did not intend to announce myself as I did. Then I saw Drona and his pupils so smug with their accomplishments, especially young Arjuna. He was brilliant, all right, but I knew I was a better archer than he was. I could not help myself; I had to challenge him. Even after I had shown them my skills, they said I could not fight Arjuna because I was not a kshatriya. Then Duryodhana took my hand, and made me king of Anga. I can never forget that day, Krishna; it changed my life.

"I was overwhelmed, and I said to him, 'I am in your debt forever. Tell me what I can do to repay your generosity. Let it be anything, my life is yours to ask for.'

"He embraced me, and replied, 'You are a great warrior; Anga is the least you deserve. I want nothing from you, Karna, but your love. Give me your heart.'

"How could I not? Krishna, only two people have loved me like that. My mother Radha and Duryodhana; and it is for the sake of these two that I am still alive. I care little enough for my life; it has brought me nothing but anguish. But don't ask me to ever sit in judgement over Duryodhana, whatever he may do. I know a Duryodhana who is my friend, who loves me, and who is the truest of men."

There were tears in his eyes. Krishna nodded, "The debt of gratitude, the most difficult thing to pay back on earth." Then, out of the blue, he said casually, "Karna, I suppose you have made your choice knowing who your real mother is?"

Karna was startled: how did Krishna know Radha wasn't his mother? Recovering at once, he said, "I never knew who my real mother was, but I dreamt of her. I sometimes felt she was a princess who lived in a palace beside a river; as if a dim memory of her has stayed with me. I must have been illegitimate, and she cared more for her reputation than her child. She floated me down the river in a box; that is how much she loved me. She must have other sons now, and has forgotten me like some bad dream she had once, briefly. But I have left all that far behind me. Why speak of it now? Anyway, what does my mother have to do with whether or not I stand with Duryodhana?"

Krishna was looking at him so queerly, and Karna felt disquieted. But he said, "And besides, Radha is my mother, even if she didn't give birth to me. She loves me, she is proud of what I have achieved, and that is all that matters."

Gently, Krishna said, "Your mother was indeed a princess, and she did abandon you because she feared what the world would say, and what her father, who was a king, would say. She was not married when she had you. But Karna, since the moment she floated you down the river, she has thought only of you. Yes, she has five other sons, as splendid as any mother could wish for. But her heart yearns for the beautiful baby she once abandoned. The baby born with the golden armour, her first child she lost. She pines for you, Karna."

Karna breathed, "If my mother is a king's daughter, I am a kshatriya! Small wonder that I longed to be an archer." He seized the Dark One's hands. "Krishna, do you know my mother? Is she alive? Who is she? Tell me!"

Krishna gazed into Karna's face, trying to decide if he should tell him the terrible truth. At last, he said, "Karna, your mother had five sons after you, and your brothers are the greatest kshatriyas on earth."

For a moment, Karna did not understand. Then he whispered, "Five sons ... the greatest kshatriyas. Krishna, do you mock me?"

Full of pity, Krishna shook his head. Karna clutched his hands more fiercely, "It cannot be!"

"But it is, Karna," the Avatara told him. "Kunti is your mother, the Pandavas are your brothers."

Karna's roar echoed in that wild place. "And my father? Who is my father, Krishna?"

"The God you worship every day, your Ishta Devata. Surya Deva is your father."

Karna swooned; Krishna caught him as he fell. When he came to his senses again, he began to sob helplessly, as he had not done for years. With such sorrow in his eyes, he said to Krishna, "Now I am certain that I am the most cursed man alive. Surya Deva is my father; Kunti Devi is my mother; Yudhishtira, Bheema, Arjuna, Sahadeva and Nakula are my brothers, my flesh and blood. And what am I to the world? An upstart sutaputra!" He laughed bitterly. "Now I know why Bhargava cursed me. He knew who I was: not who I thought, but more a kshatriya than I knew myself. But oh, how will I live with the truth with which you have struck me, Krishna? The Pandavas are my brothers, and I..."

His face hardened. He wiped his tears, and his voice full of suspicion, he said, "But you haven't just discovered this, have you? You have always known who I am. Why do you tell me this now? To disturb me, so I will not be able to fight my brothers. Ah, you are a crafty one."

But Krishna's black eyes were full of love. "I tell you this, Karna, because I want to save your life. Not only that; I have an offer to make you, an honourable one. You know kshatriya dharma as well as anyone. You know that if an unmarried woman has a son, when she marries that child becomes her husband's heir. You are a Pandava on your father's side. Karna, on your mother's side you are a Vrishni. You and I are cousins. Come away from this city of sin; come with me to your brothers.

They will welcome you as the eldest of them. Yudhishtira will set his crown on your head; dark Panchali will be your queen.

"They will make you sit in a golden chariot. Yudhishtira will lead you to it, Bheema will hold the white parasol over your head, Arjuna will be your sarathy, and Nakula, Sahadeva and I will walk behind you in train: on the way to your coronation! Who is more worthy of being lord of the earth than you are? Karna, your dharma is as staunch as Yudhishtira's. Your heart is as warm as Bheema's, your archery as deep as Arjuna's. You are regal in all your parts, and I think you are learned past what anyone realizes, since you never flaunt your learning as other men do.

"And more than any of these, you have suffered as not even the Pandavas have. You have had scorn heaped on you, and lived with the constant pang of being a sutapura. Only men who have suffered know the value of compassion; above anything, a king must be compassionate.

"You have lived thinking your mother who gave birth to you did not love you. She longs for you. Not seeing you, not knowing you, causes her more grief than you can imagine. Come away with me, Karna. Don't look back, come now."

For a moment, Karna stood staring at Krishna. Then he smiled, "Ah, Krishna, who could make it sound more enchanting than you? And I see that you do it out of love. But it is not as simple as you make it out to be. True, by law I am a Pandava, a Kaunteya and your cousin. But just the facts of blood cannot change the course of my life as it has been. Krishna, my mother floated me down the river when I was an infant. I could have drowned; but her reputation was more precious to her than my life. Such a woman is not worth calling one's mother.

"Atiratha found me, abandoned and adrift, as I am sure God meant him to. When his wife Radha saw me—she always marvels at it—her breasts filled with mother's milk! She took me in her arms, and fed me. Not Kunti, but Radha is my mother. Atiratha has loved me like his own son. My heart belongs with them; they will always be my parents.

"Then, there is Duryodhana. How can you think I would abandon him? No, not for all the kingdom and wealth on earth would I betray Duryodhana. What you don't account for is that I am a grown man; it is too late for me to change. My loves and hates, my friendships and enmities have already formed. The only way I can change them is to die."

With pity and admiration, Krishna looked at this remarkable warrior. Karna said, "It is honour and fame that I live for. More than anything else, I live to fight Arjuna in what I have sworn shall be the last battle of one of us. If I join the Pandavas now, how will the world witness the duel we have both promised it? Above all, I am an archer, and so is Arjuna. Each of us claims to be the finest bowman on earth. Mustn't we discover the truth in battle?"

Krishna began to say something, but Karna went on, "I know what you want to tell me: that you, great one, protect the Pandavas, and no force on earth can conquer them. I am not a fool that I do not know this. But honour demands that I fight my own brothers. My place is beside my deluded, doomed friend. I will fight for Duryodhana, and die for him. I am fate's plaything, its victim, and have always been; not even you can suddenly turn me into her favourite son. It is too late for that, sweet cousin. If I betray Duryodhana now, I shall not only be time's victim, but her clown."

Krishna heaved a sigh, and shook his head sadly. Then Karna's eyes were full of fear. "How will I fight Arjuna when I know he is my brother? Krishna, did you have to pierce me with this savage truth? I have never lived in peace, and now I will not die peacefully either. Yet, how do I hold it against you, when you are trying to save my life? But since you love me, and since we are cousins, there is one service you can do me."

Krishna's eyes were bright and moist. "Tell me what it is, and I will do it."

"Swear you will keep this secret, until I am dead. Yudhishtira will never fight me, if he knows we are brothers. He will offer me the kingdom he is fighting for, and that would never do. We are kshatriyas, Krishna; we are born for battle.

"As for me, I know I fight for a cause that is lost, before the first arrow is loosed. Yet, though I am doomed by my choice, I will stand with Duryodhana. There is a heaven above for kshatriyas who die on the field of battle; I aspire to that swarga. The earth holds no charm for me, and my life is worthless, especially now, after what you have said. What use is living, when my heart is in pieces and I can never be sure of who I am? I prefer death, because I have never been comfortable in life. And my way to death lies clear before me: fighting Duryodhana's hopeless war."

"What makes you so certain the Pandavas will win this war?" asked Krishna.

"Why, my lord, because this war is to be a yagna, your awesome sacrifice. It is the end of the dwapara yuga, and the earth's burden must be made lighter; the wise say you have been born for that. The rest of us are but players in your lila. You will be the ritvik, the high priest on the field of Kurukshetra, and Arjuna will be your fire. The rest of us, Dhritarashtra's sons, Bheeshma, Drona and I, and all the kings who fight for Duryodhana, we shall be your havis, your offerings; we shall all burn.

"I have dreams, Krishna. As I used to dream of my mother once, I now dream of the war of the Kurus, and its end. Repeatedly, in my dream I see Yudhishtira, bright as a star, with a golden bowl of payasa in his hands out of which he drinks. I saw Bheema on a mountain, immense himself, glaring down at the world spread below him like a tapestry. I saw you, Krishna, and Arjuna, like two suns, your light streaming down over the world. In my dream, I saw Nakula, Sahadeva and Satyaki clad in white silk, with garlands around their necks, and jewels glittering on their bodies, to signify their lordship over the earth. They smiled at me.

"But that is not all I saw. I saw the warriors of Duryodhana's army, all of us wearing black, and our heads bent, walking south, always south. Those who walk south in a dream never have long to live. Krishna, I saw the end of your sacrifice on Kurukshetra. Dusasana lay bleeding on the earth, his chest torn open; Bheema stood over him and his lips were stained with blood. Drona and Bheeshma fell, killed by Dhrishtadyumna and Shikhandi. I was cut down by Arjuna's arrow, and I fell. And at last, Bheema broke Duryodhana's thigh, as he swore he would, and left him to die slowly, to pay in agony for everything.

"I see it all as if it has already happened. Inexplicably, these dreams fill me not with dread, only elation. I am more than ready to die. I began my lonely journey the day I was born. I have borne my burden long enough; I am impatient for death to free me! There is indeed a swarga above for kshatriyas who die in battle. I dream of that place, too; only there, shall I find my peace. Only there, will I find my brothers, my father and mother again. And then it shall truly be heaven.

"But now, Krishna, I see in your eyes that you must be going. This is perhaps the last time we shall meet like this, kindly. When we see each other next, it will be as mortal enemies on the field of war." He paused, and a wistful look touched his face briefly. Karna said, "But then, we shall meet again as friends, cousin, in Devaloka after I am dead."

Krishna clasped Karna to him, and for a moment, Karna had tears in his eyes. He wiped them quickly, and wrung Krishna's hand one last time. They walked back together towards Satyaki waiting in his chariot.

SEVENTEEN

The Pandava Senapati

Exhausted by his embassy, Krishna came back to Upaplavya. The Pandavas were waiting anxiously for the word he brought. He greeted them warmly, but his face was strained and he said he must sleep a while, before he told them what had happened in Hastinapura. Krishna retired to his apartment. It was evening when he appeared again in the court of Upaplavya. Yudhishtira welcomed him formally, and, when everyone was seated, the Pandava said, "Krishna, I see sadness on your face, and it is not difficult to imagine what the news is from Hastinapura. But tell us what happened."

Krishna said, "I fear your inference is true, Yudhishtira. My mission failed, and our dream of peace remains a dream. I did all I could to turn Duryodhana back to dharma. But he was obstinate." He sighed, "There will be war, Yudhishtira, you will have to fight."

A spasm of anguish twitched on Yudhishtira's face. In a low voice, he said, "Tell me everything that happened. I want to hear each detail."

"I was taken to the sabha in Hastinapura, where the Kuru elders sat on their thrones, and where Narada and Vyasa waited, and other rishis, to hear the destiny of the world being decided."

Krishna told them how the elders tried to convince Duryodhana to relent, how Dhritarashtra, Bheeshma, Drona and Vidura spoke for peace. He told them what he himself had said, and Duryodhana's angry reply, arguing his innocence; and how the Kaurava walked haughtily out of the court. Krishna described how Gandhari came to plead with Duryodhana, and how he walked out again in fury, without answering his mother.

Finally, smiling, Krishna came to the plot to take him a hostage in Hastinapura. For once Yudhishtira lost his composure, and cried in a terrible voice, "For that he will die! My days of forgiving him are over. The earth is thirsty for the blood of these beasts, and she shall drink her fill. *War! Let there be war! Let there be war at once!*"

Bheema threw his mace into the air. He ran to Yudhishtira and embraced him wildly. He roared, "War! At last, my brother cries for war! Nothing can save Dhritarashtra's sons now. Arjuna! Karna's blood will darken the earth of Kurukshetra. Sahadeva, my brother, my eyes will watch you spill the vile Shakuni's blood, and shed tears of joy. Ah, Krishna! This is the happiest day of my life, I feel I have drunk amrita."

Krishna said, "When I left for Upaplavya, Duryodhana had already ordered his army to march on Kurukshetra." He was grave again, "Bheeshma will be the Senapati of the Kuru forces, its Supreme Commander. Dharma is on our side, but let us never underestimate the enemy. Your Pitama vanquished his guru Bhargava in battle; first of all, we have awesome Bheeshma to face. Arjuna, and you Shikhandi, who have sworn to kill Bheeshma, prepare yourselves!"

Krishna did not say a word about his meeting with Karna in the woods. Yudhishtira rose to address the kings who had come with their armies to join him. "We have done our best to secure peace, but Duryodhana will have none of it. The war we must fight is a war thrust on us, a war we never wanted. The time of trial, the ruthless time, is upon us. I thank you all for coming to help me in the name of dharma. Krishna, Lord, seven aksauhinis are yours to command. Drupada, Virata, Dhrishtadyumna, Satyaki, Shikhandi, Chekitana and Bheema could, any of them, lead our army. You must decide what role each one will have. I also want to hear my brothers' opinions, about who our Senapati should be. Sahadeva, child, you are the youngest, but the wisest in many ways. Let us hear what you think first."

Sahadeva rose and said, "My lord, any of those you named can lead our army, for they are all great kshatriyas. But to stand against Pitama Bheeshma, I would choose King Virata of the Matsyas. He is a seasoned soldier, his age and experience commend him."

Yudhishtira turned to Nakula, "Nakula, whom would you have as our Senapati?"

Nakula said with no hesitation, "Drupada, lord of the Panchalas. He is Bhargava's sishya, and Drona's sworn enemy. Acharya Drona will play at least as crucial a role in the war as our Pitama. Drupada is a tapasvin, a master of astras; let him lead us into battle."

Yudhishtira said, "Arjuna, whom do you choose for our general?"

"Let youth confront age and triumph. Let Dhrishtadyumna ride at the head of our army. None better than Drupada's son to take fire to the enemy."

"Bheema?"

Bheema said, "If Pitama Bheeshma is to be their Senapati, ours should be the one who has sworn a solemn oath spanning two lives to be the death of Bheeshma. He, too, is Drupada's son. He is also a kshatriya. Let Shikhandi face Bheeshma, and keep his vow."

Yudhishtira said, "If our army has so many warriors that are fit to lead us, it must indeed be a force to contend with! But night wears on now, and we have a choice to make before we sleep. If I had to choose anyone to lead us into war, I would not hesitate but choose Krishna. True, he is younger than some of us; but can anyone match his wisdom? It matters little whether he bears a weapon or not. All our destinies lie in his hands, and I will submit to whatever he decides. Krishna, you tell us who our Senapati shall be."

Krishna said, "It is a hard choice to make. All the kshatriyas you have named could hold up the host of Devaloka. The Kaurava army will perish before any of them."

"But who shall be our Senapati, Krishna? The soldiers are awake and impatient to hear."

Krishna said, "I agree with Arjuna. Drupada's son Dhrishtadyumna is the one to lead us into battle."

That sabha erupted in cheers, and when Yudhishtira sent word to the army, the men were jubilant. Dhrishtadyumna was the choice of most of them, as well. Krishna and Yudhishtira then decided on commanders for each of the seven aksauhinis: Bheema, Nakula, Sahadeva, Dhrishtadyumna, Satyaki, Draupadi's sons, and Abhimanyu. The other kshatriyas were to be free to fight wherever they chose. Tired as they were, those kings of the earth, the soldiers of dharma, turned in for the night. The next day would be a momentous one.

The Pandava Senapati

Yudhishtira was up before the sun and, with Dhaumya and his other priests, he worshipped the Gods. He performed the sacred rituals that must be done, before fighting a war. As he finished his worship and the sun rose over Upaplavya, the other kshatriyas emerged from the palace and made their way to the soldiers' tents. The Kekaya brothers were there, Dhrishtaketu, Sreniman, Vasushena, Virata, Shikhandi, Drupada, Sudharma, Kuntibhoja, the new Senapati Dhrishtadyumna, Anadhrishti, Chekitana, Satyaki, the Pandavas and their sons, Abhimanyu, and dark Krishna, resplendent.

Dhrishtadyumna went to greet the troops, then the camp at Upaplavya was struck. That endless force moved majestically on foot, horse- and elephant-back, and in chariots, singing lustily, to Kurukshetra. At last, they arrived at fate's field, where the war at the end of the yuga would be fought, the war that would change the world. It would end the old order, come down from time out of mind, and usher in a new, bizarre age on earth. The warriors all raised their conches, and sounded them in thunderous unison; in an oceanic roar from a few million throats, the common soldiers shouted their exultation at the tremendous bass.

The Pandava army made fresh camp at the edge of the level field stretching away to the horizon; that place was transformed into a hive of activity. Dhrishtadyumna took charge of the arrangements. The site was measured and marked for soldiers' tents, tents for kitchens to feed that teeming army, tents for the kings and their guards. Krishna and Satyaki oversaw the digging of a moat around the camp, to keep wild animals out at night. With so many hands to attend to its every aspect, work progressed swiftly; in less than a day, Yudhishtira's flag fluttered above an established military camp, already functioning harmoniously. At the heart of the camp, was a mountain of weapons of every kind. Bows, quivers full of arrows, lances, swords, maces and axes of battle, and a hillock of armour and finger-sheaths: for all to take from, when the fighting began.

The truth was that every man had been preparing for this for weeks. In the palace and in the camps at Upaplavya, kings, princes and soldiers together had planned meticulously how they would make their camp at Kurukshetra. Then they had waited impatiently for Krishna's return from Hastinapura, to know if the war would indeed be fought.

When they arrived at Kurukshetra, every soldier knew exactly what he must do.

Yet, when later, exhausted by the long march and the day's hard labour, the men lay down to sleep under a slender moon, each one knew the war itself would be another matter. Then nothing could be predicted: not if they would ever see their families again, not life itself, from moment to moment, not though they fought on the side of dharma, and that was an honourable way to die.

EIGHTEEN

The Kaurava Senapati

After Krishna left Hastinapura at noon, Duryodhana ordered his eleven aksauhinis to march to Kurukshetra the next day. The same night, he gathered his brothers and his intimate coterie together. He was sombre as the hour of truth drew near, sombre as one who, at least in his deepest heart, was aware of having incurred a greater debt than he could ever hope to discharge. But there was no turning back, and if Duryodhana was anxious after Krishna's revelation in the court of Hastina, he gave no sign of it.

Evenly, he said to those he had called to his apartment, "Krishna has gone back to Yudhishtira without having fulfilled his ostensible peace mission. I know he wants war; he has always plotted for it. He will not forget to tell Yudhishtira how we planned to take him hostage. He will exaggerate everything that happened here, and Satyaki will bear him out. Already, Bheema and Arjuna are keened for battle, and now Krishna will break down Yudhishtira's last resistance. They have Virata and Drupada with them, who also want this war for their own reasons."

He paused, then said, "For years we have dominated them with strategy and guile. Now they are certain they can have revenge on the field of war. What they forget is that we have eleven aksauhinis against their seven. Krishna may be more powerful than anyone else in the world; but he has sworn he will carry no arms during the war. Long privation robs men of their reason. The Pandavas will find swift death at the end of their exile, for the folly of daring to fight us. And that will finish the contention that began when our cousins came out of the wilderness, as they never should have. When they lie dead upon the earth, we shall be undisputed masters of the world, as we were born to be.

"Dusasana, my brother, Karna, dearer to me than a brother, let us not waste another day of this precious, fleeting life. Let word go forth that we march at dawn!"

The next morning, at crack of dawn, Duryodhana's army marched towards Kurukshetra. Weapons and armour glinting in the early sun, wave on wave of soldiers flowed in tide across the earth. Eleven aksauhinis, each with a great commander at its head: Kripa, Drona, Shalya, Jayadratha, Sudakshina, Kritavarman, Aswatthama, Bhoorisravas, Shakuni, Baahlika and Somadatta. Duryodhana stood among these kshatriyas, all of them ready to die for him, and watched his interminable legions wind their way out of Hastinapura.

The Kaurava prince turned to Bheeshma, and said, "Look, Pitama, don't our men seem like an unending line of ants?"

After months, he spoke in the friendliest tone to his grandsire. The others around them fell silent, knowing what Duryodhana was about to ask the Kuru patriarch. Duryodhana continued, "This is perhaps the greatest army ever mustered under the Kuru flag; and, to my mind, there is only one kshatriya among us who can command this force." Emotionally he knelt at Bheeshma's feet. "Pitama, I beg you, be the Senapati of the army of Hastinapura!"

Bheeshma's face softened. Gently, he said, "If you truly want me to command these legions, so be it, my child. But I have two conditions before I accept. The Pandavas are as dear to me as you are; I will not raise my bow to kill any of them. But I will harry their soldiers and their allies. I will kill ten thousand men each day we fight!"

Duryodhana said, "Pitama, you have no equal in this world."

But Bheeshma replied, "That isn't true, even if it pleases my old heart to hear you say it. Arjuna is a greater archer than I ever was. If anyone can kill me, it is he. But hear my second condition, before you decide you still want me to be your Senapati."

"What is it, Pitama? There is no condition I will not accept to have you lead our army into battle."

"I will not fight beside Karna. I cannot brook his arrogance, either he fights or I do."

This was no more the Kuru sabha that Duryodhana could walk out of it. He turned pale. He had no answer to Bheeshma's second condition.

But Karna said quickly, "I am happy with this condition! As long as Bheeshma fights I will not." Then his voice grew softer, "But if Bheeshma is killed, Karna will come to fight for Duryodhana. Besides, your Pitama has granted me my dearest wish: that he will not kill Arjuna, but let me have that satisfaction. What else do I live for but to prove I am the best bowman on earth?"

No expression touched Bheeshma's face. After a moment's silence, he said, "I will command the Kuru army."

Beaming, Duryodhana touched his grandsire's feet again, and embraced him. Word flashed forth that Bheeshma had agreed to be Senapati of the army of Hastinapura, and a sea of cheering rose among the soldiers. Amidst the solemn chanting of mantras, Bheeshma was given the ceremonial bath of consecration. Then he climbed into his chariot and rode to the head of that endless force.

NINETEEN

On the banks of Yamuna

VIDURA AND KUNTI SAT TOGETHER IN HER APARTMENT IN HIS PALACE, both of them dejected. It was the day Krishna left for Upaplavya. In a strained voice, Vidura had been telling Kunti what had happened in the Kuru court.

"Duryodhana would rather see the world end than give up his obstinacy. Again and again, Yudhishtira asked to make peace; but Duryodhana will not listen. He won't give back five towns, which are all your son wants." Vidura sighed. "I have no doubt the Pandavas will win the war; but at what a cost. Blood will flow in rivers on the holy land. Perhaps, Duryodhana might have been persuaded by wise counsel, but Shakuni, Dusasana and that wild Karna are his advisors. I haven't slept a wink these past few days, Kunti, thinking of the pass we have come to."

Kunti sat listening, without saying a word. She knew how powerful her sons were. But she also knew the Kaurava army had four aksauhinis more than the Pandavas did. And when she heard that Bheeshma had agreed to command Duryodhana's legions, fear clutched at her. What unnerved Kunti even more was the thought of her other son. Above anyone else, she feared Karna and her terror of him was heightened by guilt. When the exhausted Vidura left her, she told herself, 'Not Duryodhana's hatred for my sons can match Karna's envy of Arjuna. Karna is Surya's son; he is every bit the archer Arjuna is. He may well kill Arjuna, or Arjuna, him; either way, I will lose a son.'

She wept in despair then decided: 'There is only one thing to do.' She also retired for the night, which was a long and sleepless one.

The next day at noon, when the sun was at his zenith, burning down on the earth, with her head covered to protect her from the searing heat, Kunti went down to the banks of the Yamuna. Among the mirages that rose from the river, she saw Karna worshipping the Sun God. He stood bare-bodied, his arms raised straight above his head, his face lifted to the calescent star. Motionless he stood, chanting the Surya mantra.

Kunti approached him softly, her heart pounding. She stood behind him, unmoving. It is told that Karna was so tall and magnificent, she sheltered comfortably in his shadow, as in the shade of a tree. In a while, he lowered his arms, then his head, and opened his eyes. Her shadow fell across his own, and he turned. For the first time Karna saw his mother, like a wreath of wilted lotuses, and his heart gave a lurch. She stood before him, not saying a word, her head and face still covered. Gently, he took her hand and led her to a tree that grew at the edge of the water.

He folded his hands to her, and said, "I am Atiratha's son Karna. This is the hour when I grant a boon to anyone who comes to me. I see you are noble, and unused to the heat. Tell me, what can I do for you?"

She gazed and gazed at his face, and at first made no reply. He saw tears in her eyes, and they spilt over. She is uncannily familiar, he thought: her eyes, her exquisite hands, her regal bearing! But for the life of him, he could not tell where he had seen her before. For her, after the fateful day she floated him down the river in the wooden box, this was the first time she had seen him so close.

She dried her eyes and said, "Perhaps you know me, or then again you might not. But I have come to beg a boon from you."

He still stared at her, then he said slowly, "I cannot remember having seen you, but I feel I know you. Why, I feel I have known you all my life."

He broke off, and stared more intently. Then he breathed, "It's you! The woman in my dreams. Of course I know you, I have always known you."

He knelt before her. She said, "I don't understand. How can you say you know me, when we have never met? How have you seen me in your dreams? I have time to listen, if you care to tell me. I have come to spend some time with you."

Karna did not take his eyes off her, and his gaze scathed Kunti. He said, "I never told anyone except my mother Radha about the woman in my dreams, and I never felt the need to. Today, I know I must tell you about her, and about myself. Though Radha raised me, she is not my natural mother. One day, my father Atiratha found me floating in a wooden box on the Yamuna, an abandoned child. He brought me home to his wife, and they adopted me. I never knew any other parents, never knew Radha was not my real mother, or Atiratha my father. For many years I was called only Radheya, Radha's son."

Gravely she listened to him, tenderly. Karna went on, "Since I was a child, ever since I can remember, a dream has haunted my sleep, the same dream over and over again. A woman would appear with her face covered, and in sorrow and love, she would bend over me. Her tears would drip onto my face, burning me.

Still dreaming, I would ask her, 'Who are you? Why are you crying?'

Her voice choking, she would answer, 'I am crying because of what I have done to you, because this is the only way I can see you. But I am such a sinner that I may not speak to you even in our dreams.'

She would turn to leave. I would run after her, and try to lift the veil that hid her face. I would cry, 'Show me your face! I want to see who you are.'

But she would vanish, and I would awake trembling."

His eyes still searched her face. "As I grew, the dream became rarer, and the woman hardly appeared any more. It has been years since I saw her at all. But I am sure it was my mother who came to me in my sleep. At first, she thought of me a good deal, and she frequented my dreams. But later, when she had other children, she thought of me less and less, or did not want to; and she did not come any more.

"That is the story of the woman in my dreams." He paused, then said, "But you look exactly like her. Who are you, gracious one? What is the boon you seek from me?"

Kunti could hardly look into his eyes, full of the years' long pain. She bent her head down, down, and gazed at her fine hands. Then, quietly, she said, "It is true, I am your mother."

No expression flickered on his graven face. She went on without pausing, "I am the Pandavas' mother Kunti. You, Karna, are my firstborn son."

Karna began to laugh. He said, "Kunti Devi, mother of the Pandavas, has come to her son Karna to beg a boon! Surely, I am asleep and dreaming, for this can't be true."

He stopped. They stared at each other, and then with a cry, she was in his arms, sobbing. Karna moaned, "You have come! At last, you have come, and I knew that one day you would. Mother, how I have longed for this moment, how many times I have lived this day in my imagination. Why did you wait so long? You who bore me in your sweet body, by my Lord, my father Surya Deva whom I worship!"

She gasped. He said, "I know everything."

"How could you? When did you know? And once you did, why didn't you come to me?"

Karna said evenly, "I knew only yesterday when Krishna told me. But why speak of the past now? When, at last, at last, we are together! Let us not waste these moments. Come, sit near me, and let me lay my head in your lap. This is a perfect moment; let us not spoil it with words. Be quiet, mother, our time together will last just briefly, though I wish it would go on for ever."

He laid his head in her lap and shut his eyes. Her hands were on his face, in his hair, stroking him, and her tears fell on him. The Yamuna murmured along beside them, the only witness to their precious moment.

TWENTY

'Come away to your brothers'

THEY SAT LIKE THAT, INTERMINABLY, KARNA WITH HIS HEAD IN HIS mother's lap and his eyes shut. Neither knew if moments passed, or hours. Then Karna roused himself. He said, "Never in my life have I known such peace. I don't know if hours have gone by, or years. But tell me why you came, for what boon? Radheya Karna waits to hear what you want from him. He is impatient to do anything for his mother."

Kunti said, "Don't say Radheya any more, my son. Say Kaunteya Karna. You are Kunti's first son, and she is proud of you. Kunti has six sons now, not five, and she cries for joy."

But he stopped her lips with his hand. He was trembling. "You make me cry as well, mother, because I long to be called Kaunteya too. But that cannot be in this life. Karna is Radheya, and Radheya he must remain. No more of that; tell me what you came for. If it doesn't taint my honour, and it is in my power to give, you shall have it, be it anything."

Kunti said, "You have suffered such indignity, such shame: because the world never knew you are Kunti's son, and Surya Deva's. Your time of torment is over, my child. You hated your brothers, never knowing who they were. Put all that behind you; now you know the truth, you cannot fight the Pandavas. Come with me, I will take you to them. They will worship you, and make you lord of the earth. From today, your destiny lies with them; you must leave Duryodhana and come with me. This is the boon I came to beg."

A wry, familiar smile was on Karna's lips, "Strangest times are upon us! These last two days, two of the noblest ones alive have offered me the earth. Both say that Yudhishtira himself will serve me. But, tell me mother, what will really happen if I do come away with you?"

Without hesitation, she said, "Your brother Arjuna will fall at your feet, and the hatred between you will vanish like darkness before the sun. The Pandavas will win the war, and the world will be yours to rule, because you are my eldest son. Karna will not be a sutaputra any more, but the emperor of Bharatavarsha. All your shame and suffering will be paid back to you in honour and glory! Come away with me."

Suddenly, the disc of the sun on the river grew blinding. Kunti and Karna were swathed in uncanny light, dazzled. A voice spoke out of heaven, earth and river, the voice of Surya Deva, Lord of the day. "My son, do as your mother asks. Long shall you live, and be master of the earth."

Karna jumped up with a cry, but the unworldly radiance faded in a moment. Karna stood staring at Kunti. Slowly, he said, "Mother, you have no idea how much I hated you all these years. I told myself I would abuse you if I ever saw you, because you were to blame for everything I suffered." He took her hands, "But now I see you before me, your eyes full of tears, and all I feel is this great love, which I can hardly believe that I, Karna, am feeling. That, and a sadness I cannot describe.

"I have loved my mother Radha as I have loved no one else. But even my love for her pales before what I feel for you."

He went on, "A tide of love for my brothers overwhelms me. I, who am so used to hatred, find this hard to bear! How will I deal with this terrible love that tears at my heart?"

With a cry, Kunti embraced him, as if to clasp him back into her mother's body. From above, Karna's father, the westering Surya Deva, watched them.

TWENTY-ONE

For love of his friend

KUNTI SAID, "COME WITH ME TO YOUR BROTHERS."

Karna's powerful body shook with sobs. "No! I must not even think of it."

"Why do you say that? You know the truth now, come away to your brothers. Surely, you don't mean to fight them when you know who they are."

He gazed out across the rippling Yamuna, her currents livid with the light of the setting sun. His face turned from her, he said, "Yes, I do mean to fight them, because I cannot abandon Duryodhana. All these years, when the stigma of being a sutaputra attached to me, only he stood with me. He gave me his love, never holding back. He set me beside him in the sabha of Hastinapura, and when the war is over, he means to share the earth with me.

"My life has been harsher than you can imagine. I was raised a sutaputra, yet my blood raged that I must become an archer. Who has heard of a sutaputra being an archer? I came to Drona and begged him to teach me, but he turned me away because I was not a kshatriya. I took myself to a score of gurus, and every one refused me; most laughed at me. At last, I went to Parasurama Bhargava, and by now I was so desperate I had resolved to put an end to myself if he also turned me away. I lied to the Bhagawan, telling him I was a brahmana, and he took me in. He was kind to me, and generous; he taught me all he knew. But finally, when my tutelage was complete, he discovered that I was not a brahmana. Perhaps, with his seer's vision, he saw who I really was and my guru cursed me.

"Then I came to Hastinapura. It was the day of a tournament."

He turned to her again; a shadow flitted across his face and there was anguish in his eyes. Kunti wept silently. Karna said, "You knew me as soon as you saw me, didn't you? From my kavacha and kundala. Your mother's heart would have known me, anyway. But you chose to say nothing, you did not come near me. I will not ask you what your reasons were; I do not want to cause you any more pain.

"I was telling you about Duryodhana. When Bheema and Arjuna mocked me on the day of the tournament, and Arjuna refused to fight me because I was a sutaputra, Duryodhana crowned me king of Anga. When I asked him what he wanted in return, he said to me, 'All I want from you is your love, Karna.'

"That is how it has been between him and me, since that day. My heart belongs to him, and he has loved me more than he has his brothers. I will never betray that love, not if I have to sacrifice my life for it."[2]

He sighed. "And until yesterday, it wasn't hard for me to love Duryodhana and be loyal to him. But these last two days have been like two lives and deaths. Ah, mother, the truths with which Krishna and you have struck me are too fierce! Suddenly I feel no more anger or hatred for Yudhishtira or Arjuna, but only this overwhelming love. You think you need to beg me to come away with you to my brothers. You don't know how I long to do just that! I would give this life and ten more to be able to come away with you. Alas, I am cursed, the most unfortunate man alive, that I cannot."

He fell silent, and grew still beside the deep river. Kunti said in despair, "Why not, my child? Karna, I have always loved you. Whenever Arjuna spoke scornfully of the sutapura, I felt my heart would break. My son, have mercy on me. Your mother has borne the burden of her guilt for too long. What I made you suffer is unforgivable. But I was young, and afraid of the world. See how savagely my sin has come to roost. Oh, my sweet child, all these years I have felt an emptiness in my heart, and my other five sons could never fill it. I yearned for you, Karna. Today is the first day I feel whole, and as if God has finally taken pity on me. Let both our torments end here. I have paid in full for my sin. Now I have found you, at last, I could not bear losing you again. Come with me, Karna, let us heal each other."

---

2 See Appendix.

She sobbed again. He took her face in his hands. "Though I long to, I cannot come with you. Duryodhana depends on me. You have come to me at this eleventh hour; he has always been with me. A thousand bonds of love bind me to him. Honour has always meant more to me than my life. What honour will I have if I forsake my friend in his hour of need? Your love seizes my heart, and I ache to come with you to my brothers. But my heart is not mine to give; it belongs to Duryodhana. I am dearer to that man than his own blood, and I will not betray his love. That he couldn't bear."

She began to speak, but he said, "Mother, I know why you have come today. You are frightened for your sons. You know who I am, and you fear me. But you have no reason to be afraid. Duryodhana's cause is doomed, and with it all those who fight for him. Dharma is with the Pandavas; they must win this war, and we their enemies must die. Besides, Krishna is with them. Who in this world, or any other, can stand against the Dark One? He is the Avatara; have no doubt the side he is on will prevail."

She still looked anxious. He smiled, "You are most afraid for Arjuna's sake because he and I have sworn to kill the other. Kunti Devi, I will tell you why Arjuna must win the duel between us, and why Karna must die.

"First, when my guru Bhargava cursed me; he said that when I fought my most powerful enemy I would forget the mantras for the devastras. Then a brahmana, whose cow I killed, cursed me saying I would be shot down as I had his beast: when I least expected it.

"And haven't you noticed a change upon me? My father's kavacha and kundala, which made me invincible, have gone. Indra himself came begging for alms at my hour of worship. He took my armour and earrings, so his son can kill me. Finally, now, Krishna and you have taken my greatest weapon, my hatred. You have robbed my mind of its strength. How will I kill Arjuna when I know that he is my brother, whom I love him?"

Karna covered his face with his hands, and sobbed. Kunti took him in her arms; she pulled his head down into her mother's lap. Thus they sat, for a long time, as twilight fell around them. Karna raised his face, and said, "Stop crying, mother. You must not cry today, when we have found each other again. A son needs his mother's blessing as long as he lives. So bless me now, Kunti. Say my fame will last for ever, and that I will find honour, at last, in heaven."

He prostrated himself at her feet, and, with her tears falling on him, Kunti laid her hands on him in a blessing. Rising, Karna said, "I have never refused anyone who came to me at my hour of worship, whatever they asked me for. Yet, I have denied my own mother the boon for which you came. I will not send you empty-handed from here. I have a boon for you: not the one you asked for, but one that I give you anyway. I swear I will not kill four of your sons in battle: Yudhishtira, Bheema, Nakula and Sahadeva, none of them shall die at my hands."

She waited, breathlessly. He went on, "But Arjuna I must fight. We must face each other in a mortal duel, and the world must know who is the better archer. Of course, now, one of us knows it is his brother he must fight and the other does not. No matter, either he or I must die. And when the war ends, you will still have five sons, as you have all these years."

Then he could not endure it any more, and said hoarsely, "Now go before my heart breaks. I beg you, go!"

Kunti began to wail loudly. Karna embraced her. "What use are your tears now? For both of us it is too late. Not a line, not a word of what the Gods wrote for you and me can change. Our lives were already decided, long before we were born: every moment of them, their last ones, as well. Don't cry now, uselessly; rather, pray for me. Pray that I reach the swarga where kshatriyas go when they die, and pray that at least there I find peace.

"I feel light! As if my grief has been taken from me, as if my sins have been washed away by my mother's tears, more sacred than the waters of this Yamuna."

Feverishly, he kissed her hands, her eyes, her lips. He said again, "Now go, while I can still bear it. It is late, and no one must discover that you and I have met. Let these hours be as just another dream."

He had to help her to her feet, and she stood swaying from the pang inside her. Again, they embraced. Sobbing, she clutched him to her. After a long moment, she released him, turned, and, without another glance at his face,—for then she would never be able to walk away—Kunti stumbled blindly back towards the city. Karna stood turned to stone, watching her. Long after she was out of sight, he stood on.

TWENTY-TWO

Balarama and Rukmi

W ORD REACHED THE PANDAVAS IN THEIR CAMP AT KURUKSHETRA that Bheeshma had been made Supreme Commander of the Kaurava army. Here, Dhrishtadyumna was the Senapati of Yudhishtira's legions.

While the Pandava force waited for Duryodhana's army to arrive on Kurukshetra, Yudhishtira received a visitor. Balarama came to see him. Yudhishtira welcomed him in some excitement. Had the great Yadava, perhaps, changed his mind about not fighting the war? Yudhishtira prostrated himself before Balarama, and the other Pandavas did as well. Krishna stood by, his arms crossed over his chest and a slight smile on his face.

Balarama's eyes were red with wine. He was tense. Yudhishtira led him into his tent. For a long moment, the visitor sat silent, his gaze resting on all the Pandavas, in turns, and on Krishna. When he spoke he seemed to address Yudhishtira, but his eyes kept straying to Krishna's face. The Dark One stood there, laconic, the smile never leaving his lips.

Balarama said thickly, "I hear a great war will be fought on Kurukshetra. I hear the kings of the earth have come here to die, and their blood will flow in rills on this field. I have come to tell you I pray that all of you cross this sea of peril safely."

He paused, moistened his lips, and continued, "I am told this war could not be avoided. Repeatedly, I said to Krishna, 'Be impartial to the Pandavas and the Kauravas. They are both dear to us; Yudhishtira is dear, and so is Duryodhana.'

"But it seems my words fell on deaf ears. Against my wishes, Krishna has decided to take sides in this war. He has chosen to be with you, though he will only be Arjuna's sarathy and bear no arms."

He gave a short laugh. "But Krishna doesn't need to carry weapons to give you victory. I know him, we all do. In his hands, the reins of Arjuna's horses will be more terrible than all the Kauravas' arrows. Poor Duryodhana, I pity him. What chance has he of winning, when my brother is against him?

"But I did not come here to tell you what you already know. Bheema, I see the questions in your eyes. Yes, indeed, you are my sishya and dear to me; but Duryodhana was always my favourite. Why, I love him as much as Krishna does Arjuna. But I will not be part of Duryodhana's army, though he has sent word begging me to fight for him. How could I even think of fighting against my brother, however much I may abhor what he does?"

He drew a breath. "I mourn the ancient House of Kuru, at war with itself! I mourn the House of Kuru, which no enemy could ever bring down, but which now turns on itself, and thus to its doom. Why, I mourn the earth, as we have known it; this war will be its end. Yudhishtira, I have come to tell you I am going on a tirtha-yatra, because I cannot watch this war, let alone fight in it. I cannot watch brother slaughter his noble brother. I am going on a pilgrimage, first to the banks of the Saraswati, and then to a hundred other tirthas, to the very south of Bharatavarsha. And I will pray for you all, yes, I will pray for you all."

Suddenly, tears stood in his eyes. Krishna stepped forward. Balarama rose and clasped his brother in his arms. Choking back his grief, he blessed the five Pandavas. Abruptly, the mighty Yadava stalked out and rode away from Kurukshetra. Krishna had tears in his eyes, too, and memories of a wild and wonderful childhood and youth spent with Balarama in the green arms of a virgin forest: enchanted Vrindavana on the banks of the midnight-blue Yamuna.

At about that time, another kshatriya came to Yudhishtira, unexpectedly. Rukmi of Vidarbha, Krishna's brother-in-law and his sworn enemy, arrived in Kurukshetra with an aksauhini of his own. The world knew how Krishna had once humiliated Rukmi. The Dark One carried away his sister, Rukmini, on the day she was to marry Rukmi's dearest friend, Sishupala. Since then, Rukmi had secured Siva's blessing and had become a king of some conquests and influence. Yet, he was known more for his arrogance than his considerable valour; and today he came haughtily before Yudhishtira.

Yudhishtira received his visitor cordially. When Rukmi sat in the royal tent, he began to speak before Yudhishtira could ask what had brought him to Kurukshetra. Rukmi did not address Yudhishtira at all, but Arjuna.

"I have come to help you win this war, Arjuna! Fear the Kaurava army no more, I am here to raze it for you. Without your lifting your bow, Pandava, I will make corpses of Duryodhana's best kshatriyas. No matter if they have eleven aksauhinis or a hundred, they will not stand against Rukmi of Bhojataka."

He smiled smugly around him, then, declared, "And when I have slain your enemies, I shall make a gift of the earth to you! Fear nothing any more, Arjuna, your war is already won."

Arjuna's eyes glittered. He glanced at Krishna, but his cousin was impassive. Tense as he was on the eve of battle, the Pandava flashed angrily at Rukmi, "Dare you come here and speak to me of my being afraid? Rukmi, there are many kshatriyas here, twice as strong as you; none of them has ever mentioned the word fear to me. Who are you, that you dare speak of winning the war for us, and of making us a gift of the earth? We have no need for the likes of you. You may stay or leave, as you please."

For a moment, Rukmi sat very still. Without a word, he rose and walked out of the tent; he left Kurukshetra with his aksauhini. Rukmi rode straight to Duryodhana, and spoke to the Kaurava in much the same vein. Duryodhana laughed in his face, and the lord of Vidarbha returned to his capital, seething. Thus, Balarama and Rukmi were the only two kings of Bharatavarsha who did not fight the war at Kurukshetra.

The Kaurava army arrived on the banks of the Saraswati, and made camp there. The golden river separated the two immense forces, and their soldiers stared at one another across the water. Duryodhana called his cousin, Shakuni's son Uluka.

"Take a message from me to the Pandavas, Uluka. Go into the presence of Yudhishtira. Be certain the five brothers are there; be sure Krishna is there, and all the kings who are their allies. Then speak boldly to them, your head held high and your words ringing clear. Tell them Duryodhana says: 'The time for bragging is over, cousins. We shall have no more words, but war. Thirteen years ago, you swore many oaths of the revenge you would take on me and mine. More recently, you sent back an arrogant message to Hastinapura with Sanjaya. The time is here when you cannot brag, or threaten me any more. The time for deeds is here, for keeping the oaths you swore so loudly. The time for arrows and swords and maces is here, the time for war, your time to die.'

"Don't be cowed by them, Uluka, their fame is greater than their worth. Speak defiantly, remember you are Duryodhana's messenger."

He took Uluka aside privately, and gave him individual messages for each of the Pandavas, and one for Krishna. When he heard what he must say to the sons of Pandu, poor Uluka trembled. But he had no choice except go; indeed, Duryodhana thought he was conferring a rare honour on Shakuni's son by making him his messenger. With trepidation, Uluka set out for Yudhishtira's camp.

TWENTY-THREE

Uluka's embassy

ULUKA ARRIVED UNEASILY IN THE PANDAVA CAMP. HE WAS SHOWN into Yudhishtira's presence. All five Pandavas were in the capacious tent; Krishna was there, as well, with some other kings of their alliance. Uluka found his palms clammy with fear. He greeted the Pandavas stiffly, and said, "I have come as Duryodhana's messenger. He sends word through me for each of you. But, Yudhishtira, I am afraid to deliver his messages; I fear for my life if I do."

Yudhishtira said kindly, "Have no fear, Uluka. A messenger is never to be harmed, and I guarantee your safety."

Uluka drew a deep breath, and said, "My cousin and king, Duryodhana, says to you, and these words are his, not mine: 'Yudhishtira, you were my slave once, and we dragged your wife into our sabha like a slut. Which kshatriya would have allowed his woman to be treated like that, and let the insult go unavenged? If you were ever a man, Pandava, on that day you lost your manhood. We took it from you as Draupadi's shame.

"'You spent twelve years in the forest like a beggar. Then you spent one year as Virata's menial, a calling you are better suited to than kingship. And now you dare come back and challenge me? Yudhishtira, the hour of reckoning is here, and fine talk of dharma will not serve you any more. This is the moment of truth, and it will show you up for what you have always been: a common coward, cousin!'"

Uluka paused. Bheema began to rise, but Yudhishtira motioned him to hold his peace. Yudhishtira said, "Is that all, Uluka? You said Duryodhana sent messages for my brothers as well."

"He has. Would you hear them?"

"We must," said Yudhishtira, with a sad smile.

"Duryodhana says to Bheema, 'You, braggart, swore to drink Dusasana's blood. From what we hear, you have become a magnificent cook. Loudmouth, wielding a ladle and wielding a mace are very different things. Carving dead meat is easy, but we shall see how you carve my brother's heart. Since your skills at cooking have become such a legend, I can offer you work in my kitchen, if you like.'"

Bheema was so taken aback he sat mildly dazed. Uluka didn't pause for him to recover.

"Duryodhana says to Arjuna, 'As for you, Arjuna, who boast you will kill Karna, I hear you spent the last year among the women in Virata's court, teaching them to sing and dance. I hear you have become a eunuch, cousin. How can a eunuch even think of fighting Karna?

"'Nakula and Sahadeva, their mother's darlings, have also found their true vocation with Virata. Boys, I could find work for you too in my stables and cowsheds. But then, you have sworn to kill my uncle Shakuni and his son, haven't you? I fear you will be meat for scavengers before I can employ you.

"'Yudhishtira, your lofty dharma has finally led you and your brothers to my quenchless army. Prepare to meet your God.'"

Uluka paused, red-faced; he glanced anxiously at Krishna. Complete silence had fallen in that tent. Krishna said smoothly, "I am sure Duryodhana sent a message for me, Uluka. We are eager to hear it."

Uluka hesitated. The Dark One said, "You have our word you will not be harmed, whatever message you bring."

Bracing himself, Uluka said, "Duryodhana sends this message to you, Krishna. 'We are not fooled by your magic trick in Hastinapura. You spoke brave words that day. You said you would destroy the world with Arjuna and Bheema beside you. Cowherd, this is not Vrindavana where you seduced the gopikas with piping and dancing. This is war, and we are kshatriyas. We are not impressed by your ludicrous fame as the Avatara. We laugh at these grandmother's tales, and at your conjuring.'"

The Pandavas looked like fire just kindled. At the insult to Krishna, Bheema began to get up again, growling. Uluka was certain his last moment on earth had arrived. Krishna nodded to Bheema to sit down.

Calmly, Krishna said to Uluka, "Go back safely to your cousin, Uluka, and take him this message from me. Tell him Krishna says, 'Evil one, you have not lived like a kshatriya; at least, let us see you die like one. Duryodhana, you dare send such a message to me today because you know I have sworn not to fight. Otherwise, your army would burn even now like dry grass in a forest-fire. But Yudhishtira has asked me to carry no arms during this war. He says revenge belongs to him and his brothers, and I have sworn to be just Arjuna's sarathy.

"But I also swear, Duryodhana, my warrior's chariot will strike terror in your heart. Asleep or awake, you will see my horses. In your dreams, you will hear their hooves drumming your death. You will see Bheema kill your hundred brothers. You will see him drink Dusasana's blood; and you will not be asleep or dreaming when the ghastly sight lights your eyes, though you will wish you were. All that the Pandavas have sworn they will do. You forswear yourself as you please; but their oaths are solemn, and each word of them shall be kept.'

"Take my message to your king, Uluka."

Bheema growled, "Tell Duryodhana Bheema hasn't forgotten a syllable of what he swore. Tell him to be prepared to see all his brothers die in Kurukshetra, his sons and nephews as well. Tell him when those gruesome sights darken his eyes and break his heart, he will remember this message bitterly. He will see me drink Dusasana's blood. Finally, he may hide himself in heaven, earth or hell, but I will hunt him down and break his thigh, as I swore. And he will die."

The smouldering Bheema sat down, much to Uluka's relief. Shakuni's prince was afraid that, at any moment, the son of the wind might change his mind about keeping Yudhishtira's word, and kill the messenger.

Grimly, Arjuna said, "Your king is beneath contempt. He is such a coward that he has made Bheeshma his Senapati. Has he no shred of shame that he calls an old man to defend him? If Duryodhana thinks Arjuna will stay his hand because his Pitama takes the field, he is mistaken. I will kill my grandfather if I have to. If Bheeshma comes to fight, he will die. One by one, every warrior who fights against us, every kshatriya Duryodhana relies on to secure his evil purpose, will fall. And at last my brother Bheema will kill your king. Tell our cousin that Arjuna says the Pandavas do not make empty threats; what we have sworn, we will do. Let him be ready to die."

With these fierce messages, Uluka went back to Duryodhana. Night had fallen, and Duryodhana's mocking laughter echoed among the campfires when he heard what Krishna and the Pandavas said.

He cried, "They are afraid! They know their army will not last a day against Bheeshma; I need no other other kshatriya. Arjuna speaks bravely, but his heart quails within him. I know him. He will hardly dare fight when he sees our grandfather take the field."

There was drinking and celebration in the Kaurava camp. Then, Duryodhana and his warriors slept; a sleep of those who felt more confident than they should have.

Across the darkling Saraswati, Yudhishtira could not sleep. Krishna and Arjuna sat up with him, while the moon rose over the river, setting her currents alight in burning silver.

Into the silence of the midnight hour, Yudhishtira said, "Krishna, I feel sick at the thought of this war. Darkness has come over us all, Krishna, as if the age is perverted. How can I feel anything but horror, when I think we must attack our Pitama with arrows tomorrow?"

In rare anger, Krishna snapped at him, "This is no time for regrets! It is a great war you face tomorrow. You are the lord of this army. How will your soldiers fight if their master is so hesitant? For you there is no sin in this war, Yudhishtira, your kshatriya dharma is to fight."

Krishna's eyes shone in the firelight. "When I was in Hastinapura, there was only one voice I heard raised unambiguously against Duryodhana, Vidura's. Bheeshma was there, but I heard no strong words from him against your cousin; nor from your precious Acharyas, Drona and Kripa. I thought to myself, aren't the Pandavas also Bheeshma's grandsons; why does he love only Duryodhana so much? Aren't Yudhishtira and his brothers Drona's and Kripa's sishyas; why are the brahmanas so loyal to Duryodhana? If your Pitama loved you as much as he should, Yudhishtira, would he agree to be Duryodhana's Senapati? I hear the only condition he made was that Karna would not fight beside him."

It is uncertain if what Krishna said was more for Yudhishtira to hear, or Arjuna. Yudhishtira said, unsteadily, "Arjuna, I spent thirteen years in the wilderness to avoid fighting our cousins. Bheema wanted war, even you did. I begged you to be patient, and you were noble enough to respect my wishes. Yet, here we are on the brink of this hideous war. Oh, my brother, the kali yuga is upon us, and the God of wrath has been born into the world." He sobbed, "How will we kill our grandfather and our gurus, whom we have worshipped all these years? Whatever you might say, Krishna, this is a sin!"

To console Yudhishtira, Arjuna said, "There is no sin in fighting those who have decided to kill us anyway. Our Pitama, Drona and Kripa know the goodness of your heart and that yours is the way of dharma, but they have cast their lot with Duryodhana. Couldn't they have joined us instead? We must not falter now. Once the river flows down the mountain where it springs, it must run on into the sea. The river does not turn back, and neither can we. Don't grieve any more, my noble brother, but sleep now. Tomorrow is a momentous day, and you must be strong for all our sakes."

Krishna's heart was full of thoughts too deep to plumb. As always, he was alone with them.

BOOK SIX*

Bheeshma Parva

AUM, I bow down to Narayana, the most exalted Nara, and to the Devi Saraswati, and say *Jaya*!

---

* In Ganguli's translation, the 4 parvas of the war amount to about 1,200 pages. They are full of all sorts of details, especially of duels and battles between minor clans, Kings and other characters. Some sections are definitely repetitive, as well. In Sanskrit, all these perhaps have an atmospheric, incantatory effect. Here, I believe I have described all the important events of the war.

ONE

Sanjaya's gift

To THE WEST OF THE FIELD OF KURUKSHETRA WAS THE PANDAVA army, facing east, where the sun rose, facing the sea-like Kaurava legions. On the banks of the Saraswati and the lake called Samantapanchaka, Yudhishtira's soldiers swarmed. When the sun rose on the momentous morning, it lit a shining white parasol at the heart of the Kaurava force, and coursed a thrill through the Pandava legions. It was Duryodhana's sovereign parasol. Even as a lover's blood quickens to see his beloved, the kshatriyas quickened at the fierce spectacle of their enemies, and at the imminence of war. What other excitement was there on earth to compare with this one? Arjuna and Krishna saw the white parasol unfurled, and raised their conches and blew on them: dawn thunder! The Kauravas replied at once with blasts of their own, loud cheering and ferocious shouts, and Kurukshetra reverberated with the aggression of ten million kshatriyas.

The air was electric, when a formal meeting of some commanders of the two armies was called on neutral ground to lay down honourable conditions before the fighting began; so the war would be a righteous one, a dharma yuddha. They agreed that only peers should fight: archers would fight archers, warriors in chariots would fight other rathikas, mace-fighters would battle mace-fighters, swordsmen other swordsmen, and so on. If any warrior withdrew during battle, or fled, he would be allowed to go unharmed, and not pursued or shot in the back. If an attack was with words, so, too, would the reply be, and not with arrows. No one who was unprepared or afraid would be attacked. Flag-bearers, conch-blowers, drummers, and their chariots, horses and elephants would never be harmed. There were other codes of honour, agreed upon and declared, which must be adhered to without exception. War might be a brutal contention, but it was a sacred thing as well. Once they agreed upon the laws for a dharma yuddha, the various commanders of the two forces withdrew to their camps.

At dead of dark, the previous night, Vyasa came to his son Dhritarashtra. That king sat alone, and forlorn, faced with the inexorable conclusion of his long folly. He leapt up in alarm when Vyasa entered.

"Hah! Who is it at this hour?"

"It is I, your father."

Vyasa sat down beside his son, and took his hand in compassion. Sighing, he said, "Don't blame yourself too much, it is the nature of the times. Savage days are upon us, and there will be a massacre such as the earth has not yet seen; finally, dharma will prevail[1]. There is nothing you can do now to save your sons. They will all perish, and the vain kshatriyas who have allied themselves to Duryodhana." He felt Dhritarashtra's hand tremble. Kindly, he asked, "Would you witness this war, Dhritarashtra? If you want, I can give your eyes vision."

Dhritarashtra shivered at the thought. He whispered, "My lord, I have been blind all these years, and I would not have my sight restored just to see the deaths of my sons. All my life my ears have been like my eyes. I will be satisfied if someone describes the war to me."

There was a knock on the door, and, as if by fate, Sanjaya entered his king's chambers. Vyasa said, "Sanjaya will describe the war to you. I bless him with vision that only great rishis have. He will see the battle miraculously, every sword-stroke, every arrow loosed, every slaying and each death. More, he will know the warriors' very thoughts; and be it day or night, he will see everything that happens on Kurukshetra.

"Each morning, he will travel subtly to the battle's edge, and from there have use of his occult vision. No weapon will touch him, or tiredness lay its hands upon him. Every night, he will return to you and describe all that transpired. Sanjaya, you will never know tiredness, and your memory will be like a God's." Vyasa sighed. "But you will seldom

---

1 See Appendix for the omens Vyasa describes.

bring news to your king to gladden his heart. You will see all his sons killed, as the omens of the earth and the air cry out. You will bring Dhritarashtra word of how the Pandavas raze the army of Hastinapura, and the torment of each day's news shall be expiation for your king's sins."

The muni said more gently, "And in your time of anguish, remember that dawn comes after the night's darkest yaama. The worst sinner finds redemption, and the hour of retribution is the time when his salvation begins. You, too, will find your peace, though you must first pass through fire to be purified. Remember that, when grief threatens to break your heart."

Vyasa embraced his blind son. He passed his hands over Sanjaya's eyes, blessed the sarathy as well, and left. The next morning, Sanjaya stood on the field of Kurukshetra in a spirit body, light as air, and with magic vision flooding his eyes, he saw all the happenings of the first day of the war. That day, Soma approached the realms of the manes*. The seven large planets blazed as if they were on fire. The face of the Sun seemed to be bisected.

From now, it is from Sanjaya, the witness, that we hear about the Mahabharata yuddha, the war at the end of an age**.

Sanjaya said to his king, Dhritarashtra:

Your son Duryodhana formed his legions into a fighting vyuha. He called his brother Dusasana, and said, "Our first task is to protect Pitama Bheeshma's chariot. He, by himself, will bring us victory. Let him be guarded by our best kshatriyas. There is only one enemy that our grandfather needs fear: Drupada's son Shikhandi. Let our warriors kill Shikhandi as quickly as they can. And then who will stand before Bheeshma? I hear Arjuna watches over Shikhandi. Drupada's sons Yuddhamanyu and Uttamaujas ride beside Arjuna. We must be careful of that force. Go my brother; take our boldest men, protect Bheeshma with your life!"

---

* Upon dying, men have to first pass through the realms of the pitrs, before acquiring a celestial body, with which they can ascend into heaven. Here, the implication is that those dying in the war would gain their heavenly spirit bodies immediately.
** Ganguli notes that, at times, Sanjaya himself fights in the war.

The day's sun was still young and crimson on the horizon, when ten aksauhinis of the Kaurava force, six million men, were marshalled into an awesome vyuha of war, with ten commanders to lead them. The eleventh legion was deployed ahead of these ten, and Bheeshma himself had charge of it. Yoked to a silver chariot, Bheeshma's horses were as white as wave-froth. His banner bore a golden palm-tree with five stars above it. His hair was blemishlessly white, he wore white silk upon his body; and to look at him in his chariot, it seemed a full moon had risen upon the earth. The Pandava soldiers gazed at Bheeshma, and were afraid.

The Kuru patriarch stood up in his chariot and spoke to his army; his voice was like the sea at night. "The gates of heaven have yawned open to welcome those who die in battle! I say to all of you, fight with no thought for tomorrow. Let your courage rule you, for glory is in store for every man here. A warrior does not wish for a peaceful death in his bed, of old age, or illness. He longs to die in battle! Know, then, mighty warriors, that for you there is no defeat on the field of war. For either dying nobly, you will find Devaloka, or victorious, you will inherit the earth! There is no defeat for those who fight; but only heaven or victory. So tell me, my friends, are you prepared to die?"

Like an ocean, they roared back, "We are!"

Only Karna did not answer Bheeshma. He had sworn he would not fight as long as the Kuru patriarch did. The aksauhini Bheeshma had chosen to be at the van of his army was Aswatthama's. Bhoorisravas and Shalya were part of that legion, and seven exceptional kshatriyas formed a ring around Bheeshma to protect him against Shikhandi.

Duryodhana set his chariot at the heart of his army. His banner fluttered in the early breeze, with its black serpent embroidered on golden cloth.

Seeing the Kaurava legions in battle array, Yudhishtira turned to Arjuna. "Duryodhana has eleven aksauhinis to our seven, and only now I realize how much bigger than ours his army is. Arjuna, my brother, the enemy is formidable. How do you mean to deploy our men against Bheeshma?"

Arjuna replied serenely, "We will form our men into a Vajra, a diamond phalanx. Indra uses this vyuha; it is both a fluid and an impregnable formation, which manoeuvers more quickly than any other."

The Pandava army, of four millions, moved forward to face the Kaurava legions. Dhrishtadyumna was at the head of that force, and Bheema was at his side. Yudhishtira rode at the heart of the diamond, and Satyaki patrolled its right flank. A murmur went up from the Kaurava soldiers when they saw Arjuna ride out to take his place at Shikhandi's side. The banner of Hanuman flew above Arjuna's chariot. To keep his promise to Bheema, the legendary vanara had come to animate his image on the silken cloth: the form on the banner was alive; its eyes moved and saw everything!

Arjuna's pale horses, given him by Chitraratha the gandharva, shimmered in the early light. But none of these was the most lustrous feature of Arjuna's ratha, not even the kshatriya himself with the Gandiva in his hand like an arc of the moon. No, the sight of his sarathy drew a gasp from the Kaurava legions. With the reins in his left hand and a whip in his right, Krishna was like a dark sun risen on that field of fate.

Seeing Krishna and Arjuna* in their chariot, Drona and Kripa knew this was no less than a vision of Nara Narayana they saw before them. In their hearts, they worshipped the vision.

Krishna brought Varuna's chariot to the front of the Pandava army. Softly he said, "Be strong now, Arjuna. Bheeshma is the lion we must face first. It is him we must hunt, he is the one you must kill."

---

* They are both dark and are frequently referred to as 'the two Krishnas', throughout the parvas of war.

TWO

Kurukshetra

WHEN THE TWO FORCES WERE FACE TO FACE, A HUSH FELL ON THEM: a moment of stillness. All eighteen aksauhinis were like armies in a painting. Then, at the heart of that numinous silence, a strange thing happened. Yudhishtira peeled off his armour, and put down his bow. He removed his sandals, climbed down from his chariot with the white banner, and walked barefoot towards the enemy!

For a moment, no one moved. Then Bheema, Arjuna, Nakula and Sahadeva all laid down their weapons, and followed their brother. Krishna, who wore no armour and carried no weapon today, went with Arjuna.

When he caught up with Yudhishtira, Arjuna said anxiously, "What are you doing?"

Bheema asked hoarsely, "Where are you going, Yudhishtira, without your weapons?"

Nakula said, "You are making me afraid, my brother!"

And Sahadeva, "You are exposing yourself to the enemy!"

Yudhishtira did not look at his brothers. He strode on towards the Kaurava army. Krishna said quietly, "A kshatriya who seeks his elders' blessings before he goes out to fight is certain to win his war. Your brother wants to get Bheeshma, Drona, Kripa and Shalya's blessings, before he fights them."

The Kaurava soldiers began to jeer when they saw Yudhishtira coming.

"He is coming to beg his Pitama to stop the war."

"He has lost his nerve, seeing our army."

"The coward."

Yudhishtira walked on towards Bheeshma's chariot. The ring of warriors around Bheeshma parted to let the Pandavas through. Bheeshma waited for Yudhishtira with a smile. The Pandava emperor, Dharma's son, noblest of men, came up to his grandsire and, with tears in his eyes, prostrated himself on the earth at the patriarch's feet; and so did his brothers. His old eyes teary, as well, Bheeshma laid his hands on their heads, then, raised them up and embraced them.

Yudhishtira said, "Pitama, we have not been able to prevent the war. I have come for your blessing, so my brothers and I will win."

Bheeshma said, "My son, victory already belongs to you. Krishna is on your side, and where he is so is dharma. Alas, men are slaves to wealth, and I must fight against you today. The throne I renounced a life ago has supported me all these years. My duty is to fight for the king who has kept me; but Yudhishtira, my love and my blessings are with you, because yours is the cause of dharma in this war. Jaya vijayi bhava! Fight and be victorious, noble child."

Yudhishtira went to Drona and Kripa, his gurus, and to his uncle Shalya. He prostrated himself before each of them and asked for their blessings, and their permission for him to fight them. They gave both to the Pandava, warmly. To Drona, Yudhishtira said, "My lord, besides your blessing, I seek your advice. How can I win this war?"

Drona said, "King of dharma, victory is already yours. I hate to fight against you, but I, too, owe my livelihood to the Kuru throne. I cannot betray the king who has kept me these long years. Yet I do have some advice for you." He called Yudhishtira nearer. In a low voice, he said, "I myself can only be killed when I lay down my weapons; it is a boon I have from my guru. Remember that when my time to die arrives, as it must during this war."

Yudhishtira knelt again before his master. As the Pandava approached Shalya, Krishna saw Karna come out to look at the armies. Quietly, the Dark One sought him out. Taking him aside, Krishna said urgently, "I am told you will take no part in the fighting until Bheeshma dies." He gripped Karna's arm, "It is still not too late, Karna, come away with me now! At least for a few days, fight for the Pandavas. Fight Bheeshma, who has mocked you repeatedly, and let the world see your worth. When you have killed the old man, you can go back to Duryodhana, and Arjuna will fight you then."

Karna began to laugh. "I am not a child, my Lord, that you can persuade me with children's temptations!"

"We are all children of one kind or another," replied Krishna.

Karna said, "I am moved to see how much you love the Pandavas, and, perhaps, even me. But I have already told you, Krishna, my life and my loyalty belong to Duryodhana. It would break his heart if I did what you ask." He laughed again to think of it. "Even for a few days!" Then, he was full of sorrow. "Krishna, leave me to my fate; not even you can change what was written for Karna before he was born. Go now. I thank you for your concern, but I am with the Kauravas."

Krishna turned away sadly. When Yudhishtira had the blessings of his Pitama and his gurus, he turned back to his own army. As he walked across the empty ground between the two forces, a thought struck him. He stopped, and turned back to the legions of Hastinapura. Loudly he called, "If there are any Kaurava soldiers who want to fight for dharma, they are welcome to join us!"

The Pandava's arms were opened wide to receive anyone who came to him. A lone voice called, "I will join you if you will have me, Yudhishtira!"

A fine kshatriya, and a loyal childhood friend, came forward. It was Yuyutsu who, from his earliest days, had preferred the friendship of the Pandavas to that of his half-brothers; Yuyutsu, who had once warned Bheema that Duryodhana meant to kill him.

Yudhishtira welcomed Yuyutsu, embracing him; while, some way off, Duryodhana was tight with fury. Yudhishtira said loudly, so all the Kaurava army heard him, "At least now, when my uncle Dhritarashtra dies, he will have one son left alive to offer tarpana for him."

He glanced at Bheema, who shone ominously on that field. For a moment, the Kauravas felt a tremor of fear as they remembered Bheema's oath that he would kill Dhritarashtra's hundred sons. Back among their own soldiers, the Pandavas donned their armour again. They picked up their weapons and they were stern and fearsome to behold. They climbed into their chariots, and their legions seethed around them. Conches were blown, trumpets blared; the drums of both armies rolled like spring thunder.

Duryodhana watched the Pandava army forming the formidable fighting Vajra and he rode up to Drona. The Kaurava said, "Here we are at last, my lord. The moment of fate is upon us, the moment we have waited a lifetime for."

Drona stared across Kurukshetra at the sea of men massed against them. Weapons and armour flashed in the sun, vivid banners waved; the whinnying of horses filled the crisp air, and the lusty shouting of footsoldiers, to embolden themselves. Excitement swept the field, over both armies. Drona smiled at his pupil, and said, "Yes, Duryodhana, the moment of truth is upon us. Do you see the enemy, all the kshatriyas?"

Duryodhana's gaze was riveted to the Pandava force. As in a dream, he said, "I see Yudhishtira's vast legions, Acharya, I see his jewel-like vyuha. I see your sishya Dhrishtadyumna at its head. I see Satyaki, his eyes full of fire, I see mighty Bheema, and Arjuna in Krishna's chariot. I see all these matchless kshatriyas turned out against us, and my blood thrills to the occasion. So many of these warriors are your disciples. All your lessons will find final fruition today, as if this war is being fought for just that. I exult at it, Acharya. Truly, this is the most glorious day of our lives!"

His pale eyes ranged over the enemy ranks. "Look, beyond the front lines are Drupada and Virata, side by side, masters of experience. How youthful they seem, their faces flushed with anticipation. Beyond them are Dhrishtaketu, Chekitana and the lord of Kasi, breathless for the fighting to begin. Acharya, I see the pulse throbbing at their temples, and they moisten their lips in eagerness. Beside them, are Purujit, Kuntibhoja and Saibya; flanking Arjuna's chariot, are Drupada's other sons, Yuddhamanyu and Uttamaujas, so tall and bright. And, away to their left, another cluster of maharathikas: Draupadi's brilliant princes, Abhimanyu a crest-jewel at their head."

Drona listened to Duryodhana in surprise, that the Kaurava was so admiring of the enemy. Now, Duryodhana turned his gaze back to his own legions. He said, "But we are greater than the sea of men that confronts us, my lord. For here, we have you, Acharya, and Pitama Bheeshma who has never known defeat in battle, and Acharya Kripa, and the tameless Karna. Aswatthama and Vikarna are with me, and Somadatta's son Bhoorisravas, who is as strong as a hundred men. These are just a few of the kshatriyas, who have come to risk their lives for my sake. If the enemy is a sea, Acharya, we are an ocean; and we shall drown them!"

Drona, the master, could not help but smile fondly at his sishya, so dauntless on the brink of war. Drona thought, regretfully, what a magnificent king this prince would have been but for his one overmastering weakness: his envy. Duryodhana was saying, "Truly, we have an ocean with us, my lord. Yet, to my mind, Pitama Bheeshma is our key to victory. The Pandavas will not contain him; the rest of us must guard him with our lives at all times."

From across the Kaurava army, his fond grandsire Bheeshma saw Duryodhana, with Drona at his side. Bheeshma saw a frown knit Duryodhana's brow and, wanting to hearten his favourite grandchild, the Kuru patriarch raised his war-conch and blew an echoing blast on it; then he threw back his head and let out a roar. Duryodhana turned with a smile and waved to his Pitama. But to answer Bheeshma's bass, from across the battlefield, from the Pandava army, floated the crystal notes of an unearthly conch. That sound was at once beautiful and terrible, and it shook the Kaurava soldiers to their very souls. In Arjuna's chariot, his dark sarathy had raised the Panchajanya to his lips!

Now both armies erupted with conches of every pitch, ringing back and forth across Kurukshetra. Arjuna echoed Krishna's clarion call with a long note of his own on the Devadatta. Bheema raised his Paundra to his lips, and thunder rolled across the field. Yudhishtira took up the Anantavijaya, and blew into the echo of Bheema's sea-call, a sound as tremendous as his brother made. Nakula and Sahadeva blew in unison on the Sughosha and the Manipushpaka.

After being taken briefly unawares by the Pandavas' conches, the hundred Kauravas raised their own sankhas and blew resoundingly on them. Without a moment's hiatus, they were answered by Kasiraja, Shikhandi, Dhrishtadyumna, Satyaki, Virata, Drupada, Draupadi's sons and Abhimanyu. All these kshatriyas blew on their great sea-conches at once; heaven and earth quaked at the sound they made.

THREE

A moment of crisis

As a multitude of conches shook Kurukshetra, Arjuna said to his incarnate charioteer, "Krishna, let us ride out some way between the armies before the fighting begins."

Krishna coaxed his gandharva horses forward; Hanuman was a little lion-tailed monkey on his banner. A hush fell again on the two armies, when they saw Arjuna's chariot emerge from the Pandava ranks on its own. The sea of men grew quiet, watching that chariot. They saw the warrior in it spoke earnestly with his sarathy, the dark Avatara[2]. But they could hear no word the two exchanged; the space between the chariot and the legions was considerable.

A morning breeze ruffling their hair, Krishna said to his soldier of light, "Look, Arjuna, at the glorious Kuru armies! And the one we must fight, with Bheeshma and Drona at its head. Look at all the kshatriyas who have come to die at your hands."

Suddenly, Arjuna grew very still, Krishna saw the Pandava tremble. Arjuna bit his lip, and moaned. In an excruciating insight, he saw not enemies before him any more, but sires and grandsires, masters, uncles, brothers, sons, grandsons and childhood friends! A sob tore its way out of Arjuna, and he cried, "Krishna! My hands shake and my mouth is dry. My body shivers and my hair stands on end."

---

2 Here, at Krishna's behest, Arjuna worships the goddess Durga before the battle begins. See Appendix for the hymn.

His eyes were full of tears as he looked at the Kaurava army. Stricken with fear, Arjuna whispered, "The Gandiva slips from my grasp, my skin burns as if it is on fire. I see omens of evil in the sky, and my head reels when I look at the enemy I am meant to kill. Oh, Krishna, what good can come from killing one's kinsmen?"

Krishna realized it was best if Arjuna confessed what disturbed him so much; a yawning sense of destiny was upon the Dark One. He, too, shivered, knowing that he, Krishna, had been born for this moment between two armies, *senayor ubhayor madhye*, which divided two ages of the earth, more than for any other time of his life. It was the Avatara's loneliest hour. Yet, he knew this was a moment of infinite opportunity, an hour of miracles, when he could speak to dim generations of the future. Arjuna was the key to this war. If Krishna could not convince the Pandava to fight, the cause of dharma would be lost on Kurukshetra, and the forces of darkness would have sway over the world.

Krishna knew that, though he bore no weapons to this war, he must fight now: a battle of the spirit, a deeper battle than any he had fought before. As the two armies on both sides froze in time, as if in a mural of war, evil, which had already seized Arjuna in coils of dread, clutched at Krishna with cold tentacles. Krishna knew the price of defeat if he lost this duel of the soul.

But Arjuna, possessed, ranted at him, "I don't want victory! I don't want a kingdom, its power or pleasures. Of what use is a kingdom, or life itself? Men who could be my father and grandfather, others that are my masters, uncles, nephews and cousins—with whom, for whom, I could enjoy a kingdom—stand armed to fight us to the death. I cannot bear it!

"Even if they kill me, how can I think of harming them? No, I don't want this terrible war. I would not have it if it were for the throne of the three worlds, how much less for a miserable earthly kingdom. How can I even dream of killing Dhritarashtra's sons? They are my cousins. Let them be the most monstrous men. I shall be worse than they are if I kill them; my crime shall be more horrible than any of theirs. How can I dare spill the same blood that flows in their bodies and mine, blood that unites us? How will I ever find peace again?

"Even if they are demented with envy and greed, even if they see no fault in murdering family, or in being treacherous to childhood friends, should we imitate them? Shouldn't we know the sin in this hideous thing and shun it?"

Krishna said nothing yet. He saw what Arjuna did not: that this battlefield trembled on the verge between one age and another; both were unsteady now. Arjuna burned with anxiety. He swayed in his chariot like a green sapling in the wind. Helplessly, he said, "When a noble house like ours is divided by war, it is ruined. The old ways are forgotten, the ancient rituals and truths. And when laws perish, evil and vice take all the clan. You know what happens then; the women become loose, castes are mixed, and the age turns dark.

"My Lord, it is straight to hell that such a clan goes, first of all, those who began its destruction. Because the spirits of the manes fall from heaven! The sacred covenants are broken, and all the generations of such a house are doomed to hell. What a heinous sin you and I have plotted: to murder our family out of greed for a throne. Instead, let Duryodhana kill me in battle while I am unarmed and unresisting!"

Arjuna sat down in the chariot, buried his head in his hands, and wept. Krishna realized he must answer the Pandava, coax him out of his despair, or all would be lost. As calmly as he could, he began, "From where this cowardly spirit at such a critical time? This is not for a kshatriya. It will not lead you to heaven, Arjuna, but to disgrace. Don't give in to this womanliness, it is beneath you. Cast it aside and arise, O Vijaya!"

But evil was truly upon the Pandava. He cried in anguish, "How will I attack Bheeshma and Drona with arrows in battle? When I should worship them instead! I would rather be a beggar in the world than kill my gurus. How could I dream of enjoying a kingdom stained with my masters' blood? When I see who the enemy is, I don't know if I would rather win or lose this war. This is not weakness; it is the strength of compassion. How could I live if I killed my cousins? Krishna, help me! Confusion roils my mind; my soul is weak with pity. I am sick with sorrow and fear. Teach me, my Lord, tell me what I must do."

Again, Arjuna sobbed. "No! Nothing can drive out the grief that dries up my senses, paralyses me. Not unrivalled kingdom on earth, why, not the sovereignty of the Devas could rid me of this terrible sorrow!" His face grim, he said, "I will not fight," and fell silent.

Krishna smiled at him as at a petulant child. He said indulgently, "You grieve for those you should not, Arjuna; but you speak to me of wisdom. Wise men do not grieve for either the living or the dead. You and I, and these kings of men, have always existed, and always shall. Childhood, youth and old age are three stages of life, and death is only the fourth: as natural, as inevitable, as the other three. Death is the stage by which the soul passes from one life to the next; with death, the soul assumes a new body. The wise are not troubled by this; because the soul, which pervades all the living, the aging and the dying, never dies itself. It was never born or begun; it neither kills, nor is killed. It is primeval and indestructible. It always was, and shall always be.

As the body sheds worn-out clothes, so the soul sheds worn-out bodies. And just as we put on new clothes, the soul dons new bodies, as if they were its raiment. But the soul is not touched by fire or weapons, by wind or water. Inmost, subtlest element, always the being of beings, it is changeless, eternal."

Arjuna was still downcast, unconvinced. He had the uncanny feeling the words the Blue God spoke were meant for a multitude of listeners other than himself: unborn, yet avid listeners. As if their chariot out on Kurukshetra stood not just in their own time, but at the heart of all the swirling ages of men. Deep and secret futures swelled around them, gazed on them with a billion unseen eyes, and brushed their souls with ghostly fingers.

Arjuna frowned. He felt he was alone on the bank of a timeless river of light flowing from dark Krishna; flowing for him, yes, but not only for him. The Pandava sensed numberless presences gathering around, and the pristine river shone at them, as well, to drink from its grace. Now Krishna began to speak in some hidden rapture; as if he played on his flute.

"Even if you believe the soul is born again and again, and dies as well like that, still you shouldn't grieve. For certain, then, is death for he who is born, and the moment of it already decided at his birth; and equally certain is birth, again, for the dead. Why grieve for the inevitable? You do not determine when any man, even yourself, is born into the world. How can you hope to decide when or not he will die?"

Arjuna seemed to grow calmer now, and to listen to his dark sarathy. Relieved that at least his warrior's panic grew less, Krishna went on, "But this is not what is crucial. You are a kshatriya: for you, a battle of dharma is the highest fortune. How can you be so full of doubt at such a time? You should rejoice, Arjuna, the gates of heaven are open!

"If you deny your own nature's glory, and do not fight, then you will sin. Through all time, men will speak of your shame; for a man like you, who knows honour, shame is worse than death. They will say Arjuna was afraid on the great occasion. Even your friends will scoff; think, then, what will your enemies say? Could anything be sadder? So arise, Pandava! If you die in battle, you will go straight to swarga. If you triumph, you will enjoy the earth before you find heaven. Fight Arjuna, and I swear you will not sin."

Lulled by Krishna's voice, absorbed in his smile, his eyes, his presence of grace, Arjuna began to float away down the river of light. The sarathy now spoke softly, hypnotically, to the Pandava, touching his inner mind. As if in prayer, he chanted his wisdom, as much to himself as to his cousin.

In exorcism, Krishna continued, "Along the infinite way, no effort, even the smallest, is in vain or lost, and no obstacle prevails. This is the wisdom of union, of yoga. Arjuna, I am with you. Free yourself from attachment to what you do; make no anxious difference between success and failure. Act! Act in purity, act serenely: even-mindedness is yoga; detachment and skill are yoga.

"For one who is determined, his understanding is single and lucid. But the thoughts of the undiscerning are many-branched, endless, endlessly confused."

Arjuna was a portal to unborn generations, as Krishna's words spilled through him, each a being alive, tender and rampant: a bright host of masters! They reached beyond him into veiled times, dim, dim, down mysterious trails of history, taking fire to the hearts of bizarre and visionary heroes, who would one day walk a very different world, and make war again. In his perfect passivity, while Krishna exhorted him to immaculate action, pure war, Arjuna became the Blue God's unwitting ally in another, older contention. He stood at a crossroads of the mythic universe and, listening absorbed, gave his astral body to become Krishna's prophet.

Krishna said, "The wise who have yoked their intelligence are freed from the bonds of birth. They reach Brahman, the sorrowless state.

Arjuna, your mind is confused with all that you have read and heard. Your heart is bewildered. When true insight dawns on you, you will see beyond bookish Vedic learning, and your spirit will be profound and unshakeable."

The earth received the Avatara's song.

FOUR

The Bhagavad Gita

Sensing that Arjuna was calmer, Krishna paused. The Pandava did not tremble any more. Arjuna asked, "Krishna, who is the wise man? What is he like? How does the man of Brahman speak, how does he sit or walk?"

Krishna threw back his beautiful head and laughed. "When a man knows the bliss of the atman, his soul, all the cravings and torments of his heart vanish. And when his spirit is absorbed in itself, perfectly satisfied, he is wise, illumined."

Arjuna saw Krishna exulted, his eyes shining!

"The heaviest sorrow doesn't perturb him, nor does the most pleasant desire move him. When lust, fear and rage have left him, he is a Brahmarishi. The bonds of his body are broken; he is enlightened.

"He who is beyond affection, who does not rejoice or grieve when he is fortunate or unfortunate, but is imperturbable: he is an illumined one. As the tortoise draws in its legs, the rishi withdraws his senses. Arjuna, the abstinent run away from what they desire, but desire does not leave them. Only the vision of God removes desire itself.

"Even a man who knows the way can be dragged from it, because the senses are powerful and wild. But he who tames the senses, collects his mind in serenity and fixes it on me, he is illumined.

"Desire springs from attachment to the objects of the senses. Anger springs from desire, confusion from anger, and from confusion, forgetfulness. When he forgets the lessons of experience, a man loses his discrimination. Then, he is destroyed.

"But when a man's mind is disciplined, his spirit is pure. In purity, there is peace, and in peace sorrow ends. The intelligence of a quiet man is established in the peace of the atman, his immortal soul.

"What is night for most men, is when the quiet man is awake. And when the world is awake and abustle, is night for the sage who sees."

Arjuna floated above the field of Kurukshetra, carried by Krishna's spiralling song. The currents of that song were the tides of time. The ages roared around him in legendary magnificence; just the silver umbilicus of the Gita held him secure. The dark charioteer sang on, "When a man becomes like the ocean, perfectly calm, when his desires come to him like water to the ocean, and never move him, then he comes to peace. When a man works in the world without any desire, he comes to peace; and this peace is the ocean of the soul, the divine Brahman. Once a man comes into it, he does not return to delusion. At the hour of his death, he is alive in that eternal enlightenment. He attains the bliss of God."

Darkness and doubt clutched at Arjuna once more. Evil would not succumb tamely to Krishna in the subtle battle he waged against it. This battle would decide the outcome of Arjuna's war, and those of a thousand more to be fought on the strangest fields by unborn heroes, in impossible futures, long before they were joined. Primordial evil battled dark Krishna for Arjuna's soul: the soul of that rarest of men, an evolved disciple on the verge of final grace.

His voice full of despair, Arjuna cried, "Krishna, you say the way of the mind is finer than the way of action. Why, then, do you goad me into this savagery? You bewilder me now, and I am lost! Show me one straight path by which I can be free."

Though evil attacked his heart, Krishna spoke quietly. "The dual path has been taught in it since the world began: the way of gyana, knowledge, for men of contemplation; for men of action, the way of karma, of deeds, of battles. You do not become free by doing nothing; by abstaining from karma, you do not become perfect. He who does nothing, but broods over his desires, is no sage, he is a hypocrite. Do the work you are born to, for without working you cannot sustain even your own body. Let war be your worship, Arjuna."

The dream closed around Arjuna. He was a time-traveller again; Krishna's song was his vimana. His bright craft was rocked by the thunder of ages, buffeted by distant mysteries of violence and terror, by awesome miracles. The ship of light was proof against them all. Krishna's song withstood the last tests of time.

"In the beginning, God made men, each with his own nature and dharma. He said, 'By doing this you will prosper. The work of your nature will yield the fruit of your desires.' By doing your natural dharma you worship the Gods, and they nurture you. By working unattached, you come to immortal bliss. Such karma is the ritual that maintains the very earth. Look at me, Arjuna. I am not bound by any karma in all the worlds, nor is there anything in them that isn't already mine. Yet, I am always working.

"Only the deluded man thinks 'I am the doer'. Everything is done by the gunas, the essences of nature at their eternal play. Those who go astray become attached to their karma; they begin to take the gunas for the soul. But no wise man should unsettle the minds of those who don't see whole, because work must go on, always, or the worlds fall into anarchy."

Arjuna was entranced again, as the river of grace flowed from the Blue God.

"Every creature can only follow its innate prakriti; even the wisest man lives by his own nature. What can repression accomplish, Arjuna? It is always better to do one's own dharma, however imperfectly, than the dharma of another, even immaculately. It is better to die in one's own law; for to live by an alien law is perilous."

Like a child, Arjuna asked, "But what makes a man sin, even against his own will, helplessly, Krishna?"

"Rage and lust, ravening, deadly: the enemies! Why, the intellect itself, deluded, feeds the fires of these two. Lust veils the soul as smoke does a fire, as dust does a clear mirror. To pass beyond lust, you must transcend the intellect. For powerful are the senses; greater than they are, is the mind; more potent than the mind is the intellect. But greater than intellect is the atman who sets you free."

Krishna's eyes were far away from Kurukshetra, why, from the age. Then, smiling, he said coolly, "I taught this yoga to Vivasat once. Vivasat gave it to Manu, Manu taught it to Ikshvaku; and, handed down the generations, the Rajarishis all knew it. Until the great yoga was lost in the world in a forgotten time, when darkness came. Arjuna, today, on this chosen field, hear the deathless secret from me."

But Arjuna looked at him incredulously. He cried, "Vivasat? He died long before you were born! How did you teach Vivasat the yoga?"

Krishna laughed. "My past lives, and yours as well, are many, more than you dream; only, I remember them all and you remember none. I am not born into this world, but only seem to be; and I am master of my prakriti, my immortal nature, and not its subject. Whenever evil dominates the world, I send myself forth into it: to protect the good, who else have they? To destroy the evil, who else will redeem them? To establish dharma I come, again and again, from age to age.

"The man who knows me is never born again. When he leaves his body, he comes to me. Absorbed in me, he is delivered from lust, anger and fear. He is burnt pure in the fire of my being; I become his home. All men come to me, at last, and I deliver them all. Whatever path a man walks, it leads finally to me. I am not bound by karma, and neither are those who know me. So like the ancients, who worked for moksha, you must also fight.

"The way of karma is not easy, Arjuna, and even maharishis are perplexed about action and inaction. Only the realized yogin sees restlessness in inaction, and repose in deeds. When he acts, he remains poised in the serenity of the atman. He has no attachment to the fruit of his actions. Contented in the atman itself, he acts and is beyond karma. He is satisfied with whatever comes to him by chance. He is free from envy, untouched by success and failure. He acts and is not bound by what he does.

"All his work is a sacrifice, a ritual of worship. His enlightened heart beats as one with Brahman, the Holy Spirit. For him, all things are Brahman. The sacrifice, the oblation, the sacrificer and the fire of yagna: they are all one, and they are the Brahman.

"And he who offers no worship; this world is not for him, then how shall any other world be his?"

When he heard the tone in which Krishna said this, another dread seized Arjuna, who had laid down the Gandiva and said he would not fight.

"Worship," the Dark One went on quietly, looking out at the motionless armies, "is greater than any material sacrifice, and all worship ends inexorably in Brahman. Let the rishis of wisdom and vision be your masters. Learn from them by serving them, by worshipping and questioning them.

"As fire does wood, wisdom burns karma to ashes. Nothing on earth is as pure as wisdom; on the ship of wisdom, the worst sinners cross over the sea of evil. He who has seen the atman, slowly but inexorably, peace comes to him. Take up the sword of discernment, Arjuna, cut away the doubt that lurks in your heart."

Now Arjuna looked into the Lord's face, and saw his black eyes alight with compassion. The Pandava said, "Krishna, first you say renunciation is the way, burning karma with wisdom. Then you say the opposite, that karma is the way. Tell me, which is the true path?"

"Both," said Krishna, "lead to freedom. But yours is the way of karma. You are not greedy for kingdom or its power; that is half your battle already won, you will be freed easily." Krishna smiled, the crow's feet around his eyes cracking deep. "But, Arjuna, the wise do not speak of the ways of wisdom and action as being separate, only the ignorant do. You cannot renounce action without knowing what it is. Only he who engages in karma knows its inner emptiness. Purified, he realizes the still Brahman. In detachment, he occupies the senses with the objects of sense, but not himself. He is like a lotus leaf, resting on water, but not wetted by water. The yogin does not act out of desire, but to make himself pure, to make himself wise.

"In the city of nine gates, the body, only he shall have peace who has mastered his nature by giving in to it perfectly, without desire, renouncing whatever he does, even as he does it. He knows the soul does not act, nor is it acted upon; but just nature's gunas. Such a man's sins are cut away from him. He reaches the Brahman, from where there is no return. His wisdom illumines the immortal self.

"When the soul's light ends your darkness, that light shines forth from you: the Brahman revealed, splendid as a sun. The enlightened man sees all creation equally. He knows pleasures that spring outside the self are ephemeral, and they inevitably bring sorrow. He has no use for these. He is master of the surge in his blood of lust, of anger. He finds his joy within himself, his light within himself, in his own soul; and he comes to Brahmanirvana," said the Blue God, who had come to cleanse the world.

"Whose sins are put out, whose doubts are dispelled, to whom the welfare of every creature is his joy, finds Brahmanirvana. The austere man, set free from lust, anger and fear, is rooted in enlightenment. He comes to me, who enjoys all karma and all austerity. I am Lord of the worlds, and a friend to all men. And he finds Brahmanirvana."

FIVE

The Song of God

KRISHNA'S SONG, THE RIVER OF HOLY LIGHT, FLOWED THROUGH Arjuna, and it made him see. He was borne away from Kurukshetra, into other realms. It even seemed to the Pandava that the war—why, all his life—was a pretext to be out here, now, in his chariot with Krishna, and to hear his Gita. It was an hour of revelations, when ends more profound than he could imagine were achieved. Krishna was a sacred flame beside him.

The Dark One said, "He who works serenely, with no desire for the fruits of what he does, success or failure, he is the sannyasin; not he who lights no lamp on this earth. Arjuna, what men call yoga is sannyasa, no less. For no man becomes a yogin until he renounces his selfishness.

"Karma is the way of the rishi who wants to attain yoga, to yoke himself to the eternal. Once he attains to that union, he is at peace. The warrior's way is his own will. The will alone is the soul's dearest friend, and it is the atman's worst enemy. The restrained man's will is his soul's friend, but the self-indulgent man's will is his enemy. The rishi is absorbed in the atman. He is a master of his will, he is unchanging.

"Arjuna, the light of a lamp does not flicker in a windless place. He who has realized the Brahman never wanders again from the deepest truth of his being. When his mind is yoked to his soul, set free from craving, the yogin is united with Brahman."

Krishna sent his peace to invade the Pandava. "When you gain the atman, you know there is nothing left to achieve. Then, no sorrow will move you: the yogin is disconnected from pain; he is one with Brahman.

The body, the mind, and the life are pure; the light shines through clearly. Infinite bliss is as natural as breathing to that man. The atman is plain to him in all beings, in all things and everywhere."

Tears filled Arjuna's eyes, and ran down his face. Krishna said, "He who sees me everywhere, I am with him, and he is with me forever. The perfect man sees all things in the image of his own self, equally."

Another spasm of anxiety struck Arjuna. He said, "Krishna, it is hard to see all things equally. The mind is fickle, prone to terror. It is impetuous, strong, obstinate, and so are its passions. It is simpler to tame the wind!"

Krishna laughed again, "Who said yoga is easy to achieve? Remember it is the last achievement, beyond which there is no other. Yet, it is not impossible; I tell you, you can attain it."

But Arjuna wanted to know, "Krishna, where does he go who believes, but cannot control himself? Is he like a cloud in the sky, with no support anywhere? Does he fall forever?" The Pandava's face was pale. "Krishna, doubt grips my heart like an evil spirit."

Krishna spoke like the sun now, radiating light. "Not in this world or the next does such a believer perish. A man who seeks Brahman never comes to a bad end. The bhakta who falls away from yoga is reborn into the homes of the pure and the prosperous, of kings, or into a family of yogins; the second birth is the rarer. From there, again, the soul treads the way towards enlightenment. Inexorably, the seeker's belief takes him on. Arjuna, the man who worships me, to me he is the brightest yogin, more precious than the tapasvin, the gyani, or the man of karma. The man of bhakti is dearest to me."

Like a temple bell calling him out of sorrow and futility, Krishna's words rang in the morning. When Arjuna looked into his sarathy's black eyes, he saw such love in them. He smiled wanly at the Blue God, as if he had awoken from a nightmare to find the sun risen and daylight in the world.

Krishna let his song taper into a silence full of mercy, which enveloped his warrior in a deep respite. Arjuna felt his fear recede. The Avatara gathered himself within his resonant stillness. As always, his battles were only beginning; and he was the eternal seeker. He knew that Arjuna he could save from his crisis of courage. But who would save Krishna from his long aloneness, from himself? Who would redeem him?

But then, deep destiny was upon him. He knew his Gita would change the very heart of the dreaming, myth-making earth; and it would change him, as well, in some incalculable way. It was as if, with his song to Arjuna, the epic of man was begun again, *mutant*!

Vision washed over Krishna. He saw his words percolate through Arjuna into the seeds of unborn generations, waiting, waiting to metamorphose, to transform the nature of mythic and fabulous time: the earth's legendary heart. From them, his song redefined all the paths to freedom, all the images of the future: bodies of legend, the races of men, their nations, histories, wars, their every ordeal, and, more than anything else, death and dying.

Krishna's song flowed again, unknown, ineluctable. "Listen, Arjuna, to how in yoga, with your mind devoted to me, you will know me. Then there will be nothing left to know. Among a million men in the world, perhaps one seeks perfection; of a million such, who do, each by his chosen path, perhaps one truly knows me. Arjuna, you know me, don't you?"

Otherwise, they would not be out here together.

"My nature is made of earth, water, fire, air, ether, mind, intellect and ego: eight aspects. But this is only my gross nature. My other aspect is the soul, and the world is founded upon it. It is the seed and the end of all things. I am the cause of everything, no other.

"Like pearls on a string, the worlds are strung on me. Kaunteya, I am the essence of the waters, the light of the sun and the moon.

"I am *AUM* and the Vedas, the sruti of the mandalas and the manhood in men. I am the sacred smell of the earth, and the brightness of fire.

"I am the life of all lives, the purity of the sage, the wisdom of the wise, the lustre of the illustrious, the might of the mighty. And all creatures I am, of sattva, rajas or tamas."

Clouds had gathered in the sky. It would rain on Kurukshetra today. Great kshatriyas' blood and common soldiers' blood would mingle with rainwater, and flow in red streams for a while—in scarlet rivers if Krishna had his way—before the earth absorbed it all, and what remained was dried by the wind and the sun in brown patches of violent memory.

"It is the three gunas that delude, Arjuna; all this maya of life and death is because of them. Who makes me his sanctuary safely crosses the ocean of the world, the sea of samsara. Demons, evil ones, do not seek refuge in me yet. The virtuous that worship me, my bhaktas, are of four kinds: the man in trouble, the seeker after knowledge, the seeker after happiness, and the man of discrimination. The discerning man is dearest to me. Why, he and I are one. Unlike the others, he comes to me after many lives, having realized that I am all there is. He is the rarest of the rare: the mahatman, the great soul.

"Minds that are full of desire worship the Devas with rituals. I give them what their hearts want; I make their faith fruitful, whatever forms it takes. Those who worship the Devas go to the Devas, but my bhaktas come to me. Those who are confused think of me as my manifestations. They do not know my transcendent nature, Un-born, changeless and supreme. Arjuna, I know all the beings, those alive now, those of the past, and all those yet to be. But who knows me? Only the illumined, who have died to sin. Those who are freed from duality's delusions find sanctuary in me, and are saved from age and death. They know the atman and Brahman, and all about karma. They know that I rule both this world and the next, and they come to me when they die."

Arjuna said, "What is Brahman, Krishna? What is the atman? And what is karma? Which is the domain of the elements and which that of the Gods? How can a man know you, as he dies?"

"Brahman is the imperishable. Brahman alive in the individual being is atman, the soul; and karma is the force of creation. He that thinks of me, as he dies, certainly comes to me. Indeed, whatever a man thinks of as he dies, he attains to that, absorbed in the final thought forever. He who says *AUM* as he dies, thinking of me, he attains the absolute: Brahman, the seer, the ancient, the subtlest, the supporter beyond darkness.

"Those who come to me, Arjuna, never return to impermanence, to the places of sorrow. They have reached the final perfection; they are not born again. From Brahmaloka down, all the worlds are subject to rebirth. But he who reaches me, never comes back."

SIX

The Bhagavad Gita

ARJUNA SAW HOW KRISHNA SHONE BETWEEN THE TWO ARMIES, A still blue flame, unearthly. In perfect calm, the Dark One sang his Gita, "He who knows the day of Brahma is a thousand ages, and a thousand ages are his night, he knows day and night. At daybreak, all the hidden lives come forth to be born. At twilight, they dissolve again into the dormant seed of life; and again, helplessly, the same lives stream forth once more at dawn of Brahma's next day.

"But beyond this being and return, beyond the day and the night, there is another unmanifest, eternal Being who does not perish when other lives do. He is not born with Brahma's day, nor dies with Brahma's night. Those who reach him do not return. He is my abode. He pervades all this birth and death; he can be reached by bhakti.

"Fire, light, day, the bright half of the moon, the six months of the northern sun: at these times, the yogins of illumination go to the Brahman.

"Smoke, night, the dark half of the moon, the six months of the southern sun: these are when the yogins obtain the lunar light of Pitriloka, the world of the manes, and they return to birth.

"Light and dark are the primitive and enduring paths of this world. By one the yogin goes and never comes back; by the other, he returns."

Arjuna did not tremble any more, but listened raptly to his sarathy's Gita. Krishna said, "Arjuna, my song contains the secrets of knowledge and wisdom; it will set you free. This is the highest knowledge, easy, imperishable and known directly. It is my way, the way of the Avatara. I pervade the universe with my spirit; all things abide in me, but not

I in them. This is my mystery. As the tameless air that moves everywhere abides in cosmic ether, the akasa, so too existence dwells in me.

"When the ages have made their round, every creature is gathered back into the seed that I am. When the next creation dawns, I send them forth again, helpless, bound in my maya. I, the Lord of maya, send the multitudes forth and gather them back into my being.

"The ignorant pass by this human form of mine; of me, they know nothing. The enlightened ones, the great souls that know me, worship me with an unwavering mind, and with the rite of wisdom. They know who I am, that I am the source undying.

"I am the ritual, I am the sacrifice; I am the ancestral oblation, I am the herb that heals. I am the holy mantra, I am the melted butter; I am the fire, Arjuna, I am the burnt offering.

"I am this world's father, its mother, its supporter and its grandsire, too. I am the end of all knowledge, the purifier. I am *AUM*, I am Rik, Sama and Yajus," whispered Krishna, humming to a spellbound Arjuna.

"The goal, the upholder, the Lord, the witness, the abode, the sanctuary and the friend am I. I am origin and dissolution, the ground, the refuge and the immortal seed.

"Worship me, I am the heat of the sun. I withhold and send down the rain. Deathlessness I am, and death; manifest am I, and the hidden germ of life.

"Worshippers of the Vedas, drinkers of Soma, stray from the path. They reach Indra's realm, and enjoy the pleasures of the Devas. However, they are transients in heaven, and when their punya is exhausted, they are born again into the world of men. But those who worship me, I secure what they have and bring them what they do not. Anyway, the worshippers of the Vedas and the Devas worship only me. For I am all the Gods and the Vedas, as well.

"Those who worship the Devas go to them; those who worship the sires go to the Pitrs; and to the spirits go those who worship bhutas and pretas. And my bhaktas surely come to me.

"Every offering made with love, I receive with joy: a leaf, a flower, a fruit, and a palmful of water. Whatever you eat or sacrifice, whatever you do, offer it to me, Pandava.

"I dwell in all creatures; none is hateful to me, none special. But those who worship me, they are in me, surely, and I in them. Let even the most evil man but worship me and I will be with him; swiftly, he will become a muni and come to peace.

"Arjuna, know one thing for sure: those who worship me will never perish. Let them be rich or poor, let them be men or women; let them be anyone, my bhaktas reach the final sanctuary."

"Krishna's eyes twinkled at his friend. "How much more should devoted kshatriyas worship me in this impermanent, sorrowful world."

Arjuna was startled in his absorption, the song of peace snatched at his mind. Now the Pandava hung on the Dark One's every word; he was convinced he must fight, and he did not know if he would see the light of another day.

"Fix your heart on me," said Krishna, "be devoted to me; love me, and to me you shall come in life and in death. Arjuna listen, now that you have a mind to: not the Devas, or the maharishis know my beginning. I am their source.

"From me came the Saptarishi and the four Manus, and from them all these generations of men. I am the origin, and so the sages worship me. I give them fixity of understanding. I light the lamps of their wisdom, and dispel the ignorant dark."

Arjuna said, "Krishna, you are the Brahman, first of all the Gods, Un-born, pervasive. Narada, Asita, Devala, Vyasa, all the rishis say as much, and now I hear it from your own lips. And I believe it all. Not the Devas or the Asuras know your manifestations; only you know yourself. So, tell me, on which of your forms shall I meditate? Tell me, Krishna, your words are like amrita to me."

Krishna said, "Hear my divine forms, but only some of them; because to all my forms there is no end. I am the atman in every being, their soul. I am the beginning, the middle and the end of everything that ever is.

"Of Adityas I am Vishnu, of lamps I am the Sun; of planets the Moon, Maricha of the Maruts.

"Of Vedas I am the Sama, Indra of the Devas; of senses I am mind, consciousness in the living. Of Rudras I am Sankara, Kubera of the Yakshas; of Vasus I am Agni, Meru of the mountain peaks.

"Of priests I am Brihaspati, Skanda of the generals; of waters I am the ocean, Bhrigu among the rishis. Of speech I am *AUM*, japam of the offerings; and of ranges, the Himalaya.

"Of trees I am the Aswattha, Narada of the seers; of gandharvas I am Chitraratha, Kapila among the perfect.

"Of horses I am Ucchaisravas, nectar-born, Airavata of elephants; of weapons I am the Vajra, Kamadhenu among cows. Of lovers I am Kama, Vasuki among serpents.

"Of Nagas I am Ananta, Varuna among the marine beings; of the manes I am Aryaman, Yama among judges.

"Of titans I am Prahlada, I am time of measures; of beasts I am the lion, Garuda among birds. Of purifiers I am the wind, Rama among kshatriyas. Of fish I am the whale, Ganga of rivers.

"Of creations, I am the Beginning, the End and the Middle, Arjuna; of sciences I am the science of the spirit, the dialectic for debaters. I am death that devours everything, and the source of all, all that is yet to come. Fame I am among the feminine beings, and prosperity, speech, memory, intelligence, firmness and patience, too.

"Of hymns I am Brihatsaman, the Gayatri of mantras; Mrigasirsa of the months, of seasons I am spring. I am the dice-play of deceivers, I am the splendour of the splendid; karma am I and the punya of the good."

Krishna smiled, "Of the Vrishnis I am Krishna, Arjuna of the Pandavas; of the munis I am Vyasa, Usanas among poets. Of kings I am their sceptre, the policy of conquerors; of secrets I am the silence, their wisdom of those that know.

"And, more, I am the seed of all beings, for nothing which is exists without me. But what do you want to know all this for? There is no end to me, my friend: I support the universe with an atom of myself."

Knowing clearly that Krishna's Gita was more vital than the war before him, Arjuna said to his divine cousin, "Of those who worship you, Krishna, and those who worship the Parabrahman, who has the greater yoga?"

Krishna replied, "Those who worship me are the most perfect yogins. And those who restrain their senses, are serene, compassionate to all beings, and worship the Parabrahman: they, also, come to me. But surely, the task of these is harder, because the unmanifest Brahman is difficult for embodied beings to attain to.

"Have no doubt, Arjuna, that I deliver my bhaktas quickly from samsara, this sea of grief. Fix your mind on me, let your thoughts come to me, and in me you will live forever. If at first your mind wanders, meditate slowly on me, by stages. If you cannot do this, act in my name. If this is also impossible, offer your life to me, whatever it is. Better than gyana is dhyana, but better than dhyana is bhakti, and surrender. Then, comes peace."

Arjuna gazed at Krishna with such absorption that the Lord ruffled his hair like a child's.

"He who has no malice toward any creature, who is compassionate and friendly, free of egotism, always serene: he is my bhakta, dear to me. Who does not shrink from the world, and from whom the world does not shrink, who is no slave to joy or sorrow, anger, fear or agitation, he is dear to me.

"Who is pure, with no expectations, skilled, serene, and has surrendered to me: he is my bhakta, precious to me. Who is devoted, who does not rejoice or grieve, does not hate or lust, who has passed beyond good and evil; he is dear to me. Who is the same with an enemy and a friend, to slander and fame, in pain and pleasure, cold and heat; whose spirit is unattached, to whom praise and blame are one, who is content and tranquil, his speech controlled, his mind steady, who has no permanent dwelling: he is my bhakta, and dear to me.

"And dearest of all is he who surrenders to me in faith, with all his heart."

Thus, spoke Sri Krishna.

SEVEN

The Bhagavad Gita

ARJUNA ASKED, "PRAKRITI AND PURUSHA, KSHETRA AND THE KNOWER of the kshetra; what are they, Krishna?"

Krishna said, "The body is the kshetra, the field. The seeds of karma are sown in it, and their harvest reaped. Munis say that he who knows the kshetra watches what happens within his body. Arjuna, I am the knower of the kshetra in every body. Discernment between field and knower is the highest knowledge.

"Listen to the nature of the field and the knower.

"Prakriti, the cosmos, first; then, ego, intellect, the ten senses—five of the body, five in the mind—the five subjects of sense, pleasure and pain, desire and revulsion, the entire organism, intelligence and will: all this is the field of kshetra.

"Humility, honesty, non-violence, patience, self-effacement, and the perception that birth, death, old age, illness and pain are evil; detachment, no dependence on a wife, children or a home, and absolute equal-mindedness to pleasure and pain; unswerving devotion to me, a life in solitary parts, far from the crowd; constancy in the yoga of the atman, insight: all this is knowledge."

Weightless, always on the verge of an explosion of freedom, Arjuna was carried upon the wave of light that crested Krishna's song. The Pandava surrendered to the magic absolutely; it held him like its child.

"I will tell you how to reach the Brahman who has no beginning or end, and is transcendent, eternal. He is beyond both what is and what is not. His hands and feet are everywhere, in all times; his heads, faces and eyes are on every side. His ear is this world, and He lives in the world as well, all-enfolding.

"He moves the senses, but is beyond them. He is perfectly unattached, yet supports the universe. He is free of the gunas of nature, but enjoys them. He is within every creature and beyond them all, always working, ever still, subtle beyond the mind's grasp: so near us, so utterly remote.

"He is one, and with every creature, at once, creating them, nurturing them, destroying them, and creating them afresh. He is the light of lights, beyond darkness. He is knowledge, all wisdom's only object and its sole purpose, innate in every heart.

"Nature and soul, prakriti and purusha, both have no beginning. The soul in nature enjoys the infinite essences in nature. Attachment causes the soul to incarnate in wombs of good and evil.

"The witness is the Brahman in the body. He is the atman, the last self, and the final experiencer. No matter how a man has lived, if he once experiences the Brahman directly, beyond nature, he will not be reborn.

"By dhyana, some reach the atman, some by gyana, and others by the way of karma. Yet others are ignorant of these three paths, and they resort to worship. They, too, cross over the sea of death by their bhakti, their devotion to what they have heard.

"All that live do so by the union between the kshetra and its knower, nature and soul, prakriti and Brahman. The man who sees God abiding in all things, and all beings, God dwelling deathless in the mortal world, he truly sees.

"The man who sees that only the gunas of nature act, and never the atman, he truly sees. For the soul is actless. When a man sees that manifold, multifarious being is centred in just the One, and how from that One it spreads, he attains the Brahman.

"The Brahman has no beginning; it is before and beyond the gunas. Arjuna, the Brahman lives in the body, but it does not act, nor do actions touch it: just as the all-pervasive ether is untainted, immaculate, because it is so subtle.

"Even as the sun does the world, the Lord of the field illumines every kshetra. The man who sees the difference between the kshetra and its knower, who sees the liberation of man from nature, he becomes free."

Arjuna was awash on that sea of calm, the Song of God. Krishna's song radiated shafts of light that pierced the marmas, the fine portals to the Pandava's spirit, and through him entered distant men in unborn times, on strangest battlefields. Arjuna heard Krishna *within his heart, under his skin now*, speaking to those multitudes, beginning his eternal work of salvation again.

"Listen to the wisdom of ages. The sages on whom it dawned became perfect; they were freed from the bonds of the body. They became like me. They are not born at creation, they are not destroyed at the dissolution.

"Great Nature is my womb. I cast the seed of all things into myself. Of any being born into any world, Arjuna, I am the father who casts the seed, and prakriti is the mother. Sattva, rajas and tamas, the three gunas of nature, bring the deathless dweller into the body.

"Sattva is pure, and reveals the atman by blemishless light. Yet, sattva binds with attachment to goodness and to knowledge.

"Rajas is attraction, passion sprung from desire and attachment. It binds the soul to the body with hunger for action.

"Tamas is dullness, born of ignorance; it is blind delusion. It binds with darkness, sloth, and stupor.

"From time to time, age to age, sattva dominates, then rajas, and tamas, too, prevailing over the other two gunas.

"When the light of knowledge shines at all the body's gates, sattva prevails. Unrest and greed are the signs of rajas, and complete delusion dominates when tamas rules.

"If death comes when sattva prevails, the soul attains to the higher world of beings that know God. If death comes when rajas rules, the soul is reborn among those who live the life of power and action. And if a man dies when tamas reigns, he is born among the deluded, once more.

"The good rise upwards, the passionate remain in the middle realms, and the tamasic sink; they devolve down to the realms of darkness."

Arjuna felt a seismic disturbance in his heart. It was the labour of the ending of a yuga, and the birth of another; and he could not fathom it. Krishna, who saw it clearly, Krishna, who had caused it, sang on to his bhakta. The ripples of enlightenment were on his lips, and his depths were like the ocean's, unmoving. The Dark One calmed Arjuna, who was churned by the spirits of the two ages at whose very edge they stood, out on Kurukshetra.

"When the dweller in the body transcends the gunas that cause the body, he is liberated from life and death, decay and pain. He becomes immortal."

His terror quieted again, Arjuna said, "How do we know the one who is beyond the gunas? How does he live? How does he transcend the gunas?"

"He does not despise illumination, restless activity or dark delusion, when they prevail. Nor does he long for them, when they cease.

"For him pain and pleasure are alike. He never wavers. For him a clod of earth, a stone, and a bar of gold are the same; blame and praise are the same to him, because he is established in the atman's inner peace. He who has relinquished the initiative of action, but lives in harmony with his nature, he has grown beyond the conflicting gunas.

"The man who is devoted to me transcends the gunas. He becomes the Brahman, because I am that abode of bliss."

Krishna's every word was a scripture.

"The everlasting Aswattha, the Tree of Life, has its roots in heaven and its branches down in the earth below. Its leaves are the Vedas." He spoke in some wonder, as if his own birth's greater reasons were being revealed to him, even now: the secrets of incarnation being laid bare to the Avatara. At the end of his lonely anguish, sublime calm stole over him.

"Like the banyan's, the branches of the Tree of Life reach above and below, nourished by the gunas, down even into the world of men.

"Its true form is never seen in this world: not its beginning, its end, or its nature. The bhakta cuts down the tree with the sword of detachment, saying, 'I seek refuge not in the tree, but in the Primal One from whom this current of the world flows.'

"He who is free of pride and delusion, who has conquered the evil of attachment, whose lusts are stilled, who is devoted to me, he who is freed of the opposites of pleasure and pain, comes to the changeless state.

"Not fire, not the moon or the sun illumines the self-lustrous Being who is my abode. He who attains me shall never be reborn."

EIGHT

The Song of God

In the chariot between the two armies frozen in time by the Dark One's power, Krishna said to Arjuna, "In this world, the Avatara dons the five senses of nature, and the sixth, of the mind: the garment of prakriti!

"When I take a body and leave it, these come and go like the scent of flowers on the wind. I enjoy the senses, Arjuna, as you do, and suffer by them as well. But they do not delude me. The splendour of the sun, the moon and fire are my own.

"I nourish the world while I am in it. Then, as the moon, as precious Soma, I bring sap and water to the living world of plant and herb; as the fire of life, I nurture the bodies of animals. All the foods of this earth I consume, and make inner and outward breath of them.

"I am the heart of every man who lives. I am the source of memory and knowledge, and their loss as well. I am the Vedas, the Vedanta, and the knower of the Vedas, too.

"Arjuna, there are just two beings in this world: the dying and the undying. The one who dies is all these changing lives, and the undying one is changeless. But beyond both these the supreme Spirit, the Lord, pervades the three worlds and sustains them.

"I am beyond both the dying and the undying beings. I am the supreme person, in the world and in the Veda. Blameless Arjuna, he who knows me becomes truly wise," said Krishna.

"If you want to understand this war, you must know the two different kinds of men who fight it.

"Pure, fearless, wise, generous, self-controlled and sacrificing, knowing the scriptures, austere and honest;

"Non-violent, truthful, relinquishing, serene, never finding fault, compassionate to all the living, free from greed, gentle, humble and steady;

"Energetic, forgiving, patient, above arrogance and malice: this is the man with the divine nature.

"Ostentation, vanity, rage, harshness and ignorance: Arjuna, these are the qualities of the demonic man.

"The man with the divine nature finds deliverance, and the demoniacal one is bound in darkness."

Arjuna looked up anxiously at Krishna, who laid a hand on his head. "Don't be afraid, Pandava, your nature is divine and so is your destiny. But let me tell you about the evil ones. They know nothing of the paths of karma or renunciation. They know nothing of purity, truth, or dharma.

"They say the world is unreal, without a basis, without a Creator. These ruthless men of feeble understanding rise as the enemies of the earth to destroy her.

"They are full of hypocrisy, vanity and delusion, and abandon themselves to insatiable desire. They live in ceaseless lust and foolish cares, which end only when they die. Their single mission is to amass all the wealth they can, by the vilest means.

"'I am the lord, the great one,' they think. 'This is mine and the other shall be mine, as well. I am mighty, successful and happy. I am rich and wellborn; who is there like me? I shall sacrifice, I shall be bounteous, I shall always be joyful!' Yes, so they think, deluded.

"Bewildered by a dark jungle of thoughts, entangled helplessly, they fall into hell. Conceited, obstinate, arrogant with wealth and power, they perform hollow yagnas, with much ostentation and no regard to the inner content. Given completely to lust, anger and violence, they hate me in others, and in themselves, too.

"These ruthless spirits I cast again and again into dark wombs, in the great cycle of deaths and rebirths. And fallen into demon wombs, birth after birth, the malignant ones never rise to me, but devolve to the lowest, bestial state.

"Three-fold is the gateway to hell, three-fold the way to the ruin of the soul: lust, greed and anger. The man who is free from these naturally does what is best for his soul, and attains perfect bliss, the changeless condition.

"But he who discards the scriptures and follows his baser nature's call, he does not come to perfection or joy, or the highest peace.

"Arjuna, in this world, let the scripture be your guide; it is sacred, it comes from me."

Arjuna asked, "Those who don't regard the scripture, but sacrifice to God in faith, what place have they? In sattva, rajas or tamas?"

Krishna said, "Each man believes according to his nature, and he is what he believes.

"Sattvic men worship the Gods, rajasic men worship wealth and power, and men of tamas worship the spirits of the dead. They make gods of their ancestors' ghosts.

"Because vanity and lust fill them with egotism, the demonic ones mortify their bodies with violent austerities, which the scriptures do not ordain. These fools weaken their organs of sense and outrage me, who dwell in them.

"The sattvic sacrifice is scriptural; it seeks no reward. The rajasic one is all for show and gain, and the sacrifice of tamas distributes no food, no hymns are sung, and it is faithless.

"Worship of the Gods, of rishis and gurus, purity, uprightness, continence and non-violence: these are the tapasya of the body. Sweet words that offend no-one, but are truthful and kind, and the charity of the Veda are the tapasya of speech. Serenity of mind, gentleness, integrity of purpose, self-control and silence are the tapasya of mind. Together, these are the three-fold tapasya of sattva.

"The rajasic tapasya is done out of pride, seeking fame, for the sake of exhibition. The obstinate penance, performed for the lust of pain, or to hurt someone, is the tamasic tapasya.

"The sattvic charity is dutiful, made to the deserving, at an auspicious moment and place, and seeks nothing in return. The rajasic gift is always made with a selfish purpose, for some gain. And the tamasic gift is a contemptuous one, made without regard for time and place, and neither for the one that receives it.

"*AUM TAT SAT* is the three-fold symbol of Brahman. The brahmanas, the Vedas, and the yagnas were ordained, of old, by this.

"*AUM* say the bhaktas of Brahman at sacrifice, penance and charity. *TAT* they say at sacrifice, penance and charity. *SAT* means the Absolute, Arjuna, everything that is auspicious, good and true. All penance, sacrifice and charity are called *SAT*.

"But if a man performs any of these without faith in Brahman, it is *asat*, unreal, of no account here or hereafter."

NINE

The Bhagavad Gita

Near the end of the Dwapara yuga, between two armies, the Pandava warrior Arjuna said to his cousin, the Avatara, "Krishna, tell me about renunciation and relinquishment, and the difference between the two."

The kali yuga yawning before him, the Dark One of Dwaraka said, "Renunciation is when you abandon karma out of desire. Relinquishment is when you act, but abandon the fruit of what you do.

"The karma of sacrifice, penance and charity must be performed; these are the purifiers of the wise. But they should be done with no attachment for their results.

"The tamasic renunciation is through ignorance, the rajasic through fear. But if a man does his duty, forsaking its outcome to me, his relinquishment is sattvic.

"The sage of relinquishment does not doubt; his nature is sattvic. He does not shrink from what is unpleasant, nor is he drawn to the pleasant. No embodied being can renounce karma entirely, but he who relinquishes the fruit of his work is enlightened.

"The consequences of karma are pleasant, unpleasant and mixed, each in its season. But those who are detached reap no consequence at all, in this world or the next.

"The Vedanta says there are five participants in any deed: the body, the ego, the senses, the motions of life in the body, and providence the fifth. All karma, of speech, of body or mind, good or evil, is caused by these five. He who thinks that he is the one that acts, is deluded. But the man who is unattached, untainted by egotism, who acts naturally, perfectly: no karma binds him with any bond. Though he kill thousands, he is no killer.

"Arjuna, there are three kinds of conscience, and three kinds of happiness, too.

"The sattvic conscience knows right from wrong, what is safe and what dangerous. It knows discrimination and relinquishment, what binds the spirit and what frees it. The rajasic conscience cannot distinguish wrong from right, what to do and what not to. And when a man's conscience tells him wrong is right, that evil is goodness, and distorts the world, it is tamasic.

"So, too, with happiness. The man who knows the atman has the joy of pure knowledge, like poison at first, and ambrosial finally: the joy of sattva, the end of sorrow. The joy of rajas is of the senses uniting with the objects of sense: sweet in the beginning, deadly at last. The warped pleasure, which deludes the soul at both beginning and end, bestial satisfaction born of stupor, sloth or cruelty, is of tamas, always fatal.

"There is no being on earth, none among the Devas of heaven, who is free of the gunas of prakriti. Every man's inner nature ordains his dharma; brahmana and kshatriya, vaishya and sudra, each has his innate, natural dharma.

"The brahmana's dharma is to know the atman, to be serene, restrained, and pure; the kshatriya's is to be battle-skilled, fearless, generous and resolute; the vaishya's is to breed cattle, to till the earth, to trade; and to serve all men is the dharma of the sudra.

"But all men are born equal, and equally for perfection, and each shall find it if he follows his nature's dharma.

"A man worships God when he performs his prakritic dharma, and so he finds perfection. It is better to perform one's own dharma, however imperfectly, than the dharma of another flawlessly. For there is no sin in following one's own true nature.

"As to imperfection, all karma is clouded with imperfection, as fire is with smoke. But that is no cause to give up one's natural duty, no reason to stop worshipping God, or seeking Him.

"Listen, Arjuna, to how the perfected man is one with Brahman.

"His mind and heart are free of delusion, full of compassion. His senses are subdued, naturally, by a steady will, without regret. He seeks solitude, eats little, speaks less, and is always absorbed in the Brahman, the truth.

"Vanity has gone from him, pride, violence, lust, anger, and so have all his possessions, that once possessed him. Entirely serene, he is fit to be with Brahman. And he who is with Brahman, past sorrow, beyond craving, all beings the same to him, he loves me most dearly.

"To love me is to know the inmost truth that I am; knowing me is to enter my being. Everything that man does is offered to me in surrender, and my grace is upon him. He finds the eternal, the place unchanging."

Krishna felt a great war won within himself: the worst over, evil overcome, retreating. Arjuna, radiant with faith, said to him, "You have removed my fear. I feel I have already triumphed in all my battles. I know that whatever you have said to me is true; but Krishna, I want to see your divine form. Lord, if you think I deserve that revelation, show me your imperishable self."

The armies vanished from Kurukshetra; the world vanished from Kurukshetra. Only Krishna, the Blue God, stood smiling and tremendous before Arjuna.

"You cannot see me with your human eyes, but I will give you other sight. Behold, Arjuna, my forms: a hundred, a thousand, endless. See the Adityas, the Vasus, the Rudras, the Asvins, and the Maruts. See the hidden realms, the Universe, and whatever you care to see. *Arjuna, behold Me!*"

And Krishna stood transformed before his bhakta: speaking from many mouths, seeing with numberless eyes, carrying countless weapons, wearing divine raiment and garlands, heavenly perfumes, of endless visions and marvels, irradiant, boundless. His face was turned everywhere, the nebulae were his ornaments. If a thousand suns rose together into the sky, their light might approach the splendour of that Being.

It was the vision he had shown a shadow of in the sabha of Hastinapura; now it was complete, refulgent. Arjuna saw the universe with his gifted sight, all its eternity gathered in One, in the body of the God of Gods. His hair stood on end, he folded his hands in awe, and the Pandava fell on his knees. "Oh, Lord, I see the Gods and their hosts in you! I see Brahma on his lotus throne, and all the rishis and heaven's nagas. I see you with numberless arms, bellies, mouths and eyes, but I do not see your end, your middle or your beginning, O cosmic, infinite One!

"I see you with your crown, mace and wheel of fire. You are the light of lights, incomparable!" cried Arjuna in ecstasy, and terror verging on death. "The sun and the moon are your eyes, your face is an eternal fire whose brilliance lights the universe. The void of space between the stars is full of you. The three worlds are in awe of this Form of yours, and I tremble seeing you shouldering the sky, blazing in more colours than I had dreamt could be. Oh, Vishnu, this vision makes my soul weak with fear. I see your endless mouths, dreadful with tusks, full of Time's devouring flames, and I quail. Be gracious, Lord of Gods, sanctuary of the galaxies!

"I see not just my enemies and friends, but all men and women, humankind, fly like moths into your flaming jaws. Lord, I see the earth and the constellations spinning into your fanged mouths, and you licking them up. Have mercy, O Godhead, I know nothing of thee!"

God said in thunder, "Time am I, waster of worlds. Fight or stay your hand, no matter: these kshatriyas will die in me. For that I am come. So, take up your weapons! Win glory by killing your enemies, and enjoy a kingdom, O ambidextrous bowman. I have already slain your enemies; you are only my instrument. Kill Drona, Bheeshma, Jayadratha, Karna, and the rest, whom I have damned. Fear nothing, fight and you will conquer."

His face in the grass, his eyes shut tight, Arjuna prostrated himself at the Vision's feet. He breathed, "O Krishna, it is well the world honours you, I understand it now. Hail, hail to you! A thousand times, hail! For whatever I said rashly to you, thinking of you as just my cousin, not knowing who you really are, calling you Krishna, Yadava, or friend, I beg your forgiveness, O Father of worlds. Bear with me as a father with his son, as a friend with a friend, as a lover with his beloved. I cannot endure this vision of you. Be merciful; be as you were before, O million-membered One!"

God said, "My love has shown you this Form of fire, luminous, primeval, which no one has ever seen before on earth. Not by the Vedas, by sacrifice or study, not by the sternest tapasya, will anyone else in this world ever see this Viswarupa. But look, and do not be afraid."

Again, Krishna, his cousin and friend, stood smiling and gracious before Arjuna, and gently pulled the Pandava to his feet.

Red-faced, hands still folded, Arjuna panted, "Lord! I am quiet again."

The panic drained from his body, though he still shook where he stood. And Krishna was reminded of another purpose of the Avatara: to allay the terror of man faced with absolute Godhead.

He said, "Even the Devas, Arjuna, are always eager to see me as you just did. Only by bhakti can I be seen like that." He embraced the trembling warrior, "He who worships me, and has no enmity with any creature, he comes to me, O Kshatriya. Consecrate all that you do to me; think of me as your nearest kin. Know that I am your only refuge, be one with me in your heart.

"When you are with me, I will take you over every trial and sorrow. But if your are conceited, and do not listen, you will be lost. It is your vanity that says, 'I will not fight'. You will fight, Arjuna, your own nature will compel you to. You yourself create the karma that binds you; and caught helpless in its power, you will do even what you want to avoid.

"God abides in the hearts of all his creatures. He turns them round on the wheel of his maya. Surrender to him, Arjuna. By his grace you will find supreme peace, and the place beyond change."

Krishna smiled at Arjuna, "Now you know the wisdom that is the secret of secrets. Think carefully on it, and then do as you decide. These are my last words to you for now. You are the friend I chose over all others, and I speak for your good."

The Blue God was a being of pure love. He said, "Give me your heart; love me, worship me always. Bow only to me and you shall find me. This is my promise, who loves you more than you can imagine.

"Relinquish your karma to me, I am your sanctuary. Fear no more, because I will save you from sin and from bondage. Arjuna, you must never tell this holy truth to anyone who has no faith or restraint, or who hates his guru and mocks me. But the man who loves me, and teaches my bhaktas this supreme secret of the Gita, will surely come to me.

"If any man meditates upon this song of ours, I will know he has worshipped me in spirit. And the man who just listens to it, without derision, will be freed of his sins and attain the swarga of the just."

His deep hour between the two armies over, his battle of the spirit, Sri Krishna embraced his cousin and soldier. Around them, time unfroze: horses moved, chariots and soldiers. Kurukshetra resounded again with conches, drums and tabors. Arjuna stood forth; the river of light, the

Song of God, was a sea in his heart. Enfolded in his charioteer's fathomless calm, at peace with himself, the Pandava shone with faith.

Krishna said, "Has your soul heard everything I have said, Arjuna, have I dispelled your fear?"

From his new peace, Krishna's given peace, the archer replied, "Achyuta, your grace has made my mind firm, its doubts have gone. I will do as you say. I will fight." And he picked up the Gandiva again.

Krishna looked at Arjuna and wondered whether, when faced with his kin, the Pandava would truly aim to kill. The Dark One's eyes twinkled at his cousin.

Krishna took the silver horses' reins in his left hand. With a flick of the whip, he plunged his chariot towards Bheeshma and the Kaurava army. With a ringing cry, the Avatara bore his warrior of light into the war on the crack of the ages.

TEN

The ghastly war

THE WAR OF KURUKSHETRA BEGINS FIERCELY, AS, ROARING, THE TWO armies rush at each other. A clash of armor and weapons rends the air like spring thunder, and men fall in hundreds. Death dances there, horrific and celebrant. Above every other noise ring the roars of Bheema, excited as a lion let loose from a cage! Like a hunting lion, he charges Duryodhana's army, while elephants and horses spray urine and excrete in terror.

The enemy is prepared for him. Twelve Kauravas, Duryodhana's brothers, cover him in arrows, beating him back for a time. Seeing their uncle beset, Draupadi's sons fly to his side, their bows singing. Quickly, Abhimanyu, Nakula, Sahadeva and Dhrishtadyumna are with Bheema, too, drawing blood, driving the twelve Kauravas back. Arrows flash in the sun climbing towards his zenith.

Elsewhere, Bheeshma rides at the Pandava army, and Arjuna bars his way. They match each other shaft for shaft. Satyaki faces Kritavarman; the two Yadavas fight, one for darkness, the other for light. Abhimanyu finds himself facing Brihadbala, lord of Kosala, the kingdom perfect Rama once ruled. An inspired Brihadbala cuts down Abhimanyu's banner.

Breaking through the enemy flank, Bheema sees Duryodhana before him. The Kaurava roars, "So, at last we fight like men, cousin! Are you ready to die?"

Bheema replies with a rash of arrows. Dusasana faces Nakula, and Durmukha, Sahadeva. Yudhishtira sees his uncle Shalya before him. The Pandava bows to his elder, and raises his bow to fight. Quick as thinking

Shalya breaks his nephew's weapon in his hand with a sizzle of arrows. Roaring, Yudhishtira seizes up another bow and covers Shalya's chariot in a cloud of fire, forcing him back.

While the great kshatriyas fight exhilarantly from their wheeling chariots, all around them millions of common footsoldiers battle, and a hundred die every moment. The very first hours of the war are horrible. It is a macabre dance performed to the roars of fighting men, the screams of the dying, and deafening conches and horns that echo under the bland sky: a dance inspired by a savage God, who would purify the earth in a day by washing her in blood.

No duel lasts long, and antagonists change in moments. For, when a contest is too even, the charioteers veer away to seek a weaker adversary. But Dhrishtadyumna and his master Drona fight, evenly for an hour. Morning wears into noon; though, in the violent mandala of battle, the passage of time is counted not by moments or hours, but by deaths. It is quickly obvious that, just as Duryodhana shrewdly predicted, the Kuru patriarch takes the heaviest toll. Bheeshma is like Yama on the field of fate. Not Arjuna, no-one can contain the old master. His bow is a wizard's staff, and his arrows are spells of fire that flow from it like the ancient bowman's wishes. He kills thousands, even while he holds up a magnificent Arjuna.

It seems no one can stand before Bheeshma, or stem the wave of death he brings to the Pandava army. Then, a splendid young kshatriya's chariot erupts on the knot of warriors that surrounds the Pitama. From a flank, Abhimanyu scythes through the legion that rings Bheeshma, and attacks Shalya, Kritavarman and Bheeshma himself. He strikes Shalya's arm deep, so he drops his bow, and has to leave the field. Kritavarman stands just briefly against Abhimanyu, before he has his bow snatched from his hand by a shaft of huge velocity. Then, no warrior stands between Arjuna's son and his great-grandsire.

Abhimanyu fights like an angry Deva, and, stunned by his archery, the older kshatriyas cry that the youth is a match for his father. The Kaurava army shrinks from Abhimanyu's brilliance, and he cuts his Pitama's banner from his chariot. The Pandavas, who fled before Bheeshma's inexorable advance, come roaring back to fight; and the Kaurava soldiers, who had surged forward with Bheeshma, sensing swift victory, now cower from Arjuna's son.

The advancing Kaurava frontlines are breached; through the breach ride Virata and his sons, Dhrishtadyumna, Bheema, the wild Kekayas and Satyaki. As Duryodhana's footsoldiers flee in panic, the Pandava archers kill a thousand of them. From other parts of the field, mighty Kaurava warriors rush to stop the rout.

Drona, roaring, splits Dhrishtadyumna's bow in his hands. Aswatthama sees Shikhandi flit forward, manoeuvering towards Bheeshma; and Drona's son looms before Shikhandi, and covers him in a mantle of arrows, arresting his dangerous careen. Shouting in fine fury, both draw blood.

Battle is truly joined, and the feral spirit of war grips the two armies. Now, as always happens, the sacred conditions of a dharma yuddha are violated everywhere. In the heat of war, its madness, few care to remember that a warrior in a chariot must not fight a footsoldier, or that the elephant-mounted must not use their beasts to trample men fighting on the ground. Why, Bheeshma kills a thousand Pandava soldiers, none of whom is remotely his equal. War has its own dharma. It is a world unto itself, where everything is measured by the violent moment, when each man either kills or is killed. All their lives swimming before their eyes, death an immediate presence, the two immense forces fight, common soldiers and kshatriyas. Kurukshetra exists as much in Yama's realm, as it does on earth.

Renewed by rage that young Abhimanyu smashed the bow in his hand, Shalya comes roaring back into battle. In moments, he kills a hundred Pandava soldiers, until, another youthful kshatriya mounted on a grey tusker lumbers up to him. It is Virata's son Uttara Kumara who, just days ago, fled at the sight of a raiding Kaurava force. Now, Duryodhana's soldiers fly before him, because today he also fights like a young god, death riding with him.

As the sun creeps towards the western hills, Uttara Kumara and Shalya fight a radiant duel. The prince shoots his arrows in a blinding flurry, and it seems that Shalya must give way before him. Shalya's horses rear at the grey elephant's advance, and his sarathy cannot hold them. In a flash, prince Uttara shoots down those beasts; he draws blood on Shalya's sarathy, and smashes his chariot under him with a terrific volley. Shalya finds himself stranded, his bow fallen and Uttara Kumara advancing on him.

Then, the Matsya prince gives in to a moment of youthful exhilaration. He roars that he had vanquished such an opponent, and raises his own bow over his head in triumph. In a blur, Shalya seizes up a javelin from his broken chariot and casts it like a bolt of lightning. The prince's roar dies in a gurgling scream, as the lance flashes into his chest, striking his young heart in a crimson burst. Like a bird from a tree, he topples from his elephant's back.

Nearby, his older brother, Sweta, hears Uttara Kumara roar when he had Shalya at his mercy, and turns his chariot just in time to see him die. Shalya still stands on the ground, unarmed beside his shattered chariot. With a howl, Sweta flies at his brother's killer. Fortunately for Shalya, seven Kauravas quickly form a ring around him. Still, Sweta fights like ten kshatriyas.

Red-eyed, Virata's son rushes at the enemy, and beats back the seven warriors around Shalya. Across the field, Bheeshma sees the threat to Shalya, and aims a terrible shaft at Sweta, plumed with the feathers of the kanka bird. It is an astra, the first of the war, and it flares at that prince from a long way. Weaving elliptically through a hundred chariots, the missile finds Sweta. It burns his armour to ashes, then pierces his heart. Shalya heaves a sigh of relief. His tears streaming, Sweta's sarathy drives his prince's corpse away from the field.

The sun sinks behind the western hill. Conches blare from both sides, and the first day's fighting ends. The Senapatis withdraw their legions, and each army collects its dead, to cremate them beside the golden river. So many have died, that they are burned in coarse heaps, with hardly any dignity. A brazen moon rises over Kurukshetra, and the blood spilt on the field glimmers in its flowing light.

The first day belongs to the Kauravas. Bheeshma by himself has killed ten thousand men. Uttara Kumara and Sweta have died, and their father Virata cries like a boy, all night. Across the Saraswati, a delighted Duryodhana calls for a fireside feast to celebrate; there is drinking and singing, dancing-girls entertain the Kaurava troops. Duryodhana has no doubt that victory will be his sooner than he could have hoped: in three or four days, no more.

Across Kurukshetra, Yudhishtira is plunged in despair. Late at night, after all the others are asleep, he comes alone to Krishna's tent. In a whisper, he says, "The Pitama is more terrible than we imagined.

Thousands of precious lives have been cut off in a day, and I am to blame.

"Bheeshma is invincible, Krishna; we can never win this war against the Pitama. I have no right to ask millions to die for me, because I want a kingdom. I should return to the forest before all our men are slaughtered. Another day like this one, and that is what I will have to do anyway.

"Only my Bheema fights with any heart, but I know they have marked him out. How long will he escape the astras of Bheeshma and Drona? You saw how Uttara Kumara and Sweta died, and Virata cries in his tent. What will it matter to him now, even if we win the war? Can victory restore his sons to him? How will I live with myself, if anything happens to Bheema?

"Krishna, dread fills me. How can we reverse our fortunes tomorrow? Only you can help us against the Pitama."

Krishna says, "You take too much upon yourself, Yudhishtira; we are all with you. The men who have come to fight your cause are not children. They came knowing their lives are at risk. They know what is at stake in this war, and for what they are fighting. If you do not stand against the evil ones, Yudhishtira, who will? Darkness will rule the earth.

"Don't lose heart so easily, not after what you have suffered. I am here with you, Satyaki and Dhrishtadyumna are here, and a thousand others." Krishna lowers his voice, and his eyes shine in the lamplight in that tent. "Besides, it was written long before you dreamt of this war that Shikhandi shall kill Bheeshma; what is written in the stars must come to pass. Yet, your Pitama is too great a kshatriya to die on the first day of battle. He has killed thousands, and he will kill thousands more. Then he will die, and I promise you victory shall be yours. This is war, cousin, and possibly the greatest war ever. There is a price to be paid for victory, and you must be prepared to pay it."

Krishna speaks so gently and gravely that Yudhishtira is somewhat pacified. The Pandava goes back to his tent, to sleep a few hours if he can, before another bloody morning. As he lies on his bed, around him he can hear an uneven sea of murmuring from his sleeping army: where nightmares of the brutal day stalk his men. Once or twice, some young soldier, whose first war this was, cries out in his sleep.

ELEVEN

The second day: two kraunchas

THE SECOND MORNING OF THE WAR, AND YUDHISHTIRA DECIDES TO form his legions in the vyuha called the krauncha, after the crane. Drupada and his aksauhini are the vyuha's head, Kuntibhoja and the king of the Chedis are its eyes, Satyaki and his men its throat. At the krauncha's tail is Yudhishtira himself, at its wings Bheema and Dhrishtadyumna, with their legions. The other Pandavas are between these two, with the sons of Draupadi.

The sun is still low in the sky, when, from across the field, Duryodhana sees the enemy's vyuha. A frown on his face, the Kaurava comes to his Acharyas, Drona and Kripa. "My lords, Yudhishtira has brought out more men than he did yesterday."

Just then, Bheeshma joins them, after his morning ablutions and worship. Smiling to see the vyuha across Kurukshetra, the patriarch says, "Let one krauncha bird fly against another."

He begins to form his troops in the same vyuha, mirroring the Pandava phalanx. He sets Bhoorisravas and Shalya at the left wing, and Somadatta and the king of Kamboja at the right. Aswatthama, Kripa and Kritavarman he sends to the bird's tail, while Duryodhana and his brothers are between its wings and Bheeshma himself is at the krauncha's beak.

Deep conches boom, drumrolls rise and fall, and rise again, and the armies fly at each other. Blood leaps under the sun, and flows in spate on Kurukshetra. In a brief infernal hour, the field is strewn with the corpses of countless men and their beasts. The anguished cries of the dying, especially their screams for a sip of water before life left their bodies, mingle with the roars of those who killed them. Wheeling in the sky above Kurukshetra, and crowding the trees around that field like death's sentinels, are crows, kites and vultures, eager for the rich pickings. And in the undergrowth all around, not daring to steal in yet, but slavering in anticipation of a feast, other scavengers slink: hyenas, wild dogs, wolves and jackals, packs of them, astounded by this war.

Bheeshma is even more terrible this morning than on the first day, and it seems the Kaurava bird will win the second day, as well. As his Pitama mows through the enemy lines, Duryodhana's laughter and his shouts of glee echo above every other sound. His chariot flitting everywhere, Bheeshma gives battle to Bheema, Abhimanyu, Satyaki, the Kekayas, Virata and Dhrishtadyumna, all together, even as he cuts down another thousand footsoldiers, his every arrow deadly.

Some way off, Arjuna watches his grandsire in absorption, admiringly. He says to Krishna, "We must ride against Pitama, or the war will be lost today."

Krishna whirls the chariot round to where the Kuru patriarch straddles the field. Now Arjuna is ablaze; the arrows from his Gandiva are a crystal storm. Bheeshma has to pause his slaughter to face the third Pandava. In all the Kaurava army only Bheeshma, Drona and Karna can stand against Arjuna in battle, and he sweeps at Duryodhana's legions like a forest-fire with the wind behind it. The Pandava's archery is uncanny, and his sarathy's manoeuvres in the chariot of the white horses, are unearthly.

They are an army by themselves, the Pandava warrior and his dark charioteer. The gandharva horses' hooves hardly touch the ground, and that chariot seems to divide itself in a hundred rathas, and to be everywhere on Kurukshetra at once. Even Bheeshma's valour pales when Arjuna takes the field. The Pandava's arrows of light, every one a killer, spring like a river in his hands, like the Ganga risen in flood to make the earth pure again.

Arjuna takes Bheeshma's breath away, and the patriarch is driven back. Duryodhana cries in dismay, "Acharya! To the Pitama, fly!"

Drona flashes to Bheeshma's side, where no other warrior can remain because of Arjuna's arrow-storm, enveloping Kurukshetra in its own darkness, killing hundreds, while Krishna's laughter rings above the screams of the dying. Through that tide, Drona hews a path for himself. Behind him ride Jayadratha and Duryodhana: to relieve the beleaguered Bheeshma. At first, it seems that it makes no difference to Arjuna if he fights one kshatriya or three. Vikarna plunges forward in the path Drona clears.

But not four fine archers make any impression on the Pandava. He only grows fiercer, and Krishna's chariotry more incredible than before. The Pandava's ratha is an evanescent target the Kaurava bowmen can hardly aim at. The white horses seem made more of the stuff of time and dreams, than flesh and blood: they are everywhere and nowhere, at once. But the tide of arrows from the Gandiva is real enough, and soon Drona and Bheeshma are bleeding, while their own shafts find no mark on their brilliant adversary.

Holding the Kaurava archers at bay all around him, Arjuna kills thousands of their soldiers. Then, Satyaki flies up to Arjuna's side, and with him come Virata, Dhrishtadyumna, Abhimanyu and the sons of Draupadi, who engage Drona so he must turn away from Arjuna. The advance of the Pandava force is more determined than ever, Duryodhana's army is beaten back; numberless soldiers die, and for the first time, the Kaurava feels a stab of fear.

He flashes up to Bheeshma, and cries, "Pitama! Arjuna kills a hundred men every moment. Yet, Drona and you fight him like a favoured son. I wish Karna had been here! You insisted he should not fight, and now you hardly raise your bow against Arjuna."

Bheeshma roars in sorrow, "Aaah! I am cursed to be born a kshatriya!"

He raises his conch and blows a desperate blast on it. He cries at his sarathy, "Ride at Arjuna, fly at my grandchild!"

Across the field, Krishna sees the Kuru Pitama hurtling towards him and, with a blast of his own on the Panchajanya, flicks his whip at his horses and dashes forward to meet Bheeshma's charge. Both chariots yoked to white steeds, it is such a sight to see them sweep at each other.

The Earth and the Devas gathered invisibly in the sky hold their breath when Bheeshma and Arjuna duel. They fight as they never have before. Their bows seem to have lives of their own, and the arrows from them are the notes of an eerie song. Time stands still, and so do the other kshatriyas around the peerless two.

Neither gives an inch; neither can quell the other, they are so perfectly matched. Yet, there is one difference between them: Krishna in Arjuna's chariot. All else being equal, the Dark One's time-like manoeuvres drain Bheeshma, threatening to tilt the duel Arjuna's way. Suddenly Bheeshma looses a Brahmastra at Krishna, taking him squarely in the chest, so he slumps over his reins.

In a flash, Arjuna kills Bheeshma's sarathy with an arrow through his throat that affixes him to his seat. Bheeshma has to take the reins himself, and they fight on. Krishna, whom no astra can harm, clenches his teeth and draws out Bheeshma's shaft, dripping blood. The deep wound heals instantly! The Dark One takes up his reins again, and Bheeshma cannot drive his horses and fight Arjuna at once. He rides off the field to fetch another sarathy.

Lusty cheering breaks out among Yudhishtira's legions, and, renewed in the courage that even Bheeshma can be put to flight, they swarm forward to have revenge on the Kauravas for the previous day's massacre. Duryodhana's eyes blaze, he roars; but he is helpless to check the Pandava onslaught.

Across the field, away to the left of where Bheeshma and Arjuna fought, another duel rages between two old antagonists. Drupada and Drona fight wildly. Here, too, the rest of the battle pauses around them; their soldiers stand gaping.

However, this is no exhibition, but war. Seeing his father absorbed in the nuances of archery, instead of fighting to kill his enemy, Dhrishtadyumna rides to help Drupada. Drona greets him with a lance of fire, a gash of lightning. Bheema sees Dhrishtadyumna reel under Drona's assault, and flies at his Acharya from a flank, drawing his fire. Duryodhana sees Drona fighting alone against three men, and cries to the king of Kalinga to help him. Kalinga arrives with his son beside him, and seeing them Virata rides to Drupada's side. Drupada and Virata battle Drona, while Dhrishtadyumna, the Senapati, has already wheeled away to bolster his legions elsewhere.

Kalinga, his son Sakradeva, and Ketuman attack Bheema from three sides. But Bheema roused is like a bull-elephant in season. His very roars are unnerving, and he fights like a force of nature. Sakradeva makes the fatal mistake of lowering his bow for a moment. From an impossible angle, and from behind his back, Bheema strikes Sakradeva through his face with an arrow, killing him at once.

Blood leaping in his eyes, Kalinga rushes at Bheema with Bhanuman at his side. Bheema casts a mace at Bhanuman with his left hand, smashing his head, and he falls with a sigh, his brains spilling out. Duryodhana cries out to Satya and Satyadeva that they must protect Kalinga. Bheema, having tasted kshatriya's blood, is exuberant. His roars ring across the field, and when he is not sorely pressed for a few moments, he kills a hundred common Kaurava soldiers. He is in his element! Here, at last, is the revenge for which he had waited thirteen years. Bheema is dreadful, he is inexorable; he is a hot wave of death.

The enemy can neither stand against him nor flee. Satya and Satyadeva barely begin fighting Bheema before he kills them both, almost at once: one with an arrow through his eye, and the other's head he strikes off with an axe. Next moment, he finds Kalinga with a humming shaft, and that king falls in his chariot, struck through his heart. Bheema's roars echo in the noonday sun, and brave men's limbs turn weak.

Seeing their king die, the Kalinga army rushes at the Pandava, a thousand men. Shikhandi flies to Bheema's side with a part of Drupada's legion. Bheema slaughters a hundred soldiers in delight, but the enemy's numbers begin to tell even on him. From across the field, Dhrishtadyumna sees the son of the wind surrounded and, blowing a blast on his sankha, dashes up to help his friend. None of the Pandavas is as dear to Dhrishtadyumna as Bheema is, and none of the Yadavas as Satyaki. Some way off, Satyaki hears Dhrishtadyumna's conch, and in a moment, he too is at Bheema's side. The three fight, back to back, and wreak havoc on the Kalinga army. They crush the enemy as if they were, indeed, columns of ants.

Away to the left, Bheeshma hears the screams of those who faced that trio, and plunges at Bheema. A pure kshatriya now, on fire, the Kuru Pitama casts a javelin charged with an astra at his grandson. For the long moment of the missile's flight, battle freezes around the Pandava. Burning with power, the lance flashes straight at Bheema's chest. Bheema is so busy butchering Kalinga's soldiers, he has not seen it. At the last shred of an instant, Dhrishtadyumna yells, "Bheema!"

Turning his head, the Pandava sees the spear flying at him and leaps right out of his chariot! The lance whistles by. In rage, Satyaki kills the new sarathy Bheeshma has brought into battle; and, once more, the patriarch has to leave the field. Seeing Bheeshma sent off, what remains of the Kalinga army turns tail. Satyaki rides up to Bheema and cries, "Vayuputra! How many kshatriyas have you killed today? Kalinga, Ketuman, Sakradeva, Bhanuman, Satya, and Satyadeva too! Bheema, you by yourself are enough to finish this enemy."

Glowing, they embrace before climbing back into their chariots for more hunting. The sun has climbed past his zenith, and begins his descent in the sky, when Aswatthama rides to check the bloody progress of Drupada's sons. Drona and Kripa ride with him. A pitched battle breaks out, a thing of beauty and terror.

Duryodhana's son Lakshmana challenges Abhimanyu. The war unfolds all around in shifting tides: Yama Deva's dark nritya. Duryodhana sees his son pressed hard by the wizardly Abhimanyu, and goes to his rescue. Duryodhana's royal guard rides with him, and Abhimanyu is surrounded by enemy chariots. He is as magnificent as his father, and gives them a breathtaking fight.

Meanwhile, Bheeshma has returned to the field and, with Drona at his side, he faces Arjuna again. It is quickly plain that not his Pitama and Acharya together can contain this Pandava. Arjuna's archery is of another order, a supernatural thing. Soon, Bheeshma cries to Drona, "I can't hold him! The sun is sinking, we must withdraw."

Bheeshma blows his conch, giving the signal for the day's battle to stop. Both armies withdraw, and set about the grisly task of gathering the dead, and burning them beside the river.

Tonight, the mood in Yudhishtira's camp is in some contrast to the previous night's. There can be no doubt: this day belongs to the Pandavas. Bheema is the day's hero; no one else has killed as many great Kaurava warriors as he has. Satyaki and Dhrishtadyumna cannot praise him enough, as they sit around the blue-gold flames of a campfire. Then, Yudhishtira says, "Our fortunes turned when Arjuna beat Bheeshma back. Or, who knows if we would all be sitting here now?"

Arjuna murmurs, "My strength is my sarathy."

Krishna's eyes shine in the firelight; at least, tonight there is no talk from Yudhishtira about abandoning the war and going back to the jungle.

Across the Saraswati, the mood is one of dejection; there is no singing, no dancing or feasting. Duryodhana huddles in his tent with Karna, Dusasana and Shakuni. They hardly say a word to each other; there are no illusions about who has won the day.

TWELVE

The third day: the eagle and the crescent

Bheeshma is up before the sun the next morning, the third day of the war. He, too, has lain awake, thinking how best to confront the Pandava army after its triumph on the second day. Bheeshma gathers his commanders, and says, "Yesterday, we made the mistake of using the same vyuha as the Pandavas. It seems Dhrishtadyumna is a master of the krauncha, and they scattered us as they pleased. Today, we will use a garuda vyuha."

So, Bheeshma himself is the eagle's beak, Drona and Kritavarman are its eyes. Just behind them, Aswatthama and Kripa are its head, the Trigartas and Jayadratha are the bird's neck, Duryodhana is its heart, with his brothers around him, and Vinda and Anuvinda, the Avantis. The king of Kosala, Brihadbala, is the garuda's tail.

Across the field, as first light of day spills over the armies, Arjuna and Dhrishtadyumna watch Bheeshma deploying his legions. Arjuna says, "The garuda vyuha. The krauncha was lucky for us yesterday, but the eagle hunts the little bird."

Dhrishtadyumna thinks just a moment, before he says, "Against the garuda always use the chandrakala!" He smiles, "At least, that is what Acharya Drona used to say."

Bheema positions himself at the very tip of the crescent, on the right, where it is slenderest. Coming into the vyuha, Drupada and Virata with their armies are its curving length, their soldiers and chariots thickest towards the heart of the vyuha, like the moon at the end of its first quarter. At the crux of the crescent is Yudhishtira, with his army of elephants.

Again, to the thinning left, are Satyaki and Draupadi's five sons, then Abhimanyu and his stepbrother Iravan, the naga princess Ulupi's son.

Another warrior has arrived in Kurukshetra in the night, summoned by his father with just a thought. He is a magical being, a rakshasa: beyond Iravan, is Ghatotkacha, a legion by himself. Past Ghatotkacha are the Kekayas; and, finally, at the left tip of the crescent is Arjuna, blue Krishna his sarathy.

Soon, the Senapatis face each across the field, and sea-conches echo around them. Bheeshma and Dhrishtadyumna raise their arms high, and bring them down dramatically for the fighting to begin. The two forces plunge at each other, raising clouds of dust. Today Jayadratha, Drona, Purumitra, Vikarna and Shakuni encircle Bheeshma in protection. On the other side, facing them, is Bheema, with Satyaki, Ghatotkacha, and Draupadi's five sons around him.

Bheema's son by Hidimbi looms ominously on Kurukshetra. The Kaurava army shrinks from Ghatotkacha. The first hour of battle belongs to the young rakshasa. He is a fell wind that blows everywhere, and there is no escaping him. He kills a thousand Kaurava soldiers, with weapons, with his bare hands. Then, from a flank, Duryodhana himself marshals a hundred chariots and rides at Ghatotkacha, at least to contain him. To kill him will be hard, since arrows do not pierce his skin and great strokes of sword and axe glance off him.

Meanwhile, Bheeshma fights to have revenge for the rout of the previous day. He reaps the Pandava soldiers as if they are a field of ripe corn before him. Krishna takes his chariot to face Bheeshma, and another intense duel begins between Arjuna and the patriarch. Today Arjuna finds it hard to match his grandsire, and he cannot stop Bheeshma from killing hundreds of men around him even as they fight.

Elsewhere, Abhimanyu and Satyaki encounter Shakuni and his legion. Here, too, Shakuni fights more with deceit than courage. Yet, he is also a formidable archer, who can always make an enemy think he is less of a bowman than he truly is. Shakuni smashes Satyaki's chariot and kills his horses when the Yadava's back is turned. It is not the noble way, but definitely Shakuni's; and this is war. Cursing, Satyaki leaps into Abhimanyu's chariot and fights on.

At his age, Bheeshma finds Arjuna's archery more than he can bear for long. He soon finds the Pandava absorbs him so he cannot raze the enemy army around him. Bheeshma swerves his chariot from the duel, and rides away to challenge the advance of Yudhishtira's elephant legion, which crushes a hundred Kaurava soldiers every moment. Nakula and Sahadeva fight at Yudhishtira's side, and Bheeshma does not find this contention much easier than the one against Arjuna.

Away to the left, Ghatotkacha has all but destroyed Duryodhana's force of a hundred chariots. They lie broken everywhere, horses in pools of blood, warriors and charioteers with their heads struck off, or arrows stuck deep in their chests, dead and dying, as if they had the mischance to cross the path of an armed typhoon. Ghatotkacha, his roars chilling, still pulls Duryodhana's soldiers from their chariots and wrenches their heads from their necks with his hands. When he chooses, he towers over the rest of the field like a small hill, or flies through the air, wingless, to fall on another hapless foe.

When Duryodhana confronts a tiring Ghatotkacha and overwhelms him with a rage of astras, Bheema storms up to take his cousin unawares. The mace he hurls strikes Duryodhana on the side of his head, felling him in his chariot. At once, the Kaurava's sarathy rides out of battle, while Bheema's triumphant roars rock Kurukshetra.

Drona and Bheeshma have to ride, themselves, to quell Bheema and his rakshasa son. Satyaki flashes to Bheema's side, and the battle turns the Pandava's way again. Bheema kills hundreds, roaring so dreadfully that his enemies stand petrified before him. Duryodhana recovers from his swoon, flies back into battle, to find Bheema desiccating his army.

Duryodhana rides to his grandsire, and cries, "Pitama! Our army shrinks every moment, when Bheeshma commands it, when Drona and Aswatthama fight for me. It is your love for the sons of Pandu; none of you fights as you would if the enemy were someone else. Pitama, if you won't fight as you can, let Karna take your place as my Senapati."

Duryodhana is panting; his eyes are full of anger. Bheeshma laughs in his face. "My poor child, your envy blinds you to the truth. For so many years, we have told you that Pandu's sons are invincible. They are Devaputras; they fight with the strength of their fathers. How can mere mortals stand against them? But this was the only way you would be convinced. As for loving you, aren't we fighting on your side, Drona, Aswatthama and I, that you say we don't love you? I am an old man, but watch me take fire to the enemy!"

The third day: the eagle and the crescent

The ancient warrior charges the Pandava army. He is like an elephant prodded by his mahout, and this is just what Duryodhana intends. Pandava soldiers flee, screaming that Yama Deva, the God Death, had come to hunt on Kurukshetra. Not Bheema or Arjuna is half as fearsome as Bheeshma is now. Arrows flare from his bow, endlessly, and they see him in the north and the east, the west and the south, as he lets a froth of blood.

Krishna says grimly to Arjuna, "You swore you would kill Bheeshma, Drona and the rest. The time has come to keep your word. Whenever you face Bheeshma, you seem to remember only that he is your grandfather. Look how he tears through our lines, don't the screams of our men move you? Haven't they come to fight for your honour, that you let Bheeshma slaughter them? Our army melts before him like snow at the sun's touch."

His face taut, Arjuna says, "Take me to him, Krishna."

Krishna points his horses at Bheeshma's chariot. As they flash forward, Arjuna cuts the patriarch's banner from over his head. Bheeshma roars in delight, "Arjuna, there is no archer like you on earth! Come, let us fight."

Hearing his Pitama's voice, Arjuna grows soft at once. While Bheeshma's arrows are flames, the Pandava seems content just to defend himself, cutting down his grandsire's searing volleys, but hardly attacking the old lion himself. Bheeshma kills a hundred footsoldiers around them, while Arjuna does little to stop him. Again, Krishna is wounded, and Arjuna himself. Bhoorisravas, Drona, Vikarna and Jayadratha rush to Bheeshma's side, and push Arjuna back so ferociously it seems they will have his life. Satyaki flies to Arjuna's side, and so does Yudhishtira's legion. They are certain Bheeshma will kill Arjuna, who still hardly resists his Pitama.

Suddenly, Krishna throws back his head and gives a roar that shakes the earth, *the roar of an angry God!* Every soldier pauses at that sound. Krishna cries, "Satyaki, watch me kill Bheeshma! It seems the sarathy must take a hand in the fighting, for his kshatriya has no stomach for battle. I swore that Yudhishtira will be crowned lord of the earth. I swore that Draupadi will have revenge. But how will they, if Arjuna fights like this? Satyaki, watch me burn the sinners!"

In a moment, Krishna is Narayana the Destroyer on the field of death. Darkness falls on Kurukshetra, and the only light upon it is the light from the Blue God's body. He is so bright and awesome, that all the fighting freezes in a wink; the men stand rooted in terror of him. The Sudarshana Chakra a wheel of flames in his hand, raised above his head, Krishna leaps down from his chariot and strides towards Bheeshma's chariot. It seems his body is made of blue fire, so blinding they cannot look at him; and his eyes are cold, and wild as stars. The Chakra shines like the primordial lotus that sprouted from Vishnu's navel.

Seeing Krishna like that the wise men on Kurukshetra think the end of the world has arrived. They stand praying. But Bheeshma is not perturbed; he bows his head to the God coming to kill him. A smile on his lips, he says calmly, "Devadeva, I beg you, kill me with your own hands. For what greater glory can I hope? Knower of hearts, you know how I loathe my life, and long for death. I beseech you, kill me, give me my freedom!"

Solemnly, Bheeshma raises his bow to fight. Arjuna leaps down from his chariot, and is at Krishna's side in a flash. The Pandava clutches the Avatara's hand with the Chakra blazing over it. Krishna hardly sees his warrior; he is blind with rage. Wailing, Arjuna falls at the Dark One's feet and clasps them.

"No!" cries the Pandava. "You mustn't be so angry. You must not do this thing. Krishna, I will fight, I swear I will fight as you want me to. On the head of my Abhimanyu, I swear I will fight as I have never fought before. Let it be my Pitama or my Guru: I will fight to kill them! My Lord, you must keep your oath. What will the world come to if you break your sacred word?"

Krishna still stands with the Chakra at his finger. Arjuna cries again, "I swear I will fight, Krishna!"

For a long moment, the Blue God stares at Arjuna. Then, he lowers his arm and the Sudarshana vanishes. His body does not burn, any more, and the night of dread over Kurukshetra lifts away. Light breaks on the hushed armies. Krishna lays his hands on Arjuna's shoulders, and raises him up. He says, "I believe you, Arjuna. Come, let us ride."

Hand in hand, they run back to the waiting chariot. Krishna lifts the Panchajanya and blows a mighty note on it. Arjuna follows with an echoing peal on the Devadatta, and the quarters shake with that twin sound. Frustrated, that death at the hands of the Avatara has eluded him, Bheeshma flies at them like a comet spewing flames.

Now, Arjuna stands forth in his chariot like the kshatriya he truly is; and not a shaft can the Kuru patriarch spare for any soldier but him. Arjuna's archery presses Bheeshma back; a hundred Kaurava soldiers fall, each moment, and the Pandava legions surge forward yelling Arjuna's name.

A delighted Krishna drives his horses forward, as if he means to finish the war in an evening. Spurred by his sarathy, Arjuna invokes an astra called the aindra, his father's missile, and shoots it at the Kaurava host. A flash like a star exploding flares through Duryodhana's army, and five thousand men fall. With a cry, Bheeshma turns to Drona and Baahlika.

"Sound the retreat!" cries the Kuru Senapati, as the sun sinks in the west, the hue of blood.

Conches announce an end to the day's fighting. The Panchajanya rings above all the others, as a radiant Krishna turns his white horses back to the Pandava camp, with a tired but triumphant Arjuna, who seems to have finally mastered his worst enemy: himself.

Across the Saraswati, Duryodhana sits in his tent, in a black silence. Fear seizes him, and no amount of wine can stop the shaking that breaks out over his body. This is the second day the army of Hastinapura has been routed. For the first time, the unthinkable thought enters Duryodhana's heart: had his elders perhaps been right? Would he lose the war? Were the Pandavas invincible? For the first time, he had seen Arjuna fight as he had today. Can anyone kill Indra's son?

Duryodhana is terrified lest the answer is no.

THIRTEEN

The fourth day: Bheema and his son

Dawn of the fourth day of the war of Kurukshetra. Conches sound to begin the fighting, and the two hosts rush at each other, roaring like two jungles full of wild beasts. Death's release snatched from him yesterday, when Arjuna stopped Krishna from killing him, Bheeshma is grimmer than ever. With Drona beside him, he rides at the van of the army of Hastinapura. Krishna steers his chariot to face the patriarch: only Arjuna can contain his Pitama today.

True to his word, Arjuna fights as a man transformed. The last reserve within him gone, he fights as if he no longer knew whom he fought, or no longer cared. He brings Bheeshma up with such a salvo that it would have cut the old man in half had Drona not intervened with a shield of arrows. Seeing Arjuna godlike, Kripa, Shalya, Vivimsati, Somadatta and Duryodhana fly to Bheeshma's side. The Panadava holds them all up. Then, it seems a second Arjuna appears on Kurukshetra; arrow for arrow the newcomer matches Arjuna, forcing the enemy back: it is Abhimanyu, as resistless as his father.

The battle grows with each moment of the day. It shifts, inscrutable and fabulous, like some fleeting tapestry of violence; the roars and screams of vanquisher and vanquished are a dire symphony. Abbreviated in an hour on Kurukshetra, ten thousand lifetimes find brutal conclusions. A gory work of art, the war rages.

Aswatthama, Bhoorisravas, Shalya, Chitrasena and Sala's son ride at Abhimanyu. The young hero holds them all off, easily, until Kripa and the Trigartas attack him, too. From across the field Arjuna shouts proud encouragement to his son. But Kritavarman and Shalya ride at Abhimanyu from two flanks, and the boy is pushed back, and wounded. Dhrishtadyumna, who ranges the field, sees the unequal fight and flits to Abhimanyu's side. Krishna, also, swerves his chariot nearer the scintillating youth.

Dhrishtadyumna casts a mace at Sala's son, and smashes the young kshatriya's head. Screaming, Sala rushes at Dhrishtadyumna, who coolly fells that king; Sala is borne off the field in a swoon. A scathing duel breaks out between Dhrishtadyumna and Shalya. Seeing Sala's son killed, the other Kauravas who fought Abhimanyu turn on Dhrishtadyumna in wrath, which is what the Pandava Senapati intends. Quickly, Abhimanyu and Arjuna draw some of the Kaurava fire, and the three of them hold up twenty kshatriyas.

Duryodhana shouts to his brothers and, from different parts of the field, ten sons of Dhritarashtra ride to their king's side, arrows streaming to cover the chariots of Arjuna, Abhimanyu and Dhrishtadyumna. Away to the left of the Pandava army, another warrior raises his head from butchering the Kaurava legions. He sees his brother, his brother-in-law and his nephew beset by a swarm of enemies. Bheema gives a roar that drowns every other sound on Kurukshetra, and flies to the rescue! He kills a hundred men on his way, his mace smashing heads like fruit. Drenched in blood, he flashes at Dhritarashtra's sons. He has sworn to kill them all, and in a moment, the Kauravas' assault turns weak.

Duryodhana sees Bheema coming, bloody-eyed, like death's spectre, and roars to the king of the Magadhas, who fights from elephant-back, "Stop him!"

The Magadhan, the other Sahadeva, orders his elephants to charge Bheema. He himself leads the charge, and they thunder down on the Pandava. From the corner of his eye, Abhimanyu sees the danger to his uncle. Quick as thought, he shoots an arrow straight into the heart of the first elephant, the king's, and the leviathan collapses with a scream, just a few paces behind a surprised Bheema. Jarasandha's son is on his feet in a wink, and takes to his heels. Then Bheema is a lion loose among the elephants of the Magadhan army. He hews at them with his mace, and the lumbering creatures fall, with grey brow and temple split open, their gore splashing everywhere, their trumpeting filling the air. The

Pandava massacres the kshatriyas that rode on the beasts' necks, those not crushed under their falling mastodons.

Soon, Bheema dances, roaring, among the hilly corpses of the elephant legion, and blood flows in streams around his ankles. His face is crimson, and he drips blood as if he had bathed in it in a savage ablution. The son of the wind is like Siva, dancing his tandava on Kurukshetra. Dhritarashtra's sons tremble to watch him.

Duryodhana sends more soldiers, a thousand of them, to stop his cousin. Dhrishtadyumna, Shikhandi, and now, Draupadi's sons rush to Bheema's side. Bheema stands like the peak of Mount Meru ringed by clouds: the corpses of the warriors and elephants he has killed. With every moment that passes, he fells more beasts and men. Mayaa's mace in his hand, the strength in his sinews, the swiftness in them, of his father, the airy Deva, he is a storm that blows on Kurukshetra: his roars are thunder, his mace is lightning, and blood is his rain.

Bheeshma comes to stop Bheema's carnage. He shoots a hundred arrows at his grandson. Bheema's arms are a blur, as he knocks the whistling shafts aside with his mace, disdainfully as he might a barrage of twigs. Seeing him struck by some barbs, Satyaki rides to Bheema's side, covering Bheeshma with fire.

Now the Kaurava lines part, and a weird and wild being comes to battle, mounted in a black chariot. He is twice as tall as any other warrior, has claws for hands and fangs for teeth; his lean, naked body is covered in coarse fur. He is a spy and friend of Duryodhana's: the rakshasa Alambusa. He is so hideous, his eyes green and his breath awful, that even the Kaurava footsoldiers shrink from him. As he comes, he kills a hundred men with a curved sword, from which he licks the blood from time to time. He is a devil with power; arrows fall tamely off his hide.

Alambusa springs into Satyaki's chariot, and they fight hand to hand. Strong as the rakshasa is, he is no match for the Yadava, who is perhaps the finest swordsman on earth. Their duel lasts just moments, before Satyaki buries his blade to its hilt in Alambusa's chest, drawing a geyser of black blood. The jungle demon flees, screaming; he will heal his wound with herbs and sorcery. Satyaki steadies his chariot, wipes his sword, and picks up his bow.

Suddenly, Bheema sees an opening in the Kaurava ranks to the left of Bheeshma's chariot. He darts through it and, running headlong, he is among Dhritarashtra's sons like a wolf at a herd of calves. Before the first of Duryodhana's brothers can flee, the son of the wind has felled him with a blow of his mace, which strikes that prince's head off his neck, so it lands ten feet away.

With a laugh that transfixes the other Kauravas, Bheema yells, "Ninety-nine to go!"

As they stand stupefied by him, he kills another eight, while they hardly raise their weapons to defend themselves. Bheeshma calls desperately to Bhagadatta, the lord of Pragjyotishapura, who fights from a wonderful Airavata-sired elephant's back. "Bhagadatta, ride between Bheema and the princes!"

That warrior thunders up on his beast. His elephant is one of a kind, as big as two common elephants, and the earth shudders at its tread. The kshatriya who sits on its neck is the son of the Asura Naraka, who was a son of Bhumi Devi and Vishnu's Varahavatara. Krishna once flew to the secret Himalayan city, Pragjyotishapura, on Garuda, and killed Bhagadatta's father. Bhagadatta is immense, and as fierce and strong is his elephant Supritika. With ichor, the juice of rut, flowing down its temples, the beast fights like a vyuha by itself, goring and trampling Pandava footsoldiers.

Bhagadatta casts a sorcerer's lance at Bheema. It strikes the Pandava senseless. Supritika rushes forward to crush Bheema underfoot, but suddenly another elephant looms in his path, with a black and implacable warrior on its neck, whose smooth head shines in the sun: Ghatotkacha come to save his father! Hidimbi's son fights with maya. At times, Bhagadatta sees him, and at others, he is an eerie mist. He fights from elephant-back and from the ground; and then, again, he flies through the air, so it seems he is in many places at once. Wherever he is, invisible or plain to the eye, he fights splendidly. Ghatotkacha's smaller elephant locks tusks with Bhagadatta's monumental animal, and, mastering him with sheer courage, pushes him back. Trumpeting shrilly, Bhagadatta's elephant turns tail.

Meanwhile, Bheema is on his feet again; shaking the stupor from his head, he fights more wildly than before. Bheeshma cries to Drona and Duryodhana, "Fly to Bhagadatta! Before he is killed."

They surge forward in their chariots, and a hundred men with them. They cannot stand against Bheema and his rakshasa son. Ghatotkacha's maya bewilders the Kaurava legions; the very sight of him, black, sleek and ferile, strikes terror into them. The soldiers panic, and the rakshasa lets another sluice of blood on Kurukshetra, with Bheema roaring encouragement. Until, Bheeshma roars above the hellish bedlam of war, "Sound the conches! We will fight again tomorrow."

He turns his chariot and leaves the field. The conches blare and, at once, the fighting stops, two hours before sunset today. Bheema and Ghatotkacha cease their festival of slaughter, and stand glowing and bloody with their arms around each other. A cheer goes up from the Pandava ranks, and they carry Ghatotkacha back to the camp in triumph, where Yudhishtira embraces his favourite nephew. There is no doubt the day belongs to the quiet rakshasa who, now that the fighting is over, is shy of the praise showered on him.

There is celebration in the Pandava camp, and even the cautious Yudhishtira allows himself the thought that victory might well be theirs, and soon, if the war continues like this.

Darkness has fallen over the Kaurava legions. Dejected soldiers seek their beds early that evening. Duryodhana cannot sleep. He sits alone in his tent, spurning even the company of Karna and Shakuni. He sits with his head buried in his hands, and hot tears flow down his face. The night amplifies his fears that he will lose this war.

He has lost eight brothers today. Duryodhana feels as if eight organs of his body have been cut from him. Terror grips him that, before this war is over, Bheema will keep his oath: he will kill Dhritarashtra's hundred sons. Duryodhana remembers what the Pandava had sworn he would do to Dusasana, and he shudders.

After a time, Duryodhana crosses to his bed and lies down. Still, he cannot sleep. The night wears on with visions of doom, and near midnight he gets up and walks out from his tent. Wrapped in a shawl, under a glaring moon like an angry eye above, he walks to Bheeshma's tent. He enters, and sits in a chair beside his Pitama's bed. He feels a little comforted in his grandfather's presence, just as he used to when he was a boy, and would grow unaccountably afraid at nights.

For a while Duryodhana sits there, thinking Bheeshma is asleep; until the old man speaks softly from his bed, "Couldn't you sleep as well, my child?"

Duryodhana grasps Bheeshma's hand. Fervently he says, "Pitama, I am afraid! Bheema killed eight of my brothers today, even when our greatest warriors protected them. Every day, we go out to fight and they rout us. Already, I fear their numbers are greater than ours though we began with four aksauhinis more. I cannot understand it, Pitama, this is not natural."

He clutches the old man's hand and sobs. Bheeshma holds Duryodhana to him, as he had when the prince was a boy. He strokes his head, and says gently, "My child, my poor child, this is what we tried to warn you of, all these days. It is not too late, Duryodhana. Go to Yudhishtira, make peace with him. It will hurt you, surely; but it will be far cheaper than losing all your brothers and friends, your elders and masters, and then your own life. At least now, you must realize that no force on earth can stand before the Pandavas. Do you know why? Why not Drona or I can contain them? It is because they have Krishna with them. No host of heaven or earth can resist the Dark One. He is God come down as a man to purify the earth. I have lived many years in this deep world; I know it well, and all that is in it. I know the Avatara when I see him. Duryodhana, you must relent.

"In just four days, they have killed a third of our men. If you still cannot see how this war is going to end, you are blind. We shall all be killed; those like me, who are more than ready for death, and others who are young and far from prepared. All our fates are in your hands. Come with me, let us go to Yudhishtira and offer him an honourable peace. You will be remembered as the king who saved the world, as Duryodhana who conquered himself. Come, this is the time to be a kshatriya!"

Duryodhana has grown stiff as a corpse. For a while he sits gazing numbly at his grandfather's face. Then he lets go the patriarch's hand, rises and, without a word, walks out of his tent. Bheeshma sits staring out of the open tent-flap at the mooned night outside. Duryodhana would never relent; his pride would not allow him. His mind wanders back to the day's battle. He sees Arjuna on the field again. He sees Abhimanyu, as great an archer as his father, his face a boy's. Bheeshma smiles in the dark. The House of Kuru was still the noblest house on earth. A pang of grief convulses him again, for this house divided against itself in war; and to think what its glory would have been, if all its sons had stood together. Tears fill the old man's eyes.

Bheeshma lies on his bed. He remembers another moment from the day, when he thought his salvation had come to him: when Krishna leapt down from his chariot, and strode at him in wrath, the Chakra livid over his hand. How ecstatic that death would have been! But it was not to be. The aged warrior sighs.

As he lies there, he drifts back to his childhood, to the tangled banks of a holy river. He sees his mother's face, Ganga's face. She seems so real he can almost reach out and stroke her cheek. He imagines he is a child, once more, lying with his head in her lap, and her telling him wondrous tales of the eldest days of the earth. He hears her soft voice clearly; sleep steals over the tired old kshatriya.

FOURTEEN

The fifth and sixth days

Dawn of the fifth day of the war and Bheeshma is up with the sun and deploys his troops in the makara vyuha. Across the chasmal field, Arjuna, Dhrishtadyumna and Yudhishtira decide that the garuda vyuha will hunt the patriarch's crocodile. They set Bheema at the beak, behind him is Satyaki, the eagle's head, and behind Satyaki, Arjuna is the bird's neck. Drupada and Virata form the avian's left wing, and the Kekaya brothers, the right. Abhimanyu and Draupadi's sons are the eagle's back, and its tail is Yudhishtira, with Nakula and Sahadeva beside him.

Again, the bass of conches, as the cinnabar sun climbs over the horizon. The armies run roaring at each other, with Bheeshma and Bheema at the head of the Kaurava and Pandava legions. Arrows hum across the field, in fatal song, and stick quivering in enemies' flesh. Sword rings against sword, spear on spear. Thousands die, quick as thinking, all their intricate days on earth cut suddenly short.

Bheeshma and Bheema meet, but the Pandava has little taste for the fight with his Pitama. Bheema prefers fighting from the ground, with his mace, to the subtle skills of archery. He veers away soon enough, as Arjuna arrives to face his grandsire, and earth and sky are lit up with a treat of astras. Weapons that could quell an army extinguish one another. Bheeshma and Arjuna are finely matched, and they are the heart of the war. Neither gives an inch; each absorbs the other.

Today, more than ever, Duryodhana is determined that he will reverse the tide of the war in his favour. All night he has sat plotting nothing else. He rides to Drona's side before the Acharya begins to fight. "Acharya, I depend on you to turn this war around. Pitama and you could conquer the Devas if you wanted; these Pandavas are not your equals at all."

Drona replies, "They are invincible, and nothing you say can change that. The Pitama and I, and all of us, will do our dharma by you. But we can never win this war."

He doesn't pause to hear what Duryodhana begins to say, but flies at the enemy. Drona, Bheeshma and Shalya battle against Bheema, Satyaki, Abhimanyu and Drupada's sons. For the first time, Shikhandi dodges past the protective ring around Bheeshma, and engages the Kuru patriarch in frenzy. Seeing Bheeshma in mortal danger, Drona skims up to challenge Shikhandi, as Bheeshma slips away.

Seeing this, Arjuna confronts his grandsire. The other Pandavas are not far behind him. They, too, now use the Kaurava tactic of singling out the most threatening kshatriya, and trying to overwhelm him all together. Bheeshma is pleased that Bheema is among those he faces: at least, he can keep the Vayuputra away from Dhritarashtra's sons.

The sun climbs to his zenith, and blazes down on the war, searing the dead and the living. Once more, the field is slippery with blood, awkward with the corpses of men, horses, elephants, and broken chariots. Manoeuvering through these, Krishna flies at Bheeshma. The Kaurava footsoldiers flee from that chariot. They would be anywhere but in Arjuna's path. At once, the other Kaurava warriors rally to Bheeshma's side.

And now, another king flashes at the Kuru Pitama from a flank; Virata strikes Bheeshma with a shimmer of arrows with golden wings. Eyes crimson, Bheeshma turns on that kshatriya and covers him in a sheet-rain of silver shafts. Aswatthama fights Arjuna, with Drona watching in some pride: his son, and the disciple dear to him as a son. The encounter is even, but Arjuna is too fond of Aswatthama to enjoy the duel. As soon as he can, he cries to Krishna to turn away.

They see Bheema and Duryodhana fighting, and pass on. Now Bheema fights from a chariot, with a bow and arrows. Bheema strikes his cousin deep in his side. Duryodhana battles on as if he did not notice the wound. Arjuna seeks Bheeshma out once more. As he goes, he sees a kshatriya who has killed more Kaurava soldiers than any other Pandava warrior today: brilliant Abhimanyu in his chariot, blowing through the enemy.

The fifth and sixth days 211

Duryodhana's son, Lakshmana, dashes forward to check Abhimanyu. Briefly, he holds up Arjuna's son. Not for long, and Abhimanyu strikes Lakshmana with a long silver arrow, and he staggers in his chariot. Acharya Kripa snatches the Kaurava prince into his own ratha and rushes him out of battle, before Abhimanyu can kill him.

On this fifth day, Satyaki fights like Arjuna himself. It is easy to see the Yadava is the Pandava's sishya; he has the same smoothness to his archery, the same effortless artistry. An old enemy rides up to confront him: Bhoorisravas, who has come late to the battle today. He is fresh, while Satyaki has already been on the field for some hours, and slowly, but surely, he dominates the Yadava. Bheema sees Bhoorisravas pierce his shoulder with an arrow like light, and Satyaki cry out and stumble in his chariot. Bheema flashes up, beating Bhoorisravas back with a fury of arrows. He pulls Satyaki into his own chariot and rides off with him.

Meanwhile, from Krishna's chariot, Arjuna kills another thousand men, until Bheeshma storms up again to stop him. For an hour, the two duel, and by now the sun is low in the west. Bheeshma looks around him and sees the common soldiers and even the kshatriyas of both armies haggard. He raises his hand for the conches to sound. Gathering their dead to burn, the armies withdraw gratefully for the night. The day's honors have been shared more equally. Between them, Arjuna, Abhimanyu and Satyaki have made sure that more Kaurava soldiers have died than Pandava; but Drona, Kripa, Bheeshma and Aswatthama have done their share of killing.

Perhaps because he is tired after five days of war, this evening Arjuna is silent and pensive. No doubt remains in his heart that he must fight, and as well as he can; he still hates this war and Duryodhana for having caused it.

The evening meal, by firelight, is sombre in both camps. The faces of those who have survived to fight on seem older not by five days, but years. Young boys have deep lines around their eyes. They have seen friends and brothers die, and tasted blood by sword and arrow for the first time. Some have their hair turn grey, in these days long as lives. The war they fight is truly in death's realm as much as in life, and they are so young they can hardly distinguish between the two. There is no more singing or dancing, chat or laughter left in them. Most sit silent, staring into the flames while images of the day's killing sway before their eyes.

On the sixth morning, Dhrishtadyumna and Arjuna are out on the field before Bheeshma. They form their legions in the vyuha the Kauravas had used to advantage the previous day: the makara. Bheeshma deploys his forces in the krauncha vyuha he used on the first morning of the war, the only day that belonged to him so far.

Refreshed by a night's sleep, the armies charge each other. It is as if, despite themselves, they are eager for battle, for its violent magnificence, as if nothing but war can satisfy their spirits any more. All their pasts are like dreams now, unreal; the only reality is this gruesome contention; nothing matters any more except kill or be killed.

Bheema and Drona meet head on, and the Pandava slays his guru's sarathy. Drona, the master, takes the reins in his own hands and fights on. Today, it is the Pandava army on which both he and Bheeshma vent their ire. If any of the Pandavas challenges them, they veer away from the encounter and cut short the lives of a hundred common soldiers instead.

Just as these two kill thousands of Yudhishtira's men, the Pandavas and their sons decimate the Kaurava legions.

Suddenly, Bheema feels left behind by the others. With a roar, he seizes up his mace and leaps down from his ratha. He fights again as he does best; he is at the dazed Kauravas like a freak storm of his father. He smashes down horses, men and elephants unlucky enough to come in his way. He runs blindly into the Kaurava vyuha, roaring like ten tigers. No one dares stand in his dreadful way; they fly from him in every direction. On and on he plunges, deep into the heart of the Kaurava army, where he no longer has to wait for the enemy to come to him, but is surrounded by men he can kill. His mace a blur, he is soon drenched in blood again.

Bheema rushes into the Kaurava army like a storm cloud into a clear sky. A hundred kshatriyas attack him together, those that dare. Arrows pierce his back, chest and sides. He hardly notices the pain, only plucking them out if they came in the way of his swinging his mace freely.

Meanwhile, Dhrishtadyumna, ranging the field, comes upon Bheema's chariot empty of its warrior. The Pandava's sarathy, Visoka, sits gazing anxiously towards the enemy lines.

"Where is Bheema?" cries Dhrishtadyumna, his heart in his mouth.

Visoka replies, "He leapt out of my chariot, and ran towards the enemy. I saw him kill a hundred men. He did not turn back, but ran on into the Kaurava ranks. He vanished from my sight, and I did not heard him roar any more. I fear for him."

Dhrishtadyumna lashes his horses at Duryodhana's legions, cleaving their ranks with death. Ahead of him, he sees there is already a path to follow: the crimson one Bheema has made with his mace, littered with dead men, their blood still leaking on to the earth. Then Dhrishtadyumna hears a commotion, screams and roars. He sees Bheema at the very heart of the Kaurava army, surrounded by the enemy, covered in blood, and having the time of his life!

Bheema, on foot, faces a hundred adversaries. He fights on, roaring above the screams of men whose heads and limbs he smashes. Dhrishtadyumna rides to Bheema's side, crying out his name, arrows flaring before his golden chariot. The Kauravas that dared stand against Bheema flee at the Panchala's advent.

Duryodhana roars, "Stand and fight! Stand and fight you cowards! There are only two of them."

But they are like two thousand. Duryodhana roars to his brothers, and they stream forward, fifty royal kshatriyas. They have decided there is little point running from Bheema, he would hunt them down wherever they ran. Rather, they would do their best to kill him: to avenge their dead brothers, or to die themselves, trying. Dhrishtadyumna cries, "Quick Bheema! Into my chariot."

When Bheema staggers in, the Panchala's charioteer rides away briefly, so Dhrishtadyumna can draw out some of the arrows stuck thickly as quills in his friend's body. Bheema cries impatiently, "We'll look at the wounds later. This is the time for war. At them, sarathy!"

Roaring like two prides of lions, they fly at the Kauravas again. They fight side by side, Bheema's mace the thunder and lightning, and Dhrishtadyumna's arrows the killing rain. Fifty kshatriyas, all taught by Drona, face the two; and the odds are overwhelming. Suddenly, Dhrishtadyumna shoots an astra called Pramoha at Duryodhana's brothers. It is a weapon of sleep, and covers them in a mantle of slumber. The Kauravas swoon in their chariots. Bheema is about to leap down and finish Dhritarashtra's sons, when, from across the field, another astra spumes up in a burst of silver and falls on the unconscious Kauravas, a shower of stardust. At once, they wake up and raise their weapons

Duryodhana rages for reinforcements, and a thousand Kaurava soldiers from other parts of the field surround Bheema and Dhrishtadyumna. Yudhishtira has word that the two are fighting alone in the thick of the Kaurava army, and he sends Abhimanyu at the head of a Pandava legion to them. Formed in a sleek vyuha called the soochi, the needle, Abhimanyu's troops arrive, every man a maharathika.

Dhrishtadyumna peels away from that encounter, to face Drona who rides at him from a flank and behind. The Acharya comes quick as light, his arrows a web of magic before him. In a wink, Drona kills Dhrishtadyumna's horses and shatters his chariot. Luckily, Abhimanyu sees the danger he is in, and thrusts his horses between Drona and the Pandava Senapati. Dhrishtadyumna leaps into Abhimanyu's chariot and fights on.

Meanwhile, Bheema's sarathy Visoka takes courage in both hands and follows Abhimanyu into the Kaurava army. When Drona smashes Dhrishtadyumna's chariot, Visoka is at hand. Bheema climbs back into his own chariot and, wrath undimmed, flies at Dhritarashtra's sons again.

Abhimanyu and Vikarna fight, a hundred shafts flaring from their bows every moment; no one can tell which the finer archer is. Seeing Bheema attack his brothers again, and them shrinking from him, Duryodhana arrives to challenge his cousin. At once, his eyes shining, Bheema turns on the Kaurava, focusing his rage on his old enemy. Like two bull-elephants, they battle, but in a while Bheema begins to prevail. He beats Duryodhana back, then, strikes him down in his chariot with a clutch of fire-shafts, so his cousin faints again. With a cry, Bheema leaps down to finish it all, when Jayadratha rides up quick as a wish and spirits away the unconscious Kaurava.

A lion that has its prey saved by a jackal, Bheema charges Jayadratha. Kripa rides up and takes charge of Duryodhana, going off with him, while Jayadratha turns to face a roaring Bheema. A hundred Kaurava soldiers converge to save Jayadratha, and the fighting becomes diffuse again. The sun is on the western rim of the world, once more, and the day darkens quickly. Bheeshma and Dhrishtadyumna give the signal for battle to end. Deep conches blow from behind the fighting lines, and the killing stops.

Twilight falls on the field of dharma, and slowly, the dead are gathered in heaps beside the blood-red Saraswati, and set ablaze. Once more, the day belongs to the Pandavas: twice as many of Duryodhana's men have died as Yudhishtira's. Tonight, in the Pandava camp, Bheema and Dhrishtadyumna are the heroes; between them, they have killed twenty thousand men, perhaps more. Tonight, there is music and celebration again among Yudhishtira's soldiers. They have cause to be jubilant: except for the very first one, every other day of the war has belonged to them.

Later that night, a distraught Duryodhana seeks Bheeshma in his tent. For a long time, he sits staring mutely into his grandsire's eyes. Finally, he says, "Pitama, if you don't put your heart into the war, we will lose. You saw what Bheema and Dhrishtadyumna did to us today. But you will not kill the sons of Pandu, neither you, nor Acharya Drona; and I know that the two of you can finish the five of them. If you stay your hands in love, how will we ever win this war?"

Bheeshma is silent for a moment. Then, he says gravely, "I told you before the war began that I would never kill Pandu's sons. But I do kill thousands of their men every day. If their army is razed how will they stand against us by themselves? But you underestimated them, and those who fight for them; especially when they fight for the truth."

Then, Bheeshma sees the cloths that bind the wounds Bheema gave Duryodhana, and at once, his old eyes are moist. He rises, and fetches a crystal vial from a recess of the tent. He gives it to Duryodhana, "Drink this, my child, it will take away the pain of your wounds. Then go and sleep. You must be fresh for the battle tomorrow."

When Duryodhana has drunk the potion, warm languor steals over him, soothes the throbbing agony in his body. Bheeshma sees Duryodhana as a child before him, once more, and he tenderly embraces the prince, his old heart breaking yet again. He sends the Kaurava away, and lies on his bed, numb, watching the moon climb into the sky outside. His eyes hardly notice Soma Deva's silvery splendour.

FIFTEEN

The seventh day: many duels

Bheeshma deploys his troops in a circular galaxy on the seventh morning of the war, the mandala vyuha. Dhrishtadyumna and Arjuna form a vajra vyuha. Both formations manoeuvre quickly, and are almost impregnable. The din of conches rises, and the armies fly at each other.

At a spinning perimeter of the mandala vyuha, Drona faces Virata and Drupada. Aswatthama faces Shikhandi; Duryodhana comes up against Dhrishtadyumna; Nakula and Sahadeva, their uncle Shalya. Vinda and Anuvinda confront Arjuna. Bheema faces Kritavarman, Abhimanyu holds up Chitrasena, Vikarna and Dusasana at once. Ghatotkacha and Bhagadatta meet again, like two thunderheads. The rakshasa Alambusa, whom Satyaki wounded two days ago, returns to battle, healed by his own occult powers, and faces the Yadava once more. Bhoorisravas fights hand to hand with Dhrishtaketu; Srutayas duels Yudhishtira, while, next to them, Chekitana faces Kripa.

Today seems destined more for fervid duels than general battle. Arjuna says to his dark sarathy, "The Pitama thinks his soldiers will be safe inside his mandala. Look, Krishna, the Trigartas are spoiling for a fight, and they shall not live to see the sun set. Ride at them, my Lord, it is time the earth was lighter by their burden."

Krishna sets his horses at the Trigartas, nestling in a whorl of the mandala vyuha. Arjuna pulls on the Gandiva's string, and the ground shakes. The Pandava looses an aindrastra at the enemy. The missile flares up into the sky above the Kaurava legions, and hangs there, a gleaming jewel. From it, thousands of arrows fall in a bright torrent on Duryodhana's men. As they run for their lives, Bheeshma's careful vyuha is broken in slivers.

Susharma has to flee. Duryodhana's roar rings across Kurukshetra. But a kshatriya in a silver chariot yoked to white steeds, his hair like mane behind him, pale as his horses, rides to challenge Arjuna. It is Bheeshma, and the Pandava soldiers run every way from him. Arjuna stands his ground and meets Bheeshma's charge with a scorching salvo.

Duryodhana yells, "Susharma, ride with me! We must watch the Pitama's flanks."

He thunders after his grandsire, and Susharma after him. The duel between Bheeshma and Arjuna lights up the field with coruscating astras that lock on high, and then die away in cascades of sparks. Both warriors' bodies shine uncannily with the power of the weapons they invoke, and one cannot look at them for long. All round Kurukshetra the fighting stops. Every soldier gazes in awe at the duel between Bheeshma and Arjuna; they have never seen anything like it before.

Both fight from a protective enclave of kshatriyas, so they cannot be surprised from a flank or from behind. Then, Drona, not content to be a spectator, attacks Virata with a roar. Today that king is prepared for the Acharya. Swifter than Drona expects, Virata breaks the brahmana's bow in his hands, cuts down his banner, and kills his sarathy. Drona seizes up another bow and dispatches Virata's sarathy with a light-like shaft.

Virata's son, Sankha, rides up at once and takes his father into his ratha. The two then fight Drona together; while the Kuru Acharya drives his own chariot and holds them off with a stream of fire. Drona finds young Sankha a formidable adversary, and looses an astra like a meteor at the boy. The shaft takes the prince in his chest, cuts through his armour like butter, and breaks into his heart. Sankha dies without a sound, his blood splattering his father.

This is the third son he has lost to the war. With a howl, Virata leaps out of the chariot and runs away. Drona fights on, in icy calm, killing a hundred men every moment. Aswatthama and Shikhandi fight across the field: evenly matched and brilliant. Shikhandi strikes Aswatthama with three arrows, in swift succession. Crying aloud in pain, Aswatthama cuts Shikhandi's sarathy's head from his neck with a wedge-tipped arrow, and kills his horses with shafts through their eyes.

Undaunted, Shikhandi leaps down and, sword in hand, rushes at Aswatthama. Aswatthama covers him in fire, but Druapada's son whirls his blade round and strikes down every shaft. He is a hawk fighting in the sky, the whirling sword his wings. Just then, Satyaki rides up. Shikhandi flings his sword at Aswatthama, a streak of light, climbs into Satyaki's chariot and flashes away.

Alambusa arrives to face Satyaki. They fight, and the rakshasa uses maya, making himself invisible to confound his enemy. The Yadava pierces him with a subtle astra, which lights up the forest-devil's body so he cannot vanish anymore. Alambusa flies up into the sky, and lashes the Vrishni with a storm of arrows. Satyaki shoots an aindrastra at him, and it pursues the rakshasa, blasting a score of livid barbs at him every moment. Alambusa flees, and Satyaki kills a hundred Kaurava soldiers to celebrate.

Duryodhana seeks out Dhrishtadyumna again. Dhrishtadyumna smashes Duryodhana's chariot-wheels, but Duryodhana leaps down to the ground and battles on. Shakuni rides up, and gives his nephew his chariot; but Dhrishtadyumna is the quicker archer, and soon, fearing for his life, the Kaurava turns away. Not far from the fire-prince, Satyaki still razes Hastinapura's legions.

Kritavarman faces Bheema coming into battle. Bheema does not roar today; his silence is exceptional, quite deafening. But he fights as powerfully as ever, and in moments he has slaughtered Kritavarman's horses, and cut down his banner. Flying past the Yadava in his chariot, Bheema fetches him a blow with his mace, and Kritavarman collapses with a scream, feeling every bone in his body is broken. Luckily, Shakuni is at hand to save him from Bheema. Now Bheema lets out a full-throated roar, his first of the day. He leaps down from his chariot and, like a hurricane, sets on the elephants of the Kaurava army.

As the sea does the Ganga, the Pandava army quells the Kaurava legions. Not that Duryodhana's warriors fight tamely. No, they are ferocious, they are inspired; but they are small match for Yudhishtira's men. Inexorably, the army of Hastinapura dwindles, as if its soldiers have just one ambition on Kurukshetra: to die, and find the swarga meant for those killed in battle.

In a chariot glowing like the morning sun, Ghatotkacha accosts Bhagadatta mounted on his white elephant. The lord of Pragjyotishapura seems like Indra himself come down to Kurukshetra; and Ghatotkacha cannot match the asura today. Bhagadatta kills his horses. Ghatotkacha casts a glimmering javelin at the demon, but Bhagadatta cuts it in three pieces. Ghatotkacha wisely leaves the field; the asura spurs his pale beast forward, and it tramples the Pandava soldiers, gores them dead.

Madri's brother Shalya battles Nakula and Sahadeva, and the uncle is delighted by his nephews' valour. Even when they wound him sharply, he shouts encouragement to them. But Shalya does not stay his hand because he is fighting his sister's sons. He covers them with arrows like silver hail, and soon kills Nakula's sarathy and horses. In a blink, Sahadeva is at his twin's side, and his brother leaps nimbly into his chariot. He sees how violently Shalya shoots at Nakula; Sahadeva casts a heavy lance at his uncle and fells him. Shalya faints, and is driven off the field.

High noon, and Yudhishtira and Srutayus face each other on the field of the Kurus. The gentle Pandava is a cobra spitting venom! Srutayus is a gifted archer, and he strikes Yudhishtira's armour off his back with a blistering volley. Yudhishtira fights on as if he has not noticed. He kills Srutayus' horses and sarathy, and the Kaurava warrior runs away without ceremony. Yudhishtira wades into the unprotected enemy, killing a hundred men.

Elsewhere Chekitana overwhelms Kripa, and the Acharya is carried off the field. Three of Duryodhana's brothers attack Abhimanyu from different sides, but not together are they a match for Arjuna's son. He breaks their bows in their hands, kills their horses and charioteers, and has them at his mercy. Then, he remembers his uncle Bheema's oath that he would kill all Dhritarashtra's sons. Abhimanyu stops himself.

Bheeshma storms to the Kaurava princes' rescue. Nearby, Arjuna says to Krishna, "The old lion and our young one will absorb each other for a while. Come, Krishna, let us range the field, and reduce the size of my cousin's army."

A wind sowing death, that chariot blows at the Kaurava forces, while Abhimanyu holds Bheeshma up. Susharma confronts Arjuna once more, with his legion of Trigartas.

They surround the Pandava and fall on him from every side. But it seems Arjuna has a hundred hands and a hundred Gandivas in them. In moments, blood flying everywhere, half Susharma's men are dead.

Stunned by the Pandava's valour, Susharma retreats, and a smiling Krishna turns his chariot to seek out Bheeshma.

Shikhandi rides at Arjuna's side; in wonderful synchronicity, the other four Pandavas appear there as well, and all of them attack Bheeshma. If they can kill him now, the war would be good as won. But Duryodhana, Jayadratha and a score of others force a way to where Bheeshma battles five Pandavas and Shikhandi, at once. They rain arrows on him from every side, but not one strikes him. Like some unearthly dancer, he cuts them all down.

In a moment, Kripa, Shalya, Sala and a mortal Chitrasena are at Bheeshma's side, drawing the Pandavas' fire from him. But he has scant need of them; already, he has beaten his grandsons back with some ineffable archery. Bheema, Yudhishtira and Sahadeva have their bows plucked from their hands; Nakula and Arjuna are struck down in their chariots. Yudhishtira turns to Shikhandi, and cries in rare fury, "You have sworn to kill him. If you don't hurry, we will all be dead."

Shikhandi charges Bheeshma's chariot; but Duryodhana's kshatriyas have been warned about the oath of Amba. Shalya plunges between Shikhandi and Bheeshma, and a duel ensues. Nearby, Bheema and Jayadratha fight. Each has killed the other's horses, and smashed the other's chariot. Now they fight on foot, maces ringing together in showers of sparks. Jayadratha is no match for the Pandava. Bheema fells him with a huge stroke, and Jayadratha jumps up and runs. Chitrasena rides up to challenge Bheema, but the son of the wind greets him by flinging his mace at him like a thunderbolt. Chitrasena falls, and his sarathy rides off with his unconscious kshatriya.

Bheeshma confronts Yudhishtira, lord of the Pandava army. Intensely they fight, grandsire and grandson, like old enemies, neither giving an inch. It is hard to believe this same Yudhishtira always worshipped his Pitama; it is harder to conceive Bheeshma is his doting grandfather. Bheeshma shatters Yudhishtira's chariot; Nakula is nearby and Yudhishtira climbs into his brother's chariot. The twins and he attack Bheeshma together; but he fights not merely like a man a fourth his age: he fights like five Arjunas. As he holds off the three sons of Pandu, he strews Kurukshetra with their soldiers' corpses.

The Trigartas still surround Arjuna and shoot at him from every side. They draw him away from Bheeshma, fearing that if all the Pandavas

The seventh day: many duels **221**

combine for long enough against the Pitama, they may well kill him. Arjuna makes them pay dearly, he lets a swash of Trigarta blood. But he cannot stem the death Bheeshma brings to the Pandava legions. Twilight falls suddenly, as if a God above, heartsick of the carnage on Kurukshetra, sent an astra of darkness to stop it. Conches announce the end of the day's battle. Soldiers across the field put up their arms, blessing kindly fortune that they will live another night, while thousands of their comrades have perished.

Today, there is scant celebration in the Pandava camp. The individual duels have gone their way, on that seventh day; but at least ten thousand more Pandava soldiers have died than Kaurava. Bheeshma has killed most of them. Yudhishtira sits forlorn, while, in the camp across Kurukshetra, Duryodhana is excited as a boy.

He drinks wine, sitting with Karna, Shakuni and Dusasana, and predicts, "The worst is over. They have done everything they could, and they have found Bheeshma invincible. This lucky seventh day, the course of the war has turned. Now we shall win."

Shakuni says, "The Pitama is the key to victory. As long as we can keep him safe from Shikhandi, no Pandava, or any kshatriya on earth, can kill Bheeshma. You made no mistake, Duryodhana, when you made him our Senapati."

Karna's eyes are like embers, but he says little tonight of all that burns his heart.

Much later that night, across the field of death, when the others are asleep and the moon sinks in the west, one warrior lies awake, and an uncanny transformation comes over him. Shikhandi lies in his bed, sleepless. These seven days he has stalked just Bheeshma, and whenever he came near the Kuru ancient, another Kaurava had always come between them, even like fate. Shikhandi has hardly shot an arrow at the man he has sworn to kill. Tonight, like every other night, his lean body and his handsome face take on a strange aspect when he is alone.

The spirit of Amba comes over Shikhandi, and he feels himself as he was a life ago, when he was she. His skin is hers. His thoughts, his senses, his very body, and most of all, his obsession with Bheeshma, are all Amba's. And how she longs to kill him; but not—after two lives and a death, after all she has endured—with any hatred. Amba yearns to kill Bheeshma to set him free. She has always loved him, and she knows, now, how much he suffers; and she knows that he, also, has always loved her.

Amba smiles. Her long wait is almost at an end. Perhaps tomorrow, she tells herself again, she can finally pierce his heart with an arrow.

SIXTEEN

The eighth day: the field of death

DAWN OF THE EIGHTH DAY OF THE WAR AND BHEESHMA FORMS HIS legions in the expansive oormi vyuha: the ocean phalanx, its waves of kshatriyas splayed a league on either side. Across the field today, Yudhishtira tells Arjuna and Drishtadyumna that the most potent vyuha against the oormi is the sringataka, the horned phalanx. Arjuna is a master of this formation, and soon both armies are ready for the day's bloodletting. Once more, conches blare, death's knell, and glazed-eyed legions rush at each other.

It is another morning of duels. First, Bheeshma meets Bheema, who is in great heart, and finds the young lion implacable. The Pandava covers his Pitama's chariot in a cloak of arrows, with such artistry that those who watch can scarcely believe it of him. Even Bheeshma is taken aback at his grandson's virtuosity, and before he knows it Bheema kills his horses and sarathy, and advances menacingly on him. Away to the left, Duryodhana sees Bheeshma in danger and flies to the rescue with a force of his brothers. Seeing the Kauravas coming, Bheema immediately loses interest in his grandsire, and charges his cousins in joy. They hardly know how, and eight sons of Dhritarashtra die, their heads crushed or struck off, or their hearts stopped with whistling shafts.

Duryodhana watches, helplessly, and Bheema's oath echoes in his mind. He howls at Bheeshma, "The monster kills my brothers! While you watch as if they are not your grandsons. You don't love me, Bheeshma, only the sons of Pandu."

Bheeshma cries angrily, "You are cruel, Duryodhana! If I did not love you, would I be here fighting at your side? Even when I know you are wrong. If we did not love you, Drona and I could have kept away. When I told you the Pandavas are invincible, you would not listen. The price you pay is your brothers' lives. Every time Bheema sees them, he will kill them, as he would swat flies. You tried to save your brothers just now, but could you? Then why point your finger at me? I am as helpless as you are. All I can say to you is: Duryodhana prepare to die, and die like a kshatriya. Keep your mind on the war, not on things that are beyond it."

Bheeshma turns away in disgust, and rides off to vent his grief on the Pandava legions. Noon again, and the Pandavas attack the Pitama, all together; but he blazes on the earth like the sun at his vertex. Bheema wheels away in frustration to demolish the Kaurava elephants; while Nakula and Sahadeva turn on Duryodhana's cavalry, cutting down hundreds of fine horses, and picking off their fallen riders when they stood defenceless on the ground. The Kaurava legions suffer, but this is as nothing compared to the massacre Bheeshma and Drona bring to the Pandava army.

On the eve of the war, an unusual young warrior presented himself before Arjuna, and said, "My mother heard about the war that was to be, and sent me to fight for you."

His green eyes were somehow familiar, and Arjuna felt a surge of affection for the lean, handsome youth. Arjuna said, "Who is your mother, young Kshatriya?"

The young man smiled, "The naga queen Ulupi."

A longago sinuous night swam up before Arjuna's eyes, and, with a cry, he clasped his son in his arms. That youth Iravan had proved himself as brave and skilled as Abhimanyu. He had been a bane of the enemy these past seven days. He brought a small legion of naga warriors with him, and they fought with eerie weapons and serpentine sorceries, razing whole columns of Kaurava soldiers.

Today, Iravan watches Shakuni, who fights more with cunning than valour: always making sure he faces only inferior antagonists, whom he kills without mercy. Iravan sees Shakuni kill common Pandava soldiers by shooting them in the back, and he rides to challenge the Gandhara king. Iravan's changeling nagas ride with him, and they account for a good part of Shakuni's legion. Inexorably, Iravan moves nearer Shakuni, who cringes from him. He cannot escape anywhere, because the prince's snake-warriors ring him round.

Duryodhana cries to Alambusa, "Arjuna's naga brat is dangerous. Kill him!"

Alambusa flies through the air at Iravan, intent on fighting his way to Shakuni, whom he is determined to finish today. Ulupi's son doesn't see Alambusa, mantled in maya, fly at him from above. Alambusa materializes abruptly before an astonished Iravan, and hacks his head off with a massive sword.

Bheeshma, Drona and Aswatthama take fire to the Pandava army, even as if they are the three points of Siva's trisula; the Pandavas themselves cannot contain them today, not when they combine. When Iravan dies, Ghatotkacha leaps into the forefront of battle. He, too, fights with maya, and Duryodhana has to contend with Bheema's terrific son. Today, Ghatotkacha attacks the Kaurava king himself, and the kshatriyas that defend him.

Bheeshma cries to Drona, "Duryodhana is hurt. Fly to him!"

Drona, Jayadratha, Aswatthama and a score of Kaurava warriors peel away towards Duryodhana. Kurukshetra rings with Ghatotkacha's roars, when he sees more of the enemy coming to challenge him. Yudhishtira hears that sound, and cries to Bheema, "Ghatotkacha is beset by a hundred men!"

In a moment, Bheema is beside his son. They fight, back to back. Enemy footsoldiers shut their ears and flee. Ghatotkacha and Bheema destroy Duryodhana's crack guard, which surrounds him when he goes into battle. Mortal screams and wild roars mingle, two rivers flowing into the sea of death. Red-eyed to see his guard slain, old hatred flaring high, Duryodhana rushes at Bheema with Aswatthama at his side. Laughing in their faces, Bheema pushes them back easily.

A thousand soldiers from both sides stream forward, and the battle spreads out again. Bheema is full of incredible strength; he bristles with weapons. He flings a hundred maces at the enemy. He is invincible; he seems ubiquitous; and no one can stand before him. And when roaring, his mace raised high, he charges Duryodhana, the Kaurava feels the touch of death on him and bolts. Beside Bheema, Ghatotkacha is like five storms, and so macabre that Kaurava soldiers run at just the sight of him. Or else, they stand rooted in terror, and he murders them.

Duryodhana rides trembling to Bheeshma. He cries, "You must kill Ghatotkacha or the war is lost!"

Bheeshma says impatiently, "I cannot leave this battle. Take Bhagadatta, he turned the rakshasa back yesterday."

Bhagadatta comes on Supritika, his white elephant. Word flies to the Pandavas of the asura's arrival, and quickly, Bheema, Ghatotkacha, Abhimanyu, Draupadi's sons and some others, too, stand together to meet the lord of Pragjyotishapura. Bhagadatta charges Bheema. The Pandava warriors cover the elephant with spears and arrows, and the beast's head is slick with blood, red on white. Still, it comes on, making for Bheema. All around, kshatriyas in chariots and footsoldiers cower before the pale leviathan.

When Bhagadatta's elephant is almost upon Bheema, the king of the Dasarnas confronts Supritika on his own elephant. This grey animal is barely half Supritika's size. But its heart is great and brave, and it charges the bigger animal, goring its side, so it turns away from Bheema with a scream. The Dasarna king's elephant will not retreat before Supritika's trumpeting or his short rushes. He stands like a rock, and Supritika backs away from him. The mammoths' trumpeting rings across the field and neither will give way.

Furious at being frustrated by a mortal, Bhagadatta looses a calific volley at the Dasarna king. Sensing peril to its master, now his elephant turns away. The Kaurava army roars from ten thousand throats, and teems forward behind Supritika. But the Pandava warriors have had time to recover. Now many of them face Bhagadatta, at once, and he can make no headway through their ranks. Supritika's rage at being pierced by a hundred lances and arrows shakes Kurukshetra.

Arjuna joins Bheema, Ghatotkacha and the rest. Behind Bhagadatta, Duryodhana calls up a legion of five thousand soldiers, and sends them to fight near the asura on his elephant. Another massacre; Bhagadatta kills thousands from elephant-back, and so, too, Bheema, Arjuna and Ghatotkacha from their chariots. Direst of all is Arjuna. He has news of the death of Iravan, and his wrath is dreadful. Hissing like a serpent, he fights with tears stinging his eyes for his changeling son, who was his mother Ulupi's only child. Arjuna lets a cataract of blood, human fat its froth.

As he fights, he cries to his sarathy, "Now I see why Yudhishtira would take just five towns to prevent this war. It is more horrible than I ever imagined. My son is dead, what will I tell his mother? How many mothers have lost their boys on this hellish field! All this killing: and for what? For one man's vanity, for Duryodhana's ravening envy! How does fate allow this?" He is quiet for a while; but the tide of arrows still flames from his bow, as if someone else was the archer. Krishna drives his horses in silence, immaculately.

Arjuna cries again, "Surely, it is better to die a beggar than kill these millions for a throne. How I hate this war! More than anyone else, Shakuni is to blame for all this murdering. He first corrupted Duryodhana. If only someone had killed him before he ever came to Hastinapura.

"Look how I wilt them, and they crumple and lie down to sleep forever. Oh, look at the blood spurt from the mouths of their wounds. How I wish I had never been born a kshatriya!"

He is quiet again, before Krishna hears him sob, "Iravan, how glad I was to see you, my son. Now I wish I had never met your mother. I would not have to bear this grief that tears my heart more painfully than any arrow." Then he roars, "Krishna, they have killed my boy! Ride at them, I will make a sea of their blood!"

As Krishna rides at the enemy, Arjuna's arrows mow down the Kaurava soldiers in a russet flash flood, glimmering in the last light of day. Bheeshma sees Arjuna raging, and comes to contain the Pandava. Meanwhile, the butchering continues everywhere. Hundreds die each moment, and by now their screams, the shouts and the roars of those who kill them have become commonplace. They who have been at war for eight days are inured to these sounds.

Bheema still strews the field with corpses, as if killing were as natural to him as drawing breath. He is dripping gore again; for, often, he leaps down from his chariot and goes among the enemy, bludgeoning them with his mace, and their blood splashes over him copiously. Then he climbs back into Visoka's chariot, and fights with bow and arrows. Ghatotkacha fights near his father, and he is more terrible than Bheema. Bhagadatta is there: in the steaming, mindless, thick of battle, somehow containing Bheema's rakshasa son. Supritika, the elephant, is disdainful of the arrows that pierce him.

Suddenly, a roar on that field eclipses every other sound. Bheema has hewn his way through the Kaurava ranks and come face to face with a knot of Duryodhana's brothers, who huddle together in terror. There are eight of them, and the sight of him exploding through the rest of the legion paralyses them. Whimpering, they stand transfixed in their chariots, and he makes short, brutal work of all eight. They die with hardly a cry; as if they are grateful he delivered them from the long fear of him that darkened their lives.

Duryodhana sees the slaughter from a way off, and his howls rock Kurukshetra. He cries out like some mythic beast that had eight more of its limbs cut away by a shining hunter. Bheeshma hears that awful sound. He sees the Kaurava army shrink from the enemy, everywhere, and he gives the signal for the conches to sound. Numb with the killing they have seen and done, the soldiers leave the field, their heads bent, neither victor nor vanquished speaking, their experience of these days beyond the ken of words.

The field they leave for the brief reprieve of night is a bizarre spectacle, with corpses sprouted everywhere. Now there seem to be more of the dead than the living on Kurukshetra; both armies, especially the Kaurava, have waned. On their way back to the camps, the men step wearily over headless trunks, and severed heads struck off so savagely that their bodies are nowhere near. Those still alive often recognize a friend's features on such a face. Jewelled arms lie with bracelets and rings glinting in the last rays of the sun. Arms hacked from their shoulders, and hands cut off at the wrist clawing the air, or clasping a sword, a javelin, a bow, as if for life itself, or salvation: these lie everywhere. Among them lie the carcasses of horses and elephants, their eyes still staring, killed in a war that has little to do with their species.

Today, not all the dead are gathered for burning. There are too many corpses, and the living are too exhausted. Finally, the wait of the jackals, hyenas and wolves, the kites, vultures and wild dogs is rewarded. They feast without favour for Pandava or Kaurava. Hideous pisachas drink from the river of blood, which resembles the very Vaitarani. Both armies have lost more men than on any previous day of the war, but once more, the day indubitably belongs to the Pandavas. Bheema, Ghatotkacha, Arjuna and Abhimanyu are its heroes. Duryodhana is forlorn again, his hopes of last night dashed. There is no celebration in the Pandava camp, either. Arjuna and his brothers mourn Iravan.

SEVENTEEN

Duryodhana's despair

On his way back to the Kaurava camp, Duryodhana sees all his dead, lying dismembered on the earth. Again and again, he sees Bheema killing his brothers. He finds Karna waiting for him in his tent, and breaks down, sobbing.

Desperately he cries to his friend, "These last three days, I have seen that monster kill twenty-four of my brothers. Their screams ring in my ears, and I have no peace. I see my mother crying for her sons. But Bheeshma has not killed even one Pandava, and I fear he doesn't mean to. Each day, we return from the war, routed again, and every night Bheeshma says the same thing to me, that my cousins are invincible. I cannot stand it any more, Karna. We must do something quickly, or we shall all be dead."

Duryodhana, of course, has no inkling of the secret Karna now carries, which has changed him so profoundly. The Kaurava believes his friend is eager to take the field against the Pandavas. He does not know these eight days have been a miraculous respite, a Godsend to Karna, and a time when he has really begun to think of the Pandavas as his brothers. Duryodhana has no clue of the secret that bisects Karna's life. He, who once longed to take the field against Arjuna, hardly dares let the thought enter his mind now, but prays that Bheeshma will save him from the exigency; though, deep inside him, he knows it is inevitable.

Karna can reveal nothing of his secret to Duryodhana; least of all, when the war is being lost so swiftly. Now, he says bravely, "I can't bear to watch you cry. There is nothing I want more than to see a smile on your lips. Don't forget I am here: to fight for you, to die for you if I must. I grieve for your brothers, my prince. What can I say to soften your pain, except that their deaths were destined? All that happens in this world is by fate: life, death, everything; and there is nothing you or I can do to change what fate has written. How I wish I could comfort you, or bring your brothers back to life! Nothing saddens me as much as to see you like this."

Karna, too, has tears in his eyes.

Duryodhana says, "Drona, Bheeshma, Kripa, Shalya, none of them fight to kill the sons of Pandu. They raze the enemy army, but that is not enough. The Pandavas are that army's soul; if the soul isn't put out, they will win. It happens every day: we come home defeated, our soldiers more terrified than ever, because they have seen their comrades die. Even our great kshatriyas are dispirited; no one believes we can win this war any more. How I wish you were on the field, Karna, how different things would have been. You wouldn't hesitate to kill Arjuna or the others."

Karna says sombrely, "Your Pitama loves his grandsons too much. Besides, I am not sure that at his age he can kill them even if he wanted to. There is one solution. Tell Bheeshma to stay away for a day or two, and I will come to fight. I will hunt just Arjuna; when I have killed him, the others' hearts will break. I will leave the field again, and your Pitama can win the rest of the war. Arjuna is the key to victory. Why do you think Krishna chose to be his sarathy, and not Yudhishtira's or Bheema's? If we can kill Arjuna, the rest will be easy."

Nothing in his voice or his face gives away what it costs Karna to make that offer. Duryodhana stares at him, for a moment, then he gets up. "I will go and speak to Pitama."

Bheeshma is waiting for him; he has been expecting his grandson. Usually so direct, Duryodhana is uncomfortable with having to tell his grandsire what he has come for. He folds his hands, then sits down near Bheeshma, but never looks into the patriarch's eyes. Bheeshma waits for him to speak.

"Pitama, there is no kshatriya on earth like you. When you took command of my army I was certain victory would be mine, and I thought it would take no more than a day or two. But we have fought eight terrible days, and my certainties were mere dreams. You haven't killed even one Pandava."

Bheeshma begins to speak, but Duryodhana holds up his hand so he may finish. "Your love for Pandu's sons is stronger than your love for me. I know you kill ten thousand soldiers every day. But that will not win the war for us, because they kill more of our men than you kill theirs. And, finally, this war will not be won or lost by the ordinary soldiers who die, but by the lords of men that do."

He lowers his voice, "Pitama, I have lost twenty-four brothers already, all killed by that beast. Weren't they your grandsons too? Were their lives cheaper than my cousins' lives, that they can die but not the Pandavas? On whose side do you fight, O Bheeshma, on theirs or mine? If you will not attack Yudhishtira and his brothers, I beg you, relinquish your command. Let Karna take the field tomorrow."

Having said what he found so hard, Duryodhana falls quiet. Bheeshma sighs. He says in his slow, sad way, "Why are you so cruel to me every day, Duryodhana? Here I am at this bloody yagna, for your sake, and the yagnapasu, the sacrificial animal, is I. And you still doubt my love for you? You wound me so casually with your accusations. Instead, why don't you face the truth? I do my best, but I cannot kill the Pandavas. Even if my heart was set on killing them, I would not be able to. Krishna is with them; the armies of Devaloka could not harm the sons of Pandu.

Duryodhana, the root of your troubles is that you do not realize who Krishna is. You think of him as the Pandavas' cousin, or as the prince of Dwaraka. You are engulfed in such darkness that you don't recognize the lights of lights when he stands before you. It is God you are fighting, poor child, the master of all things, the lord of galaxies, the king of time, the creator, sustainer and destroyer of not just us, but the worlds. He showed himself to you in Hastinapura, so you might believe; and you fell down in fear when you saw him like that. Yet, later, you chose to ignore what you saw, and accused him of performing a conjuring trick to deceive you. Ah, my son, you are so stubborn, and so afraid, that I fear you will submit to Krishna only in death. What can Karna or I, or anyone else do for you? Duryodhana, the dying and the defeat are not on Kurukshetra, but in your own heart."

Duryodhana sits very still. Bheeshma says, "Let me fight tomorrow, and watch me burn their army. I will be a fire among the dry trees of summer, and the earth shall never forget how Bheeshma fights. Now go and sleep, my child, you must be strong for battle. And let me rest as well, so I can show you in the morning how much I do love you."

Bheeshma lies down on his bed, and turns his back on Duryodhana. Mollified by his grandfather's promise, Duryodhana leaves the tent. He doesn't see the tears Bheeshma sheds: for him, for his slain brothers, for all the men who have lost their lives, and, most of all, for Duryodhana's immortal soul, plunged in darkness, its final ruin drawn near.

Later that night, another kshatriya, who has taken no part yet in the war of Kurukshetra, lies awake long after he has left Duryodhana's tent. Karna lies roiled in his bed. He does not cry for himself, that he had such a cruel burden thrust upon him: the knowledge of who he was. He weeps for Duryodhana, that his cause was a lost one, and only defeat and death would reward his struggle. Yet, Karna chooses to stay at his friend's side, even at this impossible time.

Duryodhana still believes that if one man on earth hates the Pandavas as much as he himself does, it is Karna. How can Karna confess to him that, now, his hatred has turned into a love that has wrought a miracle in his spirit? Changed the way he saw the world. How can he tell Duryodhana that now Karna loves Arjuna and his brothers more than Bheeshma does? That, as nothing else, would break his friend's heart. Karna, whose life has been a long injustice from its first moments, cannot bring himself to do the thing his body cries out to: to run away from Kurukshetra until the war is over!

No, he will stay. He will fight Arjuna, and his other brothers. He knows life will not spare him that final trial, that last ordeal, before he finds death's release.

Karna does not cry for himself, as he well might. He is so used to suffering that he feels hardly any pity for himself. He cries for Duryodhana: because, like Bheeshma and Drona, he knows Duryodhana will lose this war, and his life with it. Karna knows who Krishna is, and that victory will come inevitably to those that fought on the Avatara's side. But who can make Duryodhana see the truth? No one on earth: not even Krishna, who had revealed the shadow of his Viswarupa to the Kaurava. Duryodhana rushes headlong towards an abyss; and Karna, whose heart has been exorcised by the truth, will not abandon him. This night, like every other night of the war, Karna lies staring into death's very face. He will not allow fear to master him.

EIGHTEEN

The ninth day: the terrible patriarch

THE SUN RISES OVER THE REMAINS OF THE DEAD ON YAWNING Kurukshetra. Jackals and hyenas have picked the corpses clean. Bare bones shine by first light of day, like fossils on the bed of a dry lake. Duryodhana is full of hope again, this ninth morning of the war. He tells Dusasana, "Today we will see a long-cherished dream fulfilled. Today, my brother, our Pitama has sworn to fight as he has never fought in his life."

They have just come out into the crisp morning and, shading their eyes, gaze out across the field at the Pandava legions, already deployed. Duryodhana points to Arjuna's chariot at the heart of the enemy army. "Uttamaujas guards Arjuna's right wheel, and Yuddhamanyu the left; and, look, Arjuna himself guards Shikhandi today. They mean to make their attempt on Pitama's life. Dusasana, you must see that Shikhandi never comes near Bheeshma. That is all you must devote yourself to today."

Across the field, Arjuna says to Dhrishtadyumna, "Let Shikhandi take no part in the general fighting. I will watch him with my life: today, let him go after Bheeshma."

Bheeshma forms his legions in the sarvatobhadra vyuha, which means 'safe from every side'; and so it is, that square formation. As always, Bheeshma himself is at the head of the vyuha, and Dusasana has arranged for Kripa, Kritavarman, Shakuni, Jayadratha, Kambhoja and fifty of Duryodhana's brothers to protect the Kuru patriarch. The Trigartas form another ring around this inner one.

The ninth day: the terrible patriarch

The Pandavas form their legions into another mandala vyuha. Yudhishtira, Bheema, Nakula, Sahadeva, and Draupadi's sons are at the very front. Just behind them are Arjuna, Dhrishtadyumna, Shikhandi, Ghatotkacha and Chekitana; after these, Abhimanyu, Drupada, and the five Kekaya brothers.

Bheeshma gives the signal. Conches resound, and the two armies surge at each other. Arrows light up the morning like rays of the rising sun. Swords gleam and clash, and lances drift through the air. Screams ring out over the field, as the morning claims its first lives. Soon the killing begins in earnest.

Suddenly, the sun climbing into the sky is eclipsed by an uncanny cloud appeared from nowhere. Darkness falls on the field and, from the woods that fringe Kurukshetra, another army howls dismally: an army of jackals and wolves baying at the gloom. The underside of their wings pale, vultures wheel into the bizarre twilight. Everywhere the soldiers are terrified, and stop fighting. The sinister cloud showers down a rain of fine pebbles on the legions, and all around on the horizon, meteors fall on the earth like fantastic fireworks. Then, as abruptly as it appeared, the cloud vanishes. The howling beasts run back into the jungle, and the sky is clear and speckless again. This is the dawning of the kali yuga.

While the others stand rooted by the weird omens, Abhimanyu recovers first and charges the enemy, loosing a cloud of his own at them, of arrows. Horses, elephants and footsoldiers fall to his firestorm, and chariots explode when his incendiary shafts strike them. The omens of earth and air, and then Abhimanyu's onslaught, are too much for the Kaurava soldiers. They turn and run, when the day's fighting has barely begun.

Like his grandsire Indra, Abhimanyu shines on Kurukshetra. The jewels on his arms and chest sparkle; his bow is a blur, so it seems that weapon bent in a golden circle is a halo round his beautiful head. Drona and Kripa ride at Abhimanyu together; he beats them back with a crescendo of arrows. Aswatthama and Jayadratha attack him from two flanks, but they cannot even approach him this morning. Abhimanyu rules Kurukshetra like a resplendent Yama.

Duryodhana rides to call Alambusa from a far corner of the field: perhaps the rakshasa's powers will be of some avail against Arjuna's son. Alambusa comes to the heart of the battle. He fights with maya. But it seems that Abhimanyu has occult vision so he sees the demon clearly, even when he is invisible to everyone else. The prince's aim is unerring. Swiftly, Draupadi's sons are at Abhimanyu's side, and they, too, find the rakshasa with shafts of flames.

Roaring, Alambusa grows tall as a palm-tree in his chariot. He raises his pale sorcerer's hand above his head, and intones an evil mantra. In black tides, his maya shakti shrouds the Pandava army in an unnatural night. Abhimanyu looses a bhaskarastra over the darkling field, and light breaks across it again. His maya dispelled by the weapon of the sun, Alambusa stands revealed in his chariot. In fresh rage, Arjuna's son and his brothers attack the rakshasa, wounding him sorely. Alambusa invokes the siddhi of anima. He becomes a little homunculus, leaps out of his chariot unnoticed, and flees.

Bheeshma rides to challenge his great-grandchild. But the prince who bears both Pandava and Yadava blood in his veins is more than a match for his Pitama. Then, Arjuna is at his son's side, and they face the patriarch together. Duryodhana sounds an alarm, and fifty of his brothers surround Bheeshma. They know that neither Arjuna nor Abhimanyu will kill them, for Bheema's oath; and they fight marvellously in that certainty.

Seeing Arjuna and Abhimanyu outnumbered, three other Pandavas arrive beside them. A general battle breaks out. Satyaki confronts Acharya Kripa, who fights like a tiger today. The fleet young Yadava is too much for the old master, and, after a hot exchange, Satyaki fells Kripa in his chariot. Quick as wishing, Aswatthama is at his uncle's side, beating Satyaki back. The Vrishni recovers from the unexpected assault, and breaks Aswatthama's bow in his hands. Meanwhile, Kripa's sarathy has ridden off the field to safety.

Aswatthama seizes up another bow, and takes the fight back to Satyaki. He looses an astra that could shear the peak off a mountain. Struck squarely in his chest, Satyaki falls unconscious. In a moment, he jumps up again and fights in such fury now, that, fearing for his son's life, Drona rushes up to draw the Yadava's fire. Like Budha and Sukra battling, Satyaki and Drona duel. The Kuru Acharya covers Satyaki in a blaze of arrows: in fury that he attacked his precious son. Taken unawares by the master's ferocity, Satyaki is beaten back. In a flash Arjuna is at his side, matching his guru shaft for shaft, holding him off.

For a while, master and pupil fight as if they mean to settle a hatred they have nurtured for years. In the mandala of war, it seems Drona does not see Arjuna, his favourite sishya, before him, but only an enemy; and so, too, Arjuna no longer sees his guru, but a dangerous adversary. Their archery is a holy offering. Seeing his kshatriya so determined, Krishna exults.

From a way off, Duryodhana watches the duel with concern. He is anxious lest Dhrishtadyumna ride to help Arjuna. The encounter between guru and sishya is the converse of two sublime artists. They are like Gods speaking together about the mysteries of the universe; hardly anyone else on that field can decipher their communion. They exchange their very lives with winged shafts; soul brushes soul. Often, Drona laughs aloud in delight at a frenzied, delicate volley from Arjuna.

Once, the master flings up his arms, crying, "How you have grown, Arjuna! No one on earth could have taught you that."

Arjuna bows to Drona. Then the Gandiva hums again, its deep song. At times, Arjuna's archery is such a sacred thing there are tears in his master's eyes! This sishya is a spiritual son, who is now clearly his guru's equal, and, frequently, his superior. Drona cries, "Today I learn from you, Arjuna!"

Yet, these two also grieve that they must fight each other. Arjuna thanks fate that among the crimes he must commit on this field, killing his Acharya is not one. With reverence, the disciple attacks his master, and with transcendent elegance.

Arjuna invokes Vayu, the Wind God, and looses a vayavyastra at Drona. A towering gale sweeps across Kurukshetra, and the Kaurava soldiers are blown about like straws. His chariot caught in the eye of the storm, his horses rearing, Drona summons a sailastra. Arjuna's tempest dies in a moment.

The duel between master and pupil swells into the esoteric realm of devastras. Around them, the Trigartas run in stark fear. Meanwhile, a way off, Duryodhana and a host of his kshatriyas surround Bheeshma in a tight crescent of protection. The Pitama faces the other Pandavas. Directly before him is Yudhishtira, and the Kuru patriarch fights him most intensely. From a side, Bheema leaps down from his chariot, mace in hand, and rushes at Bheeshma with a roar. At once, Duryodhana's elephant legion, detailed to guard Bheeshma against such an attack, comes between the son of the wind and his grandsire.

Far from being put out Bheema roars louder than ever and sets about the huge beasts. Some he strikes down, even as they charge him with lowered tusks. He fells each one with a single blow of his mace, smashing their lofty temples. Others, he attacks from side and rear. At times, he even leaps up on to their necks, then, kills the warriors perched there, knocking them off disdainfully, before he beats the animals to their knees. Some with their trunks cut off by his sword, fell screeching like mortally wounded birds. Like his brother's vayavyastra, like a fell wind of his natural father, Bheema destroys Duryodhana's elephant legion. Quickly, the level field of Kurukshetra resembles a land of hillocks with the carcasses of the Kaurava tuskers, and it is beautiful!

The elephants that escape Bheema turn and crash away, trampling the soldiers of their own army. Meanwhile, even as he promised Duryodhana the previous night, Bheeshma makes his bow sing on Kurukshetra; indeed, no one has ever seen him fight as he does today. Even Drona stares. Bheeshma summons supernatural power today; he fights like the Vasu he was before this human life. He is Ganga's son again, who dammed her swirling waters with his arrows once: a life ago.

Seeing the Kuru ancient, Dhrishtadyumna calls his forces to combine against the Pitama. Shikhandi, Virata, Drupada and all the Pandavas together cover Bheeshma with a thousand shafts. These never reach him, or his horses or sarathy, not one barb. They fall around his gleaming chariot like a rain of flowers. In grave calm, Bheeshma continues his decimation of Yudhishtira's army. Bheema and Satyaki join the battle; to no avail: each moment, a hundred more Pandava soldiers die on Kurukshetra, every one killed by an arrow from Bheeshma's bow.

Dread grips the Pandava army. The bravest men run from the Kuru patriarch's cool wrath. It seems that all the other kshatriyas on the field are numb spectators to the old warrior's blood-ritual. He is so calm, and he is elemental. He has no need of his legions' insignificant prowess. It seems that, by himself, Bheeshma will wipe the Pandava army from the face of the earth.

Arjuna begins to draw his grandfather's fire. The Trigartas have returned to the field after they fled from the vayavyastra. They come frothing to challenge Arjuna, and save some face. At first, he ignores them: he is so absorbed in his duel with Drona. Then, Bheeshma cuts loose, and Arjuna sees from some way off that there is no containing him. The Pandava decides, at least, to divert the patriarch. Drona has stopped his duel with his pupil; the Acharya has become rapt watching Bheeshma. Arjuna, too, has watched his Pitama in awe. Krishna cries to him, "We must turn Bheeshma's head to us!"

Waking from his absorption, Arjuna raises the Gandiva again, as Krishna already lashes his horses towards Susharma and his legion. At the first screams of the dying Trigartas, Bheeshma turns his chariot and rushes at Arjuna. Quick as light, Yudhishtira, Nakula and Sahadeva flit between Bheeshma and their brother. The three combine to hold up their Pitama.

Duryodhana sees his grandsire's fury stemmed. More, he sees Yudhishtira and the twins kill five hundred chariot-mounted kshatriyas of his guard. The Kaurava turns to Shalya in despair. "These three will kill all our best men. You aren't shy to fight your sister's sons, are you, O Shalya?"

Shalya has no choice but to ride at Yudhishtira and the sons of Madri. Seeing that king plunge at his brothers, Bheema dashes to their side. The four Pandavas defy Shalya and his legion. Away to their right, Bheeshma has broken Arjuna's shackles; once more, he sweeps the Pandava legions before him. It seems the climbing sun fuels his wrath. Blood splashes everywhere in harsh noon light, and the screams of those Bheeshma kills are an eerie song on that field.

Krishna cries to Arjuna, "Bheeshma will kill every soldier in your army, except you five sons of Pandu. You must save those that have come to risk their lives for you. I will ride at Bheeshma, kill him now!"

But then, sorrow is upon the Pandava. He says, "How I hate to fight my blood! Of what use is the kingdom we win by slaying our kin? I would rather go to hell than live in a world worse than hell."

Krishna favours him with a glare. Arjuna says, "But it is too late to think of all that now. Ride at my Pitama, Krishna, I will do what I can."

When they see Arjuna's chariot fly to face Bheeshma, a hopeful shout goes up from the Pandava army. Arjuna's first arrow cuts down Bheeshma's banner, so it falls over him. The next clutch breaks the bow in the Kuru elder's hands. Quick as thinking, Bheeshma snatches up another. With absolute genius, Arjuna breaks that weapon, as well.

Bheeshma stands unarmed and vulnerable for a moment. At that critical instant, Arjuna's fingers waver at his bowstring. His arrow whistles harmlessly past his grandfather's ears.

In a wink, Bheeshma has another bow in his hands and fights again. Once more, he not only engages Arjuna, but kills a Pandava soldier with every other shaft; a hundred flare from his bow each moment. Arjuna's response to his relucent archery is pathetic. Krishna watches this for a while. Then, without a word, he flings his reins aside and leaps down from the chariot-head. Once more, the Sudarshana Chakra blazes over his hand, and he stalks grimly towards Bheeshma, with the battle all around fallen still.

Soldiers shrink from Krishna. His wrath is a cosmic rictus, as if the galaxies with their limitless fires twitched in anger on his blue face. Among the Pandava soldiers, a tumultuous whisper of joy flashes. "Bheeshma is slain!" they breathe among themselves, like a sea.

Bheeshma smiles radiantly at the terrible Dark One advancing on him. It seems all the killing he did on Kurukshetra was just to provoke this rage from Krishna; so he could die at the Avatara's hands. Bheeshma folds his palms together, and cries in an ecstasy to the Incarnation, "Come, Lord, kill me now! There is nothing in all the worlds I would rather have than death at your hands." He raises his bow, "I offer you a kshatriya's worship, before you kill me. The world will know that Devavrata was not only the most unfortunate man on earth, but the luckiest one, as well. For, Narayana killed him with his own hands. Come, Lord!"

He is begging Krishna. All this has taken just a moment, while Arjuna stands petrified in his chariot. Krishna raises his hand higher, the Chakra flaming over it. He takes another step forward. Then, with a cry, Arjuna falls out of his chariot. In a moment, yawned wide as a life, he flings himself at Krishna, clasping his knees. At that crucial moment, Arjuna's voice fails him. His throat is dry as deserts.

Krishna growls dreadfully. He does not look down at the warrior clinging to his legs, but tries to shake free of the Pandava. The Blue God's body glows with cold light, and strange sounds come from him, like the hissing of an unimaginable hamadryad.

Then the frantic Arjuna finds his voice, "My Lord! I beg you, do not do this. You name is as pure as Pranava; don't let this deed besmirch it. The killing I have done has darkened my mind. For a moment, I forgot who you are, and who I am. Forgive me once more. I swear I will fight, Krishna, and the greatest kshatriyas will stop to stare. I will fight in your name, for love of you. From this moment, I offer my war to you; accept it as my worship. Lord, save me from sin!"

Krishna sees the cloud of darkness lift away from his Pandava's heart. Reluctantly, he lowers his hand and the Sudarshana vanishes. Bheeshma still stands in his chariot, his palms folded. Krishna turns his back on the Kuru patriarch. His face still like thunder, he strides back to Arjuna's chariot and climbs into it. Tears in his eyes, Arjuna runs after him and climbs into his place. Krishna says no word, but only takes up the reins and cracks them over his gandharva horses.

An anguished roar breaks from Bheeshma, "Aaaah! Why have you abandoned me again?"

Bheeshma rides in fury at the Pandava soldiers. He is more awesome than before, but now Arjuna raises his Gandiva and gives him battle. They fight like Devas: wounding each other, and killing hundreds of soldiers. Bheeshma is still tameless. As if being denied death at Krishna's hands has provoked him to frenzy, he kills twice as many men as Arjuna.

After what appears to be a few moments of supreme anarchy, but is in fact some hours, and countless deaths, the sun sets. It seems he crosses the sky quickly because he cannot bear to see the killing below him, with his eyes of white fire. Numb and weary, the armies withdraw. Already, the wolves, hyenas and jackals have gathered in slavering excitement at the edge of the field, and the vultures, the kites and crows in the trees that fringe Kurukshetra: for the night's feasting.

All the talk in both camps is of Bheeshma. In the Pandava camp, there is deep gloom. If Bheeshma fought again as he had today, the war would swiftly be lost. Across the field, beyond the ravening wild dogs, wolves and all that third army of carrion-eaters, which tears at the human dead on Kurukshetra under a blooming moon, Duryodhana is exultant. His eyes shine with satisfaction, as he sits with Shakuni, Dusasana and Karna in his tent. Tonight, even Karna is pleased with what Bheeshma has done. For, it saves him from what he now fears most: having to take the field against his brothers.

Duryodhana is more than certain victory will soon be his.

NINETEEN

The last night of an age

On the night of that ninth day of the Mahabharata yuddha, during which the Pandavas have lost twice as many men as the Kauravas, stark despair seizes Yudhishtira. The Pandavas and Krishna sit conferring, and Yudhishtira is so shaken he cannot speak. His eyes full of tears, he turns repeatedly to Krishna, but not a word can he utter. It seems everything he has lived for has been snatched from him in a day: worst of all, his faith. His brothers, who have never seen him like this, are shocked, even Bheema.

At last, Yudhishtira whispers, "We will never win, not when Bheeshma fights as he does. Another two days, at most, and all our men will have perished. Krishna, do you see the jackals feasting under the moon? How horrible this war is. Hours ago, all those corpses were living men, who had mothers, fathers, wives, children and friends, and rich lives. They gave their lives so we could have a kingdom. Look at them now; and we are too exhausted even to cremate them with honour. And our Pitama killed eight out of ten who died today.

"No, not Arjuna or Bheema, not Dhrishtadyumna, Shikhandi, not all of us together can stop him. He melts our army as Agni would a pat of butter; and if he spares our lives, we will have to return to the jungle with the deaths of a million men on our conscience. What use has it been fighting this war? We should have never come back. Bheema, my brother, it is too late for revenge; too many years have elapsed between the crime and its punishment. Don't you see, we, the avengers, are being punished instead, by our own grandfather."

Yudhishtira's hands shake. His words come in a rush, as if his nerve is gone, and tears roll down his noble face. "We have fought as well as we can, for nine days that seem like nine lifetimes with all the killing we have seen and done. But Bheeshma is no sinner, and he cannot be killed. His celibacy wraps him in impenetrable armour. I have seen Arjuna's arrows glance off his skin like lotus stems. Our army is among the greatest the world has ever seen. We could vanquish Indra or Varuna; we could quell Kubera or Yama; but Bheeshma is invincible. His arrows are nagapasas that make ash mounds of living men.

"I cannot have any more deaths on my conscience. I do not want the kingdom for which we are fighting. The only way I see for us is to abandon this mad war, and go back to the peace of the jungle. As long as Bheeshma lives we will find only death and defeat on Kurukshetra; and Bheeshma is impossible to kill. Let us not deceive ourselves. Arjuna's best efforts have been in vain, and Shikhandi can go nowhere near our Pitama. A king must care for his men. When defeat is certain, he must not sacrifice them for his vanity, but retreat.

"Krishna, I have caused my brothers so much misery. I had hoped that, because dharma and you are on our side, I could give them at least victory. They suffered fourteen years of exile for my foolishness. And now they must endure shameful defeat and, perhaps, death on this vile field."

Just then, the howling of some sated jackals floats in on the night breeze, and Yudhishtira shivers. "Only you can save us, Krishna! You must find a way, or I will leave this war and go back to the forest. Bheeshma must die, or everything is lost."

He falls as quiet as the vast graveyard outside. After a moment's silence—and none of the others has a word to say—Krishna says, "Your brothers are full of love for their Pitama, and will not kill Bheeshma. Not I: tomorrow, under Duryodhana's eyes, I will finish the patriarch, and victory will be yours. Your enemies are mine, Yudhishtira, and this war is mine as well. And this brother of yours, this Arjuna: for him I would cut my body in pieces to feed the jackals outside, if he asks me to. And I know that he, too, would die for me.

"If you remember, before the war began Arjuna sent a brave message with Uluka to his Pitama. He swore before all the kings who are with us that he would kill Bheeshma. I love Arjuna more than he understands, and I will not let him abjure himself. I will kill Bheeshma for him, and it won't be hard for me."

All eyes turn to Arjuna. Krishna continues, "Of course, I do not say that Arjuna cannot kill Bheeshma himself. Far from it; for we are speaking of Indra's son, who humbled his father in battle. For such a man killing Bheeshma cannot be very hard. But a kshatriya must die to pity and kindness before he can find perfection; and perfection is a hard thing to find. It isn't that Arjuna is not archer enough to kill Bheeshma, but his heart is soft; not that he cannot kill his Pitama, but he will not. He cannot find the detachment within himself, the pure spirit of vairagya.

"Indeed, all of you are too kind, too good, to be killers cold enough to cut down your grandfather. But not I, Yudhishtira; such goodness doesn't bind me. I am the warrior for you. I will do what your kind hearts don't permit you to. The bonds of this earth, its thongs of attachment, do not hold me. I am indifferent to joy and grief, good and evil, pain and pleasure. I make no difference between one enemy and another. Why, I make no difference, if you knew it, between my friend and my enemy. The world seems alike and one to me. Only my dharma matters, for what I have been born. Blame and praise are nothing to me; I am beyond the taint of these earthly things. No sin clings to me, Yudhishtira, I am the warrior for you. Leave Bheeshma to me; I will kill him tomorrow. Sleep in peace, you shall win this war."

Yudhishtira takes the Dark One's hand, and says, "Do you have to tell me you can kill Bheeshma? Krishna, you speak as if I don't know who you are. You are the beginning and the end of this world; you are the seed of the universe. Without you, there would be no darkness or light, no sun, moon or stars. What is Bheeshma, what are a thousand Bheeshmas, before you? Krishna, you are not just Arjuna's sarathy, but the sarathy of us all: the one who shows our spirits the way to light. I have no words to tell you how grateful I am that you have taken our cause for your own. But I will not allow you to perjure yourself, and have the world say ever after that Krishna was a liar.

"You swore to Duryodhana that you would take no part in the fighting, that you would bear no arms, shed no blood by your own hand. I will not allow you to break your sacred word; not if it costs us this war, not if it costs us our lives. Why, the very earth will crumble into dust if Krishna breaks his word. No, we must find another way to kill Bheeshma."

Krishna smiles to hear the new determination in Yudhishtira's voice. After a moment, the Pandava says, "I have a thought. On the first day of the war, when I went to Pitama for his blessing, he said to me that he was fighting only because he was obliged to. He said his heart lay with us; somehow, even after these nine days, I still believe him. I know of only one way in which we can kill Bheeshma. I will go to him tonight, and ask him how he can be killed." He turns to Krishna, "If you think it is the right thing to do, I will go now."

The others seem a little bewildered by the extraordinary idea. But Krishna says at once, "Bheeshma loves you and, if you ask him earnestly, how will he not answer you? Who better than the one you hunt to tell you how he can be hunted? Come, let us go at once."

It is past midnight, and Kurukshetra is perfectly still. The wolves and jackals, hyenas and vultures, all the scavengers have finished feeding and returned to the woods. The bones they have cleaned glisten in the setting moon, as the Pandavas and Krishna thread their cautious way past skeletons, slicks of blood, and lengths of intestine the carrion-eaters have disdained; they come to the sleeping Kaurava camp. No guards stir, none are posted. Only a sea of breathing ruffles the silence of the night. Quietly, the Pandavas steal into Bheeshma's tent.

He has not slept. He says in the dark, "Duryodhana, is that you?"

Yudhishtira answers, "No, Pitama. It is I, Yudhishtira, my brothers, and Krishna."

With a cry, Bheeshma rises and lights a lamp. When the Pandavas prostrate themselves before him, he raises them up and embraces them. He takes Krishna's hand, "Welcome, my Lord! Come, there are places for all of you to sit, for Yudhishtira, Bheema, and you, Arjuna, and my handsome Nakula. Wise boy Sahadeva, come sit beside me on the bed. How are you, my children? How happy you have made an old man by coming to see him."

His eyes shine with tears. There is no trace here, any more, of the dauntless enemy they have faced the past nine days on the field; but just their doting grandfather, again, stroking their faces in love, overjoyed that they have come to see him. A pang of guilt clutches at Yudhishtira and, seeing it on his face, Krishna smiles: how hard it will be to ask the question that has brought them here!

Bheeshma says, "Arjuna, you don't know how proud you have made me. There is no archer like you on earth, and perhaps even in heaven. And Abhimanyu: what a revelation that child has been! There are times when I think he is greater than you are, or soon will be. You are a fortunate father, my child."

Then he stops himself. He sees how they fidget, and do not look at him. He says, "But tell me, what brings you here at this hour? You have come unarmed. Is there anything I can do for you?"

A lump in his throat, Yudhishtira says, "We have come to you for advice. We have come not to the Senapati of the Kaurava legions, but to our Pitama, to whom we have always turned in a crisis."

"Tell me, child."

"Before the war began, you said to me that victory would certainly be ours: because ours was the cause of dharma, and Krishna was with us. But there is one kshatriya among our enemy whom we cannot face. As long as he fights us, we can never hope to win this war. Each morning, he rides out in his silver chariot and, bending his bow in a circle, spills our soldiers' blood in scarlet streams. In two days more, three at most, he will have killed all our men. Yet, he is the very one who swore to me I would win the war: Pitama, that kshatriya is you."

Bheeshma says with a smile, "And what have you come to ask me, child? Not to abandon the war, I hope, this war I am so sick of."

"I have come to ask you something that fills me with shame."

"Between a grandfather and his grandson there should be nothing like that. You can ask me anything, and I will answer truthfully. What else am I here for? Don't feel ashamed; ask me, and if it is in my power to satisfy you, I will."

Bheeshma strokes Yudhishtira's head with a gnarled hand. Yudhishtira braces himself, and says, "My lord, unless you die we cannot win our war. I have come to ask how we can kill you." Then, his heart breaking, "Oh, Pitama, I must see you dead, because I must win this monstrous dharma yuddha. *Tell me how we can kill you!*"

Yudhishtira covers his face with his hands, and piteous sobbing shakes him. Bheeshma still strokes his head, tenderly. He says, "I fear you are right, my son. If you do not kill me, you cannot win the war. So kill me you must, and quickly."

Yudhishtira sobs, "I can't bear to think of you dead! Is there no other way? Pitama, we love you as part of ourselves."

Bheeshma says serenely, "There is no other way. I wish I could tell you the war would claim me in its course; that one day, soon, I will die. Alas, a lifetime of celibacy confers invincibility or something near it. Not Indra could kill me. Krishna here, yes; he can kill me, but he will have to break his vow. That he must never do; or the sun, the moon, all the stars and this earth would cease to be."

Yudhishtira says wonderingly, "You sound as if you want to die."

"Of course I want to die! Who in my place would not? I have seen the ruin of the house I have loved and nurtured all my life. I have seen so many generations perish, and now I have seen the House of Kuru divided in war against itself, cousin against cousin. The kali yuga is upon the world. I feel its hot breath, and I am still alive. I hate my life, every moment of it is poison to me. My heart is broken, many times over, and I long for nothing except death. Don't you see, Yudhishtira, my life is an endless torment, and has been for a long time? The world as I knew it, the world of honour and faith, the earth of dharma, has long since passed away. Twice Krishna stood before me with his Sudarshana Chakra, and I begged him to kill me. Both times, he turned away.

"But tonight, I am so glad you have come to ask how you can kill me. My son, you feel ashamed you have come, and guilty. But death will be sweet release for me, from a tortured life I am deeply tired of."

They listen to him, amazed; only Krishna smiles slightly. Bheeshma sighs, and goes on, "I curse my celibacy and the strength it gives me! How I loathe the very thing for which other kshatriyas envy me. But listen, children, besides Krishna there is someone else who has the power to kill me. Arjuna."

Tears start in Arjuna's eyes. Bheeshma wipes them with his fingers. "Why do you cry, child? You say you love me. If you truly love me, you should be glad to set me free me from the dark bondage of this life. Mortal life is cruel; a punishment for old sins we have committed and forgotten. Death is a joyful liberation. I beg you, Arjuna, kill me tomorrow, and deliver me to peace. I have carried life's burden for too long. I cannot bear it any more."

Arjuna comes into his grandfather's arms, and sobs like a child. Bheeshma takes the Pandava onto his lap, as he used to when Arjuna was a boy! He says, "Even you cannot kill me while I am fighting, Arjuna; but if I lay down my weapons, then, yes, you can end my miserable life. In dharma, I cannot allow you to kill me, unresisting, which I would do except for the solemn word I have given Duryodhana. Yet, there is a way to make me put down my bow on the field. In your army, is a kshatriya born just to kill me. He has crossed two lives to come as my death. Set Shikhandi before you, and I will not fight him: because he was once a woman."

Dim mists fill his old eyes, sad memories. A wistful smile touches Bheeshma's lips. "Amba was the daughter of the king of Kasi. I abducted her sisters and her on the day of their swayamvara. Ambika and Ambalika became your grandmothers, but Amba wanted me to marry her. And that could never be, because of my vow."

Bheeshma tells them about Amba's trials. He tells them about Siva's boon: and how she burnt herself alive to be born as Drupada's son. Like the rest of the world, the Pandavas have heard something of Shikhandi's vow. Only now do they learn the whole truth. Bheeshma says, "Shikhandi remembers his last birth perfectly; so strong was Amba's love, and, when it was thwarted, her thirst for revenge. Now, she will come before me on Kurukshetra to be my deliverer. Only she has ever plumbed my heart, and seen all that I have kept locked away in it."

Yudhishtira and his brothers cannot take their eyes from Bheeshma's crevassed face, for the change they see there when he speaks of Amba. Soft light is in his eyes, and the great Kuru goes on, slowly, "Yes, Amba hates me and loves me at the same time; after all these years, the two are hardly apart. Only the passion remains. Love and hate are different faces of the same obsession. I know beyond doubt, that without her I shall be chained to this unbearable life forever. Is it her hatred or her love that brings her inexorably to me?" He smiles again. "I could not tell."

He pauses, then says briskly once more, "Yes, Arjuna, that is the only way you can kill me. Set Shikhandi before you, when you attack me. I will not see Drupada's son before me, but Kasi Raja's daughter, who once touched my spirit as no one else ever has. She has survived every test of time, to become my death. How will I shoot arrows at a woman who has spent two lives thinking of me? How will I raise my bow against any woman? When I put down my weapon, Arjuna, you can kill me. You must!"

He squeezes Arjuna's hand, insisting. He turns to Krishna and says, "My Lord, at that moment you must not allow him to hesitate." There can be no doubt he longs to die. Bheeshma smiles at them again, "And when I am dead, victory will not elude you. Tonight, you have made an old man happy. I will sleep tonight, as I have not done for many years. My precious, noble children, your Pitama thanks you with all his heart."

They see he is crying in relief. Chastened by his tears, they kneel at his feet for his blessing. He lifts them up, one by one, embraces them, kisses them repeatedly, all of them sobbing.

Bheeshma says, "You cry in sorrow, and I for joy. Dry your eyes, and go back to your camp. Sleep in calm tonight, knowing tomorrow will be the dawn of your victory. Say nothing more; go now, leave me with this joy."

Heads bent, they leave his tent. As they go, they see him enveloped in light. All his cares seem to have fallen away from him; an unearthly smile is on his lips, and his eyes shine. He sits there like a God who visited this world briefly and is now ready to return to his true and timeless home. Krishna is the last one out. He turns at the tent-flap, "Be joyful for ever more. You will never be born again into this world of sorrow. And you will be remembered as the greatest Kuru ever."

The Dark One raises his hand in a blessing, and Bheeshma feels a tide of grace surge in his heart. He cries, "My Lord!" but Krishna has gone.

Still later, in the final yaama of the night, Arjuna comes to Krishna's tent. He sits beside him and takes his hand. Krishna sees he is crying. Arjuna says in a strangled voice, "He is my Pitama, who has always loved me. The man I am meant to kill tomorrow is my grandfather. How can I do this, Krishna?"

He sobs like the boy who once sat in his grandfather's lap. Krishna holds Arjuna against him. Gently, but with complete firmness, he says, "You have to, Arjuna. You are a kshatriya. It is your dharma to win this war for your brothers, for yourself, for Draupadi and your sons. Bheeshma's death is written at your hands, and no power on earth can change that. Long ago, before you were born, why, before he was born, it was written that Bheeshma would die by his Arjuna's arrows. However you torment yourself with guilt tonight, tomorrow you will kill him. What is fated will happen; not you, not I, can change that.

"Arjuna, you are not killing him from hatred. You are not killing your Pitama, but the enemy's Senapati. You are killing him because if you do not you will lose this war, and evil will rule the earth. Evil will sit upon your ancestors' throne, and enslave all the generations to come. Be certain of that: either Yudhishtira or Duryodhana will inherit the throne of this world, not both of them. Bheeshma stands in the way of Yudhishtira ruling the earth in peace and dharma. If you do not kill him—and remember he longs to die—Duryodhana will win this war. Then, the coming age will be plunged in a sinister night, the rule of hell. There is more at stake here than your love for your grandfather. You must act without attachment; it is your dharma. The future of the world is in Arjuna's hands. He cannot sacrifice it, not for love of his Pitama."

By the power of the Avatara, Arjuna has a glimpse of what is truly at stake on Kurukshetra, field of dharma. It shatters his pity in a moment, with terror. Trembling with the fleeting vision, Arjuna kneels before Krishna in the dark. His throat parched, his hair standing on end, he breathes, "My Lord! I will do it. I swear I will kill Bheeshma."

TWENTY

The tenth morning

On THE TENTH MORNING OF THE WAR, FOR THE FIRST TIME IN YEARS Bheeshma wakes after a restful night. It seems to him that tranquillity suffuses the world, and the rising sun is more brilliant, more resonant, today. The very air seems full of deep enchantment. Bheeshma worships the saffron star, and is enfolded in peace. The earth wells with grace. Outside, the birds sing just for him; the trees speak to him, heart to heart. He knows they have always been full of this ecstatic speech: only, he had never heard it before. The golden Saraswati flows songs of fire, psalms of heaven. The earth is transformed around him, and Bheeshma knows Krishna has blessed him. There are secret worlds hidden in the morning, calling him irresistibly. Intangible, holy waters of life purify him for the ceremony of his last day on earth: the ritual of his death.

His heart soaring as never before, Bheeshma deploys his legions on Kurukshetra. Across the field of fate, Arjuna has come out, with Krishna beside him. A vast sense of destiny fills the Pandava also. There is no doubt left in Arjuna's mind what he must do. Sorrow sits on his heart like sacrament, freeing him from fear.

Arjuna says to Krishna, "I will set Shikhandi at the head of our army, and shield him from the arrows of the enemy. Let what is written in the stars be fulfilled."

Just then, another slight figure appears beside them. Arjuna starts at Shikhandi's appearance this morning. That prince wears armour, and carries his bow in his hand. But his body and his face have changed; soft curves swell beneath the mail, at breast and hip. Most of all, his black eyes have changed. It is hardly a man who stands there, but a strange and lovely woman, her every limb quivering in anticipation of what she will do today. The expression on Shikhandi's face is so disturbing that Arjuna cannot look at him. Tensely, the Panchala prince stands beside them.

They set him at the head of the Pandava army. Yudhishtira forms his legions into the most sacred vyuha of all: the Deva vyuha, the phalanx of the Gods. Just behind Shikhandi, at his chariot-wheels, are Arjuna and Bheema. Directly behind him are Abhimanyu and Draupadi's sons. Satyaki and Dhrishtadyumna flank the Pandavaputras; behind them, are Yudhishtira, Nakula and Sahadeva. These kshatriyas form the heart of the vyuha. They will ride just against Bheeshma and those that guard him. Virata and Drupada lead the rest of the Pandava forces, with the Kekayas, Ghatotkacha and Dhrishtaketu.

Across the field, the Kauravas form their legions in the ancient Asura vyuha. Bheeshma leads the army. Drona is at his side, with Duryodhana and his brothers. Seeing the finest Pandava warriors all concentrated at the core of their legions, seeing Shikhandi before all the rest, Aswatthama, Bhagadatta, Kritavarman and Kripa also ring Bheeshma round today, knowing the Pandavas mean to attack the patriarch. Around them are Shakuni, the Kambhoja king and Susharma's Trigartas. Bheeshma is radiant on the field of Kurukshetra; he is like an immortal.

The conches announce the battle, and yet again, the armies run at each other, shaking the sky with their roaring. This morning, Bheeshma is more terrible, and fluent, than ever. Duryodhana exults: victory will be his. For the Pandavas, Nakula fights resplendently today, and Satyaki and Sahadeva beside him. Duryodhana wonders that his Pitama has the appearance of a youth of twenty this morning! How bright he seems, how quicksilver is his archery. All the lines of care seem to have vanished from his face, as he cuts the enemy down as he likes. Duryodhana thinks his grandfather is excited because he also scents victory.

Then, Shikhandi rides at Bheeshma and brings him up with an effulgent volley. In a ringing woman's voice, that turns the other Kauravas' heads, Drupada's strange son cries, "Fight me now, Devavrata! I have waited two lives for this day."

Bheeshma snorts at him, "You may have a man's body today, but I know who you are. I will not fight a woman!"

He begins to ride away. Shrilly, Shikhandi cries, "They say you are the greatest kshatriya of all! I know you fought your guru Bhargava to spurn Amba's love. But her love has come to Kurukshetra to bring death to you. Fight me, Bheeshma! I will kill you today."

He strikes Bheeshma with five thought-like arrows, sharp and sweet as Kamadeva's flower shafts of love. Bheeshma growls in pain like a lion; but he will not raise his bow to fight back. Swift as Shikhandi's arrows, the other Kauravas are at the patriarch's side, and in front of him. Arjuna cries to Shikhandi, "Ride him down, Shikhandi, we are all with you!"

Abhimanyu, Dhrishtadyumna, Yudhishtira, Bheema, Nakula, Sahadeva, Satyaki, Ghatotkacha and the Kekayas ring Shikhandi round, and answer the Kaurava fire on him, ferociously. Duryodhana says to Dusasana, "They are all after the Pitama. We must keep him safe from Shikhandi at any cost. Let that be the only mission of all our kshatriyas."

He rides to Bheeshma's side and cries, "Look how Arjuna and Abhimanyu, Bheema, Nakula and Sahadeva cut our men down without mercy. I beg you, kill the Pandavas today, and let this ghastly war end. Kill them, Pitama, and save a million lives!"

Bheeshma gives him a look that is beyond contempt. He roars, "I will not kill the Pandavas! Even if I wanted to, I could not kill them. Arjuna can kill me, but not I, him. Can't you see, blind child, who Arjuna's sarathy is? Can anyone on earth, in heaven or hell, kill him, when Krishna drives his chariot? I swore to you that I would kill ten thousand men every day I fought. I reckon, Duryodhana, I have killed twice that number, and today I will discharge what remains of my debt to your father. Then, perhaps, I will be free to die."

Fear starts in Duryodhana's eyes. Before he can speak, Bheeshma whirls away at the Pandava army again. He kills a hundred men; then Dhrishtadyumna and Abhimanyu attack him, and, soon, Nakula, Sahadeva, Yudhishtira and Kuntibhoja. Aswatthama, Drona, Kripa and some of Duryodhana's brothers ride between the patriarch and the Pandava heroes. Bhoorisravas sets himself stubbornly between Bheema and Bheeshma. Chitrasena fights Chekitana, Kritavarman covers Dhrishtadyumna with a rash of silver arrows. Vikarna faces Nakula; Aswatthama attacks Drupada and Virata, at once. Drona fights Yudhishtira; Arjuna and Dusasana duel. And all around these warriors, their armies battle like two seas trying to drown each other in blood.

Rishyasringa's son Alambusa faces the brilliant Satyaki. The rakshasa uses maya, so Satyaki must summon astras against him, which light up the demon's body when he makes himself invisible. Invoking the devastras drains Satyaki, and slows his fabulous archery. Still, he begins to prevail over the tiring rakshasa. Seeing Alambusa in danger, Duryodhana sends Bhagadatta to help him, "Satyaki fights like a hundred men. Kill him today, and victory shall be ours!"

Bhagadatta comes on the looming Supritika, and the Pandava soldiers run from him. Trampling a hundred men, the elephant charges Satyaki. From the beast's white back, its demon warrior, his fangs gleaming, covers the Yadava in a cloud of arrows and javelins that glow like strips of the sun and the moon. Satyaki is quick as thoughts, powerful as a Deva, and he fights back resolutely. Yet, being at a height, Bhagadatta has the advantage; Satyaki has to shoot up at the asura, often with the sun in his eyes.

Eagle-eyed Duryodhana misses nothing on the field. He sees Bhagadatta gaining over Satyaki, and sensing a chance to kill one great Pandava warrior, he roars at the crack legion that always surrounds him, "Ride at Satyaki! He is tired and alone, he can be killed."

The arrival of those kshatriyas does not cow the young Yadava. Rather, their arrows, some of which find their marks, make him fight more radiantly than ever. Shining with courage, Satyaki beats them all back. He puts Bhagadatta to flight.

Another duel rages between Arjuna and Dusasana*, and soldiers around them stop to stare; some die as they stand absorbed. Abhimanyu and the Kambhoja king fight like two great winds trying to still each other. But one of the most enthralling contentions of the day is the one between Sahadeva and his old master, Kripa. Today, slowly, his sage pupil forces his Acharya back.

Aswatthama and Drona fight side by side. Above all the roaring and screaming around them, the father says to his son, "Do you see the omens of earth and sky? They all cry out that some calamity stalks our army. Look how Arjuna manoeuvers Shikhandi, to inveigle Drupada's prince between himself and Bheeshma. My mouth is parched and my body shivers. The kali yuga enters the world through the portal of this

---

* Dusasana is often shown as fighting at the head of a ferocious legion of mlecchas.

field! Bheema lurks near Shikhandi and Arjuna, and I fear for Bheeshma's life."

He sees another Pandava cut his way towards Bheeshma, and then another. Drona draws a sharp breath. "Fly to the Pitama! Go like the wind, Aswatthama. Don't think of your own life, Bheeshma must be guarded at any cost. Look! They form a ring around him, and hem him in from every side. Satyaki, Abhimanyu, Dhrishtadyumna, Bheema, Sahadeva and Nakula, too. Fly Aswatthama! Or they will kill him."

Aswatthama streaks forward in his chariot at his father's word.

TWENTY-ONE

The bed of arrows

SOME FINAL RESISTANCE TO DEATH IN BHEESHMA GIVES WAY. IT IS as if he has cleared the last shred of debt he owes Duryodhana and his blind father in Hastinapura. He feels a pure spring of peace gush within him again. There is light everywhere. The war seems like a child's distant, comical game. He feels blissful eternity brush his cheek. A beatific smile lights Bheeshma's face, with the miracle beginning in his spirit. He sees Krishna at Arjuna's chariot-head, smiling back at him in fathomless mystery and tenderness. For an interminable moment, the Blue One is all he sees.

Around him, the Kaurava warriors swarm, Aswatthama and a hundred others, determined to guard him with their lives. Sublime laughter fills Bheeshma: how amusing it is that they are so desperate to save his life, when he is as eager to die. Once more, he feels the nearness of other worlds, calling him inevitably. Bheeshma cries to Yudhishtira, "I am ready to go, my child. Come, free me!"

In the sweetest dream, he raises his bow and fights again. Thus he would spend his final moments; thus, he would die. Astonished Kaurava soldiers think they had imagined what he said to Yudhishtira. For here he is, fighting like before.

Yudhishtira cries grimly to Arjuna, "Let Shikhandi ride at Bheeshma!"

Aswatthama, Susharma and his brothers, Shalya, Dhritarashtra's sons, Drona and Kripa, and a score of other Kaurava warriors set themselves between Bheeshma and the Pandavas. Arjuna rides at them, his arrows a river in the air. Hearing Yudhishtira's call, Bheema flies at Bheeshma

The bed of arrows

from another side; so do Satyaki, Dhrishtadyumna and Abhimanyu. The Kaurava warriors are beaten back. Bheeshma stands his ground and the Pandavas ride at him.

Suddenly, Dhrishtadyumna, Satyaki, Abhimanyu and Bheema are between Bheeshma and his protectors, holding the Kauravas away. Krishna cries, "The moment is here! Shikhandi, ride before us."

In a trance, sensing the moment Amba has waited so long for, Shikhandi flies at Bheeshma. Krishna's chariot is perfectly positioned, a hand's width behind Shikhandi's. Yudhishtira, Nakula and Sahadeva fly at their Pitama, their eyes terrible, and their arrows. His grandsons surround the Kuru patriarch; Shikhandi and Arjuna face him.

Bheeshma sees the noble Yudhishtira, who was prepared to take five towns to prevent this war. He sees Bheema, made older by the years of exile, the sinews of the wind standing taut in his great body. He sees the motherless princes, Nakula and Sahadeva. In his mind, he sees Kunti, her eyes brimming. He sees the day, fourteen years ago, when the sacrosanct sabha of Hastinapura was desecrated. He sees Draupadi before him again, sobbing in wretchedness. He hears her cry to him, 'Pitama! You are the eldest in this sabha. How can you let this happen? Won't you say anything to protect me?'

A sob wracks Bheeshma. He sees Arjuna and dark Krishna. His mind a storm, the mighty Kuru thinks, 'Ah, I could kill all these young men except that Krishna watches over them. But what am I thinking? I have done enough killing for this life and ten more. My debts are paid. I will not spill another drop of blood. Enough, Devavrata, enough!'

In the echoing silence, the Pandavas move closer. Shikhandi glides closer. Vivid memories sweep Bheeshma's mind. At the heart of these final moments, he sees his father Shantanu before him. He sees him on the day he took his oath. Shantanu says, 'I grant you a boon, my son. You will die only when you will it yourself.'

That was it! He had forgotten. He would die only when he called his death to him. He sees Amba in Shikhandi's chariot, lovely and young, as she was on the day he took her from her swayamvara in her father's house. She says to him again, smiling so strangely, 'You took me by my right hand. You are my husband. Make me your wife, Devavrata.'

A cry breaks from Bheeshma. He says in an ecstasy, 'I forgot my secret over the years. I can die when I please. I will die now, this very moment.'

There are subtle voices everywhere, speaking from the sky and within his heart, unearthly voices. They say, 'Your time has come, Devavrata.'

Bheeshma hears another voice, the tenderest of all. He hears his mother's river-voice calling him, 'Come, my son, come to me. You are so tired, poor child. Your body burns with the burden of the years. Set the burden down. Let me wash you in my waters of light. Let me heal you, Devavrata; come to me, my son.'

So far, the Pandavas' arrows glance off Bheeshma like flowers. Krishna watches his face intently. The Dark One sees the moment has arrived. He cries to the waiting, trembling Shikhandi, "Your time is here, Amba. Kill him now!"

Shikhandi cries out, long and loud, a woman's thin roar, and plunges at Bheeshma. In his chariot, Bheeshma throws down his bow and folds his hands to Shikhandi. A hush deep as the sky falls on Kurukshetra. From five sides, five grandsons ride at their Pitama, and once his bow is down, once he has decided to die, their arrows pierce him. Still, he stands like a rock before their onslaught. Everywhere across Kurukshetra the fighting stops. Only Amba's frenzied screams break the silence; and from the depths of the Kaurava army, Duryodhana's desperate cries.

Bheeshma stands, pierced but unharmed, invincible to all the shafts with which they have shot him so far. But one Pandava has yet to shoot at his Pitama. Arjuna still hesitates. Then, Krishna roars at him in the huge silence, "Kill him, Arjuna, or the war is lost!"

At the critical moment, Arjuna cannot resist that command. His eyes bright with tears, he raises the Gandiva. With a heartbroken cry, Arjuna looses his first arrow at his grandfather. Even Shikhandi is quiet. The silence is broken by the hum of Arjuna's arrow, and the soft noise it makes when it crashes into Bheeshma's body: the sound of skin and flesh being ruptured, of bones giving way, of blood spurting, all in an instant. Bheeshma roars.

Dusasana has dodged past Satyaki and Abhimanyu, to be at his grandfather's side. Such a smile lights Bheeshma's face. He shines like a lamp of heaven on that field, when Arjuna's arrow strikes him. He cries to Dusasana, "That was not Shikhandi's arrow. It was Arjuna's!"

Another shaft from the Gandiva smashes into his chest, drawing a font of blood. Bheeshma, the kshatriya, cannot help himself. He seizes a javelin and casts it at Arjuna like a bolt of light. Arjuna cuts it down.

Another arrow takes his grandsire in his stomach, flinging him back against his flagstaff. Bheeshma cries out again, in agony, in joy.

"Yes! These are Arjuna's arrows. How powerful he is, stronger than I ever was. Aaahh!"

Three more shafts shatter his chest. The other Pandavas and Shikhandi shoot at him again, from every side, their barbs more telling, now that Arjuna has broken him. Bheeshma staggers in his chariot, hardly an inch of space left on his body where no arrow protrudes. Time assumes an extraordinary aspect on the field of war, when his grandsons cut their Pitama down. Each shaft with which Arjuna strikes his grandfather seems to age the day by an hour: as if the sun fled from this slaying. Shaking with grief, but his hands steady as if they belonged to someone else, and his aim unerring, Arjuna strikes Bheeshma with five more arrows, burning astras that could consume legions. They light up Kurukshetra like five suns. They flash into the Kuru patriarch's breast and light him up like a God being worshipped with lamps.

His eyes never leaving Krishna's blue face, Bheeshma falls out of his chariot with a sigh. So many shafts have pierced him that he falls not on to the earth, but on a bed of arrows! Some are longer than others and, with the weight of his body, they pierce him right through, so their points break out of his chest; blood from a hundred wounds forms a sacral pool under him. Yet, he lies in uncanny contentment, having set down his intolerable burden. His face shows no sign of the pain he is in; instead, the smile still creases it. A fine lambency enfolds his body, torn by his grandsons' arrows, ruined by Arjuna's virile arrows.

From the Kaurava soldiers the most dreadful lament rises, a great scream, as if the earth cried out at the fall of Devavrata: a cry to shake the Devas in their heaven. A shower of rain falls on Kurukshetra. Bheeshma sees stern figures of light in the twilight sky; he hears divine voices all around him. The voices speak to one another. "The son of Ganga is the greatest of men. How has he fallen during the dakshinayana, when the sun moves south? This is not an auspicious time to die."

A pale flight of birds lights the dim sky. A flock of luminous swans flies down to the fallen patriarch. Ganga sent the rishis who live in dhyana beside the Manasarovara to her dying son, and they have come as swans.

Bheeshma says in a whisper, "Devavrata has fallen, but he is not dead. My spirit will stay in this body until the sun resumes his northern course. Tell my mother I must not die before uttarayana, if I am to be who I was before."

The swans rise away from the earth with his message. The soldiers watch them, until they vanish in the deepening night. Again, Kurukshetra echoes with bitter wailing. Duryodhana's brothers are afraid now; they sob like children. Some of the Kauravas faint at the sight of Bheeshma like that. Panic rips through the Kaurava army, while the Pandava soldiers shout their jubilation.

Bheeshma lies with his eyes shut, his head lolling back. Near him stands Duryodhana, stricken.

When the patriarch fell, Dusasana roared in shock, turned his chariot and dashed away from the field in terror. He met Drona riding towards the alarm.

Drona shouted, "What is it, Dusasana? What is the outcry about?"

Dusasana panted, "Pitama has fallen!"

Drona keeled over. Some men had to rush back to the camp to fetch water, and salts, to revive the Acharya. When Drona awakes, the first command he gives is to sound the conches to stop the fighting. Like sleepwalkers, the Kaurava soldiers move slowly back to their camp. One by one, the kshatriyas from both sides begin to arrive at Bheeshma's side. They come divested of armour and weapons: to pay homage. He lies there on his bed of arrows, like Brahma surrounded by the Devas. Kauravas and Pandavas alike weep, but not Duryodhana.

Daylight fades swiftly from the world, and torches are lit around the patriarch. His body still glows with its own lustre. His voice low and hoarse, Bheeshma says, "My head hangs loose, I need a pillow."

At once, a score of men run to the camps, and fetch the softest silk pillows and bolsters. The patriarch turns his face from them in disgust. "These are fit for sleeping on at home. I am a kshatriya fallen on the battlefield. Arjuna, give me a pillow for a warrior's head."

Arjuna raises the Gandiva in the gloom. Three arrows flash down into the earth behind Bheeshma. Arjuna kneels beside his Pitama, gently lifts his head and sets it on those shafts. Bheeshma sighs, "This is a pillow for a kshatriya."

His breath comes hard. He shuts his eyes, and falls silent. After some moments, he flutters them open again. He beckons to the princes to come nearer. Bheeshma says, "I will wait for uttarayana, before my life leaves my body, like a friend leaving his dearest friend. Have a ditch dug around me, so I can worship the sun, undisturbed by the scavengers, until Surya Deva returns to his northern course."

Duryodhana has called his royal physicians to attend to the fallen patriarch. They have come to remove the arrows from his body, and smear his wounds with potent herbs. Bheeshma sees them standing at his side. He sees Duryodhana beside them, speechless for once. Bheeshma says, "Reward them for coming, my child, and send them away. I have no need of physicians. I have fallen as a kshatriya should, and here I am on a bed of arrows, which is also as it should be. These shafts are sacred to me. They must remain in my body, and be burnt with it when I am dead."

The physicians are sent away. Bheeshma is tired, and shuts his eyes again*. His breath heaves, shallow and rasping. He must rest if he is to live to see the sun turn north again. Night advances and, one by one, the kings and warriors return to their tents. By flickering lamplight, Duryodhana keeps a lone vigil near his grandfather. The ancient kshatriya seems to drift away, at times, and his breath is low. Then he opens his eyes, and *stares* at the moon and stars above.

Duryodhana sees his Pitama in intolerable pain, which he fears will force his spirit from his body. The Kaurava sits frozen in the night, unable even to cry for the tumult of grief he feels. Then, Bheeshma says through bloody lips, "Water! Duryodhana, I am parched with thirst."

Duryodhana rushes away, and brings sweet water, and syrups and wines that were his grandsire's favorites. When he kneels to offer them to Bheeshma, the old man says, "No. None of these will quench the thirst that burns me. Send for Arjuna, only he can give me the water I crave."

Arjuna comes running when he gets word. In agony now, but his face still bright, Bheeshma manages to smile at him. Arjuna kneels beside

---

* Ganguli says that maidens by thousands gently showered sandalwood powder, fried rice grains and soft flowers over Bheeshma. Also, countless women, old men and children flock to see him on his bed of arrows.

him. Bheeshma whispers, "Water, my child, only you can give me the water I want."

Arjuna runs back to his tent for the Gandiva. He murmurs a mantra to invoke the parjannyastra, the weapon of rain. Arjuna drills an arrow into the ground beside Bheeshma. The earth trembles under them. She opens in a cleft deep as a hand, and from it a crystal spring wells, like amrita, and scented like nectar. The water rises into Bheeshma's lips, bathing his face, letting him drink where he lies, whenever he wants. The holy spring is the Ganga herself, and his mother slakes the raging thirst of Shantanu's dying son: the thirst of his soul.

All the Pandavas and Kauravas have returned to Bheeshma's side, all his grandsons. The light on his face is brighter, after he has drunk. The water seems to have quenched his pain, as well. Bheeshma smiles more easily at them. He says, "Only Krishna and Arjuna know the mantra for the parjannya. They are Nara Narayana. Duryodhana my son, come closer, listen to what I have to tell you. Let my death not be in vain; let your enmity with your cousins end with it. You cannot vanquish Nara and Narayana. Look how Arjuna has cut me down, as not even my guru Bhargava could. Give Yudhishtira back half the kingdom, or you and your brothers will perish. I am a dying man, and as I love you, you must listen to me. End this war tonight."

The breath rattles in his chest, and Bheeshma cannot go on. Duryodhana's eyes smoulder in the torchlight, and, by the look in them, his dying grandfather knows his plea has been fruitless. Agony sears through him again, and he shuts his eyes over his twin torments: the one which feeds on his body, and the other that feeds on his heart even as he lies dying. Bheeshma drifts away on a dream of his mother. Tenderly she caresses him, wafts him out of reach of the anguish of the earth.

Seeing him suspended between pain and forgetfulness, his grandsons touch his feet, and leave him on his bed of arrows, watched by the guards they have posted around him. Bheeshma must lie on Kurukshetra for sixty days and nights more, before the sun turns north at the solstice and he can finally leave the world.

TWENTY-TWO

'I never hated you'

In his tent, Karna gets news of Bheeshma's fall. At midnight, Duryodhana comes to Karna's tent. Duryodhana has not shed a tear yet. But when he sees his friend, when Karna rises silently to embrace him, the Kaurava breaks down. He sobs piteously in Karna's arms.

Then, Duryodhana goes limp, and Karna gently leads him to his bed, and makes him lie on it. He pulls off his sandals, loosens his clothes, and sits beside him, stroking his head. The Kuru prince shuts his eyes and mercifully falls into sleep. Now and again, a sob wracks him; but he does not wake up.

Karna sits in the dark, gazing at his sleeping friend. He knows that, with the sun the next day, he must take the field against his brothers. Bheeshma had fallen, and no one stood between Karna and the war. Seeing Duryodhana, curled up like a child in his bed, gives him strength: in his moment of crisis, the Kaurava had not gone to his uncle or his brothers for comfort, not even to Dusasana. He had come to Karna.

Thus, Karna sits for a long time. The moon sinks in the west, dawn is not more than three hours away. Suddenly, an irresistible compulsion to go out into the night seizes him, as if a voice called him clearly across silvery Kurukshetra. Silence reigns over the last yaama of the night. Karna leaves Duryodhana asleep, and comes into the open. Exhausted with the day's battle, and most of all, with the shock of Bheeshma's fall, the Kaurava army sleeps like the dead. Karna makes his way stealthily through corpses strewn everywhere like large dolls, towards the torches that show where Bheeshma lies on his exceptional bed, in the long wait for the sun to turn north again.

Karna's body is in soft upheaval; he is terrified to approach Bheeshma. He knows the patriarch never liked him. He remembers all the times the old man put him down in the sabha of Hastinapura. Even the memory of Bheeshma's acerbic voice makes him shudder. But Karna knows Bheeshma is as much his grandfather as Duryodhana or Arjuna's, and this brings him inevitably to the fallen elder. The guards around Bheeshma have dozed off. Karna pads forward, hoping he can pay his respects to a sleeping warrior, and steal away.

Bheeshma's eyes are shut on his great sad face. Karna creeps closer, like a thief in the night. But, when he is near enough to see the magnificent body stuck with a hundred arrows, and the blood that has flowed and congealed in the dark pool below it, a sob breaks from Kunti's eldest son. All his resistance gives way. Karna falls at his Pitama's feet, bathing them in tears.

Bheeshma's eyes flicker open, they are full of light. He breathes, "Who are you? Your tears burn me more than these arrows. Why do you cry at my feet? Come near me, let me see your face. My head is full of fire, and I cannot turn it to look at you. Why don't you speak?"

Karna rises, and crosses to where Bheeshma can see him; but his face remains hidden from his grandfather. Bheeshma says again, "Your form is familiar, mighty child. Who are you?"

Karna breathes, "It is I, Karna! Whom you hate, my lord. I would have come earlier, except that I feared what you might say to me when the others were here. But I had to come; my heart would not be still until I did. Forgive me if I cause you distress."

Karna sees tears fill the old man's eyes, and trickle down his face. Bheeshma raises a hand to call him nearer, as if to whisper in his ear. Instead, he reaches out with both his arms to embrace the amazed warrior, and kisses him fervently! Bheeshma says, "I have never hated you, my poor child. How could I, when I have always known you are my grandson?"

Karna gasps.

"Long ago, Vyasa told me. But I had to keep the secret, and so did Vidura, who also knows. Ah, my son, whenever I spoke harshly it was only to curb your pride, so it may not lead you to ruin. You must remember I knew the Pandavas were your brothers. How could I listen to you raving against them? If you knew who you really were, you would never say such things; or goad Duryodhana on as you did. Karna, if you were not with him, Duryodhana would never have dared fight the Pandavas for fear of Arjuna. But he believes you are the greater archer; and, Suryaputra, perhaps he is not wrong. Why do you think I made it a condition you would not fight, while I did? Not because I hate you, noble child, but because I could not bear to see you go to war against your brothers. Oh, I don't dislike you at all, Karna. I love you as much as I do Duryodhana or Yudhishtira."

The old man strokes Karna's hand. "My poor, poor child. God alone knows why, but from the first day of your life, fate has been cruellest to you. But now, everything is clear. I beg you, cross the field of death; go and join your brothers. Possibly, that will shock Duryodhana into abandoning this insane war. You are the eldest of your generation. Let it be you that makes peace, and my dying fruitful."

Karna's face is ashen. "Pitama, you are the last of the Kurus, the end of a noble line. None of us is your blood. Perhaps, that is why this house is at war against itself: because the last of the Kurus had no sons. And because the kali yuga is upon us. Pitama, how I wish I could do as you ask, but it is too late for that. We cannot fight fate: the destiny of the very earth. The age grows dark, and I do not have the strength to stand against time; or the strength to betray Duryodhana, no, not for the noblest cause.

"I love him more than a brother. Once, I said to him, 'I will do anything to please you: even what seems impossible. I will give my life for you, for that is how you have loved me.'

"Pitama, I have never broken my word to anyone. How can I betray my only friend? When the Gods decide to destroy a man, who can save him? I love the Pandavas now, more than I ever hated them. But I must fight them on cursed Kurukshetra, and die on this field. I have no doubt I will die, and Duryodhana will lose this war. Every omen cries out that Dhritarashtra's sons and all those who fight for them will perish. Isn't it enough that Krishna is with my brothers: what force on earth can withstand them? I know who the Dark One is, and he has already decided all our fates."

He pauses. Bheeshma sighs, but still keeps Karna's hand in his own. Karna resumes, "The world thinks of me as a sutaputra. But you know who I am, and now I do as well. A kshatriya must die on the field of battle, and I mean to die on Kurukshetra. My life has been full of shame. Bless me, Pitama, that at least I die an honourable death!"

Bheeshma draws Karna down, and embraces him again. Karna says, "Forgive me for all the harsh things I ever said to you."

"My child, my child, how can a grandfather hold anything against his grandson? There is nothing to forgive. You are a great kshatriya. You are Arjuna's equal, his superior. Your mind is also noble, my son, as noble as Yudhishtira's. I see now that the kali yuga has indeed entered the world. The old ways must pass on, and vileness and evil replace them. Not you or I are responsible, not Duryodhana or Yudhishtira. Fate herself conspires to darken the age. Who are we to fathom her purposes, or to oppose her?"

He lays his aged hands on Karna's head, as the Suryaputra kneels before him. "I bless you, child, with all my heart I bless you. Few men have suffered as you have, and so alone. I bless you to die like a kshatriya on the field of war, and find heaven for yourself. Do your dharma as a warrior; die for your friend if you must, there is no shame in it. And your name will be remembered, and your fame last as long as the stars shine down on the world. For no fault of your own, you have been tormented to your very end. And I fear you will find death even before I leave this broken body. But I will see you in swarga soon, my prince! As soon as it is uttarayana again."

Karna folds his hands to his grandsire. He says, "I have a boon to ask you, Pitama."

"Ask me for anything I can still give you."

"Let my secret die with me. I fear you may be tempted to tell Duryodhana or Yudhishtira who I am, to stop the war. I beg you not to."

Bheeshma smiles; love for this grandchild of his fills his heart. "When you are dead I must tell Duryodhana, and no one else, who you really were. He must know how much you loved him. But I will make him swear the Pandavas don't learn of it."

Karna's tears fall on his Pitama. Bheeshma clasps him, kissing him repeatedly, whispering, "Noble, noble child! There is no kshatriya like you on earth. Of all my grandsons, I am proudest of my Karna."

Kissing his grandfather's hand one last time, his own heart full, Karna rises and walks away. His eyes streaming yet, he finds his tent in the

Kaurava camp. He sees Duryodhana as he left him an hour go, curled in sleep. Karna caresses his friend's face lightly with his fingers, then lies down beside him. Through an opening in the tent-flap he can see a lone, bright star in the sky from which the moon has sunk. He is at peace after seeing Bheeshma. The sight of that solitary star fills Karna with quiet joy. Unaware that this is the first night of the kali yuga, he falls asleep beside Duryodhana.

BOOK SEVEN

Drona Parva

AUM, I bow down to Narayana, the most exalted Nara, and to the Devi Saraswati, and say *Jaya*!

ONE

Drona, Senapati

THE ELEVENTH MORNING OF THE WAR DAWNS, COLD AND CLEAR, AND despair grips the Kaurava army. As long as Bheeshma had led them, they could always win the war. Now he lay on his strange deathbed, waiting for the sun to return to his northern path. As Sanjaya said to his stricken king, blind Dhritarashtra, the Kaurava army is like the sky without a sun, the earth without its verdure, speech without refinement, a woman who has lost her husband, a dry river in summer, like a mountain-cave empty of its lion and his roar!

As naturally as seasons change, when their times come, the Kauravas turn to Karna for assurance. On that eleventh morning of the war of dharma, the army of Hastinapura resounds not with blasting conches or drumrolls, but a single name cried out by a million throats.

"Karna!" they roar. "Karna to beat the Pandavas!"

In his tent, Karna hears them with a grim smile. He is putting on mail, readying himself for battle.

Duryodhana and his brothers arrive in Karna's tent. Duryodhana puts his arms around him and begins to cry again, as do all Dhritarashtra's sons. Karna comforts them like an older brother.

"Nothing is certain in this fleeting world; not when we live, or die. Bheeshma has fallen when all of you guarded him with your lives: when Drona and Aswatthama, Duryodhana, Kripa, Dusasana, Shalya and a thousand others watched over him. His time had come and no power on earth could save the Pitama. Yet, it is easier for you to imagine the sun fallen out of the sky."

He puts his hands on Duryodhana's shoulders, "I know why you have come to me this morning. Look, I have put on armour. Duryodhana here I am, ready to die for you. The enemy is powerful: righteous Yudhishtira, tameless Bheema, brilliant Arjuna, Nakula and Sahadeva who fight like Devas. They have Satyaki, who is hardly less of an archer than Arjuna himself. Then, the most formidable, if the youngest: Abhimanyu who has both Krishna and Arjuna's blood in his veins. We must not forget Drupada and the fire-prince Dhrishtadyumna, whose valour no one has fathomed. And their fierce, loyal legions.

"This is the enemy. We would be fools if we deceived ourselves that they will be easy to vanquish. We must do our best, and if we win, the world shall be yours. If we lose, we will still have earned immortal fame for ourselves. Let us not be anxious about how the war will end, but take courage in both hands and leave the rest to fate. Let us go and fight!"

How his dark eyes shine. Duryodhana thinks Arjuna will not live much longer and he is consoled. Of ambition and mercy, ambition will always rule the Kaurava's heart. Duryodhana returns to his own tent. Karna goes again to his dying grandsire. Now he comes as a warrior, in his chariot, wearing mail and armed. He alights and approaches Bheeshma. Folding his hands, he says quietly, "I mean to follow you, Pitama. You have laid your life down for Duryodhana, and so will I. Bless me again."

He kneels beside Bheeshma. Bheeshma takes his hand, "You are Duryodhana's only hope. Fight as well as you can: that you must do in kshatriya dharma. Karna, I have thought long about you, and I have no doubt you are the greatest of all my grandsons." He lowers his voice, "Let your death be as noble as you are. I bless you that your fame will live forever, after you die, and it shall be blemishless; and when you fall, Kurukshetra will be like a mother's lap to you. Men of generations too distant to dream of, men in the heart of the kali yuga will name their sons after you. I bless you that you will die with a smile on your lips, and joy in your heart. Noble Karna, after everything you have endured, you will never be born again into this world of sorrow. You will have moksha, my child."

Bheeshma lays a loving palm on Karna's head. Karna takes the dust from his Pitama's feet and walks back to his chariot. Splendid as his father, Karna rides up to the Kaurava army. They see him like a sun risen for them, after the fractured night. A huge cheer goes up, echoing over Kurukshetra, "Karna! Great Karna for victory!"

"Karna is with us now, how long will the Pandavas live?"

A smile on his drawn face, Duryodhana welcomes his friend, taking his hands. "You tell me what we should do next. My mind is dark with grief, and I cannot reason clearly. We must have a Senapati for our army, but I can't think who it must be."

Adroitly, he leaves the decision to Karna. Karna says, "All these kshatriyas are fit for the charge; each is the others' peer. But if you choose one, the others will feel slighted. Yet, is there a warrior among us who towers over the rest in both age and experience; only he can command respect from us all. Duryodhana, let Drona be your Senapati."

Duryodhana goes to his master. "Acharya, you have been as close to us as our Pitama. It is only just that his mantle passes to you. I beg you, assume command of the army of Hastinapura."

Drona, the brahmana, is pleased no end. He says, "I will lead your army as best I can."

Duryodhana calls for holy water, and Drona is consecrated Senapati of the Kaurava army. When Karna stands beside the Acharya, the soldiers feel a surge of hope. They say, "Karna is a better archer than Arjuna. He can win this war for us."

"Remember the tournament in Hastinapura. He showed he was the better bowman."

"He has no love for the Pandavas, as Bheeshma did. He will kill them for Duryodhana."

Drona deploys his soldiers in the shakata vyuha, phalanx of the cart; while, Dhrishtadyumna forms the krauncha vyuha once more. The Pandavas peer across Kurukshetra at some excitement among the Kaurava legions. They see Karna, bright as a God, take the field for the first time. He is as pure, as radiant as the sun springing from the dragon Rahu's mouth.

Before he rides to the van of his army, Drona says to Duryodhana, "I will fight all the Pandavas, but there is one man I will not face, one kshatriya you must shield me from. For he was born to kill me."

"Dhrishtadyumna, my lord?"

"Keep Drupada's fire-prince away from me, if you want me to stay alive." The guru smiles at his sishya. "I will not pretend I am not delighted to be your Senapati. I want to do something exceptional for you, to show my gratitude."

Duryodhana reflects on this for just a moment, before he says, "Can you take Yudhishtira captive, and bring him to me alive?"

Drona's eyes flash. "If you mean to kill him, let it be in battle, not by deceit."

Duryodhana laughs. "Oh no, Acharya! Would Arjuna spare our lives for an hour if I did that? And even if we kill all the Pandavas, Krishna will burn us with his Chakra. No, if you bring Yudhishtira to me, I will challenge him to another game of dice. He will lose, and we can send him and his brothers to the jungle again, and end this war."

Drona considers this, and likes it even less than the war. But he must keep the word he has given. "If you can lure Arjuna away, I will bring Yudhishtira to you."

Duryodhana knows how fond his Acharya is of the Pandavas. To hold him to his word, he has it proclaimed to their army that Drona will take Yudhishtira alive. The news travels quickly to the Pandavas. Arjuna cries in fury, "Have the great sunk so low? But we shall see how they take my brother, when I won't leave his side for a moment."

TWO

The eleventh day

THE CONCHES BOOM AGAIN. BHEESHMA SHUTS HIS EYES AND DRIFTS away on a vision of another world. The Kaurava army whirls into battle: a great wheel of men. The Pandavas' krauncha swoops to stop its spinning advance. Sahadeva, who has sworn to kill Shakuni, meets him in a duel. Storming up at the head of the Pandava force today, Dhrishtadyumna confronts Drona before any other Kaurava warrior can intervene. Duryodhana's brother Vivimsati rides straight at Bheema, but he does not take him unawares. With a roar Bheema charges Vivimsati, killing his horses, shattering his chariot and the Kaurava flees on foot.

Bhoorisravas faces Shikhandi. To Shikhandi, this is the first day of a new life: nothing remains of Amba's steaming memories, of her single obsession. Serenity sits on the Panchala prince's heart; son of a great father that he is, he gives Bhoorisravas a scorching fight, turning the heads of the soldiers around them.

Some way off, black Ghatotkacha and pale green-eyed Alambusa are locked in a battle of sorcery. They fight with maya, crying chillingly at each other in the tongue of wild rakshasas: dark curses that no one else can understand. The Avanti brothers Vinda and Anuvinda meet Chekitana in a fervid duel. Blood flies in the day's young sun, and the spotless sky echoes with the screams of those cut down. After ten days of war, a skin of dry blood covers Kurukshetra, and fresh crimson splashes brightly on to this russet patina.

Virata is the first Pandava warrior to face Karna in battle. Holding their breath, the Kaurava soldiers watch to see if their new hero is indeed the archer they have heard he is. He exceeds all their expectations. His hands are like light, his aim is unerring, and he is more fluent than Arjuna. It seems he only looks at an enemy, and arrows flare from his bow by themselves. A deep roar of excitement rises from the Kaurava ranks.

Yet, another kshatriya eclipses even Karna: Abhimanyu. He hunts like a gandharva on Kurukshetra, and no one can stand before him. Breaking easily through the rim of the shakata vyuha, he kills a hundred Kaurava soldiers. Duryodhana's warrior, the king Paurava, surprises Abhimanyu from a flank, smashing his bow. Abhimanyu draws his sword and leaps down from his chariot. Seizing Paurava by his hair, Arjuna's son lifts him into the air and flings him down to the ground.

Sword in hand, Jayadratha comes to challenge Abhimanyu. The prince is eager to show off his sword skills. On the ground between their two chariots, they hew at each other, their weapons ringing together in an efflorescence of sparks. Jayadratha is a fine swordsman; but though he has twice Abhimanyu's bulk, the slender prince beats him back with dazzling speed. He breaks Jayadratha's blade, that king runs back to his chariot.

Word spreads of Abhimanyu's havoc. Back in his chariot, the prince picks up his bow again, and a rash of arrows leaps from it. One Kaurava warrior matches Abhimanyu shaft for shaft: Shalya harries him. They fight a blinding duel. Shalya invokes an astra; burning with secret fires, the missile flames at Abhimanyu. Arjuna's son catches it in his hands! In a wink Abhimanyu fits it to his bowstring and shoots it back at Shalya. The astra explodes, killing Shalya's sarathy, consuming his chariot and flinging him out.

Unhurt, but dazed and furious, Shalya seizes up a mace and runs at Abhimanyu. The slight youth cannot hope to match the massive Shalya with this weapon. Yet, honour demands that he fight. As Abhimanyu hefts his own gada, another kshatriya arrives between Shalya and him, roaring a challenge. It is Bheema, swinging his mace. Shalya turns away from Abhimanyu to the equal opponent.

Like a tiger and an elephant, they circle each other. The soldiers around them step back to give them room. Shalya and Bheema battle like beasts out of a mythic wilderness. Their maces clash like earthquakes, and storms of blue sparks fly around them, and they look like trees covered by fireflies at twilight. For an hour, they fight, exhilaratingly. Neither gives an inch, smashing out wildly and, also, with superb control. Until, with the loudest roar of the day, Bheema crashes such a blow on Shalya's mace that the king's weapon ignites in his hands. Bheema's next blow takes Shalya on his head. Shalya's knees buckle. Out of nowhere, Kritavarman appears, sweeps the fallen kshatriya into his chariot and flits away.

Lusty cheering breaks out among the Pandava soldiers. The moral victory has been theirs, and Shalya has escaped death by a whisker. Karna's son Vrishasena takes the field with his father today, and he is a sudden comet appeared on Kurukshetra. Nakula's son, Satanika, faces Vrishasena; he can hardly match Karna's ferocious boy. Seeing him in mortal danger, Draupadi's other sons come flying to their brother's rescue. Like five sunflares, they attack Vrishasena, beating him back. Then, Aswatthama appears at his side, and together, those two hold the Pandavaputras at bay. But how graceful the five are, how handsome!

This eleventh day, the Kauravas have lost many more soldiers than the Pandavas. No Bheeshma holds up Pandu's sons any more, and Bheema, Abhimanyu, Satyaki, Dhrishtadyumna and Arjuna devastate the enemy. To stop them, somehow, to turn the tide on his first day as Senapati of Hastinapura's army, Drona thinks he must take Yudhishtira captive. He sees the eldest Pandava fighting on his own, with Arjuna nowhere near him. Drona cries to his sarathy, "Ride at the white parasol! Go like the wind."

They fly at Yudhishtira's chariot. Drona's bow streams five fires and no enemy soldier dares stand before him. In a moment, they are upon Yudhishtira. The Pandava turns to fight, but he is hardly a match for Drona with surprise on his side. The Acharya breaks his bow. He rides at Yudhishtira's chariot; but Dhrishtadyumna, who misses nothing, flashes between them. Arrows fly like locusts between the chariots. With wonderful skill, and some fear as well, Dhrishtadyumna contains Drona as a shore the sea.

Shikhandi and Uttamaujas are at hand. Drona beats them back in the frenzy that takes him. Draupadi's sons try to intervene, but they cannot stand even a few moments against the raging Acharya. He is possessed. His students see him like this for the first time: truly terrible. Dhrishtadyumna sees the peril to Yudhishtira, and fights desperately well. But he and his warriors are being pushed back, inexorably, farther and farther from the Pandava king.

The Pandava soldiers panic. Someone cries, "The war is lost. No one can stop Drona, he will take Yudhishtira today!"

Drona's chariot comes nearer, and Yudhishtira waits helplessly to be killed or taken by his master. Suddenly, a cry splits the arrow-thick air; the rumble of a great chariot drowns every other noise. Pale gandharva horses seem to fly above the ground, their reins held taut in the dark hands of an Avatara. The shimmering chariot appears out of the dusk, and at the last moment, darts between Yudhishtira and Drona. In its wake, it leaves a thousand dead; so, in the gloom, it seems like some uncanny ship fording a lake of blood. Arjuna falls on Drona like an army.

In Arjuna's mind turbulent images rise: first, of a day when a stranger fetched a little vita out of an old well for some young princes; then, of Bheeshma fallen just yesterday; and finally another day, fourteen years ago, when he and his brothers lost everything. How could his Acharya be an accomplice to such treachery? After all that had happened, how could he now stoop to this? In that moment, Arjuna loses a reverence he has nurtured over a lifetime. Drona had been bought with position, and he falls in his sishya's eyes. Blind with anger, and even more with grief, Arjuna flies at his master who taught him so much of what he knows. Drona cannot face him. The Pandava shames his guru on Kurukshetra, driving him off like some common soldier. The Acharya's opportunity to take Yudhishtira is lost; worse, he knows he has lost Arjuna's respect.

The sun sets in sorrow over the field of the dead. Conches sound to call the armies back to their camps. Though Drona has fought as never before, the eleventh day also belongs to the Pandavas, if narrowly.

THREE

Susharma

Duryodhana is frantic. In front of the other kings and his brothers, he says to Drona, "You asked me if you could do something exceptional for me, and I told you to take Yudhishtira alive. You had every chance to take him today, but, Acharya, you didn't keep your word."

Drona bristles at the censure. He says coldly, "I said I would take Yudhishtira, if Arjuna was far from him. The task of keeping Arjuna away was yours. If Arjuna had not descended on me, Yudhishtira would be here now, bound hand and foot."

Susharma says, "We Trigartas have old enmity with Arjuna. All these days we have tried to kill him; but his blue sarathy is as elusive as the wind in the trees. Tomorrow we will challenge Arjuna as soon as battle begins, and lure him away to the south of the field; there, either he or we will die. Drona should have all the time he needs to take Yudhishtira."

Duryodhana cries, "An excellent plan! And if you can kill Arjuna while the Acharya captures Yudhishtira, not even Krishna will deny us victory. But to make resolutions here in the safety of the camp is easy. I have seen you face Arjuna many times, Susharma, and each time you Trigartas fled from him."

Susharma's face twitches. "We will swear an oath by Agni that either Arjuna or the Trigartas will live at twilight tomorrow: but not both."

At once, Duryodhana orders the sacred fire fetched. The Trigarta brothers—Susharma, Satyaratha, Satyavarma, Satyasu, Subahu, Sudhanva and Satyadharma—swear a solemn oath that they would not leave the field of war unless either Arjuna or they were dead. With this oath, they are called the Samsaptakas. After the grim brothers return to their tents, Duryodhana says to Drona, "With Arjuna out of the way, I hope you won't balk at taking Yudhishtira tomorrow."

Drona says woodenly, "If Arjuna is kept away, I will bring Yudhishtira to you alive."

He also walks out of Duryodhana's tent, disgusted at what noble war has come to, at what he himself has fallen to. Duryodhana smiles at Shakuni, Dusasana and Karna.

Dawn of the twelfth day; Drona forms his legions in the garuda vyuha and, across the field, Dhrishtadyumna has chosen the chandrakala, the phalanx of the crescent moon. Battle begins, the two forces fall at each other. Arrows cover the sky, fingers of orange flames in the early light. Swords and maces gleam in the morning, and again Bheeshma on his arrow-bed hears the roar and the scream of the slayer and the slain.

Arjuna sees Susharma and his brothers with their men at the southern wing tip of the Kaurava eagle; usually, they would come from the rear as the day's battle grew. He sees all their burning gazes fixed just on him. He sees Duryodhana staring intently at the Trigartas, and guesses what is afoot. Arjuna says to Yudhishtira, "The Trigartas mean to challenge me again, and I cannot refuse to fight them."

As he speaks, Susharma hails him harshly across the field, "Arjuna! Come and fight us. We have sworn by Agni that today either you or we, but not both, will live to see the sun set. We are the Samsaptakas, Arjuna, and we challenge you!"

Yudhishtira is alarmed. "You must stay beside me, Arjuna. I don't care to be taken by Drona!"

"I cannot refuse a kshatriya's challenge. But here is Satyajit: let him be your custodian today. As long as he has life in him, not Drona or anyone will come near you. But if he should be killed, Yudhishtira, promise me, my brother, that you will be a coward for all our sakes and flee."

"Drona will not take me, Arjuna. Answer Susharma's challenge, let this be the Trigartas' last day on earth."

"Bless me!" cries Arjuna.

Leaving Yudhishtira in the care of Satyajit, who is Drupada's brother and no less a kshatriya than him, Arjuna says to Krishna, "Come, my Lord, let us ride at the Trigartas."

FOUR

Bhagadatta's elephant

An army by themselves, the Trigartas have formed a crescent of their own beyond the southern wing tip of the garuda vyuha. Arjuna rides alone against that legion of thousands, like a lion at a vast herd of deer. Duryodhana sees Arjuna's white horses flying like foam across a wave, and cries to Drona, "Our plan is working! Arjuna rides at Susharma's men. Take Yudhishtira, Acharya, no one can stop you now."

Susharma has brought his legion to the south, a fair way beyond the main Kaurava army. From here, Arjuna will not be able to ride back in a hurry to his brother's side. They are so far that he will not be able to hear a call for help. As they draw near, Arjuna turns to Krishna, "Do you see the smiles on their savage faces? Are they so glad I will send them to hell, that they smile?"

Arjuna lifts his Devadatta, adorned with gold, and blows a deep note on it. For a moment, the Trigarta force stands paralysed; their horses' eyes bulge wildly and the beasts pass dung in fear. Then a thousand conches' bass answers his call, a thousand arrows flash at his chariot, obscuring the face of the sun. Arjuna replies with an astra that spumes up as a calid fireball, then, falls on the enemy in a hundred burning shafts. Every arrow claims a life: a hundred Trigarta soldiers are immolated.

The Trigartas have sworn a solemn vow, and they shoot bank upon bank of dark arrows at Krishna and Arjuna, falling on them like swarms of bees upon a flowering tree, engulfing them. Because of Krishna's chariotry and the white horses' speed, the Pandava's chariot is a hard target to find. Their finer marksmen's barbs Arjuna cuts down with his own fire.

One of the Trigarta's bravest kshatriyas, Subahu of the gifted hands, rides out of the throng to face Arjuna alone. He is an excellent bowman, and wounds both Krishna and Arjuna. Roaring, Arjuna breaks the bow in Subahu's hand, then severs the hand from its wrist in a red font. Screaming in horror, Subahu flees. Susharma himself dashes forward with ten of his truest archers. But Arjuna is a warrior of another ilk. As in a nightmare, Susharma sees Sudhanva's head cut from his neck by the Pandava's golden-winged arrow, its scream stilled on its lips. Turning, he sees the other nine around him have met the same fate, in the space of a wish.

Arjuna fights as if from another dimension; where he has all the time he needs to shoot at the enemy, while he is protected from their arrows by a threshold they cannot breach. He seems to defy nature: his one to their thousand is more than they can subdue. He burns them at will; the common Trigarta soldiers panic, and want to run back to the main Kaurava army. Susharma roars at them, "Stand and fight, cowards! You have sworn to kill or be killed. I will shoot you down myself if you run."

And he sends a few warning arrows after the deserters, so they scramble back to the crescent. Susharma cries, "Shoot all at once! Cover them in a night of arrows."

The wind whistles towards Arjuna from behind the Trigarta legion, and suddenly a dark cloud of arrows drifts at him as if at midday an unnatural night has fallen over Kurukshetra. It is an endless cloud. The Trigartas now shoot in waves; and in terror: so they can hide in that darkness from the Pandava. Such an impenetrable darkness; Arjuna can hardly see his hands. In fury, he summons his first greater astra, the weapon of Tvashtar. He looses that missile, then blows a rolling blast on the Devadatta.

Tvashtar's astra is a weapon of hallucinations. Every Trigarta soldier sees the Pandava beside him. They fall on each other, thinking they are attacking Arjuna. Thousands die in the surreal confusion, cut down by their comrades; those that are not killed, Arjuna picks off. Yet, the darkness persists around the white chariot, for the Trigarta brothers themselves are masters of maya and they are not deluded by the astra.

The heavy darkness afflicts Krishna at the chariot-head. He feels exhausted, so he can hardly hold the reins in his hands. His body is drenched in sweat, and blindness films his eyes. In that eerie night, Krishna cries, "Arjuna! Where are you? I cannot see you in this accursed blackness. Are you still alive, Arjuna? Answer me!"

A roar of anger answers the Avatara. Dimly, Krishna hears the kshatriya behind him invoke the vayavyastra, the wind's weapon. He sees an arrow glowing in the sinister dark, a shaft charged with a thousand storms. Next moment, the golden arrow flashes out in the unnatural night and a hurricane sweeps Kurukshetra. Like the sun, it dissolves the darkness of the Trigarta cloud. It also blows away whole columns of soldiers as if they are dry leaves of summer. The gale of the vayavyastra blows the Trigartas across the plain of war—beautiful they seem, like flights of birds!

His enemy hopelessly scattered for the moment, Arjuna cries to Krishna, "I fear the Acharya. We must ride back to Yudhishtira."

Meanwhile, as soon as Drona saw Arjuna ride against Susharma, he makes straight for Yudhishtira. Drona knows the Trigartas will not hold Arjuna for long. Dhrishtadyumna is beside Yudhishtira. The Pandava cries to Drupada's son, "Here comes Drona, he must not take me."

The fire-prince laughs. "I am beside you, my lord, and my father's army is here with Satyajit. Drona can promise Duryodhana anything he likes; but he will not keep his word. We will make him pay for it!"

Drona arrives at the outer ring of the warriors who guard Yudhishtira, and sees Dhrishtadyumna riding at him. He swerves away from the encounter. Drupada's army surrounds Drona, shooting at him from every side. Durmukha, the ugly Kaurava, one of Duryodhana's fiercest brothers, rides at Dhrishtadyumna. Dhrishtadyumna fights him, and also shoots smoking shafts at Drona. Durmukha fights as if for his life today, and contains Dhrishtadyumna. He looses a renitent astra at Dhrishtadyumna; for a moment, Drupada's army is dazzled. Seeing his chance, Drona flits through the protective ring.

Drona is dangerously close to Yudhishtira when Satyajit sees him. Stealthy as a lion come to pounce on a calf separated from the herd, the Acharya stalks his royal prey. Satyajit veers his chariot round and attacks Drona. The brahmana, roused, is more than he can contain. In a flash Drona cuts Satyajit's bow in two, and plunges on at Yudhishtira.

Drupada's other brother, Vrika, flies between Drona and the Pandava king. Drona finds Vrika's heart with a wooden arrow and that kshatriya falls dead from his chariot.

Satyajit seizes up another bow, and sets on Drona. Now Satyajit breaks Drona's bow in his hand, and kills the Acharya's sarathy with a silver shaft that transfixes him to the chariot-head. Drona's time is short. He pulls a crescent-tipped arrow from his quiver and severs Satyajit's head from his neck, scarlet spouting at the naked part.

Panic takes the Pandava army. The Kekayas, Virata and some more of Drupada's brothers rush to where Drona closes ominously on Yudhishtira. Virata's brother Satanika sets his chariot between Drona and Yudhishtira. Growling, Drona decapitates him, too, in a flash of blood. Drona has killed three kshatriyas in a few moments, and the Pandava soldiers shrink from him. He flares on towards Yudhishtira. Shikhandi, Vasudhana and Satyaki challenge the Acharya. He beats them back easily, with fire-headed arrows that kindle their chariots.

Yet, the few moments for which the three held Drona up are fateful. Yudhishtira leaps nimbly from his chariot. He mounts the swiftest horse he can find, and flees the battle! When Drona realizes his quarry has escaped, it is too late for him to give chase. He turns on the Pandava army around him and they feel his wrath. Today, Drona fights as if to prove that he is more than Bheeshma's equal. There is a bloodbath again on Kurukshetra, more copious than any before.

Many of Drupada's brothers and Dhrishtadyumna storm back to fight Drona[1]. The old master, his white hair flying in the wind of death that blows on that field, is tameless. He kills thousands, their blood falling like rain upon the caked earth. Drona finds the prince Suchitra's heart with a serpentine naracha. All around, Pandava soldiers cry, "Kill Drona! Kill Drona or the war is lost!"

Who can kill the Acharya? In a brief hour, alone, he routs all the Pandava army. A way off, Duryodhana stands with Karna at the heart of the Kaurava legions, which have hardly any fighting to do for the slaughter Drona takes to the enemy. His eyes shining, Duryodhana cries to Karna, "Look at him scatter them! Dhrishtadyumna and the rest flee

---

1 See Appendix for a description of the horses, the standards, and the bows of some of the Kshatriyas.

from him. Look at Bheema run!" He roars with laughter. "The Pandavas will forget their dreams of a kingdom, they will hardly hope to live through the day!"

But with the queerest look in his eye, Karna replies, "Don't belittle your enemy too quickly, Duryodhana. These are kshatriyas, they will not be beaten so easily. Look where Bheema comes to fight, his eyes red as plums. And look at the rest, streaming back after him. We must ride to the Acharya, he is in danger."

Duryodhana glances sharply at his friend, startled at the warmth in his voice for the Pandavas. Then he sees Drona surrounded and rides to his Senapati, with Karna and some of his brothers. A sharp battle breaks out. Nakula and Sahadeva are twin incarnations of death; behind them, Draupadi's sons are implacable; and away to the right, Abhimanyu is the most terrible of all. The Pandavas fight in great heart after Yudhishtira escapes Drona.

Farther away, to the left of Abhimanyu, Bheema, elemental as his airy father, is among Duryodhana's elephants, tormenting them with arrows, smashing them down with his mace, as is commonplace for him by now. Then, to avenge all his kind that Bheema slew, comes a white beast, a titan among elephants: Bhagadatta's Supritika bears down on the son of the wind. Like Indra mounted on Airavata comes that ancient mountain-demon, Narakasura's son; and Airavata's son Supritika charges Bheema's chariot.

The Pandava army parts like the sky for a Deva. Soldiers hapless enough to come in his way, he tramples as if they were hardly there at all. Enjoying himself among Duryodhana's lesser beasts, Bheema does not see Supritika until the immense creature is upon him. With a shrill scream at the sight of the corpses of the other elephants Bheema has felled, Supritika lifts a gigantic foot and brings it down thunderously on Bheema's chariot. The ratha is smashed. The horses bolt, whinnying. The sarathy Visoka is pulp, and Bheema himself nowhere to be seen.

Supritika raises his pale trunk and trumpets his triumph; the sound rings across Kurukshetra. A cry of anguish goes up from the Pandava soldiers, "Supritika has killed Bheema!"

The Pandava, meanwhile, is under the mastodon, dazed but unhurt. Sensing him there, the beast begins to settle on its stomach, to crush him. As its hilly bulk descends on him, Bheema, who knows something about elephants from his boyhood, begins to rub its belly furiously with his hands*. Supritika cannot resist this. For a moment, all the rage flies out of him, and he basks in the sweet tickling! In a trice, Bheema escapes between his legs and runs for his life.

Hearing the awful cry that Bheema was dead, Yudhishtira flies back into battle with Drupada's army. Like the God of wrath he comes, bow singing. The lord of the Dasaarnas comes with Yudhishtira, bringing his greathearted elephant, which stood up so bravely to Supritika. But Bhagadatta and his beast are denizens of a lofty realm that borders Devaloka, and Yudhishtira's most ferocious volleys fall away from them like raindrops.

Bhagadatta is an endless font of all kinds of missiles, some common, others sorcerous. Columns of men he burns up, in an eyeflash, with blazing javelins that explode with enormous violence. There are hypnotic arrows, full of haunting music, which lulls Yudhishtira's soldiers into dreams. They stand stupefied, forgetting where they are, and are easy picking for the Kaurava archers.

Satyaki rides against the lord of Pragjyotishapura. The Yadava covers elephant and rider in a hum of arrows like dark bees. Supritika charges Satyaki's chariot, and once more, smashes it in splinters with a stamp. Satyaki leaps out, just in time. But another roar shakes the field, and Bheema returns to face the white elephant. He fetches Supritika a staggering blow with his mace. Quick as anything, the creature darts out its trunk, seizes Bheema and lifts him high above its head. The elephant is about to dash Bheema on the ground, when with great presence of mind Bheema stabs its soft trunk with an arrowhead. The animal screams and loosens his grip for an instant, which is time enough for Bheema to wriggle free and leap down.

Supritika lifts a leg, wider than the bole of a tree, to stomp on him. Bheema darts under the creature's belly again, and stabs him from below. It runs round and round in a fever, but cannot find its tormentor. Giving up, Supritika sees Abhimanyu's chariot before him and charges it. Bheema leaps out from between its legs, but Abhimanyu is not quick enough to pull his horses out of Supritika's way. The white giant crushes his chariot, and the prince himself jumps free at the last moment.

---

* The Ganguli text refers to this knowledge of elephants as Anjalikabedha.

It is an unusual battle being fought on Kurukshetra: the Pandava army against Supritika the elephant! The elephant surely has the better of it. He keeps the enemy army at bay, crushing so many chariots, trampling any men who come in his way, holding up Bheema; while Bhagadatta on his neck sows death all around him in a scarlet flurry.

Panic grips the Pandavas, and their soldiers' cries ring plaintively across Kurukshetra.

FIVE

An ancient and his beast

ARJUNA'S VAYAVYASTRA HAS JUST SWEPT AWAY THE TRIGARTA ARMY, when he hears the alarm of the Pandava forces being savaged by Bhagadatta and Supritika. Arjuna says, "He was my father Pandu's friend, but he kills thousands of our men. Bhagadatta must die today, if I have to kill him myself."

But as soon as Krishna turns his horses round, Susharma roars at Arjuna again, "Are you afraid to fight that your little wind has died down, Pandava? Why do you run from us at every chance?"

Krishna holds his horses, and says, "Enough of these Trigartas. Burn them with the Vajra, there are more important battles to fight elsewhere."

Already, Susharma and his brothers cloak the white chariot again in a bank of arrows. Arjuna invokes the Vajra, and shoots a silver shaft charged with that final weapon at the Trigartas. It is an adamantine thunderbolt, and gashes across the field in a jagged thousand-jointed streak. Like a small sun, it erupts among the Trigarta legions and nine of every ten men Susharma brought to war are pillars of ash. Susharma himself survives, and some of his brothers. That king still calls arrogantly to Arjuna, "Fight me to the end, Pandava. You will not live to see the sun set. Fight me if you dare!"

Arjuna says in amazement, "Susharma isn't dead. You decide, Krishna, shall I fight him or ride against Bhagadatta?"

Without a word, Krishna turns his chariot back to the Trigartas. His ire up, because he can hear the screams of the Pandava army beset by Supritika, Arjuna faces Susharma and his men. Arrows radiate from the

Gandiva like rays from a star, and he lights up the field with a clutch of astras. The Trigartas have not yet seen such battle from Arjuna: he wilts them. He takes Satyaratha's head off with a crescent-tipped shaft, like the one with which Drona killed Satyajit, and attacks Susharma himself with such violence that king faints. The rest of his men, those left alive, take to their heels.

Krishna laughs, "At last you fight as you can. One man has wiped out the dreaded Trigarta legion. Today I am proud of my kshatriya!"

And Arjuna's heart is full with his sarathy's rare praise. They turn back to the main Kaurava army on Kurukshetra. Seeing the gandharva horses, a cheer goes up from the Pandava ranks. Like a bright and dangerous wind comes Arjuna, and Kaurava soldiers run from him for their lives. Their roars turn quickly to cries of fear. Seeing how many of his men had died while he fought the Trigartas, Arjuna blazes on Kurukshetra like Siva's son Karttikeya did when he fought Tarakasura's fell legions!

Krishna steers his chariot to confront Bhagadatta. The Pandava and the Asura fight. The air is an opaqueness of arrows, some plain and sharp, others astras, locking with each other, burning the sky. Bhagadatta prods Supritika with his goad so the elephant rushes at Arjuna's chariot. The Pandava does not have the heart to shoot the magnificent beast, so, at the last moment, Krishna has to veer out of the way and the colossus thunders by, his tread missing the chariot by a hand's width.

Swirling his mount round with astonishing speed, Bhagadatta covers Arjuna with arrows. Arjuna fights back powerfully, and Bhagadatta begins to shoot more at Krishna than his warrior. He burns him with flaming shafts, while the dark sarathy bears no arms and can make no reply. Bhagadatta has remembered that Krishna killed his father Narakasura, and means to have revenge. In fury, Arjuna cuts the demon's bow in shards. At once, fourteen eerie lances appear one after another in Bhagadatta's hands; he casts them, bands of light, at Krishna. Arjuna smashes them in the air with some ethereal archery.

Arjuna aims at Supritika's armour, cutting it away piece by piece. Bhagadatta casts a livid shakti at Krishna. Arjuna snuffs its fires in flight, and the next two missiles. With a roar, Bhagadatta casts another shakti at Arjuna himself, knocking his crown askew. Smiling, the Pandava rights the jewelled kirita with his hand, while the Gandiva still streams arrows, miraculously! Once more, he breaks Bhagadatta's bow.

Maddened that this mere boy shames him yet again, the lord of the mountain chants a deep mantra and hurls the elephant-goad in his hand at his antagonist. The goad turns into an occult ayudha, which lights up earth and sky with towering flames, as it flares at Arjuna. The Pandava shoots ten arrows, quick as thoughts, at the infernal thing. It consumes them easily, and flies on at him. A cry goes up from Yudhishtira's men that Arjuna would be killed. At the last instant, Krishna stands up and receives the weapon in his chest!

A flash of light as of a star exploding: then, utter darkness for another moment. When the darkness clears, Krishna stands smiling, unhurt, and the vaishnavastra that Bhagadatta cast has turned into a garland of blue lotuses around the Avatara's neck. Rapturous cheering echoes across the Pandava ranks. Bheema hugs Yudhishtira, crying, "They are both alive!"

But Arjuna says, "Krishna, he cast the astra at me; why did you take it upon yourself? You swore to be just my sarathy."

Krishna smiles, "A sarathy will save his kshatriya's life, won't he? Besides, I only took back what was mine."

"How is that?"

"It was the vaishnavastra he cast at you, which Bhumi Devi begged from Vishnu for her son Narakasura. Naraka was invincible for it, until I killed him. Before he died, he gave the astra to his son. It is not only an astra of fire, Arjuna; it protects whoever has it against every other weapon. The vaishnava was Bhagadatta's strength, and his elephant's. Now you can kill them."

Arjuna raises the Gandiva again. He feels a new current of power in his fingers. He looses an orient shaft at the white elephant Supritika. It hums into the beast's lofty brow, from where Arjuna has shot away the armour. Splitting the creature's temples as thunder does a mountain, the arrow pierces deep into the animal's brain, like a snake into an anthill, and, with a long scream, the pale giant sinks to his knees, already dead. Bhagadatta roars in shock. Another crescent-headed shaft from Arjuna crashes into his chest, cleaving his old heart, and the lord of Pragjyotishapura falls from his elephant's back, dead himself.

Jubilation breaks out among the Pandavas. Both armies stop fighting and gather thickly around the fallen ancient. Arjuna climbs down from his chariot and approaches the dead asura. Folding his hands to one of the last kshatriyas from a bygone age, and both his fathers, Pandu and Indra's, friend besides, Arjuna walks around Bhagadatta in a reverent pradakshina.

SIX

Drona's vow

It is high noon when Bhagadatta dies. Soon, the fighting resumes, fiercer than ever. The Kauravas surge forward to avenge their slain warrior. But now Arjuna leads the Pandava army: resplendent in his chariot, inspired by his triumph over the Trigartas and Bhagadatta. He kills hundreds of enemy soldiers, burns them with many fires. Shakuni's brothers ride to challenge Arjuna. From two sides, they attack him at once. They are gifted archers. But the ambidextrous Arjuna switches the Gandiva from hand to hand, and he kills both in a moment, so you cannot tell which one dies first: the one whom he shot through the heart, or the other whose neck he severed.

Roaring shrilly to see his brothers die, Shakuni flies at Arjuna. Serpent's eyes glinting, he raises a soft hand and casts a spell at the Pandava. The earth cracks open; a pride of lions leaps from the fissure and surrounds Arjuna's chariot! But Shakuni's maya has no power over the Gandiva. A gleaming arrow dissolves the beasts, and the moment's fright they brought.

Arjuna roars at Shakuni, "This is war, not a game of dice! Come, fight me if you dare."

He covers Shakuni's chariot with flames from the Gandiva. His rage forgotten, Shakuni bolts, the Pandava soldiers laughing at him. Arjuna pulls on his bowstring and Kurukshetra trembles with that sound, even as Lanka did when Rama once pulled on the Kodanda at the gates of that evil city. The Kaurava soldiers run to Drona to save them from the dreadful Pandava.

Bheema, Satyaki, Dhrishtadyumna, Abhimanyu, Nakula, Sahadeva, Shikhandi and Draupadi's sons are beside Arjuna at the head of the army. Drona rides against his invincible sishya. Dhrishtadyumna sallies to meet him, unnerving the master. With Arjuna back, Yudhishtira comes to fight again. Some of Dhritarashtra's sons confront him. Seeing his father unsure of himself before Dhrishtadyumna, as bright as the fire from which he was born, Aswatthama dashes to his side. Drona's son fights like another Arjuna. In fury at all the death inflicted on the Kaurava army today, and for the honor of his father who commands Duryodhana's legions, Aswatthama fights like ten kshatriyas.

Neela, prince of Mahishmati, a splendid archer, has killed five hundred Kaurava soldiers. Aswatthama rounds on him. Valiantly though that prince fights, he is no match for Drona's son. Aswatthama cracks his bow and, without waiting for Neela to pick up another weapon, cuts his head off with a scythe-tipped shaft. In rage, the Pandavas surround their guru's son. At once, twenty Kaurava warriors appear at his side, and the battle spreads evenly again.

Mace in hand, Bheema leaps out of his chariot and fells anyone foolish enough to stand before him. Drona turns to the son of Vayu, and now Karna goes with him. Seeing Karna, Krishna steers Arjuna's chariot straight at him. At once, the fighting stops everywhere; all eyes are on the two sworn enemies. Their rivalry has been a legend for so long. For so long millions of men have waited for the moment when Arjuna and Karna would meet on Kurukshetra.

Karna wastes no time, or paltry weapons; he greets Arjuna with an agneyastra. Quicker than seeing, Arjuna extinguishes the weapon of fire with one of the blue sea, a varunastra like a river from his bow. It is a breathless moment on Kurukshetra, when the two astras meet like a wave and an island of flames, and subside against each other. But then, as if the time for these two heroes to fight has not yet come, other warriors join the fray and the battle becomes diffuse again.

Still buoyed by his victories of the morning, Arjuna kills Shatrunjaya, in a carmine flash. Dhrishtadyumna rages as if he is in contention with Arjuna, to see which of them can kill more of the enemy. Now they fight in knots of kshatriyas: Dhrishtadyumna, Satyaki, Arjuna and Abhimanyu against Drona, Karna, Aswatthama and Duryodhana. The sun sinks, at last, on the frenetic spectacle and conches boom to call an end to the twelfth day of the war.

There is no doubt to whom the day belongs. Arjuna has destroyed the Trigarta army, and a thousand other Kaurava soldiers; and Drona could not take Yudhishtira. A red-eyed Duryodhana comes to his Acharya, his Senapati. He does not come alone, but with many of his brothers and some of the other kings, his allies.

When he speaks to his master, Duryodhana's voice is soft, but his words are like knives. "Susharma lured Arjuna away from Yudhishtira, and he lost most of his army, and his brothers. You had all morning to take Yudhishtira, but you did not. Either you are no more the warrior you once were, or your love for the Pandavas prevents you from keeping your oath. I never asked you to do anything special for me; you made the offer. We pinned our hope on you, Acharya. Susharma sacrificed his army and his brothers' lives; but you broke your word."

Bheeshma had grown used to Duryodhana's sharpness. But Drona is not his Pitama. The Acharya rasps, "You know I did everything I could! And I would have had him, but Yudhishtira fled. Before he returned, Arjuna was back."

Duryodhana says nothing to this, but his mood does not change. If anything, his silence is more contemptuous that his words were. His face burning, Drona cries, "I swear I will kill one of their best warriors tomorrow. I will kill a maharathika for you. There is a vyuha for such hunting: the chakra. Tomorrow, we will form our legions in the chakra vyuha, and snare a great kshatriya. None of the Pandavas, except Arjuna, knows how the chakra vyuha is breached. He must be lured away again, and I will kill you an archer who has killed ten thousand of our men!"

A slow smile breaks on Duryodhana's face. He turns to Susharma, who says, "I will take Arjuna far away, and tomorrow he won't escape us."

Duryodhana hardly believes this. But he is happy to allow Susharma to sacrifice himself for the life of one of the Pandava maharathikas. One warrior who had killed ten thousand men was worth Susharma's life, and his brothers'. Drona nods curtly, turns on his heel and walks away. Within him, he seethes; he even thinks fleetingly of renouncing his command. But he was not born a kshatriya, and being Senapati of the army of Hastinapura is not a charge the ambitious Acharya will easily relinquish. He swallows his pride, and promises himself he will prove worthy of his position. Tomorrow, Duryodhana would lavish his praise on him. Drona's vow is to cost the Pandavas dearly.

SEVEN

The chakra vyuha

DAWN OF THE THIRTEENTH DAY OF THE WAR, THE THIRD OF DRONA'S command: the sun rises amidst weird haloes, portending some tragedy. Tall and grim, Drona stalks on to the field, a man who has left conscience behind him. He deploys his legions in the chakra vyuha, phalanx of the spinning wheel. The formation is almost flower-like, with Duryodhana at its heart, and around him ring upon ring of kshatriyas. Karna, Dusasana and Kripa are among the inmost layer; in the next, is Jayadratha with his aksauhini. At Jayadratha's side is Aswatthama, and Duryodhana's brothers form the next ring of the chakra. Shakuni, Kritavarman, Shalya, Bhoorisravas and their legions are the outer rim of the wheeling flower, with Drona himself beyond the perimeter. On the fateful thirteenth day, all the Kaurava soldiers wear red clothes and garlands of red flowers, and from afar, by the light of dawn, it seems that a gigantic carmine lotus has bloomed upon the earth: a blood lotus.

The fighting begins. Today, Bheema leads the Pandava army. He rides out before Satyaki, Dhrishtadyumna, Drupada, Kuntibhoja, Kshatradharma, Brihadkshatra, Sisupala's son Dhrishtaketu, Sahadeva, Nakula, Ghatotkacha, Yuddhamanyu, Uttamaujas, Shikhandi, Draupadi's sons, Virata, Yudhishtira, the Kekaya brothers, and a hundred other kshatriyas. In a throng, they attack the scarlet vyuha. But the brahmana is there at the rim of his formation, and he is like a mountain against which the waves of a sea dash in vain. His chestnut horses flit everywhere, and his arrows are an impenetrable veil. Behind Drona's veil, the other Kaurava warriors seem to wheel, round and round, never showing a still target. It is a subtle vyuha, and its kshatriyas' shafts fly out in hot swarms from where they are least expected.

The chakra vyuha melts the Pandava legions in a sludge of gore, and they have no Arjuna with them to cleave the spinning wheel. First thing after the conches blared, Susharma challenged him again with a fresh complement of Samsaptakas: now, mercenaries recruited in the night for fine sums of money. Once more, Arjuna and the Trigartas face each other, far from the rest of the battle.

There is no breaching the chakra vyuha. Not Bheema's elemental strength and the inspired archery of the others, combined, can break a way into the turning maze, which vomits death out of its hermetic confines. Exhilarated, the Kaurava soldiers fight as never before, and hardly a handful lose their lives from stray arrows, from inescapable fate; while thousands of Pandava soldiers perish. Drona's esoteric vyuha is perfectly secure against Yudhishtira's army. It is an almost magical formation, and only a maharathika knows exactly how to penetrate the fluid chakra.

Yudhishtira cries in despair, "Doesn't anyone but Arjuna know how this vyuha can be breached?" Then he remembers; of course, another kshatriya knows the secret of the chakra vyuha: Arjuna himself has taught Abhimanyu.

Yudhishtira turns in excitement to his nephew, "Abhimanyu, only four men know the mystery of the chakra vyuha. Krishna, Pradyumna, Arjuna and you. You are our only hope, child, will you break into the wheel of death?"

Abhimanyu hesitates, a frown on his face. Yudhishtira says, "What is the matter?"

That prince replies, "I can break into the chakra vyuha quite easily. But my father had time only to teach me how to enter the spinning maze; he did not show me how to come out again. I may be trapped inside."

Yudhishtira says quickly, "Once you make the breach, we will all follow you in."

Bheema cries, "I will be at your heels, Abhimanyu, and Dhrishtadyumna, Satyaki, the Kekayas, Panchalas, Prabhadrakas and the Matsyas. Make the first break, and we will smash the vyuha."

How Abhimanyu's eyes shine at the privilege. He cries, "I will bring glory to the Houses of Kuru and Vrishni. My father and my mother, and my uncles will be proud of Abhimanyu today!"

The chakra vyuha

Yudhishtira embraces the boy of sixteen summers, that great kshatriya. The Pandava says, "May all the Gods bless you! Our best warriors will ride with you, Abhimanyu. Go, my child, bring us glory."

Abhimanyu has no doubt he can break into the chakra vyuha. Only, the wheel is known to snap shut as soon as an enemy enters, as some carnivorous flowers do around a bee. But his uncles have assured him they will not let the vyuha close behind him. They will shatter the wheeling thing, as soon as he breaks in. His kshatriya blood coursing, Abhimanyu climbs into his chariot. With a radiant smile, he salutes his uncles. Yudhishtira orders two fine archers to climb in behind the prince, to watch his back. Then, the other Pandavas and kings all climb into their rathas, and follow Arjuna's son.

Abhimanyu says to his sarathy, "Fly at the chakra vyuha!"

The man can hardly believe the command. "My prince, Drona is a wily brahmana. This is a trap laid for you. He knows your father is away against Susharma's Samsaptakas, and I hear he has sworn to kill a maharathika today. Don't ride into mortal peril, Abhimanyu, I fear for your life."

Abhimanyu snorts at the man's fears. "Drona is so smug I look forward to fighting him! Have you forgotten who I am, that you fear for me? I am Arjuna's son, I am Krishna's nephew! Not all the Kauravas together can hold me. After today, they will tremble at Abhimanyu's very name. This is no time for faintheartedness; our men are dying like flies. Why, I would not fear Arjuna, Indra, or Vishnu himself in battle. Ride, sarathy, ride at the chakra vyuha!"

With a sigh, and dread in his heart, the charioteer cracks his whip and rides at Drona's cunning wheel.

EIGHT

Jayadratha's moment

Like a bolt of lightning upon the earth, Abhimanyu's chariot streaks at Drona's vyuha. But for the banner that ratha flew, it could be Arjuna himself flying at the enemy. Abhimanyu knows how to penetrate the vyuha; he knows the soft parts of the outer wheel. Ignoring all the more obvious targets the other Pandavas aimed at, before him, he looses a torrent of fire-shafts to the right and the left of where he rides. He sweeps past Drona with that tirade, and the vyuha crumbles at its rim. In the panic that follows, the chakra is breached at exactly the place Abhimanyu rides at, though he hasn't shot a single arrow directly ahead of him. He flits through to the inside of the vyuha, and the Kaurava soldiers run from him in terror.

Just behind Abhimanyu ride Bheema, Yudhishtira, Satyaki, Dhrishtadyumna and the others, straight at the fracture in the vyuha, while Drona rallies his men, quickly. But it isn't the brahmana but another who snaps the vyuha shut in the Pandavas' faces.

Within the chakra vyuha, Abhimanyu hunts like Yama. He is hardly a human prince, any more, but a young God in his chariot, his bow radiating astras all around him. That boy cuts down a thousand men before the Kaurava warriors recover and attack him in an angry throng. Already, though it isn't noon yet, the field within the chakra has the appearance of Kurukshetra when the sun is setting: littered with corpses, the ground blood-drenched. The common Kaurava soldiers run blindly from Arjuna's son.

Roaring, Duryodhana charges Abhimanyu. In a flash, Drona is at his king's side, knowing how dangerous it is for him to face the youth alone. Duryodhana is at the heart of the lotus and Abhimanyu has broken right through to him in moments. At Drona's anxious call, Aswatthama, Kripa, Kritavarman, Karna and Shakuni rush to protect Duryodhana. They form a ring around Abhimanyu, and attack him all at once. But he is indeed Arjuna's son, Krishna's nephew, and he is indomitable! Arrows flare from him in every direction, rays of light, banks of death.

Not all those warriors together can contain Abhimanyu. Bhoorisravas, Dusasana and some other sons of Dhritarashtra ride at him. Even as he holds them off, easily, beats them back in a wrath of arrows, he cuts Karna's armour from his chest, and strikes him deep with a shaft like a serpent. Karna staggers in his chariot, and his bow falls from his hand. And how proudly the uncle's eyes shine to see his nephew's valour. But he cannot show at all what he feels; not though part of him longs to fly to Abhimanyu, and begin fighting at his side!

Arjuna's illustrious son scatters the enemy as a storm of light will some shreds of darkness. Karna and Shalya make a brave stand, but not together can they face his stunning archery. Abhimanyu knocks Karna out of his chariot with a virile gust of arrows. He strikes Shalya unconscious, so that king has to be borne out of battle.

Drona watches the young man approvingly. He says to Kripa beside him, "He excels his father! Look at him, he can burn up all our army if he wants. But it seems he restrains himself, or fate holds him back. Mark my words, he doesn't yet fight as he can."

Duryodhana hears this. His face darkening, he turns to Karna, "Do you hear him? Do you hear the love in his voice? Ah, this Drona can vanquish Indra and Yama if he wishes. But he loves his precious Arjuna, so how will he kill Arjuna's brat? I doubt the young fool could have broken into the chakra vyuha, if the Acharya had not let him. And now, knowing he has Drona's protection, he fights like twenty kshatriyas. It is not that Abhimanyu is exceptional, but that our Senapati will not harm him."

Karna makes no reply, though he longs to tell Duryodhana that there is no archer on Kurukshetra like Abhimanyu. But Dusasana hears his brother, and says, "You are right. Drona will not harm Abhimanyu; we must do it ourselves. Watch me kill the whelp, Duryodhana. That will break Arjuna's heart, and Krishna's, too. They may even die of grief. This is a fine chance, my brother: we can win the war by just killing this boy!"

With a roar, he flies at Abhimanyu, imagining that he, Dusasana, will be the kshatriya who wins the war. Karna smiles to himself. The battle between the ambitious Dusasana and Abhimanyu lasts only a few moments. Seeing the Kaurava ride at him, Abhimanyu breaks the bow in his hand from an incredible way off, before Dusasana has even raised it. Then, five more searing shafts, quick as one, cut Dusasana down in his chariot, and his sarathy rides off the field with his unconscious warrior.

Karna rides at Abhimanyu once more. But his heart is not in this fight, and anyway the youth is irresistible. Karna is wounded again, and has to flee from his nephew. Abhimanyu fights on, a vyuha by himself. Often, his boyish laughter rings above the roars and screams of his enemies.

Meanwhile, at the rim of the chakra, the other Pandava warriors find themselves held up, extraordinarily. Yudhishtira, Bheema, Shikhandi, Satyaki, Dhrishtadyumna, Drupada, Virata, Nakula, Sahadeva, the Kekaya brothers and Dhrishtaketu streamed after Abhimanyu like its tail behind a comet. But only Abhimanyu breaks into Drona's wheel; and, once he does, the vyuha seals itself around him like the arms of death. Bheema and the rest are hardly a chariot's length behind the Arjuna's son, when he makes his rupture and storms in. He turns briefly, and smiles beatifically at his uncles. Then, a lone kshatriya looms before the Pandavas, barring their way. To their surprise, they see it is Jayadratha.

At first, Bheema roars with laughter. Just he and Arjuna had routed this villain in the jungle, when he had abducted Draupadi. But there is something Bheema does not know about Jayadratha, nor do any of the others. Yudhishtira and Satyaki are the first to charge him, contemptuously; Jayadratha gives them such a fight! They had expected to sweep past him before the Kaurava chariots rode back to fill the breach Abhimanyu made. Jayadratha holds up not just Yudhishtira and Satyaki, but soon enough, all those matchless kshatriyas. He does not let them advance a foot.

Yudhishtira breaks his bow, but, quick as light, Jayadratha picks up another and fights on. He kills Bheema's horses and plucks his bow right out of the wind-son's hand. Arrows stream from Jayadratha with sureness and swiftness far beyond anything he ever possessed. The dullard fights like Arjuna or Karna today! The Pandavas can hardly believe what they are seeing. With a superlative fusillade, Jayadratha drives back not merely Bheema, but Dhrishtadyumna, Virata, Drupada, Shikhandi and Yudhishtira. He bars their way with a wall of arrows worthy of Bheeshma himself; and as he holds them up, a hundred Kaurava chariots fly forward to seal the crack in the chakra vyuha.

In moments, the vyuha is as it was before Abhimanyu broke in. Siva's boon to Jayadratha is fulfilled: that if Arjuna and Krishna were not near, one day he would hold up the other four Pandavas by himself. And this was a day of sweet revenge for Jayadratha, for the way they had humiliated him in the forest; though he would not savour that sweetness for long.

Yudhishtira and Bheema fling themselves at the chakra vyuha, but to no avail. The horror of what has happened dawns on them. They remember what Abhimanyu said, 'I can break into the vyuha quite easily. But my father had time only to teach me how to enter the spinning maze; he didn't show me how to break out of it again. I may be trapped inside.'

Yudhishtira is numb with guilt, to remember his thoughtless answer to the boy, 'Once you make the breach, we will all follow you in.'

Bheema shudders to recall his own rash promise, 'I will be at your heels child, and Dhrishtadyumna, Satyaki, the Kekayas, Panchalas, Prabhadrakas and Matsyas will fly in after you. Only make the first break, and we will smash the vyuha in moments.'

Bheema stares helplessly at Yudhishtira, who is as stricken as he is.

NINE

Abhimanyu

WITHIN THE CHAKRA VYUHA, ABHIMANYU IS A HUNGRY TIGER LOOSE among a wilderness of deer. He kills thousands of men, his face so young and innocent, his archery so mature, so awesome. Like Karttikeya among the Asuras, Abhimanyu is at the Kaurava legions: bodies are scattered everywhere, one heaped on the other, and blood runs in little streams. Those whom he kills hardly cry out any more. It is as if they expect to die at his hands; indeed, as if they would rather die quickly, than suffer the torment of fear with which he stalks them. Soon, no one can count how many men that handsome prince has killed. He strews the field with corpses and severed limbs as priests do blades of Kusa grass upon a vedi. He scatters Kurukshetra with noble heads of Kings, adorned with crowns, turbans, ear-studs, pearls and diamonds, like lotuses cut from their stalks and flowing blood.

He looses a gandharvastra at the enemy. It is a missile of dreams, and suddenly they see a thousand Abhimanyus everywhere, each one shooting at them. The Kaurava soldiers run in every direction. Many of them fall on their own comrades in panic and hack one another down. Abhimanyu's clear laughter crests that wave of death.

Moved by foolhardiness, envy and a hope for quick fame, Shalya's son Rukmartha challenges Abhimanyu. The duel between the two is intense, but brief; and Arjuna's prince severs Rukmartha's young head. Rukmartha's incensed brothers rush at him from four sides. But he strikes them all down, quicker than seeing, and they are carried unconscious from the field.

Duryodhana's beautiful son Lakshmana Kumara* rides at Abhimanyu from a flank. A wild duel breaks out between the cousins. Fire in his eye, Duryodhana roars encouragement at his boy; and for a while, it seems Abhimanyu is contained. He cannot lacerate the Kaurava legions any more; Lakshmana absorbs him. Duryodhana's son fights like the prince of old, Rama's brother, after whom he is named. But then, Abhimanyu pierces his throat with a perfect arrow. With his father watching in horror, Lakshmana Kumara dies.

Duryodhana's roar echoes on Kurukshetra, as if he himself had been shot. His face a mask, he cries, "Kill the wretched boy, he has killed my son!"

Six maharathikas stream forward against Abhimanyu. Drona, Kripa, Aswatthama, Karna, Brihadbala and Kritavarman surround the meridian prince. Meanwhile, Abhimanyu has seen who sealed the chakra vyuha against his uncles. He attacks Jayadratha with a gale of silver shafts. It seems he does not mean just to break the wheel open again, but to destroy it. But Jayadratha bars his way with a legion of elephants, and some exceptional archery of his own.

Like thunderclouds around the rising sun, the six maharathikas surround Abhimanyu. But he fights like the sun himself, and not the six together can quench him. Like a dancer in his chariot, he, infuses a lifetime's heroism into an hour; as if he knows he hasn't a lifetime but just this hour to make his name immortal. Abhimanyu knows the other Pandavas have been kept out of the chakra vyuha, but he fights as if they are all with him, in his very body. The six maharathikas have their horses killed by lightning from the hands of Arjuna's son. They have their bows shredded, and their chariots shattered beneath them by impossible volleys.

Wounded and bloody, Karna runs from the fight, and Shalya rides up to take his place. Abhimanyu's fiercest assailant is Brihadbala, who fights as if he knows his own final moments on earth are here. The prince shoots the armour off his chest, with inspired precision, then pierces him through his heart, and Brihadbala dies. Dusasana's son flies at Arjuna's boy. Abhimanyu cries, "At least you stand and fight! It must be your mother's blood in you, because your father is a coward."

---

* KMG: He is 'as handsome as a yaksha prince, even a son of Kubera'.

Aswatthama looses a flaming astra at Abhimanyu. It glances harmlessly off his clever mail and, in reply, the prince covers Drona's son in blood. Breathlessly, Shakuni says to Duryodhana, "We must attack him all together."

Karna cries to Drona, "We must kill him, or he will kill us all! Acharya, tell us how this terrible boy can be slain."

Drona says wistfully, "Ah, he is a golden storm, isn't he? Arjuna's son is greater than Arjuna! It is the armour he wears that keeps him safe; and the way his father has taught him to wear it."

Karna cries, "Tell us how to kill him, or the war is lost!"

Slowly, Drona says, "You must kill the two men who guard his rear. Then break his bow, and his chariot."

"Easy to say, Acharya, but haven't we tried?"

"Only when you face him. You cannot vanquish this child when you face him, not you, Karna, or anyone. But there is a way, a desperate way. You must ride behind him, and sever his bowstring when he isn't watching you."

Karna winces, and Drona has turned away before he can answer him. The spirit of war possesses the warrior completely. Karna steals behind Abhimanyu and cuts his bowstring with an exact shaft. That prince spins around in shock, with a roar on his lips, "Coward! Who are you?"

Kripa kills the two guards protecting Abhimanyu's back. Drona kills his horses; Kritavarman shatters his chariot under him. Then, six mighty archers attack him together, as he stands unarmed before them. They are like a pack of wild dogs running down a golden stag. They cover him with arrows. His eyes bloodshot, his body shaking with the ignominy of what they have done, he roars at Drona, "You are my father's guru. They say Drona is a great warrior. This is the deed of a coward!"

He turns on Karna, while they still shoot at him. Abhimanyu sneers, "You are Bhargava's sishya! You dare call yourself my father's equal, and my uncle says you are a man of dharma. Is this your dharma? All of you are known as noble men, but I see today how such maharathikas fight. Cowards! How does the earth not open for shame and swallow you?"

He seizes his sword and shield, and leaps down from his ruined chariot. Staving off the tide of fire in which they seek to consume him, Abhimanyu runs forward: to kill them all. Drona breaks his sword at the hilt, and Karna smashes his shield. Abhimanyu stands bared before his sanguinary enemies, and they strike him with a hundred shafts, that crash into him one after the other, drawing maroon geysers.

Blood streaming down his body, Abhimanyu runs back to his chariot, and has a thought of his father. 'Arjuna, I will not see the pride in your eyes when you hear what I have done today.'

Then, his own eyes fill with tears; he thinks of Subhadra, and knows she will be heartbroken when she hears he is dead. Abhimanyu thinks of Krishna, while they shoot at him at will, and his armour still shields him from most of their arrows; of Yudhishtira and Bheema, he thinks. How stricken they would be at what had happened today, how tormented with guilt that they could not come to him when he needed them. But Jayadratha would pay for what he did; he would pay with his life.

Abhimanyu pulls a wheel free from the broken axle of his chariot. By now, he is a setting sun on Kurukshetra, crimsoned by enemies' arrows he wears like a kshatriya's proud ornaments, in profusion. He whirls the chariot-wheel over his head and stands radiant before them, his spirit undimmed by the least tinge of fear. Abhimanyu cries, "Save your honour, Kshatriyas! Don't let shame stain your souls. Come and fight me one by one, if you dare!"

Even as Krishna did at Bheeshma, he strides at Drona, wheel in hand. His hair flies in a breeze blowing just around him, his face shines supernaturally. He raises the wheel to cast it at Drona. The Acharya splinters it in his hands with ten wish-like arrows. Abhimanyu seizes up his mace from the ruins of his chariot. He cries through bloody lips, "Come, Kshatriyas, fight me one by one!"

He charges Aswatthama, taking Drona's son unawares. Though Abhimanyu is gravely wounded, he kills Aswatthama's horses with blows like falling thunder. Aswatthama's rear guards leap at him; he crushes their heads like eggshells. Aswatthama flees. Knowing death is near seems only to embolden Arjuna's son. He smashes chariots, and their warriors run from him. An entire legion of elephants he kills, blowing like death's wind among the grey beasts.

Then, Dusasana's son leaps down from his own ratha and rushes at Abhimanyu. Abhimanyu's face lights up when he sees him. He roars gladly, "At last a kshatriya! Come cousin, let us fight: for our elders are all cowards."

They fight with ringing mace-blows. No Kaurava warrior dares shoot at Abhimanyu, for fear of killing their own prince. But he has lost a lot of blood from the shafts of the six maharathikas. Dusasana's son and he strike each other a tremendous blow, at once. Both fall together, but Abhimanyu faints. In a moment, he wakes and reaches for his weapon. But Dusasana's boy has already got up and hefted his mace. Just as Abhimanyu begins to rise, the other youth swings his weapon down squarely on his head, flattening it, so blood and brains spurt out. Blemishless Abhimanyu falls back without a cry, dead at twilight.

Around the golden prince, Arjuna's sixteen-year-old son, the Kaurava warriors erupt in coarse joy. Their yells echo in heaven: treacherous Drona's hot shouts of jubilation, and terrible Karna's, and Aswatthama's, Duryodhana's, Kripa's and the roars of all the rest, as if they had killed a hundred great warriors.

As the sun sinks sadly over that crime, it seems not just the day but all the age has grown dark at how they killed beautiful Abhimanyu. If any of them feels remorse, none shows it, not even Karna. Instead, their cries of celebration swell in an obscene squall, deafening the elements. The chakra vyuha has served its purpose; Drona has kept his word to his malignant sovereign, even if he has lost his soul by doing so.

Across the field, Yudhishtira and Bheema hear that awful roar, and they know Abhimanyu is dead. Yudhishtira swoons in his chariot. The Pandava soldiers dash from the field in irrational terror. Arjuna has not yet returned from his battle with the Trigartas.

TEN

Arjuna's vow

THEY HAVE CARRIED HIM BACK TO THE CAMP, BUT WHEN HE WAKES from his faint Yudhishtira sits on the ground, holding his head and sobbing. He wails, "I sent the child to his death. I killed him. He said, 'I can break into the vyuha, but not out of it. I am afraid I may be trapped inside.' And without thinking I replied, 'We will all follow you in. Once you make the breach, we will smash the vyuha.' I sent Abhimanyu to his death. With my child gone, what will I do with a kingdom, or even a throne in heaven? What will I do living?"

Bheema stands there, crying silently, too shocked to speak.

In a while, Yudhishtira says, "Drona and Kripa, Karna and Aswatthama, Duryodhana and Shalya could not contain him. So the cowards killed him with treachery, or my heroic child would have finished them all today!" He turns to the others, "I beg you, one of you kill me before Arjuna comes back and asks, 'Yudhishtira, why did you send my son to his death?' How will I face him? How will I tell him? How will I tell Subhadra and Krishna?"

He faints again. In his swoon, Vyasa comes to his grandson and says to him, 'Though he was just a boy, Abhimanyu died like a kshatriya. He has found heaven for himself. All that are born will surely die, and you must not let your grief consume you. The war remains to be fought and won, and you must keep courage.'*

---

* Actually, Vyasa discourses at length here to Yudhistira, on death. This discourse runs into some twenty-five pages.

Yudhishtira awakes, somewhat consoled. But he thinks, "What will I say to Arjuna?"

Arjuna is turning home from his encounter with the Samsaptakas. After a day's battle, Susharma had been routed, his brothers all killed and most of his army as well. The sun sets and Krishna turns his chariot back from the field. Suddenly, Arjuna touches his sarathy's shoulder and whispers, "Look at the omens, they are all evil. My body trembles, my heart beats wildly and I am full of fear. I hope Yudhishtira is safe."

Krishna replies, "No evil has befallen Yudhishtira; for none can. Put away your fear, Arjuna, and rejoice that Susharma has no men left with whom to challenge you. Tomorrow, you can fight beside your brothers again."

As they arrive in the Pandava camp, terrible anxiety rears its head again in Arjuna, like a serpent. Silence rules the camp. Arjuna asks frantically, "What is this dreadful quiet? No vinas are playing, and the men slink away as if they want to avoid me. Where are my brothers? Where are my sons, who come to greet me every evening? Where is Abhimanyu today? He is the first to run up, with his smile, and embrace me. Something awful has happened. Krishna, terror grips my soul!"

They climb down from the chariot and come to Yudhishtira's tent. Walking in, they see all the others sitting there, stricken. Arjuna stares at Yudhishtira. His brother does not raise his face, only wipes the tears that flow incessantly from his eyes. Bheema makes to rise when Arjuna enters. But he falls back with an anguished moan, as if his legs cannot support him, or his tongue utter the words that his lips try to form. Nakula sits very still, gazing at the floor. Sahadeva stares out fixedly through the tent-flap, and does not meet his brother's eye. Draupadi's sons are there, but they also turn their faces away.

No lamps burn in that tent. Night occupies it entirely, as it does the hearts of those within. Dread grips Arjuna in a vice. He asks, "Where is Abhimanyu? My son is the first to receive me every evening. Why are you all so quiet? Say something!"

Only Yudhishtira's sobs break the silence. Arjuna dare not think the unthinkable thought that licks at him like a flame. He breathes, "I hear Drona formed the chakra vyuha today. You didn't send my child into it, did you?"

Only silence answers him. Slowly, he continues, speaking to himself, "None of you knew how to enter the chakra vyuha, only my son. I taught him. But I hadn't time to show him how to come out of it." He stops, a horrible certainty dawning on him. He whispers again, "Yudhishtira, did you send Abhimanyu into the chakra vyuha?"

Yudhishtira gets up and puts his arms around Arjuna. "Don't say another word, just kill me. Then ask the others your questions, of why and how, because I have no answers to them. Kill me, my brother, I killed your son." Yudhishtira is beside himself. "You must avenge your son's death now, you must kill me! Kill me Arjuna, kill me! I killed Abhimanyu, I swear it is true, I killed your son!"

Arjuna falls as if he has been cut down with a sword. Even Krishna sits abruptly on the floor, his eyes filling. Then he sees Bheema beside him, devastated. He takes Bheema's hand in compassion, and the son of the wind falls sobbing into his arms. Yudhishtira stands turned to stone.

Arjuna wakes with scented water sprinkled on his face. He sits up and cries, "How did it happen? Tell me everything! How could he die? Couldn't all the Pandavas and Panchalas together protect him? He knew he could not come out of the chakra vyuha. He must have told you that I had only taught him how to break in. He knew he would die if he was caught inside the wheel of death. He knew it is a trap. Ah, my son!" He faints again.

Then, waking once more, "Oh, Abhimanyu, you were the flower of chivalry. You would never begin a duel, even against your worst enemy. You always waited for the first arrow to be shot at you. How could the Gods allow this? How will Arjuna live when Abhimanyu is dead? Who had the heart to kill my beautiful boy?"

And he is wracked with sobs. Abruptly, he turns on Yudhishtira, "How could you let him go alone into the chakra vyuha? You were there, Yudhishtira. Bheema and Sahadeva, Nakula, Dhrishtadyumna and Satyaki were there. How did you let him go in alone, when you knew he could not come out? How did you, Yudhishtira? Answer me!"

There is no answer. Arjuna cries again, "But who actually killed Abhimanyu? There is no one in the Kaurava army that could match my child. He was a greater kshatriya than them all. Tell me, who killed my prince? Surely, there was some treachery! Ah, my son, they must have surrounded you and shot you down like a dog. I see your sweet face all bloody, as you lie on Kurukshetra as meat for jackals and vultures. How will I face your mothers? How will I break this news to Subhadra and Draupadi? How will I face his wife, the child Uttaraa?"

He staggers to his feet, flings his quiver and bow from him. He cannot bear the violence of this sorrow, and faints again. Once more, they revive him with scented water and salts. Now, Krishna takes Arjuna's hand, and speaks to him gently, "You mustn't grieve like this. Your son died a hero's death. He gave his life that many others may live, and in peace. In his sixteen years, Abhimanyu achieved what the greatest kshatriyas hardly do in a lifetime. Those whom the Gods love very much, they call back quickly to themselves. Abhimanyu is in Devaloka now, with his grandfather Indra. But your brothers are here around you, Arjuna. Look at them. Are you blind that you don't see the guilt that savages them? Are you made of stone that you cannot see how they suffer? Instead, you indulge your own sorrow, and make their burden insupportable. Abhimanyu was not only your son. He was the child of us all, and we hardly loved him less than you did."

With a moan, Arjuna runs to embrace Bheema, who breaks down completely, like a child himself. Arjuna falls at Yudhishtira's feet, crying, "Forgive me! Oh, forgive the harsh things I said to you! I beg you, forgive me, my brothers."

Yudhishtira embraces Arjuna, and their tears flow together. Nakula and Sahadeva come forward to clasp their brother, then, Dhrishtadyumna, Shikhandi and Satyaki, all crying as if each one had lost his own son.

In a while, Arjuna says, "Tell me now, what happened? I am calm enough to hear everything. Satyaki, tell me. Dhrishtadyumna, my friend, tell me the name of the man who killed my child. Yudhishtira, my brother, tell me."

A storm of tears takes him again, and he says, "My heart is made of stone, that it doesn't break in a thousand pieces when my child is dead! I am a devil that I still live, when my Abhimanyu is gone."

Yudhishtira takes Arjuna's hand, and makes him sit beside him. "I will tell you, Arjuna. I will tell you everything that led to the death of the jewel of our line. Early in the day, Susharma lured you away from the main battle, and the Acharya formed his chakra vyuha. The fighting began, and we could not stand against them at all. The chakra wheeled round, and from every part of it, arrows flew out at our men. We tried to break the vyuha, all of us together, Bheema and I, Satyaki and Dhrishtadyumna, Sahadeva and Nakula. But Drona stood at its rim and held us off.

"Our legions were being shredded. If the chakra was not breached the war would end by evening, and all our men would be dead. Arjuna, thousands of our soldiers died each moment, and we were not able to kill more than a handful of theirs. In despair I called Abhimanyu, and said to him, 'Among us only you know how to breach the chakra. We must break in, Abhimanyu, or the war is lost.'

He said, 'My father taught me how to break into the chakra vyuha, but I don't know how to come out again.'"

Yudhishtira cannot go on, and, in a whisper, Bheema takes up the story. "He did tell us he could not come out of the vyuha once he had broken in. But we said to him, 'We will be at your heels, Abhimanyu. Just make the first break, and we will smash the vyuha.'

"All of us stood before him, Yudhishtira and I, Nakula and Sahadeva, Dhrishtadyumna, Shikhandi, Satyaki, Drupada, Virata, the Kekayas, his brothers, and many more. How could he doubt what we said, or refuse to do as we asked, when our men were dying like flies? I will never forget the light that was upon him. Joyfully, he said he would make the breach. He climbed into his chariot and rode at the vyuha. He fought like a Deva; no, he fought more magnificently than any Deva: he fought like Abhimanyu! And the vyuha parted for him like a woman, while Drona stood helpless." Tears fill Bheema's eyes again, and he says hoarsely, "How will I ever forget how I saw him last? Just as he was storming into the chakra, he turned in his chariot and gave us all such a smile. Arjuna, that smile will haunt me for the rest of my wretched life!"

Bheema breaks down again, and Arjuna takes his brother in his arms and comforts him. Yudhishtira takes up the tale. "We were no more than half a chariot length behind him, so he had room to manoeuvre. All of us were ready to fly into the vyuha after him. We saw him split the chakra, we saw him flash past the Acharya. We saw him turn and smile, and, Arjuna, after he had entered, the chakra was still open! There was a gap in it wide as two chariots. We rode at the opening, Bheema in front, I just behind him, and then the others. But suddenly, Jayadratha loomed in our path."

"Jayadratha? And how many with him?"
Yudhishtira bends his head. He says in a whisper, "Only he."
"Jayadratha held you all up, alone?"
"He fought like a hundred Jayadrathas."
Arjuna looks around in disbelief. Bheema and the others nod their heads. Krishna says quietly, "He worshipped Siva for a boon, and this was it: that, one day, he would hold up all the Pandavas by himself, as long as Arjuna was not with them. That was his revenge for what you did to him in the forest."

Yudhishtira resumes, "Jayadratha held us up, as if Siva himself fought from his body. And before we knew it, a thousand men had filled the gap in the chakra vyuha. The vyuha was sealed again, but now with our child inside. For hours, we heard the screams within, as he burned them. They could not hold him at all; he killed ten thousand men. He did not die alone, he killed Duryodhana's boy Lakshmana."

Arjuna gasps. Sahadeva says, "He killed Brihadbala."
Yudhishtira says, "He fought them long, like a tiger a pack of dogs." He chokes again, "But in the end, they killed him."

Arjuna cries, "But how did they kill my son? Who killed him?"
Sahadeva comes near, and takes his hand. Quietly he says, "My brother, listen to the vilest crime committed on Kurukshetra. Six maharathikas surrounded him: Karna, Kripa, Drona, Aswatthama, Kritavarman and Dusasana's son. He fought like a God, and routed them all. Then, I heard Karna went to Acharya Drona and asked him how Abhimanyu could be killed; or the war would be lost by dusk, because our child would have razed their army. Drona told Karna that as long as he had his bow in his hand, Abhimanyu's armour was impenetrable. Our precious Acharya told Karna that the only way to kill our prince was to break his bow from behind, like a thief.

"Twice Abhimanyu had beaten Karna off, wounding him sorely. So now the dastard crept behind our child, severed his bowstring, and then broke his bow. The six surrounded him again. Drona killed his horses, Kripa his guards and his sarathy. And when he was defenceless, they shot him with a hundred arrows, until he was bathed in blood. He fought on, and we watched some of it and heard the rest. We were helpless, because we still could not break into the chakra vyuha.

"He killed a legion of elephants, though by now he was gravely wounded. When he staggered on his feet, Dusasana's boy leapt down from his chariot and they fought with maces. They struck each other down. Our child was exhausted, and Dusasana's boy rose before he did. He struck Abhimanyu a last blow on his head, and your son died. There was no shame in his death, Arjuna, except for those who killed him." He hangs his head, "And for all of us who sent him to his death." Sahadeva, also, breaks down and cries.

They watch Arjuna's eyes turn red. He rises softly, and stands before them trembling. In terrible quiet, he says, "I swear I will kill Jayadratha tomorrow. Let the Kauravas guard him with every man they have, let Siva himself come to protect him; Jayadratha will not live. If I don't kill him tomorrow, let all the punya I have leak away from me, and let me find the worst hell of all for myself. I swear by this sacred agni, and by this Gandiva, that if I don't kill Jayadratha tomorrow, I will make a pyre for myself and walk into it with my bow in my hand."

Arjuna picks up the Gandiva and pulls on its string, so the night resounds with that noise. Krishna raises the Panchajanya to his lips and blows a blast on it like the thunder of the pralaya. Even the Devas in their loka hear that sound; and with it, hope courses again through the Pandava camp. Arjuna has mastered his grief, and turned it to wrath. There would be a great hunt tomorrow.

Bheema jumps up, and hugs Arjuna. "I am so proud of you! I know you will keep your oath. They must have heard this sound across the field, and they may have died of fright!"

Grief turns to a searing hunger for revenge. The Pandavas leave for their own tents, to try to sleep what remains of the night. When they are alone, though, Abhimanyu's bright face comes to haunt them: how he turned and smiled at them just before he broke into the chakra vyuha.

Hardly a man, common soldier or kshatriya, sleeps, for sorrow that Abhimanyu, splendid prince, is dead. And a new anxiety tugs at their hearts in the small hours: for Arjuna's hot oath; it would not be easy to kill Jayadratha. Kaurava spies would already have carried word back to Duryodhana, and every man of the Kaurava army would be detailed to guard Jayadratha tomorrow. For if Arjuna did not kill him before the sun set, the Pandava must immolate himself to honour his solemn word.

What easier way could there be of killing the invincible Arjuna, than keeping Jayadratha alive until the sun set?

A million men, lying sleepless in their beds, mourning in the night for dead Abhimanyu, pray fervently that the Gods would deliver Jayadratha into Arjuna's hands tomorrow.

ELEVEN

Jayadratha's terror

THE EVENING ABHIMANYU DIED, THERE IS JUBILATION IN THE KAURAVA camp. Drona is lionised: he had kept his word, and one of the most feared Pandava warriors was dead. Moreover, this death, more than any other, would shatter the enemy's morale. It would break Arjuna's heart, and his brothers' hearts. There is even speculation whether Arjuna will kill himself when he hears the news.

Duryodhana learns of the massacre of the Samsaptakas. He thinks it a fair price to pay for Abhimanyu's death. Why, the Kaurava hardly mourns his own son, Lakshmana, whom Abhimanyu killed. He is so excited that Arjuna's boy is dead. The war possesses Duryodhana absolutely; everything else, even his son's life is insignificant when seen in the light of victory. No price is too high to pay, no sacrifice too dear to make. He celebrates with the others, his pale eyes gleaming brightest of all.

Suddenly, the night's silence is riven with the thunder of the Gandiva, followed by the awesome bass of the Panchajanya. In Duryodhana's tent, they all fall silent. This is not what they had expected, this triumphant pulling at bowstring and blasting on conch. It unnerves them.

But Duryodhana cries, "Hollow sounds! They don't deceive me. Their spirits are broken, and they will die soon."

The drinking and celebration continue, if less raucously than before, until Jayadratha bursts in on them, shaking. Karna cries, "What news, O Kshatriya?"

Jayadratha is in such a state he can hardly speak. Somehow, he manages to blurt, "Our spies say Arjuna has sworn to kill me before the sun sets tomorrow! I want to go back to my father's kingdom. It is against kshatriya dharma to pursue someone who has fled the field. Arjuna is a man of dharma. He won't come after me."

Jayadratha has served his purpose already; the shrewd Duryodhana expects no further valour from him. The Kaurava gives a short, cruel laugh. "You are trembling like a woman, Jayadratha. Don't be afraid: a man may swear any oath he likes in a fit of grief, but how will Arjuna kill you? Besides, we hardly killed Abhimanyu with dharma. I think you will be safer with our army than riding home alone. Besides, did you mark what the spies reported? Arjuna said, 'Even if he hides with Siva himself, I will kill him!'"

Jayadratha shakes like a leaf. Duryodhana continues, "The safest place on earth for you is at the heart of my army. All of us will protect you. Even Indra will not be able to touch you, as long as you are with us. I shall be at your side, Jayadratha, and Karna, Vivimsati, Sala, Shalya, Chitrasena, Bhoorisravas, Vrishasena, Purumitra, Kripa, Bhoja, Vikarna, Durmukha, Dusasana, Vinda, Anuvinda, Aswatthama, Shakuni, Alambusa. To name only some of those whose sole task tomorrow will be to guard your life. Why, our every soldier will have my command just to protect you.

"By yourself today you kept Bheema, Yudhishtira, Dhrishtadyumna, Satyaki, Nakula, Sahadeva and all the rest from breaking into the chakra vyuha. And now you fear just Arjuna? He is only another man, like the rest of us. He is no Deva that you should be so terrified of him. I give you my word, and I would stake my own life on it: he will not harm a hair of your head!"

Softly, Duryodhana goes on, "Then there is Arjuna's vow. Jayadratha, you will kill Arjuna: not by cutting him down in battle, but by staying alive until the sun sets tomorrow. Didn't the spies tell you he has sworn to kill himself, if he has not killed you by sunset? I swear you will not die, but he!"

He is full of dark excitement. "Everything is turning our way once more. Abhimanyu's death has achieved what we wanted: Arjuna has sworn a rash oath he cannot keep. And when he burns himself after he fails to kill you, what will the other Pandavas do? The rest will be easy to finish. Jayadratha, you have been chosen to be the pretext of our victory!"

Far from reassured, Jayadratha says, "Can all of us together stop Arjuna from keeping his oath? Duryodhana, we killed his son and fear grips me like a pisacha!"

Duryodhana sighs, "If you won't take my word, let us go to the Acharya and see what he says."

In Drona's tent, Jayadratha asks the master, "Acharya, tell me, am I the better archer or is Arjuna?"

Drona says slowly, "You are both great bowmen, and you have the same guru. But Arjuna is more dedicated than you; not a day passes when he does not practise with his bow for hours. For him archery is worship. He also has the devastras, and he is more resilient than you are.

"But all that does not matter: I will save you from Arjuna tomorrow. I will form a vyuha whose mystery he will never penetrate. We will set you at the heart of it and, guarded by us all, you will be safe."

Jayadratha is still unconvinced, anxiety plain on his face. As if this doubt is a slight to him, Drona says impatiently, "I will do everything I can to protect you. But if it is fated that Arjuna kills you, what shame is there in dying in battle? How splendidly young Abhimanyu met his death today. All that are born must die; and what finer death is there for a kshatriya than to die fighting a war like this one? If Arjuna kills you, Jayadratha, you will find heaven for yourself!"

Jayadratha trembles more than ever. With a sigh, Drona says, "Listen to me. We must save your life tomorrow, not only for your sake but for the very war. I mean to form not one, or two, but three vyuhas, and to hide you at the heart of them. On the outside, we shall have a shakata vyuha, within that a chakra, and finally a suchimukha vyuha, with you at the needle's eye, watched over by a column of maharathikas. I will stand over all three vyuhas, and anyone who enters them will first have to pass me.

"Arjuna has delivered his life into our hands. Even if he breaks past the shakata and chakra vyuhas, it will take him all day. Then, the third and most difficult vyuha will confront him; and I will be at its point again. The sun will have set long before he can reach you."

Jayadratha seems consoled. Duryodhana moistens his lips in anticipation of Arjuna's death.

Later that night, across Kurukshetra, Krishna comes alone to Arjuna's tent. Arjuna lies stiff as an arrow in his bed, his eyes streaming for his son, but his face set like stone. He must keep his vow. First, Jayadratha would die tomorrow. But the others wouldn't escape, the six cowards who had hunted his child down like an animal.

Krishna glides in and sits beside Arjuna. He says, "That was a rash oath you swore. Where was the need to say you would take your own life if you don't kill Jayadratha tomorrow? Duryodhana knows about your oath, and Drona means to hide Jayadratha at the heart of three vyuhas, with every soldier of his army charged to protect one man's life."

Arjuna lies in the darkness, silent. Krishna continues, "A shakata vyuha, first, with Drona at its threshold, then a chakra, and finally, a vyuha to confound even you: a suchimukha, with Jayadratha at its eye. And the body of the needle will have their finest warriors, one after the other, Karna, Aswatthama, Bhoorisravas, Vrishasena, Durjaya, Duryodhana, Shalya, Kripa, Durmukha, and Drona, again, following you in. Can you break past all these in time to kill Jayadratha before the sun sets?"

Arjuna is perfectly calm. He says with unusual certainty, "All these men together are not half the archer I am. Drona and his son will not stand before me tomorrow; nor will Karna or any of the others. Jayadratha will die before the sun sets. How will he not die, when my child Abhimanyu will be watching to see if I keep my oath?

"Why are you of all people so full of doubt, Krishna, when we shall be irresistible tomorrow? Think of it like this: we have the noblest weapon with us, the Gandiva. Some say Arjuna is the best archer in the world and the greatest man who ever lived is my sarathy. When you are with me, Lord, how will I fail?"

Arjuna cannot be certain if Krishna smiles in the night. They sit together without speaking for a time, and Abhimanyu fills their thoughts. Arjuna says, "I cannot face Subhadra tonight. I can't bear to see her cry. I haven't the strength to console Uttaraa. I beg you, go and comfort them for me. Tell them I will see them tomorrow, when I have kept my oath."

Krishna goes to his sister's tent. He finds her crying as mothers have since the dawn of time, whenever they lost a son to a bestial war. She sits on the floor, her hair loose, convulsed with sobs. The princess Uttaraa sits beside her, pale, numb, tears flowing down her shocked face.

Subhadra rises when Krishna comes in. With a wail she runs into his arms, and breaks down utterly. Tears springing in his own eyes, Krishna holds her, while she weeps in tides of grief.

Gradually, Subhadra calms down and they sit beside each other again; she never lets go of his hand. Long they sit, in silence. He wipes her tears with dark fingers, and says gently, "You mustn't grieve like this. Abhimanyu has reached Devaloka; he is part of the Moon. He is blessed, he is blissful, and he died as only the very greatest kshatriyas do. His name is already a legend. Men will always say he was the most perfect prince that ever lived. You must not grieve like this for a warrior who lived as full a life as he did, and died a death for which other men would vie.

"Subhadra, you are a daughter of the House of Vrishni. You are the wife of the greatest archer in the world. Your brothers are kshatriyas, you son was a great kshatriya. You must not cry. We are in the midst of a war, for which your child gave his life. This is no time for weakness."

Subhadra says, "How can I not cry, Krishna? I think of my boy, whom I carried as a golden baby in my arms, whom I nursed at my breast. I think of him lying on Kurukshetra, his body torn and bloody, his head crushed: and how can I not cry? The five Pandavas are alive, peerless Arjuna and Krishna are alive. Yet, my child lies dead, with kites and hyenas picking his bones. Oh, how could this happen, Krishna? I thought the sons of Pandu are the mightiest kshatriyas on earth, but I see I was wrong. Otherwise, with his uncles beside him, how was my son killed? He was just sixteen, and you tell me that I should not cry because he died a kshatriya's death? What do I care about that? To me, my child is dead, and that is all!"

Sobs wrack her again. Krishna holds her close. When her storm abates, he says, "This is your sorrow speaking, Subhadra. Abhimanyu was killed treacherously by the evil ones we fight. Arjuna and I were lured away from the main battle; then the murderers enticed our child into the chakra vyuha and killed him. They broke his bow from behind, because not all of them together could stand against your son in battle.

"Adharma has been born into the world, and the kali yuga rises over the earth. But the murderers will not escape punishment. Already, Arjuna has sworn to kill the man who sealed the chakra vyuha after Abhimanyu broke into it. Before the sun sets tomorrow, Jayadratha will die; and that will be just the beginning of our revenge. The cowards will all die, and their deaths will not be so noble as your child's. Think that Abhimanyu is now one of the Gods, and he covered himself in glory before he died.

"Subhadra, how is it you cry so bitterly only when your own boy is dead? Do you know how many thousands of mothers have lost their sons to this war? Their tears flow in a river that fills the night. It is a river that sprang in this world long ago, when the very first war was fought; and the river of grief will flow on until the world ends. Dry your tears, Subhadra, and console this child Uttaraa. She needs your strength now, and instead you show her your weakness."

Draupadi comes in, and she is hardly less broken than Subhadra. But she is brave, and far stronger for what she has endured these thirteen years. Subhadra and Uttaraa turn to her, almost as to a mother, and Panchali comforts them as only another woman can. Krishna returns to Arjuna's tent.

His warrior is waiting for him, now ready with his offerings. This is a nightly ritual, and Krishna sits quietly before the Pandava, who worships him with flowers, fruit, incense and honey. The Avatara places a hand on Arjuna's head, blessing him. He says, "*Jaya vijayi bhava.*" May you always be victorious. "You must sleep now, Arjuna. You must be fresh and rested tomorrow."

Turning down the lamp, Krishna goes out into the night, where his sarathy, the faithful Daruka, waits with his chariot to take him to his own tent. Krishna climbs in. They drive back slowly, with a breeze full of prophecies caressing their faces.

TWELVE

Arjuna's dream

Past midnight, Krishna lies awake in his bed. He gets up, and sends for Daruka. He makes the sarathy sit beside him. Krishna takes Daruka's hand and says, "You have heard about Arjuna's impetuous oath. So has Duryodhana, and he plans to guard Jayadratha like his own life. Drona will form three vyuhas, and keep Jayadratha at the eye of the third, protected by their maharathikas. If Arjuna doesn't kill Jayadratha before the sun sets tomorrow, he must take his own life."

Daruka sits listening. Krishna goes on, "I know what a kshatriya Arjuna is. But it will be harder to pass Drona and the others tomorrow than it was to kill the Nivatakavachas. Then, it is dakshinayana and the sun will set early. I am afraid for Arjuna. There are sinister powers, greater than we know, which watch over Duryodhana's destiny. They will bend their will to keep Jayadratha safe, and have Arjuna's life cheaply."

The sarathy has never seen his master's black eyes so anxious. "Daruka, you know how much I love Arjuna. Why, I love him more than I do anyone in the world, more than my queens or my sons. He is part of me as no one else is. If Arjuna were to die tomorrow, I would follow him into the fire."

A flicker of alarm in Daruka's eyes; he has not heard Krishna speak like this before. He remembers something he had heard from the lips of mystic rishis and wise old men: Arjuna and Krishna were born on the same day; they are Nara Narayana. The Dark One lowers his voice, "And if we both die, Daruka, how will the others resist the evil that wants to sweep everything before it? I have sworn I will not fight in this war. But I will perjure myself, and break my vow so Arjuna may keep his."

He glances around, for the night has ears. Drawing the sarathy nearer, Krishna whispers, "You must do something for me, old friend. Prepare my own chariot tonight for war. Arm it with all my weapons; put the Saringa in it and my quiver, the Kaumodaki, and my Shakti. Tie on the Garuda banner, but don't unfurl it yet. Cover Valahaka, Saibya, Meghapushpa and Sugriva in their armour, and yoke them. You also don mail, and wait at the edge of the field.

"If you hear me blow a rishabha on the Panchajanya, fly to me, Daruka. I will kill Karna, Duryodhana and the rest. I will loose the Sudarashana at them, and we will see how their fine vyuhas stand before my Chakra. Be ready from dawn, Daruka, listen for the rishabha on my conch."

Daruka says, "I will do as you say, my Lord. But when you are his sarathy, how will Arjuna not keep his vow? How will Jayadratha not die before the sun sets tomorrow?"

Krishna smiles, "It will do no harm to be prepared."

"Your chariot and weapons will be ready. So shall I."

The sarathy bows, and leaves. With a sigh and, somewhat relieved, Krishna lies down on his bed; with a prayer for Abhimanyu, he falls asleep. In another tent, Arjuna also lies in his bed, and he is full of disquiet. But he is tired after the harrowing day, and drifts off into a troubled slumber.

Arjuna dreams, and Krishna appears in his dream. The Dark One says to him, 'You must not grieve like this; you will only strengthen your enemies. Anxiety is a sickness, Arjuna; it saps you. I am with you, my friend, fear nothing.'

Arjuna answers him, 'Will I be able to kill Jayadratha before the sun sets tomorrow? If I cannot, the world will mock me and I must take my own life.'

Krishna grows thoughtful. 'Do you remember Indrakila, O Pandava? You sat on that mountain in tapasya to have a weapon from Mahadeva. Do you remember how Siva came to you as a vetala? You fought the Lord, Arjuna, and he was so pleased with your warrior's worship he gave you his Paasupatastra. You must use the Paasupata against Jayadratha, and he will not live.'

'But where is that astra, Krishna?'

'Come, sit with me in dhyana,' says Krishna.

In the dream, Arjuna purifies himself; touching holy water, he sits before the Avatara. He shuts his eyes, and feels Krishna's grace upon him. Krishna says, 'Meditate on the Lord Siva.'

In dhyana, Arjuna feels himself leave his body. Krishna is beside him, and holds the Pandava's hand. Together they fly through a cerulean sky, swift and straight as two arrows. They fly north, cleaving the wind. It is a lucid dream, and Arjuna sees everything that lies below him. Across the Himalaya, range of a hundred peaks, they flit, and still they flash on, always north. They pass Himavan and fly over a vast tableland, dotted with crystal lakes. On they fly, until they see the most pristine lake of all: the Manasarovara.

Beyond the lambent waters of the Manasa, a lone mountain looms, its peak rounded like a full moon, or a gigantic pearl. This is Kailasa, most sacred of mountains, anointed with opalescent snow. Krishna and Arjuna fly closer to the mountain like a vision. Suddenly, its higher slopes turn blinding, as if a hundred suns have risen upon it. Siva sits on a white ridge, ineffable Uma at his side, and they swathe Kailasa with their light.

Krishna and Arjuna fly down to Siva's feet. They prostrate themselves before the God of Gods. They eulogise him with the Satarudriya, his thousand names. Siva smiles. Laying his hand on their heads, he blesses them. He says in his voice deeper than the sky, 'Tell me what boon you have come for, Nara Narayana.'

Arjuna says, 'Lord, I have come for the Paasupatastra.'

Even as he speaks, Arjuna is startled to see the offerings he made earlier that night to Krishna laid at Siva's feet! Serene Mahadeva says, 'My bow and the astra I once loosed at the Tripura lie below the lake of amrita. Seek them out, Arjuna, and bring them to me.'

Krishna and Arjuna find themselves flying north again, now with a host of Sivaganas around them. The ganas bring them to the banks of a velvet lake, like a sea before them. They stand on its shore, the dark waters glimmering as far as their eyes see, and a spray of nectar flying in their faces. Suddenly, a sibilant hissing fills that place and, with a powerful swirling, the waters part. Two immense serpents, scintillating jewels in their hoods, raise themselves high into the air before Krishna and Arjuna. They are thousand-headed snakes, and flames spew from their jaws. Krishna begins to worship Siva aloud with the Maharudriya; Arjuna quickly does the same. At once, the fiery nagas grow quiescent. As the chanting continues, they are transformed into two shining weapons: a golden bow and a silver arrow float out to the two warriors. Kneeling on sands like petal dust, Krishna and Arjuna receive those ayudhas.

With that bow and arrow, Arjuna and Krishna, and the Sivaganas with them, fly back to Kailasa. They come to Siva again and offer the weapons to him. He smiles at them, and an unearthly light issues from his body. From it, a wild brahmachari stands forth, his eyes fire, his hair falling to his waist in a shimmering blue and black cascade. Bowing to Siva, the apparition picks up the ancient weapons. He shows Arjuna the only way that bow, older than the world, can be strung. He shows him how the arrow is fitted to it, and the string is drawn back. Arjuna masters the art of it instantly, as no other archer could.

As he pulls back the bowstring, Arjuna hears Siva's voice, deep in his mind, intoning the mantra for the Paasupatastra, which begins by invoking Ganapathy, the Lord's elephant-headed son, master of his host of ganas. The mantra fills every cell in Arjuna's body. In a moment, he knows it perfectly. Now, the brahmachari takes those weapons back from the Pandava and, with a cry, from where he stands he casts them back into the distant lake. Becoming fierce serpents again, they submerge below dark ripples and are gone. But Arjuna feels the lake and the weapons within himself still; and he knows the astra will return to him, whenever he needs it.

The brahmachari vanishes. Krishna and Arjuna prostrate themselves once more at holy Siva's feet. As he blesses them, Arjuna sees him again as he did in the forest near Indrakila: as the vetala! All his anxiety swept from him in a wave of joy, Arjuna touches the Lord's feet and flies back to Kurukshetra with Krishna beside him.

Arjuna emerges from dhyana, but Krishna has vanished from his dream. Other dreams flow into the Pandava's sleep, and bear him away on tranquil currents.

THIRTEEN

The three vyuhas

Dawn is yet to break over Kurukshetra, and Yudhishtira is the first one up to greet the fourteenth day of war. As always, he begins his morning with worship. When he has finished, the sun appears on the rim of the world, and the birds in the trees around the battlefield hymn the brilliant Deva. As Yudhishtira rises from his prayers, Krishna walks into his tent.

"Did you sleep well, my Lord?"

Krishna smiles, "I did. And now, seeing your serene face, I know that no harm can befall me!"

With Krishna, come Bheema, Dhrishtadyumna, Satyaki, Shikhandi, Sahadeva, Nakula, Draupadi's sons, Chekitana, Dhrishtaketu, the five Kekaya brothers wearing red mail and looking like indragopaka insects, Yuyutsu, Ghatotkacha, Drupada and Virata. One by one, Yudhishtira embraces them all. Those lords of the earth, the soldiers of dharma, are solemn on this momentous fourteenth morning of the war.

Yudhishtira turns again to Krishna. "My Lord, we rely on you to see us through this war, to bring us victory. More than any other day, we depend on your grace today." He takes the Dark One's hand, "Arjuna must keep his vow, Krishna. With you as his sarathy, he cannot fail."

Krishna is full of light, full of faith. He says, "There is no kshatriya in all the world like your brother. When Jayadratha dies, the Kauravas will know that Arjuna's vows are made not just of words, but arrows. Have you seen the omens of the earth and the sky, of the water, the wind and the birds? They all cry out that you will prevail today and that the

Kauravas are doomed. Yudhishtira, I am here with you, I swear Arjuna will keep his oath."

Arjuna walks in, and he seems entirely calm. He touches Yudhishtira's feet, and those of the others older than him. Yudhishtira embraces his brother. "Your face is as bright as Krishna's, as if the two of you have some secret you are keeping from us. I am content, Arjuna: seeing you like this, I have no doubt that Jayadratha will die before the sun sets. But if there is some good news you have, won't you share it with us?"

Arjuna recounts last night's dream, still vivid in his mind. He says, "Siva's own astra is mine to summon. Jayadratha will not see the sun set today."

Word goes out about Arjuna's dream, and soon the Pandava camp echoes with the news. Conches and trumpets blare, and excited soldiers make for the battlefield, eager for the fighting to begin. No one doubts, any more, that Arjuna will keep his oath. Who will stop him, when Siva himself has blessed the Pandava?

Krishna climbs into Satyaki's chariot to leave Yudhishtira's tent; for, they have both come as Yadavas to the early council. But when they arrive at the stables where the horses are stalled, Krishna is a sarathy again for the day's battle. The Avatara goes into the enclosure like any charioteer; with his own hands, he rubs down Arjuna's gandharva horses. He washes them lovingly, then drapes mail over their smooth bodies, while they stand for him in delight, nuzzling their faces against him.

Fortunate indeed is the Pandava who has Vishnu's Avatara for his sarathy! Krishna places his warrior's weapons in the chariot, where Arjuna can reach them easily. Finally, he hoists Hanuman's banner over the gleaming ratha and brings the chariot to his cousin's tent. A young servant is strapping the golden mail on his master, which Indra gave Arjuna. Krishna comes in, "Your ratha is here, Kshatriya, and your sarathy is ready for battle!"

Last of all, Arjuna sets his kirita, worked with unearthly gemstones, on his head, picks up the Gandiva, and the two of them emerge. Completely majestic, they mount the white chariot. Krishna takes the reins, while his pale chargers toss their necks and neigh eagerly in anticipation of battle. Regally, they make their way towards the field, the early sun blazing on Hanuman's banner, the vanara alive on it!

At the front, Arjuna says to Satyaki, "In our excitement, we mustn't forget Drona has sworn to take Yudhishtira captive. What better opportunity could he have than today? Satyaki, your task to protect Yudhishtira will be no less than mine. You are more than equal to it, my friend; I leave my brother's life in your hands."

Satyaki says, "Yudhishtira will be safe as long as there is breath in my body."

Across Kurukshetra, they see Drona's chestnut horses flitting here and there, as the brahmana forms the three vyuhas, one behind the other. In the van, facing the Pandava force, is the shakata vyuha, square and solid, the cart phalanx. Behind the shakata, Drona forms a lotus, a padma vyuha, a subtle variation of the chakra in which Abhimanyu died. Like an artist painting, he forms the indrawn petals of the lotus. Near the last of these, like a stem, Drona deploys the Kaurava maharathikas in their chariots: the final and most powerful line of defence. He arrays them straight as a needle, a suchi, one after the other, with the precious Jayadratha at the eye of the needle, which faces away from the field.

With dawn, Jayadratha is full of anxiety again. When he hears the Pandava conches, and sees Arjuna ride out to the front and stand, stern and erect in the white chariot, Jayadratha begins to quake.

Drona lays a kindly hand on him, "The three vyuhas are six krosas long, Jayadratha. Six krosas will separate you from the frontlines. A hundred thousand horsemen, sixty thousand chariots, three million foot-soldiers, fourteen thousand elephants, and then six maharathikas, each one more powerful than all these together, stand between Arjuna and you. Not even the army of Devaloka could break past such a defence before the sun sets. Your eyes will see Surya Deva rise tomorrow, but not Arjuna's!"

Jayadratha is hardly consoled. He peers across six krosas, and sees only Arjuna. He sees every feature on the Pandava's face, as if he already stood next to him. Jayadratha is terribly certain that all Drona's assurances will not keep Arjuna away. Six krosas and hundreds of thousands of fierce kshatriyas separate the Pandava from him; but when he sees Krishna's dark form at Arjuna's chariot-head, he knows that not six oceans would be enough.

Today Drona sets himself at the rim of the padma vyuha. Between him and the Pandava army lies the stolid square of the shakata. One of

Duryodhana's bravest brothers, Durmarshana, begs to command this phalanx. Drona lets him meet Arjuna's first charge. With his legion of bowmen around him, Durmarshana takes his proud place at the head of Duryodhana's army.

Duryodhana's brother is certain Arjuna will not pass him. "I won't let him through. Arrogant Arjuna shall taste Durmarshana's valour today!"

FOURTEEN

Arjuna the magnificent

ARJUNA'S ARMOUR RADIATES LANCES OF FEAR ACROSS KURUKSHETRA. The Gandiva glitters, already piercing Jayadratha's heart. To that king, hidden behind the teeming Kaurava army, Arjuna seems like the God of death. The Pandava raises the Devadatta, and blows a long, echoing blast. The Kaurava frontlines cower at the sound, and when Krishna joins a deep note to it on the Panchajanya, Jayadratha whimpers in his chariot.

Conches resound on both sides for the fighting to begin. Arjuna raises his arm high, and cries to his sarathy, "Let us burn this shoddy cart. Ride at them, Krishna, the sun waits for no man!"

Krishna flicks his whip over his horses' sleek necks. Durmarshana roars like five tigers and charges out of his vyuha to meet Arjuna. Their bows streaming, the cousins fly at each other. Durmarshana fights as never before, and for a while it seems he will hold Arjuna up. Arrow cuts down arrow in flight, or glances off warriors' stubborn mail. But the equal contention lasts only a few moments. Suddenly, Arjuna lifts his archery and heads roll off necks in a macabre pageant. When Arjuna fights like this, no one can see where he bends his bow, or draws another arrow from his magic quivers; or where he aims it, true as death. They see just a blur in his chariot. At times, it seems he hardly moves at all; but enemy soldiers fall in waves before him, blood spilling on to the dark earth from their carved limbs, and wounds through which their spirits fly out to the invisible hosts waiting above Kurukshetra to take them to other realms. Arjuna dissevers their heads so casually: as if he snipped mallika flowers from their stems, to offer Siva for worship.

The air is a murky opacity of ghosts and screams. Not a sound from the Pandava: save that of his bowstring, and the hum of his arrows. When five thousand Kaurava soldiers have died, in moments, and Duryodhana's brother realizes that today Arjuna also fights as never before, Durmarshana bolts, and his men go after him. In the time it takes to tell, Arjuna has smashed the first of Drona's vyuhas: the shakata collapses at his onslaught. And far away, at the eye of the needle he means to thread with a mighty astra today, Jayadratha is near collapse.

As Arjuna's gandharva horses flash forward, Dusasana appears on his path with a legion of elephants, roaring an arrogant challenge. But to the Pandava, it makes no difference whether it is Durmarshana or Dusasana, horses or elephants. All that matters is that they come between him and his quarry, and he will not let them stand. Grey beasts fall as facilely as men did before them: some shot with a score of wooden shafts all over their hulking bodies, others with just one silver arrow through their hearts. The Gandiva sings, calling the enemy to the ceremony of death.

Mowing through his legion, Arjuna comes face to face with Dusasana himself.

He covers his cousin's elephant in a mantle of fire. He shreds the weapons in his hands, sprouts red flowers all over the Kaurava's body, and Dusasana cannot stand Arjuna any longer than his brother Durmarshana did. He, also, turns his beast around and lumbers away quickly. On plunges Arjuna, seeing just Jayadratha before him, and all the others merely obstacles to his reaching that king, his target. It was so when he was a boy and Drona's sishya, and so it remains. Drona watches him fly at the padma vyuha, and is reminded of the day when he gathered his students under a tree in which he had set a wooden bird, and asked each one what he saw. Arjuna saw only the bird's eye, and brought it down. Today, Jayadratha is the wooden bird, and the soldiers guarding him just the leaves in the tree. Like an arrow, Arjuna makes for his prey, brushing the leaves aside.

The white chariot storms the rim of the second vyuha, and Drona rides up to stop his favourite sishya. Arjuna folds his hands to his master, and says, "I have come to avenge my child. Once you said you made no difference between Aswatthama and me, and I pray you still feel the same way. Bless me, Acharya, and let me into your vyuha."

Drona raises his bow in reply. With a smile, he cries, "You cannot enter my vyuha without defeating me!"

Though Drona was the main conniver in yesterday's treachery, Arjuna cannot find it in himself to hate his master. Without rancour, he looses his first volley at his guru, and those shafts are deadlier for the detachment with which they are shot. Drona answers with a scorching salvo of his own, and a tremendous duel begins.

How well each one knows the other's mind; how perfectly they anticipate every shaft. But they are not master and pupil any more: Arjuna is more than his Acharya's equal. The Pandava breaks Drona's bow; before the pieces fall to the chariot-floor, the master has another one out.

For an hour, they duel; and at first, one has a slender advantage, then the other. They fight at the farthest reaches of their genius, until abruptly Krishna cries, "It isn't Drona you have sworn to kill before the sun sets. Time flits by, and every moment is precious. Leave the brahmana here, we must break into the vyuha!"

Krishna swerves his horses away; he drives them round Drona's chariot in a pradakshina. Smiling, Arjuna cries to the Acharya, "My lord, I must leave you!"

Drona roars, "What is this, Arjuna? You ride away from an enemy without beating him? You have never done this before."

Flashing away to storm the padma vyuha, Arjuna calls back, "You are not my enemy, but my guru! Bless me, that I succeed."

The words are borne to Drona on the wind. For the time he has lost fighting his master, arrows flare thicker than ever from the Pandava's bow, and Kaurava soldiers fall before him in lurid waves, and a swell of mortal screams. At Arjuna's wheels, guarding his rear and flanks, ride the Panchala brothers, Yuddhamanyu and Uttamaujas, as they have since the war began. Kritavarman comes to challenge Arjuna, and with him Sudakshina, lord of the Kambhojas, and Srutayus. Their arrows darken the sky. But those shafts themselves are livid, and illumine dim Kurukshetra like strange lamps, flying.

Drona swirls round at the mouth of the lotus, and rides after Arjuna. His careful plans foiled by the Pandava breezing past him, the master dashes after his disciple in anger. The gifted Kritavarman holds Arjuna up, and it seems that Arjuna hesitates to unleash his fiercer missiles at the Yadava. Krishna cries, "He is one of the six that murdered your child! Don't stay your hand because he is my cousin. He is a traitor, and deserves to die."

No sooner has he spoken, than Kritavarman is struck down with ten sizzling shafts that break his bow and smash through his armour, so he falls screaming. His sarathy flies from the field with his bleeding kshatriya. After Kritavarman departs, Sudakshina cannot resist Arjuna for more than a few moments. The Pandava sweeps him aside, and plunges on deeper into the vyuha. A better warrior than Sudakshina looms in his path: Srutayudha who wields Varuna's mace. The mace is a magical weapon, and no one can kill Srutayudha as long as he carries it. When he casts it at an enemy, it divides itself into a hundred maces, and strikes like a flock of thunderbolts; and then, it flies back to his hand. But Varuna had said to Srutayudha he must never cast the mace at anyone who bore no arms, for then it would turn on the one who cast it.

Srutayudha harries Arjuna with the Sea God's mace, but finds he can never strike the Pandava because of Krishna's lightning manoeuvres in the gandharva chariot. Forgetting that the sarathy carries no weapon, Srutayudha flings the mace at Krishna. The occult gada takes Krishna in his chest, but softly as flowers. With a roar of its own, in anger that it has been cast at an unarmed man, the ocean mace flashes back at Srutayudha, and smashes his head like a peach. As soon as he falls, Varuna's weapon vanishes from Kurukshetra; it returns to the Lord of tides.

Seeing Srutayudha die, Sudakshina turns back into battle against Arjuna. But the duel lasts just moments and the Pandava kills the lord of the Kambhojas with an arrow through his heart. Panic takes the Kaurava army. Drona roars above the pandemonium to his legions, to surround Arjuna, they must not let him move ahead. But who can stand before the Pandava today? Drona rushes forward himself, covering Arjuna in a fever of arrows. Arjuna burns them all up with a brahmastra, and they fall away as ashes. Fifty thousand footsoldiers run at Arjuna's chariot. But he is dauntless; he is implacable, as he cuts a way of fire before him with unearthly missiles, parting the dark tide of men in streams of blood.

On through the incarnadine mire the golden chariot ploughs, as if no army stood in its way. Until, two heroic brothers challenge the

Pandava: Srutayus and Achutayus, dead Sudakshina's friends, who have rashly sworn to avenge him. They fly unexpectedly at Arjuna from two sides, and Srutayus strikes Krishna unconscious. When the Pandava's chariot lurches to a stop, Achutayus casts a javelin at Arjuna, a lance like a green star, and strikes him deep in his side. A roar goes up from the Kaurava army as Arjuna reels, and the Gandiva slips from his hand. The Pandava totters against his flagstaff.

"Arjuna is slain!" cry the Kaurava soldiers.

But in their excitement, they do not press home their brief advantage quickly enough. With a cry, Krishna recovers, seizes the reins again and veers away from Srutayus' ominous fire. By Krishna's grace, Arjuna's wound is stanched and the jade lance falls out. Quicker than thinking, the Pandava invokes the aindrastra to quell the thousand arrows that flare at him from every side. With another shaft of power, he cuts down the two brothers on either side of him. A single arrow, which severs Srutayus' head, flies on in uncanny trajectory and crashes into Achutayus' heart.

Seeing four of their kshatriyas die in moments, the common Kaurava soldiers run in panic from Arjuna. The padma vyuha is breached, and every instant the golden chariot flies nearer its quarry, hidden fearfully in the needle's eye.

FIFTEEN

At the rim of the red lotus

Beside himself to see Arjuna storm into the padma vyuha, Duryodhana rides wildly up to Drona. He cries at his Acharya, "Arjuna smashes through your legions as if they are not there at all! Your shakata vyuha fell apart at his first charge, and he has broken into your lotus as if it is made of petals, not soldiers. We do everything in our power to please you, Acharya, but you betray our cause. Your heart is not with me, but with the Pandavas. You stood at the vyuha's rim, and I know that no one could pass you unless you let them."

Drona begins to speak, but Duryodhana rages, "My lord, the deadliest enemy is the one you have taken to your heart in trust. He is like a knife hidden in a pot of honey. I believed you, Drona, when you said Jayadratha would be safe. But look how Arjuna flies at him like a naracha. Why sunset, Jayadratha will die before noon.

"I should have let him ride home; he would have been safer in his own country. I have sacrificed my brother-in-law to Yama; why, he would be safer facing Yama than Arjuna, if my cousin reaches him. You must stop him, Drona. You are this army's Senapati!"

Stung, Drona replies, "You saw me try, but he is as quick as the mind. I am old, Duryodhana, past my prime. Most warriors I can still contain; but this is Arjuna, there is no one like him. And then his horses are gandharva steeds, Krishna is his sarathy!

"But I could keep another vow today. With Arjuna away, I could take Yudhishtira. Let a younger man pursue Arjuna: none better than you, Duryodhana. It will hearten your men to see you lead them from the front; and you can avenge your four friends he killed."

Duryodhana's face turns darker. "Do you mock me, Acharya? That you send me after a kshatriya who swept past you so easily. How can I stop him when the great Drona could not? You saw him strike Kritavarman down. You stood at the lip of your vyuha, like Siva with his Pinaka. But even as you watched him, he killed Srutayudha, Srutayus, Achutayus and Sudakshina, as if they were children. And you ask me to ride after Arjuna? Acharya, you are our only hope, everything depends on you. You must save us today!"

A smile softens Drona's face. "You are like my own son, Duryodhana, I wouldn't send you to your death. Look, I have this armour I have kept just for you." He shows Duryodhana that mail, like treasure in his hands. Duryodhana gasps. "This is Brahma's own kavacha, its links are ancient mantras, and not even the devastras can pierce it. Indra wore this armour when he fought Vritrasura. Come, let me help you put it on."

Duryodhana climbs down from his chariot, and allows Drona to wrap him in Brahma's golden mail. Wearing it, he feels a surge of magic in his blood. He kneels before his guru for his blessing. Laughing, Drona blesses him. Duryodhana says, "Forgive me for what I said rashly to you."

"Even as a father forgives his son," replies Drona. "Now go like the wind, and you will beat Arjuna today!"

As if Brahma's armour touched him with unworldly courage, Duryodhana rides roaring after the Pandava. Seeing their king fly to the rescue, the Kaurava soldiers stream back into battle. This is at the very heart of the red lotus.

Meanwhile, only Arjuna, and Yuddhamanyu and Uttamaujas at his chariot-wheels have broken into the padma vyuha. Drona turns back to the rim of the lotus, where Dhrishtadyumna and the Pandava army storm the phalanx that Arjuna has breached. The two armies meet like the golden Ganga and the midnight-blue Yamuna flowing into each other during a flood. But Drona fights as if for his life and the Pandava legions can make no headway against him. The brahmana's astras light up Kurukshetra, they consume Yudhishtira's legions and, inexorably, Drona forges nearer Yudhishtira himself.

Duryodhana's brothers fight beside their Senapati. Bheema and his brothers face Vivimsati, Chitrasena and Vikarna. Vinda and Anuvinda face Virata, and Shalya confronts Yudhishtira. Dusasana and Satyaki battle, Shakuni meets Madri's twins. Shikhandi and Baahlika fight, while Ghatotkacha and Alambusa lock again in a vicious mayic duel. Far away, beyond Arjuna forging on alone through the padma vyuha, Aswatthama and Karna stand guard over Jayadratha, with Bhoorisravas and his army, Kripa, Sala and Durjaya.

Baahlika and Dhrishtadyumna duel briefly, then Draupadi's sons stream forward, an army by themselves, and their battle with Baahlika is like the war of the five senses against the mind! Satyaki and Dusasana light the air between them with igneous shafts that extinguish each other in flight. But Dusasana fights in inspiration today, and finds his mark with a blinding arrow that strikes Satyaki unconscious in his chariot. The Yadava's sarathy rides away from battle, until his warrior recovers. Satyaki is up in a moment, flaming back at Dusasana.

Dhrishtadyumna rides at Drona, and a refulgent duel breaks out. Duryodhana's sharpness has stung his Acharya deeply, and he fights beyond himself now: to reach Yudhishtira at any cost. The old master overwhelms Dhrishtadyumna. He smashes his chariot, kills the horses and sarathy of his old enemy's son. Growling, Dhrishtadyumna seizes up a sword and leaps on to Drona's horses. Nimble as the wind he runs along their backs at his master. This is not less than deliverance for the brahmana: the man born to kill him makes an absurdly easy target.

Drona raises his bow, with an astra that will blow the fire-prince to pieces at such short range. He draws back his bowstring, and for a moment that lasts a life, Dhrishtadyumna sees death face to face. He springs forward along the horses' backs, knowing he cannot reach Drona before the Acharya's arrow blasts him to bits. For an eternity, Drona's bowstring remains drawn back, and with hallucinatory clarity, Dhrishtadyumna sees every detail of the master's powerful hand, his fingers, the rings on them, the deep wrinkles on his face, the smile on his lips, every hair in his beard, the look almost of surprise in his eyes that the kshatriya born to kill him makes such a rash gift of his own life. All this is emblazoned on Dhrishtadyumna's mind.

For another eternity, Drona's hand remains, quivering, where it has pulled back his bowstring. Dhrishtadyumna wants to shut his eyes but finds he cannot. Then, he hears a noise deafening the huge silence that has fallen over his world: the sound of an arrow cleaving the air, loud

At the rim of the red lotus 339

as a tempest. Dhrishtadyumna waits in that awful moment for the shaft to tear his chest open. Instead, he sees a flicker of shock in Drona's eyes. He sees the tremor that passes through the master's hand. He sees his bowstring sag and its arrow drop on to the chariot floor. He hears its clatter mingle with the swish of Satyaki's timely barb humming past after it severs Drona's bowstring, saving Dhrishtadyumna's life.

Drupada's son still stands petrified, but Satyaki flashes up, sweeps his friend out of his daze and into his chariot before Drona can recover. With a feral roar at being done out of his priceless prey, whose life he held in the palm of his hand for that moment, Drona seizes up another bow and covers the dashing Satyaki in a swath of arrows. But the Yadava in his fleeting chariot fights like his master, Arjuna, today. Quick as light, he breaks Drona's bowstring again; and while the furious brahmana reaches for another weapon, Satyaki strikes him deep with darts like fire.

Drona cries to his sarathy, "Ride at Yudhishtira! It is him we must take today."

But Satyaki cries to his charioteer, "The brahmana who takes up arms is more terrible than any kshatriya. For his pride is great, and his mind is subtle. Drona is the heart of the Kaurava army. Ride at him, friend, fly between him and Yudhishtira!"

In a steep swirl, Satyaki confronts Drona again. Drona attacks the Yadava in wrath, meaning to kill him now. But Arjuna's pupil fights back magnificently, and the war pauses around them to watch their duel. Drona mutters to himself, between burning shafts, "He fights like Bheeshma or Arjuna, like Bhargava or Karttikeya. Arjuna's sishya is his guru's peer!"

Twice more, Satyaki breaks Drona's bow in his hand. The Acharya's face is red. He looses an agneyastra, of a hundred billowing flames, to consume Satyaki, his chariot and all. The raging weapon, used commonly against a whole legion, flares at the Yadava in flash-fire. A lesser kshatriya may have panicked to see that inferno. But serene Satyaki, poised, quicksilver Satyaki has learned well from his master. He invokes a varunastra of the Lord of the sea, and douses Drona's fireball in a crested blue wave, tall as a hill.

Not only the awestruck soldiers of both armies on the field, but Devas and gandharvas, charanas and apsaras, have gathered in the sky to watch this duel. Drenched in water from Satyaki's varunastra, his shaft of agni put out, Drona roars on Kurukshetra so the ground shakes under his chariot wheels. But before the duel can resume, Nakula and Sahadeva, Bheema and Yudhishtira ride to Satyaki's side. In a moment, Dhrishtadyumna in a fresh chariot, Virata and the Kekaya brothers are beside him, as well; and from the Kaurava ranks, Dusasana, with a score of his brothers, arrives to fight for Drona. The battle spreads out again, as the armies fall at each other.

Though he has been frustrated in his attempt on Yudhishtira, and is furious at the Yadava responsible, Drona is still warrior enough, artist enough, to admire the relucent valour of young Satyaki.

SIXTEEN

Deep into the enemy's army

THE SUN RISES TO HIS ZENITH, AND BEGINS HIS DESCENT IN THE SKY. Blazing midday finds Arjuna and Krishna battling not just the Kaurava army, but time himself. Arjuna is twice as fierce as when he began, and Krishna's horses respond not just to their reins he holds, but to his very thought. Like steeds of light they flit, weaving dizzily through the enemy, while Arjuna's arrows cut a hot path ahead of them.

But unlike the Pandava and his dark sarathy, the white horses begin to tire. Their careen through two dense vyuhas has been long and hard, and, nearing the end of Drona's lotus, they turn sluggish. Their coats are drenched in sweat; there is foam at their mouths, and their flanks are bloody with arrows. Those unearthly horses, given to Arjuna by Chitrasena the gandharva, cannot be killed; but they do tire and their bodies heave from thirst.

Jayadratha is still far away, beyond the final petal of the lotus, three-fourths of a krosa from Arjuna; and the greatest Kaurava warriors stand between the Pandava and his prey. The sun sinks in the west, and the Kaurava soldiers are heartened by the sight of the exhausted horses. Seeing the white chariot slow to a crawl, the Avanti brothers, Vinda and Anuvinda, ride at Arjuna in the hope that speed will give them a telling advantage.

They roar a challenge at the Pandava. They cover not just him, but his thirsty horses and his blue sarathy with arrows. Blinding Arjuna breaks the bows in their hands. But Krishna can hardly manoeuvre his chariot any more; his horses slow to a walk, panting. Seizing the chance, Vinda attacks Arjuna from ahead and Anuvinda from the rear. How will he resist them both, when Yuddhamanyu and Uttamaujas have been left far behind, and have rejoined Dhrishtadyumna's legion? But Arjuna will not let anyone hold him up. On another day, he may have indulged himself in a prolonged duel with the gifted brothers. Today, he takes Vinda's head off his neck with a crescent-tipped shaft, and bloodies Anuvinda's chest, before cutting off his arms and legs, and then his head.

Crying out, the Kauravas swarm at the white chariot from every side. Arjuna swivels where he stands, the Gandiva spewing an iridescence of arrows all around him. He holds them off, as fresh as when he began, killing hundreds. Then, he tells Krishna, "The horses are wounded and thirsty. They will not reach Jayadratha unless they rest."

Krishna replies, "They must be unyoked, and their wounds tended. They must drink, or they will drop. But how?"

He sounds worried. He wonders if he should raise the Panchajanya and blow a rishabha on it. But Arjuna says calmly, "Unyoke them, Krishna. Let them rest."

"Here?"

"It is as good a place as any," smiles the Pandava. "You tend to them, I will fight on foot."

Arjuna climbs down from the chariot. He looks like Kamadeva, standing there with the Gandiva in his hand as if it were the Love God's sugarcane bow. The Kauravas roar to each other, "Look! Arjuna's horses can't run any more."

"He stands helpless on the ground. This is the time to kill him!"

"Surround him. Cover him with arrows!"

So they do, running at him in excitement. But too soon: Arjuna on the ground is deadlier than Arjuna in his chariot. Rushing forward recklessly, thinking they have him at their mercy now, they hardly see the Pandava move; but a tide of arrows rises around him. It sweeps in every direction, and turns into a red wave of screams. The Kaurava soldiers shrink from him, gripped by a fear deeper than the fear of death.

Arjuna stands, a flame on Kurukshetra, and there is nothing his enemies can do about him. As disdainfully as he slew them from his chariot, he slaughters them standing on the earth. Krishna says, "There is no water anywhere, how will the horses drink?"

Hardly as if he was fighting a battle, Arjuna replies, "But, my Lord, there is water just behind you. Look."

Between scathing volleys, he invokes a varunastra. At once, where a moment ago there was only arid ground with hardly a blade of grass growing, a lake shimmers in the noonday sun, its surface covered with lotuses, why, swans floating there! That water is sweet and clear, bounded on all sides by Arjuna's incredible arrows. There is even a fine pavilion on its banks with steps leading down to the water: all made of arrows.

Krishna laughs aloud; the Kaurava soldiers stand gaping. The Dark One unyokes his horses, and leads them to the sparkling lake. First, he lets them drink, then gently plucks out the barbs that stick in their sides. He speaks softly to them all the while; he has tears in his eyes that they were hurt.

Meanwhile, the Kaurava soldiers have stopped fighting. Instead, they cry to each other, "A lake with one arrow!"

"With lotuses and swans."

"How inviting it seems. I would rather swim in Arjuna's lake than fight him."

"Look!" cries another soldier, pointing to the sky. Flights of water birds, goose and duck, ibis and teal have spotted the lake from on high and glide down onto its cool blueness. And the Kaurava legions, enchanted, stand watching Krishna tend to the elven horses with boundless love. So tranquil is his dark face, so absorbed: as if he is not on brutal Kurukshetra, surrounded by a million bloodthirsty enemies, but back in Vrindavana with his gopis, on the banks of a charmed pool in that forest.

In no hurry at all, he washes the blood from their wounds, healing them with his touch. He strokes their sides, speaking to them in a tongue of the gandharvas. When he has rubbed them down, he splashes them with the crisp water, and lets them drink again to their hearts' content. Their thirst quenched, their spirits revived, the pale horses toss their heads and whinny to show they are ready to be yoked again. The wonderful beasts know, as well as any man on Kurukshetra, that this is an exceptional day and there is a critical mission on hand.

Still in no hurry, Krishna yokes his horses once more. Taking his time, he brings the chariot to his kshatriya. With no sign of being pressed for time himself, Arjuna climbs back into it; and this complete calm, in the face of a rapidly westering sun, unnerves the Kaurava army. Seeing Arjuna's miracle with the lake, seeing how confident both he and Krishna are, Duryodhana's soldiers have no doubt that Jayadratha will die before the sun sets.

At last, the Pandava's chariot sets out towards Jayadratha again. Their morale destroyed by his cool assurance, now Duryodhana's men make easy prey for him. Like the wind in Devaloka, fly the white horses. In moments, leaving a thousand men dead in their wake, Arjuna and Krishna arrive at the very end of Drona's formidable padma vyuha, and they smash through the last petals of the lotus.

Ahead lies the needle made of the Kaurava maharathikas, with Jayadratha at its eye. Now, Krishna and Arjuna actually see that king for the first time since the day's fighting began: cowering in his chariot, his face ashen. Jayadratha sees them, as well. He knows that two of Drona's invincible vyuhas have fallen apart at Arjuna's advent, and just a slender stalk of warriors separates him from death. He stands shaking in his chariot. Arjuna forges nearer.

Then, a roar goes up from the Kaurava soldiers. Suddenly another royal ratha breaks out of the sharp tip of the suchi. In it, his lean form covered in golden mail, stands a dark kshatriya determined he will stop the Pandava. It is Duryodhana come to fight for Jayadratha, as if that king's life is his own: Duryodhana come to see that the sun sets on Arjuna's defeat.

Krishna says to Arjuna, "Be careful. Remember a desperate man fights like ten others. Duryodhana hasn't faced you yet, show him what it means to fight Arjuna! Kill this one man, and the war will end."

Arjuna says softly, "Here is the man who caused us years of grief, who broke my brother's heart. He has so much to pay for. But I wonder how he comes to fight me so boldly today."

Duryodhana stands laughing in his chariot, and cries, "Come cousin, fight! I have heard all about the astras you have, show me your valour."

Quick as love, he shoots ten arrows at them, black fire. Krishna and Arjuna cry out. Arjuna replies with a volley sharp as serpents' fangs. His arrows glance off Duryodhana, and the Kaurava's laughter rocks the field.

"Is this the best you can do? I fear for your life if it is!"

And another potent volley has Krishna crying, "His arrows are like poison. I have never felt such pain before!"

The Dark One swings his chariot here and there to avoid Duryodhana's shafts. Arjuna shoots back, a hundred astras, each of which would have killed a hundred men. But they graze off Duryodhana like green stems of flowers; his hooded eyes flash at them, his exultant roaring is louder still. Krishna assumes that Arjuna does not shoot fiercely enough at his cousin. To goad the Pandava, he says, "Duryodhana masters you effortlessly, and the sun plunges down like a fishing hawk. We might as well admit we are beaten and turn back."

Arjuna cries, "Why do you mock me, Krishna? It is not Duryodhana we are fighting but Brahma's golden kavacha in which Drona has wrapped him! Look how it shines under his tunic. But I have the astra to pierce this armour. Indra gave it to me in Amravati."

Stung by another shaft like fire, Krishna cries, "Then use it quickly! Time slips away from us."

Arjuna sets a silver arrow to his bow. He invokes the manavastra, with which Rama once killed Maricha. The arrow is a band of lava in his hands. Arjuna draws his bowstring to his ear, but in a blur another archer cuts that shaft in two. The astra vanishes with a hiss of anger. Arjuna whirls around to see Aswatthama grinning at him.

Arjuna roars his frustration. "I can't summon the manavastra again, it will kill me the next time! But watch me, Krishna, I have a way to make him run. Look how the fool wears his priceless mail: like a bullock carrying a treasure on its back, never knowing its worth. And the kavacha doesn't cover all of him."

Arjuna aims some slender shafts, like needles, at the exposed parts of Duryodhana's body; he shoots at his cousin's fingers. The fine barbs pierce the Kaurava's nails, and strike deep into his palms. Wringing his hands, Duryodhana flings down his bow and screams to his sarathy to ride away. Krishna's delighted laughter rings across Kurukshetra. Not two hours remain before sunset.

The maharathikas of the suchimukha vyuha, and their armies, surround Arjuna's chariot, so Krishna can hardly manoeuvre; they are still two leagues from Jayadratha. Krishna cries, "Pull on your bowstring, Arjuna. Let me hear the thunder of the Gandiva!"

As at some great vina, Arjuna pulls at the string of his bow. The war resounds with the twanging. Exhilarated, Krishna raises the Panchajanya, of the hue of clouds, to his lips, and blows blast after blast at the sky.

These sounds reverberate across Kurukshetra, and Jayadratha trembles even more in his chariot.

As if in response to the challenge, Bhoorisravas, Sala, Karna, Vrishasena, Kripa, Shalya and Aswatthama attack Arjuna, at once: eight kshatriyas with their legions. But Arjuna is godlike. He sees only Jayadratha before his mind's eye; all these others are leaves in his way, to be brushed aside. Prodigious Aswatthama has his fire returned to him ten-fold, so he faints in his chariot. Karna, Vrishasena and Shalya attack the Pandava in a knot. Tremendous Arjuna routs them all and the others that bar his way to Jayadratha.

Krishna looks up and sees the rim of the sun not far above the western mountain. Arjuna's heart skips a beat when he follows his sarathy's gaze. But neither of them will show, by so much as a flicker on their faces, how anxious they are; though, perhaps Arjuna's archery bears a trace of desperation. While to Krishna and his warrior the sun seems to fall like a meteor in the sky, to their enemies the star appears to sink so slowly it takes a lifetime to go down.

SEVENTEEN

The sound of Krishna's conch

MEANWHILE, A KROSA BEHIND ARJUNA'S CHARIOT, THE BULK OF THE two armies fights on. Yudhishtira faces Drona, who has sworn to take him captive. Angered by the Acharya's oath, Yudhishtira covers him in arrows, wounds sprouting on the brahmana like poppies. Drona is taken aback; it will hardly be simple to capture the Pandava if he fights like this. Yudhishtira looses a febrile shakti at Drona, which he cuts down with an astra.

Yet, all the while Drona presses forward in his chariot, nearer and nearer Yudhishtira. When he is close enough, like summer lightning he casts a mace at the Pandava. But the master has taught his pupil well: quick as seeing, Yudhishtira smashes that gada aside with his own. Still the impact rocks him back on his heels. Drona cuts down his banner, kills his horses, and lights his ratha with an astra. Yudhishtira saves himself by leaping out, just in time; but his chariot bursts apart in a flash of flames.

Yudhishtira stands defenceless on the ground, and Drona darts at him like a striking cobra. The Pandava has landed on his feet, and some of his soldiers rush forward to protect him. Drona shoots a shaft of sleep at them, and they all fall in a swoon. Like a tiger a lamb, Drona stalks Yudhishtira; he is hardly five chariot-lengths away and there is an outcry from the Pandava army. Then Satyaki flits between the brahmana and his quarry. The Yadava covers Drona in a dazzle of arrows. He flies at Yudhishtira, sweeps him into his chariot and rides away. Drona's roars echo around him.

A thousand duels rage across Kurukshetra. One of the Kekaya brothers, Brihadkshatra, battles a Kaurava ally called Kshemadhurti. Both are splendid archers. They fight long and evenly, until Kshemadhurti breaks past Bhihadkshatra's defences and draws first blood. Next moment, the Kekaya cuts Kshemadhurti's head from his neck.

A Trigarta called Viradhanva fights as if to avenge himself today on the Pandava army for all his brothers and soldiers Arjuna killed yesterday. Viradhanva kills a thousand men, before Dhrishtaketu, lord of the Chedis, rides up to challenge him. Another intense duel begins. Finally, Dhrishtaketu casts a whistling javelin at the Trigarta. It nails him to his flagstaff.

Once more, Satyaki, Nakula and Sahadeva are at the van of the Pandava army, and no one can stop them. Yudhishtira's legions forge ahead. Drona comes again to hunt the Pandava king, and again Satyaki intervenes brilliantly. Realizing he cannot reach Yudhishtira without beating the Yadava, Drona engages Satyaki in a duel. But Satyaki is young and exceptional, and the brahmana can make no headway against him.

The battle between the lord of Sala and Draupadi's five princes rages on, an interminable contention: the war between the mind and senses. But in the end, Sala cannot stand against those mercurial youths. Sahadeva's son shoots him through the throat, and Sala falls.

Bheema fights Alambusa briefly, but the rakshasa cannot face the son of the wind. He melts away with maya, and kills a hundred Pandava soldiers. More than anything, Alambusa terrifies Yudhishtira's legions because he anoints himself in the gore of those he kills. He eats their flesh, quaffs their blood and drapes himself with their entrails. He makes himself truly horrific and even the Kaurava soldiers shrink from him. But Ghatotkacha has long been stalking Alambusa, and now he arrives, sleek as a dark panther, to confront him. Rakshasa and rakshasa fight. Fangs and talons flash, blood spraying from them. The pair no longer use maya, or any weapon except their own bodies. They fight hand to hand, with sinister hisses and cries that make the other soldiers turn to watch, their hair standing on end. It is a long battle; both rakshasas are determined only one of them will live.

Yudhishtira cries to Nakula near him, "How like Bheema Ghatotkacha looks! How like him he fights. Aren't you reminded of when Bheema and Hidimba fought in the vana?"

Alambusa cries, "Rakshasa, you fight for the wrong army and you will die!"

"Not at your hands, Rakshasa," replies Ghatotkacha and, in a blur, seizes his foe. He lifts him high above his head just as his father might have. The strength of his grandsire Vayu in his arms, he flings Alambusa down again, explosively, so his limbs fly off his trunk, and his fiendish head, the scream on its white lips cut off.

A roar goes up from the Pandava army. Fear rips through Drona's legions. Alambusa came out of the jungle to fight for Duryodhana, so he could avenge his friend Baka. Now, Bheema's son has killed him, and he lies like a mountain riven on Kurukshetra.

Yudhishtira rushes up to embrace Ghatotkacha, and a glowing Bheema does, as well. It is then that they hear Krishna's Panchajanya booming across Kurukshetra, again and again, as if he was in dire distress. The thunder of the Gandiva is drowned, and Krishna does this on purpose. He knows they will need help to reach Jayadratha before sunset, and he knows Arjuna will refuse to call for any, if he asks him. Yudhishtira hears the Panchajanya resound, lonely across two vyuhas. He hears Kaurava conches blaring in response. But he does not hear the Devadatta or the Gandiva. Panic grips Yudhishtira. He is certain Arjuna is in trouble, and Krishna is calling for help.

His heart pounding, Yudhishtira rides to Satyaki. He cries to the Yadava, "Krishna calls for help, Arjuna is in danger. Fly to your guru, Satyaki, he needs you!"

Satyaki says, "Arjuna needs no one's help against these Kauravas. I have no worry for him, but for you. An hour ago, the Acharya almost had you, Yudhishtira. It would be foolish to tempt fate again. Drona by himself is more dangerous than all the others together. My place is here at your chariot-wheel, with Bheema and Dhrishtadyumna."

Yudhishtira will not listen. "All that is true. But Satyaki, I am certain Arjuna has desperate need of you. Bheema and Dhrishtadyumna, Draupadi's sons, the Kekayas, Ghatotkacha, Drupada, Shikhandi, Nakula, Sahadeva, Dhrishtaketu, Kuntibhoja and all my army protect me. They will keep me safe from Drona. But only you can pierce the Kaurava legions quickly enough to help my brother. Fly Satyaki, I beg you, don't hesitate!"

Satyaki cannot bear to think that he did not rush to Arjuna's side, when he most needed him; any more than he can bear to leave

Yudhishtira at Drona's mercy. He would never forgive himself, if either Pandava came to harm. But there is no denying the truth of what Yudhsihtira says: Arjuna fights alone and time presses him more urgently.

Satyaki makes up his mind. "I hate to leave you, my lord, but I will ride to Arjuna. The Kaurava army roars like the sea under a full moon, and I long to be at them. I need more weapons, and my horses must drink before I go. It is a long way to the suchimukha."

Yudhishtira gives orders for Satyaki's horses to be tended quickly; and for his chariot to be stocked with every weapon he might need. Satyaki must cross two vyuhas. The first Arjuna had razed; but the padma vyuha is still formidable, and Drona stands guard over it again. Satyaki has fought a long, hard day already. He has fought two enervating duels with the Acharya: once when he rescued Dhrishtadyumna, and then when he snatched Yudhishtira from Drona's clutches. The Yadava decides he needs a brief rest himself; though, his heart sings at the thought of breaking through the Kaurava army, to watch his master's moment of glory when he kills Jayadratha.

Satyaki rides back to the Pandava camp, where he pours cold water over himself, changes his battle-dress, and drinks a jar of black bees' honey to invigorate himself. All this takes hardly any time, and the kshatriya is ready for his mission. His chariot is brought back to him, its panels bristling with weapons, the horses refreshed, for they too have been bathed. Satyaki's sarathy is Daruka's brother; and above his chariot, the banner of a golden lion flutters proudly. Wearing a garland of wild flowers, a vanamala blessed with puja, Satyaki mounts his ratha: and he looks quite like his cousin, the Dark One himself, as he prepares to set out. The sun is plummeting, every moment.

Yudhishtira sends Bheema some way with Satyaki. Like two maruts, they forge through the ruins of the shakata vyuha. Seeing Drona loom in their path, Satyaki stops his chariot. He says to Bheema, "When he sees me go, the brahmana will come for Yudhishtira again. Guard your brother well, Bheema, there is more danger here than at the heart of the lotus."

"Yudhishtira will be safe. Fly now, my friend, the sun won't wait for you or me!"

They embrace briefly. Then Satyaki's chariot flashes away, and Bheema stands gazing after him, as the wind blows the Yadava's long hair behind him.

At Yudhishtira's side, Dhrishtadyumna says, "The omens of earth and sky favour us. Satyaki will cover himself in glory. But let us prepare ourselves for the Acharya."

EIGHTEEN

Terrible Satyaki

SATYAKI, THE WHIRLWIND, BLASTS THROUGH THE REMAINS OF THE shakata vyuha. The Kaurava soldiers attack him in fury, but he blows them away: blood flying everywhere, and screams ringing, as the Yadava storms on. In a few moments, at the edge of the padma vyuha, a smiling Drona confronts Satyaki. Satyaki has no choice but to fight. Shaft for shaft he matches the canny brahmana and it seems that neither will prevail.

Drona knows what Satyaki has come for, and is happy to frustrate his mission. He cries, "Your guru escaped me like a coward when we fought. He folded his hands, made a pradakshina round my chariot, and fled. But you won't escape with your life, unless you mean to be a coward as well."

It is as if Arjuna has spoken to his pupil through his master's lips. Satyaki laughs aloud, he roars back at Drona, "A sishya must follow his guru. If Arjuna was a coward before you, O Drona, I am happy to be one as well!"

Satyaki makes a pradakshina around the Acharya's chariot, and flashes away into the padma vyuha. As they skim along, the Yadava cries to his sarathy, "Ahead is Baahlika's army. Beyond him is the lord of Dravida, and beside him Karna's legion from Anga. Ride at Karna and the Dravida king. Look how Drona races after us. Go like the wind. The sun drops quickly, we must reach Arjuna as soon as we can."

Satyaki, with Drona after him, roars through the Dravida king's legions, and Karna's, in a furrow of blood. How much like the guru his sishya is: the same swiftness of hand, the same unruffled smile, as if he has all the time in the world to arrive where he is going. Kritavarman sets himself in Satyaki's path. Satyaki does not acknowledge a Yadava before him; he fights his cousin like any enemy. Kritavarman is familiar with Satyaki's style, and draws blood. For a moment, Satyaki staggers in his chariot. Then he casts a javelin at Kritavarman's sarathy, so he falls out of his seat. Kritavarman's horses bolt, and it is a while before he can seize the reins and bring them under control. By then Satyaki has gone, out of reach.

Kritavarman lets the advancing Pandava army feel his anger. He smashes their formation, scattering the likes of Bheema, Shikhandi and Dhrishtadyumna.

Satyaki ploughs on. He has crossed two great rivers on his way to his master: Drona, the first, and Kritavarman, the second. On flares the Yadava like fire through a dry forest. Jalasandha's legion of elephants appears in his path and, quick as wishing, Kurukshetra is strewn with grey hillocks tinted scarlet. The field looks as if Bheema is abroad. Roaring to see his beasts slain, Jalasandha himself charges Satyaki. He strikes the Yadava in the arm with a light lance, and next moment, breaks his bow. Every encounter saps Satyaki's waning strength. He has neither the time nor the stamina for a prolonged duel. The Vrishni seizes up another bow. Two arrows cut away Jalasandha's arms at the shoulders, and the third strikes off his head.

Quicker than ever, flies Satyaki, racing the sun to the horizon. But Drona has almost caught up with him, and from another direction Duryodhana, also, with a force of his brothers. Already, the Yadava serves the purpose Krishna intended for him: he draws some Kaurava warriors away from Arjuna. Duryodhana surprises the young Yadava. He breaks three bows one after the other in his hands, and strikes him with a dozen arrows. Undaunted, Satyaki fights on with second wind, as if he has just begun the day. But he knows his strength will soon give out; he fights as if each shaft he looses might be his last. He kills Duryodhana's horses, and the Kaurava has to flee on foot.

Kritavarman, who has just dispersed the Pandava army, charges his cousin again. As he comes, he strikes Satyaki's sarathy with two serpentine narachas and Daruka's brother falls unconscious. Satyaki's horses rear; but he leaps up onto the chariot-head, seizes the reins in his bow-hand and fights on. Kritavarman's sarathy is wounded, and his horses. Satyaki pierces his armour with a naracha of his own, and his cousin faints.

No sooner is Kritavarman quelled, than Drona flashes up to bar Satyaki's way. But an inspired Satyaki strikes down Drona's sarathy. When the brahmana takes up the reins himself, Satyaki's charioteer has recovered. Seizing the advantage, Satyaki strikes Drona's horses with slim darts, which hardly wound them but bring excruciating pain. Whinnying in frenzy, the animals bolt. Drona cannot hold them, and they hurtle all over Kurukshetra, until the agony in their blood subsides and gradually they grow calm. By then, Satyaki is far away. Drona returns to the lip of the padma vyuha in the dim hope that perhaps, on this bleak day, he may still capture Yudhishtira.

A river in spate, Satyaki rushes on through the Kaurava army and no one can stop him. Those like the gifted archer Sudarshana, who dare try, lie twitching in death's spasms and are soon still. The Kaurava army begins to make way for Satyaki, as if they know that to try to resist him is to die. Among kshatriyas, the Yadava has killed Jalasandha and Sudarshana; and he has put Duryodhana, Drona and Kritavarman to flight. As for the common soldiers he has killed, there is no count of them, but at least ten thousand men. Mlecchas of Kasi he has slaughtered, Nishadas, Tankanas, Kalingas, Magadhas, Kekayas, Kambhojas, Yavanas and Vasatis.

Looking so very much like his master, Satyaki tears on: deeper and deeper into the Kaurava vyuha. His horses are white, like Arjuna's, and he stands just like his guru in his chariot, entirely at his ease. The Yavanas try to block his way, but he smashes through them disdainfully. On he flares, and ahead of him, he sees a legion of Kauravas mustered just to bring him down. At the head of the force, resplendent in Brahma's golden mail, is Duryodhana, with his brothers around him.

His eyes shining, Satyaki cries to his sarathy, "Look! An army just to stop us. Ride at them; let me repay some of the debt I owe Arjuna. Let Duryodhana know that Satyaki is Krishna's cousin and Arjuna's sishya, and that he is invincible!"

True to his word, in a short, one-sided battle, he destroys Duryodhana's legion. He kills Duryodhana's sarathy, and stings the Kaurava's horses so they also bolt as Drona's had. With Duryodhana routed, his army runs from the dreadful Yadava and he has a clear path before him again. Throwing back his head, the Vrishni roars his triumph to heaven, as he scorches on towards Arjuna.

NINETEEN

Yudhishtira's anxiety

SATYAKI BURNS BRIGHTER THAN ARJUNA ON KURUKSHETRA; THE Yadava has killed more men than his guru. After they are routed themselves, Duryodhana and Dusasana send an unconventional legion against him. These men do not fight with bows or spears, but with slingshots and stones! Their aim is unerring, and the force with which they sling their stones phenomenal. Some five hundred of them attack Satyaki; the Kauravas hope, at least, to surprise him. But the raging forest-fire hardly cares whether it consumes the punnaga or the palasa. Laughing at the ludicrous tactic, the Yadava smashes the catapultists' missiles into dust with a bank of arrows; and, with a handful of minor astras, he kills them all. These men die almost simultaneously, and they scream louder than any others whom Satyaki has dispatched to their fathers in the next world. Greater panic than ever grips the Kaurava army.

Satyaki courses on, leaving his trail of corpses: men and horses, chariots he has riven with streak lightning, and elephants keeled over where he shot them. Far away, Drona hears the screams and turns to his sarathy. "Satyaki is more terrible than Arjuna today. We must fight him again."

His charioteer says, "He strews Kurukshetra with bodies, like riceplants in a field at harvest time. But, my lord, look how far he is from us. If you leave your place to chase Satyaki, the Pandava army will break in and then the slaughter will be ten times what it is."

Even as they speak, a legion of Duryodhana's army rides towards them, in headlong flight from Satyaki. They hardly know where they are fleeing to, only that it is away from the Yadava. At the head of that force is Dusasana, his face red, his eyes bulging from his sleek head, and his body drenched in the sweat of fear. Drona rides on to his path, and roars at him, "Kshatriya! Where are you running in such fright? You are the yuvaraja. Shame on you.

"In Hastinapura, you mocked the Pandavas louder than anyone else did. What happened to that bravado? Listen to me, Dusasana. If you run like this it won't be long before Yudhishtira sits on the throne of Hastinapura, and you and your brothers lie mouldering among the worms of Kurukshetra!"

Dusasana cringes before his master; his Acharya has not done. "If this is how you mean to win the war, I will tell you a better way, before Bheema drinks your blood. Ride to your brother and persuade him to give the Pandavas back their kingdom. Then live among the women in your harem, and tell them how bravely you fought. After this, no one else will believe you.

"Coward! You are not just ruining your own honour; you are destroying the morale of our men. Turn back, Dusasana. Go and stop Satyaki, if you call yourself a kshatriya!"

Without a word, Dusasana turns back from where he came. Mustering the last shreds of his courage, he rides to face Satyaki again. This battle does not last long, and Dusasana finds his bow snatched from his hand, his chariot broken and he himself at the Yadava's mercy. With a dreadful smile, Satyaki fits a silver shaft to his bow. He draws the bowstring past his ear, his arrow aimed at Dusasana's heart. Dusasana shuts his eyes, and sullies himself. But suddenly, Satyaki gives a shout, "I won't rob Bheema of his revenge! He has sworn to kill you, your life belongs to him."

As Dusasana whimpers in relief, Satyaki leaves him and rides on towards the suchimukha vyuha, and Arjuna.

When Dusasana rode back to face the ravening Satyaki, Drona turns to the Pandava army again, always stalking Yudhishtira, whom Bheema and Dhrishtadyumna guard like eyelids do eyes. In rage, Drona attacks some of Drupada's younger sons and kills them easily. Howling to see his brothers die, Dhrishtadyumna flies at Drona. The assault is so sudden Drona faints in his chariot. Dhrishtadyumna leaps out of his ratha. He draws his sword and runs towards the brahmana. Drona recovers just in time; he seizes his bow and drives Dhrishtadyumna back.

They fight again, and Kurukshetra is lit up with astras. Until, fighting for his life, since he knows this prince was born to kill him, Drona burns Dhrishtadyumna's bow in his hands with an agneyastra. Before the Panchala has time to pick up another, Drona rides away, thinking better of the dangerous encounter.

Duryodhana appears to stem the advancing Pandava army. He fights exceptionally today. Dhrishtadyumna, Sahadeva, Nakula, Bheema and Yudhishtira cannot match the Kaurava. He wounds many of them; others have their bows cloven, or their horses killed. His new armour glitters in the late light, and the Pandavas have no Arjuna now, to find the chinks in Brahma's mail. Seeing Duryodhana blaze like that, Drona rides to his side, and soon the two of them hold off Yudhishtira's finest kshatriyas, while thousands of common Pandava soldiers perish all around them.

The eldest of the Kekaya brothers, Brihadkshatra, challenges Drona. They fight long, with clouds of dark arrows, punctuated by flaring astras. With Duryodhana fighting close beside him, Drona wants to show off his best, and suddenly he looses a brahmastra at Brihadkshatra. The Kekaya replies with a brahmastra of his own. Kurukshetra seems lit by a second sun, as the two weapons fuse in the sky. Astra quells astra, and both fall away in showers of ashes. But the great ayudhas drain the warriors who summon them, bodily and in spirit; and now, though Drona is far the older man, it is Brihadkshatra who tires. Even as the Pandavas shout encouragement to the Kekaya, Drona strikes him with five wooden shafts through his chest. As Brihadkshatra totters in his chariot, the brahmana takes his head off with a sixth, crescent-tipped arrow.

Sisupala's son, Dhrishtaketu, charges Drona with a roar. But it seems the brahmana has lifted his archery to another plane. Dhrishtaketu dies, struck through his heart. A cry goes up from the Pandava soldiers, and Drona is a fire, ripping through them. They fly from him in every direction, while Duryodhana watches with a pleased smile.

Jarasandha's son, also called Sahadeva, rides at Drona. He hasn't time even to shoot an arrow at the Kaurava Senapati, and his head is struck off by a sickle-headed shaft. In almost the same moment, Drona kills Dhrishtadyumna's son, Kshatradharma, with an arrow that whizzes through a whole legion of soldiers and finds the prince standing idle in his chariot. It is as if the terrible Acharya already extracts revenge from Drupada and Dhrishtadyumna for his own death, which the fire-prince must bring him inevitably. He kills his childhood friend's grandchild.

Duryodhana and his army press home the advantage Drona wins for them. They hunt with terror on Kurukshetra, and kill thousands. Now the screams of the Pandava soldiers thicken the air, and it seems Drona will raze the enemy by himself. He burns them; he lets frothing vermilion streams on the field of dharma. Yet, while the brahmana turns the tide of war back in Duryodhana's favour, Yudhishtira's anxious eyes hardly notice the battle around him. Instead, they scan the distance for some sign of Arjuna. There is none: no flash of a golden banner, Hanuman animating it, no report of the Gandiva's string, nothing. And now he had sent Satyaki after Arjuna, and there is no rumour of the Yadava either.

Yudhishtira thinks he should have never asked Satyaki to follow Arjuna, when the Yadava had been fighting all day. He must send someone after him. But whom? Only Bheema is powerful enough.

Deciding swiftly, Yudhishtira tells his sarathy to take him to Bheema, who stands smouldering at the havoc Drona wreaks. He is startled to see Yudhishtira, ashen and trembling. Bheema cries, "What is it, my brother? Is it Drona who makes you tremble?"

"Bheema, I am afraid. It is so long since Arjuna rode into the padma vyuha, and there is no sign of him save Krishna's desperate calls on the Panchajanya."

Bheema scoffs, "You worry about Arjuna! Have you forgotten who his sarathy is, that you are so anxious?"

Yudhishtira has tears in his eyes. "I sent Satyaki after Arjuna, and there is no sign from him either. I hear no screams from the Kaurava army, so I know my two kshatriyas are at them. All I hear are the enemy's savage shouts. Bheema, I am terrified that Arjuna has met the same fate as Abhimanyu." He sobs, "I am sure I have sent Satyaki to his death!"

Bheema is aghast. "Yudhishtira, you mustn't let fear unhinge you. What will become of the rest of us? Tell me what I can do. I will do anything to make you calm again."

Yudhishtira says, "I want you to go after Satyaki. Go as far as you can. As soon as you see any sign of him, just roar and I will know all is well."

At that moment, the Panchajanya resounds across Kurukshetra again, in defiance, in lusty challenge. Yudhishtira blanches. He whispers, "Arjuna is dead! That is Krishna blowing on his conch, as he takes revenge on the Kauravas. Fly Bheema. For your brother's sake, I beg you, fly! You may save at least Satyaki's life."

Bheema smiles wryly. "When Krishna and Arjuna ride into battle, victory rides with them. Satyaki is hardly less valiant than Arjuna; he, too, will come to no harm. Yesterday, all the Kauravas hunted Abhimanyu like a pack of dogs. Today they are more worried for Jayadratha's life. I don't think they will even bother trying to kill Arjuna, but only try to hold him up until the sun sets. And they won't succeed even in that."

Yudhishtira hardly looks comforted, so Bheema says, "Since you are so anxious, I will ride out to them. Listen for my roar. You will hear it as clearly as the Panchajanya!"

TWENTY

Bheema arrives

Bheema rides up to Dhrishtadyumna and says, "Yudhishtira wants me to follow Satyaki and Arjuna. When Drona sees me go, he will come after Yudhishtira again. The Acharya fights like ten men, but my brother will not listen to reason. I must leave him in your hands now, my friend."

His face drawn, after his son's death and his brother's, Dhrishtadyumna says grimly to Bheema, "Drona fears me more than any man. Now he has given me more than one reason to kill him. Go with a light heart, Bheema: Drona won't come near Yudhishtira, unless he kills Dhrishtadyumna first. And we both know that he will die before I do."

Just then, another bass from Krishna's conch booms across the field. Bheema clasps Dhrishtadyumna briefly. He climbs into his chariot and cries, "Fly, sarathy! We must reach Arjuna before the sun sets."

Drona sees Bheema's chariot dash forward, and the son of the wind is the last man he wants to enter his vyuha. In a trice, the brahmana is back at the edge of his lotus, and bars Bheema's way. Between Bheema and Drona rides another host, Duryodhana's brothers all, with Dusasana at their head. Bheema gives them a welcoming roar. All day he has felt shackled to the rest of the army, and Yudhishtira. Now, on his own at last, and seeing a good score of the hundred he has sworn to kill, excitement grips him.

Dusasana casts a spear at Bheema, pale fire. Bheema smashes it in slivers, and great laughter rumbles from him. Then he is at them, and he is a force of nature. Seven screams ring across the dharma kshetra.

Seven sons of Dhritarashtra fall dead: pierced by Bheema's arrows, or their heads blown off by the mace Mayaa gave him. Thirty-one, he counts with satisfaction. The rest surround him like ants. He flails at them, killing three more, and is splattered with their blood.

"Thirty-four!" roars Bheema and the others run. On rides the Pandava, and arrives in Drona's presence. The Acharya thinks his pupil will greet him reverently, as Arjuna and Satyaki had.

Drona cries, "You cannot enter my vyuha unless you defeat me. Arjuna rode round me in pradakshina. He folded his hands, and slipped past me like a coward. Satyaki followed his guru's example."

Bheema throws back his head and laughs. "Here me well, Brahmana. Arjuna needs leave from no man, why from no Deva even! No one in heaven or earth can stop my brother. He did not beg your leave; he only honoured you as his guru. But I am not Arjuna, I am Bheema. Yes, there was a time when I, too, honoured you. Why, I worshipped the ground you walked, because you were like a father to us.

"All that is over, Drona. You are not the Acharya who loved us, any more, but Duryodhana's minion. You are not my guru, but my enemy. I am not Arjuna who is sentimental still. I am Bheema and I kill those who fight for Duryodhana!"

He leaps down from his chariot and, mace in hand, eyes on fire, charges Drona. Losing his nerve, the brahmana leaps out of his ratha and shows a clean pair of heels. Next moment, Bheema is at his chariot and his horses, smashing them down, the sarathy's scream cut off with a blow that decapitates him. Bheema's laughter rings across Kurukshetra. But he has no time to waste chasing Drona. The Pandava climbs back into his chariot, and going like his father of the air, rides again towards Arjuna.

Bheema's passage is surprisingly easy. All around him, he sees the corpses with which Satyaki has embellished the field. On he fizzes, until a legion of elephants blocks his path. Bheema is not put out: his eyes shine! He rushes at the beasts and their soldiers. Again, Kurukshetra rings with trumpeting and screams. Soon, like the sun from a bank of clouds, Bheema emerges, triumphant, and booms ahead on his quest for his brother.

From a flank, mounted in a fresh chariot, Drona rides at him again. Bheema has no patience for a duel. He casts his mace like a thunderflash, smashing Drona's chariot to a standstill. Leaping to the ground, the son of the wind runs forward. With unearthly strength, he picks up that chariot and hurls it half a league from him! It shatters where it lands, flinging Drona out. The stunned brahmana climbs into another ratha and, realizing there is no stopping the wind's son today, rides back to his place beyond the padma vyuha.

On plunges Bheema, and those who are foolish enough to cross his path lie dead on Kurukshetra. The remnants of the Kaurava army left by Satyaki make way for him, running as far as they can at the sight of his chariot. Just once, one of Duryodhana's brothers gathers a force to obstruct his way. As he comes, Bheema hurls a gleaming mace at them, an occult weapon. A thousand men fall dead at its impact, and Bheema's path is clear again. He sears on in Satyaki's wake.

He erupts out of the padma vyuha, and sees a fulvous lion-banner before him, flapping in the breeze, while the chariot that flies it streaks on remorselessly through the suchimukha vyuha, piling the bloody dead in its wake. It is Satyaki decimating Duryodhana's army, flying ever closer to Arjuna. Bheema swirls past the absorbed Yadava, and shocked at the Vayuputra's sudden appearance, the Kauravas dare not come near him.

On hurtles Bheema, and then his eyes light up: ahead of him, and not far, he sees another banner waving. He sees a white and gold chariot shining like treasure, yoked to foam-white horses, and throwing back his head, Bheema gives the most magnificent roar! Like an earthquake, that joyful sound rocks Kurukshetra. Krishna and Arjuna hear it, the rapt Satyaki hears it; and all of them yell one another's names, back and forth, on top of their voices.

Over the ruins of two vyuhas, that sound carries to Yudhishtira. He jumps up, and such a smile breaks out on his careworn face. "Arjuna is alive!" cries Yudhishtira. "Satyaki is alive, Krishna is alive, and Bheema has found them! He has always done anything I asked him to, but never before has he made me as happy as he has today. My friends, Yudhishtira is the most fortunate man on earth!"

The Kauravas hear those roars, all over Kurukshetra, and know that Arjuna does not hunt Jayadratha alone any more. Karna hears Bheema's roar and its arrogance infuriates him. He rides to challenge Bheema. Like a sunburst comes Karna, arrows streaming. The son of Surya and the son of Vayu meet in battle; Bheema brushes aside his brother's volleys, and casts a silvery mantle of his own over Karna. The Kaurava soldiers, who have heard only of Bheema's prowess at the mace, are agape at his archery. Bheema breaks Karna's bow; unruffled, the Suryaputra snatches up another and fights on.

More than anything else, the cool, mocking smile on Karna's lips enrages Bheema. He tries to outdo himself, to be more of an archer than he really is. His aim falters, as he shoots too quickly; while Karna fights calmly, well within himself, and his every arrow sharp and true to its mark. Soon, the difference between the two is plain, and who the great bowman is. His touch deft and light, Karna is as quick as thinking. The indulgent smile never leaves his face, but Bheema's turns crimson with effort. His eyes bulge, he growls and curses.

Karna knows how easily he can end this duel. Any time he wants he can break the bow in Bheema's great hands. But then, Karna also knows Bheema is his brother, and strange love fills his heart for the wild kshatriya before him. Karna never fights as he can. Instead, he slackens his own archery deceptively, and allows Bheema to break his bow for the second time. Bheema's cry of delight is reward enough; Karna's eyes are filmed with tears.

However, Bheema does not fight a brother, but a hated enemy. He kills two of his horses, wounds his sarathy and Karna himself. A shadow of annoyance crosses Karna's sere face, and he leaps into his son Vrishasena's chariot. Bheema's roar echoes there again: he has the better of the lord of Anga, and his way to Arjuna is clear once more.

Bheema rides on. But as if he enjoyed the encounter with his uninhibited brother, Karna tilts at him again from a flank. Bheema gives an angry shout, never realizing that for Karna this battle is a chance to be near him, near enough almost to caress his brother. Indeed, Karna wants to leap down from his chariot, run to Bheema and hug him; and to cry, 'I am also Kunti's son. Take me to Yudhishtira. I will fight for him from now!'

Bheema thinks Karna's reputation is exaggerated. He yells, "You can't stand before this Bheema, Sutaputra, and you brag that you will kill my brother Arjuna?"

Bheema remembers the day of the gambling, and begins to fight in anger. Karna finds it less easy to hold him off without hurting him.

Bheema carves his chariot again. Duryodhana sees this, and sends his brother Dussalan with a fresh chariot for Karna. But even as Karna climbs into it, Bheema takes off Dussalan's head in a roseate burst. Duryodhana roars in sorrow, and Bheema kills a hundred Kaurava soldiers to celebrate.

Duryodhana panics. Trembling, he rides to Drona and cries hotly, "My lord, you swore not a man would enter your padma vyuha. But three kshatriyas are at the point of the suchimukha! Arjuna, Satyaki and Bheema have halved our legions. Our maharathikas who guard Jayadratha are hard-pressed to hold them off. I thought it was easier to imagine the sea dried up, than your vyuha smashed with such contempt!"

Drona has done his best, and it has not been enough today. He says sharply, "What has happened can't be undone: better think what to do next."

Frothing, Duryodhana cries, "Jayadratha must not die! See that Arjuna does not reach him, Acharya. I count on you!"

The arrogance of the Kaurava's tone strikes his master like a blow. He was being upbraided like a boy before all the soldiers: that three men had dodged around him, two like cowards. Between clenched teeth Drona hisses at Duryodhana, "All day I have fought like a man half my age, and I have kept a whole army at bay. And if I had not, there wouldn't be three, but three thousand kshatriyas at Jayadratha's throat.

"But it seems you don't value what I have done. See to your precious brother-in-law yourself! You swore he would not be harmed. But this is not a game of dice, Duryodhana: this is war, and you once cheated your enemies out of everything they had. Today the wager is your brother-in-law's life, and the dice are arrows. You have Brahma's armour, go and save Jayadratha yourself."

Duryodhana is too taken aback to reply. He is also afraid Drona will abandon him, if he annoys him any more. He turns his chariot, and rides back towards the suchimukha vyuha. There, every moment, Arjuna claws his way nearer Jayadratha.

TWENTY-ONE

Karna and Bheema

His mind an angry fire, Duryodhana rides away from Drona. He meets two other Pandava warriors who broke into the padma vyuha at Arjuna's chariot-wheels: Yuddhamanyu and Uttamaujas still range the inner petals of the Acharya's lotus. Duryodhana attacks them. He wounds Uttamaujas' horses, but Yuddhamanyu sets on him ferociously, and then Uttamaujas, also, from different directions. They smash Duryodhana's chariot-wheels, and luckily for the Kaurava, Shalya is at hand to rescue him from the Panchala brothers. Their laughter follows him, like smoking oil in his ears.

Meanwhile, Bheema does his best to slip past Karna and reach Arjuna. It seems the only way past is to kill him. Bheema sees his enemy smile at him. He thinks he must be dreaming, that it is not a mocking smile he sees on Karna's haughty lips. The son of the wind tells himself his mind is playing tricks on him; he must be more tired than he had thought. Arrogant, spiteful Karna could not be smiling at him with such fondness in his eyes!

As the duel progresses, even Bheema has to admire his opponent's virtuosity. Though he would never admit it, it is archery Arjuna would be proud of. Sweat covers Bheema's body; this is harder than he had thought. He grits his teeth and shoots his arrows more quickly still. But his adversary is so calm he might not be fighting at all. Then, Karna shoots the armour off Bheema's chest. The fond smile widens to see the look of dismay on the Pandava's face. With a roar, Bheema breaks Karna's bow again. He strikes him with two arrows that crash through his breastplate; and while Karna stumbles briefly, Bheema breaks his chariot-wheels.

Karna leaves the field in a Kaurava prince's chariot; Bheema surges on towards Arjuna. Arjuna has been spared having to face Karna so far, because of Bheema's presence nearby. But the Vayuputra does not get far: out flits Karna from the suchimukha again, the cryptic smile still on his face. Cursing loudly, Bheema attacks him. Suddenly, the images of their long exile come steaming back to the Pandava, and he decides to kill the sutaputra if he can. In that rush of anger he breaks two bows in Karna's hands, in quick succession, and is astonished to see a gleam of approval in his enemy's eyes! Bheema cannot believe this. Beside himself because he thinks Karna is taunting him, he fights with renewed fury.

By now, Karna the kshatriya is roused. Knitting his brow, the lord of Anga draws blood with a clutch of mind-swift arrows that whistle at his antagonist from extraordinary angles. Yet Karna has the disadvantage of knowing this is his brother. He has two battles on his hands: the one against Bheema and the other with himself; while, Bheema just wants to kill an enemy. At being struck, he fights more fiercely, his roars shaking the field.

Bheema's archery is hardly less than Arjuna's now, and seeing Karna beaten back, Duryodhana cries to his brother Durjaya, "Fly to Karna's side, or the beast will have his life today!"

Durjaya is one of Duryodhana's bravest brothers, and he rides at Bheema at once. The very sight of him is tonic to the Pandava. Bheema gives a shout of joy, and strikes Durjaya's head off with a crescent-tipped shaft worthy of Drona. Karna wails. He knows each of Duryodhana's brothers well, has been close to them all. Bheema shatters Karna's chariot once more. Karna leaps out, and stands on the ground, battling on, torn between love and rage.

Duryodhana has lost count of his brothers Bheema has killed today. Like a losing gambler, he sends another one against his cousin; now, he sends Durmukha who is one of the finest archers in both armies. But Bheema is no more the student of archery he had been in Drona's asrama: today, he fights for revenge. Nine arrows so quick they are like a single unbroken one greet Durmukha. All nine crash into his chest. They rip through his armour, part flesh, bone and gristle, and the

Kaurava dies without shooting at the son of the wind. Bheema's ecstatic yell echoes across Kurukshetra.

Guilty, that he may have saved Duryodhana's brothers if it weren't his own brother that faced him, Karna feels faint in his chariot, and has to sit abruptly on its floor. The raging Bheema stills shoots at him. He cuts the armour off his body. Karna jumps up again and strikes him with an arrow deep in his shoulder. He aimed at his heart, but turned his hand away at the last moment. Bheema's reply is so savage that Karna has to ride away for a time.

Suicidally emboldened that Bheema has killed so many of them, almost as if now they have as much stake in the next world as this one, five more of Duryodhana's brothers charge the Pandava. Durmarshana rides with these. Bheema grins like a lion seeing a herd of tender deer. In a bloody blur, he kills all five. They die astonished, that the lumbering Bheema is more of an archer than they had dreamt.

Karna flares back into battle. He has decided to face Bheema as just an enemy now: it is his kshatriya dharma. Another duel begins. As daylight softens, every moment, Karna and Bheema light up the dharma kshetra with astras.

Karna is at his best; but Bheema matches him shaft for shaft. Both have their armour shot off their backs; both are bloody. Yet again, Bheema strikes Karna deeply in his arm, and the panicstricken Duryodhana sends five more of his brothers to rescue his friend. Bheema roaring, Bheema rapturous, Bheema fighting like two Arjunas, shoots them down in a garnet flurry, while Karna howls in shock.

Bheema roars, "Forty-nine, Duryodhana! Send me more."

Karna fights on. Around the two kshatriyas, soldiers collect to watch them duel. Arjuna, Krishna and Satyaki watch, cheering Bheema loudly. Even they cannot help admiring Karna's archery; it is so sublime. Of the Kaurava army, Bhoorisravas, Drona, Kripa and Shalya applaud both warriors, regardless. Yuddhamanyu and Uttamaujas are there, too, and they shout encouragement only to Bheema.

Trembling in every limb, Duryodhana sends seven more of his brothers to Karna's side. Nothing would please the Kaurava more than to see Bheema killed. The seven surround Bheema. He laughs uproariously at them, beckoning to them to come closer with his huge hands, as he might little boys. But when the Vayuputra sees the seventh Kaurava who rides against him, his laughter dries up. In grief, mighty Bheema roars, "Ah, Vikarna! Why have you come to me to die?"

On the day of the gambling in Hastinapura, Vikarna was the only Kaurava who spoke for Draupadi. Bheema cries, "I have sworn to kill all hundred of you, and I mustn't break my oath. Oh, I curse this war that you must die with the sinners. Vikarna, forgive me!"

And he strikes Vikarna's head off. The other six he has already killed, and Karna's roars of outrage rock Kurukshetra. Blind, furious Karna reverts to an old and habitual hatred; he forgets he is fighting his brother. Once more, Bheema the Pandava, Bheema the enemy, stands before him, having killed fifty-six of Duryodhana's brothers. A gasp goes up from those who watch, because Karna is transformed into another, unearthly archer, for whom the Pandava is no match at all. Quicker than seeing, Karna splits Bheema's bow, he severs the reins in his sarathy's hands, he wounds that charioteer with a shaft through his chest. All this happens in a wink, and Bheema stands with a bewildered look on his face. He cannot believe this is the same man he had sent scuttling from battle, three or four times.

Again, the maddening smile curves Karna's lips. Bheema casts a heavy lance at him. Serenely, and as if he has a day to do it, Karna divides that spear along its length, as it flies at him; the halves hum past him harmlessly. Bheema lifts a shield to protect himself; an arrow like a shard of lightning smashes it into dust. Bheema flings a sword at Karna like a knife-thrower; Karna cuts it down easily.

Far from beaten, Bheema leaps out of his chariot. He lays hold of the first thing that comes to hand, and hurls it at Karna: pieces of broken chariots, fallen soldiers' swords and shields, rocks. Then he sees the carcasses of elephants he himself killed, and Bheema picks these up and casts them at Karna! Still smiling, at times laughing aloud at the Pandava's antics, Karna cuts everything down; he truncates the elephants in the air.

Inexorably, Karna closes on Bheema. Bheema stands before him, chest heaving, uncowed. Karna raises his bow, with an arrow fitted to it, aimed at the Pandava's heart. Just a kshatriya now, his enemy in the eye of his shaft, Karna draws back his bowstring. At the heart of that long moment, he sees Kunti's face before him. He remembers his oath to her that he would not kill any of her sons except Arjuna. Suddenly, he sees not a dangerous enemy whom he has at his mercy, but his brother. Karna stays his hand. Instead, he reaches out and prods Bheema with his bow on his great chest, reviling him.

Bheema stands shaking, helpless, and Karna cries, "Pandava, you are a glutton, and a fool besides, that you dare challenge me. Go back to Virata's kitchen; you belong there more than on a battlefield. Or go back to the forest and spend your days gathering fruit and roots. Look at you, your face red, and helpless as a child! Go home, boy: this is a man's war, and no place for you."

From a way off, Krishna sees all this. He knows he must come to Karna's rescue, or how will he spare Bheema's life before all the Kaurava army? The Dark One cries to Arjuna, "Karna has Bheema at his mercy, he taunts him like fire!"

Arjuna swirls around, and covers Karna with a scream of narachas, which home into Karna's body like cranes into the Krauncha mountains. Gratefully, that warrior turns away from Bheema; he allows Arjuna to chase him off. Satyaki rides up to Bheema. The Pandava climbs into his chariot and they ride away, Bheema still trembling, humiliated by a brother he does not know. Arjuna pursues Karna briefly, his dark sarathy glad he had told Surya's prince who he really was, or Bheema would have lost his life. In rage for Bheema, Arjuna looses an astra after Karna. Aswatthama sees the weapon burning across the field, and cuts it down. With a roar, Arjuna turns on his guru's son.

TWENTY-TWO

Satyaki and Bhoorisravas

Satyaki, scourge of the Kaurava army, arrives at the front in blazing style. Dusasana surrounds him with a legion, but Satyaki brushes him aside, killing another thousand men, while siddhas, charanas, and pannagas applaud in the sky[*]. He bursts through Dusasana's force, and rides towards his master.

Krishna says to Arjuna, "Here comes your sishya. He has burned his way through two vyuhas: Satyaki of the incredible exploit!"

Arjuna is not pleased. "I left him to guard Yudhishtira like his life, and he has left my brother's side."

"Can't you think why he has come? Yudhishtira must be anxious, and has sent him to find us. Whatever the reason, I am glad to see Satyaki and Bheema."

"Look, Krishna!" cries Arjuna. "Bhoorisravas rides at Satyaki, and Satyaki is exhausted."

Bhoorisravas reaches Satyaki, and Arjuna says, "How quickly the sun sinks and Jayadratha still lives. Bhoorisravas has just begun to fight, and he is fresh. Now I have Satyaki to protect; Yudhishtira should never have sent him out so late."

They who still dare give battle to Arjuna; he kills those who come in his way, easily as breathing. Meanwhile, Bhoorisravas cries, "I have waited so long for this moment, Satyaki! You won't escape with your life today."

---

[*] This applause by the celestials is a frequent occurrence throughout the war, whenever they see any exceptional feat of heroism.

Satyaki roars back, "You are like an autumn cloud, Bhoorisravas, full of thunder but never bringing rain. Fight me not with threats, but arrows if you dare!"

Vasudeva's father, Soora, had a cousin called Sini, who was a fine kshatriya. When Kamsa was king in Mathura he held a swayamvara for his cousin Devaki. Sini burst into that swayamvara and carried Devaki away for Vasudeva, who loved her. A Kuru king called Somadatta, who had eyes for Devaki himself, challenged Sini. Before all the other kings, Sini defeated Somadatta. Heady with victory, he caught the Kuru by his hair, dragged him down into the mud, and holding a sword to his throat, planted a foot on his chest. Somadatta never forgot that humiliation. He performed a tapasya to Siva, for a son who would, one day, avenge the insult. Bhoorisravas was born Somadatta's son, and Satyaki as Sini's grandson.

The Yadava and the Kuru duel. Bhoorisravas is a bhakta and a kshatriya, and he has hardly fought today. This was exactly as Drona intended: if Arjuna broke through the two vyuhas, he must face a handful of maharathikas, who had rested all day, before he reached Jayadratha. It was to save Arjuna some of that effort, that Krishna had summoned Satyaki and Bheema.

Bhoorisravas kills Satyaki's horses with an astra that sets them alight, roasting them. As he leaps from his chariot, the Yadava kills the Kuru's horses with four shafts that find their hearts. Bhoorisravas also leaps out of his ratha. Swords out in a flash, in the grip of an older contention than this war, they charge each other. Blade rings against blade, showering sparks over both kshatriyas. They circle one another and thrust out wildly. They hew and parry, they growl, they roar, they weave and dodge. They leap high in the air and strike mighty blows down on each other. With every moment, it is clear that Satyaki tires quickly; inevitably, Bhoorisravas gains the advantage. Satyaki staggers under his blows, and has neither the strength nor the speed to answer them any more. It is all the Yadava can do to keep the Kuru from killing him. Still, he does not run, but fights on.

Krishna turns to Arjuna. "Satyaki is so tired he can hardly stand. Bhoorisravas will kill him if you don't intervene."

Even as he speaks, Bhoorisravas fells Satyaki with a tremendous stroke, knocking the Yadava's blade from his hand, sending him sprawling on his back. With a roar, Bhoorisravas is on him, crying, "The moment of revenge is here, Yadava! This is what your grandfather did to my father."

Bhoorisravas seizes Satyaki by his hair, plants a foot squarely on the fallen warrior's chest, and roars his triumph; and Satyaki goes limp. Even the Kaurava soldiers cry out in shock at the shaming of a fallen enemy. But, his eyes glinting, Bhoorisravas drags the young Yadava round and round the space where they had fought, roaring, "Today, my father is avenged!"

Krishna cries to Arjuna, "Look what that wretch is doing to my cousin! Satyaki didn't follow you through two armies to be humiliated like this."

Arjuna replies, "Bhoorisravas is honourable. He is only having revenge for what happened to his father. He will not kill Satyaki."

The words hardly leave his mouth, and they see Bhoorisravas draw his sword again. They see him raise his arm to hew off Satyaki's head. Arjuna cries, "What shall I do, Krishna?"

"To kill an unconscious enemy isn't the kshatriya dharma by which we agreed to fight this war," says the Avatara.

Between the raising of Bhoorisravas' arm and its fall, Arjuna cuts off that sword-arm with an arrow like lightning. The look on Bhoorisravas' face is unforgettable. He stares at the blood spouting at his elbow, and his severed arm which lies on the ground at his feet, the sword still clutched in its hand. Bhoorisravas whirls around with an agonal cry, and sees Arjuna behind him.

"Arjuna!" wails Bhoorisravas. "What have you done? Is this dharma? You have covered yourself in shame, Pandava. You have brought disgrace to the House of Kuru! Your wretched sarathy made you do this, only a Yadava could stoop so low."

But Arjuna rages back at him, "You dare speak ill of Krishna! Do you think I am heartless that I will let you kill Satyaki when he cannot defend himself? He is not only my friend who risks his life for me, he is my sishya. Bhoorisravas, when Sini shamed him, your father was not in the state in which Satyaki is. I could have had your head instead of your arm, and I would not sin."

Bhoorisravas stands before him, uncowed, blood gushing from his wound. Arjuna rails on, "Dare you speak to me of dharma? You stood by when the six maharathikas shot Abhimanyu down like a dog, when my child stood defenceless before them. Was that the dharma you preach? Or is dharma just for someone else, while you and yours are above it? Did you say a word to your dastardly nephews, when they murdered my son?"

Bhoorisravas has no answer to this. He hangs his head. Next moment, Arjuna is overcome with remorse, and cries, "Ah, my lord, how I hate myself that I was born a kshatriya! That I had to do this terrible thing to one of the noblest sons of the House of Kuru. But I curse Duryodhana more than I do myself: all this is his doing."

Arjuna has tears in his eyes. Now, Bhoorisravas raises his good hand over his head, to acknowledge what the Pandava says. He orders a seat of kusa grass spread for himself on the battlefield beside his chariot. He sits on it in padmasana, the posture of the lotus. Bhoorisravas shuts his eyes, yokes himself in dhyana, and prepares to die. The blood flowing from his elbow forms a pool on the field of dharma.

The Kaurava army has gathered around Bhoorisravas, in a hush. Every soldier's gaze is upon him. They watch the colour drain from his face, and slowly the pain, as the swell of the atman, his soul, washes over the kshatriya. Just then, Satyaki stirs from his faint. He seizes up his sword and rushes at Bhoorisravas, who by now is unaware of the world. Kaurava soldiers cry out in horror. Arjuna and Krishna cry at Satyaki to stop. But he is at the motionless Bhoorisravas in a blink. With a roar, Satyaki strikes off the Kuru's head so it flies from his neck in a scarlet eruption.

The Yadava stands panting beside Bhoorisravas' corpse, his eyes aflame, daring anyone to challenge him.

TWENTY-THREE

The setting sun

ARJUNA IS SHOCKED BY WHAT HIS SISHYA DOES; BUT THIS IS NO TIME for him to rebuke Satyaki, and the Pandava does not say a word. The Kauravas raise accusing voices, and Satyaki smoulders at them. They cry at him, "Is this dharma that you kill a man who had sat down to die? That you kill him while he sits in dhyana, with his eyes shut?"

Sword in hand, Satyaki roars back at them, "How easy it is to preach dharma to others! But yesterday, when that child said, 'Come, one by one, and fight me', did you listen to him? When Karna cut Abhimanyu's bowstring from behind his back that was dharma was it? When you set on him like a pack of dogs, was that dharma? The Kuru Acharya, the Senapati of this great army, was the one who trapped him. He knew only Abhimanyu could enter the chakra vyuha when Arjuna was away. To save his wounded pride, to save face, he murdered a mere boy. I know it was Drona who told Karna the only way Abhimanyu could be subdued: with treachery, from behind his back! When your Senapati's conscience is sold for a title, how dare the rest of you speak of dharma?

As for my killing Bhoorisravas, I care little what you think of it: I am a kshatriya, and I must kill anyone who insults me. When I was past fighting back, he struck me down, seized my hair and dragged me round the field. I would have killed him, anyway, or died trying to. I don't care what you think, my dharma was to kill Bhoorisravas."

Suddenly, a disembodied voice, an asariri, speaks out of the sky, "No blame clings to Satyaki. It was written that Bhoorisravas would die by his hand."

The setting sun

The Kaurava army turns away from that sanguinary place. Satyaki has no chariot to ride in; he stands there with his bloodied sword in his hand. Even after the unearthly voice speaks, Arjuna is not convinced of Satyaki's innocence. But Jayadratha still lives, and every moment the sun plunges down the sky, and the world grows dimmer.

Arjuna says, "Krishna, our time is short."

Krishna flicks his reins over the gandharva horses. Duryodhana, Karna, Vrishasena, Aswatthama, Kripa and their soldiers prepare to stop the charge of the white chariot. Duryodhana cries to Karna, "There is only one task for you now: keep Arjuna away from Jayadratha. The sun is not far from setting, and all of us will be at your side. If you can do this thing, the war is won."

But also between Karna and Arjuna stands Satyaki, sword in hand, his feet stained with Bhoorisravas' blood. Karna rides at the Yadava: to distract Arjuna again, to waste more of his precious time; or, perhaps, deep in his heart, Karna does not want his brother to fail his mission. Arjuna cries, "Quick, Krishna! Ride to Satyaki, he stands defenceless before Karna."

But Krishna does not want to face Karna now. He fears Indra's shakti that Karna has. He says, "Let Satyaki face Karna. There are others we must pass, before you can keep your vow."

"But Satyaki has no chariot!"

"Not for long," replies the Avatara. He raises the Panchajanya to his lips, and a clear rishabha rings across Kurukshetra. Hardly has that note died, when they hear a storm of horses' hooves, and no one can be sure if the sound comes from the earth or the sky. In a moment, a marvellous chariot flashes up to Satyaki, and he cannot tell whether that ratha came through the Kaurava lines, or flew down from Devaloka. It shines like treasure on Kurukshetra, and flies the banner of the golden eagle. Satyaki climbs into Krishna's chariot, the Jaitra, and Daruka's chariotry excels the Dark One's.

Satyaki and Karna fight a pitched duel. But Karna's sarathy is no match for Daruka, who flies here and there, like thoughts, as hard to aim at. The advantage of fighting from Krishna's chariot, yoked to the foam-born horses Varuna gave the Blue God, tells for the Yadava. Besides, killing Bhoorisravas has invigorated Satyaki. He cripples Karna's chariot, and Duryodhana has to rescue his friend.

The Kauravas must stop Satyaki from gaining Arjuna's side again; together, those two would make short work of cutting their way through to Jayadratha. Dusasana and some of his brothers surround Satyaki; they are dazzled by Daruka's skill and overwhelmed by the renewed Yadava's archery. Satyaki has them at his mercy. But he remembers Bheema's oath, and lets them escape; only hurting them sorely on their way.

In grudging admiration, Aswatthama says to Kritavarman, "If anyone on Kurukshetra is Arjuna's equal and Krishna's, it is Satyaki."

Kritavarman murmurs, "There is no fourth."

But Karna has swung away from the irrepressible Satyaki, and confronts Arjuna. Before they actually fight, Arjuna cries to him, "You slaughtered my son like an animal. You will see me kill your boy Vrishasena!"

Arjuna sails past, always flying nearer Jayadratha, whom he now sees clearly through the slender suchimukha. Every moment the sun sinks lower, the shadows grow longer. Duryodhana rides up to Karna, and cries, "You must hold him up, Karna! The sun has almost set. Just a while, and he will not reach Jayadratha."

Arjuna sees the sun turn the colour of blood and its lower rim touch the horizon. Krishna takes the white chariot deeper into the suchimukha, nearer and nearer the needle's eye. Five maharathikas led by Karna ride between Arjuna and Jayadratha. Satyaki and Bheema are at Arjuna's side now, holding off some of the Kaurava warriors. Inexorably, they forge closer, like two tigers hunting a ruru deer, or two hawks swooping on a shred of flesh, and, nothing else for it, Jayadratha raises his bow and fights, at least to keep his terror at bay.

Between them, battling as if for their own lives, Satyaki and Bheema hold up four of the kshatriyas who protect Jayadratha. But Karna looms before Arjuna, like a hill he must cross in a few moments. An ineffable duel breaks out between them. The astras they shoot at each other light up Kurukshetra brighter than the sun, which falls away like Arjuna's very life. Half the saffron orb is already below the horizon, and Karna still bars Arjuna's way with a hindrance of arrows.

Krishna cries to Arjuna, "We cannot reach him before the sun sets. Night is about to fall, be ready with the Paasupata. Trust me now. When I tell you, kill Jayadratha!"

In faith, Arjuna invokes that weapon with its mantra, though he does not know what Krishna means. A moment later, darkness falls on Kurukshetra, and a shout goes up from the Kaurava soldiers. Duryodhana's roar rings above all the rest. "The sun has set!"

Karna lowers his bow. Arjuna shivers with soft fear in his chariot. He still waits breathlessly, the Paasupata ready in his hand. Jayadratha's cry of relief echoes there, "The sun has set!"

All the fighting stops. The soldiers raise their eyes to the sky where a thousand stars glimmer down at them in the suddenly fallen night. Jayadratha lifts his head to gaze at the sky. As in a dream, Arjuna hears Krishna hiss at him, "Quick! Kill him now. The sun hasn't set, I have hidden it for a moment."

There is no time for doubt. In the dream, past Karna's chariot, Arjuna sees Jayadratha's bare neck and shoots the Paasupata at that throat. Just before the astra flames out, Krishna says, "His head mustn't fall on the earth. Jayadratha's father sits in sandhya vandana near Samantapanchaka. Let his son's head fall in his lap!"

Jayadratha's roar shatters the silence as Siva's astra takes off his head like a bud from a flowering-tree. As the others spin round, they see a stream of arrows, silvery as moonlight, pluck up that head even as it falls, neatly severed from its neck. They see the spectral shafts carry Jayadratha's head high above the battlefield, and beyond its perimeter. A million voices roar, "Arjuna has broken his vow. He killed Jayadratha after the sun had set!"

Arjuna has no answer to this; but then, a divine Chakra glides majestically away from the last sliver of the setting sun. Night and its stars vanish, and Kurukshetra is bathed in ruddy light again, the colour of Jayadratha's blood. Krishna says to Arjuna, "There was no other way. I hid the sun with the Sudarshana."

Arjuna's face is wreathed in a smile. Bheema's celebrant roars rock Kurukshetra, and Satyaki roars with him. Duryodhana and his army stand rooted, hardly believing what their eyes have seen.

TWENTY-FOUR

The war at night

Arjuna chants the mantra to withdraw the paasupatastra. From afar, the silver shaft flies back into the Pandava's quiver. There it vanishes, and a breeze laden with the scents of a thousand different flowers blows across Kurukshetra. His eyes alight, because he knew how close they had come to failure, Krishna embraces Arjuna. The Kauravas troop numbly away from the place where Arjuna kept his vow, Duryodhana sobbing in rage.

Far away, across the field, Yudhishtira hears Bheema's roar echoing, repeatedly, and he cries, "It's Bheema roaring in joy. Jayadratha is dead!"

As if to confirm this, golden blasts from the Devadatta and the Panchajanya are borne to them on the scented breeze. Yudhishtira is beside himself. Over and over, he cries, "Jayadratha is dead! Arjuna has killed Jayadratha!"

Meanwhile, Arjuna kneels before Krishna. The Pandava says, "This is your doing. Without you, Jayadratha would be alive and I would be preparing to kill myself. Krishna, without you I would never have crossed this sea of enemies, and kept my word to my child. Now I see what your grace is; now I believe Yudhishtira will rule the world again. This is your doing, Lord, all of it!"

Krishna smiles. How different this Arjuna was from the kshatriya who was so full of doubt before the war began. Krishna says, "Look around Kurukshetra. Between Satyaki and you, you have razed seven aksauhinis; and the Kauravas were glad to sacrifice them, as long as

Jayadratha lived and Arjuna died. How they will rue their losses now. I think our Satyaki has killed more men than you have today."

The wind in their faces, they ride back through the ruins of the Kaurava army. With darkness, the first hyenas and jackals are already on the prowl among the dead. As they go, Arjuna asks, "Why did I have to carry Jayadratha's head into his father's lap? Krishna, why did I have to kill him with the Paasupatastra?"

"Jayadratha was born after his father Brihatkshatra performed a tapasya. And when his son was born, he asked for a boon that he could be killed only by the greatest kshatriya on earth, and with the greatest of all astras! You did not know this, but that is why you had to have the Paasupatastra. Brihatkshatra's tapasya was such that he could ask for another boon. And he asked that the man who caused his son's head to fall on the earth would have his own head burst apart."

Arjuna stares at his sarathy and Krishna nods in reply to his unspoken question. Earlier that evening, as the sun was setting, Brihatkshatra sat in dhyana at Samantapanchaka, not far from Kurukshetra. He sat in padmasana, his eyes shut, his breath stilled, lost in himself. But he was roiled by nightmarish anxiety this evening. Suddenly, some silver arrows flew out of the sky and dropped their grisly load in the meditating king's lap. He sprang up with a cry, and his son's staring head fell on to the ground. Brihatkshatra had no time even to scream, and his own head exploded.

Through the remains of the Kaurava army, Arjuna, Bheema and Satyaki ride back to Yudhishtira. He gives such a shout when he sees them. He runs to Arjuna, to embrace him fervently, while tears course down his face.

"I thank God for this! I thank God a thousand times that you are alive, Arjuna. And you, Krishna, and my Bheema, and you, heroic Satyaki." One by one, he hugs the others as well. Then, taking Krishna's hand, Yudhishtira cries, "My Lord, by your grace my brother has prevailed today. You decided Arjuna would keep his oath, and then no power on earth could stop him!" And he sobs like a child before the Dark One.

A smiling Krishna says, "There you are mistaken: Jayadratha died because your eyes blazed in rage yesterday! The wrath of a good man, a serene man not easily moved to anger, is more potent than any other force on earth. And, also," he puts an arm around Arjuna, "this brother of yours is the greatest archer in the world."

Across Kurukshetra, in the Kaurava camp cloaked in gloom, Duryodhana sits alone in his tent. Today, he also realizes the truth of what Bheeshma and Drona told him, so often: that no one, not Drona, not Aswatthama, not even Karna, was Arjuna's equal in battle. By himself, the Pandava had come through three vyuhas and he had killed Jayadratha. Now Bheeshma's warnings and Krishna's in Hastinapura, his uncle Vidura's sage warnings, all return to Duryodhana in new resonance; as if only now he hears them clearly, and understands what they tried to tell him. Duryodhana sits sobbing bitterly.

But the war is not over, and not all his heroes are slain. Drona still lives, and no one has really mastered the Acharya yet. Wearily, Duryodhana rises and goes to his guru's tent. Drona is as calm as he was yesterday. Duryodhana walks in. He takes Drona's hands and says, "Look what Arjuna has done to our army. So many kshatriyas have died for me. Bheeshma lies dying on his bed of arrows; and today, ah, today has been the most dreadful day. Satyaki and Arjuna have destroyed seven aksauhinis. Seven legions razed by two men!

"All these kings came to fight for me, and now they are dead and I am still alive. I am like a coward, Drona! A man who cannot fight for himself. And look how cruel fate leaves me alive to see my precious friends slain. Each one gave his life for me." His voice is a whisper. "They paid for my sins, for my arrogance and my stubbornness. They paid with their lives. Not a hundred Aswamedhas can wash my sins from me. How will I face my sister Dussala? I swore to her husband he wouldn't be harmed. Yesterday I was so confident that no man could break through the whole Kuru army and strike at the eye of the needle. Now not only Jayadratha but Jalasandha, Srutayus, Achutayus, Srutayudha, all once invincible, are dead. Sudakshina is dead, my lord, Vinda and Anuvinda, the wild and brave Alambusa. And fifty-six of my brothers."

As he counts his dead, his tears stop flowing. Instead, his eyes turn red again. Duryodhana says, "I caused all their deaths, and I have nothing left to live for. But I will avenge my friends before I die; I will kill all five Pandavas. I will kill every Panchala, or die trying. How else can I pacify the spirits of my dead? With his friends gone, Duryodhana's place is not in this world any more, but in Devaloka with those who gave their lives for him. Acharya, I will not rest until I have avenged Jayadratha, Bhoorisravas and the rest, who were killed like animals on a hunt. Why should I wait for tomorrow? Even now, by darkness, I will ride for revenge!"

Drona is moved to see Duryodhana like that. He rises and says, "I always told you Arjuna is invincible, but there is no cure for that. I swear to you, Duryodhana, I will take such battle to the enemy, as they have not tasted yet. I will not take off this armour until all your enemies are dead or I myself am killed. Do not grieve, my prince, Drona will fight for you until no breath remains in his body. Aswatthama will fight beside me. Yes, let us not wait to begin our revenge, but go out straightaway. We will fight under the moon and the stars!"

Grimly, the two of them emerge from the brahmana's tent. Drona goes to call his legions out again, and Duryodhana to find Karna. Soon, the two friends stand at the edge of Kurukshetra, gazing across the starlit ruin of their army.

Duryodhana breathes, "Look at what Arjuna and Satyaki did to our army: more than half our men are dead. The earth drinks their blood, scavengers feast on their flesh. Look where Jayadratha's headless body lies, with hyenas tearing at him. Karna, you know Arjuna is the Acharya's favourite sishya; he loves Arjuna more than he does Aswatthama. I am convinced Drona let Arjuna into the padma vyuha; he could never have broken in otherwise. The brahmana swore to Jayadratha that he would protect him, and instead he let the Pandava in like a leopard into a calf-pen. If only I had the sense to see what would happen, I would have sent Jayadratha back to his kingdom; and now we would be rejoicing that Arjuna had killed himself, instead of this terrible grief!

"It is not only Jayadratha who is dead. Drona let Satyaki and Bheema in after Arjuna, and thousands of our men lie still forever under the stars. Look at the arrows that protrude, ghastly, from their corpses: every shaft bears either Arjuna, Bheema or Satyaki's name. And do you know how many brothers I have lost today? That beast has killed fifty-six of Dhritarashtra's sons!"

A sob rends him. Karna says, "Grief clouds your judgement, Duryodhana; you must not even think this of Drona. I have watched him: he does everything he can for you. At his age, it is a miracle he fights like this. You must be grateful to him, not suspicious. Arjuna's chariot is yoked to gandharva horses, Krishna is his sarathy. Tell me, who can stop him, when he comes like the wind? Arjuna did not fight Drona honourably. He dodged past him, and the Acharya could do nothing. Arjuna cried, 'You are not my enemy, but my guru!' and flew by.

"It isn't only at Drona that you can point a finger. I was there, and you yourself, Duryodhana. Could we stop Arjuna? It was fate, my friend, and she is more powerful than all the armies of the earth. We can only do the best we can. The rest is in fate's hands and, despite everything we do, fate has her way with us."

Karna puts an arm around Duryodhana. "Come, let us go out and fight. That is all that matters: that we fight side by side, for each other! That, not even fate can take away from us. Look at all the kshatriyas who have died for you, Duryodhana. What more precious gift is there? How many men are there in this world for whom so many others will give their very lives? The armies are out again. We will fight as never before, for the sakes of those who lie dead for us on Kurukshetra. Beyond that, whether we will win or lose this war is not for us to decide."

Even as they speak, conches sound across the dark field, and Drona streams into battle with his legions. Like a ghostly Deva, swathed in starlight, the brahmana rides at the head of his legions. And now he is irresistible. Weapons clash across the field, and sound like a burning forest of bamboo upon a mountain. Duryodhana joins his army, with Karna just behind him. The Kaurava fights in cold rage; his arrows are a river of death under the stars. Before the Pandava frontlines can adjust to the unaccustomed battle by night, Duryodhana has killed a thousand men. He is like an ancient Asura come to hunt by darkness.

The Pandava soldiers run from Duryodhana, any way they can. But from behind their melting lines rides another king as bright and noble as his enemy is fell and heartless. With Bheema at his side, Yudhishtira rides to face his cousin. As soon as Duryodhana sees the eldest Pandava, he plunges at him, and the two of them, for whom all this war is being fought, duel. Their arrows are pale clouds scudding low in a high wind. At times, they loose shaktis, or the rare astra at each other, and these light up the field of death in brief splendour.

Frequently, real clouds pass over the stars, and the darkness of the cold night is complete. At these times, no warrior could be certain at whom he shot his arrows, though roars and screams still ring out, in evil bedlam. Drona is anxious for Duryodhana; any chance arrow could kill him in the night. Just then, Duryodhana pierces Yudhishtira's sarathy with a smoking shakti, and as the man drops his reins, it seems the Kaurava has his cousin at his mercy. But Yudhishtira replies, quick as life, with two smoking shafts that flame into Duryodhana's chest, knock him down on his chariot-floor, and would have killed him except for Brahma's golden armour.

Drona rides between Yudhishtira and Duryodhana, drawing a magic curtain of arrows between them. Yudhishtira's sarathy recovers. Some other Pandava warriors ride up to their king's side, and the duel ends. The fighting spreads out again. But it seems Drona can see as clearly by starlight as by the sun. His aim is unerring, his every arrow deadly. Once the two armies flow into each other, it is hard for the kshatriyas to fight with any ease. They can never be sure if their shafts and swords find enemies, or their own men.

The war by night wears a sinister face. Somehow, the battle by daylight, brutal as it is, is not remotely as macabre a ritual as fighting under the stars. The very earth takes on an eerie aspect, as if demons are about, invisibly, partaking in the offerings of life and blood. The darkness of night seems to illumine the deeper significance of this war: that it is a timeless contention between dharma and adharma, good and evil. As if these revelations of the soul's dark and light are intolerable to the common soldier, terror stalks Kurukshetra as never before: terror woven into the screams of the dying, and the dismal howling of the jackal-packs.

But the darkness is no obstacle to one that prefers to fight close to his enemies, hand to hand, smashing them down with his mace. For the Pandavas, Bheema is as devastating as Drona is for the Kauravas. It seems that Bheema, too, has cat's eyes, as he hunts Dhritarashtra's sons in the dark. He picks them out unerringly and, riding at each one, kills them with his mace, or his bare hands, even; rending some limb from limb, covering himself with blood that glimmers under the stars, so he is a scarlet spirit ranging the field.

Yet another warrior is even more at home in the darkness, and entirely in his element. Ghatotkacha patrols the night with a legion of rakshasas. For them darkness is their daylight, and their strength at this hour is ten times what it is by day. Their eyes like torches on Kurukshetra, their weird cries chilling their enemies' blood, they sweep at the Kaurava army in a wave of dread.

There is a king that fights for the Kauravas, who has lost two sons on Kurukshetra: Somadatta, the father of Sala and Bhoorisravas. He rounds on Satyaki in the night, "Kshatriya! How could you kill my son when he sat in dhyana?"

Satyaki roars back, "And now I will kill you!"

The Yadava matches his words with a brace of fiery arrows, lighting up the dark. Duryodhana flits to Somadatta's side; but Dhrishtadyumna materializes at Satyaki's, and holds off the Kaurava prince. Somadatta is hardly a match for Satyaki, and the Yadava cracks his bow and fells him with another humming shaft. The unconscious king is borne off the field. Aswatthama rides up to confront Satyaki, who is still tired after his long day. Aswatthama seems to have the better of their encounter, when, with a heart-stopping cry, Ghatotkacha erupts on him from the night!

Aswatthama whirls round to meet Bheema's son with a lucent volley, turning night into day. Ghatotkacha uses maya against Drona's son; he vanishes, and reappears on the other side of Aswatthama's chariot. Ghatotkacha fights with sorcery: he creates bizarre hallucinations out of the black air, and the Kaurava soldiers run screaming from them. But Aswatthama is unmoved. He vaporises the demoniacal visions with an agneyastra, which lustrates the field like a small sun. Aswatthama strikes Ghatotkacha with some light-swift archery.

Roaring in pain, the rakshasa casts a phosphorescent chakra at him, but the brahmana's son smashes it in flight. Ghatotkacha has a son himself, who attacks Aswatthama from the air with a barrage of occult weapons. Aswatthama turns up at the young rakshasa and brings him down like a bird out of the sky. Ghatotkacha's roar shakes Kurukshetra.

For the first time, the two armies hear him speak in a human tongue. He cries, "Brahmana, you won't escape with your life tonight!"

Ghatotkacha creates a vast illusion. Aswatthama finds himself in the heart of a mythic forest that teems with all kinds of predators: lions, tigers and baleful incubi; every one of these stalks Drona's son, as in the most terrifying nightmare. The hallucination is like a trial the soul passes through on its way to moksha. But Aswatthama, master of weapons,

The war at night

master of himself, is warrior enough and yogin enough not to be perturbed. Serenely, he invokes the proper astra and dispels the illusion.

Ghatotkacha flies up into the sky, and now he fights like any other kshatriya, with bow and arrows. He covers Aswatthama's chariot in a hail of firestones. An anxious Duryodhana rides to his friend's side. All round them Ghatotkacha's rakshasas are at their horrible sacrifice: thousands of petrified Kaurava soldiers their offering. Their naked bodies glistening in blood, the jungle demons are on the soft rampage.

Duryodhana cries to Aswatthama, "Who can stand against the rakshasas by night?"

Aswatthama actually smiles at his king, while arrows stream from his glowing bow. He says, "Leave them to me, my lord, and their master as well."

With a shaft like Yama's danda, Drona's son fells Ghatotkacha himself. Panic among the other rakshasas; they rush to their fallen friend to revive him. Aswatthama kills three of them as they go. Some of his anxiety allayed, Duryodhana rides away to find Shakuni. He persuades that sorcerer to attack the Pandavas, at this hour that suits him well.

A roar goes up from the Pandava soldiers, "Aswatthama has killed Ghatotkacha!"

Some kings who fight for Yudhishtira are so dismayed they leave the field. But when Bheema hears that cry, he falls on the enemy with renewed ferocity, killing three thousand. Until ten of Duryodhana's brothers ring him round, determined they will finish him, before they meet their brothers' fate. But they could not have chosen a worse time for their bravado. Bheema butchers them as if they were children before him.

When the last of the ten has his skull smashed by the Pandava's mace, another shout rings out on Kurukshetra, "Ghatotkacha isn't dead, he only fainted!"

TWENTY-FIVE

Karna, Kripa and Aswatthama

Aswatthama blazes like Rudra in the night, and no one can contain him. He consumes columns of the Pandava army with his astras; and when he shoots Ghatotkacha unconscious, Yudhishtira's army runs from him in terror. As Aswatthama swirls forward, irresistibly, Drupada's splendid sons appear out of the darkness in his way. But Drona's son is master, tonight, and he engages all the Panchala princes, at once, and kills those that dare stand before him for too long. Seeing his sons die, Drupada comes roaring into the fray.

Meanwhile, Somadatta's father Baahlika, the very oldest kshatriya to fight the great war, straddles Kurukshetra like a man half his age. Until he meets Bheema in the night. Many Pandava soldiers, who fought Baahlika as if he was too old to fight in earnest, have lost their lives tonight. Bheema makes no such mistake. He hurls his mace at the ancient, and Baahlika falls, his head split open, his spirit escaped. Baahlika was even older than Bheeshma, and a lament goes up at his fall. By the light of astras, and the rushlights that some soldiers have lit, ten more of Dhritarashtra's sons surround Bheema. The son of the wind fulfils another tenth part of his vow. Shakuni arrives with his legion, and Bheema welcomes him by dispatching some Gandhara princes, Shakuni's brothers.

There is another Pandava who fights as he has never done before: Yudhishtira burns the enemy like legions of dry grass. Drona rides at him. Kurukshetra is lit up, as the astras ruled by Varuna, Yama, Agni, Tvashtar and Savita flare at the Pandava. But Dharma's son, the serene one, cuts them down even as his brother Arjuna might.

With Arjuna resting away from the field, Drona sees this as his best chance to take Yudhishtira. When the Acharya's lesser astras prove ineffectual, Drona intones the mantra for the brahmastra. Yudhishtira hears the arcane chant across the darkness, and at once, he summons the same weapon. When brahmastra and brahmastra spume at each other and lock on high, it seems the night has ended abruptly. The Pandava army roars its delight to see Yudhishtira match Drona so wonderfully. The Acharya has no answer to the Pandava king's valour. He rides away from his sishya, and the hapless army feels his wrath.

Thousands perish in the dark: their lives put out with arrows they never see from Drona's bow. Then, from two sides, two Devaputras ride to take up their guru's challenge. Bheema comes from the west of the battle, where he has been annihilating the enemy. Vayu's son now rides with his bow in his hand, covering his master's chariot in silver fire. From the south, in a ratha yoked to steeds white as milk, the moon or the kunda flower, comes a greater archer than any other. A rejuvenated Arjuna rides into battle again, like Death himself. Drona shrinks before the combined assault, and the Kaurava soldiers, sleepless and exhausted, their morale at its lowest ebb, run from the brothers like a herd of deer from two tigers.

But Bheema and Arjuna kill thousands in the dark, and it seems the war will end this very night. Duryodhana rides to Karna at the edge of the field, and cries, "The river of death breaks its banks! You must stop them, Karna, you are my only hope."

Karna says, "I still have Indra's Shakti. Arjuna will die by his father's weapon; and when he dies, the rest will be easy to kill. I ride to bring you victory, Duryodhana. I will kill all the Pandavas for you. I will kill the Panchalas, too, and lay the world at your feet!"

Kripa is beside them, and the old warrior begins to laugh. Karna whirls round, and Kripa says, "Such fine words, Karna! It is a pity that fine words don't win wars, or Duryodhana would already be emperor of Bharatavarsha: for there is no one to match his friend Karna at bragging. You say that you will kill all the Pandavas and the Panchalas? Though they have Krishna with them! But we saw how you ran when you met just Arjuna by himself outside Virata. And today you could not stop him from killing Jayadratha. They say brahmanas make fine speeches and kshatriyas are men of deeds. But Karna is a master of building palaces in the air! I wish you fought as well as you boast."

He laughs again. Red-eyed Karna cries, "I will show you tonight that Karna is not just a braggart. Duryodhana is the only one who loves me and I will lay the world at his feet!"

Kripa scoffs, "You are not master of your own mouth, Karna, then how will you master Arjuna? Wars are not won with boasts; in a few days Yudhishtira will sit upon the throne of the world. Krishna is with the Pandavas, they cannot be defeated."

Karna growls, "I don't doubt the Pandavas are great adversaries. Yudhishtira is the image of dharma, and Arjuna is a brilliant archer. What is more, so far fate has been with them. But Arjuna is not immortal. Krishna avoided me today. He knows I have Indra's Shakti, and I can kill Arjuna with it!"

Kripa only laughs again. Karna draws his sword and snarls, "Another word and I will cut your tongue out, Brahmana!"

He actually rushes at Kripa; Aswatthama comes between them, his sword drawn too. "I will kill you for this, Karna!"

Then Duryodhana is among them, pulling Aswatthama away. Karna growls, "Let him go, Duryodhana. He always taunts me, and I will kill him first, and then the Pandavas."

Duryodhana cries, "We have an enemy to face! Are we going to help them by killing each other?"

Kripa murmurs, "You are right. Let Arjuna quell this fool's arrogance."

Duryodhana says, "Aswatthama, this is no time to fall out among ourselves. Already, the enemy has the advantage. Countless men have died for us: we owe it to our dead to turn defeat into victory. I beg you, save your anger for the Pandavas. Karna is dear to me, and he fights our cause."

Aswatthama lowers his sword. Without another word, Karna mounts his chariot and rides into battle.

TWENTY-SIX

Awesome Karna

K ARNA BURNS LIKE AGNI DEVA IN THE NIGHT. AT FIRST, WHEN THEY see him ride at them alone, the exuberant Pandava soldiers rush at him. But he is dread incarnate on Kurukshetra, and as swiftly as they came they run from him, when he burns up a legion in moments. No kshatriya dares stand against him, and Arjuna rides at him.

A radiant duel breaks out. The armies stand transfixed by the spectacle; it seems two Gods duelled. They fight as if it is daylight and the sun risen on the world: their aim is so true, their archery so effortless. Then, Arjuna strains himself briefly, kills Karna's sarathy and horses, and breaks his bow. Karna leaps out and finds the nearest Kaurava chariot to escape in: Kripa's!

The Kaurava army runs blindly when Karna loses his chariot. Arjuna is at them in the night. Roaring, Duryodhana charges him. Kripa cries to Aswatthama, "The king rides at Arjuna. Stop him!"

Quick as time, Aswatthama cuts off Duryodhana. "My lord! Am I dead that you must go to fight Arjuna? It is dark, Duryodhana. I beg you, watch the battle from behind our lines. You are our king, you mustn't expose yourself like this."

Duryodhana replies, "It seems I must fight myself, since your father and you are so full of love for the Pandavas! Drona lets our enemies through our lines, because they are his favorite sishyas. And of your valour, I have hardly seen a glimmer. Is it to please Yudhishtira that you stay your hand, or to win Draupadi's favour? All those that were loyal to me have already lost their lives."

Aswatthama remains calm. He says, "It is true we love the Pandavas. We love you also, or we would not be here at all; and when we fight, we leave our affections off the field. But you have a suspicious nature: whenever we lose a day, you turn accusingly on us. Calm yourself, Duryodhana; Drona and I, Kripa, Karna, Shalya and Kritavarman are all here with you, and we shall prevail. Don't doubt me, I swear I will fight for you until there is no breath left in this body."

Duryodhana cries, "Then ride at them, Aswatthama! Show me your courage tonight."

Aswatthama sweeps at the Pandava army like a natural calamity*. They run from him any way they can, but he consumes them with many flames by starlight. Suddenly, another kshatriya looms out of the night to challenge him. Through the panicstricken Pandava soldiers, Dhrishtadyumna flies at him.

The fire-prince, whose sons Aswatthama killed today, cries, "It is easy to kill young boys, who are not your equals. Come, coward, try me!"

The hatred between the two is as deep as their fathers' is. Aswatthama is frantic to kill Dhrishtadyumna: he knows he can save Drona's life if he does. He roars back, "The Panchala weaklings are mine to kill! Stand and fight, if you dare, and I will send you after your sons to Yama."

They battle with arrows, and words sharper than arrows. But the moment belongs to Aswatthama. He cracks Dhrishtadyumna's bow, cuts down his horses and kills the soldiers who guard his back. The Senapati of the Pandava army flees in another chariot, while the Kaurava army breaks into wild cheers. It seems the night belongs to Drona's son; he is tameless under the stars.

Meanwhile, Duryodhana has not left the field: he seeks Yudhishtira out, roaring his name in the dark. But when he nears the eldest Pandava, Bheema challenges him. Anxious for the Kaurava's safety, Drona, Aswatthama and some others fly to his side; while, on the other part, all the Pandavas appear around Bheema. Field and sky are lit by astras.

Satyaki, who ranges Kurukshetra again, cries to his sarathy, "Ride at Somadatta, I will kill him tonight!"

Somadatta roars to see Satyaki again. He would avenge himself on the Yadava, not just for the old humiliation by his grandfather, but now,

---

* He kills Ghatotkacha's son, Anjanaparva, here, after a prolonged duel.

more, for the death of Bhoorisravas. Satyaki knows he must kill this Kuru, or he will hunt him down some day. They fight without a word, silent as the night beyond, each knowing this duel is for his life. Satyaki has time on his side, and presses Somadatta hard, until he saps the older man's strength. Panting, Somadatta fights on, but finds it harder and harder. Somadatta's vision grows blurred; resignation comes over his sad heart. Then, Satyaki finds that heart with an arrow that steals past the old man's defences. Somadatta falls with a roar, dead.

Ten Kaurava warriors converge on Satyaki, Drona among them. Yudhishtira rides at Drona. The brahmana turns, growling, on the Pandava king. Around them, the general carnage continues, and the screams of the dying meld with the howling of the jackal-packs. Kurukshetra is an immense slaughterhouse. It seems the earth has plunged deep into hell. And, indeed, this war marks the end of an age. The dwapara yuga sets with the war on Kurukshetra, and the kali yuga rises already on time's horizon: monstrous and malignant, eager to be loosed upon the earth. But Krishna is still in the world, and as long as he is, the sinister kali dare not arrive.

The warriors of the two armies are hardly aware of the profound transformation that is afoot. They do not realize why the denizens of night, the jackals, wolves, wild-dogs, hyenas, and pisachas, too, are abroad in such numbers. Butchering one another, the kshatriyas are too absorbed in the night's bloody ritual, to notice the macabre Spirit of the kali yuga that is almost upon them; or that their own dominion over the earth nears its end. They have no sense of the distant consequences of the massacre on Kurukshetra. The moment absorbs them completely, the mindless sacrifice of the night.

Under the sorrowing stars, no bond is sacred. Guru and sishya attack each other. Yudhishtira fells Drona in the dark; the master jumps up again, and looses a keening vayavyastra at his student. Just in time, the Pandava cuts down the tempestuous weapon with a vayavya of his own.

Krishna rides up anxiously to Yudhishtira, and cries, "Why do you face the Acharya so often? He is dangerous. Dhrishtadyumna is the one for Drona, leave the brahmana to him. A king should fight a king. Look where Bheema battles Duryodhana. Go and join him, that is where you should be."

The darkness on Kurukshetra is a night of the soul. That field is swathed in such terror, in such a blindness of the spirit, that frequently soldiers from the same side kill each other, mistaking one another for the enemy. The torches are few and far between, and far from adequate to light up a war as great as this one. Much of the fighting is done with the loud yelling of names and armies to distinguish comrade from foe in the pitched night. Seeing how their soldiers panic in the dark, and kill each other in the fearful confusion, Duryodhana and Drona confer. They have lost so many men today that they cannot hope to win the war by superior numbers any more. The Pandavas may well have more men left alive.

Duryodhana roars to his legions, "Put down your weapons! You are killing our own soldiers. Put down your weapons and every man light a torch for the maharathikas to fight by."

The Kaurava soldiers gladly obey their king. At the edge of the field, rushlights and brands are lit and passed on, hand to hand, until every tenth man holds a flame over his head. On the other side, the exhausted Pandava soldiers follow their enemies' example, and soon Kurukshetra is wonderfully lit up with thousands and thousands of flaming torches: like some unimaginable yagnashala for the huge midnight sacrifice. The fighting begins again, but now only chariot-mounted kshatriyas battle, while footsoldiers light up the darkness so they can see their antagonists clearly.

A hundred duels flare up by marvellous torchlight, and the dharma kshetra is a spectacle[*]! Swords, red with blood, make brilliant arcs. Duryodhana cries to his warriors, "Drona will consume the enemy, and no one but Dhrishtadyumna can stop him. Kritavarman, you stay close beside the Acharya on his right, and you, O Shalya, guard his left side. At any cost, Drona must not face Dhrishtadyumna alone. The rest you leave to him!"

Satyaki seems to have found second wind, and fights as if he has begun a new day. A king called Bhoori rashly challenges the Yadava, and finds immediate death. Aswatthama burns like a thousand torches

---

[*] Ganguli: The Devas, rishis, gandharvas, apsaras, vidyadharas, nagas, yakshas, uragas and kinnaras hold magic lanterns in the sky, too. Here and elsewhere, apsaras fling garlands down on the warriors, and sprinkle heaven's perfumes over them—in joy!

himself. Once more, he strikes Ghatotkacha senseless in his chariot. Duryodhana and Bheema duel briefly. Bheema smashes the bow in his cousin's hands, and Duryodhana's sarathy wisely rides away from that most dangerous enemy.

Sahadeva rides against Karna, and fights lustrously; but Karna is a warrior of another order. The encounter doesn't last long, before he kills Sahadeva's horses, and snaps his bow. Seizing up a sword, Sahadeva leaps from his useless chariot. But even as he runs at Karna, that grand marksman smashes the blade in the Pandava's hand. Sahadeva wields his mace, only to have it struck into dust. Thinking his death has arrived, Madri's son wrenches his chariot-wheel free and runs at his sneering enemy. Karna strikes the spokes from the wheel with five amazing arrows; he breaks its rim with a sixth. Sahadeva stands panting and helpless, not ten feet from Karna. Determined to die unbowed, the youngest Pandava stands with his handsome head thrown back, his eyes raking his conqueror.

Karna laughs. Slowly, he brings his chariot nearer the trembling prince. He prods his young antagonist with the tip of his bow. Grinning, he says, "You mustn't fight your betters, boy. Look there, at your brother Arjuna. Now, he is a kshatriya; go and hide behind him, little one, or else go home."

With a last mocking laugh, and such an inscrutable look in his eyes, Karna rides off leaving Sahadeva dazed that this enemy had spared his life. Shaking his head, he walks away towards the nearby Panchala soldiers, who have witnessed the miracle.

All around, duels rage. Shalya overcomes Virata, Arjuna a king called Ala, and Acharya Kripa puts Shikhandi to flight. These are honourable contentions, and a helpless enemy is never slain. At midnight, by the wonderful sea of torches, the war puts on a less bestial face. Nakula and Shakuni meet, and the Pandava allows the treacherous Gandhara no chance to use any sorcery against him. He cuts down Shakuni's banner, and strikes him down to his chariot-floor.

Dhrishtadyumna finds Drona by torchlight. A brief encounter sparks up between them, but, quickly, Shalya and Kritavarman intervene. Infected by their kshatriyas' valour, the common soldiers of both armies begin to fight again: as if war is an irresistible temptation and the brush with death too sweet to stay away from. Karna has waited just for this;

now he can kill a thousand men. He is terrible past describing at the midnight hour. He is a black sun on Kurukshetra, a hungry maw to Yama's realm.

For the Pandavas there is a kshatriya as glorious as Karna is. Wherever he goes, all heads turn to watch him. Satyaki the Yadava is so handsome he makes even his enemies wish they were women! There are those who die by his arrows, crying out his name, rapturous that he and no other has killed them. As if drawn together by fate, this night, Karna and Satyaki come face to face on Kurukshetra.

They do not fight long with common shafts. Astras of fire, water, wind and air light up the sky into which a moon rises shyly now, as if in fear of the war below. Those who die by darkness are spirited away to different worlds than those who find their end under the sun. It is inauspicious to die at night. But who thinks of such things, while the war rages?

Karna hears loud screaming among his legions, he hears the thunder of the Gandiva. Leaving Satyaki in the midst of their duel, Karna seeks out Duryodhana. He says to the Kaurava, "Do you hear the song of the Gandiva? Do you hear our men scream? I cannot ride against Arjuna yet. I have Satyaki to kill first, the sishya before the guru. Hold the Pandava up somehow, until I rid us of the Yadava. Then Arjuna will find death by his father's Shakti, and, Duryodhana, the world will be yours."

Duryodhana and Shakuni ride towards Arjuna, and Karna back at Satyaki: to fight on in the heart of the night. Fearing for him, the Pandavas and Dhrishtadyumna stream forward around Satyaki, and on the other side, Drona and Aswatthama ride to Karna. The sky is lit by jagged bolts of astras. Fighting as never before, Karna dominates Kurukshetra: in majestic inspiration, he smashes Dhrishtadyumna's bow and his chariot, leaving the Panchala breathless.

Karna is aflame, and the Pandava soldiers fly from him. They don't care who else they face, as long as it is not him. Kunti's eldest son rules Kurukshetra. Not only has he killed thousands, this night of torches, he has brought such fear to the enemy that Pandava soldiers cry out when the breeze brushes their faces, thinking it is Karna. Yudhishtira is terrified, as he helplessly watches the brother he does not know raze his army.

Arjuna cries to his dark sarathy, "Look at Yudhishtira, Krishna. He trembles like a child, and hardly hopes we will last the night against

Karna. I never knew this evil one could fight like this! It seems only now he truly reveals himself; who can stand before him tonight? I must stop him, Krishna. Come, let us ride against the sutaputra."

But Krishna knows about the Shakti Indra gave Karna. He knows that not even Arjuna can resist that weapon. And as Karna is now, a pure kshatriya, alight on Kurukshetra, he will hardly think of Arjuna as his brother, if he dares face him. Karna would use the Shakti against the Pandava, and everything would be lost. His cause deeper than anyone else can fathom, his mission in the world past common understanding, the Avatara knows that one precious life must be sacrificed to save Arjuna's. Arjuna must be kept safe at any cost: he is the key to this war; only he can kill Karna. Karna grows in stature with every life he takes. The earlier valour of Satyaki and Arjuna pales before the way the lord of Anga rages now. After seeing Karna tonight, who could say that Arjuna is the greatest archer in the world? Karna blazes on Kurukshetra, the night belongs just to him.

Krishna says softly, "There are only two warriors on our side who can stand against Karna tonight. You are one, Arjuna, and the other is Ghatotkacha. Night makes him stronger; he can kill anyone by darkness. Look where Drona stalks Yudhishtira again, stealthily through the corpses with which Karna strews the field. If the subtle brahmana takes your brother, all your valour, all the heroism of your brothers and your friends, all the lives of those that have died for you will have been in vain. Drona hunts like the night leopard, and Yudhishtira is the calf he is after. Your first dharma is to protect your brother. Send Ghatotkacha out against Karna and let us ride to Yudhishtira's side."

Arjuna wonders at the look in Krishna's eye. Was it a trick of the torches, or did he see a tear in those black depths? But he cannot ignore his sarathy's warning. Arjuna summons Ghatotkacha with a thought. In a moment, the rakshasa stands before them, his eyes glowing.

Krishna smiles at Bheema's son, and says, "Karna devours our army, and no one can stand before him. Drona and his son are also out hunting tonight. Your uncle Arjuna must watch over Yudhishtira like his very life. Ghatotkacha, if you don't stop Karna, I fear the war will end tonight and the earth will belong to Duryodhana. Karna must be killed, and no one can do this thing but you. Take your astras, open Yama's door for him."

Ghatotkacha bows gravely, "I will go at once."

A pang in his heart, Arjuna says, "Take Satyaki with you. Together, you will tame the sutaputra."

Krishna's face is bland. If any evil premonition stirs in Ghatotkacha, he shows no sign of it but seems pleased he has been chosen for this mission. Anyway, the high rakshasas are magical beings, creatures of twilight that make no stark difference between the realms of waking and dreams, or life and death, as men do.

Ghatotkacha arms himself to the fangs, and comes into battle mounted in a white chariot. Around him, again, his legion of rakshasas swarms. Lithe they are, and powerful; their skins shine by the light of the torches. Most are at least a head taller than the men they have come to fight. All of them bear eerie weapons in their hands, sorcerous ayudhas, and every rakshasa is a master of maya. Just seeing that force, the Kaurava soldiers scatter.

TWENTY-SEVEN

Ghatotkacha rules the night

Duryodhana sees his soldiers flee one side of the battlefield. He sees Ghatotkacha advance on Karna, and turns to Dusasana in alarm, "Ghatotkacha rides at Karna with his devils. Take ten men for every rakshasa, go quickly, my brother! Karna must be protected."

Dusasana turns to go, when another rakshasa speaks out of the darkness. It is Jatasura, whose father Bheema once killed, on an adventure of his. In his element, by night, he says to Duryodhana, "This is my chance to avenge my father. Let me kill Bheema's son and drink his blood under the stars."

Gladly, Duryodhana sends Jatasura* out against Ghatotkacha. On his way, the demon kills a thousand Pandava soldiers. He is taller than any of Ghatotkacha's warriors, taller than Bheema's son. He is pale-skinned, for he is of another race of rakshasas, from another part of the earth. Jatasura does not ride into battle but comes to fight on foot, like some curse. He comes veiled in maya, and can only rarely be seen.

He roars at Ghatotkacha, "You are neither a human nor one of our people. Get down from your chariot, if you dare: let us fight like rakshasas!"

He cries out a resonant challenge in their weird tongue. Ghatotkacha leaps down from his chariot. The sight of them, circling each other, one white and the other black, their eyes luminous, their ears pointed, their

---

* Ganguli says this is Jatasura's son.

movements feline, makes the human soldiers around them shiver and step back. But torches are held for the two to fight to the death.

Their roars are fearsome, their blows dark whiplashes. Soon, blood blossoms on their faces. At times they lock with each other, so the muscles on their bodies stand out like serpents, glistening with the sweat that covers them. Then, one of them wrenches free and flails at the other with a clenched fist, or a vicious kick too swift to see, felling him. But neither stays down for more than a moment. Two human armies hold their breath around the inhuman warriors. Long they fight, until Ghatotkacha decides he has had enough of unarmed combat. With a blow like an earthquake, he knocks Jatasura down. Before that rakshasa can rise, Ghatotkacha sweeps up a long scimitar, and hews off his head with a stroke that makes an arc of torches on its gleaming blade.

Jatasura's scream echoes through the field, dying only when his head lands twenty feet from his body, blood shining in a trail between. Ghatotkacha picks up the grisly head, and runs towards Duryodhana's chariot. Gore from Jatasura's neck flows over his black body, and the men around him cower from Bheema's son.

In a ringing voice, Ghatotkacha cries to Duryodhana, "One must never visit a king without a gift. I have brought you a gift, Duryodhana!"

He flings Jatasura's head into his chariot, at the Kaurava's feet. Duryodhana leaps back with a cry. His lips wet with Jatasura's blood, Ghatotkacha says, "I will bring you another gift before the night ends, one you will love. Uncle, I will bring you Karna's head!"

Duryodhana stands too shocked to retort. With a smile, Bheema's son lopes back into battle. The Kaurava army parts for him and he quickly finds himself facing the lord of Anga by rushlight. Ghatotkacha's eyes are torches burning with their own fire. The rakshasa stands heaving before Karna; he stands swirled about in maya, that mysterious being. At times, the two armies see him, but mostly he is invisible. A hush falls on Kurukshetra, but it is broken by loud, rich laughter. Karna's eyes are not deceived for a moment by Ghatotkacha's maya; he sees the rakshasa, wraith-like, even when he is invisible to all the others. Karna throws back his head and mocks him with laughter, diminishing his spell of fear.

Ghatotkacha answers the mockery with an astra that immolates a thousand Kaurava soldiers. Kurukshetra is lit up, with men burning like rushlights. Roaring, Karna looses five silver shafts at him. Ghatotkacha has been taught by his uncle Arjuna, and strikes them aside with ease. Again, the rakshasa fights with maya; and now he not only makes himself invisible, but casts potent spells at his enemy. Great winds rise out of nowhere, and blow away lines of Kaurava soldiers; or sheets of flame flash from the rakshasa's hands, ashing entire legions.

Karna douses fire with rain. He stills tempests with unerring shafts that put out their stormy eyes. Karna is effulgent on Kurukshetra, with the light of his father. His bow is a sliver of the sun in his hands, and the battle against Ghatotkacha isn't a duel merely of the earth. All around Karna his soldiers run, screaming in terror of the rakshasa, or they are slain by his sorcery. Karna himself stands unmoved, his arrows a Ganga of flames from his hands.

Ghatotkacha is quenchless. One moment, he fights with sharp wooden shafts from the ground, and Karna is hard-pressed to hold him off. The next instant, the rakshasa treads air with maya, invisibly, and now his arrows are astras of sinuous darkness. Karna fights at the limits of his prodigious ability, for his very life. Ghatotkacha is everywhere. He is all the night of a thousand forms, a thousand fears. When Karna pierces his maya in the air, in a flash he assumes some monstrous shape on the ground, goes among the Kaurava soldiers as a Beast.

Duryodhana watches from a safe distance, in concern. It does not seem even Karna will be any match, tonight, for Ghatotkacha. Only the most intrepid soldiers continue to stand around the two, holding torches for them to fight by: for to be anywhere near is to court death.

Then, another demon arrives, tall and ferile, on Kurukshetra with a hideous army. Vile, slouching beasts march behind the pale stranger, and surely never before, since the earliest days, would such fiends have dared to approach a Kuru king without being slain on sight. It is the rakshasa Alayudha, whom even his own kind shun, come to offer his services to Duryodhana. The creatures that march in his yowling, gibbering legion are monsters that never show themselves when the sun is up.

Bheeshma would not have let these devils near the army of Hastinapura. The desperate Duryodhana senses an ally, and welcomes him. In sibilant tones, the rakshasa says, "I am Alayudha. Hidimba,

Kirmira and Baka were my kin*. Bheema slew them all, and I have come for revenge. I hunt only by dark, so I waited until you fought under the stars." He bares his fangs in a grin that makes even Duryodhana's skin crawl. "Hidimbi belonged to us all in the vana. But Bheema took her for himself, and he is not even one of us. Their child is a monster, of neither your kind nor mine. He is an unnatural thing, a blot on the face of the earth. He must die, and Bheema must die. I, Alayudha, have come to drink their blood."

If he were not so repelled by the stench of this rakshasa, Duryodhana may have clasped the devil to him. As it is, he cries, "Welcome, Alayudha, to the army of Hastinapura! Bheema's son rules this night, and no one can stand before him. You have come to be my saviour. Look where Ghatotkacha burns my army. Go friend! Kill Bheema's boy, and you shall find me forever grateful."

Karna is, by far, the finest archer in the Kaurava army. He is a legion of marksmen by himself. He is better than Aswatthama, Drona, Kripa and Kritavarman; he is better than all of them together. Long ago, Yudhishtira glimpsed Karna's genius at the tournament in Hastinapura, and he knew this was the greatest bowman in the world. Yes, even greater than Arjuna. Ever since, he has dreaded Karna. Now, this naked midnight of the war, Karna dominates Kurukshetra with his immaculate gifts. Yet, the one who confronts him tonight is a match even for him. Ghatotkacha contains Karna, and even as he does, he slaughters the Kaurava army.

Alayudha comes into battle, his malignant platoon streaming behind him, many of those rakshasas shambling on all fours, their eyes green slits. Ghatotkacha greets the force of demons with weapons of fire and wind, and braids of lightning that streak along the ground through their lines. Raising their evil faces to bay at the enemy, the rakshasas come on in a wave, unmindful of their own that fall screaming among them, torched.

Soon, Ghatotkacha is contained, since now two powerful enemies assail him at once. For all his rank appearance, Alayudha is a warrior, his courage boundless. He is also impervious to most weapons, calmly plucking them out of his milk-white skin. Then, he comes on again,

---

KMG: Alayudha was Baka's brother.

death at his bow, his curved sword, and his fangs and talons he uses to tear down those who stand before him. Alayudha quaffs the blood of the men he kills, and soon his lean form is covered in deep scarlet, shining slickly by the torches.

Bheema sees his son beset by two enemies, and attacks Alayudha with a gale of arrows. Seeing the father come to battle, Alayudha turns away from the son. His army eddying around him, he rushes snarling at Bheema. By dark, the demons have the better of Yudhishtira's soldiers. Supernatural fear numbs the Pandava legions. The rakshasas kill them with fang and claw, with sinister weapons and sorcery. Alayudha and Bheema face each other at the heart of all the blood flying. Bheema is bemused by the rakshasa's maya; the duel against an enemy who is seldom visible is not one he relishes. Alayudha smashes the Pandava's chariot. Bheema leaps down from its ruins and the two fight with maces.

At the edge of the war, Krishna turns to Arjuna. "We must go to Bheema!"

Arjuna comes to battle like a spirit of light. Krishna pilots his chariot straight to Ghatotkacha's side. Arjuna engages Karna, while Krishna cries to Bheema's son, "Your father needs your help against Alayudha. Fly to him!"

Karna makes to pursue Ghatotkacha, but Arjuna raises a screen of arrows in his path. Roaring, Karna turns on his brother. Ghatotkacha flies out of the sky at Alayudha. Like the heart of the midnight wind he swoops, and hacks off the white rakshasa's head with a bright blow of his sword. Alayudha's blood sprays across his own people with the force of Ghatotkacha's arm. It is as if they have all been slain with that stroke: panic takes them. Maddened, they run every way and the avenging Pandava army cuts them down as they please.

Ghatotkacha picks up Alayudha's head from the ground. Bearing it aloft he runs to Duryodhana's chariot again. Grinning, he flings the ruddy thing at the Kaurava's feet. Duryodhana jumps back from it with a roar. Ghatotkacha has already returned to the fighting.

Bheema's son rules the night's heart. He massacres the enemy as not Bheema, Arjuna, Satyaki or any of the others have yet done. He burns them, he blows them away: whole legions with astras and with subtle, deadly maya, so they hardly know they have been killed. Only Karna prevents him from razing all Duryodhana's army, only Karna holds him up in the dark. When Ghatotkacha lashes down a torrent of fire on the Kaurava forces, Karna blows the burning storm away with a vayavyastra. When it is a cloud of arrows the rakshasa conjures in the sky, Karna dispels it with an aindrastra. But Ghatotkacha is like two armies by himself, on the ground and in the air! Not even Karna can contain him entirely. In a chilling moment, Karna sees an entire complement of Kaurava soldiers beheaded by a flight of golden swords: to this, he has no answer.

Ghatotkacha's inhuman roars fill the darkness and terror worse than death lays hold of Duryodhana's men. And the rakshasa is not alone. Beside him, his father and uncle kill thousands, and it seems the war will surely end tonight. Karna hears desperate voices cry to him, "Kill the rakshasa, Karna, or the war is lost!"

"Hah! Save us, Karna! Kill the devil."

"Use your Shakti, Karna. Use Indra's Shakti against the beast. Or we all die tonight!"

"Kill him now or everything is lost!"

Karna hears Duryodhana's desperate cry, "The Shakti, Karna! The Shakti, or we are doomed!"

TWENTY-EIGHT

Indra's Shakti

Karna lays his hand on the Shakti before him, and it begins to shine like a piece of a star. His chariot is lit up, blindingly. As he picks up the weapon, he hears the echo of another voice above the tumult of the armies.

Giving Karna his Shakti, Indra said, 'You can cast it only once, against just one enemy. Whoever he may be, he will die. But then the Shakti will return to me.'

Karna had replied, 'I need to use it only once. I have only one enemy.'

Indra laughed, 'You mean Arjuna; but Krishna protects him. Not even with my Shakti can you kill the Pandava.'

But Karna had hoped to cheat fate. Even after he discovered Arjuna was his brother, the old flame of rivalry had not subsided entirely in his heart. He must show the world who its finest archer was. Bheeshma, Drona and the others all said it was Arjuna; he knew they were wrong, he would prove them wrong. Even now, his hand rests reluctantly on the ayudha. Indra had taken his kavacha and kundala; Krishna had struck him deep by telling him Arjuna was his brother. He cannot hope to defeat the Pandava without Indra's Shakti. That would be fateful, indeed: a brother killing his brother with his father's weapon! But now, the rakshasa threatens. The war will end tonight, in defeat for Duryodhana, if Ghatotkacha is not killed. Karna knows that if he uses the Shakti against Ghatotkacha, the war would be as good as lost anyway. For then, what weapon would conquer Arjuna?

Meanwhile, Bheema's son is death's gory spectre on Kurukshetra. Again, Karna hears Duryodhana cry at him, "The Shakti, Karna, kill the rakshasa!"

Tears spring in his eyes, but he is strangely glad as well. Now he would not kill his brother; instead, he would die at his hands. Ah, sweet death: end of the long cruelty that had been his life! For his friend he would die, for his brothers, most of all, for his mother, for Kunti. That was what she wanted, wasn't it? That Arjuna kills Karna. Karna raises the Shakti above his head. It is as if a midnight sun has risen on Kurukshetra. Light floods the field. Karna stands at the heart of that splendour; tears like fire-drops scald his eyes.

With an echoing cry, he casts Indra's Shakti at Bheema's son. Time stands still as the Shakti flashes from his hands. It seems to take an age to traverse the night to its target. Ghatotkacha stands helpless in its path, his mantle of maya torn apart by the coruscance of the Shakti. Fearlessly, he watches his death come for him. All his wild and tender life flashes before him in the yawning moment the ayudha takes to arrive. With a roar beginning on his lips, Ghatotkacha grows big as a hill. He towers over the Kaurava army. Before his roar ends, with a report like ten thunderclaps, the Shakti crashes into his chest in an explosion of light. The weapon blows a great hole in Ghatotkacha's chest, killing him instantly. He falls like a mountain on Duryodhana's army, crushing tens of thousands of soldiers in his final moment, a whole aksauhini, just as he intended. In the shocked silence, Bheema's roars echo. Again and again, the Pandava roars his grief into the still night.

That sound is music to Duryodhana's ears. He flies to Karna, pulls his friend into his own chariot and embraces him. His arm around his warrior, Duryodhana rides triumphally through his army, and the soldiers cry out Karna's name, Duryodhana's, and 'Jaya'!

At the edge of the battle, Bheema sits on the ground and buries his face in his hands. A moment ago, it seemed Ghatotkacha by himself would win this war for them; now, the shock of his death lances through Yudhishtira's legions. Numbly, the Pandava king rides to Bheema's side. Yudhishtira is also sobbing helplessly. Ghatotkacha was his first nephew, and always his favourite child. He sits beside Bheema bereft on the ground, the stricken Bheema. Yudhishtira takes his brother's hand. He wipes Bheema's tears, while his own flow: their arms around each other, the two of them mourn.

All the Pandava army is stunned when Ghatotkacha falls. There is one exception: Krishna exults! Arjuna climbs down from his chariot, and stands too shocked to shed a tear. But his sarathy leaps down from his chariot-head in unashamed delight. Crying out in jubilation, he embraces Arjuna. The soldiers around them watch the strange sight curiously.

Arjuna turns on Krishna in anguish. "My Lord! Am I dreaming, or are you pleased Ghatotkacha is dead? Bheema's son has died, what makes you so happy?"

Krishna takes Arjuna by his shoulders. "This is the happiest day of my life! I don't celebrate Ghatotkacha's death, but the manner in which he died."

"What do you mean?"

"The war is won! Don't you see, Arjuna, Ghatotkacha's life was the price of victory: and I swear he will not have died in vain. Now Yudhishtira will surely sit upon the throne of the earth."

"Whatever do you mean, Krishna? I don't understand a word you are saying."

"It is so plain! Now Karna is dead. The only man I feared of the enemy. You still don't see? The Shakti, Arjuna: he could use it only once, and he has. If you knew how many sleepless nights I have spent thinking of Karna with his Shakti, perhaps you would understand my relief. Arjuna, Ghatotkacha has died in your place and I don't fear Karna any more."

Arjuna still looks puzzled. Krishna goes on, more softly now, "Everyone said Arjuna is invincible, that he is the greatest kshatriya on earth. I knew they were all wrong. Karna would have killed you with the Shakti. Do you know what Duryodhana said to me when I went to try to make peace in Hastinapura? He said, 'I have Karna on my side. He by himself will win the war for me.'

"Bheeshma and Drona scoffed at him; and they would, because they believed their Arjuna was invincible. But Duryodhana loves Karna, and his love made him more clear-eyed than the rest. Arjuna, Duryodhana was right. Only he realizes Karna's true worth." His voice is a whisper now, deafening Arjuna.

Krishna says, "You see, I also knew the truth: that of all the archers on earth, Arjuna is not the greatest one but Karna. You may have beaten him twice, but you are not his equal at all. There is no archer like Karna. Before the war began, Bheeshma contemptuously refused even to include Karna among the maharathikas of the Kaurava army. He said that, without his kavacha and kundala, he was at best an ardharathika. But your Pitama was wrong, you know. Why, as long as Karna had Indra's Shakti, not the armies of Devaloka could face him. As long as he had either his kavacha and kundala, or the Shakti, not Indra, Varuna or Kubera could defeat him. Not you, with the Gandiva, not I, with the Sudarshana, could kill Karna!

"Now he is like a serpent without its fangs, a God who is not immortal any more. Even now, only you can kill him, Arjuna. But at least it can be done."

Arjuna listens, astonished. Satyaki has joined them, he, also, amazed by what Krishna says. The Dark One goes on gravely, "Karna is the most misunderstood, most demeaned man on earth. You have no idea who he is, what he is. Ah, he is like the sun at noon, too bright to gaze upon. Arjuna, this enemy of yours is not just the best archer in the world, but the most pious, noble man on earth. Why, those who know his heart will claim he is as great as Yudhishtira, greater. Who has suffered as Karna has? You five have always had one another to take comfort from, during your trials. But whom does Karna have? He is alone, and alone he has borne his torments.

"But the time draws near for his anguish to end, in the only way it can. It is time for great Karna to die. Without his Shakti, you can kill him. Only then will this war be won, and Yudhishtira sit upon the throne of the world, as he was born to. You ask me why I rejoice at Ghatotkacha's death. I rejoice because he gave his life to save the world; he gave his life so your life may be saved. He made the noblest sacrifice of all, the needful one."

They hear exuberant roaring as the Kaurava army comes streaming back into battle, to celebrate Ghatotkacha's death. Satyaki asks, "But, Krishna, why didn't Karna use the Shakti against Arjuna?"

Krishna smiles, he says, "Every night, they would speak of nothing else in their tents, Duryodhana, Dusasana, Shakuni and Karna. All these days Karna stalked Arjuna, so he could cast the Shakti at him. But I knew he had the weapon, and that is why, Arjuna, time and again I avoided Karna. When, once or twice, we did face him, I made him forget he had the Shakti!"

The battle rages once more by the sea of torches. Krishna says, "Drona is attacking us again. His soldiers are wild with joy at Ghatotkacha's death. Come, we must rally our forces."

Some way off, Yudhishtira raises his tearful face and whispers to Bheema, "My brother, Drona rides at us again. I feel too faint to come to battle. Bheema, go and face the Acharya; he will take great toll of us if he isn't contained."

Heartbroken, and radiantly brave, Bheema wipes his eyes. He clasps his brother once, tightly, and then goes out to vent his sorrow on the enemy. Yudhishtira sits slumped against his chariot-wheel, sobbing desperately now and again. When Krishna comes to him, he finds the gentle Pandava has fainted from a grief he cannot support.

Gently, Krishna wakes his cousin. He says, "This weakness is not for a kshatriya and a king. Your army depends on you; every man in it fights for you. You must master your sorrow, all will be lost if you succumb like this."

Yudhishtira fetches a sigh. His eyes still stream, and he says, "Ah, Krishna, I know, I know. Nothing is certain in war, from moment to moment. But won't I be the worst sinner if I don't grieve for my precious child, my sweet Ghatotkacha? Let me recount, at least once, all that he did for us, and so quietly, with never a thought for himself. You did not know him as I did, Krishna. He was so loving, more than any other child in our family. He was the first in his generation, and I loved him twice as much as I do Sahadeva. And ever since he was an infant, he was specially fond of me."

Krishna realizes he must allow Yudhishtira this expiation of remembrance. Softly, as if to himself, Yudhishtira goes on, "He spent his childhood with us, and he was such an intelligent boy. He learned everything so quickly, Krishna: the Shastras from me, archery from Arjuna, fighting with the mace from his father, until he went away with his mother. Later, when we were in exile in the Kamyaka vana, Ghatotkacha heard Arjuna had left us to sit in tapasya. He knew how much we would miss our brother, and he came there and spent some months with us. How thoughtful he was! And such a joy, always self-effacing and so resourceful. On Himavan, when Draupadi and I could not climb up to Badarikasrama, Bheema summoned Ghatotkacha. He came with his people, and they carried us on their backs and flew to Nara Narayana's asrama.

"Since the war began, he has been with us. You saw how he fought, how bravely, how carelessly of his own life. And not for kingdom, or any desire for it: if he was alive and we won, he would only have gone back to his jungles. Power and kingdom meant nothing to him. He came to fight just out of love; and he, who least deserved to die, has been sacrificed to this gruesome war. Oh, how will I ever know happiness again when my pure child is dead?

"When Abhimanyu was killed, none of us was near him; but Ghatotkacha died before our eyes. What was the point in killing Jayadratha for Abhimanyu's death? Drona and Karna were to blame, and they have not paid for what they did. Even now, no one speaks of killing Karna for what he has done to our precious child."

Then, rage grips Yudhishtira. He rises, quivering. "But I will not leave him alive. I will avenge my Ghatotkacha tonight!"

Not looking back at Krishna, Yudhishtira climbs into his chariot. Krishna runs to Arjuna. In this mood, Yudhishtira must be guarded closely. In alarm, Krishna and Arjuna watch him make his way round the rest of the army. He means to ride at Karna through the Kaurava ranks. They pursue him as swiftly as they can. Suddenly, a glowing figure looms before Yudhishtira's chariot in the night. His horses rear, neighing, in fear of the dark, matt-haired apparition that bars their way. Tossing their manes, they stop still before that wild and holy one.

Vyasa says quietly to his Pandava grandson, "Ghatotkacha's death was written long ago, Yudhishtira. He was born to die for you. You must not give in to sorrow; all your army depends on you. If Karna had not killed Ghatotkacha with the Shakti, Arjuna would have died by it. And then this war would really have been in vain: for then, not you, but Duryodhana would have sat upon the throne of the world."

Yudhishtira stands, hands folded, his good sense slowly returning to him. Vyasa continues, "Just five days more, Yudhishtira. Five days more and victory will be yours. Five days and you will be lord of the earth, and the light of dharma will shine again in the dark world. And those whom you want to see punished for what they have done shall be dead.

Go back to your brothers. You will achieve nothing by riding out like this, except getting yourself killed; and if you do, everything will truly be lost."

Yudhishtira shivers when he realizes how close he has come to destroying himself and his sacred cause. He bows to his grandfather, who vanishes before him as mysteriously as he appeared. Krishna and Arjuna ride up beside Yudhishtira. Together, they turn back the way they came, and a moment fraught with danger passes.

TWENTY-NINE

Drona

THE TWO HOSTS RUSH AT EACH OTHER BY TORCHLIGHT, AND THE killing begins again; the air is shrill with the screams of a thousand dying men, thick with the roars of their killers. But past the midnight hour, deep tiredness is upon them all as well. They have been fighting since morning, and there are those that actually fall asleep where they stand, and have their heads struck off by an enemy almost as exhausted.

Arjuna's voice rings out above every other sound of battle. "All of us are tired. I say we should sleep an hour or two before we fight again."

Shouts of approval from both armies greet this. Not waiting a moment, every soldier on that field lays down his weapons, lies on the blessed earth and lets sleep come over him. Some Kaurava soldiers cry before they fall asleep, "God bless Arjuna for his mercy!"

Then, soon, silence; only a sea of breathing heaves against night's deep quiet. Kurukshetra lies darkling, a child that has sobbed itself to sleep, scarlet trails on her face. The sleeping and the dead lie side by side, indistinguishable. A moon the hue of blood rises high over this spectacle, a cardinal lotus blooming in the sky. As Soma Deva climbs higher, his ruddy complexion fades and Kurukshetra is bathed in silver light.

There is one man who does not sleep tonight. Drona sits alone at the edge of the field of death, and a profound sense of doom is upon him. At night's abysmal heart, all his life plays itself out phantasmagorically before his eyes. He sees himself as a boy again: his idyllic tutelage in his father Bharadvaja's asrama. He sees Drupada beside him, also a boy. He hears their innocent voices, full of wonder, full of love. Tears well in Drona's eyes, and roll down his cheeks. Then, later, Aswatthama is a child; his father hears him ask in his lisping voice to taste milk. An uncanny breeze starts around Drona, plucking at his face. He sees himself come to Drupada's court, hoping to find a new life, most of all for his son. For the first time, he tastes the hubris of kings, their selfishness. Drupada breaks his heart with scorn. Even then, he could have turned back to the natural forest. That should have been taste enough for him to realize he did not belong in the world of power, the harsh world of the kshatriya.

But he was young and rash; he took the wrong turn. Thirsty for revenge, he went to Hastinapura. Now, alone here in the outer darkness, he sees it all so clearly. He sees his terrible mistakes, the first steps on the road to sin. He was a brahmana; he did not belong in the court of a kshatriya king, least of all, as a teacher of archery. But he also realizes he could hardly have helped himself. Untenable sorrow turned into the rage that obsessed him: sorrow, and his pride. If only he had understood this then, they would not have consumed his life.

He sees himself walking into Hastinapura, to Kripa's house. He sees it all as if it was happening again before his eyes, in this dense night full of ghosts of every kind, full of the lost times of the earth. He went to Bheeshma, and told him how Drupada had humiliated him, and he wanted revenge. The Kuru Pitama smiled: a smile that mocked Drona's youthful earnestness. Quietly, Bheeshma said, 'You have come to the right place. I have a hundred grandsons, all eager to learn archery.'

Drona stayed on in Hastinapura. The demon revenge possessed him, and he did not think what he was sacrificing for it. Over the years, he lost the gentleness that should have been part of his nature. He lost the dignity and freedom that should have been his. He became just a hireling of the Kurus. Over the years, this gnawed at him. Yet, more than anything, he wanted revenge against Drupada.

Revenge he had, when Arjuna routed the Panchala king. But when Drona saw his childhood friend humbled before him, he cried, 'I only wanted to teach you a lesson. Let us be friends again.' How naive he had been to think a kshatriya would forget that shame, or ever think of him as his equal. Drupada prayed for a son who would kill Drona.

The breeze swells into a midnight wind, whispering death around Drona sitting alone at the edge of Kurukshetra, as the moon washes the violent field in spectral light. His life plays itself out before his weary eyes, eerily.

The brahmana sees himself as a master to the Kuru princes. There, too, he had been a failure. Very early, he had noticed the growing enmity between the sons of Dhritarashtra and the sons of Pandu. As a guru, he could have tried to put an end to that fledgling antagonism, to nip it in the bud. But he had not thought of this as being part of his duties. Indeed, he had subtly fuelled that hatred by turning a blind eye to it: because he thought it helped the princes compete more intensely, and thus excel. This was where his indifference had led them all. Out alone on the deathly field, Drona realizes he had not loved his wards as he should have. He had seen them only as warriors of the future, not as human children.

Now, Drona's eyes leak pointless tears, and the cold wind dries them on his face. He should have gone back to the forest when the princes' instruction was complete. The wilderness would have healed him. It would have eased away the worldly mantle with which he had covered himself. He would have been his own master again, and for a proud spirit like Drona, that would have cured him as nothing else. But he lingered on in Hastinapura, until the fateful game of dice was played. Even then, it was not too late. He could have spoken out for dharma; it was not as if he did not know who was right and who was wrong. Like Bheeshma, he remained silent. Was it because he revered the Pitama so much that he could not bring himself to speak out when the patriarch held his peace? On Kurukshetra tonight, as two armies lie around him, asleep and dead, Drona faces that terrible question from himself.

He shivers in the dark wind, which seeps into his bones. Drona feels what can only be death's fingers brush his cheek, and is filled with remorse. He remembers how Duryodhana came to him, after the Pandavas left for the forest swearing revenge. Duryodhana was afraid his cousins would attack Hastinapura. Even then, the Acharya could have redeemed himself; instead, he rashly promised the Kaurava prince that he would fight for him. More than any other, that promise had sealed Drona's fate. There was no turning back for him.

Now, too late, he sees that a deep sense of inferiority had led him down the path to ruin. Then the war began, and Bheeshma fell. Drona became Senapati of the Kaurava army. How proud he had been! No turning back. The cruel night mirrors his mistakes without mercy. Drona sobs like a boy, when he thinks in shame of how he agreed to take Yudhishtira captive. Even that was as nothing compared to what followed.

He remembers the chakra vyuha. He sees every chariot and footsoldier of it with pitiless clarity. He sees himself weave that web, in cold blood, to snare a child. And why? Because Duryodhana taunted him, saying he did not fight as he could. He had known very well that only Abhimanyu could breach the vyuha. It was as if he had stolen into Arjuna's son's tent, and stabbed him in his sleep. And Arjuna had treated him as a father, looked up to him even when he fought as Duryodhana's Senapati. What had he said, as he flashed by on his way to kill Jayadratha?

'You are not my enemy. You are my guru.'

But Bheema had not spared him the truth. The night burns Bheema's words like hot knives in his soul. 'Once you were our guru, and like a father to us. Now you are an enemy, just another of Duryodhana's minions.'

Suddenly, a voice speaks out of the night to the brahmana. Duryodhana says, "Here you are, Acharya, I have been looking for you."

Quickly, Drona wipes his tears, and turns to his king. By the light of the moon, for the first time he sees Duryodhana as he truly is: a beast of darkness, his eyes full of evil. Drona controls himself, and says, "Yes, Duryodhana? Is there something you wanted to say to me?"

His voice cold and mocking, as ever, Duryodhana says, "Nothing new, Acharya. Only what I have been saying to you all these days, since you became our Senapati. You have astras that can raze the enemy, whenever you decide that you will win this war for us. But Arjuna still rules your heart. Did you see how many of our men he killed today? You hardly tried to stop him. Drona, you must make up your mind if it is the Pandavas you fight for or us."

Drona growls, "I have always done my best for you. But you know, as well as I do, that it is a crime to use the devastras against common soldiers."

His eyes malevolent, Duryodhana answers his master with silence. Drona sighs, "I have already sworn I will not remove this armour from my body until I have killed all the Panchalas and Kekayas. But you are my king, and I am your Senapati. I will obey you. If you command me to use the devastras against common Pandava soldiers, so be it. My life is hardly worth living any more, and with this final crime, death will come for me: though I know that is of small concern to you.

"But listen to me, Duryodhana. I, too, have something to say to you, which I have said before. Not with the devastras, or any weapon that your warriors possess, can Arjuna be killed. No kshatriya that fights for you, not all of them together, can bring him down."

A tremor of resentment ripples through the Kaurava. He says, "We will bring down your Arjuna, Acharya. Between Karna, Dusasana, Shakuni and me, we will kill your great archer."

Drona smiles more scathingly than anything he can say, and does not reply. Duryodhana continues, "From now, let us divide our army in two. We four will take one half and ride against the Pandavas. You take the other half. Fight if you will, Acharya, or stand aside and contemplate your Arjuna's greatness."

Drona smiles. "I wish you well, Duryodhana. You have lived a full life, so you need have no regret as you set out on this brave mission. Only when you face him yourself, will you discover who Arjuna is. Until then, you won't believe what I say." There is bitterness in the brahmana's voice. "You have always been suspicious, never knowing who loves you and who does not." He laughs. "But I am forgetting you are a kshatriya born in the House of Kuru. It is only natural that you want to fight Arjuna yourself. I wondered why you hardly fought all these days, while all around you hundreds of thousands died for your sake. For the sake of your greed.

"After all, what have you to fear, when your uncle goes into battle with you? The mighty Shakuni! The one who has brought us all to this pass. The master of the dice-board will do what no kshatriya has yet: he will vanquish Arjuna in battle, as easily as he did Yudhishtira at dice!"

Drona laughs again, grimly. "Yes, how often I have heard you say in your father's sabha, 'We three, Dusasana, Karna and I, are enough to kill the five Pandavas.' Your time is here, Duryodhana. You have drunk deeper from the cup of pleasure than most kings do in ten lifetimes. You have wielded power as no other man in the world. And yes, you have been generous to those whom you love. You have done much good, as well, and as far as I know, you are not in debt to anyone. So, go boldly, and fight the Pandavas. You have tasted everything that life has to offer someone like you. Now die gloriously at your cousins' hands!"

Drona gets up and walks away from Duryodhana, who stands gazing out into the night for a long time after his Senapati has gone.

THIRTY

One white lie

BATTLE RESUMES BY THE LIGHT OF THE STREAMING MOON. AWAKENED by echoing conches, the soldiers of both armies rise[*] and, somewhat rested, fall at each other again. The moon has risen late. It is the last yaama of the night, and soon the sun touches the eastern sky with livid fingers. A cheer goes up from both armies, as the star slides over the horizon and casts his lustre across the field of death. It is the fifteenth day of the war, the fifth of Drona's command.

As the sun rises, for the first time the armies clearly see the devastation the night has left. Kurukshetra is uneven with corpses, like anthills; and, among them, a mountain: noble Ghatotkacha's body. But there is no time to mourn the dead, or to honour them with cremation. The war rages on.

Krishna sees the enemy legions now divided in two. He says to Arjuna, "Look to the left where Duryodhana, Karna, Shakuni and Dusasana fight in a cluster, like a baleful constellation."

Bheema, who is near them, shouts, "Let us turn to the left! All those we have sworn to kill ride in a pack like dogs."

Arjuna takes up the Gandiva, and Krishna points his horses at the Kaurava king and his coterie. Arjuna comes in wrath; his arrows obscure the face of the rising sun. Easy as it was for Duryodhana to imagine that he and his inner circle would vanquish Arjuna, in battle they cannot stand before the Pandava at all. He quickly puts the four to flight, their army following, and thousands cut down by the riptide from the Gandiva.

---

[*] Ganguli 'the sea of troops wakes like an assemblage of lotuses unfurling to the sun'.

Meanwhile, with half the Kaurava army, Drona rides at the Matsyas, the Panchalas and the Kekayas. He is like fire that does not smoke. Certainty of his end is upon him. The enemy shrinks from him in awe; the brahmana's body is as bright as a Deva's. Yet, he is purely dreadful, like an evil amsa of Agni. Drona does not care any more if it is a kshatriya or a common soldier that stands before him; he consumes both with astras. He torches legions, leaving nothing but statues of ashes, which the wind blows down.

Drona sees three of Dhrishtadyumna's sons riding at him, naively. He kills all three, in a moment, striking their heads from their necks with his famous crescent-tipped arrows. He kills the boys where their grandfather sees them die. Drupada's roars shake the field, and he rushes at Drona. This is exactly what Drona wants; he does not mean to leave the Panchala king alive, when his own death is so near him.

Virata rides beside Drupada at the hated brahmana. Drona is ready for them both. He engages them powerfully, fighting as Drupada has never seen him do, as Drupada had never known he could.

Drona cries at his old friend, his old enemy, "This is the end, Drupada. Everything will be over today!"

"When you die, vile Brahmana!"

Drona casts a gleaming javelin, striking the Panchala king through his heart, killing him instantaneously. Demented Drona turns on Virata and kills him with another lance, affixing him to his chariot-head. Uproar breaks out among the Pandava legions. Crimson-eyed, Dhrishtadyumna cries, "He has killed my sons and my father. If I don't kill Drona today, let all my life's punya be lost!"

He plunges at Drona; but Duryodhana's legion rings the Acharya round. Arjuna and his brothers fly to help Dhrishtadyumna, and a general battle ensues. After a wild hour, Drona still dominates Kurukshetra, and Dhrishtadyumna is no nearer killing him. To provoke him into the deed, Bheema scoffs at his friend, "It doesn't seem you will avenge your father or your sons. Let me help you, Dhrishtadyumna!"

Roaring twice as loudly as anyone else, Bheema rushes at the Kaurava army. The Pandava heroes fight, all together, trying to force a way through to where their Acharya burns like time. On the fifteenth day of the war, Drona bestrides Kurukshetra, as Bheeshma could not on the ninth day, when the Kuru Pitama was at his fiercest. But Bheeshma had fought with dharma, while Drona, in the clasp of despair after the night's revelations, has abandoned the way of truth entirely.

The brahmana incinerates Yudhishtira's common legions with the greater devastras. Fire stalks Kurukshetra, and Drona is Agni incarnate. The war is Drona, and he is death come naked to the world. Everywhere the sickly-sweet smell of burnt human flesh hangs in the air. The Kauravas rally around their Senapati, and not the five Pandavas together can contain him. Few duels are fought, the war swirls around just Drona. Duryodhana and Nakula face each other briefly; and the Kaurava has his bow snapped in his palm and hastily retreats. Dusasana encounters Sahadeva, and here also the Pandava prevails after a short, fierce encounter. In another duel, Karna and Bheema meet. In memory of how Karna humiliated him, Bheema fights beyond himself for revenge. Again, he finds Karna is an archer of superior gifts. Karna strikes Bheema unconscious in his chariot, then, spares his life once more.

Meanwhile, Krishna manoeuvres Arjuna's chariot to confront Drona, and Kurukshetra seems transported to another world by the duel between that master and disciple, each fighting at the very ends of his skill. In two brilliant bands, astras sizzle across the field of moment. Only those who are masters themselves of the missiles can fathom the subtleties of that contention; the others watch, awed.

For some time, they fight, guru and sishya, and neither prevails. Then, Drona, who by now hardly knows what he does, invokes a fearsome weapon. The brahmana summons the greatest brahmastra*. Kurukshetra is rocked by a seismic tremor and a sudden night falls, when he chants the mantra for the transcendent ayudha. Only Drona's chariot is enveloped in such light that the soldiers turn their faces from it. At its white heart, Drona draws back his bowstring, and his body is a flame. In a moment, the old master looses the weapon at his favourite pupil. Pandavas and Kauravas wait, breathless; they know this is a moment that can end the war.

The brahmastra flares up into the darkened sky, lights it like five suns. Then, like doom, it falls on Arjuna's chariot. But a gasp goes up from the armies of darkness and light. At the heart of that moment, Arjuna's chariot also blazes like a star; his body is a pale fire as well, and the Gandiva a lucific crescent in his hands. Another sun flames up

---

* This weapon is one that appears in many forms, both protective and devastating.

from the Pandava's bow, and brahmastra and brahmastra meet in the sky. An explosion like the world ending shakes heaven and earth, a million men fall dazed on the ground. Astra blows astra apart on high; they blow the darkness away and it is daylight again on Kurukshetra. With a long roar of frustration, Drona rides away from Arjuna.

The fighting grows diffuse again, as many duels break out. At least for the time being, Arjuna has broken Drona's dominance: the brahmana rides away to savage the Panchala army once more. Dhrishtadyumna and Dusasana face each other; but the Kaurava cannot stand against the angry fire-prince. Swiftly, he has his bow cloven, and his sarathy leaves the field before his warrior is killed.

Another duel rages nearby, a piquant one. Chance brings Duryodhana and Satyaki face to face. They fight fiercely, but with smiles on their faces! Though Duryodhana is some years the older, these two had once been inseparable friends. Suddenly, Duryodhana feels a pang of remorse. He roars at Satyaki, "What a despicable war this is, in which you and I must fight each other. How I hate myself sometimes, Satyaki, for my arrogance, my lust for kingdom, and that I am a kshatriya! Otherwise, we two would never face each other with arrows today."

He lowers his bow briefly, and so does Satyaki, a little startled. The Kaurava continues, "Do you remember the old days, my friend? How clearly they rise before my eyes, as if they were happening again. You were dearer to me than my very life and I to you! Look where time has brought us."

Duryodhana's confession is sharper than his arrows, and Satyaki is taken aback to see the Kaurava wipe tears from his eyes. The Yadava cries, "All that is past, Duryodhana! This is not our guru's house, when I was a boy and you a youth, and you were so fond of me that you would play children's games with me."

Duryodhana says, "Oh, where are those innocent games? This is like another life, and we are like strangers, Satyaki. How cruel time is. Look at us today. Fate is merciless, my friend, and fate is my enemy. Karna always says that if fate is against you, there is nothing you can do. It is not we but fate that decides our lives, every moment of them."

Quickly, tears fill the softhearted Satyaki's eyes, and he says, "We are kshatriyas, and war is our dharma. There is no escape from that, Duryodhana. We fight, and must not care if it is our brother or our friend we kill; if a sishya kills a guru or a guru his sishya. Duryodhana, if you still love me, I beg you, kill me quickly! I can't bear to see you like this, or hear you speak thus to me."

With a sigh, Duryodhana raises his bow and they fight again. Soon, Satyaki strikes the Kaurava down in his chariot and then rides away, with all the memories welling in his heart. He had seen his friend Duryodhana turn to arrogance and harshness, to ruthlessness; and against that Duryodhana he could fight. But now, he saw another Duryodhana, the loving friend who wept that they must fight, the one who remembered the tender past so well. This Duryodhana, Satyaki cannot bear to face in battle. The Yadava rides away as far from the Kaurava as he can. He will never speak of the moment they have shared, to anyone. Neither will he ever ride against the Kaurava again.

When Arjuna cuts down his brahmastra, he fuels his Acharya's despair. Drona turns his wrath on the Pandava army. Astra after astra he looses at Yudhishtira's soldiers; every missile consumes ten thousand men. The brahmana blazes like the sun just before the world ends. It seems his body is swathed in the flames of hell, and no one can look at him too long, let alone face him in battle. The carnage is like the slaughter of creatures at the end of a manvantara.

The Pandava warriors watch him, aghast. They cry to one another, "This isn't our gentle Acharya. It is not the same man at all."

"It isn't Drona, but the demon that has possessed him."

"Look at his face, it isn't human."

"His body is like the fire at the end of time."

Krishna sees how Bharadvaja's son consumes common soldiers with devastras. He says quietly to Yudhishtira, "This man cannot be vanquished in battle; and if he isn't killed soon, you will have no army left. Look at your precious guru. Where is his dharma, that he looses devastras at our common soldiers? He must die. And since all of you together cannot kill him, we must also use a little adharma to bring him down."

Yudhishtira waits, uncomfortably. Krishna goes on, "Drona can only be killed if he lays down his bow. The only way he will do that is if we first break his heart. Then, perhaps, Dhrishtadyumna can keep his vow."

The Dark One pauses, "If there is anyone the cold brahmana loves more than his life, it is his son. If he hears Aswatthama is dead, he will put down his bow."

"But the son is hardly easier to kill than the father!" cries Arjuna.
"I only said that Drona must be told Aswatthama is dead."
Arjuna is shocked. "Oh no!"
Bheema says, "If we don't stop the Acharya, the war is lost. Have no doubt of that."

They gaze out at Drona, the inferno, who will make ashes of their dreams, and a waste of all their trials. Nakula and Sahadeva echo Bheema's approval. But Yudhishtira is silent. Krishna waits, everyone waits for the eldest Pandava to speak. Then Bheema cries impatiently, "I will kill an elephant called Aswatthama and tell Drona his son is dead. So there will be no lie. Yudhishtira, you must allow me to do this! Look, he kills a thousand men each moment."

A trembling Yudhishtira nods his head, consenting. Bheema rides off and kills the king of Malava's war-elephant, Aswatthama, with a blow of his mace. He comes storming up to Drona, and roars, "Aswatthama is dead! Aswatthama is dead!"

Drona sways in his chariot. Darkness films his eyes and his very life lurches in shock. But he says to himself, 'Bheema is lying, no one can kill my son.'

The brahmana begins to fight again, twice as savagely as before. Once more, he invokes the brahmastra, and now not against Arjuna. Drona looses the missile at the Panchala and Somaka legions! A flash of fire as if a volcano has erupted among helpless soldiers: flames tall as trees engulf those armies, and fifty thousand men perish in an instant. Silence falls on Kurukshetra; the war will not last until dusk, if Drona is not stopped. Duryodhana's face is wreathed in a smile. At last, his Senapati fights as his king wants him to: now he would see how the Pandavas won this war.

But across the field, a subtle miracle is happening. Suddenly, Drona hears unearthly voices speaking to him from the air. When he looks up, astonished, he sees a host of shining beings materialized in the sky: only he saw them. Among those rishis*, the brahmana sees his dead father Bharadvaja. A cry escapes Drona's lips; in a moment, his eyes are full of tears.

---

* Ganguli mentions Viswamitra, Jamadagni, Vasishta, Kashyapa, Atri, Garga, the Srikatas, the Prishnis, the descendants of Bhrigu and Angiras, the Valkhilyas, the Marichis, and 'many others'.

The munis of Devaloka say, "You are not fighting with dharma, Drona; you burn men that know nothing of the astras with the brahmashtra. Your time in the world has come to its end. Lay down your weapons now, and prepare to die. Look, you see us with your mortal eyes. You are a brahmana, a master of the Vedas and Vedangas. This kshatriya's violent way is not for you. Enough now, Mahatman: cast away the cloak of darkness in which you have wrapped yourself. Turn your mind again to the Brahman, your time to die is here."

His father Bharadvaja says, "Put down your bow, my son. Your life on earth is over."

The vision fades from the sky, and Drona stands stricken in his chariot. Some way off, he sees the man born to kill him: Dhrishtadyumna hacks his way through the Kaurava army to reach his master. Away to the right, and nearer, Drona sees Yudhishtira. Another war raging within him now, Drona turns to the Pandava. Seeking a final reason to die, the guru cries to his sishya, "Is it true, Yudhishtira? Is Aswatthama dead?"

Drona knows Yudhishtira will never tell a lie. He never has in all his life, even as a child. Krishna had already said to Yudhishtira, "When the time comes, Drona will ask you if Aswatthama is dead. The future of the world will depend on what you say to him. If you don't tell this small white lie, the brahmana will fight on, and in an hour or two you will have no army left. You will have the deaths of those who came to fight for you on your soul. But if you tell this small lie, I swear no blame will attach to you, no sin."

Seeing Drona ravage his legions, Yudhishtira had reluctantly agreed. So now, when Drona cries out his fateful question, Yudhishtira hesitates only a moment before he replies, "Aswatthama is dead!" And adds under his breath, "The elephant Aswatthama."

Yudhishtira was a man of such perfect dharma that his chariot never touched the earth but rode four fingers above it. Now, when he lied, his ratha descends to the ground, and Dharma Deva's son is like any other man in the mortal world.

Drona hears Yudhishtira and faints in his chariot. Every moment, Dhrishtadyumna battles his way nearer his Acharya. When Drona recovers, it seems his spirit is broken and the will to fight has all but left him. Dhrishtadyumna storms at him, his bow streaming; now the brahmana, who bestrode Kurukshetra a short while ago, fights back weakly, with effort. Drona's hands have grown sluggish and hardly obey his will. Dhrishtadyumna harries him.

Yet the fight has not died in the Acharya; it only slumbers in grief. When the Panchala prince strikes him with arrows, the brahmana shakes off his stupor. Drona seizes up another bow, given him by his guru Angiras. He breaks Dhrishtadyumna's weapon, and covers him with fire. Dhrishtadyumna picks up another bow and fights back. But Drona is fear embodied, once more, his body is full of uncanny light. In a searing moment, he kills Dhrishtadyumna's horses and his sarathy. He shatters the prince's chariot.

Roaring himself, Dhrishtadyumna leaps down to the ground, sword in hand. He rushes at Drona. Coolly, the brahmana smashes his sword and shield, and Dhrishtadyumna stands unarmed and helpless before his guru. A thin smile curving his lips, Drona raises his bow to kill the Panchala. From his quiver, he draws some arrows called vaitasmikas, meant specially for a powerful enemy who is very close. They are incendiary shafts, and will steam away the armour from Dhrishtadyumna, before blowing him apart.

Of all the great archers only a few know anything about the vaitasmikas. They are more difficult to aim truly than any other arrow, because they are heavy, and the bowstring must not be drawn back too far. Kripa is a master of them, as are Arjuna, Drona, Karna, Krishna, Pradyumna and Satyaki; Abhimanyu, also, was a master of the weighty shafts. Only one of those warriors is close enough to prevent Drona from killing Dhrishtadyumna.

His wrist cocked, Drona draws his bowstring back in the unusual manner used for the vaitasmikas. The Pandavas hold their breath. If Dhrishtadyumna is slain, who will kill Drona? In that interminable moment, the brahmana shoots his thick barbs, ten of them, one after the other. Dhrishtadyumna stands before him, roaring, ready to die. At the very last sliver of a moment, before the vaitasmikas tear into the Panchala's breast, ten arrows flash out of nowhere, each one a saviour, and they cut down Drona's shafts in the air! Arjuna and Krishna shout aloud in relief. They turn to see Satyaki has saved Dhrishtadyumna's life.

Arjuna cries out Satyaki's name. He says to Krishna, "Satyaki is more than a brother to us! The war would have been lost in another moment."

Krishna murmurs, "It has not yet been won."

Arrows flow endlessly from Arjuna's Gandiva, and he holds the Kaurava army off, and away from Drona, just as he had on the day Bheeshma fell. On the other side, Satyaki does the same. The Kaurava warriors surround these two, but to no avail. Drona and Dhrishtadyumna still face each other.

As a flame blazes brightest just before it dies, so, too, does Drona on Kurukshetra. He fights more splendidly than ever, like a man of twenty. It is as if hearing his son is dead and seeing the rishis of Devaloka and his father have only made him more determined. He burns the Pandava army with astras, like a field of straw. He consumes twenty-four thousand kshatriyas; and, dissatisfied, rages on.

Once more, the terrible brahmana takes up the brahmastra. Dhrishtadyumna stands helpless on the ground, with no chariot, and no means to contain the Kaurava Senapati. Then Bheema rides up like the wind, spirits him into his ratha and they attack Drona together. Fighting side by side, they cut down many of his missiles; but they can hardly put out the conflagration he is. Having beaten back the Kauravas on one flank, Satyaki rides up, and he, too, turns his bow on Drona: not the three of them are enough to subdue him.

In disgust, Bheema leaps down from his chariot. Throwing caution to the winds, he runs to his old guru. He seizes Drona's chariot horses by their bridles, bringing them up. Drona pauses his hellish archery; he turns glowering to the lion that dares accost him. Bheema roars, "It is when the brahmana abandons his natural dharma that kshatriya kind is destroyed! The brahmana is meant to be gentle and compassionate, a home of all the virtues. You were born a brahmana, Drona, but you have become a butcher. You have strayed from your dharma and you have lost your mind. All the thousands you kill are kshatriyas, fighting as they were born to. But you were not born to this, which is why you burn helpless footsoldiers with devastras.

"I know what turns your head, Brahmana. It is the gold Duryodhana gives you, isn't it? But what will you do with all that wealth, Drona, when your son for whom you want it is dead? Murderer, how much you preached dharma to us when we were children. Is this that dharma you show us now?"

Bheema spits on the ground in contempt, turns his back on his guru and walks away fearlessly. His every word has struck Drona like an arrow. With his childlike directness, this pupil of his always had the power to wound his master. For he always spoke the truth, frankly and without blandishment. Now, Bheema's words push his Acharya over the edge, at which he already teetered. With a long roar, Drona flings his bow from him. The war pauses.

Drona cries in a ringing voice, "Karna, Duryodhana, Kripa: hear me! I will not fight any more. Drona's war has ended, the rest is left to you."

Drona sits on the floor of his chariot; he crosses his legs in padmasana. He shuts his eyes, and yokes his spirit; in moments, he is lost to the battlefield around him, to the very world. Sunk in yoga, the brahmana journeys back on his anguish to the wellsprings of the eternal atman. Ancestral memory opens like a sacred flower in him. In relief, in gratitude, in joy, Drona discovers himself again.

Dhrishtadyumna sees him like that. Sword in hand, he leaps down from Bheema's chariot and runs at Drona. Arjuna watches him. Seeing that Drona was again their old guru whom they loved and worshipped once, the one who taught them so much, the Pandava cries, "Don't kill him, Dhrishtadyumna! Take him alive, don't kill him!"

But he cries in vain to a kshatriya whose father and sons Drona has killed. The Panchala springs lightly on to Drona's chariot. With a swing of his sword, he hews his Acharya's head from his neck in a blast of blood. Drona never opens his eyes; perhaps, he never knows when the sword-stroke ends his life. When the head is struck off, a blinding light, of a soul, issues from the naked throat and, pulsing and awesome, rises into heaven, lighting up the sky as it goes. In the subtle akasa above, the immortal rishis are still waiting for the brahmana. Drona walks among them now. He attains Brahmaloka, a realm that the Devas hardly know.*

Sanjaya, who has been blessed with mystic sight, sees the ascent of Drona's spirit. Besides him, just Kripa, Krishna and Yudhishtira see it. The rest of the field only sees how brutally Dhrishtadyumna hacks off Drona's head, and stands drenched in his Acharya's blood. The Panchala picks up that head and leaps down from the gory chariot. With a roar, he flings it on the ground, and stands smiling and panting, while the

---

* By the Ganguli text, Drona was 58. Also, Dhrishtadyumna drags his severed head along the ground, then lifts it and flings it down before the armies.

cheering Pandava soldiers throng him. The Pandava Senapati has killed the Kaurava Senapati. He has accomplished the impossible task for which he was born! But his father Drupada is not alive to see his son fulfil his destiny.

Bheema is the first to run up to Dhrishtadyumna and enfold him in a great embrace. Unmindful of the blood he is covered in, the blood of his master, Bheema roars, "You have kept your oath! I will hug you like this again when the sutaputra dies; and once more, when Duryodhana is killed."

Kurukshetra is alight with the news.

THIRTY-ONE

Recriminations

A T FIRST, DURYODHANA WILL NOT BELIEVE THE NEWS THAT STREAKS across Kurukshetra. The cry 'Drona is dead!' echoes everywhere, and Kaurava soldiers run headlong from the field. Dropping their weapons, some peeling off their armour in terror, they fly on foot, on horseback and in their chariots. Even Karna, Shalya and Kripa flee.

When Duryodhana realizes the news is no empty rumour, his howl rings across the field, dismally. Again and again, he cries out his grief, his abysmal defeat; he cries out as if Dhrishtadyumna has hacked another limb from his body. Drona was the Kaurava's great hope, and hope had flared up when he saw how his master incinerated the Pandava army. He had been convinced the war would end before dusk, and victory would be his. But now...ah, how could a man who fought so luminously just moments ago, have laid down his bow and allowed Dhrishtadyumna to lop off his head? It would have been more likely that the ocean dried up, or that Meru stood on his crown. Then, through the panic, the story of how the Pandavas deceived Drona filters. Gripped by the mood of his army, Duryodhana also turns his horses and dashes from battle.

Suddenly, ahead of him he hears a voice that brings him up short, "Duryodhana, what happened? Karna, you look as if the war is already lost! Who is dead that you panic like this? How can you run from the field, when Drona is your Senapati?"

Duryodhana stands mute. Aswatthama cries again, "Tell me, who died?"

Not for a moment does any suspicion of the truth cross his mind. His father is invincible; who can kill Drona? Duryodhana turns imploringly to Kripa, and says in a whisper, "I beg you, Acharya, tell him. I cannot."

Gently, Kripa breaks the news to Aswatthama. He tells him how the Pandavas lied to Drona, how even Yudhishtira lied. He tells the son how his father laid down his weapons, and yoked himself in dhyana. Finally, he tells him how Dhrishtadyumna leapt on to Drona's chariot and struck off his head. Aswatthama grows very still; for a moment, it seems he has turned to stone. But his eyes are terrible, and a ripple of fear shimmers through the Kaurava legions when they sense his fury.

He does not break down, he doesn't even cry. Quietly, he says, "There was no other way they could have killed him, and they will die for what they have done. War is a fearsome thing, that it can make even Yudhishtira abandon dharma. I could have borne his death, if my father had been killed honourably. This is intolerable. Drona is in Devaloka now, because he died a hero's death; but those who killed him shall find hell before the sun sets today. Dhrishtadyumna will not live, nor Yudhishtira."

Now he raises his voice, so all the army hears him. "Duryodhana, I have an astra that not Arjuna, Krishna, Bheema or Yudhishtira will resist. It is a weapon never used against common soldiers, and I did not summon it. Vishnu himself once gave my father the narayanastra, and Drona gave it to me. In this world, only I have that ayudha, and I mean to avenge my father with it today. Duryodhana, my friend, let us return to battle. I will make you lord of the earth in a few moments!"

The Kaurava legions rally round Aswatthama. Conches resound, horns are blown, drums beaten, and Duryodhana's army wheels into battle again. Across Kurukshetra, the celebrating Pandavas hear the conches and horns. They see the cloud of dust where the Kaurava chariots, horses and footsoldiers surge towards them again. Above the rest of the distant din, they hear one voice roaring.

Standing among his brothers, Yudhishtira says, "A moment ago they fled in terror, and now they have turned around and come back to fight. Fresh hope stirs them, and I hear one voice raised like a tiger's above every other. Whose is it?"

Arjuna says grimly, "It is Aswatthama coming to avenge his father. Yudhishtira, you lied to have our guru's life; now who will save us from his son? Aswatthama was born by Siva's blessing; no one can save you from him, Dhrishtadyumna. I was not for it, Yudhishtira: what we did was adharma, and we will pay for it with our lives. For greed of a kingdom, my brother, you told the lie that killed our master. It would have been better to abandon the war, than do this shameful thing. Our sin is three-fold: of killing a brahmana, an elder who loved us like a father, and a guru. We have forsaken the truth, and now we will die!"

Arjuna stands trembling, as a stunned silence follows his outburst. Then, his eyes turning red in a moment, Bheema growls, "Such fine words, Arjuna! You speak like a vaanaprastha who has renounced the world. But I don't like what you say. Are you a brahmana that you speak like this? You are Arjuna, who can subdue the earth with your astras! Then why do you talk like a priest, whose only glory is his humility? You disgust me. And how dare you accuse Yudhishtira of adharma? Answer me!"

Bheema's reaction is so ferocious that Arjuna is taken aback. He stands confused, and makes no reply. Bheema has not finished, "Aren't we here to fight a war? Were we not cheated and humiliated? Was all that was done to us dharma? When we were exiled, when that animal dragged Draupadi into the Kuru sabha and tried to strip her? Answer me, Arjuna! Didn't you once say that we must fight to avenge ourselves? And now you whine about dharma to our brother: to Yudhishtira who spent thirteen years like a beggar for dharma's sake! Yudhishtira, emperor of the earth, who lived like a common courtier in Virata's palace, and did not protest when that king flung his dice at him as if he was his slave. Answer me, Arjuna!" roars Bheema.

"Wasn't it dharma for which Yudhishtira agreed to take five towns from Duryodhana, to sue for peace? And this is the man you accuse of being greedy for a kingdom, and of killing his guru with treachery. Are you blind that you didn't see how Drona burnt our legions with his astras? Are you witless, that the great Arjuna does not realize how all we have suffered and everything we have fought for would have been in vain, if Drona was not killed? You have courage to stand there and accuse Yudhishtira!

"Abhimanyu was killed by treachery, and most of those responsible are still alive. Karna humiliated me on the field, and he still lives. And suddenly, instead of doing what he is meant to, fighting the war, here is Arjuna preaching dharma to his older brother. And singing Aswatthama's praises. 'He was born by Siva's blessing. Who can save us from him?' I say to you, Bheema will smash Aswatthama down with his mace!

"Arjuna, you have gone too far today. You have insulted the one who drives your chariot. Look where he stands, smiling so tolerantly. He is the Lord! He asked Yudhishtira to lie to Drona. Who are you that you know more about dharma than Krishna does? You are a kshatriya, a warrior. Just that. It would be better if you left matters of dharma to those who really know about these things. You are no rishi, brother: remember that before you preach to your betters!"

Still glowering, Bheema falls silent. With a cry, Yudhishtira embraces him.

Dhrishtadyumna bristles, "Arjuna, you say that I killed a brahmana. How was Drona a brahmana any more? Do you know what a brahmana is, that you preach to me? He must perform yagnas, he must be a teacher, and always a student as well. How was Drona a brahmana? He taught, but no Veda. He studied, but not the Shastras. And what was the yagna he performed? He sacrificed a million lives in the flames of his astras! And for whom was this offering? For no God, Arjuna, but for a demon called Duryodhana. Why, even as a warrior, Drona was an adharmi. Who else would use the devastras against ordinary soldiers? He was bloodthirsty, arrogant and merciless.

"Besides, we all know I was born to kill him. Didn't we come here to fight a war? Haven't I been following Drona like his shadow, for fifteen days? Didn't you know that I meant to kill him? Now that I have, you blame me, instead of embracing me in joy that I have rid you of your most powerful enemy. This is strange indeed, Arjuna!

"If you speak of dharma, tell me, did you kill Jayadratha in perfect dharma? Wasn't the sun hidden before you cut away his head? Or is that not deceit, because Arjuna is the one whom it helped? You killed Jayadratha because you lost one son. Drona killed my father, my brothers, and all my sons. I have avenged myself on a murderer, and I feel no remorse. I have saved the lives of thousands of men whom the demented brahmana would have made ashes with his astras. And I swear I am the happiest man alive!"

Arjuna makes no reply, and Dhrishtadyumna rages on, "You say a kshatriya should not kill an elder. Wasn't Bhagadatta an elder, wasn't he your father Pandu's friend? You say a kshatriya shouldn't kill his guru, or someone who is like a father to him. What about Bheeshma? I did not see your hand falter at your bowstring, when Bheeshma laid his weapons down. Or, perhaps, he wasn't your Pitama, and far more a father to you than the wretched Drona? So what are you saying? That if Arjuna kills an elder that is no sin, but if Dhrishtadyumna does, it is." Dhrishtadyumna cries, "Draupadi is my sister, and her sons are my nephews. Or I swear I would kill you for what you have dared say to me today!"

Satyaki cries, "Dare you speak to Arjuna like this! You have done a vile thing before all these noble men, Dhrishtadyumna; and you dare turn on Arjuna? Not only do you kill your master, when he sits in dhyana with no weapon in his hand, you cut his head from his body and fling it down on the ground! How does Bheeshma's fall compare with Drona's death? The Pitama asked to be killed, but not Drona. Besides, your brother Shikhandi shot Bheeshma first, not Arjuna. Not another word from you, coward, or I will crush your head!"

Satyaki stands growling, mace in hand. Dhrishtadyumna laughs in the Yadava's face. He says coolly, "We are fighting this war on the same side, and so perhaps I should forgive you, Satyaki. But this is passing strange, that you of all people preach to me! Yadava, was it dharma when you killed Bhoorisravas? Hadn't he given up the war, didn't he sit in dhyana? That was such a noble thing you did! After Arjuna cut off his arm, and he was helpless, the great Satyaki cut off Bhoorisravas' head. And you dare accuse me!

"Listen to me, Yadava. We are here to fight a dharma yuddha. We are here to put down a tide of evil, which chokes the earth. We are here to crush the Kauravas. At times, fire must be fought with fire. You killed Bhoorisravas when he was helpless; but you had an old feud with him, and this is war. So we said nothing to you. In war, particularly, dharma is hard to define, and adharma too. The final dharma in war is to prevail over the enemy. All of us are here because we believe the cause of the Pandavas is the cause of truth, and that they have been grievously wronged.

"Yudhishtira has never told a lie in his life, because he holds truth more sacrosanct than anything. Yet, when he saw how Drona burned our men with devastras, he sacrificed his truth for his soldiers' lives. You know as well as I that if the Acharya had not been stopped, he would have killed us all, and cremated our cause with us. Better than anyone, you know what it is to inherit an old feud. You killed Bhoorisravas because of such a feud. Because of such a feud, Drona killed my father and my sons; and I killed him. But it seems you have one dharma to judge what Arjuna and you do, and another to judge me. I cannot kill Arjuna because he is my sister's husband, but no such bond prevents me from killing you. Come, Yadava, let me see how you crush my head!"

Satyaki needs no encouragement. He runs at Dhrishtadyumna, with his mace raised. Bheema leaps down from his chariot and flings his arms around Satyaki. Even Bheema is dragged along a full five paces, but on the sixth he stops the Yadava, who struggles furiously but is helpless against the iron clasp in which the wind's son holds him.

Krishna, Arjuna and Sahadeva intervene. Tears in his eyes, Sahadeva cries, "Now we are at each other's throats. Stop it! I beg you, Satyaki and Dhrishtadyumna, stop this madness. And you two are such friends. Satyaki, you are like Krishna to us, and Dhrishtadyumna is as dear as his sister is. Bhoorisravas and Drona are both dead, and we are forgetting we are standing on a field of war! Embrace each other now, and forget the harsh things you said."

Krishna and Yudhishtira add their voices to Sahadeva's. But it is the arrival of the Kaurava army, led now by Aswatthama, which sobers the Panchala and the Yadava. Together, they turn to face the enemy again.

THIRTY-TWO

Narayanastra

They watch the Kaurava army flow at them across Kurukshetra, Yudhishtira turns to Arjuna. In a sad, strained voice he says, "I want a word with you, my brother. You say I am responsible for the death of our guru, who you claim loved us like a father. Yes, I told the lie that made Drona lay down his bow. But as for him loving us like a guru or a father, was it because of his love that he trapped Abhimanyu in the chakra vyuha, where six maharathikas killed our child? Was it love for us that tied his tongue, when Dusasana dragged Panchali into the Kuru sabha? Love that made him swear he would fight for Duryodhana if there was a war? That made him burn our soldiers with his astras and loose the brahmastra at you? And even when he finally laid down his weapons, he cried out a warning to Duryodhana."

Yudhishtira speaks tensely, with uncommon pique in his voice. "Arjuna, you may still think of Drona as your guru. For me he lost that place in my heart some time ago. A man should have only one guru, who does indeed love him like a son. Krishna is my guru, and I have no other. Yes, for the first time in my life I told a lie. I lied at the instance of my guru Krishna. I lied to save the lives of thousands of men who depend on me, who risk their lives for me. Arjuna, I am proud of my lie! I would never have told it, if I was to regret it after I had. That isn't my nature."

Arjuna has no answer to this. But now, the Kaurava army is within striking distance and immediately Aswatthama summons the narayanastra and shoots it at the enemy. The earth shakes, the sky seems to catch fire, and a malefic star hangs over the Pandava army as an inferno. Towering flames flash down from the astra, ashing legions whole. A hundred thousand arrows whistle down from that ayudha every moment, reaping as many lives. Whining chakras whirl out from its blinding heart, and scythe through Yudhishtira's forces in unimaginable violence. The Pandavas train their own arrows on the dreadful thing; the narayanastra only blazes more fiercely with each shaft they shoot at it. Other weird weapons scream down: tornadoes of flames of a hundred colours.

Yudhishtira panics. "Run, my friends, run! Dhrishtadyumna, take your army and ride home: the war is lost. Satyaki, fly back to Dwaraka! My brothers, run while you still have your lives. I must stay and let the astra kill me. Let that be my penance for killing my Acharya."

But above the screams of the dying, another voice roars, "The narayanastra grows fiercer when it is resisted. Lay down your weapons and prostrate yourselves before Vishnu's ayudha. Worship the astra and it will grow mild."

Krishna's word flashes across Kurukshetra. In moments, every Pandava soldier has flung his weapons down and lies flat on his face before the apocalypse in the sky. At once, the astra grows quiet, it dims itself at being worshipped. But one kshatriya has not put down his weapons. He stands alone and defiant in his chariot, roaring, "I am no coward to bow to Aswatthama's astra. I will stand against it, even if no one else ever has!"

Blasting on his conch, Bheema rides at the Kaurava army. Erupting again in wrath, the narayanastra turns its fires on Bheema. A thousand fulminant arrows flash down out of the sky on just his chariot. Roaring like a pride of lions, Bheema turns his bow on Aswatthama, by whose will the astra hangs fire. Hardly has he drawn them from his quiver, the power of the astra burns up his shafts in his hands. A rain of fire pours down from the astra. Light-like arrows, keening chakras flame down at the kshatriya who stands alone against Vishnu's weapon on Kurukshetra. Bheema looks like a mountain covered by fireflies. He stands roaring his defiance, that wild son of Vayu!

The astra sets Bheema's chariot and horses alight. It engulfs him in a sheet of flames, until he is like a Deva materialized at the heart of a yagna fire. Now there seem to be two uncanny suns risen on Kurukshetra:

one the astra above and the other Bheema in his burning chariot. He will not give in. His roars ring louder than ever on the field of dharma. Arjuna jumps up and invokes the varunastra. But when he shoots it at Bheema's ratha, that weapon, which can drown Kurukshetra in a flash flood, turns to steam.

There is only one way to stop Bheema from killing himself. Krishna and Arjuna leap down from their chariot and run to him. Plunging through white flames, they jump on him. Before Bheema realizes what they are doing, they wrest his weapons from him. He roars louder still. They drag him out of the chariot, fling him down on the ground, and themselves beside him. He struggles desperately, but they hold him down on his face.

When the last kshatriya is on the ground, the narayanastra grows mild again. Like a majestic comet, the weapon passes over the supine Pandava army and on out of the world. The air on Kurukshetra is cool again. Healing breezes blow across fate's field. Still, no soldier rises for fear. Then Krishna is on his feet, crying, "It has passed. You can get up now."

Bheema staggers up, still furious. Krishna turns on him and says sharply, "Was it to win the war that you were trying to get yourself killed?"

There is something in his eyes and his voice, with which not even Bheema dares argue.

Across Kurukshetra, Duryodhana sees the narayanastra passing, and turns eagerly to Aswatthama, "Again, Aswatthama: summon it again! They have no answer to the narayanastra."

The crestfallen Aswatthama says, "Krishna knew the answer to the narayanastra, or their army would have been ashes by now. No matter: they fell on their faces to beg for their lives. They have acknowledged defeat, which for a kshatriya is worse than death. From now on, they live in shame. I am satisfied."

Duryodhana growls, "But not I! Call the astra again, and this time let it consume them."

"The narayanastra can be summoned only once. If I call it again, it will consume not the enemy but us."

"You command so many astras. Summon them all today, Aswatthama! Your father is dead; we depend on you now. Burn the Pandavas, I must see them die."

Aswatthama charges at the Pandava host. Dhrishtadyumna rides against him first. They fight, without pausing to draw breath. Drona's frenzied son strikes Dhrishtadyumna with twenty arrows, in a single moment. Dhrishtadyumna faints in his chariot. By the time he recovers, Aswatthama has killed his sarathy and horses.

Luckily for the Panchala, Satyaki rides up just then. The Yadava cuts down Aswatthama's horses and sarathy, even as Drona's son flies up to avenge himself on his father's killer. Duryodhana, Kripa and Karna surround Aswatthama. They have another chariot brought out to the hero of the hour. Like a tiger robbed of his prey, Aswatthama rushes again at Satyaki. Once more, the cool Yadava shoots down his horses and sarathy.

Yet another chariot is fetched for Aswatthama, and he rages from it. He calls out with a laugh to Satyaki, "Yadava, I know how much you love the Panchala prince! But today, neither of you will escape me."

Satyaki is overwhelmed by a cataract of arrows. He has his bow sliced in slivers, and it seems Aswatthama will kill him. Then, five Pandavas ride from five sides to form a ring around their Yadava, as if they guarded their own lives. Yudhishtira and the twins take Satyaki to safety, while Bheema engages Drona's son. Not for long: Aswatthama kills Bheema's sarathy with a naracha, and the Pandava's horses career across Kurukshetra.

Now Arjuna roars at his boyhood friend, his master's son, "I have heard so much about your valour, Aswatthama! I have heard how powerful you are, how wise, how fearless: how you are truly your father's son. I know how much you love the sons of Dhritarashtra, and hate the sons of Pandu. Come now, show me your courage!"

Aswatthama replies with a smoking, thought-like fusillade. They fight as if in another dimension: the son and the finest sishya of the dead Acharya. The rest of the war pauses around them, to gaze. They are so evenly matched, and they duel as if to settle which of them is Drona's best pupil. Aswatthama has long harboured a secret envy of Arjuna; and, today, with his father slain, he means to prove that he is better than the Pandava.

Drona's son invokes the agneyastra, and shoots it at the Pandava army. In a moment, night falls on Kurukshetra. The weapon of the Fire God flames into the sky, and, hanging low, vomits five meteors that immolate five columns of helpless footsoldiers in an eyeflash. Black smoke and the stench of burning flesh envelop the field of death. Plaintive screams ring across Kurukshetra, and it seems the battleground has plunged down into the last pit of hell. The son emulates his father's rage; he defies every law of dharma. Watching from a distance, Duryodhana exults.

At the heart of night, in the thick of fear, Arjuna invokes a brahmastra, which subdues every other astra. It streaks from his bow. Instantly, the murky darkness of the agneyastra evaporates. The air is clear again, and cool. An icy gale springs up, and sweeps across Kurukshetra, blowing the weapon of fire out of the sky. Around Arjuna's chariot the charred remains of thousands of his men, almost an aksauhini, bear gruesome witness to the power of Agni; but Arjuna and his dark sarathy are unsinged.

For a long moment, Aswatthama stands trembling at his failure. Then, with a howl, he flings down his bow, leaps from his chariot and dashes madly from the field. Helplessly, Duryodhana and his army watch him go. Like one pursued by demons, Aswatthama dashes across Kurukshetra and plunges into the forest beyond: never turning back, running on and on as if for his life. Tears stream from his eyes, and roars of grief and rage issue from his lips. On he runs, not knowing where he runs to, nor caring, only bellowing his despair to the trees, the earth, the astonished beasts.

Abruptly, a dark figure looms in his path. Panting, Aswatthama stops his flight. He flings himself, sobbing, at the feet of the Rishi Vyasa. Drona's son wails, "The astras failed me! Why, Muni, why?"[2]

Vyasa lays a kindly hand on the brahmana warrior's head. He says, "You summoned them against Nara Narayana, my child. What can any astra do against those two? The fault is not yours, or the weapons'. Krishna and Arjuna have come into the world to cleanse it: what force can stand in the way of their grace? Why, by their grace, your father is in Devaloka now. He is at peace, and you have nothing to grieve about. Go back; it isn't dharma to run from battle. You have come here to risk

---

[2] Aswatthama asks specifically how Krishna and Arjuna were proof against the agneyastra. See Appendix for Vyasa's reply in greater detail.

everything for Duryodhana. You must not abandon him now, when he needs you most."

Vyasa vanishes before the kneeling Aswatthama. Slowly, Drona's son rises; he wipes his eyes. Soft peace has fallen on his heart to hear that his father is in heaven. Aswatthama turns back to Kurukshetra. It is twilight, when he arrives in the Kaurava camp. The day's battle has ended; the armies have withdrawn. Only the dead lie on the black field, while jackals and hyenas begin to tear away their flesh in burning mouthfuls.

In Duryodhana's camp and Yudhishtira's, common soldiers fall gratefully into sleep. So ends the fifteenth day of the war: a fateful day, when Drona, who had stood like a fortress, fell. In the early part of the night, Duryodhana is sunk in despair; he will neither eat nor say a word. Red-eyed and grim, he sits in his tent with Aswatthama, Karna, Dusasana, Shalya, Shakuni and some others. He drinks often and deeply from the flagon of wine at his side. Not all the wine in the world can change the truth that Bheeshma has fallen, and Drona is slain. Defeat stares Duryodhana in the face; and death.

BOOK EIGHT

Karna Parva

AUM, I bow down to Narayana, the most exalted Nara, and to the Devi Saraswati, and say *Jaya*!

ONE

Senapati Karna

L<small>ATE THAT NIGHT IN DURYODHANA'S TENT, THE KAURAVA ASKS</small> heavily, "What do we do now? Tell me what you think."

A moment's uncertain silence, then, Aswatthama says, "We must not lose heart, my lord. What you need is a new Senapati to lead us into battle tomorrow: a warrior that loves you, to whom we can all look up. To my mind, the choice is obvious. Though all of us are ready to die for you, there is no archer among us like Karna. Let him be your general, and we can still win this war."

The others agree. A wan smile lights Duryodhana's strained face. He embraces Karna and says, "My friend, there is no archer on earth like you. This is my moment of crisis, and only you can help me. Pitama and the Acharya led our legions splendidly; both were killed when they had laid down their weapons. Yet, my grandfather and my master did not fight as they might have, or these Pandavas would never have stood against our numbers. The war should have ended ten days ago. But Bheeshma and Drona loved the sons of Pandu, they would never fight them as just another enemy."

He pauses: this argument is more for himself than anyone else. "Now, for the first time, we will have a Senapati who detests the simpering Pandavas as much as I do. Karna, I leave everything in your hands. I won't have to goad you each day to do your best, and you will lead us to victory. At dawn tomorrow, you will be like Karttikeya leading the army of Devaloka! It is your destiny, take command of the Kuru army."

This is typical of Duryodhana: that, in a moment, his mood swings from despair to elation, for which there is hardly cause. Karna stands before his friend, for whom he will give his life. Softly he says, "Nothing will please me more, my lord. I will kill Arjuna, and the world will be yours. Have no doubt, tomorrow Arjuna will die."

Priests are summoned, and holy water is fetched in urns of gold and earthen ones, in the tusks and horns of the elephant, the rhinoceros, and the bull—water sanctified with mantras. Duryodhana seats Karna on a throne made of udumbara wood, covered with silk. He ties the auspicious thread around Karna's wrist, drenches him with the water, himself, in midnight consecration, and the sutaputra, Suryaputra, is Senapati of the Kuru army. This is the nearest Kunti's eldest son will come to becoming the king he might have been.

Duryodhana convinces himself that the war, so far, has been a trial of his endurance. After all, they were fighting for the throne of the earth: such a prize will not come easily, but only after a man was purified by an ordeal. Duryodhana does not think of Yudhishtira's ordeal; and, of course, he has no inkling that his new general is the Pandavas' brother. The Kaurava is content to believe that, now, his own destiny would be fulfilled.

Dawn of the sixteenth day of war; Karna arrays his legions in the makara vyuha. He sets himself at the head of the phalanx of the crocodile, at its snout. The eyes of the beast of war are Shakuni and Uluka, with their troops around them. The crown of the makara's head is Aswatthama, renewed, eager for battle. Duryodhana's brothers are immediately behind Aswatthama, in a fierce cohort. At the very heart of the phalanx, protected by thronging legions all around, is Duryodhana himself, his chariot fluttering the black and gold serpent banner. The forelegs of the massive reptile are Kritavarman, with the Narayana warriors and his own Bhoja legion*, and Kripa and his company. The hindlegs are Karna's son Sushena and the redoubtable Shalya, with their soldiers.

Across the field, Yudhishtira gazes at the Kaurava phalanx being formed. He turns to Arjuna in the dawn breeze, and says, "They have

---

* KMG: A force of fierce shepherds called Gopalas also comes with Kritavarman. More recently, they are called Gowalas or Ahirs, and they are still hired for local brawls, or as musclemen for politicians, in certain areas of Bihar and Bengal.

a new Senapati. Karna shines at their head like a moon in a sky full of stars. And now, seeing them again in the same makara vyuha our Pitama used, I realize how they have dwindled these sixteen days. And we with them.

"Can we restore these millions of lives by winning the war? A generation of noble kshatriyas has perished on this field of our fathers; the world will never be the same again. Bheeshma and Drona have fallen. To my mind, Karna is the last great soldier they have, and he is the most dangerous one. More than Pitama or the Acharya, I fear Karna. Arjuna, if you can kill this man, and only you can, victory will be ours."

Arjuna and Dhrishtadyumna form their legions in the chandrakala vyuha. Bheema is the left point of the crescent moon, and Dhrishtadyumna the right. At the heart of the vyuha is Arjuna himself, with Yudhishtira, Nakula and Sahadeva around him. At Arjuna's chariot-wheels are Yuddhamanyu and Uttamaujas, and, flaring out in a curve on either side of the four Pandavas, the rest of their soldiers. It is a leaner crescent, by far, than the one they formed two weeks ago: fifteen lifetimes ago, to those that fought the war.

When both armies are ready, their conch-blowers and drummers sound a storm to begin the day's bloodletting. The armies charge each other, weapons glinting in the early light of morning. Karna leads the Kaurava army with dignity; he returns the war to Bheeshma's dharma yuddha. This is a relief to all, after Drona's vicious command. Though Karna fights with dharma, the Kauravas recover spirit under his lead; for he straddles Kurukshetra like a Deva.

Bheema opens the day's slaughter by striking off the arrogant lord of Kshemadhurti's head. Then, Karna is at the Pandava army. Nakula dashes up to confront him, killing a hundred Kaurava soldiers as he goes. Away to the left, Bheema and Aswatthama meet in a glittering duel. Satyaki faces two of the surviving Kekaya brothers. As the armies flow into each other, on wavelets of blood, Duryodhana and Yudhishtira come face to face. The remnants of the Samsaptakas ride at Arjuna, only at him, for revenge. Kripa and Dhrishtadyumna face each other, Shikhandi and Kritavarman, Srutakirti and Shalya. Sahadeva and Dusasana duel.

Blood flies everywhere, spraying freely. Limbs and heads, struck off, lie severed from their trunks. Dismembered bodies fall, spasming in death's throes, and the air is a hoarseness of screams and roars. After an exhilarating encounter, Satyaki kills the Kekayas. Part of the morning's glory belongs to Draupadi's sons, who range the field in a small patrol of their own, fleet and ruthless. Fighting well above himself, Bheema strikes Aswatthama unconscious, and the brahmana is borne off the field by his sarathy. Shalya puts Srutakirti to flight, and Sahadeva shames Dusasana.

Nakula fights his way through a hundred men to face Karna, who rides to meet his charge, with a familiar, mocking, smile on his lips. Nakula cries, "Evil one, you are the cause of this war. You are the outsider who stoked hatred between cousins. I will kill you now, Karna, and pluck a thorn from my heart."

The smile never leaves Karna's face. He says smoothly, "You are a fine kshatriya indeed, Nakula. But let me shear your pride a little."

Nakula replies with a buzz of arrows. But Karna is quicker than the mind; he splits the Pandava's bow; in a blur, Nakula seizes up another, and divides Karna's weapon. Karna also picks up another bow and fights back; and now he is truly awesome. After Bheema and Sahadeva, today it is Nakula's turn to be humbled by the lord of Anga. Karna shatters his brother's bow again; he kills his horses and his sarathy. Another scorching volley smashes Nakula's chariot.

Sword in hand, Nakula leaps down to the ground. Hardly have his feet touched the earth, when his blade is struck from his grasp, superbly. Next moment, his shield is smashed in shards. When the Pandava lifts his mace from the ruins of his ratha, that, too, is pulverized. Nakula wrenches a chariot-wheel from its axle. Smiling, Karna cuts the wheel in slivers with a wizardry of silver shafts.

His enemy laughs in the defenceless Pandava's face. Nakula loses his nerve; he turns and runs. He does not go five paces, when Karna rides up beside him and brings him up roughly by snaring his head in his bowstring! Like a fisherman his catch, he hauls the Pandava back to him. Nakula stands shaking.

Karna says cruelly, "What happened, little one? Lost your tongue, O Kshatriya?"

Nakula squirms. Karna holds him firm, the bowstring around his throat. He has not finished. "Don't be ashamed, Nakula. I promise you, one day you will remember this duel, and feel proud that you once fought Karna and escaped with your life! Here, I gift you your life, child. Run away now. Go."

He lifts the bow away from Nakula's neck. Nakula runs from his tormentor. Hissing like a serpent, in shame, he runs to Yudhishtira's chariot. Only Krishna notices, from a way off, the wistfulness in Karna's eyes.

TWO

Many duels

K ARNA BESTRIDES KURUKSHETRA, A WHITE FLAME, AN INCARNATION of the living sun. Like Surya Deva over the earth at high noon, the sutaputra shines on Kurukshetra. Emboldened by him, the other Kaurava warriors begin to fight as never before.

Shakuni's son, Uluka, routs Yuyutsu. Shakuni himself battles Sutasoma; and in rage at how Drona died, Kripa confronts Dhrishtadyumna. The Acharya fights as well as his slain brother-in-law, and Dhrishtadyumna cannot face him at all. Kripa strikes him unconscious in his chariot. Dhrishtadyumna's sarathy bears his prince out of the battle. But crimson-eyed Kripa rides after him, determined to avenge death with death. This brahmana is fearsome today, as he hasn't been so far.

Some way off, Shikhandi and Kritavarman duel, and the inspired Yadava lacerates the Panchala. Shikhandi is almost struck out of his chariot by Kritavarman, but saves himself by clinging to his flagpost at the last moment, before he faints. His sarathy rushes him out of battle. Not far from one another, like three fires from Siva's trident they rage: Kritavarman, Kripa and Karna. They kill thousands.

The Samsaptakas foolishly challenge Arjuna again. Seeing them reminds him of the day Abhimanyu died, and he lets them feel his wrath. The few he leaves alive, flee. Duryodhana and Yudhishtira come face to face: the lords of the two armies. Seeing how Karna rules Kurukshetra gives heart to the Kaurava, and he fights like ten men. The war would be won if he can kill Yudhishtira.

But his cousin, the Pandava, is here for dharma. After a brief, refulgent duel, Yudhishtira looses four arrows like one in the heart of a moment. Duryodhana's horses fall, shot through their hearts. Yudhishtira's fifth shaft takes his sarathy's head from his neck, spraying Duryodhana with the man's blood. The sixth cuts his serpent-banner down; the seventh strikes the bow from his hand. Yudhishtira's archery is elegant, effortless, and the armies gaze at him."

Roaring, Duryodhana draws his sword, but the Pandava's eighth arrow breaks it in two. Then, five arrows in a stream fling the Kaurava back against his flagstaff. Only the armour Drona gave him saves Duryodhana's life. Yudhishtira raises his bow to end the war; like three wishes Karna, Aswatthama and Kripa appear to hold him off. The Pandava's own kshatriyas arrive to join the fray, and the battle spreads out again. But the moral victory belongs to Yudhishtira; he has the pleasure of seeing rage and shame on his cousin's face.

The sun has begun to fall from his zenith, and afternoon finds the Kaurava army melting before Bheema. He kills thousands, and his roars resound above every other noise on Kurukshetra: above the whinnying of horses, the yells of kshatriyas, the whistling of a million arrows, and, most of all, the piteous screams of those cut down.

Duryodhana mounts a fresh chariot and rides at Yudhishtira again. But the tide of dharma flows against the Kaurava and, once more, he finds swift humiliation. Yudhishtira casts a javelin at him, and strikes him down. His new sarathy rides away with his king dazed on the floor of his ratha.

When Arjuna has inflicted sharp defeat on Aswatthama and Kritavarman, who challenged him, he turns on Karna. But Karna is invincible. He wounds both Arjuna and Krishna with some astounding archery, arrows like flights of bees, and the other Pandavas rally round the white chariot. The sixteenth day of the dharma yuddha wears on, and surely by now there is more death than life on yawning Kurukshetra. The sun slips to the horizon. Fearful that they may be asked to fight in the night, again, the soldiers on both sides begin to leave the field even before the signal is given to end the day's battle.

Karna and Dhrishtadyumna order the twilight conches to sound, and the armies are formally withdrawn. It has been a day when tens of thousands perished on both sides, but no kshatriya among them. The names of those thousands remain unknown, unrecorded; though, surely, they gave their most precious possession on the field of battle. This has always been the way of war, why, of life itself: that fame is an ornament worn by the few.

There is no elation or dejection in either camp. The honours of the day have been shared almost equally, even if the Kauravas have perhaps had the slight edge, because of Karna. After Drona's frantic command, the war has been restored to an even tenor. With Karna, the Kaurava soldiers feel as if Bheeshma led them again, and the Pandava legions are relieved as well.

THREE

The lucid night

D URYODHANA HAS NOT HAD THE SATISFACTION OF SEEING KARNA kill Arjuna. He had seen how Karna had Nakula at his mercy, and spared the Pandava's life: he says nothing about these to his friend. Bheeshma and Drona he would have accused of being partial to the Pandavas, but he can never utter a harsh word to Karna. Moreover, the Kaurava is convinced Karna is as disappointed as he is that Arjuna remains alive.

After the day's battle, just when they are about to retire to their tents for the evening ablutions, Karna takes his king's hand, and says, "Arjuna fights magnificently, but tomorrow I will kill him."

Duryodhana embraces his Senapati. "You will, Karna, I know you will."

Late that night, Karna comes alone to Duryodhana's tent. Complete certainty is upon him that this will be his last night in the world. He is calm, and as always, they plan the next day's strategy together. Then, Karna leans forward and says in his intense way, "There is only one way this war can be won. Tomorrow, my friend, I will either kill Arjuna, or die in the attempt. Duryodhana, tomorrow the world will see, once and forever, who its best archer is.

"Both he and I have astras we can summon, of the four kinds. He has the Gandiva, renowned in the corners of the world; but my Vijaya, which Bhargava gave me, is the greater weapon. What few men know is that Viswakarman once made the Vijaya for Indra, and the king of the Devas gave my master the bow. My prince, tomorrow, with Arjuna dead, the world will lie at your feet."

He pauses, frowning. Duryodhana says, "Something disturbs you, Karna?"

"Yes. One must not underestimate one's adversary. Arjuna's silver quivers are magical, inexhaustible. His chariot is unearthly, and his horses are gandharva steeds. He has Hanuman's blessing. Have you observed his banner? Hanuman emblazoned on it is alive: I have seen his eyes watch the war, I have heard him roar! And then, of course, there is the most telling advantage Arjuna has, the one without which he would have long since been dead: Krishna is his sarathy. You have seen him drive those horses, Duryodhana. He is like the mind, quicker. Every time our arrows fly straight for Arjuna's throat or his heart, suddenly we find him gone from where he was a moment ago. Krishna has spirited him away.

"I have no sarathy to match Krishna. All else being equal, even if I am the better archer, how can I kill the Pandava when the Dark One guides his horses?"

Duryodhana asks, "Is there no one in our army who can match Krishna as a sarathy?"

"There is one man. But will he agree to be a sutaputra's charioteer?"

"Who is he, Karna?"

Karna says, "Shalya. He is twice the sarathy Krishna is. Shalya is to charioteers what Karna is among archers! Krishna knows the aswahridaya, but Shalya is a master of the arcane art. If Shalya will drive my horses tomorrow, Arjuna will not escape with his life. But Shalya is a king, and proud; it will not be easy to persuade him. Yet, there is no one on earth like Duryodhana to persuade any man. The very war may depend on it."

Duryodhana says, "He won't refuse me, Karna! Shalya shall drive your horses. Now go and sleep, you must be fresh for tomorrow. It will be your great day, and the world will know that not Arjuna but peerless Karna is its finest bowman: and that he won the war for Duryodhana. What could be more fitting? Only so you could win the world for me, Bheeshma has fallen and Drona has died!"

Tears in their eyes, they embrace again. Karna lingers on in Duryodhana's tent. How many nights they have spent talking and drinking into the small hours: baring their souls to each other. Tonight, Karna knows, will be the last one. For a while he stays on, chatting of this and that, of the times they have shared. Then, reluctantly, he rises to go. He walks to the tent-flap, and turns back to clasp Duryodhana again. They hold each other for a long moment, before Karna breaks away and strides out into the darkness.

Visions of the past fill the night for Karna, alone in his tent. He sees his life vividly before his eyes; and he has no doubt that tomorrow he will die. He sees his mother Radha, his tender years with her. He lies quietly in the dark, and allows himself to be borne away on the crystal tide of memories. At last, those memories have no power to hurt him. He is a serene witness to his own past: almost as if he watched another man's life being played out before his eyes.

Then, the anxiety of what he has sworn to do snatches him back from calm. Karna knows Arjuna will kill him tomorrow, as he was always destined to; but he will never admit Arjuna is his superior. No, it is not skill that will give his brother victory, but the light he is enfolded in, from the beginning; while Karna's life was plunged in darkness since its first day. Karna sees his mother Kunti now, as she came to him at the river. He feels her fingers caress his cheek, he hears her sob. How futile his life has been; and tomorrow it would end. Somehow, that is so hard to accept: all that could have been, and never was, torments Karna. And because of the Dark One who held his horses' reins, the reins of his very fate, Arjuna would triumph.

Karna had lied to Duryodhana. But how could he tell his friend it was later than he imagined, that all was already lost? He could have told him before the war began that the side Krishna was on could never lose. But how could he break his heart? The only way he could break the truth to the Kaurava was by dying.

Tomorrow, Shalya might agree to be his sarathy. What was Shalya before blue Krishna? Besides, Shalya hated Karna. Karna tries to thrust aside the darkness that threatens to choke him. Inevitably, his mind wanders back to his guru Bhargava. The scar on his thigh throbs icily, where once the insect fed as his master lay asleep with his head in his lap. Before his waking eyes, Karna sees Bhargava again. He hears his voice pronounce his curse. 'When you are faced with your most implacable enemy, you will forget the mantras for the devastras!'

He thinks back to the cow he killed on the deserted beach: the brahmana's curse, 'Your chariot-wheels shall be mired on the day of your greatest battle. And you will be shot down when you are helpless, just as you have shot my cow today.'

Yes, he has no doubt, as he allows his memories to bear him far from Kurukshetra, that he will die tomorrow. He submits to the clear swell, it washes the last resistance from him. He sees Krishna's face, black eyes full of mercy; again and again, he sees that face and Karna feels deeply consoled. He feels ready to die, or nearly so.

But he must face Yudhishtira, once, before he does Arjuna. He must conquer him, as well: so Kunti would know that he had spared the lives of her four sons. In his own mind, it was his way of telling them he was their brother. After he died, and they learnt who he was, they would cherish the memory. And brilliant Arjuna, the memory of having killed him.

Shifting at will, the visionary night bears him through his whole life, starkly, gently, until he feels his deepest rancour dissolve. Karna is at strange peace when, an hour before dawn, he falls into a dreamless sleep.

FOUR

Shalya

Dawn of the seventeenth day of the war, and Duryodhana comes early to Shalya, and says, "My lord, I have come to ask a favour."

"Tell me what it is, and consider it given."

"Karna means to fight Arjuna today. Karna is the better archer; he will kill Arjuna. But there is one advantage the Pandava has that has saved him all these days."

He pauses. Shalya says impatiently, "And what is that? Come, Duryodhana, tell me what you have come to say."

"My lord, Krishna is immeasurably superior to any sarathy Karna has had. In all my army, there is only one man who can match Krishna. That man, my lord, is you. I beg you, Shalya, be Karna's sarathy today."

"How dare you!" roars Shalya. "You dare ask a kshatriya to be a suta to a sutaputra? Already, you have made the suta Senapati of the Kuru army; and now you want me to be his sarathy. Sutas are servants in the courts of kings. How can a crowned king of the earth hold a suta's chariot-reins?"

Shalya stutters in rage, "You ask me this, as if Karna is my superior. Duryodhana, I can easily kill that man in a duel. Shalya can face Indra and vanquish him! He can rout your Karna, Arjuna and Krishna all together! You have insulted me, Kaurava, I will not fight for you any more. This is not my war that I should tolerate such impudence."

Shalya turns to walk away. But Duryodhana grasps his hand, and stands before him with tears in his eyes! "How can I even dream of suggesting that Karna is your superior? I know you, mighty king. Shalya is the bane of his enemies!

"But, my lord, you will not kill your nephews, and Arjuna must die if we are to win this war. Of us all, only Karna can kill him; and how will he do that if he does not have a sarathy who is better than Krishna? Only one man on earth is better than the master of Dwaraka: you, O Shalya. I beg you, take Karna's chariot-reins in your gifted hands; this is a matter of victory or defeat.

"Millions have died for me in this war. My Pitama has fallen, and my Acharya is dead. I don't know how I will ever expiate all that sin. But that is not what we must think of now, only winning the war: which we can never do as long as Arjuna lives. Great Kshatriya, I only asked you to take Karna's reins as Brahma did Sankara's, when Siva flew to burn the Tripura!"

Shalya glows at the fulsome praise. He says, "So you meant no slight to me, Duryodhana. Since you believe I am the only one who is a match for Krishna, I will be Karna's sarathy today!"

Duryodhana actually kneels at Shalya's feet. "My lord, I can never repay you for this. Now that you have agreed to be my friend's sarathy, I must tell you something else. Karna's guru Bhargava had all his astras from Siva himself. The Lord said to him that he must never teach them to a lowborn man. Yet, Parasurama gave them all to Karna, and even his bow, the Vijaya. Bhargava is a trikalagyani, who sees through the three veils of time as you and I see the day. Would he have given Karna the Vijaya, and the astras, if Karna were a sutaputra?"

"What are you trying to say, Duryodhana?"

"That since I first met him I have always felt Karna was no sutaputra. All my instincts cry that he is a kshatriya. He is not Atiratha and Radha's natural son, but adopted. My heart always insists that Karna is not just the son of a kshatriya, but of a Deva! Perhaps his mother was a princess, and he was born from a night of secret love and abandoned. You all see him every day, my friends, you see how he shines like a God. Tell me, if you did not know he was Atiratha's son wouldn't you say he was not only a kshatriya, but the most exceptional one? Even a Devaputra! Can any sutaputra be Arjuna's equal at archery? Karna surely is."

It is obvious he believes what he is saying. "Shalya, I am convinced you will not be driving a sutaputra's chariot today, but a kshatriya's.

Some day the truth will come out, and then you will all say that Duryodhana was the only one that realized who Karna really was. I tell you, my friend is the noblest of kshatriyas. Why, I say he was born to rule the world: and so he shall, at my side! I know him long and well now; if Karna is not a kshatriya, none of us is."

Shalya embraces Duryodhana. "Noble Duryodhana, truest of friends! I will drive Karna's chariot as well as I know. But there is a condition I must impose. If I love you, I might be critical of you when I think you are in the wrong. If I am to be Karna's sarathy, I must have the same liberty: I must be able to speak to him as I please.

"There are four traits in a man I abhor: when he insults himself, because he feels inferior; when he praises himself too much; when he derides other men, and when he is foolhardy, from bravado. While I am Karna's sarathy, I must be free to censure him if I find any of these weaknesses in him. My censure will sharpen him, and perhaps even save his life. He must not mind it."

Duryodhana has already sent a messenger to Karna with the news that Shalya has agreed to be his charioteer. Just as Shalya finishes, Karna walks up, smiling. He bows deeply to that king, "My lord, I am honoured the matchless Shalya will be my sarathy. Of course you may speak freely, whenever you wish, O king."

Shalya looks at him for a moment. Then, he smiles slowly and says, "I will fetch your chariot, Karna."

Shalya prepares the chariot for battle, to his satisfaction, and brings it out to where the others wait. Karna walks around the ratha in pradakshina, he folds his hands to it. Then he worships the rising sun, chanting a quiet mantra. This done, he respectfully asks Shalya to climb on first, before getting in himself. How splendid those two are in that chariot: like Surya and Agni riding in the pushpaka vimana!

Duryodhana cries, "Today you will do what Bheeshma and Drona could not, my friend. Ride, Karna, and destroy our enemies! Come back to me covered in glory. This will be the finest day of our lives."

Karna reaches out a hand to his friend, and he chokes. "For you I will always do my best. Remember that, Duryodhana, that Karna always did his best for you. The rest is in the hands of the Gods."

Duryodhana wrings his friend's palm. Shalya flicks his reins over the necks of his superb steeds, and they are off at the enemy. Behind him,

Karna wipes his eyes. He has no doubt that it is his final journey on which he sets out, and this is his last farewell to Duryodhana.

Evil omens attend his going forth, and in the sky, which seems ablaze, the seven planets seem to fly at one another to do battle.

FIVE

The two brothers

KARNA CRIES TO HIS SARATHY, "FLY AT THE ENEMY, O SHALYA! I WILL kill Arjuna today, and win this war!"

Shalya remembers his promise to Yudhishtira that he would dishearten the Kauravas, while he fought for them; most of all, he would discourage Karna. Now he is free to speak his mind. He laughs sharply, "Why reach for the stars, Karna? Your ambition flies away with your reason! It is easy enough to talk like this before the fighting begins. Wait until you hear the thunder of the Gandiva. Then we will see how brave you are. I know Arjuna, how powerful he is: but the way you go on, it seems you do not."

Karna says serenely, "I won't argue with you today, Shalya. Ride on!"

Karna learnt the art of reading the omens of the earth and the sky from his guru Bhargava. He sees them inauspicious all around him. He is beyond caring; why, he welcomes what he sees. Knowing how cruel his life has been, he goes willingly towards death's velvet clasp.

Shalya has not finished. "Krishna and Arjuna are like the sun and the moon. You are a firefly beside them. How do you dare challenge Arjuna, except that your good sense has left you?"

Karna growls, "I have sworn to let you speak freely, my lord; but truly, your name suits you well*. Your tongue is like a dagger! For which

---

* KMG: Actually, Shalya means a dart or goad. Also, in the original text, Karna loses his temper here, and abuses Shalya, and the Madras of whom Shalya is king. He says the Madraka men are ignoble and deceitful, and hate their friends. He says both Madraka men and women are notoriously loose and vile-tongued, drinking, dancing naked, and sleeping with anyone—blood relatives, members of their own sex, even servants and slaves. Karna asks how any virtue can be expected from someone born into such a race.

side do you fight that you praise the enemy and mock me? No matter. You cannot move me from what I have set out to do today.

"Besides, Shalya, I too know something of fate. I know there is such a power, and that it is awake when the world sleeps. Its ways are strange and inexorable, and men are puppets in its hands. Yes, when I saw Bheeshma fall and Drona die, I knew it was from fate; not they could resist her. But even if we cannot decide the time of our dying, at least it is in our hands to determine how we die: whether as cowards or heroes. By the way we die, in some measure we can triumph over fate.

"I know why you speak like this to me today. It is because your heart is with your nephews, and you want to make me doubt myself. There is no need for it, O king, because I know already that Arjuna will kill me: because dharma and Krishna are both with him. I am a doomed man; don't darken my last few hours in the world by praising Arjuna."

The astonished Shalya falls silent. At the battlefront, Karna deploys the Kaurava army with vision and elegance. Across the field, Dhrishtadyumna and Arjuna form their legions in a vyuha to subdue the one Karna forms.

Yudhishtira says, "Let us fight them one by one. Arjuna, you ride against Karna. Bheema, you kill Duryodhana today. Nakula, you fight Karna's sons. Let Sahadeva meet Shakuni, Satanika face Dusasana, and Satyaki his cousin Kritavarman. Dhrishtadyumna must contain Aswatthama, or he will raze our army by himself. I will confront Acharya Kripa."

Once more, conches blare across Kurukshetra, and, their eyes full of death, the armies run at each other. It is the seventeenth day of the war, and today the roar of the soldiers is just an echo of what it had been on the first day. Both forces have vastly diminished, and tired as well. There is hardly any valour left in the men's hearts, but only prayer and the grim will to survive another day.

What remains of the Trigarta army, which swore to kill Arjuna, it seems ten lives ago, charges him again. He rides against them and makes short work of that dispirited legion, killing many, scattering the rest in the hot breath of his arrows.

Away to his left, another warrior is a wild star on Kurukshetra. Karna, too, is a legion on his own, and not a soldier who meets him in battle escapes with his life. At his chariot-wheels ride his sons: as bright as their father, as formidable. Sushena and Satyasena are beside him, and Vrishasena behind him. They are like a fiery diamond, the four of them; they cut blandly through the enemy, leaving numberless corpses in their wake. Dhrishtadyumna, Satyaki, Draupadi's sons, Bheema, Shikhandi, Nakula and Sahadeva all combine to hold up Karna and his sons. But today, Karna's sarathy is quite as magnificent as his archer is, and the Kaurava Senapati is uncontainable. Blood leaps in vivid garlands in the morning sun, around Karna it flows in rills.

Bheema breaks through on a flank and cuts Satyasena down in a fiery storm; the boy's chariot breaks into flames, and he himself has his head struck off by a shaft from his mighty uncle's bow. Roaring that he was avenging Abhimanyu's death, Bheema shoots at Vrishasena and Sushena, as well, crippling their chariots and forcing them to run. The brave Vrishasena returns at once in a fresh chariot, and guards his father's back again. Karna melts the Pandava army like his sire does the snow on the Himalaya in spring. Enemy soldiers run screaming from him, or else, die.

Seeing Karna raze his legions on that seventeenth day, Yudhishtira rides at him, his gentle eyes flaming. Yudhishtira hails the older brother he does not know with harshness quite alien to his nature. He fears this enemy the most. This is the warrior whose very sight makes the Pandava's blood run cold.

Yudhishtira cries, "Sutaputra! Dare you compare yourself to my Arjuna? I hear Duryodhana began this war because he counts on you to win it for him. Come, Suta, show me your valour! Let me save Arjuna the trouble of killing you."

Karna turns to him. A slight smile on his lips, he gazes at Yudhishtira for a long moment, almost in a reverie. Yudhishtira waits, impatient for his challenge to be answered with fight. At last, Karna says slowly, "Ah, you are a great man, Yudhishtira. Though you will hardly believe me, I am happy to spend this moment with you, even if it is in the midst of this infernal war. I greet you, O Kshatriya, as one warrior another!"

Karna raises his bow, and they fight. At first, inspired by his terror of his opponent, that he is the one who might kill Arjuna, Yudhishtira fights like a Deva. He strikes Karna unconscious in his chariot. Shalya wheels away briefly from the encounter. Karna jumps up again, and now he lifts his archery so Yudhishtira cannot withstand him at all. With razor-headed shafts he kills the Panchala princes Chandradeva and Dandahara, who rode at Yudhistira's chariot wheels.

Satyaki and some others fly at Karna from two sides. He is invincible. No one has seen such archery yet on Kurukshetra. Karna brushes the Yadava aside, and confronts Yudhishtira again.

Not Yudhishtira, who has always feared Karna, ever imagined that he is such a bowman. But he hardly has time to think: in a flash, his own bow is dissected, and his armour struck neatly off his chest. Karna wounds him sharply with a clutch of fine, short-range arrows that make him cry out in pain, as they cover his handsome body in blood. They never pierce him deeply or threaten his life.

Recovering quickly, Yudhishtira picks up a javelin and casts it at Karna like an angry thought. But it seems his enemy sees the lance come at him for an hour, and has forever to raise his bow and cut it down. Yudhishtira flings another four javelins at Karna, each one aimed at his heart. In a languid blur, Karna cuts them down, laughing softly. Karna's chariot draws ever closer, and he shoots down Yudhishtira's flagstaff and banner, so they fall out of his chariot into the dust; and with them, the Pandava's honour.

Yudhishtira stands helpless before his enemy. Karna has him in the eye of his next arrow; he draws his bowstring to his ear. The war around them freezes; this, surely, is the end. Then, Karna lowers his weapon, rides closer still. Yudhishtira stands at his mercy. Karna reaches out his bow, and touches his brother with its tip, in contempt, in tenderness. The moment is like death for Yudhishtira.

Karna says, "You are truly a high-born kshatriya, a scion of the House of Kuru, the eldest Pandava. But it seems you are no match at arms for this lowborn sutaputra! Look, your life is in my hands. That, my lord, is because you are more of a brahmana in spirit than a kshatriya. So don't challenge your betters on the field of war. Now go back to your brother Arjuna, and remember that you are not Karna's equal. I spare your life. Go."

Yudhishtira wonders if those are tears he sees in Karna's eyes! The Pandava stands petrified by the scathing disgrace. Karna turns away and rides off to assail the Pandava army again, with sublime ferocity.

Bheema has seen the shaming of Yudhishtira, and his eyes turn scarlet. Smashing his way through the Kaurava army, he rides madly at

Karna. He is so furious no sound will come from him. Shalya sees him coming and says to Karna, "Bheema rides at us in wrath. I haven't seen him like this, even when Abhimanyu died."

Karna smiles, "Yudhishtira is his God, and he can't bear to see him shamed. All the Pandavas will die for the eldest one. Come, we must fight him."

Bheema breaks on him. He overwhelms Karna, and the Kaurava Senapati faints. Now a volcanic roar explodes from Bheema. Sword drawn, he springs from his chariot and rushes at the fallen warrior. "I will cut his tongue out for what he said to my brother!"

Shalya stands in his way. "Stop, Bheema. You have struck him down and that is revenge enough for Yudhishtira. Remember he spared your life once; don't demean yourself by attacking him when he had fainted. Besides, your brother Arjuna has sworn to kill Karna. Would you have him perjure himself?"

Growling, Bheema turns back to his chariot and rides away. In a moment, Karna opens his eyes. He springs up and seizes his bow. His hands shake, and he says to Shalya, "Ride at Bheema, I must answer him!"

Some way off, Duryodhana sees Karna's chariot flying towards Bheema, and he sends his brothers, fierce Kauravas, to fight at Karna's side. These are nearer Bheema than Karna is, and they reach him first. Bheema turns on them with such a smile. He croons at them in welcome, and then he is at the sons of Dhritarashtra. He excoriates them with his arrows; he smashes their heads into vivid pulp with his mace. Their screams ring across the field, and by now, he has lost count of how many he has killed. Roaring, roaring in ecstasy, drenched in his cousins' blood, his clothes, his face stained in rich crimson, Bheema looms on Kurukshetra. By the time Karna comes near him, the other Pandavas have surrounded their brother. The battle disperses.

The Trigarta Samsaptakas challenge Arjuna again: they have the knack of confronting him whenever he is about to ride at an exceptional Kaurava warrior. Now, just when he is going to ask Krishna to ride at Karna, Susharma and his horde appear around him. Arjuna kills a thousand Samsaptakas, but Susharma himself is a master of the devastras. Fighting obsessed, he presses Arjuna hard, while the Pandava kills half his army. At last, Arjuna strikes Susharma unconscious in his chariot, and his sarathy bears the Trigarta away, the last straggles of his legion fleeing behind him.

Arjuna is about to ask Krishna to take him where Karna rules the field, littering it with the dead, as if each life counted for less than nothing: when Aswatthama rides on to Arjuna's path. Hailing each other, they begin to fight. Aswatthama casts an occult dome of arrows over Arjuna's chariot; until nothing can be seen of it and there is perfect darkness within.

Arjuna manages to keep those shafts from breaking in on Krishna and himself. Krishna's eyes glitter in the gloom. He rages at his kshatriya, "Everything I said to you has been a waste! Your love for your guru means more to you than your very soul. You see Aswatthama and your hands fumble at your bowstring. Perhaps you would rather see me killed than answer your master's son!"

With a cry, Arjuna shrugs off his reluctance, and the pity he feels for Aswatthama, who lost his father yesterday. The Gandiva in his hand is blinding; he is the sun rising to dispel the brahmana's night of arrows. Arjuna smashes the dark cupola, and overwhelms Aswatthama. Drona's son swoons, and his horses bolt from the field.

SIX

In Yudhishtira's tent

ARJUNA TURNS BACK TO THE KAURAVA ARMY. DANDADHARA, PRINCE of Magadha, and his brother Danda charge the Pandava. But they are like jackals, after he has fought Aswatthama the tiger. Arjuna strikes the first Magadhan prince's head off with a crescent-tipped arrow, and fells his brother with a shaft through his throat.

Another company of Samsaptakas rides at him, like a refrain in the horrible song, which is this war. Susharma is not with this legion and Arjuna makes short work of them, killing a hundred and the rest run. Krishna cries, "We must fight Karna, victory lies beyond his death."

"Ride at him then, Krishna! I am ready."

As they go, the gandharva horses obeying their dark sarathy's thoughts, they see Aswatthama, recovered, ride back into battle. A powerful and inordinately proud kshatriya, the Pandya king confronts him. Arjuna and Krishna watch helplessly as the brahmana kills him with eight arrows that ruin his chest and pin him to his chariot-head. He has fought like ten men for the Pandavas, and his is a loss. No time to mourn him; like death's wind, they fly towards Karna. Aswatthama sees Dhrishtadyumna across the field, and rides at his father's killer.

The Gandiva hums in Arjuna's hands, as he cuts his way to where Karna reigns over Kurukshetra. Like Yama's dire thought, Karna's chariot skims across the field, with Shalya inspired at his reins, Shalya quick as light. Krishna, who sees deeply into the tragedy of that warrior, is moved by the spectacle of Karna at war.

He says to Arjuna, "Look at him, like a dancer! How graceful your mortal enemy is, how awesome. Not for long shall this earth be blessed with heroes like him. How splendid he is, in every limb, every movement. I could just stand and watch him."

Arjuna sees briefly with Krishna's eyes, and sees the splendour of Karna. But his sarathy's moment of eulogy is past. He says quickly, "He covers the earth with our soldiers' corpses*, and he must die. Look how his face shines with unearthly light. Heaven's touch is upon him, and his days of sorrow on earth are over. Arjuna, prepare yourself for the battle for which you were born."

Meanwhile, wounded by Karna, Yudhishtira has taken to his tent, and his bed. His body is a flame of pain, and his mind a sad fire. He had never wanted this war, and it was even more terrible than he had feared. His gentle soul is mortified by the relentless bloodshed of seventeen days. Now, when Karna humiliates him, his spirit can hardly bear the strain any more. Arjuna had said he would raze the enemy's best warriors by himself. But Karna has sway over Kurukshetra, while Arjuna does little to stop him.

An abyss yawns before the despairing Yudhishtira. Now that Karna leads the Kaurava legions, the Pandava is full of fear. His own defeat at the sutaputra's hands seems ominous to him. Yudhishtira lies alone in his tent, in agony, his thoughts all black. From the field of dharma, Yama's field, the screams of the men Karna kills waft in to him, and he covers his ears.

As Arjuna and Krishna ride towards Karna, a worried Bheema appears in their path. He says, "Karna wounded him, and Yudhishtira left the field."

Arjuna cries, "I must see my brother. I cannot fight until I am sure he is well, and I have his blessing."

Krishna turns back to the camp; he brings the chariot to Yudhishtira's tent. Yudhishtira sees them enter, and springs up from his bed. His face lights up, and he clasps Arjuna with the cry, "You have killed him! With Karna dead, the war will end. I am so proud of you, Arjuna. Awake or asleep, I always saw the sutaputra's face before me; why, the universe seemed to be full of just Karna. With which astra did you kill him?"

---

* There is more than one reference to vaisya and sudra soldiers, as well as kshatriyas.

Arjuna says, "I haven't fought Karna yet. Bheema told us you were wounded and we came to see you. But bless me now, and I will keep my oath."

A spasm of darkness twitches on Yudhishtira's face. He flashes at his brother, "Coward! I counted on you. Shame on you, Arjuna, yours is a hollow fame. The Gandiva is just an ornament in your hands. Give it to me, I will go and kill the suta myself!"

Arjuna's face turns red. He is about to draw his sword to kill his brother but Krishna lays a hand on his arm. He says, "He only means to rouse you to kill your enemy."

Yet, for a moment the brothers stand glaring at each other. Arjuna breathes, "I swore secretly to the Gandiva that I would cut off the head of any man that demanded the Gandiva from me."

The moment is fraught with danger, then the darkness leaves Yudhishtira; with a cry, he embraces Arjuna*. "Karna humiliated me before both armies. Oh, he is formidable. He is greater than Pitama or the Acharya. He fights like Indra, and I fear for us all. Most of all for you, my Arjuna, because surely no one else can kill him. I am sorry I spoke cruelly to you, but I will have no peace until this terrible man is dead."

The brothers embrace again, then Yudhishtira says, "Go now, my child. Go with my blessing and return victorious!"

Arjuna touches his feet, and Krishna and he leave the tent. They have their horses rubbed down, and give them water to drink. They refresh themselves, then climb into the white chariot and ride slowly into battle again.

As they go, Krishna says quietly, "You have sworn to kill Karna, and so you shall. But remember he is a noble antagonist. He has Agni's

---

* This confrontation between Arjuna and Yudhistira is longer in the Ganguli text. Arjuna accuses Yudhistira of casting aspersions at him, while his brother lay safely in Draupadi's tent and bed, a full yojana from the battle. He says Bheema might upbraid him, for he was in the thick of the fray, having slain 800 elephants. Arjuna calls Yudhistira cruel for accusing him, when he, Arjuna, fought with all his might and heart. He tells of how he had slain countless samsaptakas. Arjuna brings up the game of dice. Only after all this, Yudhistira melts and apologises abjectly, citing his terror of Karna as his excuse. Then Krishna upbraids Arjuna sharply, asking if he would have really killed his brother.

energy, Vayu's speed, and Yama's wrath.* Never forget, Arjuna, that he is the best archer in the world." Arjuna stiffens. Krishna goes on, "Yes, he is not merely your equal, he is better than you are. Karna defeated all the kings of the earth, just as you did during the Rajasuya. When he won a bride for Duryodhana, he vanquished the lord of Kasi by himself. Why, Karna is the only man who humbled Jarasandha, whom I could not face in battle.

"Remember all this, Arjuna. Never for a moment allow yourself to think he is just a sutaputra and you will beat him easily. If you fight this enemy with that thought in your heart, he will kill you. There is no one like Karna. This will be the battle of your life: the one that will take you to the brink of death. Only there, at the very limits of your powers and your will, can you kill Karna. To do this thing you must become more of an archer than you have ever been: even while you fight him!"

Krishna pauses as they draw nearer, then, says, "He is a great man, none greater than him. In his way, he is a man of dharma. You, Arjuna, will have the fortune of killing an incomparable warrior."

The Pandava says simply, "You are with me, Krishna. I will not fail."

They arrive at the edge of the war, and plunge in. Arrows from the Gandiva clear a path for them, in light, fire and blood. Ahead, they see Bheema, raging like his father Vayu when he blows as the dread north wind. Arjuna sees his brother dripping gore, most of it from Duryodhana's brothers whom he has killed. Bheema is still not quenched; roars issue from him, like a hungry lion's. Duryodhana sends Shakuni to contain him, but Bheema strikes the Gandhara king unconscious.

Bheema hears the deep thunder of the Gandiva, and knows Yudhishitra is well. Truly like a mighty lion, he turns his head and roars louder than ever, in joy. Nakula and Sahadeva are also at hand, and soon the four Pandavas fight side by side.

Then, Karna rides at them. He burns like hell's flames on the field and Yudhishtira's army cowers from him.

---

* Krishna also describes Karna as being 8 ratnis tall. A ratni is a measure of length from an elbow to a clenched fist.

SEVEN

The tastiest drink

INEXORABLY, ARJUNA AND KARNA THREAD THEIR WAY THROUGH THE armies towards each other. Arjuna breathes, "How glorious Shalya is at Karna's chariot-head; why, he seems like you, Krishna. And, ah, how radiant Karna is!" He is quivering with excitement. "Come, my Lord, let us ride at him. Let the duel begin."

In the other chariot, laden with tiger-skins Shalya does not mock his warrior any more. He is awed by Karna's virtuosity, and quite forgets his promise to Yudhishtira! Not he has ever seen an archer who can hold a candle to the one riding in his chariot.

Now, Shalya says, "Look, Arjuna rides at us. Your time has come, Karna, kill the Pandava. As for me, I take back everything I said earlier. Now I say to you: truly, truly, you are the greatest archer in the world! I had not dreamt that any man could wield a bow as you do. Not Aswatthama, Drona or Bheeshma is your equal. I want you to know I am proud to be your sarathy. Once, already, you won the earth for Duryodhana. Kill Arjuna today, and make a gift of the world to your friend for the second time!"

Karna is speechless. Tears well in his eyes, and stream in the wind. When he finds his voice, he says, "My lord! You fill me with joy. Though I know better than anyone what an archer Arjuna is, for Duryodhana's sake I will do my best to kill him today. Take me to my enemy, Shalya, the hour of reckoning has come."

Duryodhana sees Karna's chariot and Arjuna's fly at each other, like two comets in the vaults of space. A pang in his heart, he sends some of his brothers into the fray. A general battle breaks out as the bloodthirsty Bheema bursts upon those sons of Dhritarashtra.

Satyaki cuts down Karna's son Sushena in an arrowstorm, mangling the youth's chest. In fury, Karna beheads Dhrishtadyumna's son. Five Panchalas surround him: Shikhandi, Janamejaya, Yuddhamanyu, Uttamaujas, and Dhrishtadyumna himself. Not five of them together are any match for Karna. Swiftly, in a realm of archery they can neither fathom nor endure, they are beaten back. Satyaki joins them, and more Panchala warriors. Karna holds them all at bay. Kshatriyas from both sides stream in to balance the encounter: to Karna's exasperation and Arjuna's. A hundred battling chariots separate them.

With a shout, Duryodhana rides into that cauldron and a score of his brothers with him, Dusasana leading the rest. Bheema sees Dusasana and, eyes shining, turns on him. But Dusasana fights as if destiny lays its hand on his head, blessing him.

Bheema roars, "How many years I have waited for this moment!"

Dusasana roars back, "And I, Bheema, even longer than you!"

"I owe you a debt, cousin. Remember the day you laid your vile hands on Panchali? Since then, I have thought only of when I would repay my debt to you. Have you forgotten that day, Dusasana? I have dreamt of it every night."

His cousin replies mockingly, "I haven't forgotten! And so much besides. Do you remember how you scurried like rats from the house of lac? How you hid in the forest like animals? You found a fine wife for yourself there: a rakshasi, well suited to you! Then, in Panchala, your brother won another wife for you. And she was such a woman! You talk of my touching her, but not that she shared the beds of all five of you. Like your mother before her, Bheema! It runs in your family."

Bheema roars like a lion shot with arrows. Absolutely bloody-eyed, he fights on. Dusasana contains him. He means to provoke the Pandava: to make him careless, and have his life.

Dusasana cries, "And I remember the day your wife stood before us in the sabha in Hastina. She was our slave that day, Bheema. She was ours to do as we pleased with her!"

Bheema's roars explode from him more violently than ever. He is mad with anger, just as Dusasana wants him to be. Bheema casts a javelin at his cousin, a streak of wrath. Dusasana cuts it down with an arrow like time. Bheema picks up his bow again, but Dusasana breaks it in his hands. With a curse, Bheema leaps down from his chariot, mace in hand. Unmindful of the shafts Dusasana strikes him with, he runs at the Kaurava's horses. Before Dusasana's sarathy can turn them away, Bheema kills the lot with dreadful strokes.

In a wink, the Pandava clambers on to the chariot and one blow knocks Dusasana onto the ground. Bheema jumps down after him, and plants an immense foot on his chest. Dusasana does not stir, all around them a hush falls. Bheema stands there, rolling his eyes, tossing his great head from side to side, until he spots Duryodhana.

A smile dawns on Bheema's face, when he sees the eldest Kaurava frozen in his chariot. Ring upon ring of kshatriyas, Pandava and Kaurava, circle the fallen Dusasana and Bheema standing over him. Bheema looks at Kripa, Aswatthama, Karna and Duryodhana, and he throws back his head and gives such a terrible laugh!

Bheema says to Duryodhana, "I have your brother like a sparrow in an eagle's talons! What can you do about it, Duryodhana?"

Dusasana whimpers. Bheema growls, "So you remember everything, do you, cousin? Then you must remember that I have sworn to drink your blood. Nobody will stop me now.

"Duryodhana, seventeen days ago, you sent that jackal Uluka to me with a proud message. 'Bheema, you can carve meat on a kitchen board, but let us see how you carve my brother's heart!' Look at your brother now. Do you see the terror in his eyes? He begs you to save him, but you cannot. And now for sweet revenge."

No one stirs, no one can. Quick as thinking, Bheema draws his sword and, with a clean stroke, cuts off Dusasana's right hand, jewels and all. In the vast silence, Dusasana's screams ring across Kurukshetra, as blood from his severed wrist gushes in a geyser over Bheema. The Pandava holds up the bloody hand and roars to the armies watching, entranced, "This is the hand that dared touch Panchali's hair!"

Dusasana screams on, but Bheema has not finished. Smoothly, he opens a gash on Dusasana's breast with the tip of his sword. Kneeling in a flash, he tears his cousin's chest open with his fingers, exposing his heart. Dusasana screams his last, as Bheema bends like an unimaginable beast of prey and drinks at the scarlet font. Then, he raises his bloody face, smiling, and cries, "Aaaaah! The tastiest drink I have ever had!"

Dusasana lies limp on Kurukshetra. Bheema rises away from his corpse. His roar shakes the earth, "Panchali, I have avenged you! Come wash your hair in this wretch's blood."

Crooning in ecstasy, Draupadi runs out on to the frozen field: an exquisite and vengeful spirit! With deep cries of fulfillment, she bathes her black, loose tresses in dead Dusasana's gushing blood, from his severed wrist, from his chest.

Ashen-faced, Duryodhana turns away from that spectacle. Karna breaks down and sobs. Shalya says firmly to him, "This is war, Karna; in war these things happen. You must not give in to grief, now Duryodhana's fate is in just your hands. Let us find Arjuna, only his death can pay for this outrage. His death can still win the war for us."

Shalya wheels his chariot away. Battle breaks out again on the barbarous field, and the Pandava army is in great heart. Valiant as his father, Karna's son Vrishasena rides at Bheema. He mows a bloody way through the Pandava legions, and it seems no one will stop him. With a proud gleam in his eyes, Karna pauses to watch his son. Suddenly, another Pandava appears in Vrishasena's path; one that is a dark flame in his chariot, whose bow is an arc of the moon.

Even as he had sworn to, when Abhimanyu died, Arjuna kills Karna's son while the father watches helplessly. A golden arrow hums into Vrishasena's chest, and pierces his heart in a spurt of crimson, killing him before he can even scream. Karna's roars echo across Kurukshetra.

EIGHT

Karna and Arjuna

KARNA CRIES, "AT HIM, SHALYA! I MUST KILL ARJUNA."
The death of his son has given him the anger he needs to fight his brother. As if all those countless soldiers knew the time had come, they part like two seas and the chariots of Arjuna and Karna fly at each other. The fate of the war will be decided by this battle, which would be as the heart of every other one fought on Kurukshetra.

The chariots face each other. A stirring breeze has sprung up on Kurukshetra, and like death's herald, strokes Karna and Arjuna. For a long time, they stand still in their rathas, not a muscle moving, staring at each other in a contention of wills. The two warriors are relieved that at last this moment has arrived. Not both of them would survive the duel to come, and the one who did would never fight another like it.

Queerly light-headed, Karna says to Shalya, "My lord, I think I shall win today. But if I don't, O king, what will you do?"

Shalya turns his head, and Karna is startled to see his eyes moist. Shalya says, "Karna, you are the best archer on earth. I am sure you will win. But if fate runs against you and you should lose, why, I will kill Arjuna and Krishna to avenge you."

Thus, solemnly, speaks Shalya, who had practically been Karna's enemy before this day. In Shalya's change of heart, Karna feels he has some redress for all the years he was slighted by the kshatriyas of the world.

Across from them, in the other chariot, Arjuna says to Krishna, "I hope I can kill Karna, my lord. But if I am killed instead, what will you do?"

Krishna turns back to look at his archer, and his eyes are as deep as midnight. A smile touches the dark sarathy's lips, he says quietly, "The sun may fall out of the sky, but you will not fail today. Fire may turn cold, but Arjuna will prevail." He pauses, and then, softer than ever, adds, "And if somehow Karna kills you, then be certain the end of this world has come. Karna and Shalya shall die, I will tear them apart with my hands. Why, Arjuna, I will burn up this earth." Arjuna shivers to hear him; he has no doubt Krishna will do as he says. His charioteer smiles again, "But it won't come to that, Arjuna. I know it."

Some way off, Aswatthama sees Karna and Arjuna tensed for battle. He hears silence fallen on Kurukshetra, every other contention stopped. A wave of pity, for all the men come here to kill and die, overwhelms him. At his side, in the same chariot, Duryodhana still sobs for Dusasana. Aswatthama takes the Kaurava's hand, and says fervently, "Stop the war now, Duryodhana! Make peace, it is still not too late. My father died for this war, Bheeshma has fallen for it. Dusasana died, and so many of your brothers. Stop it, before Karna is also killed.

"The Pandavas are men of dharma; they are your cousins. I will go to Arjuna and say that you want peace. Krishna will be delighted. The truth is they cannot kill me and they cannot kill Kripa. But you can still lose the war and then everything will be as ashes. Enough blood has been spilt. Let Arjuna and Karna live as friends, both jewels of the Kuru Empire.

"Yudhishtira won't refuse an offer of peace. He hates this slaughter, anyway, and the others will listen to him. Save your life, Duryodhana; save so many lives. Why, save your soul! You know I love you, my friend; why, I love you more than I do anyone else in the world. Now I am afraid for you. Karna will die if he fights Arjuna. It cannot be otherwise, as long as Krishna is Arjuna's sarathy. How much grief weighs already upon your spirit; you will not be able to bear it if Karna is killed. I beg you, send me to the Pandavas now! Offer them an honourable peace."

Duryodhana smiles grimly at his boyhood friend. "Everything you say is true, Aswatthama, and I am grateful to you. But it is too late, and has been for some time. Look where Dusasana lies, his heart torn out by the beast. How can I offer peace to that monster and his brothers? Aswatthama, my friend, it is not we who decide these things, but fate. We are her playthings, her means to achieve inscrutable ends. Karna always says that we have no armour to protect us against fate, and he is right. I thank you for your love, but we have come too far to turn back. This war will be fought until the last man on one side is dead."

Duryodhana tells his charioteer to take them to where Arjuna and Karna face each other. All the Kaurava legions have gathered behind Karna, and the Pandava army behind Arjuna. Solemnly Karna raises the Vijaya above his head. Arjuna, too, lifts the Gandiva aloft. Both armies blow conches and shout their warrior's names, until earth and sky resound with *'Arjuna! Arjuna! Jaya! Jaya!'* and *'Karna! Karna! Jaya! Jaya!'*

In a moment, the duel begins[1]. At first, they fight with common arrows and lances, unhurriedly, each one settling into the battle, feeling his adversary out. Yet, already, their archery is breathtaking! Those who watch see their bodies become lustrous, and their weapons shine. It is not that no other kshatriya on Kurukshetra can match what Karna and Arjuna do; but surely none with such ease and grace. Many soldiers wish this duel would go on forever. It is like great music.

With no warning, Arjuna summons an agneyastra and shoots it at Karna. Sheets of white flames blow at Karna's chariot. Quicker than seeing, Karna summons a varunastra and a hundred showers douse the flames. Thick smoke billows there and darkness falls. Arjuna invokes a vayavyastra to blow the smoke away with a scented breeze.

With a growl, Arjuna chants the mantra for a more powerful weapon: the aindrastra. It drifts up from his bow and hangs in the air. From it, thousands of arrows whistle down at Karna and the Kaurava army behind him. A thousand Kaurava soldiers fall each moment, and it seems Duryodhana's army will be razed.

The thunder of Karna's bowstring rocks Kurukshetra. He looses a silver shaft charged with the bhargavastra. That weapon flashes up into the sky and puts out the aindrastra, so it falls away spent. The bhargavastra hangs fire in the sky, and banks of arrows scream down from it, killing thousands of Pandava soldiers.

A cheer goes up from Duryodhana's legions, Karna's name rings across Kurukshetra. Above the deafening noise, Arjuna hears Bheema's

---

1 Both are Devaputras, and in the sky, the celestials all take one hero's side, or the other's. See Appendix.

angry voice. "The enemy laughs at you, Arjuna. Tell me if you can't fight this man, and I will kill him with a blow of my mace!"

Krishna echoes Bheema, "It seems we will never break out of the mantle Karna wraps us in. What is the matter with you, Arjuna? Why do you hesitate?"

Now, the strangest thing happens in the Pandava's chariot enveloped in Karna's shroud. Krishna speaks to Arjuna as Narayana to Nara.

"Have you forgotten who you are? Don't you remember how you killed the Asura Dambodhbhava once? Here he is again, he has returned as Karna. Don't stay your hand, Kshatriya; this enemy is more ancient and powerful than you understand. He has come across ten lives to have revenge. Use the brahmastra, Arjuna, or you will die. Rouse your slumbering self, kill Karna!"

Fantastic vision is upon Arjuna! He sees another life, and the deep reasons why Karna confronts him on Kurukshetra today. Shaking off the stupor of the bhargavastra, he invokes the brahmastra. A molten arrow flies up, and unfurls in ten thousand golden shafts. Still, the bhargavastra resists the brahmastra.

The veil of arrows that covered Arjuna's chariot falls away. No more shafts fly down at the Pandava army, as, gradually, the brahmastra absorbs the bhargavastra. No soldier can look up into the sky where the two missiles are locked.

Meanwhile, Arjuna and Karna shoot at each other again, a hundred common arrows every moment. The astras above extinguish one another, and an emboldened Arjuna covers Karna's chariot in a blaze of silver shafts. A gasp goes up from the Kaurava legions, they are certain Karna is slain. Then, like the sun rising after night's final yaama, the resplendent Suryaputra stands forth again, and Arjuna's darkness of arrows falls away around him.

Karna looses another astra at Arjuna, who knows the weapon with which to quiet it. Kurukshetra is full of spirit presences, of the lords of the astras. In his tent, Yudhishtira hears that Karna and Arjuna are duelling. Despite the agony in his body where Karna struck him, he drives out to watch the fateful encounter.

The Devas gather above Kurkshetra in invisible vimanas. Indra and Surya almost fight over the battle between their sons. Karna dominates the field of dharma. He not only holds Arjuna off, but sends an occasional teasing shaft at Bheema who stands watching, breathlessly, his eyes bulging. Beyond the two warring kshatriyas, their thermal arrows immolate columns of soldiers. Yet not a man stirs from his place; they will rather die than miss this duel.

Silence rules Kurukshetra, except for the thunder of the strings of the Gandiva and the Vijaya, and the whistling of a hundred incredible shafts that fly from them, each impossible moment. Now and again, when one of them surpasses himself for a breathless instant, a cheer goes up from this army or the other.

Suddenly, Karna severs Arjuna's bowstring. Quick as a thought, Arjuna replaces it and is about to raise the Gandiva again, when, with uncanny aim, Karna breaks the Pandava's bowstring yet again. Quick as light, Arjuna strings the Gandiva afresh and raises his bow once more. Yet again, Karna snaps his string with an unerring shaft. This happens no less than eleven times! Karna feels a surge of love for this implacable brother of his. The twelfth time, Karna does not sever Arjuna's bowstring, but shoots five scorching narachas at Krishna. In a split second, Arjuna strings his bow and slices those five serpentine shafts along their lengths.

The duel nears its crescendo; each moment of it is like an hour of any other. The brothers fight at the very ends of their skill and endurance, at death's threshold.

NINE

The mired wheel

ONCE HE SLOUGHS OFF HIS FIRST HESITATION, ARJUNA FIGHTS exceptionally. Faced with the only real rival—Karna, who even Krishna said was better than him—Arjuna's archery becomes a mystic thing. So absorbed is the Pandava, he is hardly aware of what he does. The Gandiva is like part of his body, his very soul. Together, bow and bowman are one being: godlike!

All the Kaurava warriors who stood around Karna, guarding his flanks and rear, flee. Many are killed by Arjuna's luminous volleys. Duryodhana roars at the deserters, but nothing can persuade them to go back.

Karna is hard-pressed to keep the Pandava from burying him in a night of arrows from which he will never emerge. He cuts down as many shafts as he can; they flow at him endlessly, many finding their mark on either Shalya or himself. Karna has no inexhaustible quivers like his antagonist. There comes a time when the Kaurava soldiers can no longer see their Senapati, or anything around him. He is hidden in a perfect darkness of arrows: Arjuna hides the face of the sun.

Fighting for his life now, Karna knows the moment has arrived when he must either kill Arjuna or die. At darkness' heart, Karna briefly longs for Indra's Shakti; but the Shakti had returned to the Deva, after it killed Ghatotkacha. His death drawn so near he can reach out and touch it, Karna summons the last weapon he has left with which he can still win this duel. From its scented case, Karna draws the nagastra. Chanting its mantra, which perhaps five warriors on earth know, he fixes the glimmering missile to his bowstring. Already, it seethes and hisses like a cobra disturbed in its nest. Emerald scales cover that weapon; fangs yawn at its snake's-head, below lidless eyes that gaze plainly at Kurukshetra. Karna aims at Arjuna's throat, he means to cut his head from his body.

Karna is plunged in the night of arrows, and Arjuna cannot see what he is doing. He does not see the nagastra in Karna's hands; he doesn't see him fit it to his bowstring. Shalya says to his warrior, "Don't aim at his throat, you might miss. At least, send another shaft at his heart."

Karna replies, "A warrior never changes his aim. A real archer never doubts himself, that he must shoot a second arrow. Karna never misses his mark."

He draws the Vijaya's string to his ear, and, blinded, Arjuna shades his eyes. Karna cries to his inveterate enemy, "Take a good look at the world, Arjuna, this is the last moment of your life!"

A bolt of lightning, the nagastra streaks across Kurukshetra, spitting green fire. A cry goes up from the Pandava soldiers, they are sure Arjuna will die. Karna is certain his aim is true. Shalya, watching, thinks Arjuna is a dead man. Arjuna himself sees the macabre weapon flash at him out of the darkness with which he has covered Karna, and he can do nothing against the astra. For that moment, Arjuna also thinks he will die.

They have all reckoned without a blue charioteer. Krishna sees the nagastra; he sees it presciently even before Karna shoots it. As soon as the green thing flares at his kshatriya's throat, Krishna jerks on his reins. He forces his gandharva steeds down on their knees! In a moment's core, those horses kneel and the chariot tilts forward a hand's length. The nagastra flashes true to its mark, but Arjuna's throat is a hand's length lower than it had been. The emerald arrow whisks the crown Indra gave him from his head, and leaves a deep scratch; otherwise, it does not harm the Pandava.

Arjuna feels as if he has died and been reborn. Wild cheering breaks out among the Pandava footsoldiers. The howl on Bheema's lips is stanched, and a yell of joy issues from him instead. Colour flushes back into Yudhishtira's face, which had gone pale as death in that awful moment. A sigh like a serpent's comes from Karna: that moment, despite the odds of dharma, victory might have been his. Now, all is lost. He has no other weapon like the nagastra, none that can kill Arjuna. The

Suryaputra also knows the Pandava would have been dead except for his sarathy. Then, he had always known that, no matter what, Krishna was always with Arjuna: so, he, Karna, could never win this duel.

Yudhishtira's heart had stopped beating for that life long moment. Flushed himself, Arjuna darts a grateful smile at Krishna, who is as unruffled as ever, just his eyes a shade brighter. The Pandava ties up his long hair and the scratch on his scalp with a white scarf, and he has recovered enough to resume battle.

Meanwhile, a bizarre thing happens to Karna. The crown his nagastra shot from Arjuna's head is the same one Indra gave him. From where that kirita fell, and Karna's shaft with it, a serpent thrusts itself out from the ground. Invisible to every other eye, it flies through the air to where Karna stands disconsolate in his chariot.

Startled, Karna stares at the gleaming snake. It speaks to him, "You did not know it, but I entered your nagastra subtly; but for me, your arrow would have been quicker and Krishna would not have saved Arjuna. I am Aswasena. Long ago, when the Khandava vana burned and he killed my mother, I swore that I would kill Arjuna. Set me on another arrow, Karna, and shoot me at the Pandava. This time there will be no mistake, I swear Arjuna will die."

Karna cries angrily, "Haven't you done enough? Karna needs no help to fight his enemies. I would rather die than depend on you. Leave me, before I kill you!"

Aswasena's eyes glint balefully. He hisses, "If you won't help me, I will take revenge by myself."

He flashes through the air, invisibly, at Arjuna's chariot. But Krishna sees him coming, and says, "A serpent comes to kill you!"

By Krishna's grace, Arjuna sees the snake, hood unfurled, flying to sting him. In a flash, he cuts Aswasena in shreds with six light-like arrows. Panting, Arjuna says, "Who was he that came to kill me though no one sent him?"

Krishna, who knows all things, tells him. Karna and Arjuna resume their duel, more intensely than ever. Soon both of them stream blood from a hundred wounds they have opened on each other. Shalya and Krishna are not spared either.

Karna's time runs out swiftly; every moment, his death glides nearer. Two curses stalk him close. Fate and the very earth conspire to fulfil the first one. All at once, the ground under his chariot turns soft and his chariot-wheel sinks into the yielding earth. Shalya's horses cannot pull them out. The ratha tilts backwards, and his fine steeds' hooves are off the ground. Warrior, sarathy, chariot and animals are askew. Karna cannot possibly fight as he is.

A memory from years ago floats up into his mind. He sees a windswept beach, and at its edge, the corpse of the cow he killed. Karna sees the brahmana's anguished face before him again. He hears the man curse him, his words ringing above the surf, "When you face your greatest enemy, your chariot-wheel will be mired in the earth."

A shiver runs through Karna's body: death's first touch. He fights more furiously than ever. He thinks of one final astra he has, which might still finish Arjuna. Despair stokes Karna. He decides to use a weapon, which will kill a hundred thousand men besides the Pandava. Karna summons the brahmastra against Arjuna. He draws a golden arrow from his quiver, fits it to his bow in a blur and begins to chant its mantra.

Another face floats up before his mind's eye: a face he has hardly dared remember all these years. Karna sees his guru Bhargava's face before him. He sees his master's angry eyes. He hears his curse across the years, "When you most need an astra to save your life, you will forget the mantras I have taught you."

Karna fumes. He cannot remember all the mantra for the brahmastra. Arjuna's arrows swell at him in a squall. Now Arjuna severs Karna's bowstring, again and again, as quickly as he can mend it. Tears stand in Karna's eyes. He recalls the misfortunes of his life. He cries, "They say that dharma always watches over those who keep it. I have walked the way of dharma, as I saw it: but there is no such thing in this world!"

Arjuna's arrows draw flowers of blood on Karna's body, as he stands helpless in his mired chariot. Arjuna invokes the aindrastra. At the very last moment, the mantra for the brahmastra flashes into Karna's mind, and he manages to contain the aindra with the brahma. The two astras fuse in the sky.

Every moment Karna's chariot-wheel sinks deeper into the yielding earth. With a curse, he leaps down to the ground. Kneeling, he pulls out the mired wheel, lifting the chariot with awesome strength. At that moment, Arjuna is thinking of the raudrastra. When Karna sets the chariot-wheel down on what he believes is firm ground, it promptly sinks again.

Howling, he bends again at the offending wheel, and cries, "Arjuna, wait until I lift this wheel out. You are a kshatriya. It isn't dharma for you to shoot at me when I stand helpless. Give me a moment and we will fight again."

A wild laugh rings out from Krishna. "So you want dharma from Arjuna now! Tell me, Karna, have you always walked the way of dharma yourself? Was it dharma when you plotted against the Pandavas' lives with Duryodhana? Was it dharma when Draupadi was dragged into the sabha in Hastinapura, and you told Dusasana to strip her naked? Was, perhaps, the game of dice dharma? And let me remind of another moment of dharma, just four days ago."

Krishna's face is a mask. "Was it dharma when six of you killed Abhimanyu, when he was alone and without a weapon in his hands? And who broke the boy's bowstring from behind? I hear it was you, Karna. Was that dharma? That you demand dharma now from Abhimanyu's father!"

Krishna's lips throb, and Karna reels at what he says: the Avatara's words are like arrows, tipped with terrible truth. He leaves the mired wheel, and with a roar, turns to fight. Arjuna does not summon the raudrastra he had thought of, but looses an agneyastra instead. It burns at Karna. Karna invokes another varunastra to quell the fire in the sky. The effort to remember the mantra for the sea-weapon drains him. Karna staggers against the side of his chariot.

Arjuna invokes the vayavyastra to blow away the clouds of smoke that billow around Karna's chariot. They screen Karna, give him time to lift his wheel from the sludge. He hardly has the strength any more to do this. His mind is numb. He realizes he cannot remember another mantra. Somehow, he keeps his bow raised and fights back with common arrows. Visions overwhelm Karna. He sees his life flash before his eyes, in a moment. He sees it all so vividly, and with complete detachment, as if he was watching someone else's years. Why, even the present moment, this great duel, assumes a quality of dream. Wonderful illumination floods his tired body. Somehow, he fights on.

Shalya is helpless. His horses are covered in blood, wild-eyed from the wounds Arjuna has given them. Neighing frantically, they strain against their bits. The mired wheel will not let them escape and their legs thresh the air. Shalya is also covered in blood, like his archer on the ground. Gritting his teeth in a last, tremendous effort, Karna shoots a heavy wooden arrow at Arjuna. With a crack like thunder, it flashes into the Pandava's chest. The Gandiva slips from Arjuna's hand and he falls.

A cry of dismay from the Pandava army, and an excited cheer begins on the lips of the Kaurava legions. It dies before being given full throat, because Arjuna rises as if from the dead, groggily, but his eyes turning red. He picks up his bow and cuts down Karna's banner of Anga. Karna roars as if he has been shot through his heart; then the wave of visions smothers him again. It is as if there are two men in his body: one fights Arjuna for his life; and the other a Karna wafted far from this field, from this very world on a bright current of bliss.

Karna, the kshatriya, strains again at his chariot-wheel to lift it out. By now, he is bathed in blood. Tears run channels down his cheeks. With his huge effort, the sinews on his back stand out like snakes. Again, he sees the face of the brahmana who cursed him. He hears his voice, as if the man spoke them even now, 'And just as you have killed my cow, when she least expected it, so, too, you will meet your death, when you are not ready for it.'

Krishna cries to Arjuna, "Quick! Kill him now!"

Karna kneels on the ground, bending his back to his task. Slowly, the chariot-wheel slides out from its furrow. Arjuna draws an uncommon arrow from his quiver, its head wide as two hands, and shaped like a thunderbolt. It is the anjalika, and the Kauravas who watch hold their breath. Caught in a dream himself, Arjuna chants the weapon's mantra. The moment pauses as if time will stand still in it. Fluidly Arjuna draws his bowstring to his ear and looses the anjalika at his sworn enemy, his brother. It is just past high noon.

A clap of thunder, the light of a sunflare, and the arrow flies at Karna. Karna turns his head to that sound. The livid astra seems to take forever to reach him; Karna looks straight into Arjuna's eyes, and a smile of supreme contempt lights his face. As both armies watch, transfixed, the astra takes off Karna's head in a burst of wild roses, and it falls to the earth, brilliant, like the setting sun. The last disdainful smile still curves his haughty lips, and at last, death's peace softens his face.

Karna's headless trunk sways and falls beside the chariot-wheel that was his undoing. A pulsing light issues from his bloody neck, and rises so slowly from him, as if it was reluctant to leave his magnificent body. Majestically, that light, his soul, rises into the sky and is absorbed into the sun.

TEN

The sorrowing Sun

Karna lies on the earth like a fallen star. And it seems nothing beautiful is left in the world after he left it, as if all that was noble has died with him. High noon of the seventeenth day of the dharma yuddha claims Karna's life. As the Pandava legions break into deafening cheers, the Sun above pales in grief to see his son slain by Arjuna. He shines so dimly he seems like a moon in the sky. An abrupt twilight falls on the battlefield, where Karna lies cut in two on Kurukshetra.

His head is like a thousand-petalled lotus sprouted on the earth, and his body gleams like gold. Slowly, the Sun contains his searing sorrow, and shines down again on the world: but with soft evening light though he is at his zenith.

Shocked, his eyes streaming, Shalya drives his chariot back to the Kaurava camp. Both its banner and its warrior have fallen. Strangely, when Karna dies, the chariot comes out easily from the mire, as if its wheel was never stuck at all. Amidst the exultant roaring of the Pandava army, their blasting conches and trumpets, Shalya rides back in a sad frenzy.

Numbly, he comes to Duryodhana's tent and finds him outside, in a terrible state. The Kaurava's chest heaves in gasps and no words come from his lips that seek to form them, again and again: to cry out his untellable grief. Tears course down Duryodhana's face, trails of fire. His heart, which bore the death of his brothers and his sons so bravely, cannot believe his friend is dead.

Duryodhana sees Shalya in the empty chariot. His eyes roll up; his legs buckle under him and he falls in a heap. Shalya runs to him and lifts him up gently. He carries him into his tent, where the Kaurava is ministered to with scented water and salts.

Duryodhana has gone limp. His face is ashen, as if his very life has left him, and no word comes from him still. Sitting beside him, Shalya takes his hand and tries to comfort him. "My son, don't let your heart break. All this happens only as fate wills. I saw how Karna fought today, and I tell you only fate could have brought him down. But how he raged before she could have her way with him, and I was proud to be his sarathy. Arjuna did not kill him; fate did. If it had been a duel between just the Pandava and him, Karna would have killed Arjuna five times over. Duryodhana, the greatest archer in the world has left us, and we are all poorer for his going. Perhaps the Gods love him so much, they could not bear to have him away from them any longer."

Duryodhana still cannot say a word; but listening to Shalya calms him a little. His chest does not heave as much, and he no longer struggles to speak. Some semblance of quietness comes over him. But his eyes are still full of shock; they are desperate: everything is lost now, that Karna is dead.

Shalya says, "The enemy massacres our men. Even the sun is dim that Karna is dead. Shouldn't we honour his passing by stopping the battle for today?"

Duryodhana can only nod slightly. Shalya sends word that the fighting should be stopped for the day in honour of Karna. He turns back to Duryodhana. "We saw the light of his soul rise into heaven. Your friend is at peace now; don't grieve for him."

Aswatthama and some others try to pacify Duryodhana, but he sits like a stone, only the tears flowing down his face. All night he sits like that.

The sun sets over Kurukshetra, and Karna lies on the field of death. His body glows as if it is still alive and the smile on the lips of his severed head seems so alive as well. No one dares come near him as he lies there. They say he was the noblest man who lived in the world: rivers stand still when Karna dies, the sun loses his lustre, the earth trembles and the sky turns crimson with grief. The planets wander

The sorrowing Sun

from their orbits when Karna dies, and comets flare across the sky, plain even by day. The Devas weep when that kshatriya falls, even they who are free from sorrow.

When he kills Karna, Arjuna raises his conch, the Devadatta, and blows on it, and Krishna sounds his Panchajanya. Neither blows a joyful note. It is as if they, his enemies who killed him, are sad he is gone. Arjuna feels a part of his own life has ended. So many years he had waited for this duel, since the day Karna first swaggered into the exhibition in Hastinapura and stole his thunder. Now his enemy is dead, and least of all Arjuna can believe that by killing Karna, he, the Pandava, has proved he is the better archer. All that hardly matters any more; inexplicable sorrow lays hold of Arjuna.

Yet, there is no taking anything away from his triumph. The last warrior who stood between the Pandavas and victory has fallen, and their army celebrates his death. Yudhishtira had come out to watch the duel between Karna and Arjuna; but the pain of his wounds forced him back to his tent. Arjuna and Krishna make their way to Yudhishtira's tent through a sea of soldiers, all shouting both their names, and those near enough reaching out to touch their heroes.

The news reaches Yudhishtira before they do, and he is waiting for them in a fair tumult of joy. Arjuna leaps down from his chariot, runs to his brother, his guru, and prostrates himself at his feet.

With a sob, Yudhishtira raises him up and embraces him. Yudhishtira clasps Krishna. Krishna says, "With Karna, Duryodhana's last hope has died. Yudhishtira, your wrath of thirteen years burns brightly and it consumes the Kauravas. Already, you are lord of the earth again."

Yudhishtira, the bhakta, says humbly, "You have won this war for me. You are always my hope and my strength. When you are with me, victory must be mine."

Yudhishtira is deeply relieved; some peace comes to his spirit. It was always Karna he had feared, Karna who had been Duryodhana's main hope. The eldest Kaurava and the eldest Pandava knew, instinctively, how great Karna was; and the duel that would decide the outcome of the war would be the one between Arjuna and him. Now it is over, and Yudhishtira wants to be driven to the place where Karna fell. He wants to see the corpse of the man who haunted him with anxiety for so many years. He wants to see it with his own eyes.

Krishna takes him to the field in his chariot. The Pandava sees Karna's sons all lying dead, and then at last he sees Karna himself, his head cut from his body and restored to calm, after life's brief, harsh, fever. He sees the great body pierced all over by arrows, like a Kadama flower with its thousand filaments. He sees the thousand lamps lit around that headless trunk, and fed by scented oil. A pang grips him and Yudhishtira stands gazing at his dead brother. The Sun is setting behind the western mountain, slanting his last light across his slain child's face, when finally, the Pandava heaves a sigh, and says softly, "He is dead and he is so splendid even in death. Come, Krishna, let us go back."

ELEVEN

Out under the moon

THE SUN SETS, BUT DURYODHANA SITS UNMOVING IN HIS TENT, paralysed. His mind is also blank, until he remembers the day of the exhibition in Hastinapura again, the day he first saw Karna. How glorious Karna had been on that day, when he put Arjuna in the shade. Duryodhana sees his friend once more. He sees him so clearly, he can reach out and touch his face.

A sob tears itself out from the Kaurava's very entrails. The vision of the exhibition fades, and that of Karna with it. He remembers where he is and what has happened. It is midnight now, and no one is about. A stark compulsion seizes Duryodhana: he has to see Karna at once. Not caring to cover himself against the cold, he stumbles out into the night. Like a beast of the wild to its dead mate, Duryodhana runs to where Karna lies.

A bronze moon has risen into the sky and hangs low over Kurukshetra. By its burnished light, Duryodhana finds his friend, cut in two by Arjuna's arrow. Tenderly, the Kaurava picks up the severed head. He strokes its handsome face, its eyes shut in sleep forever. He kisses those eyes, the proud lips curled in their last smile, mocking death. Duryodhana gathers Karna's headless trunk in his arms and sits on the ground, mourning.

Suddenly panic grips him. He jumps up like a madman, and dashes here and there, sobbing and laughing, crying Karna's name to the moon. He plunges across the field, falling over the corpses of Kurukshetra, while grief dissects his heart. Summoned by a subtle impulse, Duryodhana runs to his Pitama on his bed of arrows. Sobbing, he falls to his knees beside Bheeshma.

Painfully, the patriarch stirs. He reaches out a gnarled hand and strokes Duryodhana's head. Tears in his aged eyes, he says, "Don't grieve for Karna, my child. His death was fated, and he is happy now. He was a kshatriya and he died as a kshatriya should. He is at peace."

Duryodhana stiffens. His voice quivering with excitement, he whispers, "So I was right! Karna was a kshatriya, all along. Tell me who he was, whose son. I must know everything. Tell me, Pitama! I must tell the world. At least now let them know he was a kshatriya, and they taunted him vainly."

His hand trembles in the patriarch's. Bheeshma says, "I cannot tell you who Karna was, unless you swear you will tell no one else. It was his own wish that no one should know; not even you, until he was dead."

Puzzled, that Karna kept something from him that Bheeshma knew, Duryodhana says, "If he wanted it kept a secret, would I ever tell anyone? I swear it will not pass my lips. Tell me, Pitama!"

Bheeshma hesitates. "Can you bear what I have to tell you? You are already unhinged with grief."

Duryodhana says, "I have seen Karna lying on the field with his head cut from his body, and I am still alive. My heart is made of stone; it can bear anything. Tell me, Pitama, who was he?"

His grandsire says, "Listen, then. I will tell you because you must know how much he loved you. Duryodhana, Karna was Kunti's eldest son."

Duryodhana reels. He clutches Bheeshma's hand, and breathes, "The Pandavas' brother! Tell me more."

Under the witnessing moon, Bheeshma tells him all about Karna's tragic life. He tells him about Surya Deva, whom Kunti invoked, and of the child born of the Sun's visitation. He tells him how Kunti floated her infant on the river, how Atiratha saw the wooden box and took the golden child home. Of Karna's dreams, Bheeshma tells the Kaurava, and how he discovered he was not the suta's son; how he wanted to be an archer, and was refused by every master in the land, until he went to Parasurama. Bheeshma tells Duryodhana about Bhargava's curse, and the brahmana's, how Karna gave away his kavacha and kundala to Indra, and, finally, when Karna himself discovered who he was, when Krishna told him. The Kuru patriarch tells Duryodhana how, just before the war,

Kunti went to her firstborn son and begged him to join his brothers' army, as their king. Bheeshma tells Duryodhana what Karna's answer had been. 'I will never abandon Duryodhana. He is the only one who ever loved me, and I love him more than my life.'

Duryodhana listens to him in silence, his tears dripping onto the old man's hands. Bheeshma falls silent. Duryodhana says, "He knew and he still stayed with me. He died by his own brother's hand for my sake, because he loved me so much. Why am I not dead? Why doesn't this heartless earth open and swallow me for what I have done?"

Duryodhana whispers feverishly, "Karna, my friend, there is nothing left to live for when you are gone. Not now, that I know how you loved me: more than I had dreamt. I am coming to you soon, my brother, very soon."

Bheeshma says, "Karna was the noblest man that lived in our times, and he has found the heaven he deserves."

Duryodhana says quietly, "Nothing can hurt me now that I have heard who my Karna was, and what he did for me. Pitama, I do not want the kingdom any more, for which this war is being fought. Now that Karna is not here, with whom I can share it, I don't want it at all. I want nothing but to die, and I will die a noble death. You will see, Pitama, how this grandson of yours dies. You will be proud of me. I promise you: at last, you will be proud of your Duryodhana. I must leave you now, I must prepare for death."

A smile lights Duryodhana's face, one of such relief, almost of peace: the smile of a man who has finally found his true direction. He kisses Bheeshma's hand, then, rises quickly and walks away. Bheeshma lies on his incredible bed under the moon, and his tears flow for his grandson, for all his grandsons. There is also a new light in his eyes. He can feel the war drawn near its end, and his own life, as well.

BOOK NINE

Shalya Parva

AUM, I bow down to Narayana, the most exalted Nara, and to the Devi Saraswati, and say *Jaya*!

ONE

Kripa and his sishya

THE NEXT DAY, WITH THE RISING SUN, ACHARYA KRIPA COMES TO Duryodhana's tent. He finds the Kaurava wide awake, his eyes red, intent. Obviously, he has not slept all night. Kripa takes Duryodhana's hand and speaks to him.

"Curb your sorrow, my prince, it drains you. How cruel this kshatriya dharma is, which venerates killing and dying above everything else. Just look at you, my poor child. I have seen you since you were an infant, and look at the pass you have reached. Duryodhana, real dharma is to protect precious life, not destroy it.

"You know how fond Aswatthama and I are of you. Listen to an old man that loves you. When this war began you had the bigger army and you were certain of victory. That is not how it has turned out. Bheeshma fell, then Drona was killed, and now Karna is dead. So many of your brothers are dead, and your son Lakshmana. At least now, you must realize that Arjuna is invincible. Krishna is his sarathy, and no one can stop him.

"Look at your army today: like stragglers of a caravan attacked by bandits. Do you remember what it was, eighteen days ago? How many men have perished, how many noble kshatriyas. We were all there when Dusasana was killed; none of us could stop Bheema. We were all there when Jayadratha died; could we stop Arjuna then? The truth is that you are in the wrong, and dharma is against you. How can you hope to win this war? Duryodhana, even now it is not too late. You still have that most precious treasure: you have your life. Don't throw it away.

"Go to Yudhishtira; offer him peace. He will welcome you, share the kingdom with you. Krishna will welcome peace. The rishis say you must fight only when you are strong. When you are weak, peace is the sensible course. You will still save thousands of lives, and every living soldier on Kurukshetra will bless you. I beg you, Duryodhana, listen to me!"

Kripa is so overwrought his eyes roll up, and he faints. Duryodhana revives his Acharya, sprinkling water on his face. Kripa wakes, and still sobs. Duryodhana takes his old master's hand, and says kindly, "Only you, who love me, will speak like this. Everything you say is true. Before the war began, you spoke strongly against it; once battle was joined, no one fought as you did. I saw you, always in the van of our legions, like a man half your age. You are my first guru. Drona came much later. You were my master since the day I was born, and you speak not out of fear or ambition, only love.

"But it is too late to think of peace. We are men of the world. We know how much the Pandavas have suffered at my hands. Think just of the day of the dice. How will they ever forgive me for what happened on that day? This war has opened my eyes. Once, I only thought of what I wanted, and I would do anything to get it. Today I can almost feel the Pandavas' pain in my own body.

"Bheema and I played together as boys. I confess to you now, he was always an affectionate fellow, wild but loving. Did you see what he did to Dusasana yesterday? Did you see the look in his eyes when he cut off my brother's hand, ripped open his chest and drank his blood? What rage he must have carried in his heart, for thirteen years, that a loving man like him could do a thing like that. You think Bheema will forgive me? Never.

"Then, think of Abhimanyu. Perhaps if he had not died, we could still have sued for peace with the Pandavas. Now, even if they do make peace, do you think Krishna and Arjuna will forget how Abhimanyu was killed? And do you think Bheema and the others will forgive what we did to Draupadi on the day of the dice? She will never forgive us. She has sworn she will sleep only on the floor until Bheema kills me.

"Acharya, your love blinds you with hope. Peace is impossible, let us not even think of it. The Pandavas have suffered too long and too much to accept peace now. Besides, *I do not want peace.*

"Perhaps you are right and they might still settle for peace. Yudhishtira is so full of dharma, that if I make the offer he may accept it. Krishna and Arjuna might forgive me for Abhimanyu's death, since I have also lost my brothers and my son. But what will I do with peace, Acharya? You forget that for thirteen years I have ruled the earth myself. How can I bear to share it with anyone? And it will hardly be an equal sharing. Yudhishtira and his brothers will rule, and I will be no better than their servant. I have shone alone all these years, dimming the glory of every other king in Bharatavarsha. How can I bear to walk behind my cousin now? Think of the shame of it. It will be far worse than dying.

"Yes, I have ruled the earth these thirteen years, and mine has been a splendid reign. Do you think that otherwise all these lords of men would have come with their armies to fight for me? Many more came for me than for Yudhishtira. I have tasted power like no other man. I have known wealth and luxury that even other kings hardly dream of. I have given away as charity more than many kings own in all their lives. And now you want me to be my cousin's subject, and to rule half a kingdom, if that, at his mercy? Ah Kripa, you mean well, but the dying man does not relish the bitter medicine that can cure him.

"I am set on war, and for me it is the only course. I might be many things, Acharya, but I am not a coward. I have never been afraid of anyone. I have lived the life of a great king: no pleasure I have not tasted in surfeit. I have the blessings of my poor because I have been generous in charity. Night and day, since I was a boy, I have heard the Vedas chanted; and you know how many yagnas I have performed. I have set my foot on my enemies' heads, and I have been munificent with my own. I never turned away any man who came to me in need. My conquests are numberless and far-flung, and I ruled my kingdom ably. Which man who has lived the life I have will willingly serve the rest of his years as the Pandavas' slave?

"So many of my friends and my brothers are dead: all those that wanted me to rule the earth. They died for my sake, as kshatriyas should. In this fleeting world, where everything is always dying, only honour matters. I will not sacrifice my honour to save my life, and live in misery under another man's yoke. Karna always said only honour was worth striving for, since only honour is immortal. If I die fighting on Kurukshetra, all my sins will be washed from me and I will have honour forever. A kshatriya should die in battle, not of old age and sickness.

"My mind is made up. My friends have given their lives for me, and the only way I can repay the debt I owe them is to follow them out of this world. For my sake, Bheeshma lies dying. Drona has fallen for me, and Karna, Jayadratha, all my brothers, and millions more. Each of those deaths is an arrow in my heart. I must go to those who have died for me. The only thing that could have held me back is love for my kingdom. But when Karna died, the kingdom I meant to share with him lost its last attraction. I have enjoyed a kingdom for long enough, and care nothing for it any more. How can I even dream of making peace with the Pandavas, after they have killed those who loved me? That would be ingratitude past forgiving.

"No, death is my only way. You should not grieve for me. I am beyond caring for life, indeed, I am impatient to die. When Karna perished, my heart went with him. I am hardly alive any more; my life is a hollow thing without my friend. He was the noblest man that ever lived. I cannot live without him, and all I want is to be with him again. Acharya, you cannot wish it on me to die in a sickbed, surrounded by wailing women. That is not the kshatriya's way. Forgive me, but I cannot make peace with the Pandavas."

Duryodhana falls silent. For just a moment, Kripa is sure he detects something like regret in the Kaurava's voice: genuine regret that he cannot make peace with his cousins. The harshness and hatred have vanished from Duryodhana, and the best in him seems to shine forth after what he has suffered on Kurukshetra. It is as if he is exorcised of all his demons; Kripa thinks sadly that of all the Kuru princes this one, as he is now, is the most lovable. Amazing gentleness sits on Duryodhana, and Kripa sighs and says nothing more. There is still the war to be fought, and they must choose a new Senapati to replace Karna.

TWO

Tameless Shalya

THE KAURAVA WARRIORS HAVE JUST FINISHED THEIR MORNING ablutions in the Saraswati, coloured by dawn. Their bodies burn as if with fever, and the night-chilled water hardly refreshes them. Duryodhana comes to the river, and calls Aswatthama. "You are the wisest of us, my friend[1]. Tell me, whom should I make our Senapati?"

Without hesitation Aswatthama says, "Shalya. He is powerful and experienced, and he is devoted to you. At last count, we still outnumber the Pandava army. With Shalya as our general, we can win this war even now."

Duryodhana approaches Shalya, who has just finished worshipping the sun and is wading out of the golden river. The Kaurava folds his hands and says humbly, "I beg you, be master of the Kuru army. Hope is not lost, my lord, you must lead us to victory."

Shalya says, "Yesterday, before he died, Karna asked me what I would do if he were killed. I said to him he could not be killed; but if he was, I would avenge him by killing Krishna and Arjuna." He chokes, "He was the best man I ever knew, and I must keep my word to him. Shalya is a kshatriya, Duryodhana; even Arjuna will not stand against me. I will either win this war for you yet, or die trying."

Shalya is given the ceremonial bath, and made Senapati of the Kaurava army. Some semblance of hope returns to Duryodhana's legions, and they shout Shalya's name, and blow their conches and beat their drums

---

1 See Appendix for a description of Aswatthama.

to embolden themselves. Across Kurukshetra, Yudhishtira hears the sounds and says, "They have made Shalya their Senapati. He has never been defeated in battle, how will we face him?"

Krishna says, "Shalya is formidable*. In some ways, he is more of a warrior than Bheeshma, Drona or Karna. He is a powerful archer, and he fights with the mace as well as Bheema. Then, there is something else about him, a thing of fate, and not Bheema, Arjuna, Dhrishtadyumna, Shikhandi, Nakula or Sahadeva can kill him. Shalya's death is written at the hands of only one kshatriya in the Pandava army."

"Who is he, Krishna?"

Krishna smiles, "Why, you, Yudhishtira. Forget he is Sahadeva and Nakula's uncle; you must kill him if this war is to end. Dharma is with you, you will not fail."

Shalya deploys Duryodhana's dwindled legions in a complex vyuha. At its hub, he collects the few maharathikas that remain: Kripa, Aswatthama, Shakuni, Kritavarman, Duryodhana and the handful of his brothers that Bheema has left alive. Before they ride out to battle, they confer among themselves and Shalya decides, "We will not fight duels, if we can help it. Each man will fight for the others and they for him. We will attack the Pandavas together, and try and kill them all at once."

It is the eighteenth day of the dharma yuddha. The conches echo yet again, and the two hosts fall at each other. Seventeen fearsome days of battle have whittled both armies. When the war began, Duryodhana had a hundred thousand chariots, seventeen thousand elephants, two hundred thousand horses, and six million footsoldiers; and the Pandavas had sixty thousand chariots, six thousand elephants, a hundred thousand horses and four million footsoldiers. Now those numbers are a few thousands each: of chariots, horse, elephant, and some more thousands of footsoldiers, at most.

When the Pandavas see Shalya has gathered all his best warriors at the centre of his vyuha, they divide their army in three phalanxes, with Dhrishtadyumna, Shikhandi and Satyaki leading one each. At the head of his army today, and leading all the rest, rides Yudhishtira, impatient to kill Shalya. Nakula and Sahadeva ride at his chariot-wheels.

---

* Krishna calls him Artayani, too.

Tameless Shalya

Dashing Kritavarman breaks on the Pandava lines, and only Arjuna can face the Yadava. Bheema comes up against Kripa. However, these encounters do not develop into prolonged duels. The Kaurava warriors wheel away from any Pandava who challenges them for too long, and they ride quickly to help one another.

Yudhishtira and Shalya fight the only real duel, and the Pandava finds Shalya implacable, more than he can endure. Seeing his brother pressed hard, Bheema rides to his side. Meanwhile, Karna's son, Chitrasena, and Nakula face each other. Chitrasena fights with some of his father's valour, but Karna's death has made him sadder than the youth can bear. At one point, he smashes Nakula's chariot with a volley reminiscent of Karna's finest. Nakula leaps down in fury, his sword drawn, and rushes at the bewildered Chitrasena. Before the prince can recover from his surprise, Nakula springs up on to his chariot, seizes his nephew by his hair and cuts his throat.

The slain prince's brothers, Sushena and Satyasena, attack Nakula. But the Pandava's blood is up, and he kills them both in moments, with exact arrows. Seeing Shalya beset by all the Pandavas now, Kripa, Kritavarman, Shakuni and Aswatthama fly to his side. Kritavarman strikes Bheema deep in his chest, so he staggers back, the mace falling from his hand.

Acharya Kripa severs Dhrishtadyumna's bowstring, from far away, and Aswatthama easily holds up Nakula and Sahadeva. Only Yudhishtira fights the grand Shalya again. When Bheema falters briefly in his chariot, Kritavarman kills his horses. Growling, Bheema leaps down from his ratha, mace in hand, and runs at Kritavarman. He strikes the Yadava's horses down so they fall without a sound. He is too close to shoot at with arrows, and Kritavarman jumps down behind his chariot and runs.

The smouldering Bheema turns on Shalya again. He smashes down the Kaurava Senapati's white horses. With a roar, Shalya hurls a javelin at him. Bheema dances aside and catches the hurtling lance in flight. Quick as thinking, he turns and flings it back at Shalya's sarathy, so the man falls off his chariot-head to avoid being transfixed.

Shalya seizes up his mace and leaps down to the ground to face Bheema. Mace rings against mace, and the titans are covered in sparks. Kurukshetra quakes. The battle all around them pauses, as the soldiers come to watch. The two fight on with elemental blows, and it seems neither will prevail. Then, both Bheema and Shalya find a gap in each other's defences, at the same moment, with seismic strokes: each is knocked unconscious by the other's blow!

Kripa swoops on the fallen Shalya, lifts him into his chariot and rides away. Bheema lies where he fell, for a while. Then his eyes flutter open. He takes a moment to recall where he is, and jumps up with a roar, the mace still in his hand, "Shalya! I am not finished with you. Come and fight!"

He is comical, standing there so fierce, while his opponent has gone; some laughter breaks out around him, some relief in the relentless horror.

Elsewhere, Shalya mounts a new chariot and rides back to battle. Now he fights twice as ferociously as before, as if being knocked unconscious by Bheema has roused him. There are notably few duels today. Instead, the kshatriyas all concentrate on attacking the enemy army, and killing as many men as they can. From a boundless theatre for heroic duels, the war becomes a contention of fading numbers. The Kaurava Senapati, Shalya, is untameable. Watching him, hope flickers up again in Duryodhana that he may still win this war.

For the other side, Satyaki fights as boldly, and Dhrishtadyumna is awesome. Bheema and Arjuna are quenchless, as well, and no one can contain them. But nobody burns as brilliantly as Shalya today, and Yudhishtira is anxious. If the Kaurava Senapati is allowed to continue, the already reduced Pandava army will evaporate entirely. Yudhishtira mutters to himself, 'Can Krishna be wrong?' He shakes his head. 'No, Krishna is never wrong. I must kill him myself.'

Yudhishtira sees Sahadeva and Nakula flit to Bheema's side. He sees Shalya hold them off, easily, while killing a hundred Pandava soldiers. Yudhishtira sees Aswatthama ride against Arjuna, and cover Krishna's chariot in a web of silver shafts. His chest heaving, he sounds his conch to call his brothers off the field.

They come at once, and he says to them, "Krishna says that only I can kill Shalya; and so I will, or die trying. Satyaki, my friend, guard my right wheel. Dhrishtadyumna, watch my left. Bheema, you ride before me, and Arjuna you come after me."

Flanked by four majestic kshatriyas, Yudhishtira comes to kill Shalya. A duel develops. As if he senses death near him, Shalya is more than magnificent. He looks like Saturn duelling with the Moon. But it is Yudhishtira who surprises everyone. His lips pursed, his eyes flaming, he is like Indra come down to Kurukshetra. Soon after they begin, Yudhishtira ruins Shalya's chariot with a smoking volley. Fortunately for that king, the Kauravas have gathered around him, and quickly he is back in another chariot, fighting more powerfully than ever.

Still, Yudhishtira takes everyone's breath away. Five times he snaps Shalya's bowstring, and then, once, strikes him with a torrent of arrows, so that king swoons; his horses are killed and his banner cut down. Luckily, Aswatthama is near and whisks him from the field. When Shalya is away Bheema straddles Kurukshetra, killing a thousand men. The fighting spreads out again. All around Bheema ring the roars and screams of those that kill and are killed.

When he recovers, Shalya rides back into battle for the last time. He makes straight for Yudhishtira. He rakes the Pandava with a hundred arrows, in a moment. The serene Yudhishtira replies with nine perfect shafts, which disjoint Shalya's armour so it falls away. Shalya cracks the Pandava's bow. Next moment he, too, cuts away Yudhishtira's golden armour and kills his horses. Flying up just then, Kripa kills Yudhishtira's sarathy.

Bheema is at hand to protect his precious brother. He breaks Shalya's bow, kills his horses with a terrific volley, and his sarathy by flinging his mace at the man's head. Undaunted, Shalya draws his sword, picks up his shield and leaps out of his broken chariot. He runs straight at Yudhishtira, whose death can still win the war for Duryodhana. Dhrishtadyumna, Satyaki and Shikhandi surround Shalya, so he cannot escape, and no Kaurava warrior can rescue him. No thought of escape crosses Shalya's mind, he runs wildly at the Pandava king.

Bheema smashes his sword, and blows his shield to bits. Shalya stands briefly surprised, and defenceless. Then he charges Yudhishtira again, with bare hands now. Not pausing to think, Yudhishtira finds himself reaching for a silver, jewel-studded lance beside him. He casts it at the Kaurava Senapati, as Karttikeya once did his spear of agni. It pierces Shalya's chest like a serpent flashing into its hole. He falls with his arms spread wide, as if he embraced the earth, one last time, before he left her. With an echoing roar, Shalya dies.

THREE

The last men

WHEN THEIR KING DIES, SHALYA'S LEGION BREAKS AWAY FROM THE rest of the Kaurava army and rushes at the Pandavas. Duryodhana cries to them to wait, they must all fight together. They will not listen. Yudhishtira and his triumphant kshatriyas pick Shalya's men off easily, and yet another Kaurava legion perishes.

Panic takes the other Kaurava soldiers. Their nerve gone, they turn to run. Duryodhana looms behind them in his chariot, and speaks to them in a voice like the sea. "Is it from death that you flee? Death will hunt you down anyway, whether in war or in peace. It is better to die as heroes and find heaven, my friends. Why do you fear these Pandavas? I will show you how to win this war. Ride with me, and victory shall be ours!"

He charges the enemy, and what remains of his army, twenty-one thousand men, follows him into battle again. Duryodhana fights like a dark Deva on Kurukshetra. For a while it seems he will win the war single-handedly. By himself, he holds up Satyaki, Dhrishtadyumna, Bheema, Arjuna, Yudhishtira, Nakula and Sahadeva.

His uncle Shakuni appears beside him, and he fights like ten men today! On Shakuni's other side, his son Uluka is as formidable as his father is. Between them, these three drive the five Pandavas back. Seeing them, Duryodhana's brothers, the handful Bheema has left alive, rally round, their bows singing. But when Bheema sees these sons of Dhritarashtra, he throws back his head and gives a familiar roar of delight. A smile spreading on his face, Bheema comes like a comet from the Pandava ranks, flying to keep his oath!

Some of Duryodhana's brothers try to run. Bheema catches them. He kills them all, their blood splashing in the sun, staining the brown field. Soon, of Dhritarashtra's hundred sons, only Duryodhana and his brother Sudarshana are left alive.

The eighteenth day hurtles on, with men dying like rain-flies. With some incandescent archery, Arjuna decimates the scant remains of the tenacious Trigartas, and just Susharma is left alive. A sharp duel ensues, but Susharma's spirit is broken with all the defeat inflicted on him. Arjuna puts an end to that king with an arrow that tears his chest open and blows his heart to shreds.

Bheema dances among what remains of Duryodhana's elephant army. He crashes the beasts down with huge strokes of his mace, then, dispatches their riders like insects. When almost all the elephant legion is razed, Bheema, covered in blood, turns his burning gaze to Duryodhana and Sudarshana. He climbs into his chariot again and, with Arjuna and some others around him, rides at the last two Kauravas left for him to kill. As he draws near, he roars at Sudarshana to attract his attention. Even as that prince swirls around to face him, Bheema sloughs off his head with a crescent-tipped arrow, once favoured by their master Drona.

Of his hundred brothers only Duryodhana remains, and a gory, triumphant Bheema rides at his cousin to end it all. Just in time, Shakuni blunders between them with his son Uluka and the last elephants of the Kaurava army. Nakula and Sahadeva appear at Bheema's side, and they engage Shakuni and Uluka. Fine power upon him, Nakula caparisons Uluka's elephant in a sheen of arrows. Uluka strikes Nakula with thirty shafts, and covers the raging Bheema with seventy more, drawing blood in a hundred fonts. Nakula seizes a slender spear, and casts it at Uluka like sorcery. With his father looking on, the golden lance decapitates Uluka, and his corpse tumbles off his grey beast's back.

Shakuni's scream echoes around Kurukshetra. His eyes welling blind, he turns on Nakula's twin: Sahadeva who had sworn to kill him on the day of the game of dice. With every weapon he has, Shakuni attacks Sahadeva. The Pandava smashes all his missiles, and fells his elephant. Shakuni climbs into a chariot, and, his nerve gone, tries to escape. But Sahadeva is determined to keep his vow. He pursues the Gandhara, crying, "Stop and fight, coward! You are the cause of this war, of all this misery. If you had never come to Hastinapura, Duryodhana would not have become the monster he did.

"You laughed at the oaths we swore when you banished us. Who is laughable now, Gandhara? Dusasana is dead, Karna is gone. Look where your son lies without his head. Come, Shakuni, pay for your sins. Let me pluck your head from your neck like a fruit from a tree. I am happy that I can kill the most evil of all our enemies."

Knowing there is nowhere to run, Shakuni turns. They fight a short, scathing duel. Then, Sahadeva picks up a javelin with golden wings, and casts it at Shakuni. It cuts the Gandhara king's head from his throat and Shakuni dies, his hooded eyes staring, still full of malice.

Celebration breaks out among the Pandava legions, and absolute panic among the Kaurava soldiers that remain alive. Duryodhana's men flee in that frenzy, and once more the Kaurava looms threateningly behind them and brings them back to fight. But with Shakuni, the last ember of hope dies in Duryodhana. Surely, now, only one thing remains: to die himself.

Of his eleven teeming aksauhinis, of millions, just two hundred chariots, five hundred horses, a hundred elephants and three thousand footsoldiers remain. For his sake, they come back into battle. Duryodhana watches the Pandavas make short work of his final legion, scattering its corpses on Kurukshetra as the wind does blades of grass.

Of eleven immense legions just Duryodhana, Kripa, Aswatthama and Kritavarman are still alive. Of the seven Pandava aksauhinis, two hundred chariots, seven hundred elephants, five thousand horses and some ten thousand footsoldiers remain. The blood of more than ten million kshatriyas soaks Kurukshetra, field of dharma. Most of the noblest bloodlines of the earth have been extinguished. The race of kings has been destroyed forever; an age has ended.

FOUR

The Dwaipayana lake

Duryodhana surveys the field of Kurukshetra, the ruin of kshatriya kind. He realizes what Vidura had meant when he said to him, "You will destroy the race of kings."

Duryodhana's head reels. He wonders if Vidura had seen, in his mind's eye, the spectacle he now confronted himself. The Kaurava sits astride a horse, an animal wounded by many arrows. Then, even that beast folds under him and falls dead. Now he is truly alone. Sobbing like an orphaned child, when this final companion also left him, Duryodhana staggers away from Kurukshetra.

His mind ranges over the past eighteen days, but no grief touches his heart for the millions who had died for him. Only one face rises before his eyes: how Karna must have suffered when he knew the Pandavas were his brothers! Yet, he had not abandoned Duryodhana. Where would he find another Karna in this world? Nowhere, even if he lived a hundred lives. As he walks dimly on, hardly knowing where he goes, Duryodhana's body begins to burn as if a rain of fire fell on him.

He sees a blue lake ahead. Then all he wants to do is cool the fire in his body in the water, to immerse himself forever. Eighteen days ago, he had six million men to fight his cause. Now Duryodhana has his mace in his hand, and it is his only guardian. For a moment, he stands gazing at the lake, somehow unable to move into it yet.

Just then, Sanjaya comes running through that place. He stops still to see Duryodhana standing there, lost, his eyes full of tears. Before him is the man who was sovereign of the earth a few days ago. Now he stands bereft, alone. His father's sarathy approaches Duryodhana, and says, "My lord, it is I, Sanjaya."

Duryodhana turns slowly, like a dreamer. A smile lights his face and he embraces Sanjaya fervently. "Thank God you have escaped with your life!"

Duryodhana holds Sanjaya's hand, as if it were his own sanity. Sanjaya says, "When they had finished killing all our soldiers, the Pandavas arrived in our camp to look for you. They found only me, and Satyaki took me prisoner. When Dhrishtadyumna saw me, he began to laugh. He said, 'What are you going to do with this poor fellow? What does it matter any more if he lives or dies?' Satyaki growled, 'I will kill him then.'

"The Yadava raised his sword when, suddenly, Vyasa Muni appeared there, and said, 'This man must not be killed; let him go back to Dhritarashtra.' Reluctantly Satyaki released me, and I ran away before he changed his mind."

Sanjaya sees the blank look in Duryodhana's eyes, and cries, "But, my lord, I cannot bear to see you like this. I fear your mind is unhinged after what has happened."

Duryodhana smiles, "Ah, Sanjaya, if only I could lose my mind! I would be spared this agony. Look at me now: I have no one left, no one to even cry for me. Why, I can hardly cry myself."

Duryodhana falls silent for a moment, then, says, "Go to my father, good Sanjaya, tell him his son Duryodhana sent him a message. Tell him I have entered the Dwaipayana lake, because my body burns and I mean to submerge myself to cool my limbs. Anyway, of what use is my life when all my brothers and my friends are dead? And the Pandavas have won the war.

"Sanjaya, tell my father I will never see him again in this world, and say his son begs his forgiveness for all the grief I have caused him. He has always loved me and I am sure he will forgive me. Then go to my mother Gandhari, and tell her that her Duryodhana says he is not fit to be the son of a great soul like her. Tell her that I, who have never bent before anyone in my life, now set my head at her feet and beg her forgiveness. And tell her I have just one prayer left: that in every life to come, I am born her son. Go now, my friend. I must cool my limbs for a while, ah, they are on fire! Let me enter the water before anyone else finds me. I must cool myself, Sanjaya, I must cool my burning body."

Mace in hand, he walks slowly into the lake until it covers his head. He makes the blue water still above him; he knows the secret art of not breathing for as long as he wants. Sanjaya stands a moment, gazing sadly after him, then the sarathy turns and makes for Hastinapura again.

On his way, he meets Kripa, Kritavarman and Aswatthama. They say to him, "You are lucky to be alive, Sanjaya. Have you seen Duryodhana anywhere? Is he alive?"

Sanjaya tells them how Duryodhana had submerged himself in the Dwaipayana lake. "He said his body was burning, and he needed to cool it."

Aswatthama cries, "He thinks we are also dead. The four of us could still kill the Pandavas!"

Suddenly, they hear the voices of men coming towards them through the trees. It is some Pandava soldiers searching for Duryodhana, and the four vanish into the forest.

Celebrations rule the Pandava camp. The war is won, and Yudhishtira is lord of the earth. The cost has been stupendous, but victory belongs to them. Meanwhile, the Kuru princesses are sent home to Hastinapura in palanquins and carts, the widows wailing, pulling their hair, and raking their breasts with their nails. It takes the Pandavas a while to realize that Duryodhana is nowhere to be found; when they do, they send their men out in every direction to look for him.

Duryodhana's horse is discovered, dead, but there is no sign anywhere of its master. They never dreamt he was a coward; yet, now, there is no trace of him and it seems he has run away. The Pandava soldiers comb the woods around Kurukshetra, but they do not find the Kaurava. Evening sets in and they return to Yudhishtira's camp, having failed their mission.

When the enemy soldiers have gone, Kripa, Aswatthama and Kritavarman come quietly to the lake. They call, "Come out, Duryodhana, we three are alive."

There is no reply. Aswatthama says, "The four of us can still win this war. The Pandavas have hardly any army left. If we win, you will be king; if we lose, we will find Devaloka for ourselves. Come out from the water, and lead us to victory!"

For a moment, there is no answer. Then Duryodhana's voice speaks to them softly from the lake. "I am so happy you are alive. Yes, my loyal friends, we will fight the Pandavas and kill them yet. But not tonight. Darkness has fallen, and my body is on fire with the wounds I have received. I am exhausted and so are you, and my mind is full of sorrow. The lake waters will revive me in the night; tomorrow we will fight the Pandavas again and destroy them. We shall win this war yet.

"More than anything, I am moved that you are still loyal to me. I cannot think what I have done to deserve such love. That will suffice for me tonight; tomorrow, we will face the enemy."

Aswatthama is impatient. "Why wait until tomorrow, my lord? Let us fight them now. I swear we will kill them all!"

The three do not notice the knot of vetalas, carrying loads of fresh meat from their hunt, who have come to Dwaipayana lake to drink its sweet water. The hunters move as silently as wild animals. They stand hidden in the trees, listening to every word Kripa, Kritavarman and Aswatthama say. At first, they wonder whom the warriors address. Then they hear Duryodhana's ghostly voice float out of the silken water. Those hunters had heard the Pandavas are looking for Duryodhana, when they came across some of Yudhishtira's men scouring the forest for the Kaurava.

They melt back into the jungle, and run through evening's shadows towards the Pandava camp. The hunters arrive at Bheema's tent. The guards outside try to stop them, but they barge in. When Bheema hears their news, he brings the foresters to Yudhishtira.

Yudhishtira rewards the vetalas and sends them on their way. The Pandavas set out at once, with Krishna leading them. Dhrishtadyumna, Satyaki, Draupadi's sons, Yuddhamanyu and Uttamaujas, and Shikhandi go with them to the lake. The sun is low in the western sky; dusk is upon the world. Aswatthama hears the Pandavas coming. He says to Duryodhana, "The Pandavas are coming! We must hide."

Duryodhana's voice answers, "Go, my friends."

Kripa, Kritavarman and Aswatthama run from the lake. They find a large banyan tree in the depths of the jungle, and sink down under it, exhausted. They speak in whispers among themselves, "What will happen now, will they find Duryodhana?"

"Will he fight them, if they do, or will he remain under water?"

"It all depends on what the sons of Pandu decide."

FIVE

Magnificent Duryodhana

THE PANDAVAS ARRIVE ON THE BANKS OF THE DWAIPAYANA LAKE. No ripple stirs its surface; the water lies smooth as a mirror.

Yudhishtira says, "Drona taught us how to do this: Duryodhana has used a siddhi to still the lake. He is under the water, hiding like a coward; but he will not escape today. Even if Indra comes to save him, I mean to send our cousin to the next world."

Yudhishtira is trembling with the rage he has borne, so patiently, for thirteen years. Krishna says, "Then make him come out, Yudhishtira, and kill him. Today, he must pay for everything."

Yudhishtira comes to the edge of the lake, and cries angrily, "How can you hide now, Suyodhana? Every kshatriya in Bharatavarsha has died for you. Your brothers are all dead, your uncle Shakuni is dead and you hide like a common coward. Where is your pride? Where is your honour? If you are a Kuru, come out and fight! Millions have died for you, and here you are clinging to your life. Bheeshma lies dying, Drona is dead, and your beloved sutaputra is gone. I had thought that if you are arrogant and envious, you are fearless too. Come out, cousin, and fight like a kshatriya. If you kill us, you can still rule the world."

A mocking laugh wafts out from the water. Duryodhana's voice speaks to them. "You prate like a witless boy, Yudhishtira. How dare you think I fled the battle! I saw my brothers and my uncle die, and I was dazed. I sat numbly on my horse, hardly aware of the world around me. The horse wandered away from Kurukshetra on his own, and then he fell dead. I walked away from the beast, not knowing what

I did or where I went. My body felt as if it was on fire, and when I saw this lake, I thought I would cool my fevered limbs in it. You flatter yourself, cousin, to think I am hiding from you. As soon as I have rested, I will come out and we will fight. Meanwhile, you and your men must also be tired. You rest, as well, and we will fight when we are fresh again."

Yudhishtira is secretly pleased that his cousin is not, after all, afraid! Somehow, even he cannot bear to think of Duryodhana as being craven. The Pandava says, "We need no rest. We have been searching everywhere for you, come out and fight us."

A pause, then, Duryodhana says, "Yudhishtira, I don't want the kingdom any more. Those with whom I meant to share and enjoy it are all dead. My brothers are dead. My Karna is gone. The earth has lost her splendour. I will fight you; yes, I will surely fight you. But you can have the kingdom: it means nothing to me any more, it is just some barren ground. I make a gift of this lustreless earth to you, Yudhishtira; it is yours to rule. And I will put on tree-bark and deerskin and spend the rest of my days in the jungle, seeking my peace."

Yudhishtira roars, "Dare you! What right have you over the kingdom any more, that you presume to give it to me? Even if it were yours to give, I would never take it from you as a gift, but win it in battle. No kshatriya would rule a land that his enemy has given him.

Yet, there was a time when all this kingdom was yours to give. You were lord of the earth, when your uncle and you conspired to banish us for thirteen years. We came back from our exile and asked you gently to give back what was ours. Then you were not so magnanimous. When Krishna came to you as our messenger, the answer you sent with him was that you would not give us enough land to set on the point of a needle! Now, suddenly, you are the soul of generosity. You have lost your mind, Duryodhana. How else would the king of all the world, who wouldn't give his cousins five towns, be ready now to part with his entire kingdom? Cousin, you have no kingdom left to give.

Yet, you still have one thing to lose. You have your life, Duryodhana, and it is for your life I have come. Our long enmity must end today, for only one of us can be king in Hastinapura. After all that has happened, I do not mean to let you escape with your life today. So come out and fight."

Yudhishtira's voice sounds very different, so hard now. "This enmity between us has lasted too long. You have hated us since the day we first came to Hastinapura from the jungle. One way or another, you have done your best to destroy us. Today, all that must end. I will see you dead today, and send you to swarga where you do not deserve to go. Come out and fight!" roars Yudhishtira.

Duryodhana stiffens under the lake. No one has dared speak to him like this in years, not since he became master of the earth. He is also taken aback, because it is the gentle Yudhishtira who speaks so harshly. There is nothing for it but to come out and fight.

Crafty to the end, Duryodhana says, "I marvel at this! All of you are men of dharma, and you want to fight me all together, when I have no chariot, or a single soldier left. I don't even have a bow or sword, only my mace. I have no armour, and I am wounded. But I am not afraid of any of you. I do not fear Satyaki, Dhrishtadyumna or even your Krishna. I will meet you as the year does the seasons, and I will kill you all. Yet it saddens me that you, who call yourselves kshatriyas, have banded together to murder a defenceless man. Remember that a man takes only dharma out of this world with him; and you forsake dharma by this cowardice.

"But that is your concern, not mine. I am a kshatriya and a Kuru, and I am ready to fight you all, and send you to your fathers. If I die, I will be the happiest man, because I will be with my Karna again. But what do you know about Karna, or that he was the noblest man who ever lived? I will kill all of you first, then take my own life. Prepare to die, I am coming!"

With a swirling of the water, Duryodhana emerges from the lake. He rises from the Dwaipayana lake as the sun does from the sea. He is majestic. His chest is as broad as a hill, his arms are splendid, and his mace is laid across his shoulder. His eyes burn darker than ever, and despite themselves, the Pandavas find themselves quivering with admiration as he wades calmly out of the water to face them.

Yudhishtira smiles. "I am proud that my cousin isn't a coward, but a true Kuru after all!"

Duryodhana gains the shore and rasps, "I will fight you one at a time. You are men of dharma, you know what the dharma of kshatriyas is."

"Do you mean the same dharma you used to kill Abhimanyu?" retorts Yudhishtira. "It seems only when the law applies to you it is meant to be observed. But as you say, we are men of dharma. So, Duryodhana, choose any one of us and choose your weapon. If you win, you can rule the earth again."

There is a ripple of dismay among the others at the foolhardy offer. But that is Yudhishtira: as soon as he sees Duryodhana come out so bravely from the water, the Pandava's rage leaves him. The Kaurava is his young cousin, once more, and deserves a fair chance. Duryodhana stands there like a tiger eyeing a herd of cattle.

With a tight smile, he says, "It seems we are almost friends again at this final hour. I accept your offer! For my weapon, I choose this mace. As for my opponent, it makes no difference which of you I fight first: one by one, I will kill you all. Come, I am ready."

Yudhishtira actually glows to hear him, so dauntless. He says, "Then fight me first. I will kill you and send you to Devaloka, where you now deserve to go for your courage!"

Duryodhana stands before them, his body covered in wounds that have begun to bleed again. He is a mountain of sinister presence, cool, and full of slow rage. A roar breaks from him at what Yudhishtira says, "Come then! I will fight any of you, and send you all to hell. There is no one who can face me with a gada."

He stands there, red-eyed, bristling and growling like a great wild beast.

SIX

The two cousins

KRISHNA TAKES YUDHISHTIRA ASIDE. THE DARK ONE IS TREMBLING with rare fury. He lashes out at the Pandava, "I have never seen anyone as foolish as you! You dare challenge Duryodhana to a mace-fight? He will kill you before the fight even begins. It is no empty boast when he says no one can match him at the mace. For these thirteen years you were in exile, he practised every day, raining blows on an iron image of Bheema. Duryodhana's mace blows are like thunder and lightning in Devaloka! Bheema is perhaps stronger than he is, but he has neither Duryodhana's skill nor his long, hard practice."

Krishna sighs. "This is turning into another game of dice. It seems you are determined you and your brothers will spend your lives in the jungle, and Duryodhana will sit upon the throne of the world. Listen to me, if there is any of you who might be able to face Duryodhana it is only Bheema. And not even he can beat the Kaurava in a fair fight with maces. Oh, Yudhishtira, I despair for you and your dharma. *Dharma is not meant to be carried to such insane lengths.* After millions of men have died and the world is almost yours, you mean to give it all back with your foolishness!"

Krishna's lips are pale with annoyance. Bheema says, "I will fight Duryodhana. More than any of us, he hates me. But I am stronger than he is, and my mace is more powerful than his. I will kill him today, Krishna, nothing will stop me."

Bheema speaks with such fervour that Krishna takes the big Pandava's hand, and cries, "Yes! You will kill him today, Bheema, and only you can. You have killed the other ninety-nine Kauravas, and you will kill Duryodhana as well. You must keep your oath. As much as your mace, let the anger of thirteen years be your weapon. Kill your cousin, and lay the world at your brother's feet. But be careful, Bheema, never for a moment think he will be easy to kill. There is no macefighter like Duryodhana; he is strong as a mountain and quick as a thought."

Duryodhana stands growling still, ready for the last battle. He is determined to salvage some honour from it for the rout on Kurukshetra. Bheema comes up to him and says, "I will fight you, Duryodhana, and before we begin I want you to think back on everything you have made us suffer. Remember Varanavrata, the game of dice, how Dusasana dragged Panchali into the sabha in Hastinapura. Why, remember Kurukshetra, where the very race of kshatriyas has been destroyed. Bheeshma lies dying, Drona lies dead, and the sutaputra graces the field, bright as a sun even in death. Our uncle Shalya lies there, and your own brothers, glowing like embers of a great fire put out. Not only the kshatriyas, but dharma has perished on Kurukshetra; sishyas have killed gurus, uncles have killed nephews, and cousins their cousins. We have cut down our Pitama on Kurukshetra, and all this for your vanity.

"The time has come to pay, Duryodhana. I am going to have revenge on you for every sin you ever committed. I am going to kill you." Bheema's voice is frightening, though he speaks so quietly.

Duryodhana listens to him in contempt, a brow arched, a sneer on his lips. The Kaurava laughs, "I never knew you were so eloquent, Bheema! I myself prefer deeds to words. How many years I have waited to kill you. I am pleased that you are man enough to fight, rather than letting one of your brothers be killed first. Don't you see my mace like a cliff of Himavat? You will die, cousin: no one on this earth can fight me with a mace. Why, if the fight is fair, I think I could beat Indra. But of you five, certainly you are the most worthy adversary. After me, there was Shalya, until he died; and then there is you. Of course, my master Balarama is greater than any of us. It was he that said I am better than the rest of you put together. I am ready, Bheema. Let us begin."

He speaks so boldly it would hardly seem that he stands alone against the others. Smiling at his cousin's invincible arrogance, Yudhishtira brings him some armour, and a crown to contain his long hair. Duryodhana takes these graciously. He has never hated Yudhsihtira; he even admires his noble nature, thinking that here is a worthy brother to his Karna. He had only fought Yudhishtira for kingdom, the wealth and power it brought. Bheema he has always loathed.

Duryodhana dons the golden mail. He sets the shining crown firmly on his head. And he is truly splendid: every inch a kshatriya and a king, glowing by the last rays of the setting sun as if his body was bathed in blood.

Bheema steps forward, mace in hand, and the antagonists begin to circle each other warily. Before the first blow can be struck, they hear a conch and the approach of a chariot through the trees. They stop and turn to see their master, Balarama, arrive.

Krishna's brother comes from a pilgrimage*, which had taken him from Prabhasa to the source of the Saraswati, to all the tirthas along the Ganga and the Yamuna, to the Naimisa vana, down to the Sarayu, to Prayaga, on to bathe in the Gomati, to the Gandaki, to Gaya where he worshipped his ancestors, to Mount Mahendra, to bathe in the seven streams of the Godavari, to the Vena, the Pampa, and the river Bhima, to the Venkata mountain, to Kanchi, to Kamakoti, to bathe in the Kaveri, to Srirangam, Kanyakumari, the Panchaprana lake, to Kerala, Siva's Gokarna, Uma's island shrine, to the Dandaka vana, and from there to the Narmada and back again to Prabhasa from where he set out. On his way back, he met Narada who told him of the gada-yuddha his sishyas were about to fight, to the death of one of them. Duryodhana, of course, was the Yadava's favourite and the guru wanted to be present when the duel was fought.

Balarama arrives on the banks of the Dwaipayana lake. Krishna and the Pandavas greet him warmly. Duryodhana prostrates himself at his master's feet; he does not feel alone any more.

Balarama says, "I have heard Samantapanchaka is a most holy place upon the earth. It is near here. Let the gada-yuddha be fought there, for anyone who dies in Samantapanchaka goes straight to swarga."

---

* Balarama's pilgrimage is described in 50 pages in KMG. This includes the legends of every tirtha he visits.

Yudhishtira agrees, and they set out for Samantapanchaka. It is such a spectacle: those kshatriyas moving through the trees like a pride of lions. Duryodhana saunters along at his ease with his cousins, his enemies, his gait regal, his mace across his shoulder. Krishna walks with Balarama, asking him about his tirtha-yatra, and Satyaki brings up the rear, a few paces behind them.

SEVEN

At Samantapanchaka

AT SAMANTAPANCHAKA, THE ETERNAL NORTHERN ALTAR OF BRAHMA, the two titans are ready for battle. Both are Balarama's disciples, they are cousins, and tigers of the royal House of Kuru. Entirely at his ease, Duryodhana says to Yudhishtira, "The rest of you sit around us and watch the gada-yuddha. May those that love us enjoy our duel!"

The Pandavas, Krishna, Balarama and the others sit in a wide circle around the antagonists. Balarama is full of grace after his pilgrimage. His face is radiant; so is his body: fair as wave-froth, draped in shimmering blue silk. Krishna sits at his side, dark and mysterious as a blue lotus. Together, they are like the full moon and a cloud beside it.

Bheema and Duryodhana bow solemnly to each other, and the battle begins with a clap of maces ringing together, showering the two kshatriyas in sparks. The earth under their feet shudders with each stroke, and birds fly out of the trees, crying in alarm. But what Duryodhana said when he lay submerged in the lake is true, and the combatants are soon overcome by tiredness. They stagger on their feet, and can hardly swing their weapons.

Yudhishtira calls a halt to the duel. "You are both exhausted. Rest a while, and then resume."

Panting, Bheema and Duryodhana sink down on the ground, gratefully. When they have rested an hour, they rise and fight again. Like two bull-elephants in a jungle's heart, Duryodhana and Bheema battle, and the night is lit by the moon risen above them, and the streams of sparks that flow from their maces when they ring against each other are endless firefly swarms. The Pandavas light some torches, as well, for them to fight by. They fight honourably, with dharma, and Balarama, their master, watches them with some pride.

Once or twice, Duryodhana, his skills dazzling, strikes Bheema's mace out of his hands. He never strikes the Pandava when he is unarmed, but waits for him to retrieve his weapon before attacking him again. Bheema's roars shake Samantapanchaka. Now he strikes his cousin's mace from his hands, and Duryodhana's eyes blaze in the night. In a wink, he picks up his weapon and, even as he rises with it, he fells Bheema with a flashing blow. Bheema is up at once, and they fight again.

Into the small hours they duel; until Yudhishtira stops them once more, saying they should rest and begin again with the new day. They sleep for a few hours. When Bheema and Duryodhana awake, it is with fire in their eyes. With dawn, they battle once more, more powerfully than ever. Their grunts and growls, their roars reverberate through the sacred glade. Their maces flash in the sun: Bheema's, which the Asura Mayaa gave him, and Duryodhana's, as splendid.

Bheema's blows felled elephants during the war. But Duryodhana is a dancer, easily evading his stronger, but less agile adversary's extravagant strokes. The Kaurava fights with uncanny speed, and he is hardly less powerful than Bheema. Twice he knocks the Pandava down, and once Bheema faints with the strength of the blow that finds him. Once, one of Bheema's strokes lands squarely, and Duryodhana staggers back and falls, like a sala tree in bloom uprooted by a tempest. Bheema waits for him to get up; and when he does, knocks him down again.

But when Duryodhana rises again, he begins to fight as he hasn't done yet: as if he has been saving his strength. Now Bheema can't match the Kaurava at all. Duryodhana seems to be in more places than one, at the same moment. His strokes land like gashes of lightning from every direction, easily passing Bheema's defences and crashing into his body. Twice, Bheema had fought Shalya. Both times they had been almost equal, perhaps Bheema slightly the superior for youth being with him. Duryodhana is an opponent of a different ilk; most of all, his speed is unearthly. Bheema staggers about, he roars in rage and pain. But he is increasingly helpless against his cold, quicksilver adversary; it will not be long before Duryodhana kills his cousin.

Arjuna asks Krishna, "Which of them is better, who deserves to win?"

Krishna smiles, "Both are great mace-fighters, and they have the same guru. But surely, you can see Bheema is no match for Duryodhana. Your brother is stronger than your cousin; but in speed and skill Duryodhana has left him far behind. Thirteen years behind, Arjuna. It hardly matters how powerful Bheema's blows are if Duryodhana dodges them as easily as he does." Krishna sees fear in Arjuna's eyes, and sighs. "Yudhishtira has been foolish to allow the war to be decided by this duel. The beaten enemy, who comes back to battle, is the most dangerous one. If they fight fairly, Duryodhana will certainly win and Bheema will die."

Just then, Duryodhana lands a stunning, exquisite blow. Krishna breathes, "Look at that! If there was not a kingdom at stake, I could spend days watching these two. Alas there is, and Bheema must kill him if all the war is not to be in vain. I only wonder how he will do it."

Krishna grows thoughtful. Duryodhana's blows have begun to land frequently on Bheema, who totters like a wounded elephant, swaying on his feet, roaring again and again. Arjuna turns to Krishna in panic, "How can Bheema kill Duryodhana? You must help him."

Again that impenetrable smile appears on the Dark One's lips. He seems to be waiting for the right moment. Duryodhana lands two dreadful blows, felling Bheema again. Bheema shakes his head; he growls and begins to rise, when suddenly Krishna whispers to Arjuna, "If only Bheema would remember the oath he swore in Hastinapura."

Arjuna looks perplexed. Krishna murmurs, "That he would break Duryodhana's thigh."

Bheema is rising groggily from the ground. He looks at Arjuna and Krishna in despair. For the first time in his life, the kshatriya who killed Baka and Hidimba finds his confidence shaken. He knows he will not last much longer against his cousin. Then he sees Arjuna slap his own thighs with his palms, meaningfully. On the brink of everything as Bheema is, he understands immediately.

Meanwhile, Yudhishtira is losing hope with each moment that passes. With every blow, Duryodhana seems more certain to kill Bheema. Yudhishtira's face is a picture of misery. Sahadeva, Nakula, Satyaki and

Dhrishtadyumna scarcely breathe. Covered in blood, Bheema can hardly move any more. He stands in one place, turning round and round, tiredly, his mace raised just in defence, ineffectually. Duryodhana circles him like a panther, toying with him, looking for a chance to finish him. The frantic Yudhishtira calls another break. The mace-fighters sink down to rest. Bheema's eyes are glazed, while Duryodhana's burn darkly. The Kaurava knows he will win this duel. At last, he will achieve his life's fondest ambition: to kill his cousin!

Not to lose his advantage, Duryodhana is the first to rise. He calls tauntingly to Bheema to get up. Bheema does, with an effort, and they begin again. In a moment, Duryodhana fetches Bheema a stroke that knocks him down on his back. Bheema shakes the fog that rises into his eyes, and gets up again, heroically. With a roar, he aims a huge blow at Duryodhana's chest. He is so tired Duryodhana allows him to begin his stroke, before he leaps nimbly into the air and above the arc of Bheema's mace! Bheema stumbles forward with the impetus of his own swing. Landing supplely, Duryodhana catches his cousin with a smart half-blow across his back that sends him sprawling into the dust again. Now Bheema takes still longer to rise; when he does, he is unsteady on his feet.

Duryodhana closes for the kill. Bheema is good for perhaps one blow more; at most a couple, and then he would die. Duryodhana prods Bheema with his mace-head, laughing in his face, goading him into some final rashness. The tired Pandava seems to take the bait. He lunges forward and aims another massive blow at Duryodhana's chest. Once more, Duryodhana waits for him to begin his wild swing, then leaps high into the air to evade it. Bheema stops his stroke halfway. A startled look flashes into Duryodhana's eyes. As the Kaurava comes down from the top of his spring, Bheema hurls his mace with a half-swing, and with every bit of his remaining strength. It crashes squarely into his cousin's thighs, breaking them and smashing his manhood.

Duryodhana's scream echoes under the hushed trees. Still screaming, he falls, and lies wriggling like a serpent with a broken back. Like Surya's sarathy, the legless Aruna, magnificent Duryodhana lies on holy ground, and the sky erupts in a battery of thunder, peal after peal, which threatens to shake the earth loose from her orbit. Meteors streak down in their hundreds, while the cries of birds and beasts, yakshas, rakshasas and pisachas echo all around*. Bheema has felled Duryodhana with a most treacherous blow: in a gada-yuddha, it is forbidden to strike one's opponent below his navel. It is a crime, a sin, adharma.

Just now, Bheema doesn't care a whit for dharma. His tiredness vanished as if by magic, he leaps into the air, his eyes alight, roaring in joy. With his great body splattered with his own blood and Duryodhana's, he seems hardly human as he runs up to the fallen Kaurava, kicks away his golden crown and plants a foot on his head. "Thirteen years ago you laughed at the oath I swore. I have kept my oath, Duryodhana! Do you remember how your brothers called me a cow? I have never forgotten that. I swore then that your head would lie under my foot some day, and here it is. Feel my foot, cousin!"

He grinds Duryodhana's head down, while the Kaurava whimpers for the agony in his shattered parts. Bheema raises his foot up, and stamps Duryodhana's face. He raises his foot again, but Yudhishtira rushes at him and drags him away, bloody-eyed still.

"Enough Bheema! You have kept your oath and that is enough. With that, all enmity ends. Duryodhana is your brother; he is a Kuru. He is a king, a lord of eleven aksauhinis. You demean yourself by setting your foot on his head. I will not allow you to humiliate a fallen king."

Tears in his eyes, he goes and kneels beside Duryodhana. Gently he says, "Duryodhana, you will soon be in a place where there are now more of those we love than remain in this world. I envy you! The world you leave me to rule is so empty. The kali yuga is upon us, and the earth has lost her glory. Go in peace, my brother. I salute you, O king of the earth!"

Though his chest heaves in mortal agony, and sobs are torn helplessly from him, a light in Duryodhana's eyes and the ghost of a smile on his lips show that he is grateful to the compassionate Yudhishtira.

---

* KMG adds that a dreadful sound came from the bowels of the earth, while conches and drumrolls echoed. Showers of blood and dust fell from the sky. On every side, frightful beings, headless, but with many arms and legs, danced across the earth. Lakes and deep wells vomitted blood, and brave warriors trembled. Rivers flowed back toward their sources, women looked like men, and men like women. All the Devas, gandharvas, siddhas and charanas returned to their abodes, talking about the awesome duel and its end.

EIGHT

The clarity of Krishna

But not everyone at Samantapanchaka celebrates Duryodhana's fall. Balarama jumps up in a rage. His lips throbbing, his great body shaking, he roars, "Bheema, you coward! You have disgraced us all. You struck him below the waist. I will avenge Duryodhana, I will kill you myself!"

He seizes up his Halayudha, uncanny plough-weapon of a hundred fires and blades, and rushes at Bheema who stands nonplussed. In a flash, Krishna seizes Balarama and restrains him powerfully. Only he can; and how beautiful they both look at that moment, one dark and his brother fair.

Krishna cries, "Stop! There is no crime in what Bheema did. It was for the bigger cause that he struck Duryodhana down. How does this one thing Bheema did move you to such anger that you want to kill him? You found no fault in everything Duryodhana made the Pandavas suffer. I did not see you rush to kill the Kaurava, when Draupadi was dragged into the Kuru sabha. This man bared his thigh, and called the Pandavas' wife to sit in his lap. His thigh should have been smashed that same day; but when Bheema sprang at Duryodhana, Yudhishtira stopped him. Which kshatriya can bear such an insult to his wife? That day, Bheema swore he would break Duryodhana's thigh and today he has kept his oath. A warrior must keep his word at any cost. That is what Bheema has done."

Balarama struggles against Krishna, but he cannot get free. "Balarama, you can't bear this one injustice against Duryodhana, if it is even that.

But you will forget all the sins of this evil one, all the provocation he has given the sons of Pandu, why, the very earth. You choose to take Bheema's slight fault by itself, as if it were a worse crime than all Duryodhana's crimes! Since this is how you feel, listen to what I have to say." Krishna's voice takes on an edge. "Even on the day Panchali was humiliated I could have killed Duryodhana and his brothers, and set Yudhishtira on the Kuru throne. But I did not interfere. Why, until the last moment, I did my best to avert the war. When I could not, I did not bear any arms but only drove Arjuna's horses.

You swore you would take no part in the war. You must keep your word. If you did not fight against evil, at least you must not fight for it. Let this sinner lie where he has fallen; it is not for you to avenge him. Your love for Duryodhana prevents you from seeing with clear eyes. The Pandavas are our cousins. They have suffered a great deal, and they have every right to some happiness. You must not harm them."

The threat to Bheema's life is very real. Now, Balarama seems to calm down a little. He does not struggle to free himself from Krishna any more. But he still stands glowering at Bheema, and Krishna continues, "The kali yuga has come to the world. Nowhere on earth shall pure dharma be found any more, but only mixed with adharma. The first nine days of the war were fought nobly. From the tenth day, the shadow of the kali fell over the battle. Day by day, the shadow grew and monstrous sins were committed on Kurukshetra. The fault is only time's. Evil and violence are the signs of the kali. Destiny fulfils herself darkly in the fourth yuga, and this is only its beginning." Krishna's eyes are shining, "I, for one, am convinced that the end justifies the means."

But Balarama is not; he says, "Keep your sophistry, Krishna: nothing will persuade me that what Bheema did today was dharma. Duryodhana was as much a mace-fighter as I am, and he has been killed treacherously. Let the world always speak of Bheema as a cheat, and of Duryodhana as a kshatriya. I am proud of my sishya Duryodhana, and ashamed of Bheema. I say that Duryodhana has fulfilled the yagna of war, which he undertook, nobly. He will find Devaloka for himself, and live there forever!"

Krishna smiles to hear his brother, but he is relieved that he has thought better of killing Bheema. When he is certain Balarama will not attack the Pandava, he releases him. Balarama goes up to Duryodhana and kneels beside him with a sob. He takes his pupil's hand tenderly, and bids him farewell. He cannot bear to watch his torment, and mounts his chariot and rides away from Samantapanchaka, without even looking at the Pandavas. Yudhishtira has tears in his eyes, and Bheema seems dazed.

Krishna heaves a sigh, and says cheerfully, "He has been away from Dwaraka for a long time. He will forget his anger when Revati gives him his first bowl of wine."

But Bheema stands crestfallen. After Balarama's tirade, even Arjuna, who reminded him of his oath during the duel, stands away from his brother. Krishna goes up and embraces Bheema fervently. He cries, "I am proud of you! Only the rare man fulfils even some of his oaths. You, Bheemasena, have kept all yours. I am so proud of you!"

Then, from a way off, Yudhishtira smiles at Bheema. With a cry, Bheema rushes to his brother and prostrates himself at his feet. "Bless me, my lord! All your enemies are dead. The long story of hatred has ended, and I lay the world at your feet. Panchali will not sleep on the floor any more. Bless me, my brother!"

Yudhishtira raises him up and embraces him. All the Pandavas and all those with them break into loud cries, of '*Jaya*'! Now everyone rushes to Bheema to hug him. Conches are blown, drums beaten; the name of Vayu's son resounds in that place.

With an inscrutable look in his eye, Krishna turns to Duryodhana. He says slowly, "We need not bother to kill this man, he is as good as dead. He was the worst sinner, and retribution has found him. He had many wise men to tell him what the way of dharma was. Time and again, he spurned their wisdom.

"How much poor Vidura begged him to mend his ways. Duryodhana would only listen to that serpent Shakuni. The time to pay has come, and he must pay alone. Look where he lies now, broken on the ground, yes, even he who was the greatest king, the most powerful man on earth. Let us leave him here to pay in full. He is just a dry log of wood now, not worth bothering with."

Duryodhana lies gasping in unbearable pain. But at what Krishna says he rears up on his palms like a cobra, and hisses, "Stop, you son of a sudra! You are not even a kshatriya or a king, that you dare speak to me like this. Wretched cowherd, you have been the death of me. You remembered Bheema's vow. He fought fairly, until you whispered in Arjuna's ear and he slapped his thighs."

There is untold hatred in his voice, "Black cowherd, son of Kamsa's slave, you caused this war by poisoning my cousins' hearts. And you dare call me a sinner? Who brought Shikhandi before Bheeshma, and made him lay down his bow? Who told Yudhishtira to lie to Drona that Aswatthama was dead? And the Acharya put down his weapon. You think I did not watch you, cowherd? I saw everything you did. Who turned day into night, and the unsuspecting Jayadratha was murdered? Who sacrificed the monster Ghatotkacha, so your precious Arjuna would not have to face Karna's Shakti? And who told Arjuna to shoot Karna down when he knelt to lift his chariot-wheel? You did, evil one, always you. It is your cunning and not their valour that won this war for the sons of Pandu. Without your plotting, Bheeshma, Drona and Karna could never have been killed. You may deceive the world, Krishna, but I know you. Of us all, you are the worst sinner!"

Krishna laughs in his face. "So now you would blame it all on me! But the truth, Duryodhana, is that your greed cost these millions their lives. The truth is that all your brothers and friends died because of you. Bheeshma, Drona, Karna and all the rest died because they fought for you, and for evil. Bheeshma should never have agreed to fight. Drona could have left Hastinapura and gone away. Karna knew you were in the wrong; he knew you would lose this war. But he loved you too much to abandon you."

His eyes are hard as diamonds, and Krishna continues, "You blame this war on me, Duryodhana? Have you perhaps forgotten how I came to Hastinapura before the war began? Have you forgotten how I begged you to make peace? Then you would not listen. Your greed held you firm. You would not part with five towns, why, you said you wouldn't give the Pandavas enough land to set on a needle's point. What you taste now is the fruit of the bitter tree of envy, which your father and your uncle Shakuni planted in your heart when you were a boy. The tree has matured, its fruit are ripe.

You speak so glibly of treachery. What about Abhimanyu, whom you cut down in the flower of his youth? Just for that crime you should die, again and again. Yudhishtira wastes his sympathy on you. I feel no pity for you; you have got what you deserve."

Despite his agony, a familiar sneer curls Duryodhana's lip, and a thin brow is still arched in disdain. Though his breath comes torturedly from him, he wheezes defiantly, "I have lived a full life. I have studied the Vedas. I have always been generous to anyone who came to me in need. I have been king of all this earth, and tasted her fruits to the full. I have trodden on my enemies' heads. I am a fortunate man, cowherd. I have lived a joyful life, and I look forward to a joyful after-life. Dying in this most sacred place, I will find the heaven where kshatriyas go who die in battle, and there my brothers and my Karna are waiting for me. As for the rest of you, you have years still to spend in this world of sorrow, this earth that is just a shadow of what it was."

His eyes are undimmed, glittering and fierce as ever. He pauses, his breath becomes more laboured with every moment. Painfully, he resumes, "As for Bheema stamping my head, I am past caring for that. In a short while, crows and vultures will feed on this head, and by what he did, his place shall be with the scavengers." With a final effort, he manages to say again, "I have died like a kshatriya. I will find swarga for myself!"

He sinks back on the ground, and lies writhing and gasping in savage pain. Then, out of the sky falls a shower of petals, like crystal fireflies on the dying Duryodhana! They fill Samantapanchaka with the fragrance of Devaloka, for the Gods themselves bless the Kaurava for his indomitable courage. Duryodhana's body may be broken, but not his spirit. The sky has grown lambent to honour the fallen kshatriya, and the Pandavas hang their heads to see that heaven seems to take their cousin's side.

Krishna turns on them in rage. "Of course Bheeshma and Drona and Karna were killed with deceit! Did you imagine for a moment that they could have been killed otherwise? They were the very acme of the warrior's prowess. You could never have beaten them fairly, let alone killed them. They lived upon the earth like Gods; not all your devastras, not Arjuna's archery or Bheema's strength could have brought those men down. Why, this serpent Duryodhana could never be killed in a fair battle.

"Listen to me now, and hear me well. Years ago in the Kamyaka vana, I wiped the tears from Draupadi's eyes and I swore to her I would bring death to those that had tormented her. Yudhishtira, you did not seem to mind that your wife had been humiliated in the sabha of Hastinapura.

You only spoke of the dharma or the adharma of what happened. You allowed these beasts to drag her into that court, to revile her, to try to strip her naked. And you would not let Bheema kill them, as they deserved, because you said it was not dharma.

"It seems that to you there were other things more important than Panchali's tears. But to me, Yudhishtira, there was nothing in the world more momentous than her tears. I swore I would kill those that had made her cry. Bheeshma and Drona never raised a hand, never spoke a word to help her; for that, they have died. I believe in only one thing: the tears of the oppressed must be wiped, and justice given to them. Draupadi could hardly help herself against the men who abused her, and not even her husbands were sure that they would redress what she had endured. But not I. I said I would kill the devils that made her cry, and I have kept my word. I have no doubts, no regrets. I see clearly where dharma lay in this war, and where adharma.

"As for the sin of the deceit we used to kill our enemies, let it fall on my head! I care nothing for it. I will bear those crimes gladly for the sons of Pandu, because they are my very life to me. If we had not used some judicious deceit, this war would have been lost. You would all have died. Duryodhana would still sit upon the throne in Hastinapura, and the earth would be plunged in a rule of hell. For me, nothing could be worse than that."

At what he says, the Pandavas feel as if a burden has been taken from them. They breathe more easily, and guilt lifts away quite magically from their hearts. Krishna says, "The sun has sunk to the western mountain, and night is upon us. Come, let us go back."

They turn and walk away from Sampantapanchaka. Duryodhana, lord of the earth, lies alone in the gathering dusk. His blood and seed have spilt together on to holy ground, and pain sears through his every limb. He lies dying, with not a living soul at his side.

BOOK TEN

Sauptika Parva

AUM, I bow down to Narayana, the most exalted Nara, and to the Devi Saraswati, and say *Jaya*!

ONE

In Hastinapura

THE WAR IS OVER: EIGHTEEN DAYS THAT HAVE BEEN LIKE EIGHTEEN years, longer. The Pandavas ride back to Kurukshetra. Custom demands they should enter the vanquished enemy's camp; and they do now, blasting on their conches. The Panchajanya and the Devadatta resound above the rest. Krishna is the most cheerful one in the company. More than anything, he does not want the sons of Pandu dejected at what happened in Samantapanchaka. He does not want their moment of victory dimmed by remorse.

They find the Kaurava camp, which had once teemed with eleven aksauhinis, deserted. Nothing stirs save a twilight breeze, which murmurs endlessly about all the killing and dying on yawning Kurukshetra. The last shafts of the sun light that desolation with scarlet and gold. As soon as they arrive, Krishna turns to Arjuna and says, "Climb down from the chariot, bring the Gandiva and your quivers with you."

Arjuna is puzzled, but does as Krishna asks. Krishna puts down his whip and reins, and he, too, alights from the white ratha that Agni once gave Arjuna in the Khandava vana. The Pandavas stand watching curiously. The moment Krishna climbs down there is a flash of light above the chariot, on the flag with Hanuman's form. They see the immortal vanara fly out, and vanish into the sky! The banner is empty of its emblem. That is not all: the white chariot bursts into flames; it burns like tinder. The gandharva horses are ablaze, and in a few moments, all that remains of chariot and steeds is a mound of ashes.

Arjuna cries to Krishna, "My Lord! What is this? Krishna, I don't understand."

Krishna's face is stern, as he says, "Their purpose in the world is served. Arjuna, your chariot was struck by the brahmastras of Drona and Karna, by Aswatthama's agneyastra. The truth is that both chariot and horses were consumed long ago; but as long as I sat at your chariot-head, and drove your horses, they did not perish. Now we have no further use for them, and they are ashes. All things in this world exist for a purpose; when their purpose is served, they cease to be."

Krishna's face softens. More gently now, he says, "And so it is with men, Arjuna. Each man is sent out on this mysterious journey called life, and he comes into the world to achieve a purpose. Once his mission is over, the earth has no more need of him. It is so with all of us: even me. I have come into the world for a mission, and as soon my mission is complete, I will leave." He sees the look of alarm on Arjuna's face. "My tasks are not yet over, and neither are yours or your brothers'. We have much to do still. But don't grieve for your chariot and horses: they accomplished what they were created for, and now they have gone."

Krishna turns to Yudhishtira. He takes his hand and says, "You have won the war, and I am proud of you. It is the custom for the victors to spend the night outside their defeated enemies' camp. Let us spend the night somewhere in these woods."

Yudhishtira is deeply moved by the miracle of the chariot. He says fervently to Krishna, "My Lord, we have won the war only because of you. Now I understand what Vyasa Muni once said to me, 'Where there is dharma, Krishna is. And where Krishna is, there is victory.'"

Krishna says, "You and your brothers fought heroically. You deserve to have victory."

They ride a short way, and decide to stay beside the river flowing nearby. They have just settled under some trees, when Krishna sees a shadow on Yudhishtira's face. He asks, "Why are you distraught?"

Yudhishtira has turned pale. He says slowly, "By your grace we have won the war, and the earth is ours now. But, Krishna, I fear the wrath of Gandhari. She is a bhakta and a righteous queen, and she is a mother who has lost all her sons. She could burn the world with her grief, and she may curse us, when she hears how Duryodhana died. I beg you, go to Hastinapura and pacify Gandhari."

Krishna is thoughtful. He says softly, "You are right. Gandhari must not curse you: there are others to bear her wrath. I will go at once." Krishna has his own chariot fetched, and sets out for the Kuru capital.

Meanwhile, hiding among the trees in Samantapanchaka, Sanjaya saw Duryodhana fall. Shocked and weeping, he flew back to Hastinapura. His arms raised above his head, he came wailing into the palace and Dhritarashtra's presence. Dhritarashtra sat with Gandhari and his daughters-in-law around him. Vidura was there, as well.

Sanjaya ran in and cried, "My lord! Fate has robbed us of everything we had." Then he could not go on, but sobbed like a child. Water was fetched for him, and when he drank, he grew calmer. He managed to say, "The war is over, and we have lost. Shalya and Shakuni were killed, Uluka is dead, and…" he broke down again.

Vidura asked, "What of Duryodhana?"

Sanjaya cried as if he had lost his own son, "Bheema felled Duryodhana in a gada-yuddha! He lies dying at Samantapanchaka."

Gandhari slumped to the floor from her throne. Dhritarashtra swayed where he sat, and he swooned. The world spun before Vidura's eyes, and he clutched the arms of his chair. Duryodhana's queens and his brothers' wives set up a lament, many of them fell unconscious. The blind king revived in a short while, and then fainted again; and thus, twice or thrice. The palace maids came to Gandhari. They sprinkled water on her face, and held sharp salts under her nose. She lay as if she was dead.

After a while, Gandhari and Dhritarashtra revived, and poor Vidura did his best to comfort them. Vyasa arrived, opportunely; even he could hardly quieten the surging tide of grief. Gandhari wailed hysterically, beating her breast, and Dhritarashtra sobbed and sobbed.

It is now that Krishna appears in the Kuru palace and is shown into the sabha.

Tears well in his eyes when he sees Dhritarashtra and Gandhari in their sorrow. He comes forward to take their hands. The presence of the Avatara infuses their hearts with mysterious strength. Full of mercy, Krishna sits near that king and queen, speaking tenderly to them, stroking their hands, their faces, as if he was comforting two children. Gradually, their sobbing subsides; sorrow's storm blows more quietly in their aged bodies. In their moment of crisis, they clearly feel the love of the Dark One, transcending their grief, transcending everything: a timeless, unshakeable love. Like children with a father, they let him console them with his gentle words, his healing touch.

When they are calmer, Krishna says to Gandhari, "Do you remember the day I last came to Hastinapura? I came on a mission of peace, and Duryodhana plotted to take me his hostage. I have not forgotten how you stopped him then, Gandhari. Do you remember what you said to your son? You said, 'Where there is dharma, there is victory.' So it has turned out, O Queen.

"Today, also, I have come on a mission of peace. I have come to beg you not to blame the Pandavas for what has happened. Yudhishtira grieves that he has caused you such sorrow. You know how much the sons of Pandu wanted to prevent this war. They implored you to give them just five towns, and they would be content. But Duryodhana was adamant. I want you to recall clearly that it was not the Pandavas, but your son who was responsible for the war, and all the tragedy it brought. You must not be tempted to blame Pandu's sons for Duryodhana's sins. They have suffered enough for a lifetime; you must welcome them home with love. Most of all, Gandhari, you must not turn your wrath on them. It will not be dharma if you curse them for a war they never wanted."

He pauses to let what he says sink in, then, continues, "You don't need me to tell you in what esteem Yudhishtira holds you both. Now, there is no Kuru prince left, save a son of Pandu, to sit upon the ancient throne of Hastinapura. I beg you again, Gandhari, do not hate Kunti's sons. You are so pure that you can consume the very earth with your anger. All will truly be lost if you turn your fury on the Pandavas."

Gandhari's shoulders shake, and she says in confession, "I am glad you came, Krishna. No one but you could have calmed me: for my reason had left me, and I would have done some harm to Kunti's sons. Truly, you know how to speak to the heart. Grief's rage has left me, and I see clearly again. I will be just to the Pandavas. I will not harm them."

Krishna takes her hands. Gandhari breaks down again and sobs piteously. The grief she has held behind the floodgates of anger flows from her, and the Avatara's compassion washes over the queen.

Gandhari composes herself, and says, "With my sons all dead, I have only you to comfort me. Don't abandon me, Krishna."

The Dark One sits with them for a while longer, consoling them with his presence of grace. Suddenly, a premonition of evil seizes him. He divines a sinister plot that has taken root in the mind of a brahmana warrior. Krishna rises, and says quickly, "The Pandavas are in danger. Give me your leave, I must go at once!"

Dhritarashtra whispers, "Hurry! You must protect my nephews at any cost, they are all this kingdom has left."

Krishna flies back to Yudhishtira and his brothers in the Jaitra, his chariot of the air. He is relieved to find them safe beside the river, under the trees where he left them. They have Satyaki with them, but all the others have returned to the Pandava camp. Krishna tells them how Dhritarashtra and Gandhari were pacified; they were waiting for their nephews to return to Hastinapura. He also tells them of the danger he had sensed from Aswatthama.

"You are in mortal peril. We must be on our guard tonight."

TWO

The white owl's lesson

Sanjaya cannot help himself: he has to go back to Samantapanchaka where Duryodhana lies dying. It is twilight when he arrives, and, peering carefully through the trees, he sees the Kaurava is alone. He lies writhing on the ground, and sharp hisses of breath escape him, when the pain is unendurable. Duryodhana rolls from side to side, he is covered in mud. Tears course trails down his ashen face, and he sobs pitiably with torment.

Sanjaya thinks his heart will break, seeing him like that: Duryodhana who had been lord of all he surveyed, master of the earth. No one had been as powerful or as wealthy as the man who now lies in the dirt, his very manhood crushed, and no one beside him, as he dies slowly in the wilderness. Here lies a king whose feet had never felt the paving of a street; one whose palace had been like a God's temple. Sanjaya thinks of how, once, Duryodhana would pass through his city: the glittering retinue that went with him, and he riding his caparisoned elephant like Indra himself on Airavata. Where is all that majesty now? How pitiless fate is, that she lays the sovereigns of the earth so low. Everything lost, the Kaurava lies wriggling in the dust.

Duryodhana presses his palms hard against the earth, as agony rips through him. He grits his teeth, his chest heaves, and now and again a helpless cry is torn from his lips when the pain crests. At times, his body twitches in spasms, at others he shivers uncontrollably. During brief remissions, he shakes his head and growls at his helplessness. Sanjaya runs forward and kneels beside his dying prince.

Duryodhana sees Sanjaya, and at once, he grows calm. He lies back with a sigh, and Sanjaya takes his hand. Slowly, with an intense effort, Duryodhana speaks to him, "Sanjaya, what a loving soul you are that you have come back to me. My friend, I am in hell, but my life refuses to leave this broken body."

Sanjaya's tears fall onto his hands. Duryodhana smiles wanly, and says, "Don't cry for me, Sanjaya. I am very near swarga now. But it seems I have to pay for my sins, and be purified before I reach the blessed place."

A livid spasm tears through him again, and he gasps. In a while, it seems to pass, and he says weakly, "I can hardly bear it. Look at me, Sanjaya. This is I, Duryodhana, who just a few days ago had Bheeshma, Drona, Karna, Kripa, Shalya, Kritavarman, Dusasana and a thousand kshatriyas to fight for me. I was the lord of eleven aksauhinis, and I was so certain I would win the war. Look at me now."

Duryodhana weeps. Speaking exhausts him, and he falls silent for a while. Then he says, "Sanjaya, will you do something for me?"

"Anything, my lord!" sobs Sanjaya.

"Find Acharya Kripa, Kritavarman and Aswatthama. Tell them that Bheema struck me down with a low blow. Tell them I am still alive, and I want to see them before I die. Then go to Hastinapura and tell Dhritarashtra and Gandhari what happened. Tell my mother that her son died like a kshatriya. Say I did not run from battle, but fought to the last, my head held high. Tell her I was happy as I died, and I would find Devaloka for myself. Tell her, good Sanjaya, I died without any regret."

Again he subsides, gasping. His hand goes limp in Sanjaya's, and he whispers, "Go now, my friend, send my three warriors to me quickly."

Then, in sweet relief from his ordeal, he has fainted. Sanjaya runs through the forest, calling to the three warriors as loudly as he dares. They are not far and seeking Duryodhana themselves, since they do not know where he went from the Dwaipayana lake. Sanjaya tells them everything that happened, and shows them the way to Samantapanchaka. He says, choking, "I have a message from Duryodhana to take to Hastinapura. And I cannot bear to see him as he is."

Sanjaya turns back to the city. Word of Duryodhana's fall has spread like fire in Hastinapura, and some of the people come out into the wilds to see him. But they find him unconscious, and growing afraid of the jungle as night draws near, they turn back home. One tale tells how they bring Duryodhana's youngest son to see his dying father. The Kaurava cannot even take the child on to his lap, where he once called Panchali to sit, and waves him away in misery. Though his pain is intolerable, Duryodhana refuses to be carried back to Hastinapura.

Kripa, Kritavarman and Aswatthama find their king alone, lying there like the sun fallen onto the earth, the disc of the full moon shrouded in a fog, or a great tiger struck down by hunters, still raging. He is conscious, his brow furrowed, squirming on the ground, crying out at times. Aswatthama kneels beside him and takes his hands. When he sees the bloody ruin below Duryodhana waist, dizziness overcomes Drona's son.

When the others revive him, Aswatthama clutches Duryodhana's hands and cries, "What has this world come to that a king like you, O lord of the earth, lie alone in your final hour? It is a vile world, and nothing in it is permanent."

Duryodhana manages a wry smile, and, his voice lower than a whisper, says, "All things in this world only die, Aswatthama, and this is the end written for me in fate's book. But don't grieve for me, my friends, I am not sorry my life ends here. Remember that as soon as breath leaves this body, I will be in Devaloka. And in heaven, my brothers and my Karna are waiting for me. I see everything clearly now. All this is fate, and there is no use blaming anyone for it."

His chest heaves again, in mortal exhaustion. Duryodhana wipes his tears and brushes aside the dust-matted hair that has fallen over his face.

Aswatthama blazes up in anger. "The sons of Pandu are the worst sinners! They cover themselves in a cloak of dharma, but look what they have done to you. They killed my father dishonourably, and they have done the same to you. Duryodhana, just say the word, and this very night I will kill the Pandavas. I will kill them under Krishna's eyes! They are a plague upon the earth, they must not be left alive."

Duryodhana's eyes fill. He had always thought that Aswatthama was partial to the Pandavas, and now here he is swearing to kill them for his sake. The Kaurava summons the last of his strength, and says to Kripa, "Acharya, bring me water from the river."

When Kripa complies, Duryodhana says, "Sprinkle Aswatthama with the water, make him the new Senapati of my army."

Sadly, solemnly, Kripa performs the ritual; he intones the mantras to make Aswatthama supreme commander of the Kuru army. Aswatthama rises: his face dripping, his eyes shining as if he has been given command of a million men. He kneels again beside Duryodhana. The dying Kaurava lays his hand on his warrior's head. Aswatthama clasps him, and whispers fiercely, "I will not fail you, my lord. Revenge shall be ours tonight!"

The other two embrace their king, and then leave him there, alone once more. As night falls, they make their way south, tiredly towards the Pandava camp. This camp is built on the hem of some woods. Aswatthama and his army of two arrive in those woods. They find a clear, lotus-laden pool and quench their thirst from it. They move on towards the edge of the trees, and hear sounds of celebration coming from the Pandava camp. Too tired even to think of attacking the enemy tonight, they retreat deeper into the woods, and find a fine old tree, an immense nyagrodha with a thousand branches, under which to rest. No sooner have their heads touched the ground, after saying their evening prayers, than Kripa and Kritavarman are asleep.

Aswatthama cannot sleep. He lies under the tree, his eyes wide in the deepening twilight. His mind works feverishly, plotting revenge. But no plausible scheme rises into it, and he lies frustrated. The sun sinks below the asta mountains, and night, mother of the universe, arrives. Aswatthama's gaze ranges over the dense branches overhead, and he sees them adorned by so many crows' nests: like large fruit among the leaves. The dark birds have all come to roost for the night, and they are asleep. Aswatthama's eyelids are growing heavy, when he sees a flash of white wings in the darkness. It seems a shimmering spirit from another world has flown down into this one. Peering up intently, Aswatthama sees it is no spirit that has alighted in the branches above him. It is an immense owl, and when he can see its head clearly, he sees it is a terrible bird. Its green eyes flash like cold lamps in the dark.

Aswatthama lies rapt. He has the strangest feeling that the scene unfolding above him is an omen. Once it has flown down into the tree, the white owl gives the most chilling screech, and attacks the sleeping crows. The owl is a blizzard of beak and talons; it seems to be everywhere in that tree at once. The poor crows hardly have time to awake, before the marauding owl savages them. Raked and bloody, their black bodies fall dead out of the branches. The hunting owl brings such terror, and the crows are taken so unawares, they perish in the onslaught hardly knowing what killed them.

When it has killed all the crows, the owl pauses to clean its beak and claws against the bark of the tree. Its huge eyes glow like moon-lenses in the night, and the warrior below clearly sees the glint of satisfaction in them. Aswatthama wonders what the crows had done to the owl for it to wreak such revenge. The next moment, the great bird spreads it wings, and truly like an unearthly spirit, it flies off and is lost in the night.

Suddenly, Aswatthama knows what he must do. In a frenzy, he wakes the others. Thinking they are being attacked they spring up, drawing their swords. It is only Aswatthama, trembling with excitement, burning in the night.

Kripa says sleepily, "What has possessed you now, Aswatthama? Go back to sleep, child."

His nephew cries, "I cannot sleep! I know how to have revenge on the Pandavas."

"What do you mean?"

Aswatthama's eyes gleam insanely. "We must kill them when they are asleep! We must attack them now, when they don't expect us."

Kritavarman and Kripa gasp. Kripa cries, "How can you even think such a thing?"

"A sovereign of the earth, a master of eleven aksauhinis, lies dying by himself: his manhood shattered by cowardly Bheema. How else, uncle, do you suggest that we avenge him? The Pandavas have won this war with guile. Now we must also fight them with deceit. There is no other way."

Kripa says, "A warrior must be brave, but he must also be virtuous. You must remember Duryodhana was no king of dharma himself. He was greedy and ruthless. He humiliated the Pandavas. He cheated them out of everything they owned and banished them for thirteen years. Still, they sued for peace until the last moment. But Duryodhana was unrelenting. We must not take his death out of its context, or forget everything he did to the sons of Pandu. And as for the manner in which Bheema struck him down, it was only as he swore he would. Perhaps you are right that the gada-yuddha was not the occasion to do it. That isn't cause enough for us to commit the crime you want to."

But Aswatthama is adamant. "Was the way they killed my father, their guru, dharma? The time for dharma has passed. This is the time for revenge."

"And we will seek revenge, openly. We will challenge the Pandavas tomorrow, and fight them to the death. That will be honourable, and fate will smile on us. Yours is a dastardly plan, my son. I beg you, don't even think of such a sin."

Aswatthama is past listening to reason. "I have sworn to Duryodhana that I will kill the Pandavas. I am his Senapati now. This is the only way I can keep my word to him."

Kripa says, "I am tired, and I cannot think clearly. Let us seek Dhritarashtra's counsel, Queen Gandhari's, and the wise Vidura's, before we do anything we might regret."

Aswatthama says, "I have made up my mind, and I mean to do this thing tonight." A fearful smile touches his lips. "It is their first night of rest after the war. The Pandavas will be asleep. They would have taken off their armour, and be lost in dreams. They will never wake up again."

Again, Kripa says, "You are so tired and sad that you don't realize what you are saying. Sleep now, Aswatthama; tomorrow we will fight the Pandavas together."

"Sleep! How can a man who is in the grip of anger or desire, anxiety or sorrow, sleep? I am churned by all four! I will sleep only after I have killed the sons of Pandu. If you won't come with me, I will go alone. Farewell."

He strides away towards his chariot. He has not gone ten paces when Kripa and Kritavarman cry after him, "Wait! We will come with you."

They realize that it is later than they imagined. The kali yuga is upon them, and the time for dharma is past. They are all that remain of Duryodhana's army; from now, they will have to act together, whatever they did, or they would die. The last three warriors of Duryodhana's numberless legions ride in the pitched night to avenge their fallen king.

THREE

The savage camp

RIDING THROUGH THE DARKNESS ACROSS KURUKSHETRA, THE THREE warriors approach the Pandava camp. Aswatthama lets Kripa and Kritavarman down near the main gate. He says, "See no one escapes this way."

He rides off into the night. He means to find another way in. As he goes, the dark wind in his face, suddenly a rakshasa looms in his path, his hundred strangely beautiful eyes glowing red, round his waist a tiger-skin dripping fresh blood, and the skin of a black buck covering his radiant chest. A writhing serpent is his sacred thread, and his many arms hold aloft diverse weapons. Flames issue from his fanged maw. Aswatthama looses a few arrows at the demon. The rakshasa yawns open his mouth and swallows those shafts. Aswatthama summons the rathashakti. The apparition swallows that fiery missile as well. Leaping down from his chariot, Aswatthama draws his sword, golden-hafted and its blade the colour of the sky; but it vanishes from his hand, into the demon's body like a mongoose into its hole! So does the great mace he seizes up next.

Aswatthama thinks this is no ordinary rakshasa; it makes no move to come any nearer, or to attack him. Drona's son folds his hands and stands on one foot. He prays to Siva, by whose grace he was born. Abruptly, the rakshasa vanishes, and in its place, a golden altar appears before the brahmana. In moments, all sorts of strange spirits materialize from that altar.

Some have three heads, some no head at all. Some are naked, pale phalluses erect; others wear tiger-skin. Some have three eyes, and others just one. Some have four and five arms; some have tails. Some are minotaurian, others have bull's heads and men's limbs, and still others are indescribable, for they have no human feature, or any bestial one. Many have the complexion of the lotus and they carry all kinds of weapons. Yet, these weird beings do not threaten Aswatthama in any way, only sing and dance bizarrely before him. The Siva-bhakta knows these extraordinary creatures are his Lord's ganas, come to announce their master.

The golden altar blazes up in flames. Bracing himself, Aswatthama climbs the steps that lead to the vedi. He cries, "Lord, I offer myself to you! I am born in the line of Angiras, and I beg you to accept me as the yagnapasu." and is about to step into the flames, when a light illumines heaven and earth, and Siva stands before his devotee. The God wears deerskin; he is three-eyed, irradiant, and carries his trisula. Matted jata covers his head, the crescent-moon peeps out from his topknot and the Ganga glimmers there. Aswatthama falls on his face to worship that vision.

Siva says, "Krishna is my finest bhakta, and so far I protected the Panchalas for his sake. But the time of their lives has run out. Here, take this sword, Aswatthama, and may your enemies perish."

In a daze, Aswatthama takes the shining sword from awesome Sankara, and the Lord vanishes. Just the ineffable fragrance of him lingers on the midnight air. Rising from where he knelt, Aswatthama stalks into the Pandava camp, the sword a long flame in his hand. To his right and left, unseen rakshasas march. He peers into the first tent he comes to in the dark, and dimly sees Dhrishtadyumna lying asleep on a white bed, on satin sheets scented with dhupa. Aswatthama steals into the tent.

For a moment, he stands staring at the sleeping Panchala prince. His lips curl, his eyes blaze, and then, with a screech like the hunting owl's, he lashes out with a kick at his father's killer. Dhrishtadyumna is startled awake and Drona's son is at him. Dhrishtadyumna tries to get up, but Aswatthama seizes his long hair, flings him down on the ground and begins to kick him relentlessly: in his stomach, his groin, his face, again and again. Dhrishtadyumna curls up in agony. In a flash, Aswatthama rips the string from the Panchala's bow lying nearby. He plants his knees on Dhrishtadyumna's chest, and quick as rage, winds the bowstring around his throat and throttles him. Dhrishtadyumna's eyes bulge from his head, his tongue lolls out of his mouth. He grips his attacker's hands and manages to gasp, "Don't kill me like this! Kill me with an arrow like a kshatriya, or I won't reach swarga."

Aswatthama's face is a mask, its eyes slit in hatred. Drona's son, the Panchala's boyhood friend, hisses, "You killed your own guru! swarga is not for men like you. I have come to send you to hell. You will be damned forever, and that is what you deserve."

Still throttling him with the bowstring, Aswatthama drags Dhrishtadyumna around the tent, kicking him, killing him in the most brutal way. Long after life has left the fire-prince's body, Aswatthama continues to savage his corpse. At last he stands panting above the dead Dhrishtadyumna, and his eyes gleam in satisfaction.

Aswatthama takes up Siva's sword he had set down so he could kill that kshatriya with his bare hands. Now he goes through the rest of the Pandava camp as the white owl did among the sleeping crows. Aswatthama slaughters the other Panchalas, Shikhandi and his brothers. He comes to another tent and sees Draupadi's sons asleep. They are hardly more than children. The brahmana enters stealthily and, covering their mouths so they did not cry out, he cuts their throats or plunges his sword into their hearts, killing them before they awake. He finds Yuddhamanyu and Uttamaujas, and kills them*.

Meanwhile, Kripa and Kritavarman have set fire to the camp from three sides, and the tents blaze up like yagna flames in the dark. Roused by terrified screams in the feral night, the other sleeping soldiers wake up and try to run from the rakshasa attacking them at the midnight hour. Like Yamadutas, death's messengers, Kripa and Kritavarman cut them down at the only gate.

Aswatthama stalks that camp like Yama himself** His roars drown the screams of those he murders with Siva's sword, flashing like a moon-sliver in his hand. Drona's son attacks the elephants and horses that

---

* The KMG text describes several duels in this section, as also women wailing upon finding their husbands being slaughtered.

** Also, Death appears as an old black-skinned woman, her eyes and mouth bloody, wearing crimson garlands and unguents, clad in a single red rag, chanting a dismal dirge. She ties the spirits of the slain men and beasts with a cord, and leads them away into the next world.

stampede through the camp, felling them at will, and is drenched in their innocent blood. Whinnying and trumpeting in terror, those beasts plunge away from the demented avenger; and on their panicstricken careen, they trample a hundred Pandava soldiers who try to escape Drona's dreadful son.

Soon, the three Kaurava warriors meet again at the gate. Lit by the flames of the burning camp, their faces are wet with blood. Their mission is accomplished; their macabre sacrifice is complete: every man in the Pandava camp is dead, and most of their beasts. Scavengers descend on the camp and begin to feast. Rakshasas and pisachas arrive to quaff the flowing blood, gorging on flesh, fat, and sucking marrow out of the bones of the corpses, they dance in joy. Drunk with murder, Aswatthama, Kripa and Kritavarman embrace one another, roaring at the stars. They climb into the waiting chariot and ride back to Samantapanchaka like an evil, three-headed wind.

Duryodhana lies alone where he fell. He keeps his mace close beside him, because the night has flowered with a hundred baleful eyes. The jackal and hyena packs have discovered him and every moment they pad closer. He roars and screeches at them, and they retreat. But in a few moments, they come snuffling forward again, with low growls, and the hyenas' mad cackling. The pain in Duryodhana's loins threatens to make him faint at any moment, and he knows that will be the end: the scavengers will tear him apart.

Then, the animal eyes vanish as if by magic. It takes the Kaurava a few moments longer than it has the jackals and hyenas to hear horses flying towards him through the night, bearing Aswatthama and his army of two. Even before they stop and alight, Duryodhana senses their excitement. Next moment, the three are at his side. He sees they are covered in blood, and their eyes shine.

Smiling, Kripa says, "My lord, I see you mean to take your gada with you into Devaloka: a friend who remained faithful to the last!"

Aswatthama takes his king's hand fervidly, and cries, "I did not fail you, Duryodhana! I killed all your enemies tonight. The Panchalas and Dhrishtadyumna are dead; Draupadi's sons are slain. What remained of the Pandavas' army is dead, their camp burned to the ground. But I did not find Yudhishtira and his brothers there, and I did not find

Satyaki or Krishna. Of the two forces that faced each other on Kurukshetra, my lord, from your army just Acharya Kripa, Kritavarman and I still live; and from the enemy's, only the five Pandavas, Krishna and Satyaki."

By now, Duryodhana is gasping for his last breath. A faint smile touches his lips, and there is a glitter of triumph in his hooded eyes. He manages to whisper to his final Senapati, "Aswatthama, you have done what Bheeshma, Drona and Karna could not! I am proud of you. May God bless you."

Duryodhana's eyes are full of death, and his three warriors hold his hands tightly. Their king breathes, "I am going now, my friends, we will meet again in swarga."

Then he has gone, and peace suffuses his dead face. At last, the tumult and anguish of that great and terrible life have ended. One by one, his warriors embrace their dead king and, their hearts full, they walk away from him. Once more, the night sprouts hungry eyes, as the scavenger packs arrive for their feast. But then, unearthly protection is upon Duryodhana's corpse. It begins to glow so eerily in the dark that the scavengers back away from it, and run yelping into the night.

It is told that the moment life left Duryodhana's body, Sanjaya's eyes lost the miraculous sight with which they had been blessed so he could relate the events of the war of dharma to Dhritarashtra.

The most terrible morning of the Pandavas' lives dawns. They are roused by a man who comes howling to the tree under which they spent the night. It is Dhrishtadyumna's sarathy, the only one to have escaped Aswatthama's carnage: by pretending to be dead. He cries to Yudhishtira, "They are all dead, my lord! Aswatthama killed them in the night. Your sons are slain, the Panchalas are killed, my lords Shikhandi and Dhrishtadyumna have been murdered!"

Yudhishtira falls where he stands, and Satyaki catches him. For a moment, the other Pandavas stand turned to stone. It is the hour of atonement: for they, too, have killed thousands on Kurukshetra. Shock rages through their bodies, maddening them, and then, mercifully, each one of them faints. Even Krishna seems shaken.

When Yudhishtira revives, in a low voice he says, "We have been vanquished in our victory." He tells Nakula, "Go and fetch Draupadi."

They ride to the camp, and see the desolation Aswatthama has made of it: ashes everywhere, and bloody corpses, their faces peaceless even in death, because they died so horribly. They see their sons lying side by side, some still on the charred remains of their beds, other having fallen off when Aswatthama killed them in their sleep. But the sight Yudhishtira can bear least is of Dhrishtadyumna, strangled, his swollen tongue protruding lewdly from his lips, his eyes staring in terror, his body and face covered in purple welts. This was how the splendid fire-prince had died at last, the kshatriya who had been their Senapati since the war began, without whom they could have never won the dharma yuddha. Yudhishtira begins to sob. Satyaki and Bheema sit mutely beside their friend's mangled corpse.

Arjuna walks around the horrific camp. When he sees the corpses of Uttamaujas and Yuddhamanyu, who rode at his chariot-wheels all these days, he breaks down. They hear the sound of a chariot driving up. Nakula has returned with Draupadi.

The Pandavas stand helpless, as Panchali is helped down from the chariot. She takes a few hesitant steps, then, sees her sons and collapses. When she regains her senses, hysteria has its way with her: her screams ring through the tragic morning. She beats her breast, tears her hair, and cries out her sons' names, her murdered brothers' names. She screams at Yudhishtira, "Are you content now, that you have won the earth by sacrificing your sons?"

She falls across the body of each of her boys, kissing their faces, touching their wounds that smear her in dried blood, like sacramental kumkum, and whimpering like a wild mother that has lost her young. Then, suddenly, she grows ominously quiet. Like a cobra uncoiling, she rises.

She says to Yudhishtira, "I will not eat again until Aswatthama is killed. I will die in this place."

She sits down again, and her husbands know she means to do exactly what she has said. Yudhishtira tries to pacify her. "Your brothers and your sons died heroes, and they have found swarga for themselves. How can you sit here in prayopavesha, Panchali? Aswatthama has escaped into the jungle, who can tell when we will find him?"

"I want revenge for my sons and my brothers, or I will die here."

Yudhishtira cries, "Even if we do find Aswatthama and kill him, how will you believe we have?"

"He wears a red jewel on his head. Bring me that stone, and I will be content. Losing it will be worse than death for him." Yet again, she turns to her husband she relies on whenever there is violence to be done, the one she can most easily persuade. She turns to Bheema and says, "Bheema, my love, you are the only one who will help me. You must do this for me!"

That is all it takes. Bheema swells up, his eyes turn red, and he cries, "I will bring you the jewel. Nakula, come with me, be my sarathy."

Bheema sets out to find Aswatthama. Yudhishtira sits near Draupadi. He puts his arms around her and does his best to comfort her. She sobs against his chest.

Krishna says, "Aswatthama has the brahmasirsa. He has left dharma behind him, and he will stop at nothing any more. If he uses that astra, Bheema will not live. Drona once gave the brahmasirsa to Arjuna, but he did not trust Aswatthama with it: for it can make ashes of the earth in its four fires. But Aswatthama did not stop begging Drona, and at last the father relented and gave his son the astra too.

"I can never forget how Aswatthama flattered me once for a whole morning, and I wondered where his flattery was leading. In a while, he asked me for the Sudarshana Chakra*! Bheema doesn't know Aswatthama has the brahmasirsa. Arjuna, come with me, we must go after him."

They climb into Krishna's Jaitra, and set out. When they are out of the others' sight, Krishna says to his sarathy, "Daruka, fly!"

The wonderful horses take to the air, and rise above the trees. With unerring instinct, they fly straight to where Bheema has already found Aswatthama, who is with Vyasa and some other rishis on the banks of the Ganga.

---

* Finally, Krishna gives it to him, but Aswatthama cannot hold it up. Krishna then asks him why he wanted the Chakra, and he replies, "I meant to fight you with it, Krishna."

FOUR

Aswatthama's jewel

MEANWHILE, DHRITARASHTRA IS INCONSOLABLE. HE IS PLUNGED IN dark sorrow, crying without pause. Sanjaya says to him, "My lord, you mustn't grieve like this. You know there is no one to console you any more."

The blind king says, "I have nothing to live for any more."

He slides down onto the floor and lies sobbing there. Vidura kneels beside his brother, and tries to comfort him. "Your sons all died kshatriyas' deaths, Dhritarashtra. You must not cry for those that have found heaven for themselves. Come, rouse yourself for the tasks that lie ahead."

But Dhritarashtra has lost all his sons. Patiently, Vidura speaks to him, telling him about dharma, about life and death, that the soul never dies.

Hoping to provoke him out of his grief, Sanjaya says, "My lord, we told you long ago the course you chose would lead to doom. All that has happened is of your own making. A hundred kings have died for your son's sake. You must come to Kurukshetra, to ensure their bodies are brought away and cremated. The last rites for them must be performed with honour."

Finally, it is only when Vyasa arrives and adds his voice to the others', that Dhritarashtra acquiesces, "Prepare my chariot, Sanjaya. Let Gandhari, Kunti and the other women of the palace ride with us."

Soon, all the women gather on the palace steps. Their hair loose, crying, all of them clad in widows' white, and no gold or jewels adorning their bodies, these women whom not even the sun has seen now walk and ride through the streets of Hastinapura. Only Vidura remembers another day, thirteen years ago, when the Pandavas were exiled: Draupadi's curse on the Kaurava wives has come to pass. The brahmanas of Hastinapura walk before the king's chariot, chanting the Rudra hymns aloud, exactly as Dhaumya had done thirteen years ago. Vidura rides silently with the mourning procession.

Then, three wild-looking warriors in a chariot appear before the king and his train. It is Kripa, Aswatthama and Kritavarman, blood still on them from the night's exploit. Kripa says, "My lord, your army is razed, we three are the only survivors."

Kripa comes to Gandhari and says, "Your sons all died noble deaths, they have found Devaloka. Last night we attacked the Pandava camp to avenge Duryodhana, and Aswatthama killed all the Panchalas and Draupadi's sons. The Pandavas are out hunting us, we dare not stay in the open any longer."

They ride away at once. Kunti falls as if someone had cut her down with a sword. Vidura tries to console her, but all her grandsons have been murdered. Kripa, Kritavarman and Aswatthama ride some way into the jungle, and decide to part. They embrace one another, then Kripa rides home to Hastinapura, Kritavarman to Dwaraka, and Aswatthama will seek refuge in Vyasa's hermitage on the banks of the Ganga.

Bheema lets out a tiger's roar, when he finds Aswatthama in Vyasa's asrama, covered in dirt, smeared with ghee, and wearing a piece of cloth made of kusa grass. He leaps down from his chariot with his bow and quiver, crying, "Coward, I will kill you today!"

Aswatthama turns, and Bheema gasps to see his face. Drona's son has lost all his lustre. His face is twisted and bestial, the face of a nishada who sells the flesh of animals: a butcher's ghastly face! The expression in his eyes is so sinister, the look of a man who has lost his soul. Bheema stands stunned by the change in his childhood friend, the brahmana. Chest heaving, he stands ready to dispatch Aswatthama.

Drona's son draws a stalk of grass from the ground, as he rises to meet Bheema's challenge with an evil smile. He chants a mantra over the green blade, and fetches a cry from Vyasa and the other munis. The blade of grass bursts into flames. Aswatthama hisses, "May this world be without Pandavas!"

Aswatthama's jewel

Bheema stands rooted, as the four-headed brahmasirsa rises in white fire from Aswatthama's hands. Just then, the Jaitra flies down beside Bheema, and Krishna and Arjuna leap down from it. The astra rages towards them, devouring everything in its path. Even before they came down, Krishna cried to Arjuna, "You have the brahmasirsa, too. Use it or we are lost!"

The moment the chariot lands and they leap from it, Arjuna raises the Gandiva and murmurs the same mantra Aswatthama did. From his bow, also, there flares an arrow charged with the flames of the missile formed like Brahma's heads. The earth shudders as if it will crack in two. Fissures gape at their feet. Climbing steeply into the air, the two astras fly at each other, and flames of a thousand hues lick the sky: to consume the very stuff of reality. Oceans begin to evaporate; mountains shake to their roots.

It is the very last instant before the astras collide. If they do, the earth will be ashes, and the ashes blown across the fathomless vaults of space. In the final fraction of a moment, Vyasa jumps up with a shout and raises his hands above his head, "Stop!"

That moment, Narada appears there also, his body shining, and he, too, raises his hands in mudras of power. By the tapasya shakti of the two rishis, the astras are arrested in the sky. They burn there still; but they do not collide, just hang fire.

Vyasa cries, "How could you invoke the brahmasirsa? Withdraw your astras before the earth is consumed!"

Arjuna says, "I summoned the astra only to save my brother. I will recall it."

But to call back the brahmasirsa needs the will of a tapasvin. For some life-long moments, Arjuna stands in intense dhyana; slowly, the fires of his astra grow quiet. Sweat breaks out over his body, and then the arrow that bore the ayudha flies back into the Pandava's hands. It is a common wooden shaft now, and cool to his touch. Aswatthama's brahmasirsa still blazes in the sky.

Vyasa and Narada turn fiercely on Drona's son, "Recall your astra, Aswatthama!"

Aswatthama shuts his eyes in dhyana, sweat breaks out on him, too. But Drona's son has fallen from grace. He is a murderer now, and he cannot recall the astra. The brahmasirsa remains where it is, burning up the sky. Now, Aswatthama realizes the enormity of his sin. With a cry, he falls at the munis' feet. "I cannot call it back! I am a terrible sinner, and the astra mocks me."

There is panic in his voice. "What shall I do? I was afraid of Bheema, and I summoned the astra, saying, 'May this world be without Pandavas.' My lords, I am helpless. Save me from the weapon's wrath!"

Vyasa says, "If this astra is subdued with a brahmastra, there will be a drought in the world for twelve years. Not a drop of rain will fall, and the oceans will dry up. Pluck the hatred out of your heart. Think kindly of the sons of Pandu, and recall the astra."

But his crime has ruined Aswatthama's heart within him. He cannot raise a spark of mercy in it. Glowering, Vyasa says, "Give the Pandavas some recompense for what you did in the night. Give them the jewel your wear in your topknot."

Aswatthama cries, "The jewel is my life! It protects me against weapons, disease, curses and hunger."

Vyasa says grimly, "You have taken many lives. You must give up the jewel."

The muni's tone is irresistible. His hands shaking, Aswatthama gives up the magical gemstone. Then, he says, "I can't recall the astra. At best, I can turn it away from the Pandavas themselves, and ask it to consume their unborn children. But one day the world must be without any Pandavas."

Vyasa and Narada nod. Aswatthama turns his weapon into the wombs of all the Pandavas' wives, and their sons' wives. In a moment, Draupadi is barren, and Subhadra, and the astra flashes subtly into Uttaraa's womb and burns Abhimanyu's child nestling there. Then, the brahmasirsa subsides.

Now, Krishna says in a fearsome voice, "Of all the creatures born into the world, Aswatthama you are the most contemptible one. You have killed Abhimanyu's child in Uttaraa's womb, but I say to you, that child will live when it is born. I will give it life!"

The Avatara trembles with anger, "I curse you, Aswatthama. You will see that child born. You will see him crowned king and rule from the throne of the Pauravas. For sixty years of the kali yuga, Abhimanyu's son will rule, and you will live through his reign, and still not die. Go wander the earth, friendless and alone, to expiate your sin! You shall not have a single companion and no man will speak a kind word to you. Go now, I curse you to live until the kali yuga ends!"

Aswatthama howls like an animal shot with an arrow. He runs from that place as if demons are after him, and he hears Vyasa saying, "Yes, Uttaraa's son will rule the world, and let him be called Parikshita, the tested one."

Aswatthama plunges into the deep jungle, and is lost. With the jewel of power they took from him, Arjuna, Bheema, Nakula and Krishna come back to the desolate camp at Kurukshetra. Draupadi is calmer now; but she rises with a moan, when she sees them return. A glowing Bheema gives her the scarlet stone, and she takes it from him, crying out softly, knowing her sons and brothers had been avenged.

Bheema says, "Aswatthama was vanquished, and Krishna cursed him to wander the earth until the kali yuga ends. He was our guru's son, so we spared his life."

Draupadi looks at Krishna, and when he nods at her, she seems satisfied. She brings the scarlet gem to Yudhishtira, and says, "Wear this from now, my lord. Only a great king should wear a stone like this one."

To please her, Yudhishtira takes the jewel and wears it in his crown.

BOOK ELEVEN

Stree Parva

AUM, I bow down to Narayana, the most exalted Nara, and to the Devi Saraswati, and say *Jaya*!

ONE

With Dhritarashtra and Gandhari

AFTER FOURTEEN YEARS, THE PANDAVAS RETURN TO HASTINAPURA. They should come home in joy, for the war has been won and now Yudhishtira returns as king. Instead, they arrive in mourning after what Aswatthama did. Krishna and Satyaki ride with them. Just inside the city-gates, the Pandavas meet the Kaurava widows. Wearing white, the women wail louder than ever when they see their husbands' killers. Some scream at Yudhishtira, "How could you kill your own blood, Yudhishtira?"

"Is this your dharma, Pandava?"

Lamentation rings through the streets of the city of elephants, and it is not only the Kaurava widows who weep. Draupadi has lost five sons in the night; her eyes are not dry. Krishna alights from his chariot and melts into the crowd. Yudhishtira sees Dhritarashtra. With a cry, the Pandava runs to his uncle and prostrates himself at the old king's feet. Dhritarashtra raises him up, and embraces him. It is a cold clasp; the king's mighty form trembles with suppressed rage. Dhritarashtra always knew how to conduct himself before the eyes of the world, and he now speaks gentle words to his nephew.

His blind face turns here and there, seeking someone else. He says, "Bheema, where are you, my son?"

Bheema starts forward, and his uncle opens his arms to hug him. Suddenly, Krishna reappears, and he is carrying an iron image of Bheema: the same one upon which Duryodhana used to rain blows with his mace. To the others' amazement, Krishna calls Dhritarashtra, "Bheema is here, my lord."

Bheema is about to speak, but Krishna's eyes flash warningly at him. Dhritarashtra gropes forward, "Where are you, Bheema, come to my arms."

Krishna sets the iron statue before the king, "Bheema is before you, my lord."

It is told that Bheema's body was as hard as iron, and the king in his wrath does not notice the difference between his nephew and the statue. He throws his arms around the image, and clasps it with the superhuman strength with which he was born. Now the blind man's mask falls away, and naked hatred is plain on Dhritarashtra's face. He has his precious son's killer in his embrace; grimacing, the old king crushes the statue in his arms. Blood flows down his chest, blood flows from his mouth, and the iron figure buckles in his arms! The effort overwhelms Dhritarashtra, and he collapses.

He still does not realize what he has done. He feels warm blood on himself, and thinks it is Bheema's. Sanjaya runs forward, crying, "My lord! What did you do?"

Abruptly, Dhritarashtra's rage leaves him and cold sanity returns. He begins to tremble, and cries, "Bheema! What have I done to you, my child? I have killed my brother's son! Ah, Bheema, I killed you in anger."

He sobs. Krishna sees the king's fury has passed. He goes to Dhritarashtra and says, "Bheema isn't dead. I gave you Bheema's image to vent your anger. You crushed the statue your son used to practise with his mace, and the blood was your own.

"My lord, this is no way for a king to conduct himself. The Pandavas are your nephews, they need your affection. They hated the war and the sorrow it brought. You have not treated Pandu's sons with dharma; at least now, be as a father to them. You have lost your own sons, and no punishment could be worse. You have a chance to make sons of the Pandavas, as you should have done long ago."

A subtle transformation seems to come over Dhritarashtra. A smile of relief spreads on his face, and they see that, now, this smile springs from his heart. He says, "Krishna, everything you say is true. My overweening love for Duryodhana turned my mind to evil. But all that is past. I am grateful you brought the iron image to me, or I would have killed Bheema." He turns his face, "Bheema, child, forgive me! Come here, let me embrace you."

Bheema glances at Krishna, who nods. Sobbing, Dhritarashtra clasps his nephews, one by one, "Bless you, my children! All my boys have been taken from me, and I have only you five to be my sons. From now, I swear I will be as I should have always been: a father to you."

For the first time they hear sincerity in his voice, and have no doubt he means what he says. But they still have to face Gandhari, and the Pandavas quail at the thought. The queen stands some way off from her husband, her eyes bound as always, and rage rules her heart. As they begin to walk towards her, she has decided, again, to curse Yudhishtira and his brothers. She is about to utter the curse, when Vyasa appears at her side and says, "Stop, Gandhari! Your love for your sons fills your heart with sin. This is no time for hatred; it is the hour of forgiveness. Before Duryodhana went to war, he came to you for your blessing. Do you remember what he said to you that day?

"'Mother, say I will win this war and I know I shall.'

"You replied, 'Where there is dharma, there will be victory.'

"Your own prophecy has been fulfilled. Dharma was with the Pandavas, and so they are victorious. You always knew that Duryodhana's was the way of sin; if you curse the sons of Pandu now, you will desolate the virtue of a lifetime. You have always been patient and truthful. Calm yourself, daughter, the Pandavas do not deserve your anger. The sin lay with your sons, and they have paid for it. Yudhishtira and his brothers were only fate's warriors."

Gandhari hears him out in silence. Then she says, "My sons Duryodhana and Dusasana, and my brother Shakuni are to blame for the Kuru House being destroyed. When I first heard that my boys were dead, I was deranged with grief. I am calmer now; I cannot blame the Pandavas for fighting the war. How can I? They did not want this war, only my son did.

"Yet, I am a mother and my heart will not be still after hearing how Bheema killed Duryodhana. That was not dharma, O Muni. He struck him below the waist, treacherously, and my child fell. Bheema drank Dusasana's blood on the field, like an animal. He did these things out of arrogance. I cannot forgive him."

The Pandavas have just come up to Vyasa and Gandhari. In such a humble voice, that Krishna smiles to hear him, Bheema says, "Mother, I admit I killed Duryodhana treacherously. There was no other way he could be killed; and if I did not kill him, he would have killed me. I only did what I had to, to save my life. There was no other way, because there was no mace-fighter on earth like your son. I could never have beaten him in a fair fight, why, not Indra could! But your son did not walk the way of dharma. You know how he made us suffer for thirteen years. Yudhishtira never wanted this war, but Duryodhana was obstinate enough to fight it. And you know what happened in the sabha of Hastinapura on the day of the dice, you know how Draupadi was abused. Who would avenge her except me? I swore then that I would break Duryodhana's thigh, and I did.

"I should have done it on the day of the gambling, and you would have said there was no sin in what I did. For, then, your son's crime was happening before you. After thirteen years, what he did has faded from your mind, and all you know is that I killed Duryodhana by striking him unfairly. But thirteen years ago, Yudhishtira stopped me.

"I beg you, see this thing in its entirety, not just what I did yesterday. Mother Gandhari, forgive me if I have sinned."

Gandhari hears him out, and a thaw sets in on her heart. Her voice is less fierce, when she asks, "Bheema, I hear the sincerity in your voice when you say my son was the greatest mace-fighter in the world. I will forgive you for killing Duryodhana. But what about Dusasana? You drank his blood on the battlefield! He was your cousin, and you drank his blood."

Bheema is humbler still, "I swore in anger that I would drink his blood. It was no cold plan, but my temper: but I had to keep my oath. And now I swear, not a drop of your son's blood passed down my throat, but I turned away and spat it out. Karna saw me, and I remember he smiled. It was mere bravado; I did not really drink his blood. I beg you, see what I did in its true light, and forgive me."

Krishna's smile grows wider than ever at the abject contrition in Bheema's voice. Gandhari seems mollified, and says, now with less rage than sorrow, "Ah, Bheema, you killed all my sons. Couldn't you have left me just one? Your uncle and I are old. I haven't even one son left to be my support in my old age."

Bheema says, "Mother, you could have prevented your sons from banishing us. You could have persuaded them to return our kingdom, when we returned after thirteen years in the wilderness. But you did not. Am I to blame for everything that happened?"

At this, anger returns to Gandhari. She turns her face here and there, seeking someone else. "Where is Yudhishtira?"

Yudhishtira comes before her, his palms folded, and says, "Here I am, mother, your sons' killer. If you curse anyone, let it be me. I caused not just the death of your sons, but the ruin of kshatriya kind. Curse me, mother Gandhari, I deserve your curse!"

When she hears the anguish in his voice, Gandhari sighs like a serpent and remembers what Vyasa said. That queen begins to sob helplessly. As she weeps, a corner of the cloth with which she binds her eyes comes loose, letting in a ray of light. For a moment, the virgin vision of those eyes falls on Yudhishtira's feet. The Pandava cries out in pain, for Gandhari's glance burns up his toenails, charring them black!

When Arjuna sees this, he scurries to hide behind Krishna, who laughs to see the greatest kshatriya on earth running from a woman. Gandhari also dimly sees Arjuna retreat, and at once her heart goes out to him. Krishna whispers to Arjuna, "O Jishnu!" which means terror of the world, and laughs again to see him flush.

Gandhari's anger passes like a spring cloud. She blesses the Pandavas, and embraces them, saying that from now on she was also their mother, because her sons were all dead. Then it is time for them to go to their own mother: Kunti whom they have not seen for thirteen years.

TWO

Gandhari's curse

CRYING ALOUD TO SEE HER SONS, CRYING FOR JOY SHE CAN HARDLY express, Kunti runs to them with her arms flung wide. One by one, she clasps them to her, stroking their faces, kissing them, touching their battle-scars with her fingers, while she weeps and laughs at once. Then she turns to Draupadi, who stands limply, shattered by the death of her own sons.

Kunti takes her in her arms, and Panchali breaks down. She wails, "Mother, all your grandsons are dead! Abhimanyu was killed, and my boys as well. It is some time since you saw them, now you will never see them again. What use is victory or a kingdom when I have lost my children?"

She sobs in Kunti's arms. Then, the blind king's train sets out again for Kurukshetra, and the Pandavas and the women, all wearing just single cloths, follow it. Seeing Kunti helpless to comfort her, Gandhari takes Draupadi in her arms, and says, "Look at me, my child, and be consoled that you are not alone in your anguish. We have both lost all our sons; our pain is the same one. At least you are younger, and stronger, so you can bear the grief. Don't cry, my daughter, this is fate. It is the end of the world as we knew it, and a new yuga has risen over the earth. Vidura foretold this years ago, and Krishna warned us of it. Don't cry for your sons, Draupadi, they have gone where they are happier than we are."

Then, her own sorrow overwhelms her again and she sobs, "Oh, which of us will comfort the other? We are both heartbroken!"

Gandhari's curse

As they near Kurukshetra, subtle vision fills the pure Gandhari. Clearly, through her bound eyes, she sees the apocalyptic field. She sees corpses sprouted on the earth like blades of grass; she sees severed limbs, severed heads, and blood congealed everywhere. She sees the vultures and jackals that feast on the mouldering flesh of the dead. She sees her sons lying on that field, some whole, some rotted past recognition, and others with their faces eaten away by scavengers. Gandhari sees thousands of wives and mothers, all crying, many screaming: the women of an entire generation, some from far-off lands, others from Hastinapura. They throw themselves across the corpses of their sons, brothers, husbands, fathers, and a sea-storm of lamentation rises into the yielding sky, it seeps into the earth. The wild creatures of the world hear that wailing and think the pralaya is upon them.

Gandhari takes Krishna by the hand, she says, "Do you see them, Krishna, the millions that died*? Do you hear my daughters-in-law sobbing for my hundred sons?"

Krishna does not reply. He leads her to a corpse, which has just been carried to Kurukshetra from Samantapanchaka. Gandhari bends to touch the magnificent body, broken at the waist, with her fingers, which are her eyes. She feels the proud face, uncowed by an agonizing death, and she flings herself down across Duryodhana's chest, and her shrill, ululating cries echo above every other sound on Kurukshetra. Then, she faints.

When she recovers, she still sobs and calls her son's name. She runs her fingers through his tangled hair, trying to break the clotted blood from it. She runs her fingers over his face; she kisses his eyes, his cheeks, and his lips.

Trembling, Gandhari turns to Krishna. "Krishna, do you see the sea of grief around you? Look at Duryodhana's wife, she runs like a mad woman between her husband's corpse and her son's, trying to chase the jackals and vultures away from both. Look at Uttaraa; can you hear her sobbing as she lies across what remains of Abhimanyu? They were married hardly a month."

---

* In KMG, Gandhari names several dead kings and warriors, for some 10 pages.

That is far from all: a million widows, a million bereaved mothers mourn on the field of death*. Karna's quiet wife sobs softly over her husband's headless body. Shalya's wives fling themselves over him, shrieking. If anything can be worse than the war on Kurukshetra, it is the spectacle of the women mourning their dead.

Now, Gandhari turns on Krishna, "You are to blame! If you had really wanted to, you could have prevented this war; but you were indifferent. You could have cooled the enmity between my sons and their cousins. Instead, you sided with the Pandavas and fanned the flames. You have ruined the Kurus, Krishna. I, Gandhari, curse you that thirty-six years from today your clan will also perish. The Yadavas will fight among themselves, and kill one another, every man of you. And your women will weep then, even as we do today!

"As for you, you will wander the earth, friendless and alone, and you will die a common death, without glory. I curse you, Krishna, I curse you for the deaths of my sons!"

A hush falls around them. Gandhari is a queen of tapasya, and her curse cannot fail. Krishna smiles. Imperturbable, he says, "Mother, your curse is merely the course of fate. For only the Yadavas can kill the Yadavas; and if they are not killed, they will overrun the earth. They are my own people, and not men or the Devas can harm them. I thank you for your curse: it is a blessing for the world! And now your anger has been exorcised, you will not curse Yudhishtira and his brothers. Gandhari, I will do anything for the Pandavas. If the Yadavas have to die so the sons of Pandu can live, I am only happy. I say to you again, Yudhishtira and his brothers are my very life to me."

The Pandavas hear this with tears in their eyes. What love can be greater than Krishna's? But now, the Dark One's eyes glitter, and in a harder voice he says to Gandhari, "You have cursed me, and I gladly take your curse upon myself. Yet, O queen, this is not dharma. You are

---

* In a nearby section, Dhitarashtra asks Yudhishtira how many warriors had died, and how many survived. Yudhishtira replies, "One billion, six hundred and sixty million, and twenty thousand men have fallen in battle. Twenty-four thousand, one hundred and sixty-five escaped with their lives." (KMG) However, the figure for the dead is not only absurdly exaggerated, it contradicts every calculation based on the number of aksauhinis that fought the war.

griefstricken and do not see right from wrong, or the truth from a lie. Not I, but you are to blame for this war! You loved Duryodhana too much, and you indulged his every whim. You spoilt him so much that he could never deny himself anything, regardless of the cost. Duryodhana was always arrogant and envious. You are a wise woman; you knew your son's nature. Why did you never try to curb him? You could have prevented this tragedy, not I.

"You accuse me of indifference. Tell me, who came to Hastinapura to ask for peace? As for you, didn't you know your brother Shakuni's character? You still allowed him into your house. When Duryodhana was young and impressionable, you let him grow close to his uncle. Gandhari, tell me truly, did you know nothing about the house of lac?"

She gives a start, and is silent. Krishna smiles, and goes on, "You and your husband are responsible for this genocide, and you want to shift that blame to me. You spoilt your son until he did not know wrong from right, but only what he wanted. He began the war that has destroyed the world, and you cannot blame me for it.

"Dhritarashtra is responsible for what happened. And you, who are a woman of dharma, allowed evil to take root and grow in your home. As for me, I feel no sorrow for your sons. They have what they deserve; why, they have better than they deserve. Duryodhana, the worst sinner on earth, has found Devaloka! Even as he lay dying, he made sure the Pandavas would suffer; and such a one has found heaven. Gandhari, it is because he was your son that he has gone there. Your penance and your prayers have not been in vain. Your sons are with the Gods now, mother. I beg you, set aside your anger in the knowledge that your princes, who deserve the cruellest hell, have attained paradise.

"Just now, you told me about your final conversation with Duryodhana. He said, 'Bless me, mother, and I will win the war.' You replied, 'My son, victory will be only where there is dharma. Your cause is not just; you cannot win this war. But I bless you that you will die a glorious death, and, thus, find swarga for yourself.'

"Those were the bravest, most truthful words any mother could say to her son. You are not weak like your husband; you are a strong woman.

You must not try to blame me for what happened. Be yourself again: face the truth, accept your sorrow as just punishment."

Krishna speaks as to a favoured child gone astray. Gandhari is speechless at what he says*.

---

* Krishna also says, "You double your grief by indulging it. A brahmana woman bears children to practise austerities, the cow brings forth calves to give milk and bear burdens, the mare foals so her colts and fillies may be swift-footed. The sudra women's children add to the numbers of servitors; the vaisya women's children swell the keepers of cattle. But a kshatriya princess like you brings forth sons to be killed in battle."

THREE

Tarpana for a kshatriya

DHRITARASHTRA ASKS YUDHISHTIRA TO TAKE CHARGE OF arrangements for cremating the dead. The Pandava appoints Vidura, Sanjaya, Yuyutsu, Dhaumya and some others to the task. The corpses are gathered onto wood pyres, and set alight. A million pyres burn on Kurukshetra. Then, Dhritarashtra, Yudhishtira and the others come to the banks of the Ganga to offer tarpana to those who have died. The mourning women all come with them, Gandhari, Kunti and Draupadi also.

Now the men put aside their silks and their jewels; covered by thin cloths, they enter the water. Thousands of women offer prayers, among them the Kaurava widows and Draupadi. Kunti's mind is on fire today at the river, for she, too, has seen a son lying headless on the field.

It was three days ago that Arjuna killed Karna, and the Pandava camp erupted in celebration. When Sanjaya told Dhritarashtra about Karna's death, Kunti overheard him. She felt as if her heart was being carved with a knife, but, of course, she could not share her grief with anyone. She clasped it to her and wept, alone.

Today, she sees Karna lying on Kurukshetra, his head sloughed off by Arjuna's arrow. She sees his wife mourning him, and Kunti's world spins around her; but she will not let herself swoon, nor does she say a word. She comes with the other women to the Ganga, and sees the lucid currents of the same river, which once, a life ago, bore her firstborn away from her in a wooden box. Kunti hears the Kuru scions paying final homage to their dead fathers. But her Karna is deprived of the dignity of sacrament even in death: all his sons have been killed. He had lived and died the orphan she had made him. Suddenly, his spirit cries out to her that at least now let some justice be done to him. Kunti hears him; she sees his splendid form before her eyes.

Meanwhile, Yudhishtira and his brothers have entered the river to offer tarpana to their dead sons. Arjuna stands with tears streaming down his face, as he offers holy water and pinda for Abhimanyu: to quench his thirst and allay his hunger on his final journey. Kunti lays a hand on Yudhishtira's shoulder. He turns in some surprise, "What is it, mother?"

She is quivering with the sorrow that tears at her. She says, "Yudhishtira, there is another kshatriya for whom you must offer tarpana."

Krishna stands near them, watching, a sad smile on his lips. How well Kunti had kept her secret. Even when war was declared she had not told Yudhishtira what she knew; not even when Karna died, had she said a thing. She knew, and Krishna knew, that if she had, Yudhishtira would have abandoned the war and gone back into the forest. But now the time for truth has come, the moment of confession.

Puzzled, Yudhishtira says, "How is that, mother? I know our dead, and I have offered tarpana for them all. I am not such an ingrate that I have forgotten anyone who gave his life for me."

The other Pandavas come up around them, wondering whom their mother means. Kunti says softly, "Karna. You must offer tarpana for him also."

Yudhishtira is astonished. "Karna? Why should I offer him tarpana? He was a sutaputra, mother, and our enemy. His sons are dead, so his father must offer tarpana and pinda for him. I am a kshatriya; how can I offer tarpana for a suta? What are you saying? I don't understand you."

Kunti is sobbing, and many of the other women have gathered round curiously. Yudhishtira asks in some annoyance, "Mother, what is the matter? Why are you crying?"

With an effort, Kunti calms herself. Again, she says, "You must offer tarpana for Karna. He was not a sutaputra, he was a kshatriya."

A gasp goes up from the others, and word flies forth, "Karna was not a sutaputra, he was a kshatriya!"

Yudhishtira looks a little dazed. Gently, he says, "But you know nothing about Karna. How do you know he was not a sutaputra? And even if he was a kshatriya, why should I offer tarpana for him? Hasn't Karna a father?"

The moment is upon her. Kunti takes a deep breath and says in a clear voice, "Surya Deva is Karna's father, and his mother was a kshatriya princess. She invoked the Sun God with a mantra given her by a rishi, and Karna was born from their love. He was born wearing golden kavacha and kundala. But his mother was a maiden, living in her father's house, and she feared the world's censure. She floated her baby down the Ganga in a wooden box, and it was on this river that Atiratha found the child and took him home to Radha. They adopted him, raised him as their own. As for his natural mother, in time she married and had other sons. But how could she ever forget her firstborn child? Throughout her life, there seemed to be a hollow space in her heart without him. She could never forget how she had sinned against him."

Kunti stands beside the sacred river, and she, who had been so strong all her life, seems so fragile. Tears still course down her face.

Yudhishtira asks, "Who is Karna's mother? Which woman could be so heartless as to abandon her own child as soon as he was born? You must know who she is, since you know so much about Karna. Who was she that ruined what might have been such a noble life? Is the woman still alive?"

All eyes are on Kunti. She looks at her sons' faces, one to the other. She sees Krishna, and his eyes are full of mercy. Kunti feels a deep strength dawning on her from the Avatara's gaze. She turns back to Yudhishtira. She looks straight at him and, in a ringing voice, Kunti cries, "Yes, Karna's mother still lives, and she stands before you, Yudhishtira. Karna was my son, my first child!"

She sways on her feet, and falls on the soft silt of the riverbank. Vidura rushes to Kunti's side, while Yudhishtira stands as if he has been struck by lightning. Slowly, he turns to face Arjuna, who, if anything, looks more stricken than his brother. Into the hush that has fallen, Yudhishtira murmurs as in a dream, a nightmare, "We killed our brother."

A roar breaks out of Arjuna. He splashes out of the river, and falls on the ground, crying, "What have I done, Yudhishtira? I have killed my own brother!"

He cries out his shock, repeatedly, until river, forest and sky echo with it. "I killed my brother, and I gloated!" howls Arjuna. "How can I go on living after what I did?"

His eyes roll up, and he faints. Yudhishtira's eyes turn crimson; otherwise, he does not move, but stands as if his mother's confession has turned him into a statue. Bheema staggers out from the water and sits beside the unconscious Arjuna. The effect of Kunti's truth is most evident on poor Bheema. Those that watch see him turn, before their eyes, from an overgrown boy into a man.

Bheema remembers the day of the exhibition in Hastinapura. He thinks of the moment when he mocked Karna, 'Sutaputra, you are not fit to have yourself killed by my brother Arjuna. Put down your bow, and get yourself a horsewhip. That will suit you better.'

He remembers what Duryodhana said to him then, 'Karna brims with every noble quality a kshatriya should have. He is like a tiger. I pity you, Bheema, that you don't see him for what he is, and are blind to his greatness, which shines from him like a sun. I have made him king of Anga; he deserves to be lord of this earth!'

How foolish he, Bheema, had been on that day, and how prescient Duryodhana. Bheema's thoughts drift on to Kurukshetra, and the duel he fought against Karna. He sees Karna's mocking eyes, and his strange smile again, as he prodded Bheema with the tip of his bow, contemptuously, and spared his life. Karna's words are burned on his heart, 'Some day, Bheema, you will think back on this duel and feel proud. Some day you will rejoice that you fought Karna.'

Bheema knows, from now, that moment will be his most precious memory. It crosses his mind that, hereafter, for him Karna would be his eldest brother. Near Bheema, Sahadeva sits in a daze, thinking of the moment when Karna spared his life, 'Go now, boy, and hide behind your brother Arjuna. Don't come to fight your betters.'

Sahadeva sees the glittering eyes, and the haughty smile. He also sobs. Yudhishtira has come ashore now, and sits shaken and grim, never looking at his mother. His heart cries out within him that it would be better if he never saw her face again, for what she did to his brother, his *older* brother. Why, for what she had done not just to Karna but to all of them, the sin she made them commit.

Sitting with Krishna and Arjuna, Yudhishtira remembers the final day of Karna's life. He recalls every moment of it, vividly. He thinks of how he mocked his brother, calling him sutaputra. Suddenly, Yudhishtira turns to Kunti. Coldly, he asks her, "Mother, did Karna know who he was? Did he know he was our brother?"

She hangs her head, and cries. Krishna answers him, "He knew."

All the Pandavas turn to face Krishna. Yudhishtira whispers, "And you also knew, my Lord?"

"Yes."

The frantic Yudhishtira turns on Kunti, "How could you keep this from us? You made us kill our brother. Do you know, when I heard Karna had been killed, I ran to the field to see if the news was true? More than anyone else, I wanted Karna dead. I feared my brother more than I did any other man. Mother, how could you let us do this horrible thing?"

Then Yudhishtira looks into Kunti's eyes, and sees an age of grief in them, far, far greater than his own. He sees that his mother already suffers as much as she can bear. He sighs and does not say a word more. With his brothers around him, he enters the river again. Now he offers tarpana to his dead brother, and it seems the tears he sheds are all he needs as holy water for Karna's final journey. Somehow, Abhimanyu's death, and even the nearer deaths of Draupadi's sons are forgotten. The Pandavas have just one thought in their minds: they had another brother, and they killed him.

Seeing the Pandavas' mourn, the women on the riverbank set up a fresh lament. When he has finished offering tarpana and pinda to dead Karna, Yudhishtira raises his voice above the women's wailing, and curses womankind, "It is because my mother kept her secret so well that we killed our brother. May no woman ever be able to keep a secret again!"

Slowly, they come out of the whispering Ganga and make their way back to the camp. The Pandavas walk at the head of the procession. The women follow them, still crying, and a few paces behind the women, Krishna and Satyaki bring up the rear.

BOOKS TWELVE and THIRTEEN

Shanti Parva and Anusasana Parva[*]

AUM, I bow down to Narayana, the most exalted Nara, and to the Devi Saraswati, and say *Jaya*!

---

[*] The 2 Parvas have been condensed and combined. Together, they are some 1000 pages long in the KMG translation—the Shanti Parva is 600 pages, and the Anusasana Parva 400 pages, approximately.

ONE

Yudhishtira's grief

THE MONTH PRESCRIBED FOR MOURNING THE DEAD HAS TO PASS before the Pandavas can enter Hastinapura, and Yudhishtira can be crowned king in that city. The sons of Pandu settle in tents on the banks of the lotus-flowing Ganga. Every day, elaborate rituals are performed for the peace of those that have died.

Vyasa, Narada, Kanva and other munis arrive in the Pandava camp, to meet the man who will be emperor of Bharatavarsha. They find Yudhishtira plunged in despair. He hardly speaks, but sits brooding darkly, at times sobbing when grief overpowers him.

One day Narada says to him, "Put away this sorrow, my son. By Krishna's grace, and the valour of your brothers and the Panchalas, you have conquered the world. No war is won cheaply. You should be pleased that your enemies are vanquished and victory is yours."

At once Yudhishtira's eyes fill, and he says, "My lord, I am not destined to know happiness. What you say is true: by Krishna's grace and my brothers' valour we have victory. But ah, Muni, victory at what price? How many we loved like life perished in this war. What does it matter who wins or loses such a war? The only truth is that we fought, and millions died. This is the end of the world, as we knew it. The war wasn't fought with dharma: not by our enemies, and not by us."

He pauses, and tears roll down his face. The knowing Narada asks, "Is this all that is troubling you?"

"No, my lord! Even this much I could somehow bear. What torments me more than anything else is that Karna was our brother, and we killed him like our worst enemy. How can I ever hope to be happy again? Although we did not know the truth, how could we do this terrible thing? Karna knew who he was before the war began. Krishna and my mother begged him to join us. They offered him the throne of the world, which was properly his, not mine. He refused them: he would not betray Duryodhana. Once he knew the truth, no one would have censured my brother if he had abandoned our cousin, not even Duryodhana. But Karna would rather die than forsake his friend.

"That was our brother. And what did we do to him? We mocked him, whenever we could, calling him sutaputra, and finally we killed him. We cut him down when he was trying to lift his chariot-wheel from the mire. I cannot live with this sin. Not even when Arjuna's arrow was aimed at his throat did he cry out, 'Don't kill me, Arjuna, I am your brother!' And how I rejoiced when Arjuna cut Karna's head from his body."

Yudhishtira chokes, and cannot go on. Then, remembering something else, he resumes, "I will never forget that day in Hastinapura, when I lost everything. Karna was there, and he was taunting us even more than our cousins did. I stood with my head hung, but my heart blazed to hear him. Then my eyes fell on Karna's feet. I can hardly describe what happened to me at that moment. His feet were so familiar. I was astonished, for they were my mother's very feet! Looking at them calmed me. I felt at such peace just looking at the feet of this enemy who reviled us in the Kuru sabha. Of course, at that time even he did not know who he was.

"I never forgot that experience. Even when we were in exile in the forest, I would lie awake at nights thinking of how strange it was that Karna's feet were exactly like my mother's. Today, I know why they were so alike, and I feel my heart will break in a thousand pieces. You say I should be happy we have won the war. But how can I be happy after killing my own brother, and a brother as noble as great, great Karna?"

Again, he sits silent, his tears flowing. Yudhishtira shakes his head in a sorrow he can neither bear nor cure. In a moment, he goes on, speaking almost to himself, "Muni, when my mother went to Karna before the war began, he said he would grant her a boon. Not that she asked him for anything after he refused to join us; but he said he must give her something, because she was his mother whom he had found after so many years. The boon he gave her was that he would not kill any of her sons in battle, except Arjuna.

"Now we know why he did not kill the four of us, when he had each of us at his mercy. He only prodded us with his bow, as if he was blessing us! As for Arjuna: how could Karna kill Arjuna, when he knew who he was? And how could he not at least try, for Duryodhana's sake? But knowing his heart now, I am convinced that Karna did not kill Arjuna because he was his brother.

"And what did Arjuna do? He cut off Karna's head when he was defenceless. Who was responsible? I, of course! I can never forgive myself for making one brother of mine kill another. The soul knows all things. Deep in my heart I must have known the truth, or at least suspected it. I am the worst sinner on earth."

He grows thoughtful, and says, "Narada, one thing perplexes me. After my brother was killed, we all saw the place where his chariot was mired. The earth was not soft where Karna died. It seems fate plunged his wheel into the ground so Arjuna could kill him. Also, at that final moment, Arjuna tells me he thought Karna had forgotten the mantras for the astras, and could summon one only with an inordinate effort."

Narada tells Yudhishtira about the two curses Karna received: one from Bhargava, and the other from the brahmana whose cow he killed. The rishi says, "But for those curses, and that Indra took his kavacha and kundala, Karna could never have been killed. He was the greatest kshatriya on earth. Listen to the story of his life, and his suffering, if you will."

In that camp beside the golden Ganga, Narada tells them about Karna's life: of its anguish and the curse he was born with that he must suffer until the day he died. Hearing about that sad, heroic life, their eldest brother's life, chastens the sons of Pandu. They know that their own ordeals do not account for a tenth of what Karna had endured: and always alone.

Just listening to Karna's tragic story calms the Pandavas. It makes Yudhishtira forget his own sorrow, when he realizes that from the first day his brother was marked by fate for its fiercest trials. Karna had survived them all, and covered himself in glory in his lonely battle against time. He had not been beaten; he had triumphed. Finally, he had achieved the one prize he valued more than any other: immortal fame.

Yudhishtira realizes the wound in his heart for his dead brother will never heal. But hearing Karna's life from Narada, the Pandava feels that if Karna could have endured all that he did by himself, surely, he, Yudhishtira, can bear the anguish of losing him. At least, he has his other brothers and Krishna, with whom he can share his pain.

Kunti tells Yudhishtira, "You mustn't grieve like this for Karna. It is not as if both Surya Deva and I did not tell him who he was."

Yudhishtira accepts this; but the kingdom is a different matter. Yudhishtira wants no part, any more, of ruling a kingdom. He says, "We should have been content to live begging alms. What good has this war done any of us? It has destroyed the Kauravas, and the Pandavas as well. A man can atone for his sins by confession, by charity, and by penance. I mean to live in the jungle, in tapasya. Arjuna, I leave you this hard-won earth. I have no use for it any more."

Shocked, Arjuna says, "Why did you bother to fight a war, if you were going to abandon everything we fought for? It was a dharma yuddha we fought; millions laid down their lives for you. Was all that sacrifice just for you to roam the world with a begging-bowl? You could have done that without the war. If you don't do your dharma as a kshatriya king, you will mock those that died for you, and we shall have their curses on our heads. Yudhishtira, the path you want to tread is for brahmanas, not us.

"How can you even think of renouncing this kingdom won with so much blood? Remember what it is of which you make so light: the throne upon which Dilipa, Nriga, Nahusha, Ambarisa and Mandhata sat. You must not relinquish the earth now, but guide all our destinies. This is no time for you to live in a jungle, but a time for you to perform an Aswamedha yagna!" cries Arjuna passionately.

His brother replies, "Hear me clearly, Arjuna. I mean to live in the forest on fruit and roots, wearing deerskin and tree-bark, and with my hair matted in jata. Nothing will induce me to leave the path of penance I have chosen."

Turn by turn, Bheema, Arjuna, Sahadeva and Nakula come to their brother, to persuade him*. He is adamant, and will not change his mind. One day, Draupadi goes to him in his grief.

---

* This section of conversations between Yudhishtira and his brothers, and Yudhishtira and the Rishis Devasthana, Vyasa, and then Krishna himself is some 70 pages long in the KMG translation. The argument is whether sannyasa is the right course for Yudhishtira to adopt. He believes it is the only course, and the others try to dissuade him.

She says, "My lord, your brothers come to you again and again, like chataka birds, and beg you to take the Kuru throne. Listen to them. They have suffered so much for your sake. They have fought heroically for you; they have lost their sons to the war. Do you remember, when we were in exile, you would always comfort them saying that when the time came you would defeat the Kauravas and rule from Hastinapura? Your time has come, Yudhishtira, don't refuse your brothers what they ask."

Yudhishtira hardly answers her. Vyasa, Narada, Kanva and the other munis try to talk the eldest Pandava out of his despondency. They are full of legends from the past; they tell him about his ancestors who once sat upon the same throne he is now being offered. But he is obdurate.

Arjuna comes in despair to Krishna and says, "My Lord, you are the only one to whom he might listen. Speak to him, or all we have done will have been in vain."

Krishna replies, "I believe Vyasa Muni is with him even now. I think what he says will see some change."

Vyasa in the mean while tries to infuse some reason into Yudhishtira, "My child, a king has no right to indulge his own grief. A just king's time has always belonged to his people, and only to them. He is like a God to them, and their lives are his sole concern. A king has no wives, sons or brothers, Yudhishtira, only his people whom he rules. That is the truth and the deepest meaning of his life, to the exclusion of everything else. For the king, the people are his dharma, his prana, his God. His task is just to rule them; beyond that, he has no other truth, or life. Your dharma is to assume kingship in Hastinapura. Your people are waiting for you like children. They put all their faith in you, you must be a father to them."

For the first time, Yudhishtira seems moved. This is an argument that appeals powerfully to his nature, one he cannot resist. There is light on his grim face again, light breaks in his eyes. With a wry smile, he says, "I fear you are right, Muni. I have been selfish and indulged myself, and you have cleared my mind. I walked alone through a dark place, but I have come out from it now. I feel the sun on my face again, and hear my destiny calling me. I will go back to Hastinapura and be king. I beg you, tell me about the dharma of a king. I would be as just a king as the Kuru sires were. Teach me the wisdom of kings, before I sit upon that hallowed throne."

Vyasa laughs, "I am hardly the one to tell you about kingship! I have never sat upon a throne, nor do I know anything about the affairs of state. But there is someone else you might ask for guidance. Indeed, no one on earth is better suited than him, both by his experience and by his love, to advise you on the dharma of kings."

"Who is he, Swami?"

"Your Pitama Bheeshma, who lies on his bed of arrows as if he still has something left to accomplish in this world."

Vyasa sees the Pandava gives a start, and a shadow crosses his face. The rishi continues, "The first sixteen years of his life, his mother Ganga raised him to be a king who would grace the noblest throne in the world. Devavrata was to have succeeded his father Shantanu. Brihaspati and Sukracharya taught him in Devaloka, and he has no equal in political wisdom. Rama's guru, Vasishta, taught him the Vedas and the Vedangas. Markandeya taught him the rigours of renunciation; he taught him the final secret that lies beyond the veil of death. Yudhishtira, the time has come for you to go to your Pitama. He will be happy to see you, and happier to teach you everything he knows."

Yudhishtira says, "How can I go before Bheeshma, when I have killed my cousins?"

Vyasa laughs. "Do you think your Pitama doesn't know that fate, and not you, was the cause of everything that happened? He hardly interfered in the attrition between your cousins and yourselves; he knew it was no use trying to oppose destiny: what was written must take its course. An awesome task is before you, Yudhishtira, you will have need of Bheeshma's wisdom."

Krishna arrives there then with Arjuna, and Vyasa says, "Yudhishtira has decided to go to Hastinapura, and be crowned king of the Kurus."

Krishna and Arjuna embrace Yudhishtira, and he himself smiles like a man who has woken from a nightmare to find sunlight in the world.

TWO

A new king in Hastinapura

THE DAYS THAT REMAIN OF THE MONTH OF MOURNING SEE A DEEP change in Yudhishtira. He spends all his time with the rishis who have come to comfort him, enlighten him. Once he decides that he will become king in Hastinapura, day by day, the eldest Pandava appears to become more cheerful, and stronger. It is as if he has left the dark past and the war behind, and now looks forward eagerly to the future, even to kingship. He spends a lot of time alone with Krishna, mainly sharing silence with the Avatara; but at times, he asks his cousin a question, or his advice on anything he cares to. Serenity comes stealing over the Pandava. The war has ended, and with it, enmity: that at least cannot be denied.

Then, the month is over, and it is time to return to Hastinapura, time for a new king to sit on the Kuru throne. The sons of Pandu set aside their mourning cloths; they don silks and jewellery once more. They set out in a procession for the city of their fathers. Yudhishtira rides in a chariot yoked to sixteen resplendent white bullocks. Bheema has the reins, while Arjuna holds the shining white parasol, the sign of the king, over Yudhishtira. Nakula and Sahadeva stand on either side of their brother with the royal chamaras, the silver-handled whisks, in their hands.

Immediately behind Yudhishtira's chariot, rides Dhritarashtra's only surviving son: Yuyutsu, who was always loyal to the Pandavas. Krishna and Satyaki follow Yuyutsu in the Jaitra, with Daruka at the chariot-head. Behind them come the women of the entourage, Kunti, Draupadi and the others, in golden palanquins. The irresistible joy of the occasion is upon them all, and, for the moment, grief has melted from their hearts like darkness at sunrise. The long night ends today. It is indeed a new dawn in their lives, one bought dearly. Fate herself will not allow their minds to be shadowed with sorrow on this most auspicious day. The Pandavas arrive at the gates of Hastinapura, and, despite themselves, a great sense of destiny overwhelms the five brothers in the chariot; even, perhaps, a feeling that everything they have suffered is worth this moment.

The people of Hastina have turned out in crowds to welcome their princes of light. The streets are thronged to bursting, all the way from the city-gates to the palace. Despite the incalculable tragedy of the war, a fresh new spirit sweeps the city of elephants. A stagnant darkness seems to have lifted away from the ancient capital, overnight, and despair banished. Hope springs green and exuberant in the hearts of the people, and it seems the old ways of love will return to their lives, in triumph, with the sons of Pandu.

Earth and sky reverberate with Yudhishtira's name, and the names of his brothers and Yuyutsu, of Krishna and Satyaki, and the Queen Draupadi. Though it has taken many years and a dreadful war, though blood has flowed on Kurukshetra: finally dharma has prevailed, and the people rejoice. A sea of loving hands reaches out to the new king and his brothers, and they are healed by that multitudinous touch.

The gates, the streets, are decked out in a season of garlands. All along Yudhishtira's progress, the sound of the Vedas hangs in the air, mingling with incense and the scents of flowers. It is a new spring come to the city, and through avenues of white flags flapping in a celebrant breeze, the Pandavas are escorted to their palace with a thousand musicians, singers and dancers going before them. Truly, it is as if the earth blooms again in exhilaration, at the return of this king of dharma!

At the palace-gates, the brahmanas of Hastinapura receive Yudhishtira ceremonially with mantras and earthen lamps. Krishna leads his cousin into the sabha of the Kuru kings, where so many majestic sovereigns have been crowned, since time out of mind. Borne along by the tide of history, and with the Dark One still leading him by the hand, Yudhishtira mounts the dais in that sabha and sits on the throne of his fathers, the Sarvatobhadra covered in tiger-skins. Now, Krishna's eyes shine with rare tears. He had sworn that one day his good cousin would ascend this throne of the earth. Today, he has kept his word. Dharma has prevailed and rules the world again; at least, for the time being.

Two glittering, jewelled seats face Yudhishtira's royal throne: places of honour, in which Krishna and Satyaki sit. Without them, the war could never have been won. There are two other golden thrones on either side of Yudhishtira. Here, Bheema and Arjuna sit. Beside them, are two beautiful ivory thrones; in one, Nakula sits, and Kunti shares the second with her favourite child, Sahadeva. Draupadi is led in, solemnly, and takes her place beside Yudhishtira. No memory touches her mind, today, of the time when she was last in this sabha. Dhritarashtra and Gandhari are there as well, in thrones of their own, with Vidura and Yuyutsu beside them.

Krishna calls for the sacred water, fetched from the holiest tirthas in Bharatavarsha. He fills his sea-conch, the Panchajanya, with that water, and pours it over Yudhishtira with his own hands, in abhisekha. That done, Krishna takes the golden Kuru crown, glimmering with jewels given by the Devas—the crown Pururavas once wore and all the Paurava kings after him—and sets the hallowed thing on Yudhishtira's head. As Krishna marks his cousin's brow with the vermilion rajatilaka, cries of *'Yudhishtira Chakravarti! Jaya! Jaya!'* ring out through that court. These cries are picked up by the oceanic crowd outside, and the entire city resounds with the king's name, and soon, with his brothers' names and his incarnate cousin's.

The people's chosen representatives approach the throne and greet Yudhishtira formally on his coronation. He thanks them, saying, "My friends, I am moved by the love with which all of you have blessed my brothers and me. I will do everything in my power to justify the faith you place in me, and be a king of dharma to you. My uncle Dhritarashtra has been king all these years, and I pray he will continue to be head of the Kuru household, while I serve him as best as I can with the help of my brothers."

Yudhishtira gives away a thousand gold coins, each, to the brahmanas who performed the Vedic rituals at his coronation. Then, in court, he appoints his brothers to their various tasks. The king has more holy water fetched and pours it over Bheema, making him yuvaraja. Vidura is appointed the king's Prime Minister, and has charge of the defence of the realm. He will also be the king's personal counsellor. Sanjaya is given charge of the treasury and the finances of the land. Arjuna is named Senapati of the army, while Nakula is given charge of its recruitment and maintenance. Arjuna also has charge of relations with other kings and their kingdoms. Dhaumya retains his position as chief priest and guru to the king and his brothers. Yuyutsu is to administer the provinces of the kingdom, and to see to the needs of his father Dhritarashtra. Finally, Yudhishtira turns to his youngest brother, Sahadeva, waiting patiently to be given his charge. Yudhishtira says, "And you, Sahadeva, shall be my protector. You will be at my side at all times."

A radiant Krishna watches his cousin assume crisp control*. Later, that evening, last rites for those that died in the war are performed in the palace: grave rituals. When they are over, Yudhishtira and his brothers come to Krishna, who has gone to Arjuna's palace, even like a tiger entering his cave. Before all the people, Yudhishtira folds his hands to the Avatara and says, "My Lord, you have given me back my fathers' kingdom. You shared our sorrow during the years of our exile, and without you, we would never have won the war. Every time we faced a crisis, or an obstacle that seemed insurmountable, you showed us the way ahead." His voice chokes. "Lord, for our sake, you who are the eternal Brahman assumed this human form. You were Arjuna's sarathy during the war. I have only my bhakti to offer you, Krishna. This is just the beginning of our need for you. I beg you, remain with us always."

Yudhishtira, emperor of the world, washes Krishna's feet and sprinkles his own head with the water. He prostrates himself before the Avatara. Smiling, Krishna raises him up, and then, one by one, the other Pandavas, as they also worship him with sasthanga namaskara, the prostration of eight limbs.

---

* Various palaces are given to the brothers: Yudhishtira has Dhritarashtra's palace, Bheema enters Duryodhana's, Arjuna gets Dusasana's, as magnificent, Nakula has Durmarshana's palace, even grander, and Sahadeva moves into Durmukha's palace.

THREE

The dying patriarch

THE NEXT MORNING, WITH THE SUN, YUDHISHTIRA COMES TO KRISHNA'S apartment. He finds his cousin pensive. The Pandava says, "Did you have a restful night, my Lord? But you seem disturbed, Krishna, are you unwell?"

Krishna smiles at him, and shakes his head. He makes no reply immediately. Then, slowly, he says, "I was thinking of your Pitama Bheeshma. He will not live much longer, Yudhishtira, and I hear him calling me. When Bheeshma dies, all his wisdom will vanish with him. We must go to him before that happens. You must learn whatever he has to teach you about your dharma as a king. Bheeshma's wisdom is a priceless treasure. He must share it with you before he leaves us."

Yudhishtira says, "Let us go at once, Krishna, together."

Satyaki comes in just then. Krishna says to him, "Tell Daruka to prepare my chariot, and you prepare to ride with us. We are going to Kurukshetra to see Bheeshma."

They set out, Yudhishtira and his brothers, Satyaki and Krishna. Kurukshetra lies bare before them, now that its corpses have been removed and burned. It is difficult to believe, just days ago, the greatest of all wars was fought here. At the edge of the fateful field, like another sun setting over the earth, Bheeshma lies dying.

Krishna and the Pandavas alight from their chariots, and make their way to the patriarch on his bed of arrows. Many mysterious munis, whom none of them has ever seen before, sit around Bheeshma, some silently in dhyana, others softly chanting arcane mantras that have all but passed out of the world. Krishna approaches the Kuru grandsire first, and kneeling beside him, takes his hand. Bheeshma's eyes flicker open; they are sea-like, and full of pain. He sees Krishna at his side, and Bheeshma's eyes flare with light, his face is lit by a smile.

Krishna says, also smiling, "Oh, my lord, how do you bear such pain? Why, if a needle pricks me, I cannot stand it! Here you are with a hundred arrows lodged in your body, and you have been lying on them for so long. There is no one like you in all the world, no one with such a mighty will, Devavrata. Not just a will, Bheeshma, but wisdom also. Brihaspati, Sukra, Vasishta and Markandeya were your gurus, and you have always walked the way of dharma. Never in time has a greater man lived on this earth, and none ever shall.

Your grandson Yudhishtira has been crowned king in Hastinapura; he has come to see you with his brothers. Now, more than ever, Yudhishtira has need of your wisdom. He is shaken by all the killing and dying he saw on Kurukshetra. He is full of sorrow, and needs you to comfort him. It is just fifty-six days until uttarayana. When you die, all your wisdom will disappear from the world forever, unless you leave something of what you know with Yudhishtira. Your grandsons have come to you: tell them what you know about dharma, artha and yoga."

Again, the smile touches Bheeshma's face. With an effort, he begins to speak, "You are the Paramatman who pervades this universe: you tell me what I should do. I do not know how much longer I will live. This pain has robbed me of the count of time. I have discharged my debt to Satyavati. I can die in peace now. I am only waiting for Surya's chariot to change its course in the sky."

He pauses; then, another light is in his eyes. He takes Krishna's hand and says, "My Lord, I want to see your Viswarupa before I die. Won't you show yourself to me?"

"At the end of fifty-six days, when you leave your body, I will be at your side. But first, you have one final task left: you must pass your wisdom on to Yudhishtira."

Bheeshma laughs. "Krishna, you mock me! How can I speak of dharma, artha or yoga when you are here with us: you who are the beginning and the end of all knowledge? Dare a sishya hold forth in his guru's presence? And then, these arrows fill me with agony. I can hardly speak."

"You are too modest, Bheeshma," says Krishna. "You must teach Yudhishtira everything you know."

"But I am so weak. I can hardly bear the pain I am in; to speak at any length would be impossible. Besides, my memory has faded, and you want me to remember what I learnt when I was a boy. Forgive me, Krishna, but I don't have the strength for this final task."

The Avatara's body shines. He speaks as softly as before, but there is unearthly authority in his voice. Krishna says, "I grant you a boon: from this moment, until you die, you will feel no pain. Your memory will be as clear as the heart of a rishi. Your mind will be sharp as a sword, Bheeshma, to sever any knot that binds Yudhishtira's heart."

It is told the sky showered down a petal-rain on Krishna and Bheeshma. A wave of relief floods Bheeshma, as all his pain vanishes. Krishna squeezes the Kuru ancient's hand, and then he rises, saying, "We will leave you to collect your thoughts. But we will return early tomorrow to hear your wisdom."

That night is the first restful one Krishna has spent in a long time. He sleeps deeply, a dreamless slumber. Early next morning, he sends Satyaki to Yudhishtira. Soon, they are ready to set out again for Kurukshetra. An hour after dawn, the Pandavas and Krishna arrive on the field. Bheeshma lies on it like the rising sun. He has not felt a twinge of pain since Krishna blessed him, and he too has spent a restful night.

Bheeshma feels detached from his body, free to range through the labyrinths of his days. The past is clear before him in all its fabulous richness; the book of his life is his to read from at will. Indeed, most of the night Bheeshma has leafed through that marvellous tome as he pleased. There is so much he sees plainly now, which was obscured before. Devavrata sees his life for the miracle it has been, every symphonious moment.

Bheeshma welcomes Krishna in a stronger voice. Yudhishtira and his brothers still linger in the background. Narada, who is at Bheeshma's side, says, "Let Yudhishtira ask whatever he has to quickly. Time flits by, and Bheeshma will not live long."

Before Krishna can call Yudhishtira closer, Bheeshma says, "Krishna, I am free of pain, and my mind is keen and clear. I think I can answer any questions Yudhishtira has for me. But there is something I want to know. You can teach the dharma better than I can. Why have you chosen to entrust this task to me?"

Gently Krishna says, "Perhaps you are right, Bheeshma, and I can tell Yudhishtira what he needs to know. But I thought, let Bheeshma's name be a legend forever in the world. Let men hear his wisdom and count it as being equal to the Vedas. What you say to your grandson shall be immortal, and men will live their lives by it. A man is said to live in the world for as long as his fame does. You are the greatest man ever to grace the earth, and I want your spirit to be with humankind forever. So, I ask you to teach the dharma to Yudhishtira and his brothers."

Tears start down Bheeshma's face, as he listens to the Avatara and feels his love upon him. Bheeshma is speechless for that stupendous love. At last, slowly, the Kuru patriarch says, "Let Yudhishtira ask me whatever he wants. I will be happy to tell him anything I know."

"Yudhishtira is afraid to approach you. He thinks you might blame him for what happened during the war."

Bheeshma raises his voice and calls Yudhishtira. When the Pandava comes hesitantly, and kneels at his side, Bheeshma lays both his hands on his head, blessing him. Laughing, the patriarch says, "Why should you be afraid to come to your Pitama? I know your noble heart; I blame you for nothing. My child, every kshatriya's dharma is to fight and kill his enemies, whoever they may be. You have only followed your dharma; why should you feel guilty? Call your brothers also, and ask me whatever you want. I learnt what I know from unworldly masters, long ago. And I will tell you everything I learnt: by the grace of this immortal one who has come among us, and is pleased to call himself Krishna."

FOUR

Bheeshma's wisdom*

THE KURU SOVEREIGN YUDHISHTIRA ASKS HIS GRANDSIRE BHEESHMA, lying on his bed of arrows, "I have heard that a king's is the highest dharma. Pitama, I would learn my dharma from you."

Bheeshma says, "A king's first dharma is to worship the Gods, and to honour brahmanas who are illumined men. But he himself should always be a karma yogin, a man of deeds. There are those that say destiny is all-important in a king's life. Karma comes first, Yudhishtira. Destiny is important, but his own actions shape a king's destiny. Indeed, I would even say a king's deeds are more powerful than destiny.

"The king's second dharma is to be truthful. If you are a man of truth, your subjects will honour you, trust you. A king must be above reproach. He must be restrained, humble and righteous. He must be a master of his passions.

"Justice must be like breathing to him: it must come naturally. As for his weaknesses, he must know how to conceal them, to be perfectly secretive about them. He must know his enemies' weaknesses, and hardly let them know he does. A king's plans must be opaque, known only to himself and, perhaps, one or two counsellors whom he trusts.

---

* The patriarch's discourse on the dharma of kshatriyas and kings teems, among other things, with creation legends, tales of the devas and asuras, the rishis, parables and other stories, descriptions of many royal houses and bloodlines, the nature and art of kingship, legends of great kings of the past, the yugas and ages gone by, the Avataras of God, and expositions on the nature of time and God. In Ganguli's translation the discourse, which runs through both parvas, is about 900 pages long.

"A king's demeanour should be unafraid and straightforward. He must not be too mild. He will be disregarded if he is, and his subjects will have no respect for him. That does not mean he should be harsh or tyrannical, and that his people should be unduly frightened of him.

"Most of all, a king must know how to choose those who serve him. He should be a judge of men, and know whom he can trust and who are dangerous. Compassion must be part of the good king, but never weakness. If he is weak, the lowest men will take advantage of him.

"Vigilance is integral to a king's every moment. He must always be alert, and study both his friends and his enemies. Above all, he must remember his first duty is towards his subjects. He must nurture them as a mother does the child in her womb. His dharma is never to please himself at his people's expense. As a mother is with her child, a king should be with his people: their welfare should be his only concern.

"A king must be the loneliest man in the land. He must not share his inmost thoughts with anyone, not even his closest advisors. He must be adept at dealing with the stronger enemy, the equal, and the weaker one. He must know how to employ spies and sow dissension in his enemy's city, to divide those that serve his enemy. He should know how to bribe his enemy's soldiers and officials, make them betray their master.

"A king should speak pleasantly at all times. He should surround himself with those that are as noble as he is, whose natures and thoughts concur with his own. Indeed, the only difference between himself and those that serve him should be the crown on his head.

"The noblest king is the one in whose country the subjects are like children in their father's house. They are contented, because it is their own home they are living in. There is no deceit or pretence among them, no envy or dishonesty.

"The essence of a king's dharma is to secure his subjects' prosperity, their happiness. There is no harder task on earth, and he must use varied methods to achieve his ends. Most important are the men he appoints to positions of power. They must be honest and sincere men, yet he should never trust them entirely. The treasury must always be full, for the king's power stems from his wealth, as well. He must always have a powerful army to protect his kingdom, for that, too, is the secret of his strength. He must be a master of creating discord in his enemies' kingdoms, because therein also lies his strength. He should be wary and always on his guard against his enemy, who would do the same to him: create dissension within his country, his very court.

"The king is the justice in the land. He is the one who metes out punishment to wrongdoers, and protects the righteous. He should be honest; but he must know the ways of the world, how to fight fire with fire. He can never afford to be a simpleton. And yet, the world must never see him as being other than candid and straightforward."

Thus, Bheeshma of the Kurus discourses on the dharma of a king to Yudhishtira. He dwells on the many nuances and secrets of kingship, and they soon find the day has flown by and the sun is sinking in the west. Yudhishtira takes his Pitama's hand and says, "You must rest now. I will return, first thing in the morning. There is so much I have to ask you still."

Bheeshma lays his palm on Yudhishtira's head. He shuts his eyes, and peace steals over him. He falls into a deep, healing sleep.

The next morning, Yudhishtira and his brothers arrive with the sun. Yudhishtira has a question for his grandsire. "Pitama, how does a king come to be called Rajan? He is just a man like all other men. He is subject to joy and grief. His mind and his senses are like those of other men. His lives for as long as other men do. Among his subjects, are men that are his superiors in intellect, in wisdom and courage. Yet, the king rules all the others. Why is one man elevated to being a Rajan, Pitama?"

Bheeshma says, "Long ago, in the first ages of krita and treta, there were no kings or kingdoms. The world was one, and all men lived as one, in love, sharing the plenitude of the earth. The pristine spaces of nature were man's inheritance and he was fulfilled in them, he rejoiced in them. All men were like brothers; they cared for one another as parts of themselves.

"As time advanced, evil crept into the hearts of men. Covetousness was the first darkness to cloud the light of men's minds: they became greedy, and wanted possessions. Ancient man was free of such possessiveness; he knew his natural place in the order of things, and exulted in time and its subtle fruit of wisdom and delight.

"The first step towards darkness was covetousness, but lust was not far behind. Lust never hunts alone; wrath arrived with it. The age grew dark, and anarchy and confusion swept the world. The original Veda vanished from the lips and the minds of men; dharma vanished with the Veda. The guardians of the world, the Devas, took panic and came trembling before their sire Brahma in his sabha.

"Indra cried, 'Lord, the world you created is plunging towards destruction. You must save it.'

"It was then that Brahma composed the Neeti Shastra, an interminable treatise on conduct. It contained a hundred thousand edicts. So far, men had been pure, and had needed no more than their untainted natures to be their guru. Now they were corrupted, their hearts had grown dark; they had need of a law outside themselves. When there is a law, someone must enforce that law. For the first time, men were divided into rulers and the ruled.

"The Neeti Shastra dealt with the four concerns of human life: dharma, artha, kama and moksha. Brahma dwelt on these, at length. An important part of the Neeti Shastra dealt with crime and its punishment: what constituted a crime and how each crime should be punished. There were two kinds of punishment the Shastra dealt with, the open and the secret punishment. It dealt, for the first time, with traders and trade, and the conservation of wealth. It dealt with rishis and tapasya. It spoke of thieves and other criminals, and how they should be treated.

"Another section of the Neeti Shastra dwelt on religious observances and rituals, and the conduct of the various officials in the kingdom: of counsellors, spies, ambassadors, and the method of conciliation.

"Brahma composed that Shastra in a mere moment, and he said, 'Let this be called the Dandaneeti, the way of chastisement. There has never been crime or punishment before in the world. Now, there is already crime, and let there be punishment as well.'

"The treatise was studied and abridged by the great Gods, Siva being the first. Just before it was given to men, the wise Sukra saw it. He knew men's lives were short, and most of them would hardly have the time to study such a voluminous Shastra. Sukra pared the original Dandaneeti down to its present form of a thousand essential edicts. Then, the Devas brought the tract to the Lord Vishnu who lies upon eternity's ocean of bliss. They said to him, 'Lord, show us a man on earth worthy of ruling all other men.'

"Vishnu said to them, 'I will enter the body of one man. He and his sons shall be lords of the earth.'

"A man called Vena was chosen to be king. From Vena's right arm, a son was born and he was as glorious as Indra. He was born wearing a coat of mail, and with all the occult and earthly weapons. He was born knowing the Vedas and the Shastras, the art of war and of kingship, and all the other arts, too. His name was Prithu and the rishis made him king of the world. Men said, in those days, that Prithu was the eighth son of Vishnu himself.

"Prithu levelled the uneven earth. Vishnu and the Devas came down to witness the coronation of Prithu. Bhumidevi came as a Goddess bearing treasures of gold and jewels for King Prithu. Prithu asked her to be a cow, and he milked her for the seven foods, which all living creatures would eat. Prithu was the lord not only of men, but also of the forests and the trees, and the birds and beasts in them.

"It was Prithu who first established dharma in the world, and elevated it above all else. Prithu brought peace and righteousness back to the earth, and because the people loved him, he was called Rajan: 'He who pleased all men'. Because he healed men's sick minds, he was also called Kshatriya; because the earth was pervaded by virtue during his reign, she was named Prithvi, after him.

"Vishnu is said to have entered that first king's body, and Prithu was blessed with divine intelligence, superior to any other man's. Thus, a king was created by the Gods themselves, and was not to be trifled with. That was why he ruled the world, but not the world him. And so, Yudhishtira, a king is called Rajan."

Yudhishtira asks, "What is the dharma of the people?"

"Their first task is to choose a king, and crown him. For his treasury, they must give up a fiftieth part of their livestock and gold, and a tenth part of their grain. They should help him choose from among them men that are proficient at arms, so the kingdom can have an army. It is said a fourth part of the people's punya, their virtue, accrues to their king, and so, too, a fourth of their paapa, their sins. Before their king, the people should be as a sishya before his guru, humble. A king whom his own subjects honour will naturally be feared by his enemies."

"What are a king's other duties, Pitama?"

"First of all, a king should subdue himself. Then it will be easy to subdue his enemies. There is no conquest as hard as that of his own five senses. Every king must wage a lifelong war against these.

"A king must have an army to defend his kingdom and his people. He must be vigilant, because danger is always near. He must have spies who warn him of everything that goes on in his enemies' kingdoms, why, in their very hearts. His spies must be the cleverest of his agents. They must seem like fools before whom an enemy will speak freely, without fear; or they must seem like men that are deaf and blind. In fact, they must be wise men, sharp and loyal, a king's eyes and ears in his streets, and in distant parts. His spies must be the hardiest, most incorruptible men, strong, and able to bear long privations: exile, cold, heat, violence and hunger. A king must have secret agents in his own court, that spy on his ministers, his friends, even on his sons. His spies should report only to the king himself. They must not know one another, or they will become too powerful.

"The king, on whom his people rely, must never hesitate to be ruthless with his enemies. It must not be beneath him to use treachery, fire and poison against them. He should take a sixth of his people's income for himself, as tithe, to maintain his army for their protection. His people are a king's children, but he must not be overly compassionate when punishing the criminals among them, or he will lose respect.

"Honest men, who are perfectly trustworthy, must be appointed to administer justice in the kingdom. If they are corrupt, the nation becomes weak. The old adage is so true, Yudhishtira: that the king makes the age; and not the other way, that the age makes the king.

"Yet, the four yugas have their different natures and gifts to bestow on the earth. The age when the kings of the world rule entirely by the Neeti Shastra is called the satya or the krita yuga. Dharma prevails perfectly in this yuga, and evil is unknown. It is an age when there is hardly any need for a king. The earth yields food without being tilled or sown, and life-giving herbs and sacred plants, which cure every disease, grow abundantly. Sickness hardly exists during the halcyon krita, and men live long lives. Every season is full of delight, and peace and harmony suffuse the earth, and its rulers reign immaculately by the Dandaneeti.

"Then, comes an age when the king rules with three parts of dharma, and one of darkness. This is the treta yuga. The earth no longer yields food on her own, but waits to be tilled. The third yuga is the dwapara, and its sovereigns employ a half part of dharma to rule, and the other half adharma, evil. The earth gives only half of what she can, and the foods she yields are only half as nourishing as they once were. The herbs of healing, also, have lost their power by half, and men too have lost half their dignity, strength and splenduor.

"In the last age, the kali yuga, the kings of the earth oppress their own people. Adharma is the rule of the day, and hardly a fourth of the Dandaneeti is used. The earth is governed by anarchy and violence. All kinds of diseases sweep the world, and men live short, harsh lives. The men of this yuga are diminished in every respect; indeed, they are hardly men in the sense that men of old were. They are creatures of darkness, their hearts ruined by greed, lust, malice and envy. The clouds do not bring the rain in season; drought and famine have their way with the world.

"These are the yugas, Yudhishtira, and the king is said to cause them."

"Pitama, the king is the lord of wealth. Whose wealth does he own?"

"The Vedas say that the wealth of all men, except brahmanas, belongs to the king. It is the king's dharma to support the holy ones, who bless the kingdom."

The Pandava asked, "No king can accomplish even the smallest task by himself, but he needs his ministers. What are the traits and the dharma of the king's ministers? What kind of men are worthy of being ministers?"

Bheeshma says, "A king is usually surrounded by four kinds of men. The first kind is the one whose opinion is always the same as his own, dharma or not. The second kind is the man who is sincerely devoted to his sovereign. The third is related by blood; and the fourth may be those who began as enemies, but have been won over with gifts.

"There is also a fifth man, who serves only dharma. This fifth kind is rigid, and a king should exercise caution while confiding in him. A king has to rule not only with dharma, but with adharma, too; and the fifth kind of friend or minister will censure him whenever he uses the dark ways. He might even betray him.

"Most important is choosing the ministers with whom a king will surround himself. When power and position are involved, no man can be trusted entirely. A dishonest man can appear honest, and an honest man, a villain. Power also changes men. A man who was scrupulously honest can be corrupted by power, and become dishonest. Thus, no one must be trusted implicitly. Yet, a king cannot be unduly suspicious either. He must blend trust with mistrust, judiciously. He should use one minister to spy on another.

"But of all those close to him, a king should fear his own blood like death. A kinsman always considers himself the king's equal or his superior, and he is more envious than anyone else. His own kinsman cannot bear to see a king prosper." A wry smile twitches at the Kuru patriarch's lips. He says, "But you know all about that, Yudhishtira. Yet, a king needs his kinsmen more than anyone else. With them, also, he must behave as if he trusts them completely, but in truth he must always be watchful."

Yudhishtira asks, "What kind of men should be made legislators? What qualities should the ministers of war have? Which men should be a king's courtiers, and which ones his counsellors?"

"The legislators should be modest, restrained men; they must be honest and sincere, and have the courage of truth with them at all times. The ministers for war must be men who are close to the king, ever at his side. Most of all, they must be brave men, and kshatriyas. They must be learned, too, and their only fault should be their excessive love for their master. A courtier should be from the noblest lineage, and the king must always treat him with honour. He, also, must be one who is always loyal, a man who never abandons his sovereign, whatever the circumstances.

"The officers of the army must be from noble stock, and born in the king's own country. Let them be handsome, learned and powerful men, so they inspire loyalty and devotion in their soldiers. They must be of impeccable conduct, and, above everything else, loyal.

"As counsellors a king must have four brahmanas, learned in the Vedas, all of them snatakas, and dignified past reproach. He must have eight kshatriyas, strong men and proficient warriors. He must have twenty-one vaishyas, all wealthy, three sudras, pure, humble and intelligent, and one suta. Remember that these counsellors must all be above fifty years of age.

"Among a king's main tasks is to punish those that commit crimes in his land. The wealthy criminal should have his riches or property taken from him, while the poor criminal should be imprisoned. Corporal punishment may be used to check the more hardened law-breakers.

"A good king levies taxes as a bee gathers pollen from flowers: gently, without injuring his people. He is like a tigress who grips her cubs firmly in her teeth, but never hurts them."

Bheeshma imparts his treasure of wisdom to Yudhishtira over many days. There is much he shares that has not been recorded: for, at times, he speaks in secret. At dusk, the Pandavas go back to Hastinapura, and they return each morning with the sun.

Once, Yudhishtira asks, "Pitama, tell me again how a king should conduct himself."

"Dharma must be his very life, for there is nothing greater than dharma in the world. Dharma makes one king better than another; and, with dharma, a king can conquer the earth. Remember his ministers must be men of dharma, as well, as pure as he is; and their truth should radiate, by word and by deed, throughout the land. Malice has no place in a king's heart. His senses must be perfectly subdued. He must love his people as a father does his children, and he should use his intelligence without passion. Then, his reign will be glorious, and his greatness swell like a sea fed by a thousand rivers."

Yudhishtira says, "The way of dharma is long, it is said to have a hundred branches. Which are the main duties to be followed?"

"First of all, the mother, the father and the guru must be worshipped, and what they command must be obeyed without question. Serving his father helps a man cross the sea of samsara, serving his mother raises him up into Devaloka, and serving the guru bestows the realm of Brahma on a sishya."

"Tell me about dharma, artha and kama, Pitama. Which of them helps take one's life in the right direction?"

"The three exist together; they are indivisible when a man creates artha, wealth, for himself, always treading the path of dharma. Wealth is rooted in virtue, and kama, pleasure, is the fruit of wealth. All these come to be by the effort of a man's will. In this world, there are objects created for the gratification of the senses, and the acquisition of these is the will's concern.

"When a man is unattached to the objects of pleasure, he is liberated. One needs virtue, punya, to protect the body. One requires wealth to be virtuous. However, dharma, artha and kama must never be pursued just for themselves, but always as a means to knowledge: the knowledge of the Self. Virtue must be acquired not for pleasure, but to purify the soul. Wealth must be acquired so it can be spent with perfect relinquishment, and pleasure must be pursued not to gratify the body but only to support it.

"Thus, dharma, artha and kama are founded in the will, and all three are necessary means to an end. The end is moksha, the final goal, the only one. As a man approaches moksha, he must abandon dharma, artha and kama by tapasya, ascetic penance."

FIVE

Dharma

ANOTHER TIME, YUDHISHTIRA ASKS, "THEY SAY INTELLIGENCE IS superior to everything else. Intelligence helps a man plan for the future, to provide for it; with intelligence, a man meets every emergency. Pitama, tell me about intelligence and how to use it. Especially when a king is beset by many enemies, how does he protect himself with intelligence?"

"When a king is in distress, he often finds that a friend becomes a foe, and an enemy a friend. There are times when fate makes everything uncertain, and a king hardly knows what to do. There are times when an enemy must be befriended, and times when a friend must be treated as an enemy. What a king does depends on the times, and the king who does not hesitate to do what the time demands seldom fails. While a king who is unbending, seldom succeeds.

"Of course, a man must be investigated thoroughly, before he is accepted as a friend. Enemies must be studied even more carefully, their every strength and weakness examined. In this life, which is a play of masks, often friends appear in the guise of foes, and foes disguised as friends. The terms friend and enemy are relative: when a man suits one's interests, he is a friend; when he opposes them, he is an enemy. If a man serves one's purpose as long as he lives, he is a lifelong friend. Ultimately, friendship and enmity are matters of self-interest.

"Selfishness is the most powerful impulse in every man: the world turns on this pivot. No man is precious to another unless he stands to gain by him. Of course, men's needs are varied, and one man is popular because he is liberal-minded, another because he is sweet-tongued, and a third because he is religious. Like-minded people generally become friends, until time changes their affections. It is the rule and not the exception that friendships last as long as they serve some purpose. As soon as the reason for the friendship ends, so does the friendship itself.

"An intelligent man knows when to make peace with an enemy. When two enemies become friends, it is obvious that each one only bides his time until he can get the better of the other. And it is invariably true that the wiser and the more patient of the two is the one that succeeds. Until the proper opportunity presents itself, you must pretend there is no one dearer to you than your enemy, no one you trust as much. When the time comes, never hesitate to wage war! Yudhishtira, this policy applies not only with enemies, but friends as well."

Another day, Yudhishtira asks, "Pitama, what is the font of sin? From where does evil spring?"

"Greed is the single root of evil. Greed destroys dharma and punya. From this single spring the river of sin flows. When a man covets, he becomes full of hypocrisy and cunning. Anger and lust come from covetousness, and so do a hundred other sicknesses of the mind. The loss of judgement comes from it, deception, arrogance, malice, vindictiveness, shamelessness, the loss of virtue, anxiety and infamy all spring from covetousness. These are not all. Miserliness, cupidity, arrogance of birth, arrogance of learning, of beauty, of wealth, every impropriety, harshness of speech, speaking ill of others, ruthlessness, malevolence, insincerity, gluttony, a love of lies, indeed, a love of every kind of sin: all sprout from the root of covetousness. My son, no man in this world has been able to relinquish greed. Life on earth may decay, men may diminish in numbers and stature; but the power of greed will never fade. Even the greatest men, those of deep learning, whose minds are a treasury of the scriptures, those who are so able at advising others: these are found wanting when it comes to managing their own lives. Greed nestles in their hearts and makes them weak and cowardly—its slaves."

"Tell me about ignorance, Pitama," says Yudhishtira.

"Ignorance, too, springs from the same covetousness. As greed grows, so does ignorance, and the mind becomes dark and hardly sees clearly any more."

Yudhishtira is thoughtful, then asks, "What are the first duties of a king, which must have precedence over the rest?"

"Restraint is the quintessential dharma. Just as giving in to his greed leads a man to every sin, restraining himself leads him to glory. From restraint come the virtues of compassion, forgiveness, patience, mercy, impartiality, truth, sincerity, humility, modesty, steadiness, tolerance and liberality, serenity, contentment, sweetness of speech, benevolence, and a heart free of malice. A restrained man will never be a slave to the attachments of this world, nor to his greed. Once he learns to restrain himself, he is already upon the threshold of moksha."

"Tell me about the truth, my lord, if you are not tired."

Bheeshma smiles. "All my pain and tiredness left me, when Krishna blessed me. Truth is the dharma not just of kings, but every human being. Truth is the eternal dharma; it is the final sanctuary, the last tapasya. Truth is the highest yoga; why, it is the immortal Brahman. There is no yagna as profound as truth: the three worlds are founded in truth and nothing else.

"There are many aspects to truth, Yudhishtira. Impartiality, self-control, forgiveness, modesty, endurance, goodness, renunciation, contemplation, dignity, fortitude, compassion, and non-violence are some. But the Truth itself is single, eternal, immutable."

"What must a man strive for in his life?"

"All the living are in death's shadow. The nights come and go, but every moment death draws nearer. Death waits for no man; it frequently arrives before a man's desires in this life have been fulfilled. Even when a man is plucking flowers in his garden, death snatches him away, like a tiger a ram. So, my child, avoid procrastination in your life. Finish today what you had planned to do tomorrow. Do in the morning what you had left for the afternoon. Time is always shorter than we believe, and a man must acquire virtue as quickly as he can. Thus, one must be ready for death: for he comes at his whim, without notice. Only virtue bestows fame in this world and the next.

"On earth, man is plagued by a thousand desires, endlessly. He grows attached to possessions and people; he grows attached to places and houses. His work, his home, his lands, his wife and children all weave a subtle web of bondage. Death brutally tears every thread. Nothing but truth can resist the web of attachment. When a man realizes how ephemeral this world is, he sees the truth; then death holds no fear for him. For, the fear of death springs from attachment. In every man, there are the seeds of death, and the seeds of freedom. It is left to each man which seeds he chooses to nurture. It always seems the seeds of attachment are easier to nourish. But the truth of time is otherwise.

"Thus the wise man restrains his senses; he rises above desire and anger. He learns how to treat pleasure and pain alike. Serenity comes to him and, then, nirvana. What he thinks and what he says, what he does: all his life is founded in Brahman, and such a man does not die, but is born to eternal life.

"There is no vision like knowledge, and truth is the greatest tapasya. Attachment is the most terrible sorrow, and relinquishment the only, deepest joy. Yudhishtira, we are born from Brahman, the eternal current; by Brahman, we are born. If we devote ourselves to that supreme Spirit, we can return to Brahman. My son, always seek the self hidden in the deepest cave of the heart."

Yudhishtira asks, "Which is the man whom all the world loves? Who is he that is perfectly accomplished?"

"He will be learned, good and wise. He is never so proud that he will lose his composure from arrogance. He is contented, and serene. His senses do not lead him astray, and he is always possessed of the peace that comes from knowing the supreme truth."

"Why does a man become a sinner or virtuous? How does he achieve relinquishment, and liberation?"

"It is desire that makes a man sin, when he grows so attached to the objects of the senses that he will do anything to gain them. With attachment, the mind becomes clouded and a man abandons the path of virtue. When he is no longer virtuous, he pretends to be so and becomes a hypocrite. The acquisition of wealth by hypocrisy is not difficult, and the man plunges down the way of sin. He does not listen any longer to the advice of elders and wise men; and soon there is hardly any hope of salvation for him.

"The man of dharma always seeks the welfare of others. He is sage and knows how to avoid the pitfalls of the senses, how not to let them rule him. He knows the difference between brief, empty pleasure and true joy. A man is virtuous when he is a master of his senses. But just this does not give him freedom; he must practise renunciation, so desire tself leaves him, slowly. At the final stage, knowing this world is merely a passing pageant in death's halls, the virtuous man casts off his very virtue and its rewards: heaven and happiness. He sets out to seek moksha, the unchanging condition."

"What are the qualities a man needs to be free from attachment, to achieve moksha?"

"The man who is near moksha has passed beyond the senses and their world. Hunger and thirst do not approach him; his body makes no demands. His mind has grown far beyond anger, greed and sin. He never forgets himself, the truth that is within him. A bamboo hut and a king's palace are the same to such a man. Pain and pleasure do not touch him, he knows both are conceived in delusion. He sees the world clearly, as only the coming together of the five elements. Pain, pleasure, loss, gain, defeat and victory are all the same to him. Fear and anxiety lay no claim on his heart. He knows that a thousand kings of majesty have lived briefly, and then passed on from the earth; he knows the evanescence of life. He has learnt the truth that all things in the world are fleeting, insubstantial. With such wisdom he attains moksha, be it in the jungle or in his home."

The spiritually inclined Yudhishtira is intrigued. He asks, "How can a man attain moksha without leaving his home and its bonds, and going into the forest?"

Bheeshma says, "A king need not abandon his kingdom to attain nirvana; only, he must not be attached to his throne. So, too, with everything else in life, your wife, children, work or wealth. If you can turn your mind away from all these to the eternal Brahman, you will find salvation. Your state of mind is what is important, not where you are. Knowledge comes from relinquishment, and yoga, which is union, comes after knowledge. If his spirit is enlightened, it does not matter if a man lives in his home or in the forest. He is a sannyasin."

Yet another day, Yudhishtira asks, "Where is the Devi of prosperity to be found?"

"She dwells in the eloquent man, the active man, the attentive man. If a man is high-minded, free of anger, and has his passions under control, prosperity comes to him. A man of little energy does not find the Goddess of prosperity, nor does he who is full of anger, or he who is diffident. She lives with brahmanas who are devoted to studying the Vedas, kshatriyas who are men of dharma, vaishyas who are absorbed in their trade, and sudras who are bhaktas."

"What should be the dharma of a man who wants to pass pleasantly through this world, and have heaven in the next?"

"There are three sins of deed such a man must avoid: killing, thieving and adultery. He must avoid four sins of speech: evil talk, harsh words, lies, and speaking ill of others. He must resist three sins of the mind: coveting what belongs to someone else, injuring another in his heart and disbelief in the scriptures. If a man can avoid these ten sins, he passes safely through this world and finds swarga for himself."

"Is there any virtue superior to brahmacharya? What is the highest punya, grandfather, which is the greatest purity?"

"Abstinence from wine and meat is superior to celibacy. Indeed, you can hardly aspire to being a brahmachari if you cannot first control what you eat and drink. Dharma is the highest punya, it is also the greatest purity."

"Which are the times in life for dharma, artha and kama?"

"The first part of a man's life is for earning wealth. Then, dharma must be followed, and the enjoyment of kama comes after. Remember, one should not be attached to any of these, but always be reaching beyond them for moksha."

Another time, Yudhishtira asks, "Which is the holiest tirtha?"

"All the tirthas can purify a man, for they are all blessed; but, my son, there is no tirtha like truth. The deepest, fathomless tirtha is the mind. It is in that tirtha one should bathe, for it is the most untainted of all holy waters. If a man bathes in the Manasa sarovara called truth he becomes sincere and gentle, truthful, compassionate, restrained and tranquil."

"Who is man's truest friend? Is it his mother, his son, his guru or his companion? When a man dies, he abandons his body as if it were no more than a clod of earth. Who is the friend who follows a man into the next world?"

Bheeshma smiles, "Man is born alone, my child, and so, too, he dies. Whether he knows it or not, he is quite alone all through this wondrous journey called life. Once you are dead, who stays with you? Your mother and father, children and guru, your friends and all the others turn away from your funeral pyre, and return to their own lives. But, Yudhishtira, dharma follows you out of this world. Dharma stays with a man even after he is dead. At last, dharma is the only true friend."

There is a lot else that Yudhishtira asks his Pitama and Bheeshma answers the Kuru king patiently, giving freely of his wisdom to the Pandava. At last, one evening, Yudhishtira asks his last questions. "In this world who is the one God in whom we may seek final refuge? Who is the God I can worship, and have everything I want from him? Which is the one true religion that is above all others? Which is the mantra by which a man can free himself from the bonds of life and death?"

Bheeshma takes Yudhishtira's hand. His face full of light, he says, "My son, Krishna is Lord of the universe. He is the God of Gods, who has come among us as a man. There is no one greater than him: among all the stars, in all the ages. He pervades the akhanda, and if you meditate on him, and his many names, you will pass beyond every sorrow." Bheeshma smiles, "You ask me which the greatest religion is. It is Krishna. He is the highest tapasya, the final refuge, and the holiest one. He is the beginning of creation, and its end. Dark Krishna is the eternal Brahman. He is the Paramatman, Lord of the past, the present and the future. Surrender to him, Yudhishtira, and you will find eternal bliss, the place beyond change."

Bheeshma keeps Yudhishtira's hand in his for some time, and they are lost in a living silence, as the sun sets. Yudhishtira is content. Like cobwebs from his mind, his Pitama's wisdom has brushed away his doubts and anxieties. His heart is full of faith again; the tiredness and despair of the war have all but left him.

Muni Vyasa arrives there. He says to Bheeshma, "You have restored Yudhishtira's faith, why, he glows with it. And now, great one, your treasure of wisdom will remain in this world for a time more."

Bheeshma lays his hand on the Pandava's head. "You have no more questions. Go back to your kingdom now, and begin your reign; and let it be a just and prosperous one. I know your heart, Yudhishtira, your subjects will be as happy as the people of the earth were when Nahusha, Harishchandra and Yayati ruled them. Bless you, my son. Go now, and live a joyful life. But when the sun turns north again, at uttarayana, come back to me. I must see you once more at that time, ah, the time I have waited for all this long life!"

Yudhishtira takes the dust from his Pitama's feet. He kisses his hands tenderly, and walks away from him, as night falls. Full of new hope, the Pandavas return to Hastinapura. Slowly, the memories of the war begin to fade from their minds, and they have sense of a new day dawning in their lives. Quiet joy is upon them, welling in their hearts.

On Kurukshetra, profound peace again enfolds Bheeshma upon his uncommon bed. His heart is as light as the air, soaring: at last, he knows he has no task left in this world to fulfil. Death draws near like an old friend.

SIX

The passing of a patriarch

THE DAYS PASS, AND THE SUN TURNS NORTH. THAT MORNING OF THE solstice, Yudhishtira and his brothers return to Kurukshetra, where Bheeshma still lies. With them come Dhritarashtra and Krishna, Gandhari, Kunti, Draupadi, Satyaki, Vidura and Yuyutsu. They bring flowers, incense, silks, sandalwood, jewels, rice grains and fruit. Bheeshma knows his time has finally arrived; he lies waiting. All Hastinapura follows its king to the field of fate.

Bheeshma lies with his eyes shut; Vyasa, Parasara, Narada and the munis from Devaloka surround him. Yudhishtira approaches the patriarch, takes his hand, and says, "Pitama, it is I, Pandu's son Yudhishtira. All of us have come, as you wanted. Dhritarasthra is here, my lord. Krishna is here; the people have come to pay homage to you. I beg you, open your eyes and look at them."

For a moment, Bheeshma does not respond. Then slowly his eyes flutter open, and they are far away, as if they already saw other worlds. Bheeshma sees a sea of people around him; a faint smile touches his lips. He says softly, but very clearly, "Yudhishtira, my son, I am happy to see you with our people. At last, Surya Deva has turned his chariot north again. I have lain here for some sixty days, more. I feel a hundred years have passed. Now, finally, it is time for me to leave this earth."

Bheeshma turns his gaze to Dhritarashtra, "My son, you know the dharma of a king. Yes, you are wise, there is nothing you do not know. All that happened was by fate, none of it could be helped. Don't grieve over your sons who died. Pandu's sons are with you, treat them as your own. Be fulfilled in them, be joyful with them."

Bheeshma pauses, then, says to Yudhishtira, "Fetch me some flowers, child. I want to worship Krishna."

The flowers come; Bheeshma worships Krishna, ritually, and his eyes are so very bright. The Kuru ancient says fervently, "You are the Lord of the universe, you are the Creator of this earth. I beg you, Krishna, show me your Viswarupa, and let me leave this world forever. Bless me that I find the highest sanctuary."

Though all the others see no change in Krishna, Bheeshma's eyes see his Cosmic Form, infinite, ineffable. Krishna takes Bheeshma's hand, he says, "Devavrata, return to your home on high. Go back to the Vasus, and never again shall you be born into this world of men. As for your death, why, you are like Markandeya: death waits for you, you can summon him when you want."

Bheeshma's face is lit by a brilliant smile, and the people see a miracle before their eyes. Devavrata shuts his eyes and calls his death to him. The people of Hastinapura see Bheeshma's body blaze with light, and, limb by limb, from his feet up, the arrows that pierced him fall out and his wounds vanish. Then, the uncanny lustre rises, and leaves his body through the subtle opening on his skull. Scintillating, Bheeshma's soul ascends into heaven.

The sky is full of music; a fine breeze blows, laden with the scents of a thousand flowers of Devaloka. The earth is cool and mild, and the heart of every man and woman is full of the peace beyond understanding.

They make a pyre of sandalwood on Kurukshetra. Yudhishtira and Vidura wrap Bheeshma's body in cerements of silk, they cover him with flowers. In a solemn procession, the Pandavas bring their Pitama on his final journey, while Yuyutsu holds the sovereign white parasol over him. They lift the Kuru patriarch on to the fragrant pyre, around him they lay the hundred arrows that brought him down. The brahmanas and munis all chant the Sama hymns, and Dhritarashtra touches Devavrata's pyre alight with a burning branch. Yudhishtira, his brothers, Vidura and Dhritarashtra stand to the right of the blazing sandalwood. All of them cry, as flames clasp the greatest man who ever lived, make ashes of his body.

Early the next morning, they collect Bheeshma's remains, bones the fire spared and ashes, and come to the Ganga. As they offer tarpana to the departed one, suddenly the river stops flowing! Ganga rises from her waters, lamenting.

She says to the other mourners, "My child is dead, and there was no one like him in all the world. He was a devoted son. He was invincible; even Bhargava could not vanquish him. Today, you have come to float his ashes down my currents, for Shikhandi, who was not even a man, killed my child. Oh Devavrata, all my hopes for you have been proved vain. I thought you would be king of the earth, and now look what is left to me."

She sobs inconsolably, as the others watch in some awe. Then Krishna goes to her, and says, "Don't cry for your son, mother of the world. You know he was your child only briefly. You know who Bheeshma was before he was cursed to a mortal life. He was not merely a man, and he could not be merely a king like one. He was not just a kshatriya; he could not be killed like one. The time of Bheeshma's curse has ended, and he has returned to his kingdom in Devaloka, where he sits on a loftier throne than any of this earth. Your son is a Deva, and he is with the Devas again. Rejoice, Mother Ganga, that at last your Devavrata is free."

Shimmering Ganga bows gravely to Krishna. Her eyes still tear-laden, she vanishes. When they look at the golden river, they see that she flows again, as she has since the world began. Now, standing in the water after offering tarpana to his dead Pitama, Yudhishtira breaks down. Sobs shake him, and he staggers out from the river with Bheema helping him.

Yudhishtira sits on the riverbank, covers his face in his hands and grief convulses him. His mood passes to his brothers, and all of them sob like children, as wild remorse grips their hearts. Before the war began, Dhritarashtra had sent a message to Yudhishtira through Sanjaya. He had said Yudhishtira should abandon all thoughts of war, because, with his gentle nature, even if he won he would regret it ever after. The blind king had not been wrong.

As Yudhishtira sits crying like an orphan, Dhritarashtra comes to comfort him. The uncle raises his nephew up compassionately and enfolds him in an embrace.

Dhritarashtra says, "Come, my son, you cannot lose control of yourself. You are a king now; you have a kingdom to care for. Look at Gandhari and me, Yudhishtira. What is your loss compared to ours, what is your remorse compared to ours? All you did was dharma and you have not sinned. That is not true of us, and we have lost a hundred sons. Come, my son, this is no time for tears, but for courage and fortitude."

Krishna, also, comes and takes Yudhishtira's hand. The Dark One says, "Yudhishtira, your Pitama taught you everything he knew before he left us. You are setting all that at nothing. What will your people do, if you give in to yourself like this?"

Yudhishtira controls himself, and they return to Hastinapura.

BOOK FOURTEEN

Aswamedha Parva

AUM, I bow down to Narayana, the most exalted Nara, and to the Devi Saraswati, and say *Jaya*!

ONE

Krishna says farewell

IN HASTINAPURA, THE PANDAVA TAKES UP THE REINS OF THE CHARIOT of the kingdom. Guilt still haunts him. He blames himself for the war, and all the death it brought. Krishna, Vyasa and Narada pacify him. They speak to him at length, and at least he has the everyday serenity to discharge his dharma as king. Dhritarashtra spends hours talking to his nephew, and Vidura comforts him as well.

Now, that the war is over, Krishna and Arjuna take to spending their time with each other, as they used to in the old days. They go back to Indraprastha, and rediscover the places where they first grew close. They wander the gardens of the city and spend hours, alone together, in the Mayaa sabha. They range the forest around Indraprastha, hunting, speaking of everything under the sun, of the war, and, especially, the events that led to it*.

It hardly seems a few days since they were last here, but in fact fifteen years have gone by. They ride out to the Khandava vana that they helped Agni burn. It was there that they first met Mayaa. The thread of time shimmers clear, its silver strands. Krishna asked Mayaa to build a sabha for Yudhishtira; and then the tide of fate swept them along, helplessly. Perhaps, it began even before that: when dark Panchali entered their lives. That was the very day Krishna first met his cousins, the Pandavas.

---

* In this section, Arjuna questions Krishna further about the Gita that the Avatara revealed to him before the war. There is a spiritual discourse (of some 70 pages) by Krishna, called the Anugita—the little Gita.

They were given a wilderness for their patrimony, and the Avatara raised Indraprastha in the desolation. Narada came and told Yudhishtira that Pandu was unhappy in Yama's halls. The Rajasuya followed, and stoked Duryodhana's envy. Krishna killed Sishupala, and everything else had come like a flash flood: the game of dice, Dusasana dragging Draupadi into the Kuru sabha, the swearing of the oaths of revenge, and then exile.

Arjuna remembers how he went to Dwaraka to ask for Krishna's help. Duryodhana had been there, that day. Arjuna chose Krishna for his sarathy, and that sealed the fate of the Kauravas. Then, the war to end all wars. Finally, Yudhishtira sat on the throne to which he was born.

One day, Krishna says to Arjuna, "The war is won, your enemies are dead and Yudhishtira sits where he belongs, on the throne of Hastinapura. I have served my purpose, Arjuna, and I must return to Dwaraka. I have not seen my mother and father, and they must be anxious. I haven't the courage to ask Yudhishtira if I can leave. I beg you, ask him for me, Arjuna. If he agrees, I will go; if he says I must stay, I shall. What Yudhishtira wants is more important to me than what I want myself. But tell him I said he has his brothers with him to help him rule, he has the wise Vidura at his side. Arjuna, you must also let me go now."

Before he has finished, he sees tears in Arjuna's eyes. Krishna takes his cousin's hand. The Pandava can hardly bear to think of parting from his sarathy. The eighteen days of the war had been the most wonderful days of his life. Krishna had been with him every moment! Fear and triumph they had shared, sorrow and courage. During the war, they had been like one person: two bodies, but one spirit. Arjuna thinks he would not mind reliving his life, every day of it, just to be as near Krishna as he had during the war.

Arjuna cries, "You have served your purpose! How can you say that to me?"

Krishna smiles. "I only meant the war, Pandava. I know you need me still, and I need you. I can hardly live without you, my friend. Don't you understand? You and I are not apart from each other. Half Krishna's soul is Arjuna!"

For the first time, Krishna tells Arjuna about the anxious night he spent before the day Jayadratha died. He tells him how he told Daruka to keep his chariot ready, because he would kill Jayadratha himself if Arjuna could not. Arjuna cries again to hear him. He clasps Krishna to

Krishna says farewell

him, and they sit thus, in silence, for a long time. Then, softly, the Pandava says, "I will let you go back to Dwaraka, but only if you promise to return to us soon."

"How will I stay away for long?" replies Krishna.

The next day the two of them ride back to Hastinapura. They spend that evening with Dhritarashtra and Yudhishtira. In the morning, Arjuna and Krishna come to Yudhishtira's apartment. They sit chatting pleasantly of this and that, though Yudhishtira's face continues to show signs of a deep grief.

After a while, Arjuna says, "Krishna feels he must return to Dwaraka. He says his father will be waiting for him."

Sighing, Yudhishtira says, "Of course you must go back to see your father and mother. But oh, my Lord, how will we live without you?" Krishna only smiles. Yudhishtira wipes his tears, then, says, "Very well, I will let you go. But on one condition: that you come to me in Hastinapura, just as you used to in Indraprastha, as soon as I think of you. Whenever I needed you, Krishna, you always came. Let that never change. Go now; go home to Vasudeva and Devaki. They must long to see you. So much has happened in our world since you were last with them."

Krishna says, "I will be here whenever you need me, that will never change. One war has ended, Yudhishtira, but another, greater one is just beginning. You still have the war against yourself to win."

The Avatara takes leave of his cousins. Satyaki bids the Pandavas farewell; after embracing his friend, Bheema stands in a daze, staring dully ahead of him. After everything they have been through together, at death's very gates, parting is hard indeed. Krishna prostrates himself before Dhritarashtra and Gandhari, Kunti, Vidura, Yudhishtira and Bheema. He takes tender leave of Draupadi, Nakula and Sahadeva. Finally, he embraces Arjuna, quickly, then turns away and climbs into his chariot. Daruka flicks his reins over his horses, and Krishna and Satyaki set out for home. The Pandavas stand gazing after the white chariot long after it has vanished from view.

When they have driven some way, Krishna lays a hand on his sarathy's shoulder, "Come, Daruka, now fly!"

The horses flash across the ground, then rise steeply into the air and go the way of the wind: home to mysterious Dwaraka, jewel in the sea.

TWO

The Aswamedha yagna

THE DAYS PASS, AND HIS KINGDOM PROSPERS LIKE THE EARTH blooming in a sacred spring; but Yudhishtira still grieves. One day, Vyasa returns to Hastinapura. He finds the Pandava king dejected, wasting. Bheema and Arjuna tell the muni that remorse still torments their brother.

Vyasa says to Yudhishtira, "It seems all our advice has been in vain. You still mourn for what is past, which cannot be recalled or mended. Your brothers are distraught to see you like this, your mother is anxious for your health."

Sadly, Yudhishtira says, "My lord, I cannot help myself, though I try."

Before he came, Vyasa has already thought of a remedy for Yudhishtira. "There is a remedy prescribed of old that will help you subdue your sorrow. Undertake an Aswamedha yagna."

Hope flickers in the Pandava's eyes. He says, "The Aswamedha will purify the earth of the sins of war, but a king must have vast resources before he can even think of the yagna. The war has emptied our coffers. I cannot dream of performing an Aswamedha. Why, the commonest sacrifice would tax me sorely."

"The Ikshvaku king of old, Marutta's, treasure lies buried under the Himalaya. I know where the stone vault is, and the trove is waiting to be unearthed by a needy king of the earth."

"How was such a treasure hidden on the mountain?"

"Once, Marutta wanted to perform a profound yagna, and approached Guru Brihaspati to be his priest. Brihaspati said, 'I am the guru of the

Devas of light, of Indra himself. How can I be the priest of a mere mortal king? Find someone else to be your ritvik.'

"Marutta sought the counsel of some munis. No ordinary priest would suffice for the yagna he planned, he had need of a great brahmana. He was advised to seek the services of Brihaspati's brother, Samvarta, who now lived in a forest on earth. Samvarta had left Devaloka because he could not bear his brother's envy any more, and Indra always took Brihaspati's part against him. Marutta found Samvarta, and begged him to be his priest. Samvarta said, 'I will be your ritvik, Kshatriya. You must first worship Lord Siva. Only he can give you the wealth you will need for the yagna of yagnas that you plan.'

"Marutta of the House of the Sun was a rajarishi. He sat in tapasya, and Siva blessed him with a treasure like the world had never seen. Marutta and Samvarta decided to perform the yagna upon the Himalaya. A thousand craftsmen were commissioned to create the golden urns for the sacrifice, and build a wonderful yagnashala on the mountain. When Brihaspati heard who Marutta's priest was to be, when he heard about the wealth with which Siva had blessed that king, he was livid with envy. He grew pale, thin, and wasted day by day.

"Indra asked him, 'My lord, what ails you? Don't your servants care for you well?'

"Brihaspati said in a low voice, 'Marutta has begun his yagna with wealth won from Siva. Samvarta is his priest.'

"'But you are my own priest, the Devaguru. How can Samvarta harm you?'

"Grimly, his master replied, 'Who can bear to see an enemy prosper? Indra, you must do something to put out the fire in my heart!'

"Indra sent messengers to Marutta's court, offering him Brihaspati's services as priest for his yagna. Marutta sent his reply to the Deva king, 'Samvarta shall be my ritvik.'

"Furious Indra wanted to cast his Vajra at Marutta, but Samvarta prevented him with his tapasya shakti. Finally, Indra and the other Devas attended Marutta's yagna, and, pacified by that king, gave him their blessing. When the sacrifice on the Himalaya was complete, Marutta gave away gold by the sack to the brahmanas who had come to chant the Vedas. Siva had been so generous that, even after this, a huge treasure was left over, gold and jewels to fill a storehouse. Marutta had this wealth sealed in a rock chamber on the mountain, in a secret place, and he returned to his capital, Ayodhya."

As Vyasa speaks, Yudhishtira looks around at his brothers, and sees how eager they are. Bheema will do anything to see his brother get over his sorrow, and be enthused by something again. Arjuna, essential kshatriya, is always delighted at the prospect of a campaign. For, of course, Yudhishtira will send him to ride with the sacrificial horse of the Aswamedha, daring any king to arrest its careen.

At last, a smile dawns on Yudhishtira's face. It is perhaps the first time he has smiled since the war ended. He says to Vyasa, "My lord, let us go to the Himalaya and uncover Marutta's treasure. We will perform an Aswamedha yagna."

Before anything else, Yudhishtira sends word to Krishna in Dwaraka, informing him of their plans. He asks his cousin to come to Hastinapura with his Yadavas for the sacrifice. Suddenly, the eldest Pandava's disposition is transformed. Once more, he seems to look forward to something; there is a light in his eyes again. Vyasa smiles to himself, he knows the immediate reason for Yudhishtira's change of heart. The Kuru king loves no place on earth as he does the Himalayas, where he was born. There is no other place, which can comfort him and return peace to his troubled spirit like those holy mountains.

The Pandavas leave Yuyutsu to care for Dhritarashtra, Gandhari and Kunti, and, on an auspicious morning, they set out for the Himalaya with a force of chariots and men.

Word of the Aswamedha reaches Krishna, and he and his Vrishnis set out from Dwaraka. They arrive in Hastinapura a month before the Pandavas return. Having quite forgotten the rage that seized him when he saw Duryodhana felled, Balarama also rides with Krishna. There is another reason why Krishna arrives early; there is another task for him in the city of the Kurus. Abhimanyu's wife Uttaraa is in mourning. She cannot forget her dead husband, that the time they spent together was so short. Uttaraa carries Abhimanyu's child in her womb, and her confinement is near.

Krishna arrives early in Hastinapura because, after Aswatthama's curse that the brahmasirsa would destroy every unborn Pandava, the Dark One swore he would restore life to Uttaraa's child. Great anticipation is alive in the city as the day draws near. At last, on a bright still morning, the princess delivers a fine son. But their cries of celebration die on the midwives' lips, and shrill wailing breaks out. With Satyaki at his side, Krishna rushes to the chamber of birth.

They meet Kunti stumbling out from Uttaraa's room, her face covered, sobbing. Kunti sees Krishna and cries, "Only you can save us now! Abhimanyu's son is stillborn. Oh, he looks almost alive and he is so handsome. But no breath stirs in him, and his heart doesn't beat in his chest. It will be the end of the Kuru line if he does not live. You must give life to Uttaraa's son, Krishna, you must!"

She falls on the floor, and clasps her nephew's feet. Gently, Krishna raises her up. He says, "I have sworn Uttaraa's son will live, even if I have to use up all my punya to give him life."

Krishna enters Uttaraa's chamber, where Draupadi is in tears, and Subhadra is inconsolable. When Uttaraa sees Krishna, she jumps up naked from her bed and runs dementedly to him. She also kneels at his feet, "Lord, save my child, or I will take my own life!"

She faints, and her women lift her up and set her on her bed again. Krishna approaches that bed and sees the perfect infant lying there, as if he slept. Though his eyes are wide open, they stare glassily and no breath moves his chest. Krishna grows very still. The smile vanishes from his face, and his eyes glow uncannily. The women fall hushed, they have never seen him like this before.

Krishna gazes intently at just the lifeless child, as if the rest of the world has ceased to exist. In a whisper, he asks for holy water. Pouring some into his palm, he murmurs quiet words over Uttaraa's child, and sprinkles the water over him. The air in the room is electric, no one stirs; why, they hardly breathe, for the dhyana of the Blue God. In a trance, Krishna takes the baby in his hands. Unearthly light is upon the Avatara. He shines like the night sky when a full moon rises into it.

The child is limp in his hands. Slowly, Krishna passes his hands along the infant's body, from his feet up over his legs, his belly, and chest, to his fine head. The women in that room can almost see the prana passing from Krishna's fingers into the unbreathing child.

Krishna says, "If I have always served dharma, let this child have life!"

The baby stirs, his limbs twitch. His tiny mouth puckers up, a spark of life ignites in his eyes. Next moment, he kicks his legs and begins to cry in a magnificent little voice!*

In a dream, Uttaraa's eyes fly open. In a dream, she hears her son crying. In an incredulous dream, she sees a radiant Krishna bring her baby to her: a living child that wails for her breast. In an ecstasy, Uttara takes her son in her arms. Around them, the other women stand frozen, like women in a painting. Krishna turns and, smiling, walks out of the room. A tumult of joy breaks out behind him.

Krishna comes out of Uttaraa's door. Now sweat streams down his ashen face, his body is drenched in it. Trembling, he staggers down the passage to a dark corner. He looks as if he has aged a hundred years, since he went into Uttaraa's room of labour. Krishna thinks he is alone. Satyaki stands at the far end of the passage, and seeing his cousin, comes forward quietly. Krishna crosses unsteadily to a stone seat in an alcove, and sits on it, his chest heaving. Satyaki stops himself, when he sees the state in which Krishna is.

He stands in the shadows, watching, as the Avatara shuts his eyes and yokes himself in dhyana. Krishna slips into samadhi; Satyaki stands watching him. Gradually, the Dark One stops shaking. Satyaki sees the unearthly light that enfolds him, pulsing. Krishna sits for some moments, wrapped in the light. When his breathing is even again, and the colour flushes back into his face, the mystic light begins to fade, until it vanishes.

As long as he lives, Satyaki will never forget those moments. Krishna was so far away then; he could have been on another world, or in another kalpa. Satyaki stands transfixed by what he has seen, and then Krishna opens his eyes. The familiar, slightly mocking smile is back on his lips. He is quite himself again, as if nothing exceptional had occurred.

Satyaki approaches him with folded hands, and says, "Abhimanyu lives in Uttaraa's child. This is a greater victory for you than the war!"

Krishna takes his hand, and says quietly, "Yes, Satyaki, this was harder than winning the war. But come now, surely it is time to celebrate."

Arms linked, they walk back to the main palace.

---

* Ganguli: The rakshasas that had gathered invisibly in the room, melted away.

A month passes; then, word comes to Hastinapura that the Pandavas are on their way home. Following Vyasa's directions, they have discovered King Marutta's treasure-trove. With Dhaumya their priest, Yudhishtira and his brothers worshipped Lord Siva on the Himalaya. Then they excavated the mountain, and when they dug fifty hands, they found a buried rock chamber. In it lay an unimaginable hoard, wealth like the Pandavas had not owned even during the days of the Rajasuya yagna in Indraprastha. They found gold and golden vessels, chests and caskets full of incredible jewels.

It took them ten days to bring up that treasure. It was loaded onto elephants' backs and in chariots*, and a thousand men helped carry it all back to Hastinapura. Miraculously, the Kurus were masters of untold wealth once more.

The entire city has turned out to welcome them home. Indeed, on the very day they discovered the treasure on the Himalaya, Abhimanyu's son was born in Hastinapura and Krishna restored him to life. The palace in Hastina is a temple of hope, surging again through the kingdom. Even the forlorn Subhadra hardly cries any more but grows engrossed in the little one, her grandson.

Krishna gives the heir to the Kuru throne the name Vyasa Muni wanted. "He is born after the war, and he has already known death. He is a tested one, let him be called Parikshita."

Word arrives that Yudhishtira and his brothers have returned. Krishna rides out of the city to receive his cousins. Yudhishtira jumps down from his chariot and runs to the Dark One, and they embrace. A sea change has come over the Kuru king. His dejection has vanished; instead, he glows with new contentment. They are a wealthy kingdom again, and Yudhishtira is not past rejoicing at this for his people's sake. Besides, the Himalaya has healed a favoured son. One by one, the other Pandavas come to embrace Krishna, and they tell him about their quest for the treasure.

As they enter the city-gates, Krishna says to them, "Uttaraa is a mother now. Your grandson is called Parikshita."

---

* KMG: Sixty thousand camels, a hundred thousand elephants, a hundred and twenty thousand horses, and as many chariots. The mules and men that helped carry the treasure were countless.

Such joy breaks out on the Pandavas' faces. Bheema gives a roar of delight. Yudhishtira cries, "And he lives, Krishna?"

"I swore he would, didn't I?"

They cannot wait to see Parikshita, and they ride quickly to the palace. The people crowd the streets to welcome their king home. When they see the wealth the Pandavas have brought, singing and dancing break out, and the celebrations last through the night.

Back in the palace, Abhimanyu's father and his uncles can hardly put the little prince down. Any straggle of gloom in Yudhishtira's heart vanishes, when he sees Parikshita and takes him in his arms. They pass the handsome child from hand to hand, and the quaintest sight is Bheema holding him in his arms. There is no doubt left in anyone's mind that a bright new time has dawned over the destiny of the Kurus; and the time of darkness that Duryodhana brought has ended. Once more, there is a future to look forward to, a future that Abhimanyu's son will rule one day.

More enthusiastically than anyone else, Yudhishtira throws himself into planning for that future. Vyasa returns, timely as ever, to Hastinapura. Yudhishtira says to his grandfather, the muni, "We have treasure now, my lord. If you bless me, I will perform the Aswamedha yagna."

Vyasa says, "The yagna will purify the earth, and all of you of the sin of the killing you saw and did. You must not waste any more time."

Yudhishtira has another thought. He goes to Krishna and says, "My Lord, if it hadn't been for you, we would never have won the war. You must perform the Aswamedha yagna, to exorcise us of the sins of Kurukshetra. I beg you, do this for my sake."

Krishna laughs, "Now I know beyond any doubt that you must perform the Aswamedha. My noble cousin, no other king has the relinquishment you do. You are lord of the earth, king of the Kurus, and I am happy to serve you. The performance of the Aswamedha yagna is a tradition in your royal House. I am content as I am, but my joy increases, day by day, as I see all my dreams being realized. Perform the yagna, Yudhishtira: to me, it will be just as if I did it myself."

Plainly, Krishna means what he says. The truth is that he has been deeply concerned about Yudhishtira; he had feared the Pandava might never recover from his remorse. Now he sees him full of hope at the birth of Parikshita, and he is relieved. For the Avatara, it is another battle won.

Vyasa finds an auspicious day for the yagna to begin. The finest white horse in the king's stables is chosen to be the sacrificial animal. Yudhishtira asks, "Everything is ready. But who will ride with the horse through the kingdoms of Bharatavarsha?"

"Arjuna is the archer; let him go with the horse," says Vyasa. "Let Bheema, Nakula and Sahadeva remain here with you, and do whatever needs to be done in Hastinapura for the sacrifice."

Yudhishtira turns to a beaming Arjuna, "My brother, go with our army and invite all the kings of Bharatavarsha to the Aswamedha. If any of them opposes you, subdue him in battle. But, Arjuna, as much as you can, avoid bloodshed."

Arjuna takes the initiatory bath. He sets out in his chariot with the white horse going before him, and an army and some brahmanas following. The Pandava goes forth in elation. The people mill in the streets and the thunder of the Gandiva's bowstring resounds through the city.

After Arjuna leaves, preparations begin in earnest in Hastinapura, and Bheema and the twins oversee them. A hundred kings will arrive shortly in the Kuru capital, and they must be housed and feted royally. Another small city comes up quickly within Hastinapura; at its heart is a wonderful yagnashala with golden pillars. Meanwhile, Yudhishtira takes his vows as the sacrificer, and sits before the yagna fire, his chest covered with the skin of a black buck, his loins with red silk, and a staff in his hand. Vyasa and countless other brahmanas gather in the city of elephants to bless the Kuru emperor. They have come to usher in the new age that is upon the world, the kali yuga, as auspiciously as they can. Of course, at the back of their minds, a shadow lingers: of the other bloody yagna on Kurukshetra with which the kali began. But they have seen enough evil for a lifetime; and if anyone thinks of what sort of age this is that began with such a war, no one says anything about it. They are content to mind the day, as best they can.

Meanwhile, Arjuna follows the white horse through Bharatavarsha. They ride north first, and hardly a king dares obstruct them. They turn east and a few lords of the earth have to be quelled with battle. After the war at Kurukshetra, there are hardly any kshatriyas left in the world with stomach for a fight against Arjuna. West and south, also, the Pandava conquers, and all the kings of the sacred land submit once more to Yudhishtira's sovereignty, as they did during the Rajasuya yagna*.

A month before Arjuna rides home, these kshatriyas begin to converge on Hastinapura with their legions for Yudhishtira's horse sacrifice. They bring treasures for the Kuru emperor. The awareness of a new age is upon them all, and they come keenly to the Kuru capital, to forge and renew their ties with the most powerful monarch in the world, and to establish a new peace on earth.

Bheema and the twins have seen to it that Hastinapura is splendid with its new mansions and sabhas. The guests are wonderstruck by the yagnashala that stands at the heart of the city, reminiscent of another sabha in another city: a sabha that sparked such envy that a war to end all wars was fought in the world.

Bheema, of course, is in charge of the kitchen that serves the visiting kings; and it can be safely said the fare in Hastinapura is even more extraordinary than it was fifteen years ago in Indraprastha. For, in between, Bheema had served a year in Virata's kitchens and he had learnt a good deal of the culinary art during that year. With typical humility, Yudhishtira receives his guests, and shows them to the mansions where they will stay.

All the kings have arrived, and at last, one day, the white horse canters into Hastinapura, with Arjuna just behind it. Dhritarashtra and Yudhishtira go out to the gates to welcome home the conquering kshatriya, and the city begins its celebrations. The next morning, with Vyasa and his hundred rishis presiding over the ritual, the horse is sacrificed to the Gods.

The animal is cut into pieces, and then Draupadi, the Queen, is made to sit next to these. The brahmanas then cook the marrow of the dead

---

* KMG lists the sons and grandsons of the Trigartas, Bhagadatta's son Vajradatta of Pragjyotishapura, the Sindhus, his own son Babhruvahana of Manipura, Jarasandha's grandson Meghasandhi of Magadha, Sishupala's son Sarabha of Chedi, the Kasis, Angas, Kosalas, Kiratas, Tanganas, Chitrangada of the Dasarnas, Ekalavya's son—king of the Nishadas—, the Dravidas, Andhras, Mahishakas, the hillmen of Kolwa, and the Saurashtras. In Dwaraka, the Yadava youths arrest the horse's careen, but Ugrasena comes out and forbids them. The Gandharas and Shakuni's son—all these resist Arjuna, and he defeats them in battle.

steed, and the Pandavas sniff the fumes from the boiling marrow—which would remove every stain of sin from them. The other portions of the horse is fed to the sacred fire, and for the second time, Yudhishtira is crowned emperor of Bharatavarsha.

Those who were there say that the Pandavas, Krishna and all the Yadavas are present at Yudhishtira's Aswamedha yagna. But the other kings who attend are either sons or nephews of the lords of the earth that came to the Rajasuya in Indraprastha: their sires and elders have all perished in the war.

The yagna is concluded, and Yudhishtira the sacrificer turns to his grandfather Vyasa, and says, "Take all this earth we have conquered, Muni, as our gift to the brahmanas who came to our sacrifice."

The performance of the Aswamedha yagna requires the sacrificer to give all his lands as alms. The custom was seldom observed literally, only a token offering was made. Vyasa replies, "I return this gift to you, my child. We brahmanas have no use for lands, but we have use for gold."

Yudhishtira is insistent. "Not my brothers or I can keep what rightfully belongs to the brahmanas."

Vyasa says, "We are moved by your generosity. But give the brahmanas gold, and keep the lands for yourselves."

Yudhishtira is about to protest again, when Krishna says, "Do as the muni says, Yudhishtira. He knows best."

Yudhishtira gives the brahmanas millions of gold coins, as well as the golden vessels from King Marutta's hoard that was used at the yagna. One by one, the visiting kings depart: dazzled by the sacrifice, overwhelmed by the wealth and the generosity of Yudhishtira Chakravarti.

Just as the Aswamedha yagna is being wound up, the queerest thing happens. In the midst of the brahmanas, the Pandavas and Vrishnis, a blue-eyed mongoose makes his appearance. He is an extraordinary creature, for half his pelt is shimmering gold! The mongoose speaks to the Kuru king and the others in perfect human speech, "Yudhishtira, your yagna isn't half as great as the sacrifice of the Kurukshetra brahmana."

The brahmanas and kshatriyas crowd around the exceptional creature. One priest asks, "Everything at this Aswamedha has been conducted according to the Shastras. What fault do you find with it?"

The mongoose laughs. "It isn't a lie I tell, and I don't speak from vanity. But neither your yagna nor your king's generosity is equal to those of the poor brahmana of Kurukshetra, whose only offering was four bowls of gruel."

The munis are incredulous. They say, "We have followed the Shastras in every particular. How can you compare the poor brahmana's sacrifice with this one?"

The mongoose replies, "I was there at that yagna of yagnas, and just seeing it made half my body turn golden. Listen, if you want to hear about that sacrifice.

"Long ago, in Kurukshetra, a brahmana lived on the grain that his neighbours, the farmers, threw away. This hardly amounted to anything, and he, his wife, his son and daughter-in-law ate but once in three days. Sometimes, they ate only once in five days, barely keeping body and soul together. A terrible drought fell upon that land. It did not rain and the earth grew parched, and all the fields dried up and lay desolate. The poor brahmana's family starved.

"One day, they could not bear the pangs of hunger that tore at them, and went to forage for some food. After wandering for hours, in blazing heat and blinding dust, and they often collapsed from weakness, they managed to collect a few handfuls of coarse barley, and came home with it.

"They cooked gruel from the arid grains. They divided the gruel in four bowls and sat down to eat, when a guest arrived at the door, a stranger. The brahmana rose and offered him a place at his table. The silent stranger came in and sat down. Shyly, the brahmana set his bowl of gruel before the man. The stranger quickly ate the gruel. He looked up when he had finished, and he was not satisfied.

"The brahmana was embarrassed, hardly knowing what to do. His wife called from the kitchen. She pressed her bowl into her husband's hands and said, 'Give the visitor my gruel as well. If you can go hungry, so can I.'

"Almost in tears, he gave her portion to the stranger. In no time, the guest licked the second bowl clean, then looked around, obviously not sated still. The brahmana's son called his father, and pressed his uneaten gruel into his hands. 'I, too, can starve, father. Let our guest eat.'

"The brahmana began to protest, but his son was adamant and the stranger had the third bowl of gruel. He still looked around him hopefully. The daughter-in-law called the old brahmana, and handed him her bowl. The brahmana said, 'No, my child! I cannot take this from you.'

"She would not listen, and the fourth bowl of gruel was also set before the stranger, and he emptied it quickly, as if it was the finest delicacy he had ever tasted. Suddenly, the stranger's body shone with heaven's light. He said, 'Brahmanas, your generosity isn't of this world.'

"A shower of petal-rain fell in that humble home, its fragrance was divine. The poor brahmana and his family stood astonished. Their guest went on, 'Your generosity has earned you a place in Devaloka.' He pointed through the door, 'Look, Lord Indra has sent a vimana for you. Your sacrifice is greater than any Aswamedha or Rajasuya. Come, let us go.'

"The poor brahmana family followed the stranger into the vimana, and he took them into heaven. I had been hiding in my corner, watching all this, and when the brahmanas flew away with the messenger, I came out. I was also hungry, and I saw that a few drops of the barley gruel had fallen onto the floor. Oh, it smelled so wonderful, better than any other food! I crept up and licked up those fallen drops, at once half my pelt turned golden.

"Since that day, my friends, I make it a point to visit every yagna in the land of Bharata to see if I can turn the other half of myself golden. So far, though I have been at countless sacrifices, a Rajasuya and an Aswamedha among them, I have not found a yagna to match that of the brahmana of Kurukshetra. Look, the proof is upon my pelt: only half of me is gold. Yudhishtira, non-violence, self-restraint, contentment uprightness and gentleness, sincerity, austerity, truthfulness and charity are superior to the greatest ritual sacrifices. All the fine offerings of your yagna are not equal to a few drops of the poor brahmana's gruel!"

With that, the mongoose vanishes[1]. Krishna stands smiling to himself, and all the others have something to ponder. Soon, it is time for their royal guests to depart, and last of all, Krishna, Balarama, Satyaki and their Yadavas leave Hastinapura to return to Dwaraka on the ocean. Though the Aswamedha yagna might not have been as great as the poor

---

1 See Appendix to discover who the mongoose was.

brahmanas' sacrifice, it does wash their sins of the war from the Pandavas. Peace returns to Yudhishtira's spirit. The nightmares that ravaged him since Kurukshetra no longer stalk his sleep. With Parikshita as their hope for the future, the sons of Pandu begin a long and blessed reign from Hastinapura.

BOOK FIFTEEN

Asramavasika Parva

AUM, I bow down to Narayana, the most exalted Nara, and to the Devi Saraswati, and say *Jaya*!

ONE

The passing of the elders

WHEN THE ASWAMEDHA IS COMPLETED, YUDHISHTIRA GOES BACK in earnest to his task of ruling the Kuru kingdom. The eldest Pandava is a king of dharma, blessed by the Gods in heaven and by Krishna on earth, and his reign is all that was expected of such a noble prince. The kingdom blooms at his touch. The people are contented: their lives flow pure and fruitful. Prosperity sweeps Bharatavarsha, as if a Deva sat upon the throne of Hastinapura.

Yudhishtira is king of the Kurus; but whenever he has to take an important decision, Pandu's son is careful to consult Dhritarashtra. Uncle and nephew grow close, and the bitterness between them melts. Yudhishtira still treats Dhritarashtra like a father, and Gandhari with as much love he shows Kunti. Indeed, if anyone ever disparages the old king or queen, he runs the risk of incurring Yudhishtira's wrath[*].

Acharya Kripa lives in Hastinapura again, and perhaps the noblest thing Yudhishtira does is to reinstate him in the Kuru sabha. He even appoints Kripa as young Parikshita's guru. Fifteen peaceful years pass, and as is the way with men, the war is almost forgotten. Kripa and

---

[*] KMG: Yudhishtira brings costly robes, the finest maireya wines, rare and delectable fish, sherbets, honey, and countless other delicacies to Dhritarashtra. When kings of other land visit Hastinapura, they all come to meet the blind one even as they used to when he was the king. Kunti herself shows Gandhari the utmost respect, while Panchali, Subhadra, and Ulupi and Chitrangadaa, when they come to Hastinapura, all wait upon her like serving maids. Gandhari's bitterness melts, and she begins to love the Pandavas as her own sons.

Vidura have the responsibility of seeing Dhritarashtra never wants for anything. They are his constant companions. Vyasa often visits his son, and recounts ancient legends from the Puranas—tales of rishis of the olden days, as well as those of the pitrs and the rakshasas. Yudhishtira is as loving as a son, and Yuyutsu also takes to spending time with his aging father. But Dhritarashtra's heart is not in Hastinapura. It is far away, with a son of his whom he can never forget, his favourite, who is no longer in the world. Dhritarashtra pines for Duryodhana.

The old king is so well cared for in Hastina that he has no cause for complaint. He has no immediate reason to tell Yudhishtira that he longs to go away to the forest, to embark on the final journey of his life: that he longs to die and be with his Duryodhana again. But one day, fifteen years after the war, fate takes a hand in Dhritarashtra's life.

There is someone in Hastinapura who has never forgiven the blind king for everything that happened. Bheema cannot forgive his uncle. In deference to Yudhishtira, he is never openly hostile towards Dhritarashtra or Gandhari; but within him, he is full of rancour. For fifteen years, somehow, Bheema controls himself and gives neither Dhritarashtra nor Gandhari any offence. But he seethes every time he sees them, certain that they have not been punished as they deserve.

One evening, Bheema sees Dhritarashtra and Gandhari sitting on an open terrace, taking the air outside their royal apartment. He himself is out for a walk with some friends. Suddenly, a compulsion to hurt the old people seizes him. Pretending he has not noticed them, he boasts loudly, "No man on earth is as strong as Bheemasena. With these arms I crushed all the hundred sons of that blind fool!"

Bheema gives a gory account of how he killed some of his cousins on Kurukshetra. When he finishes, he wanders off with his companions. Dhritarashtra and Gandhari sit very still. Finally, with a sigh, Dhritarashtra says, "I feel weak, I must lie down."

He goes in and Gandhari follows him. Four days pass, and the king neither eats, nor stirs from his bed. On the fifth day, Dhritarashtra calls Yudhishtira, Vidura and some others to his chambers.

He says, "We all know the Kuru House was divided because of me, because I would not listen to wise counsel. I have been happy here in Hastinapura, and well looked after, these fifteen years. But I have thought about my sins, and their horrible consequence. Yudhishtira, my son, I have decided the only way for me to find expiation is to go into the jungle and do penance. I must atone for my crimes, before I can leave this world in peace. Gandhari and I have made up our minds to spend the rest of our days in the vana, in tapasya.

"Yudhishtira, you are the king in Hastinapura now, and I beg you to let me go."

Yudhishtira cries, "What a fool I am that I did not see how unhappy you have been! You look so weak, my lord, what has happened to you? I swear I will mend all that, if I have to serve you myself. For heaven's sake, do not speak of going away. Don't even think of it."

Dhritarashtra says, "My child, since the eldest times, our ancestors renounced the world in their final days, and sought peace in the jungle."

"I will not let you go! If you do, I will come with you into the forest myself."

The argument continues for some time, then, Dhritarashtra becomes very agitated. He gets up and cries, "Sanjaya! Kripa! Vidura! Explain to Yudhishtira that I am exhausted, and I cannot argue any more. Tell him I must go into the jungle to find my peace!"

He sways on his feet and almost falls, except that Gandhari reaches out blindly and catches him. Yudhishtira takes Dhritarashtra in his arms and helps him sit down. "Look how weak you have grown. The king who crushed an iron statue in his arms can't stand a moment's argument."

His uncle says, "It is four days since I ate, child. But your loving touch has refreshed me. You must let me go to the forest."

"I will do anything you want, but you must eat something first."

"I will eat only after you say you will let me go."

Timely as ever, Vyasa arrives in the palace and knocks on Dhritarashtra's door. He is told what has happened there, and, after listening gravely to both Dhritarashtra and Yudhishtira, the rishi says, "Yudhishtira, you must allow your uncle to leave. His time for penance and prayer has arrived."

Yudhishtira looks stricken. After a long moment, he assents numbly, "If you say so, my lord."

Once the matter is decided, Yudhishtira himself brings food, and Dhritarashtra eats a little. Later that evening, they sit together, uncle and nephew, and the old man has some kindly words of advice for the Pandava. The most important counsel he has is: "Always surround yourself with wise men, who are good-hearted. And on all vital matters, be sure you consult them and heed what they say."

That night, Gandhari asks, "When do we actually leave?"

Dhritarashtra replies, "Very soon. I must speak to the people first."

Yudhishtira is told his uncle wants to address the people, and arrangements are made for men from every walk of life, the citizen's representatives, to gather in the palace yard.

Dhritarashtra says to them, "My friends, Gandhari and I have decided to leave for the forest to do tapasya. Yudhishtira and Muni Vyasa have agreed to let us go. I want to ask your permission, as well. I also wanted to tell you all that I have been happier during Yudhishtira's rule than I was during Duryodhana's. My nephew has looked after me as if I was his own father, and I have enjoyed peace of mind as never before. But I am old, and all my sons are dead. You must let me go away."

His eyes are moist. "Friends, try to forgive me for whatever happened when I was your king. My sons were selfish and arrogant, and I beg your forgiveness for them, too. I beg you, let me go in peace."

A whispered discussion follows among the crowd, and then a brahmana called Samba mounts the palace steps where Dhritarashtra stands. Samba says, "My lord, the people have chosen me to speak for them. We want to tell you that you have been like an older brother to us. It was not you or your sons that caused the great carnage, but irresistible fate. If you truly want to go into vanavasa, you have our leave. We will miss you, Dhritarashtra, you will always be in our hearts."

Dhritarashtra's blind eyes spill tears. One by one, the men in the crowd come up to him, and they take his hands tenderly, some embrace him.

The next day, Vidura arrives in Yudhishtira's presence with a message. "Dhritarashtra wants to leave on the day of the next full moon, in the month of Kartika. Before he goes, he wants to perform a sraddha for Bheeshma and Drona, and his sons. He wants some gold for this."

Yudhishtira and Arjuna say what a good idea it is, but Bheema jumps up and cries, "We shouldn't give him a cowry! That hypocrite is responsible for everything we suffered, and he dares ask for gold."

Arjuna says gently, "Whatever happened, he is our uncle, and he kept us for many years in Hastinapura. We all have weaknesses and make mistakes, Bheema. This is the last thing he wants from us. We must not refuse him."

Bheema says hotly, "We will do whatever sraddha is needed for the dead. Dhritarashtra need have no part in it!"

Beside himself, and guilty as well, since he knows the immediate cause for the old king's leaving, Bheema begins a tirade against Dhritarashtra, listing everything he had done to them, or acquiesced in. Yudhishtira cuts him short, "That will do, Bheema! Be quiet now."

From the look in his brother's eye, Bheema knows Yudhishtira has guessed the truth. He falls silent, squirming. Yudhishtira tells Vidura, "Uncle, please tell Dhritarashtra he can have whatever he wants for the sraddha. No expense, no effort, shall be spared."

Dhritarashtra undertakes an elaborate ten-day ritual, as an offering to all those who had lost their lives in the war*. On the last day of the sraddha, Yudhishtira learns Kunti means to go to the forest with Dhritarashtra and Gandhari. He is shaken. All the Pandavas, Draupadi, Subhadra, Uttaraa and Parikshita beg her to change her mind. But she is adamant.

Yudhishtira clasps her feet and cries, "Mother, you asked us to fight the war and win back the kingdom. How can you even think of leaving us and going away? All this is for you, don't abandon us now."

"Whatever I did was for my sons' sake. I have lived long enough to enjoy my great-grandchild for fifteen years. My place is not here, any more, but with Gandhari and Dhritarashtra. Our time in the world is over, let me go in peace."

The next day, when Yudhishtira actually sees Dhritarashtra, Gandhari and Kunti emerge from the palace, wearing deerskin and tree-bark, he flings his arms around his uncle and cries, "Don't leave me!"

He will not let them pass, until Arjuna draws him aside firmly, saying, "Calm yourself, my lord. This is not how you must send them on their way."

There is another shock in store for the Kuru king. Two more figures, clad in valkala, emerge shyly from the palace. They have not had the courage to tell Yudhishtira that they, too, mean to go away. When he

---

* KMG: By Yudhishtira's command, untold wealth is distributed on Dhritarashtra's behalf. He that was to receive a hundred gold coins gets a thousand, while the one who was to be given a thousand receives ten times as much.

sees them, he begins to sob more loudly: Vidura and Sanjaya mean to follow Dhritarashtra into the forest.

The Pandavas walk through the thronging streets behind the renunciates, with Panchali, Subhadra, Uttaraa, Chitrangadaa, and other women of the city, brahmana, kshatriya, vaisya, and sudra, wailing like a swarm of bereaved birds. The people have turned out to bid farewell to the elders. At last, at the city-gates, with many an embrace, they part. On Vidura's arm, Dhritarashtra walks away into the open spaces of Aryavarta, and Kunti leads Gandhari by her hand. They are heading first for the Ganga and Vyasa's asrama on her banks, where Dhritarashtra receives his first initiation into sannyasa. Then they go to the forest asrama of the Rishi Satayupa, who at Vyasa's behest, instructs Dhritarashtra further.

The munis of the wilds welcome Dhritarashtra and his companions, and they begin living an ascetic life in the forest. Vyasa's eldest son proves an eager tapasvin, and in a few months little remains of the Kuru king of measureless power. Instead, an austere rishi takes his place. Dhritarashtra mortifies himself, and spends his days and nights in ceaseless prayer. Soon he has reduced himself to macilence, and his body takes on a fine lustre. Slowly, the blind king's sins are burned from him.

A year passes, and in Hastinapura not a day goes by without Yudhishtira and his brothers thinking of their mother Kunti, and missing her more than they can bear. They never speak of her, for that would make them unbearably sad. One day, when all five Pandavas sit together with Draupadi, Yudhishtira says, "I wonder how our uncles fare in the forest."

Sahadeva, who has been waiting a year for this, cries, "And our mother! Yudhishtira, can't we visit them just once, to see how they are?"

Draupadi puts in, "I long to see mother. The women of the palace can't wait to go and meet Gandhari and Kunti again!"

Yudhishtira looks at the others, and sees the eagerness on every face. He calls the captain of his guard. "We will leave for the forest tomorrow to visit our uncle. Make preparations, and let it be announced in the streets that anyone who wants to go with us shall be welcome."

Sahadeva can hardly contain his excitement. Early next morning, a royal party, with elephants, chariots, horses and palanquins for the women of the palace, sets out from Hastinapura; with them, go a hundred mules, laden with provisions. Yuyutsu and Dhaumya are left in charge of the kingdom. Yudhishtira waits five days outside the city, for anyone that cares to join his party. Then, after a day's journey, the company arrives on the fringes of the forest where Dhritarashtra has taken sannyasa.

Yudhishtira orders camp made at the edge of the vana, for they must not disturb the tapasvin rishis within. The Pandavas enter the forest on foot. Asking directions from the hermits they meet, they make their way to the asrama where Dhritarashtra, Kunti and Gandhari live. An aged muni in the asrama tells them, "You will find him at the river. He has gone to bathe and to gather flowers for his worship. Gandhari and Kunti are with him."

The Pandavas set out towards the Yamuna, and coming towards them from a distance, they see their uncle, aunt and mother. Sahadeva gives a cry, runs to Kunti and flings himself at her feet. She raises him up, and hugs him: kissing him, sobbing to see her favourite child again. The others come up, and Dhritarashtra weeps for joy to see his nephews. At last, he has truly become the loving uncle he would have always been, except for his overpowering attachment for Duryodhana.

Sanjaya is there, faithful to the last, serving Dhritarashtra as he has always done. Later, when they sit together in the asrama, and the people greet their old king, Dhritarashtra says, "Having you all here makes me feel I am back in the palace at Hastinapura."

Yudhishtira asks, "But where is Vidura? Doesn't he live with you?"

One of the rishis says, "He has gone beyond us all. He lives by himself in the deepest jungle. He does not eat, but mortifies his body. Only rarely he comes to visit us, and then he never says a word."

At that moment, another muni gives a shout, "There he is! It is Vidura."

They catch a fleeting glimpse of a wild-looking figure at the edge of the hermitage, darting away into the trees. Dhritarashtra says, "He is shy of men now. He will not come where there are even two or three people."

Another muni says to Yudhishtira, "If you want to see him, we will show you the way to where he sits in dhyana. But you must go alone, or you won't find him."

Yudhishtira gets up, and follows the rishis into the deeper forest. Soon, the others point him ahead, and say he should go on by himself. As he walks on, the trees grow closer together, and the awning of branches overhead is so thick hardly any sunlight penetrates it. The silence here is a reverberant presence, as if God is very near.

Slowly, Yudhishtira goes forward, until suddenly he senses he is not alone any more. He pauses to let his eyes grow accustomed to the gloom. Nothing stirs, and the Pandava walks on again. He hears a low cough to his left and spins around. He can hardly recognize the emaciated hermit leaning against a tree. The bizarre and naked figure is covered in mud and leaves, as if the jungle has claimed him entirely. He is hardly more than a skeleton, for there is so little flesh on him and his skin hangs loose. But Vidura's body is luminous in the forest's dimness; his eyes glow like torches.

Yudhishtira calls softly, "Uncle, Vidura, it is I, Yudhishtira."

Vidura makes no reply, only the burning eyes seize Yudhishtira's in an irresistible gaze. The Pandava realizes Vidura is past being able to speak, but those eyes hold him in their brilliant trance. They are surely mad, but in the most sublime way: *with having seen God*. Yudhishtira stands rooted by that gaze; and then the strangest thing happens to the Kuru king. Uncannily, he begins to feel older and wiser, as if another, sager, being was entering his very body, limb by limb, breath by breath. The Pandava trembles at the subtle possession. He feels his mind being immeasurably enriched, with an intelligence and wisdom far beyond his own.

Then, Vidura's glowing eyes flicker, and burn no more; they are lamps put out. Yudhishtira approaches the attenuated form, which still leans against the tree. He reaches out and touches Vidura's face, but life has left the skeletal body. Yet, within himself, the Pandava can clearly feel his uncle's gentle presence. He stands for a moment, astonished, and a little uncertain. He thinks he must carry Vidura's body back to the asrama to be cremated.

An asariri speaks to him: "Vidura was an incarnation of dharma, just as you are, Yudhishtira. He is with you forever now. You must not burn his body, nor remove it from this place. Your uncle was a sannyasin when he died, and now he is part of you. Let the forest absorb his mortal remains."

Yudhishtira turns back to the asrama, and recounts his experience to the others. He and his brothers light a fire and spend the night under the trees. The people of Hastinapura return to the city in a day or two, but the sons of Pandu stay a month in the forest with their mother and their uncle, and, also, visiting other asramas.

During this time, the Pandavas notice that, for all his tapasya, Dhritarashtra is not yet at peace with himself. Some nights, they see him come out of his hut and stand staring at the dark jungle; often, a spasm of grief convulses him, and he shakes with sobs. Then, one day, when the Pandavas themselves are away in another asrama, Vyasa arrives in the asrama. When they sit together, speaking of many things, Dhritarashtra bursts into tears.

He prostrates himself before Vyasa, and cries, "Father, I cannot bear this sorrow any more! Where are my sons now, in which world? Are they in some terrible hell, paying for their sins?"

Draupadi, Subhadra and Uttaraa also begin to sob. Panchali asks, "Where are my sons, Muni? I hardly knew them, before death snatched them from me."

Subhadra and Uttaraa wail, "Where is Abhimanyu?"

Dhritarashtra says in anguish, "Ten million men perished for my sin. How can I ever forgive myself? Where are they all now, who died such violent deaths? Oh, where are my grandsons?"

Gandhari adds her voice to the others. "No grief is as cruel as not knowing where our husbands and our sons are. No prayer, not all the wisdom in the world can cure the uncertainty and anguish we women feel."

Kunti says, "Where is my Karna? I was his mother, and I was responsible for everything he suffered, and for his death. Now he is gone forever, who can tell me where?"

Dhritarashtra says, "Father, this is what torments us. Who has ever died and returned to the world to tell us that there is indeed life after dying? No one knows for certain."

Vyasa shuts his eyes in dhyana. Silence falls on the company. After a short while, the rishi rises, and says, "Come to the Ganga with me. You shall have an answer to your doubts."

Away in the west, the sun is sinking, and twilight falls over the world when they arrive on the banks of the sacred river. They bathe in her warm currents, worship the setting sun and come ashore. Vyasa remains standing in the Ganga, waist-deep in her flow. He begins to chant some resonant mantras in a primitive tongue. Like flights of birds they fly out from his throat and seem to glimmer everywhere through the twilight world. At last they fly over the river, and plunge into her waters, setting them alight.

The Ganga takes silver fire. White waves rise as from a stormy sea; from them, a spirit host emerges and stands forth upon those waves between heaven and earth. Bheeshma is there, and Drona. With them, are Karna, Duryodhana, and Dhritarashtra's hundred sons. Abhimanyu and Draupadi's sons rise from the Ganga, down which their ashes floated so many years ago, Dhrishtadyumna and Shikhandi, Drupada and Virata, Uttara Kumara, Bhoorisravas, Jayadratha, Susharma, Bhagadatta, Shakuni and his sons, and a thousand kshatriyas: like fish from a sea!

With these, is the teeming host that perished on Kurukshetra: ten million men, a generation of warriors. Those shining legions fill the river, the earth, the trees and the sky. Their bodies are lustrous, heaven's grace is upon every man. They wear unearthly raiment and jewellery, and enmity has vanished from their hearts. They are like brothers now, all of them. Elven gandharvas appear with them, and sing their praise, apsaras dance for them upon the phosphorescent Ganga.

It is told Vyasa Muni opens Dhritrashtra's eyes for that night, and he sees his sons and all the others, whom he had, indeed, never seen with mortal sight before. The place by the river is like Devaloka, where no fear or envy, anger or hatred can come. The living and the dead spend that night together, in joy.

At dawn, the legion dead vanish, leaving the river flowing serenely again*. Vyasa still stands in it, worshipping the rising sun. He says to some of the women, who have also lost their husbands to the war, "If any of you want to be with your men, enter the river now."

---

* Ganguli says some went back to Devaloka, others to Brahmaloka, some to Varunaloka, some to the realm of Kubera, and others to Surya Deva's world. Some returned to the worlds of the rakshasas and pisachas, while celestials spirited others away in their vimanas.

Some widows do so, and by Vyasa's power their bodies dissolve in the Ganga. They rise as bright spirits, and are free. Deeply consoled, Dhritarashtra, Gandhari, Kunti and the younger women return to the asrama. The next day, the Pandavas also return.

The sons of Pandu give away the gifts they have brought, and at last they come to Dhritarashtra and Gandhari, and ask their leave to return to Hastinapura. The elders bless them, cling to them fondly, before saying farewell.

Kunti takes Yudhishtira aside. She has become more composed than he has ever seen her, and says to him, "We may not meet again in this world. You must look after my Sahadeva: of all of you, I have always loved him the most. Even now, I can only think of him as a child. Bless you, Yudhishtira, my noble son. Rule long and wisely, and God be with you. Go now, for my love for you impedes my tapasya."

They part in tears, Sahadeva the most visibly upset. Finally, they tear themselves away and return to Hastinapura. The Pandavas settle down again to the routine of their royal duties, which keeps them busy indeed. They have a kingdom to rule, and not even in times of dharma was that an easy task.

Two years slip by, and one day Narada arrives in Hastinapura, his face grave. Yudhishtira's blood turns cold to see the look in the muni's eyes. All the Pandavas are present in the sabha, so Narada launches directly into what he has come to tell them.

"When you left the forest, Dhritarashtra, Gandhari, Kunti and Sanjaya went to Haridwara. After Vidura's death, Dhritarashtra increased his austerities ten-fold, subsisting on just air, with stones in his mouth, and never speaking, until he was as lean and wild as you found Vidura. He roamed the jungle, with no fixed dwelling, all the other hermits of the forest worshipped him. The women and Sanjaya, also, spent their time in prayer and fasting. Gandhari only drank water, while Kunti took some every sixth day. One day, they were returning to their little asrama after a bath in the river, when they saw that a forest-fire had broken out around them. A stiff wind fanned the flames and they spread like light on every side. Birds and beasts fled in panic, as the fire swept closer.

"Dhritarashtra cried to Sanjaya, 'Run, Sanjaya! Save yourself, before it is too late.'

"Sanjaya hesitated, but Gandhari and Kunti also cried, 'Run Sanjaya, and take news of us to the world outside. We are too weak to go with you. We will offer ourselves in the agni, and find moksha.'

"Sanjaya knelt at their feet, and then ran for his life. Dhritarashtra, Gandhari and Kunti sat cross-legged, still as posts, facing east. The fire burned the jungle down, and Dhritarashtra, Gandhari and your mother perished in it."*

Yudhishtira falls where he stands. Sahadeva's heartbroken cries ring through the sabha. Again and again, he calls piteously to his dead mother, and Draupadi has to lead him away. The other Pandavas stand dazed. Narada tries to console them; Vyasa arrives and attempts to comfort them. But this is not a grief they will get over in a day, a year, or ever. They will carry it to their deaths.

Yudhishtira asks in a whisper, "What happened to Sanjaya?"

"He climbed the Himalaya, and sits in tapasya. He has also become a sannyasi."

The Pandavas and their women come to the banks of the Ganga, each of them wearing just a single garment. With them, come all the people of Hastinapura, and even many from the kingdom's provinces. Setting Yuyutsu at their head, they perform tarpana for Dhritarashtra, Gandhari and Kunti. They return to the city to ritually perform cremation rites for the three dead. On the twelfth day, purified by a fast and other vratas, Yudhishtira performs the sraddha, and gives away bounteous gifts in the names of his uncle, aunt, and his mother.

Slowly, the sons of Pandu learn to carry their newest burden of grief, and they plunge themselves entirely, especially Yudhishtira, into ruling the Kuru kingdom. Now they are the elders in Hastinapura, and their greatest delight is watching young Parikshita grow into a handsome, brilliant prince: the very image of Abhimanyu.

---

* Actually, the fire began as Dhritarashtra's sacrificial fire, which his yajaka brahmanas allowed to spread by their carelessness. Thus, the old king met death by being united with his own sacred fire on the banks of the Ganga. It was an auspicious and blessed passing.

BOOK SIXTEEN

Mausala Parva

AUM, I bow down to Narayana, the most exalted Nara, and to the Devi Saraswati, and say *Jaya*!

ONE

Ritual at Prabhasa

THIRTY-SIX YEARS PASS AFTER THE WAR, AND THEY ARE PEACEFUL and prosperous. Yudhishtira is king in Hastinapura, and his dharma pervades Bharatavarsha. Then, in the thirty-sixth year of his reign, the Pandava sees sinister omens all around him, like those seen before the war. Yudhishtira is certain some calamity stalks the earth, but he does not know what it is. Jackals and wolves howl in the city-streets at noon; kites, crows and vultures wheel in dense swarms in the sky. The horses and cows of Hastinapura are restive, and hardly touch their feed.

Not only in the Kuru city are evil omens seen. They are everywhere, as if the earth herself has premonition of a tragedy more terrible than any other. Storms of fire spring up, with no obvious cause, and lick down whole forests. Eerie meteors streak through the sky, by day and night. Unseasonal rains lash the earth, and the sea rises in tidal waves and savages the shores of Bharatavarsha. The sun and the moon shine dimly, as if stricken by sorrow, they are wrapped in black haloes. Violent tremors rock land and sea, and in Dwaraka, Krishna sees the omens[1] and remembers Gandhari's curse. He knows the end of the Yadavas is near.

The dwapara yuga was over on the tenth day of the war, and for thirty-six years the pale kali has crouched, awesome and sinister, on time's horizon: a Demon impatient to be loosed upon the earth. Not as long as Krishna, the Avatara, lives in it, can the kali yuga claim the world. Krishna has a final task to fulfil, before he departs.

---

1 See Appendix.

His Yadavas—the Vrishnis, Andhakas, Kukuras, and the rest—are invincible. Even he has been hard-pressed to contain them, as a shore does a raging sea. Their hubris will be their undoing, and Krishna knows their time has come. For his own time has come, and if he leaves the world without destroying his powerful clan, they will overrun the earth. He knows that not men, why, not the Devas can tame the Yadavas of Dwaraka.

The omens are plain on the land, in the sea, and the sky. In Dwaraka, only Krishna reads them clearly, and what they portend. One day, Viswamitra, Kanva and Narada arrive with some other munis in the ocean city to pray at the temple of Pindarika. Deluded by fate, the Yadava princes decide to poke a little fun at the holy ones. They dress Krishna's son, Samba, in some clothes borrowed from a fisherwoman in a nearby village, and lead him, face covered, to the august rishis.

Mockingly, they prostrate themselves before the sages. One bold spark says, "This doe-eyed beauty has something to ask you, Brahmanas. She is too shy to ask herself and bids me speak for her. She is Babhru's wife. She is pregnant, and is anxious to have a son. Sages of vision, tell her if she will have a boy or a girl."

The young men had expected a mild reproof, at worst, and they are taken aback at the ferocity of the rishis' response. His lips white, one of the wise curses them, "She will give birth to an iron club, and that club will destroy the arrogant Yadava clan!"

Trembling with fright, the young men come running to Balarama. They tell him, and not Krishna, what has happened: and there is, indeed, suddenly something growing in Samba's belly. The same night, his stomach has to be incised and yields an iron club. Balarama has the club ground into powder, and the powder cast into the sea, where it floats on green waves. Floating landwards with the tide, it settles fatefully on a blessed shore of confluence, at Prabhasa. That powder transforms itself into a shimmering pollen. Under the moon, the pollen grows with supernatural swiftness into a bank of silvery eraka reeds.

One perfectly arrowhead-shaped sliver of the club cannot be ground. Balarama thinks that, surely, a small sliver cannot harm the Yadava clan; he has that cast into the sea, as well. A fish swallows the sliver. The next morning, it swims into the net of some fishermen. While gutting their catch, they discard the piece of iron they find in the fish's belly,

Ritual at Prabhasa

and it lies shining on a white, nocturnal beach, on a full moon night. An old hunter called Jara, abroad on his poach, spots the sliver. Jara is attracted by its perfect shape. He picks it up and fixes it to the head of his hunting arrow.

The sea swells in fury and lashes the marble walls of Dwaraka. The evil omens are out in the open, everywhere. Astrologers see cataclysmic syzygys in the heavens, and Krishna, who misses none of the signs, is eager to leave the world.

One day, he says in his sabha, "Thirty-six years have passed since the war, and it is time for Gandhari's curse to take effect. We must go to Prabhasa, to seek expiation. Our ancestor Soma Deva found redemption at Prabhasa from Daksha's curse; we might also find salvation there, from Gandhari's. Let our men prepare to travel to the place from where the Saraswati flows west."

Krishna has a cousin, Uddhava, of whom he is particularly fond. As preparations get underway in Dwaraka for the pilgrimage to Prabhasa tirtha, one evening Uddhava comes alone to see Krishna. He kneels at the Dark One's feet.

"Lord, I am frightened!" he whispers, and he is shaking. "Krishna, I cannot bear to be apart from you. I see signs of doom all around us. I believe you mean to kill the Yadavas and leave this world yourself."

Krishna raises Uddhava up, and embraces him. "Uddhava, go to Badarikasrama upon Mount Gandhamadana. There, in the temple of Nara Narayana, you will find moksha. After I leave Dwaraka, it will sink beneath the waves."

He speaks to Uddhava, gently expounding the eternal dharma, as he had done for Arjuna on Kurukshetra. Finally, he gives him his own wooden padukas, the ones Krishna had worn for years. Hands folded, Uddhava walks around the Dark One in pradakshina; he kisses the Avatara's blue feet, bathing them in tears. Laying a hand on his cousin's head, Krishna blesses him to attain nirvana. Uddhava leaves on his final pilgrimage, not with the other Yadavas, but alone, in another direction, bearing the precious sandals on his head.

When Uddhava has left, Krishna goes into the temple that stands in his garden, beside the parijata tree he once took from Amravati. He stands in dhyana before the stone idol in that shrine, the image he had himself created for his father Vasudeva. With a thought, he summons two resplendent beings there. They stand before him as soon as he calls them, their bodies made of heaven's light. One is Brihaspati, the guru of the Devas, and the other is Vayu, the tameless wind.

Gravely, Krishna gives the sacred idol of Dwaraka into their hands. He says, "Take this holiest of my idols to Kerala, which is divided from the rest of Bharatavarsha by the western mountains. Establish it there, and let it remain as a blessing upon the land, secure from the invasions of darkness that will sweep the country in the centuries to come. Let this idol stand in a shrine you must fashion yourselves in Kerala: to be a solace to all men, a lamp that will burn in the darkest nights of kali yuga."

The unearthly ones receive the image in reverent hands, of wisdom and air. They kneel before him, and when he blesses them, they vanish from there with the idol. They scour the southern country of Kerala, seeking an appropriate place in which to install it. One day, they find Siva at worship in a sylvan grove beside a lake. As soon as they see him, Siva vanishes, and Brihaspati and Vayu install Krishna's stone image where he sat. Thus, they found the most holy Krishna temple in Guruvayoor, named after both of them.

Carrying provisions for a long excursion, the Yadava men set out for Prabhasa, with Krishna and Balarama going before them. As they ride out from the ocean city, Krishna knows his people will never see it again, bathed in the first light of day, a vision among the waves. Sorrow surges in his heart, but he forces himself to ride on. As they go, the Dark One thinks of the last time he persuaded his people to visit Prabhasa. It was a life ago, when Arjuna the yati came to Dwaraka, and eloped with Subhadra. Krishna sighs; a smile touches his lips.

At Prabhasa, the Yadavas pitch their tents, and as the brahmanas they have brought with them chant the Vedas, they themselves begin to celebrate. The crisp sea air exhilarates them, and the drinking and feasting begin in earnest, with Krishna joining in. The tirtha-yatra turns into a raucous outing. The Vrishnis mix wine with the food prepared for the brahmanas, and feed this mixture to monkeys. They have some games between the different clans, and these continue through the day and the night, hardly as if they have come to expiate their sins. A week passes; then one morning, Krishna calls them together for a ritual bath.

He initiates them into some unfamiliar mantras, which he says will turn away Gandhari's curse. In fact, these are last rites for safe passage from the earth.

Later that day, just before the noon meal, they all drink large quantities of the sweet and potent stimulant, maireyaka. Krishna had the maireyaka brought, and he begins the drinking. The Yadavas do not notice that fate flutters down on every kshatriya's shoulder like a dove of death. They have not seen the unusual reeds, shaped like jagged thunderbolts, growing in clumps at the water's edge: silvery, ominous, eraka reeds, rustling sibilantly in the hot breeze that hums over land and sea.

Soon, every Yadava is roaring drunk. Krishna watches them, a tear glistening in his eye. Tensely, he watches them, an instinct of imminent calamity awoken in him. The different clans, the Andhakas, the Bhojas, the Kukuras and the Vrishnis, have always envied one another, and only Krishna's masterfulness has held them together for so long. Now, the maireyaka and the intense games they have been playing have made them all more than a little rumbustious.

Suddenly, with a hard look at Kritavarman, whom he has never forgiven his part in the war, Satyaki cries, "There are some here that call themselves kshatriyas, but murder their sleeping enemies at night! And then run back to their homes, never to face the consequences of what they have done."

Kritavarman's face turns crimson. "Who was it that cut off Bhoorisravas' head when he had put down his weapons and sat in dhyana? That was truly the deed of a kshatriya!"

Drunk as they are, all the others quickly take sides and a hundred voices are raised in anger. Krishna sees death everywhere, in the waves and on the sand. He sees the silver reeds glistening in the sun, which seems to stop in mid-heaven, with prescience of the massacre to come. Krishna watches his son Pradyumna take sides with Satyaki, the Vrishni, against the Bhoja, Kritavarman. Hot words fly back and forth.

Then, Satyaki roars, "Today I will avenge Dhrishtadyumna, the finest kshatriya who fought on Kurukshetra!"

In a blur, he draws his sword and hews off Kritavarman's head in a scarlet explosion. The other Vrishnis are some way off, and hardly has Kritavarman's head struck the earth, when the Bhojas and Andhakas fall on Satyaki, and hack him to pieces. Pradyumna is the only Vrishni at

Satyaki's side. He draws his sword and slashes out wildly. He is badly outnumbered, and the Andhakas and Bhojas kill Krishna's son, too.

By now, the Vrishnis arrive and a pitched battle breaks out. Like characters in a nightmare, the Yadavas helplessly enact the tragedy that follows. Akrura flies at Bhoja; Aniruddha and Samba fall on each other. Soon, they hardly know anymore who the enemy is, nor care. Son hews at father, brother at brother, all of them unhinged with maireyaka and with Krishna's potent maya. They fight like a pack of dogs, felling one another with savage sword-strokes. But then, they are the invincible Yadavas: the dead rise again, intoxicated and laughing! Their wounds heal miraculously, and death is their ally, because they are Krishna's own people, his flesh and blood.

Aniruddha sees the eraka reeds growing in shallow water. Moved by an instinct he hardly understands, he throws down his sword and grasps at the glittering things. Balarama cries out to him to desist; too late. When Aniruddha pulls up a clutch of the reeds grown out of the powdered club of the rishis' curse, they turn into a dark blade in his hands. Anyone he strikes with it falls dead instantly and never rises again.

All the Yadavas pull up those macabre reeds to be their weapons, powerful as thunderbolts. Now the killing begins in earnest. Those even scratched with a silver reed die, by the curse in them. Krishna has seen his son and Satyaki both killed before his eyes. With an anguished cry, he runs forward to stop the fighting. Like any man, the Avatara had hoped some miracle could save his people at the last moment from Gandhari's curse, from the sages' curse. His sons Samba, Charuka and Charuvarman turn on him, growling. They attack him viciously, like children who have repressed a lifetime of resentment and raging, festering *envy*. Now they are sons who hate their father more than they can bear any more, and must kill him.

His cousin Akrura and all the others surround Krishna menacingly. His own head turned, with a heartbroken roar, the Dark One snatches up a handful of the deadly reeds and sets on his murdering clan. In his hands the reeds turn into a gleaming club, and, roaring for fate, roaring like the God he is, roaring wild for sorrow, Krishna slaughters his Yadavas with that club. He smashes their noble heads and their splendid bodies. Blood flies everywhere, brightly in the sun, splashing into crystal water. Heads are broken like melons, handsome limbs shattered: a grisly orgy of killing, and Krishna roaring above it all, above the screams of the others.

In moments, all the Yadavas are dead, and Krishna stands alone among the corpses of his people, drenched in crimson, his chest heaving. Still, bloodlust rages in him.

"Balarama, where are you?" he roars, red-eyed. In a whisper, his heart calls him to the waving sea.

There, Balarama sits, calmed, under a giant aswattha tree growing at the forest's edge. Daruka appears there, and his master and he watch Balarama seated in padmasana, perfectly withdrawn in dhyana, lost to the world. Light enfolds his brother, and at once Krishna grows calm. He knows he has accomplished everything for which he came into the world.

He says quietly to Daruka, "Ride to Hastinapura, my friend. Tell Arjuna what happened here, and Yudhishtira. Tell Arjuna to come at once to Dwaraka, he must look after our women and children. The curse is on me, as well, and my time is near."

Daruka stands numb for a moment, hardly believing what has happened, so suddenly. Without a word, he prostrates himself at Krishna's feet. Krishna raises him up and embraces him. He says, "Fly now, Daruka!"

The sarathy finds a chariot and rides like Vayu to Hastinapura. Krishna goes near Balarama and says, "Wait for me, brother. I must go briefly to Dwaraka, but I will fly back to you."

There is no sign that Balarama has heard him. Black turmoil churns Krishna, as his death glides nearer. Quietening himself, somehow, he climbs into the Jaitra and flies back to Dwaraka through the air. At the palace, he runs up the marble steps and straight into Vasudeva's presence. The world spins around Krishna, strange and terrible fires burn him. Panting and bloody, with the killing he has done, he comes into his father's chambers. Krishna runs forward and kneels at Vasudeva's feet. "Bless me, father, my end is upon me!"

With a cry, Vasudeva blesses his son. Krishna gasps, "I have sent for Arjuna, he will be here soon. Until then I leave the women and children in your care."

Vasudeva looks helplessly at his son, on whom he has always depended. Summoning all his strength, the old Yadava somehow whispers, "Go in peace, my child."

"Balarama is waiting," cries the Avatara, and runs out.

On his way, he hears wailing and screaming, as the women hear the news. In passing, he cries to them, "Arjuna will be here soon, he will look after you."

Then he is gone. Krishna flies back to Balarama. He finds him still locked in padmasana, but now his body seems to be on fire: such light blazes from him. Krishna goes nearer. Suddenly, Balarama's eyes fly open, *staring*. He sees Krishna standing before him, and smiles. Balarama's eyes close again, and even as Krishna watches him, he begins to metamorphose. An immense white serpent slides slowly out of his mouth. As it comes, the snake transforms Balarama's body for its own flesh; so that when it has emerged fully, nothing is left of the man. The brilliant Naga pauses a moment, its hood inclined to gaze at Krishna. It lowers itself, glides majestically into the sea and vanishes. Varuna himself, countless celestial nagas, and sacred rivers receive Ananta with padya and arghya.

Krishna knows his own time has come.

TWO

Krishna

In a tide of memories, he sees his life flit before his eyes. After the white snake enters the sea, Krishna roams the forest around Prabhasa in a daze. It is part of Gandhari's curse coming true: that he would wander the earth, alone. He ranges a whole life in vast, crystalline remembrance.

Arjuna sits alone in his apartment in Hastinapura. All at once, he begins to think of Krishna. The Pandava's heart races, and he hears Krishna's voice, 'Go and lie down, Arjuna. I want to speak to you.'

Arjuna goes to his bed. As soon as he lies on it, he falls asleep. In a dream Krishna comes to him, and takes his hand. 'Arjuna, do you remember I once told you that all things in this world are born to serve a purpose? And when each one's purpose is served, it passes on.'

'You said that when my chariot burned down after the war.'

'And so it is with men. When a man has served every purpose he is born for, he doesn't live another moment in the world, but death comes for him.'

'Yes, you told me, Krishna.'

Krishna's eyes are bright in Arjuna's dream. 'Arjuna, all that I came for has been accomplished. It is time for me to go.'

'My Lord!'

'You must also come soon, Arjuna. We cannot be apart, you and I.'

'I don't understand what you mean.'

'I wanted to see you once, before I went. Now I can go in peace.'

A smile lights the Avatara's face, as he fades from Arjuna's dream, and the Pandava awakes.

His soul in tumult, Krishna runs through the forest and arrives back at the aswattha tree under which Balarama was transformed. With a sigh, he sinks down on the ground. With every moment now, he feels his death draw nearer; he can feel its breath on his neck. Krishna lies on the earth in shavasana, the posture of the dead, and the Brahman, the timeless Spirit, washes over him in an infinite swell. He yokes himself deeply into that Godhead and is lost in samadhi.

Jara, the hunter, is out looking for a deer. From a distance, he sees Krishna's feet around the bole of the tree under which the Dark One lies. Jara sees the feet red with forest earth and blood from the slaughter of the Yadavas. The old hunter thinks he is seeing a red hind, and he stalks the crimsoned feet. When he is within range, he raises his rough bow, and taking careful aim, looses his fateful arrow. The Muni Durvasa had once blessed Krishna that every part of his body would be invulnerable to all weapons, save the soles of his feet. The arrowhead made from the sliver of the accursed club flares into the sole of the Dark One's foot, piercing the base of the thumb toe. Krishna roars in shock, as fate's shaft plunges agony through him.

Jara comes running to hear that cry. Gasping to see Krishna, knowing him at once from rumour, the hunter falls on his face before the dying Avatara. Krishna places his hand on the wild man's head, and tells him, "It is only as I willed it, and, my friend, you have set me free. Your mission in the world is fulfilled, and you will find swarga for what you have done today."

Sobbing, the hunter takes Krishna's head onto his lap. The Avatara's face is serene, wreathed in a smile. Next moment, he is dead. His spirit issues from his body, and makes all the earth glow mysteriously, as it courses into heaven, where Indra, the Aswins, Rudra, the adityas, the vasus, the viswedevas, devarishis, and siddhas come to receive him. Greeting them, he ascends beyond, as Vishnu Narayana, into his own, most exalted realm.

Then, the very world is dim: like a flower that has lost its fragrance, like a body from which the soul has gone. At that moment, the sacred river, the golden Saraswati, also vanishes from the earth forever; and, black lightning into the void Krishna leaves, the kali yuga flashes into the world, entering her fully.

THREE

Arjuna's anguish

Riding all night with the wind that flows like a dark river across Bharatavarsha, Daruka arrives in Hastinapura early the next day. He runs into the sabha, cries, "Gandhari's curse has come true, the Yadavas are all dead!" and falls unconscious before the throne. Yudhishtira's world crumbles, and the Kuru king also faints. The other Pandavas sit petrified. When Daruka revives, he tells them that Krishna wanted Arjuna to ride to Dwaraka and take charge of the Yadava women and children.

Arjuna realizes the meaning of his dream. He calls for his chariot and sets out with Daruka. They come to Prabhasa first, and find the bloody remains of the Yadavas. Arjuna sees Satyaki, Pradyumna, Aniruddha, Samba and the others. They are queerly preserved in death, no scavenger has touched their corpses. Controlling himself as best he can, he says in a whisper, "Where are Krishna and Balarama?"

Daruka leads him to the giant aswattha. They see the trail in the sand where the white serpent slid into the sea. There is no sign of either Krishna or his brother. They seek them in vain, for a time, then Daruka says, "We must ride to Dwaraka, the women will have panicked."

Suddenly, a terrible cry breaks out of Arjuna. Around the massive bole of the tree, he sees Krishna lying dead, a familiar smile still on his lips. Arjuna falls on the ground and clasps the blue body. In a while, Daruka says quietly, "My lord, we must go to Dwaraka."

Sixteen thousand women wait on the palace steps, and, when they see Arjuna's chariot drive up, and the Pandava alight from it, they begin to wail loudly. Slowly, Arjuna climbs the marble steps, and the sobbing women lead him in. There, he sees Rukmini and Satyabhama, and the mighty Arjuna swoons. Krishna's women carry him on to a couch. The kshatriya revives slowly; but he cannot speak and tears stream down his face. He sits mute, crying, with Krishna's queens around him.

At last, he rises and goes to meet Vasudeva. When Krishna's father sees the Pandava, he puts his arms around him and sobs. Arjuna spends some time with Vasudeva, and the old man says sadly, "Your sishyas Satyaki and Pradyumna are dead. They began the fighting. But, my son, the fault wasn't theirs: it was Gandhari and the rishis' curses that killed them. It was fate. Krishna did nothing to stop the carnage. He watched his sons and his people kill one another, and did nothing to stop them."

Vasudeva speaks haltingly, deep age and sorrow in his voice. After a moment's pause, he says, "Arjuna, I have no wish to live any more. I commit our women and children to your care."

Arjuna says, "I cannot live in this world without Krishna, and I am sure Yudhishtira feels the same. I will take the women and children and the old people to Indraprastha with me. Allow me, uncle, I must find the ministers and make the arrangements."

Arjuna meets with the elderly courtiers who did not go to Prabhasa. He tells them, "Seven days from now, you must leave Dwaraka forever. Take whatever gold you can with you. In Indraprastha, we will crown Krishna's grandson, Vajra, king of the Yadavas."

That night, Arjuna lies in his precious cousin's bed, while memories bear him far away. He thinks of the first time he saw Krishna, it was after Draupadi's swayamvara; and all the other times, brilliant and dangerous, which they shared. Arjuna lies awake through the night in lonely vigil. He knows the meaning has gone out of his life, and there is nothing left to live for.

The next morning, he has the corpses of all the Yadavas, Krishna's among them, brought to Dwaraka to be cremated. With his own hand, he touches alight the Dark One's pyre, while the sea rises to lash the ocean-city's walls. Four of Krishna's wives cannot bear to live without him, and immolate themselves on his pyre. Again, a night full of memories and intolerable grief; in the morning, Arjuna finds Vasudeva locked stiff in a yogasana, dead.

Arjuna performs the last rites for Vasudeva and the Yadavas. Then, with as much of the gold of Dwaraka as they can carry, he, the Yadava women and elders, and the brahmanas, vaisyas and sudras leave the city of dreams in a procession of chariots. Now, only the wind sighs in the empty streets. Even as the last chariot drives out through the gates, the ocean rises on every side and rushes into the crystal city. A seismic, submarine earthquake shakes land and sea. As if riven by a God's awesome hand, exquisite Dwaraka breaks in two and sinks below mountainous waves. Arjuna and the women watch, the shining palaces, the wide avenues and marvellous parks submerge, in moments. Last of all, Krishna's palace sinks. No trace remains of fabulous Dwaraka, and the sea grows calm before their eyes, still as a lake.

His heart broken, Arjuna rides towards Indraprastha with the Yadava women and children. They travel for two days, then make camp, once, in the land of five rivers. They have not noticed the mleccha bandits who have been stalking them like a pack of wolves. Evening sets in and Arjuna and the women are about to begin their meal, when, with fierce yells, the bandits attack. The camp rings with the screams of the Yadu women. Arjuna jumps up and seizes his Gandiva: but he cries out in dismay when he finds he cannot string the great bow! The Pandava's hands shake, his body trembles, sweat stands out on his brow, while the brigands take whatever they want, unopposed. With a huge effort, Arjuna manages to string his weapon. When he tries to summon an astra to burn the marauders, he cannot remember a single mantra.

Roaring in despair, Arjuna reaches for his magic quivers. They are empty! The greatest kshatriya in the world stands, watching helplessly, while the bandits carry away most of the gold from Dwaraka, and many of the Yadava women, too. Arjuna sinks to the ground, in tears; realization dawns on him that all this is, indeed, fated. Gandhari's curse has come true with unthinkable ferocity: it is truly the end of Krishna's people.

Gathering the handful of women, children and elders that remain, Arjuna arrives in Indraprastha, where Aniruddha's son, Vajra, is crowned king of the Yadavas.

Krishna's wives Rukmini, Saibya, Hymavati, and Jambavati make pyres and immolate themselves. Satyabhama and some others go away into the forest to perform tapasya. They live on roots and fruit, and meditate upon Krishna. They climb past the Himalaya, and begin living in the sacred place called Kalpa. Finally they all attain moksha. Arjuna does not stay even a day, but rides away from that city. He fears he will lose his mind for the grief that ravages him. Something draws him inexorably to his grandfather Vyasa's asrama. Glazed-eyed, panting, he comes before the serene maharishi.

Vyasa says, "Welcome. Why so stricken? Have you slept with a woman during her period? Or killed a brahmana? Has someone vanquished you in battle? Tell me what ails you, if, of course, there is no harm in telling me."

"Gandhari's curse has come true," says the Pandava dully. "Krishna and Balarama are dead, all the Yadavas are killed. Oh, Muni, how can I go on living, after what I have seen? I lit Krishna's pyre with my own hands. And once I would have believed the seas had dried up or the mountains had fallen into them, but not that he could die."

Vyasa says simply, "Arjuna, it is time for you to leave the world as well. There is no peace or purpose in it for you or your brothers, any more. You have accomplished everything you were born for."

Arjuna tells him about the bandits, known as the Abhiras: how he could hardly string the Gandiva, or remember a mantra for the astras, how his quivers were empty.

Vyasa says, "You have no further need of the devastras, the Gandiva or the quivers. You must seek Devaloka now. Leave this world of sorrow behind you, your time in it is over."

They sit together in rich silence, for a while, as the Pandava absorbs what Vyasa said. In that mystic silence, the warrior fancies he hears his Krishna's voice calling him, blithely as ever, from another world. Arjuna takes his grandfather's blessing, prostrating himself at his feet, taking the padadhuli from them, and he rides slowly back to Hastinapura.

Arjuna walks into the Kuru sabha. He looks at Yudhishtira's face, and cannot say a word, but falls unconscious at his brother's feet.

BOOK SEVENTEEN

Mahaprasthanika Parva

AUM, I bow down to Narayana, the most exalted Nara, and to the Devi Saraswati, and say *Jaya*!

ONE

The final journey

They revive Arjuna with scented water. Haltingly, often breaking down, he tells his brothers everything that had happened. He tells them about the carnage at Prabhasa: how Satyaki, Balarama and Krishna had died, and how he had lit Krishna's pyre. He tells them about the women and the bandits, and finally Yudhishtira whispers, "It is Gandhari's curse come true, in every detail."

Arjuna tells them how he had dreamt of Krishna, and the strange things his cousin said to him in the dream. The Pandavas are too shocked to even cry; it is as if their own lives died within them when they heard Krishna was dead. Yudhishtira, Bheema and the twins have already made plans while Arjuna was away.

Yudhishtira says, "There is no reason for us to live any longer. We always belonged to Krishna: we learnt how deeply during the war. We have decided we will crown Parikshita king in Hastinapura, and leave this world."

Arjuna murmurs, "I agree. Finally, time is the only victor."

Arrangements have already been made; within days, Parikshita is crowned king of the Kurus in the palace in Hastinapura. Yuyutsu is to be the new king's guardian and advisor, and Acharya Kripa, old as he is, will remain with his sishya, at least until the prince grows accustomed to the kingship. The Pandavas are ready to set out on their final journey, from which they will not return.

On the momentous day, Yudhishtira and his brothers appear on the palace steps wearing tree-bark and deerskin. Draupadi is with them, and she has put away her silks and jewellery. She is also clad in valkala and soft animal hide. The people fill the streets in sorrow at the news, and a cry goes up when the Pandavas emerge. But when the crowd sees the lustre upon Pandu's sons and their queen, it falls silent. Powerful grace enfolds the brothers and their Panchali.

The people part, in a wave, to let them through. Blessing them, asking them to be loyal to Parikshita, the Pandavas and Draupadi walk away from the city of their fathers for the last time. As they leave the city-gates, an unusual companion attaches himself to them. A little brown dog appears out of nowhere, and follows at Yudhishtira's heels, making them a party of seven. When they talk to him, wondering to whom he belongs, he turns soulful eyes up at them and wags his tail. Draupadi says, "Oh, he is so friendly. Let him come with us if he wants."

They travel south first, and arrive at the place where, just a few days ago, magical Dwaraka thrust its crystal towers at the sky from the waves. Now, a calm sea stretches away to the horizon on every side, and no trace remains of the marine city. But subtle visions reach out to the sons of Pandu from the jade and plumbless depths. Memories inundate them, particularly memories of a dark face and its inscrutable, always smiling, black eyes. They hear his voice woven into the surf and the mourning wind, which cries out his name endlessly.

As they stand there, a blazing Deva appears before them. Agni says to Arjuna, "You have no need any more of the Gandiva and the quivers I gave you. Give them back to the Lord of the ocean."

Agni vanishes as abruptly as he came. Full of grief, for he is parting from friends with whom he had passed through the valley of death, Arjuna sets his weapons down on the white sand. His hands folded, he walks solemnly around them in pradakshina. He strokes them with his fingers, kisses them, and casts his bow and quivers out into the smoky sea. There is a flash of light when they strike the waves; then they are gone. Varuna receives them again, as Arjuna stands forlorn, the wind blowing tears from his eyes.

It is told Varuna comes to them in an illustrious form, and takes the sons of Pandu below his waves, to the city of Dwaraka on his ocean bed.

Vivid schools of fish now swim in her streets, where she waits for the ages to turn slowly round, and for the Dark One to be born into the world again. So she can rise once more to be his home on earth. After they pay homage to Krishna's palace, Varuna brings them ashore and now they turn north.

With the brown dog always at their heels, Draupadi and her husbands cross the plains of Bharatavarsha, and arrive at the Himalaya. They mean literally to climb into heaven! Climbing for months on feet light as air, their punya their strength, they arrive on the white slopes of majestic Meru, mountain at the heart of the earth, from which the continents unfurl like petals from a calyx. With fervent prayers, they climb higher and higher, through breathless passes, along paths hardly as wide as their feet, and the mountain falling sheerly away below them. Clinging to smooth rock faces, they climb on, with Panchali between them.

Suddenly, Draupadi slips and, before any of her husbands can catch her, she falls off the slender trail they are on, plunges to her death thousands of feet below. The cries of the others echo off glacial gorges.

Bheema turns to Yudhishtira in anguish, "My lord, she was sinless all her life. Why has she died like this?"

Yudhishtira appears unmoved. Calmly, he says, "Though we were all her husbands, in her heart, she always loved Arjuna more than any of us*. Except for that, she was pure: which is why she could climb this far. That was her only sin, but it took her down."

They climb on, and then Sahadeva loses his footing and falls to his death. Again, Bheema asks Yudhishtira why he fell, when he was always so selfless. Yudhishtira says grimly, "He was proud of his intelligence, that was his sin."

On they climb and a blizzard howls across the icy precipices. It blows Nakula away. Yudhishtira says, "He thought he was the most handsome man on earth, and so he died."

---

* Yudhishtira once asks Krishna why Arjuna's life had been such a restless one, when he was perfect in every respect, with every auspicious mark on his body. Krishna replies that he agreed Arjuna was almost perfect, but his cheekbones were slightly high—this is why he had a life of frequent wandering. Draupadi, who is there, flashes an angry glare at Krishna! She can never bear anyone saying a word against her precious Arjuna.

Also, Krishna always calls Panchali 'sakhi' in the Sanskrit text—friend.

After a while, Arjuna lies down on the very path and breathes no more. Bheema cries, "Arjuna never told a lie, not even in jest! How has he died?"

"He boasted that he would kill all his enemies in a day but did not keep his word. He was proud of his archery, and his pride killed him."

Just they two climb on. Then Bheema feels his head spin viciously. He cries, "What have I done, my brother?"

Yudhishtira answers, "You ate too much, and you bragged about your strength, my Bheema. That will cost you your life."

Bheema falls to his death. Now it is only Yudhishtira and the surefooted, cheerful brown dog who climb on. Yudhishtira walks blindly, for he can hardly see anything around him any more. This is no longer the mountain of the earth; he is sure he has climbed into heaven. He comes into a place full of unearthly brightness. He sees a supernal chariot fly down before him. A radiant Deva rides in that vimana. Indra says, "Yudhishtira, I have come to take you to swarga."

"My lord, my brothers and my wife have fallen by the way. I do not want to go to swarga without them."

"They have abandoned their mortal bodies, and are already in heaven. But you, O king of dharma, shall enter the realm of the immortals in your human body!"

Yudhishtira says, "If you assure me I will meet them there, I will go with you." He pauses shyly, then, "But this dog has followed me all the way from Hastinapura. I beg you, let me bring him with me."

Indra, lord of light, laughs. "Do you know what you are saying, Pandava? You are being offered immortality. You will be equal to the Gods, and you want to bring a dog with you! You are the most fortunate man that ever lived in the world. Don't ruin your fortune with this foolishness. There is no place in swarga for a dog. Leave the beast and come with me. Come, Yudhishtira, no blame will attach to you."

"The dog has shared my journey, he shared my grief. He loves me and is loyal to me. I cannot abandon him now."

Indra says angrily, "You are still full of attachment. You have arrived at heaven's threshold, and you are being stubborn. Leave the dog, I cannot have him in my vimana."

Yudhishtira says, "All my punya will perish if I abandon this dog now. He is dependent on me, I cannot leave him. It would be a worse sin than killing a brahmana."

"You left your brothers and your queen. Does the dog mean more to you than they did?"

"My brothers and my wife were dead when I left them. I could do nothing for them any more. The dog is alive and he is helpless. I cannot abandon him. I will not come to swarga, unless he comes with me."

There is the strangest smile on Indra's face now, as he gazes past Yudhishtira. The Pandava turns his head, and cries out. The furry brown dog has vanished: Yudhishtira's father, Dharma Deva, stands in its place. The astonished Pandava folds his hands to his sire. "My lord!" he breathes.

Dharma says, "There is no other king like you on earth or in heaven, my son, none as compassionate. I tried you once in the Dwaitavana, and you asked for Nakula's life to be restored. Now I have tested you again, and you have earned heaven for yourself with your mercy."

Numberless presences have gathered above that mountain, great spirits come to see the first mortal man who ever gained Devaloka in his human body.

Yudhishtira climbs into Indra's vimana, and they flash away from the world, quickly as light. The sky parts like a blue sea, and they break through its veil to the realms on the other side: wonder everywhere, light everywhere, grandeur and beauty past describing.

Indra says, "Look, Yudhishtira, every star you saw from the earth is a separate mandala of the Devas."

At the heart of ineffable legend, they arrive in fabled Amravati, the deathless city. The Lord of the Devas brings Yudhishtira into the Sudharma, his incomparable sabha. The great kings of the ages all have thrones in that court.

Indra says, "Your ancestors are all here, Yudhishtira, kings who made time fragrant with their dharma. You are one of them now, your fame is eternal."

Yudhishtira looks around him. "I don't see my brothers here, my lord. I don't see my queen. I beg you, take me to them. I have no use for all this glory, if Panchali and my brothers are not with me."

Indra says, "Stay here with us. You have earned your place in heaven with your dharma. This is not the earth any more; you must leave your worldly attachments behind you. Forget about your wife and your brothers, that life is past. They cannot hope to gain these heights,

Yudhishtira, every man is given only what he deserves. You will be happy with us here, forget the past."

Yudhishtira hardly hears him. His eyes seek his brothers everywhere in the sabha. He does not see them, and the Pandava says, "I realize what an honour you bestow on me. But I cannot stay here, without my Bheema, my Arjuna, my Nakula and Sahadeva, and my dark Panchali. Where are my sons, Lord, whom Aswatthama killed? I beg you, take me to those whom I love!"

Then, Yudhishtira grows very still. Seated before him on a lofty throne, with a smile on his face, he sees Duryodhana.

BOOK EIGHTEEN

Swargarohanika Parva

AUM, I bow down to Narayana, the most exalted Nara, and to the Devi Saraswati, and say *Jaya*!

ONE

The law of heaven

AMONG KINGS OF YORE WHO ENRICHED THE EARTH WITH THEIR noble lives, Duryodhana sits in Indra's sabha on a jewelled throne. The Kaurava is as majestic as any of the other kshatriyas.

Yudhishtira cannot contain himself. "How is Duryodhana here in your court of dharma? He caused the deaths of millions. He destroyed kshatriya kind with his greed. This man had Draupadi dragged into the Kuru sabha by her hair, and tried to strip her naked. There is no sinner like him in heaven or earth. I cannot bear to be in the same place as him, not for a moment!"

Narada is in the Sudharma, and he says to Yudhishtira, "Ah, don't say that! This is swarga. Before you enter here, you must forget your old enmities. Listen to me, Pandava, all these kings of men love your cousin. He died like a kshatriya, offering his body as libation in the fire of war, and they love him for that. He died bravely, in agony, and his death purified him. Moreover, he was a just king when he ruled. He was fearless and generous. Pandava, the laws of heaven differ from the laws of the earth.

"Don't judge Duryodhana anymore. He was forgiven everything when he died, and he died in a most holy place. Balarama said he would find Devaloka, and his mother Gandhari was a bhakta. You must leave your anger behind you, Yudhishtira, there is no place for enmity here."

Yudhishtira stands trembling. "I know nothing of the laws of Devaloka, but I wonder why I don't see my brothers here. If Duryodhana deserves to be here, what about them? They were all great men, who never strayed from the path of truth. Where are they now? Where is my noblest brother Karna? Where are Satyaki and Dhrishtadyumna? Where are all the kshatriyas who laid down their lives for me? Where is my child Abhimanyu? Where is Krishna? Where is my mother Kunti? Where are Shikhandi, Virata and Drupada, where is my queen Draupadi? I beg you, my lords, take me to my brothers. I want to live in the place where they are, wherever it is. I don't understand the dharma of heaven, I want to be with my brothers!"

Yudhishtira's voice has risen in despair. Indra sighs, "Very well, then, let Yudhishtira be taken to where his brothers are."

The king of the Devas summons an attendant, and Yudhishtira follows that bright servitor out of the Sudharma. They hardly walk a short way, when suddenly they tread a sinister trail. This path snakes on, interminably, and Indra's servant walks briskly along it. A glowing blackness engulfs them. The air is still, breathless; a fetid smell hangs heavily. On both sides, they hear groans and screams of souls in torment. In the gloom, Yudhishtira dimly sees the monstrous forms of demons: some entwine horribly; others are dismembered or headless, and some have mouths like needles. Corpses are strewn everywhere, hideously disembowelled, entrails hanging out, smeared with fat and blood, their stink intolerable. A thousand human hands reach out to them, in agony.

Everywhere they hear sobbing and the gnashing of teeth. Weird howls ring out, now and again, and at times serpents slither across the narrow path. Sulphurous pools bubble beside the eerie trail, and there are living creatures in them: burning slowly, never dying, suffering endlessly. With every step they take, the sights, smells and sounds grow worse, and the heat becomes unbearable.

Soon, Yudhishtira cries, "This is an infernal place! Which God rules this part of Devaloka? Ah, where are my brothers?"

Indra's servant replies, "This path leads to your brothers; but we will turn back, if you cannot bear it."

The stench is intolerable. Yudhishtira gags. The sights around them are so vile he cannot look at them, and he wants to shut his ears for the dreadful sounds that fill the darkness. The heat begins to scald the skin from his arms and face. Steadfast as he is, the Pandava cannot go any further into that hell.

He stops, and says, "Friend, I cannot stand this place any more. Let us turn back. How far did Lord Indra tell you to bring me?"

The man smiles, "Only as far as you could go."

Then, many voices wail dismally out of the darkness. "Yudhishtira, don't leave us!"

"Don't go, Yudhishtira!"

"Take pity on us, stay a while!"

"Your presence soothes us like a soft breeze of heaven—don't leave!"

"Just a few moments, stay a few moments more!"

Yudhishtira's hair stands on end: the voices are familiar! He cries, "Who calls out to me? Why are you in this naraka?"

All together, the voices reply.

"I am Karna."

"I am Bheema."

"Arjuna."

"Nakula."

"Sahadeva."

"This is I, Draupadi."

"I am Dhrishtadyumna."

"I am Satyaki."

All the others he loved, who had fought and died for him, call out to him.

Yudhishtira cries, "My sinless brothers, my Panchali and my friends are all in hell, while Duryodhana sits on a crystal throne in the Sudharma! Am I dreaming? Surely, this is a nightmare from which I will awaken."

Again, the piteous voices call out, begging him to stay with them just a little longer, ah, his presence soothed their torment. Tears in his eyes, Yudhishtira turns to the divine servitor who brought him here, "Friend, go back to Indra, and tell him I will remain with my brothers. They say that my presence soothes their anguish."

The man bows, and leaves Yudhishtira alone. The darkness, the purulence, the heat and the terror of that hell are all magnified, when he is alone. The voices cry out more plaintively. Yudhishtira sits on the path, sweating, wondering how long he can endure it. He has been there for an hour, when there is a flash of light, then another, another, and more. Indra stands before Yudhishtira, the king of heaven come with his host. In a moment, the darkness, the pestilential vapours, the scathing heat, the sulphur pits, the demons, all vanish. No more groans and screams bruise the air. Instead, it is sweet and pure, and that place is full of light, and living silence. A fragrant breeze blows, plucking at Yudhishtira's face. He stands blinking in the soft lambency of Devaloka.

Indra says to him, "Now you have earned swarga for yourself. The law of heaven is that every king must pass through hell to purify himself. You experienced naraka briefly, to atone for your one sin on earth. Yudhishtira, you deceived your guru Drona on Kurukshetra. It was your lie that made him put down his weapons, and then Dhrishtadyumna killed him. You have paid for that sin now. Forget what you saw, it was an illusion. Come with us."

Yudhishtira stands, hands folded before the effulgent Gods. He murmurs, "My brothers?"

"Your brothers are already in swarga! With them, are all the kings who fought for you. They, too, served a brief time in hell for their sins, and were purified. You say you do not understand the law of Devaloka. Let me tell you what it is. If a man's sins outweigh his punya, then he comes straight into heaven when he dies. When his punya is exhausted, he sinks into hell to suffer for his sins. But if a soul's virtue exceeds his sins, then he pays first for his crimes, and then comes into swarga forever.

"Your brothers are not here, Yudhishtira. Come with me, I will show you where they are."

"Yudhishtira's father, the Lord Dharma, appears before him again. Blessing his son, he says, "This was the third trial, the last one. Nothing could induce you to leave the path of truth; nothing could quell your love for your brothers. Come to those whom you love so much."

The Devas bring Yudhishtira to the banks of the Ganga, flowing through heaven in her celestial form. The Pandava bathes in her waters of light and she takes his mortal body from him, like a worn set of clothes. He rises in glory, a king of Devaloka. With Indra and the others, Yudhishtira comes back to Amravati, to its incomparable sabha. First of all, he sees Krishna on the loftiest throne, with Arjuna beside him and all the Yadavas around them. They rise to receive Yudhishtira.

Yudhishtira sees his brother Karna sitting among the twelve Adityas, all sons of Surya. He sees his brother Bheema, his body a swirling air; he sits amidst the Maruts, who are Vayu's magnificent people. Nakula and Sahadeva are with their fathers, the brilliant Aswin twins. Then, sweeping the sabha, Yudhishtira's gaze finds Draupadi. She wears a garland of undying lotuses, and she is a great flame in that court; all her sons surround her. Her brother Dhrishtadyumna sits not far from her, with rutilant Agni, the Fire God: their father. Yudhishtira sees Abhimanyu, seated beside the glowing Moon, luminous Soma Deva. The Pandava sees Bheeshma among the Vasus, and Drona at Brihaspati's side. He sees his uncle Vidura, now a lord of heaven beside Dharma Deva. In joy, he sees his father Pandu, and Kunti and Madri.[1]

His brothers rise and come to welcome Yudhishtira. Karna also rises; and with them comes another familiar figure, his body luculent, kindness and grace in his eyes, and his face wreathed in a smile. It is Duryodhana, who is also a king in Devaloka. Now Yudhishtira feels no twinge of resentment, and embraces his cousin just as he does his brothers.

Indra, Lord of the Devas, presents Yudhishtira, the Pandava, in his sabha in Devaloka: Yudhishtira who is Dharma's son, and the very soul of truth.

---

1 See Appendix.

Phalasruti

DARK KRISHNA WAS THE EIGHTH AVATARA OF THE LORD VISHNU, who lies upon eternal waters. He was born into the world to cleanse it of the tide of evil that darkened the age. He came to establish dharma on earth again. The Devas Indra, Vayu, Dharma, and the Aswins were also born into the world, in amsa, as the sons of Pandu: to fight at Krishna's side. The earth was purified because these Gods walked upon her. And at the war on the cusp of the ages, the seed of dharma was sown in holy ground made fertile by the blood of the kshatriya.

Once their lives' purpose was accomplished, the Pandavas left the world and were absorbed again into their fathers in heaven, the Lords of light. Most of all, the earth was enriched forever that blue Krishna walked upon her for a brief human life.

The legend of the Pandavas, the Mahabharata, the tale of the war on the crack of two yugas, is an immortal story. As long as the earth lives, as long as the sun and moon light the sky, and there is even a spark of goodness in men's hearts, this legend of the sons of Pandu will be told in the world. It is a sacred epic, a tale of truth, and whoever reads or hears it will have his sins washed from him, and his heart made pure. He will finally come to the blessed realm of Mahavishnu, who lies on the serpent, Anantasesha, upon the Kshirasagara, ocean of eternity, and of bliss.

AUM SHANTI SHANTI SHANTI! AUM SHANTIHI AUM!

Glossary

Abhichara – sorcery. Also a spirit raised by an occult ritual.
Abhichari – sorcerer.
Abhisheka – investiture.
Acharya – a brahmana master.
Achyuta – immortal; a name of Vishnu's, and Krishna's.
Adharma – evil.
Adi kavya – first Poem. The Ramayana.
Adisehsa – great Serpent, Vishnu's rest.
Aditi – mother of the Devas.
Aditya – son of Aditi. Being of light, also son of the Sun God.
Adityahridaya – lit. heart of the sun.
Agni – Fire God
Agni – fire.
Agnihotra – fire ritual.
Agni kunda – fire pit.
Agneyastra – fire weapon, missile.
Agneyi – self-immolation by invoking inner fire.
Aindastra – Indra's astra.
Airavata – Indra's four-tusked white, flying elephant.
Akasa – sky, cosmic ether, fifth element.
Akhanda – universe.
Aksauhini – a legion. One version of its size is 21,000 chariots, as many elephants, 65,000 horse and 110,000 footsoldiers. (But this count does not tally with the total number of men killed during the Mahabharata yuddha, in 11 aksauhinis.)
Alakananda – a name of the Ganga.

Alidha – archer's stance.
Amavasya – new moon.
Amravati – Indra's heavenly city.
Amrita – nectar of immortality.
Amsa – essence, part.
Ananta – Sesha cosmic Serpent on which Vishnu rests.
Anarta – Krishna's kingdom.
Anarya – ignoble.
Andhaka – a Yadava tribe.
Angaraka – Mars.
Anima – the occult power to make oneself small.
Aniruddha – Krishna's grandson.
Anjali – offering.
Antapura – harem.
Apsara – nymph.
Arani – a twig from a sami tree. A fire kindeld with these is always sacred.
Aranya – jungle.
Arati – worship with lamps.
Ardha – half.
Arghya – offering of welcome.
Arya – noble.
Aryavarta – land of the noble. India. Bharatavarsha.
Aryaman – ancestor, the first man. Also, the Sun. Lord of the manes.
Asariri – disembodied voice.
Asrama – hermitage.
Asramas, the 4 asramas of life – brahmachari, grihasta, vanaprastha, sannyasi. Celibate, householder, renunciate, hermit.
Astra – unearthly weapon.
Asura – demon.
Aswamedha yagna – horse sacrifice.
Aswattha – pipal tree.
Aswins – heavenly twins, known for their beauty.
Atharva – the fourth Veda, concerned with sorcery, spells, etc.
Atman – the individual Soul.
AUM/OM – holy syllable, represents the Ultimate Reality.
Avatara – Incarnation.

Ayudha – weapon.
Bala/atibala – strength, extreme strength.
Bhajan – devotional song.
Bhakti – devotion, worship.
Bhakta devotee.
Bharatavarsha – India. The land of Bharata.
Bhasha – language.
Bhasma – holy ash.
Bhiksha – alms, begging.
Bhoja – a Yadava tribe.
Bhumi – the earth.
Bhumidevi – Earth Goddess.
Bhuta – ghost, spirit.
Bindu – point; mystic singularity.
Brahma – God of the Hindu Trinity. The Creator.
Brahmachari – a celibate.
Brahmacharya – celibacy.
Brahmahatya – murder of a brahmana.
Brahman – Ultimate Godhead; Holy Sopirit; different from Brahma.
Brahmana – priestly caste, also 'Brahma's people'.
Brahmarishi – sage of Brahman.
Brahmavadi – knower of Brahman.
Brahmavidya – knowledge of Brahman.
Brighu – an ancient rishi.
Brihaspati – guru of the Devas. Also the planet Jupiter.
Budha – Mercury.

Chaitra – an auspicious lunar month.
Chaitra – Kubera's garden.
Chakra – a wheel. In the body, a subtle centre of energy along the spinal column and in the brain.
Chakravaka – a water bird.
Chakravarti – emperor.
Chamara – silken whisk.
Chandala – an untouchable.
Chandra – Moon.
Charana – unearthly being.

Chiranjivi – long-lived, almost immortal.
Chital – a kind of deer.
Chitraratha – king of the gandharvas.

Daksha – Brahma's son, Sati's father. A prajapati.
Danava – demon, son of Danu.
Danda – a staff, also punishment.
Daitya – demon, son of Diti.
Dakshina – south.
Dakshinayana – the sun's southern migration.
Darbha – a kind of grass.
Darbhasana – seat made of darbha grass
Deva – a celestial, elemental, being. A God. Also 'Being of Light.' 'Divya' is light.
Devaloka – heavenly realm of the Devas.
Devaputra – son of a Deva.
Devi – Goddess.
Dharma – truth, justice.
Dhanu – Sagittarius.
Dhanusha – bow.
Dhanvantari – the original physician, who rose from the sea of milk with the amrita.
Dharma – truth, justice, duty, righteousness.
Dhruva – North Star.
Dhyana – meditation.
Dikpala – lord of a direction.
Diksha – gift/offering for a brahmana.
Dvividha – a vanara.
Dwapara – yuga third great age.
Dwaraka – Krishna's ocean city, raised for him by the Devas.
Dwarapalaka – gatekeeper.

Ekarnava – the original sea of life.

Gada – mace, club.
Gana – servitor, companion of Siva.
Gandharva – heavenly warrior minstrels. Elf.

Gandharva – vivaha marriage by abduction, elopement.
Garuda – Vishnu's Eagle.
Gayatri – the mother of all mantras.
Ghee – clarified butter.
Gochara – planetary transit.
Gopa – cowherd. Krishna was raised by gypsy cowherds.
Gopi/gopika – cowherdess.
Gotra – family, clan, lineage.
Graha pravesha – formal entry into a new home.
Grihastha – householder.
Guna – essence in nature. Sattva, rajas and tamas.
Guru – preceptor, master.
Guru dakshina – a formal fee or gift given to a master by his pupil, when tutelage is complete.
Gurukula – stage of life as a student, under a guru.
Gyana – knowledge.
Gyani – a wise man.

Halahala – original poison, which Siva drank.
Hari – Vishnu.
Hatya – murder.
Havis – the burnt offering from a sacrifice.
Himavan – Himalaya.
Hiranyagarbha – pregnant with the Golden Egg of the Cosmos.
Homa – ritual worship.

Ikshvaku – Ancestor. A race of the Sun is named after him.
Indra – king of the Devas.
Indradhanush – rainbow.
Ishta devata – personal God.

Jatakarma – caste ritual.
Jambavan – king of bears.
Jambavati – Jambavabn's daughter. Krishna's wife.
Janaki – Janaka's daughter, Sita.
Janardhana – Vishnu.
Janmanakshatra – lunar birth star.

Japam – chant of God's names.
Jata – dreadlocks like rishis wear.
Jaya – victory.
Jaya vijayi bhava! – Be victorious!
Jitendriya – one who has conquered his senses.
Jivatma – embodied soul.

Kaala – time.
Kadamba – a tree.
Kalakuta/Halahala – Poison churned up from the kshirasagara.
Kali yuga – the fourth, and the most evil, of the ages. Not the black Goddess, Kaali.
Kalpa – cosmic tract of time. 1000 yugas.
Kalyana – marriage.
Kalyanamantapa – marriage hall, enclosure.
Kama – God of Love. Also pleasure, enjoyment.
Kamadhenu – first, sacred, cow of wishes.
Kamandalu – brahmana's water-pot.
Kama shastra – sacred arts of loving.
Kanchana – golden.
Kanya – virgin, maiden, young woman.
Kapila – great sage. Vishnu's incarnation.
Karma – action, duty, also the fruit of past deeds.
Karttikeya – Siva's son.
Kavacha – armour.
Kirita – crown.
Kiriti – Arjuna, after he wore the crown ndra gave him.
Kirtana – devotional song.
Kohl – black substance used to line the eyes.
Koyal – cuckoo.
Krita yuga – first of the four ages; the purest, most pristine yuga.
Krodhagraha – chamber of anger.
Krosa – about 2 miles, a fourth of a yojana.
Kshatriya – warrior.
Kshetra – field; also, field of experience, knowledge etc.
Kshirasagara – mythical sea of milk.
Kubera – Lord of treasures. A Deva.

Kula – clan.
Kulaguru – the teacher of a royal family.
Kulapati – head of a clan.
Kundala – earrings, ear-studs.
Kurma – tortoise: Vishnu's second Avatara.
Kushti – wrestling.
Kutila – hut.

Lagna – ascendant, rising sign.
Lakshmi – Goddess of fortune. Vishnu's consort.
Linga – phallus, phallic emblem, Siva's.

Madhurpaka – sweet offering to a guest: usualy, honey and milk.
Maha – great or powerful.
Maharathika – great warrior.
Mahavishnu – second God of the Hindu Trinity. The Preserver.
Mahima/anima – the occult siddhis to grow big and small.
Mahodadi – great sea.
Mahodara – consumption
Malaya – of a mala, a mountain.
Manasa sarovara – holy lake on the Himalaya that Brahma made from his mind.
Mandala – dimension, galaxy.
Mangala – Mars.
Mantapa – pavilion.
Mantra, mantram – sacred incantation.
Manu – ancestor, law-giver.
Margasirsa/Mrigasirsa – an auspicious Hindu lunar month.
Maricha – demon who turned himself into a golden deer in the Ramayana.
Marma – a vulnerable place in the body.
Marut – divine companion of Vayu, the Wind God. There are 49 Mauts.
Mathura – city of the Yadavas.
Matrihatya – matricide.
Matsya – fish: Vishnu's first Avatara.
Matsya yantra – a fish device.
Maya – illusion, cosmic illusion; as different from the Reality of God. Also, sorcery.

Maya – Goddess of illusion.
Mayaa – great demon builder and king.
Mayavi – sorcerer.
Meru/Sumeru – sacred, golden mountain north of the Himalayas, from which the continents are said to have unfurled. Heart of the world.
Mlechcha – alien, untouchable.
Mohini – enchantress: Vishnu as a woman.
Moksha – liberation, salvation.
Mowna – silence.
Mrityu – death.
Mrityunjaya homa – a ritual to keep death away.
Mudra – hand-sign, gesture of occult power.
Muhurta – a small measure of time, esp. an auspicious moment to begin a new enterprise.
Muni – seer, rishi. Silent one, knower of minds.
Musth – elephant's season/rut.

Naga – great serpent; also magical, serpentine beings.
Nakshatra – asterism in lunar Hindu astrology. They are 27 stellar goddesses, wives of the Moon.
Nandana – Indra's garden.
Naracha – fiery missile.
Narada – a great rishi. Brahma's son, born from his mind. A devotee of Vishnu.
Naraka – hell.
Narasimha – manticore incarnation of Vishnu's.
Narayana – the Sleeper on eternity's waters, which are called the Naara. Vishnu.
Nilakanta – blue-throated One: Siva.
Nilgai – a species of deer.
Nirvana – moksha, liberation.
Nishada – untouchable.
Nritya – dance.

OM, Omkara – the primal, holy syllable, which represents Godhead. AUM. Pranava.
Oshadhi – healing herb.

Paapa – sin.
Paasa – noose.
Paativratya – fidelity.
Padadhuli – lit. 'dust from feet'. A spiritual emanation from a holy person or elder's feet.
Padma – lotus.
Padmanabha – lotus-navelled. Vishnu. Brahma is born in the lotus that sprouts from Vishnu's navel.
Padmasana – lotus-posture.
Padya – water for washing the feet.
Panchabhuta – the five elements.
Parabrahman – Brahman. The ultimate, undifferentiated Godhead.
Paramatman – Supreme Soul, God.
Parasurama – brahmana incarnation of Vishnu. Axe-bearer.
Parivrajaka – mendicant, holy man.
Parthiva linga – an earthen phallic symbol.
Parvati – Siva's wife, lit. mountain-daughter.
Pasupati – lord of animals: Siva.
Patala – under-world, nether world.
Pativrata – a devoted wife.
Paurnima/Purnima – full moon.
Payasa – a liquid sweet.
Phalasruti – a description of the fruit, results to be had from listening to or reading a holy text.
Pipal – holy tree.
Pisacha – evil spirit.
Pitama/Pitamaha – grandfather.
Pitr – ancestor. Lit. father.
Pitriloka – realm of the manes.
Pradakshina – circumambulation, in worship, respect.
Pradyumna – Krishna's son.
Prahlada – son of the Asura Hiranyakashyipu, but Prahalada was a great Vishnu bhakta.
Prajapati – a lord of the first races of men.
Prakriti – nature. Ying. Feminine principle.
Pralaya – the Deluge.
Prana – life breath.

Pranava – AUM.
Prayatna – difficult endeavour.
Prayaschitta – penance.
Prayopavesha – fasting for a cause, or a boon.
Preta – a spirit.
Prithvi – the Earth.
Puja/Pooja – ritual worship.
Punnaga – a tree.
Punya – virtue, merit.
Purana – ancient legend, revelation. Also, collections of such legends about the Gods and their lives and deeds.
Puranika/Pauranika – a raconteur, expert on the puranas.
Purohit – priest.
Purusha – the masculine principle. Yang. Also, soul as opposed to the feminine prakriti, or nature.
Purushottama – 'best among men', Vishnu.
Pushkara – lake sacred to Brahma.
Pushpaka vimana – sky chariot. UFO!
Putrakama yagna – sacrifice for the birth of a son.
Putrasneha – attachment/love for one's children.

Raga, raaga – special combination of musical notes.
Raghuvamsa – the clan of Raghu, an ancient king.
Rahu – dragon's head, a demon.
Rajarishi – a king who is a sage.
Rajas – the second guna: active, energetic.
Rajasuya – an imperial sacrifice.
Raksha – protection, amulet of protection.
Rakshasa – demon.
Rakshasi – demoness.
Ratha – chariot.
Rathika – expert charioteer.
Rekha – line of power.
Rik/Rig Veda – the first Veda.
Rishabha – the second note of the scale. Re.
Rishi – sage.
Ritvik – priest.

Rohini – asterism, goddess, the Moon's favourite wife.
Rudra/Siva – also a class of fierce beings associated with Siva.
Rudraksha – holy beads; lit. Siva's tears/eyes.
Rukmini – Krishna's wife.

Sabha – court, hall.
Sachi – Indra's queen.
Sairandhri – flower girl to a queen.
Sakhi – female companion.
Sama – a Veda.
Samadhi – absorption in the Soul/God. Mystical trance.
Sambur – a species of deer.
Samsara – the world of illusion. This life of appearances.
Sanatkumara – one of four original sages, born from Brahma's mind.
Sandhi – conjunction, cusp.
Sandhya – twilight.
Sankara – Siva.
Sannyasa – asceticism, renunciation.
Sannyasi – hermit.
Saptarishi – seven sages, born from Brahma's mind.
Sarabha – great mythical bird.
Saras – lake.
Sarasa – water bird.
Saraswati – Goddess of learning. Brahma's consort.
Sarathy – charioteer.
Saringa – Krishna's Bow.
Sati – Daksha' daughter. Siva's first wife, who immolated herself, and was then born as Parvati.
Sati – when a widowed woman kills herself by sitting on her husband's pyre.
Sattva – the first, pure guna.
Satyabhama – Krishna's wife.
Senapati – general; lit., lord of an army.
Shastra – scripture.
Shimshupa – a tree.
Siddha – a self-realized being.
Siddhi – occult power.

Sirasasana – yogic posture, headstand.
Sishya – pupil, disciple.
Siva – third God of Hindu Trinity. The Destroyer.
Shavasana – corpse-like yogic posture.
Skanda – Siva's son, Karttikeya.
Sloka – sacred verse.
Soma – the Moon God. Also, lunar nectar.
Srarddha – death ceremony.
Sruti – tone, sacred recitation, text.
Sruva – ladle.
Stamba – post, pole.
Sudarshana Chakra – Vishnu's weapon, a blazing disc.
Sudharma – Indra's court in Amravati.
Sudra – fourth Hindu caste, the servitors.
Sukra – Venus, guru to the Asuras.
Sukshma/sthula – Subtle/gross. Incorporeal/corporeal.
Surya – Sun God.
Suryanamaskara – yogic ritual for worshipping the sun at dawn.
Suta – bard, charioteer.
Sutaputra – son of a suta.
Swamini – female of swami, saint.
Swapna – dream.
Swarga – heaven.
Swayamvara – the ceremony at which a princess chooses her own husband.

Taala – rhythm, beat.
Tamas – the third and grossest guna in Nature.
Tandava – Siva's dance of dissolution.
Tapasya – penance, long meditation or austerity.
Tapasvin – one performs tapasya.
Tapovana – grove of worship.
Tarpana – offering of water for the dead.
Tilaka – auspicious mark made on forehead.
Timmingala – mythical whale-eater, possibly giant squid.
Tirtha – holy place of pilgrimage.
Tirtha yatra – pilgrimage.
Treta yuga – the second great age.
Trikalagyani – one who knows the 3 times.

Trimurti – trinity: Brahma, Vishnu and Siva.
Tripathaga – of three paths.
Tripura – three sky cities, built by Mayaa, which Siva brought down with a missile of fire.
Trisula – trident.

Ucchaisravas – horse of the Sun.
Upanishad – holy book, dealing with the Brahman, the formless God.
Usanas – Sukra. A male God, guru to the Asuras, as Brihaspati, Jupiter is to the Devas. Greatest of poets.
Uttara Phalguni – a nakshatram.
Uttarayana – the northern migration of the sun.

Vaastu – land, property, house etc. also, the sacred science of these and building. Ancient Indian feng shui.
Vaastu shanti – rite for peace in a new dwelling.
Vaikunta – Vishnu's celestial city.
Vairagya – detachment, relinquishment.
Vaisya – third Hindu caste; the traders.
Vajra – Indra's thunderbolt.
Valkala – fabric made of tree-bark, worn by hermits.
Vamana – dwarf: Vishnu's fifth Avatara.
Vana – jungle, forest.
Vana devata – forest god.
Vanara – ancient, magical race of monkeys. Lit. dwellers in the vana.
Vanavasa – living in the forest as a renunciate.
Vandana – worship.
Varaha – boar: Vishnu's third incarnation.
Varanasi – city sacred to Siva.
Varsha – continent. Also, rain.
Varuna – God of seas.
Vasantha – Spring.
Vasuki – king of the nagas.
Vayavyastra – wind weapon.
Veda – ancient book of sacred hymns.
Vedanta – lit. the end of the Vedas. Includes the Upanishads. Discourses on the Brahman.
Vedi/vedika – altar.

Vetala/i – hunter, huntress
Vidya – an art.
Vidyadhara – magical being.
Vimana – sky ship.
Vina – Indian stringed instrument, like a lute.
Vina nadam – the sound of a vina.
Viswakarman – divine artisan.
Viswarupa – Cosmic Form.
Vivasat – ancestor: the Sun.
Vrata – vow.
Vrishni – a Yadava tribe, to which Krishna belongs.
Vyuha – battle formation.

Yaama – a measure/hour of the night.
Yadava – Krishna's clan.
Yaga, yagna – sacrifice.
Yagnapashu – sacrificial beast.
Yagnashala – enclosure for a sacrifice.
Yajaka – one who undertakes a yagna.
Yajus, Yajur Veda – a Veda.
Yaksha – a forest spirit.
Yama – God of Death.
Yamala – a tree.
Yamaduta – death's messenger, servitor.
Yantra – occult symbol. A device.
Yatra – journey, often with religious significance.
Yoga – 'union'; union with the Self, with God.
Yogi, yogin – one who is united with his higher Self, with God.
Yogini – female yogi.
Yojana – 8/9 miles approximately.
Yoni – vagina. Vaginal symbol at the base of a linga.
Yuddha – war.
Yuga – an age.
Yuganta/Yugantara – conjunction of two ages; a time of great change.
Yuga sandhi – the cusp between two yugas.
Yuvaraja – crown prince, heir apparent.

Appendix

Book 5. Udyoga parva

1. The names of some of those kings: Hardikya, Ahuka, the king of the Mallas, Rochamana, Brihanta, Senabindu, Baahlika, Mudrakesa, Suparshva, Subahu, Paurava, the kings of the Sakas, the Pahlavas, and the Daradas, Surari, Nadija, Karnavest, Nila, Viradharman, Durjaya, Dantavakra, Rukmi, Janamejaya, Ashada, Vayuvega, Purvapali, Bhooritejas, Devaka, Ekalaya and his sons, the Krausha king, Kshemamurti, the Kamboja and Richaka kings, the kings of Kashi, the Sindhu, the son of Kratha, the mountain kings, Jananki, Susarman, Maniman, Potimatsyaka, Dhrishtaketu, the Pansu king, Paundra, Dandadhara, Brihatsena, Aparajita, Srenimat, Nishada, Vasumat, Brihadbala, Bahu, Samudrasena, Uddhava, Kshemaka, Vatadhana, Srutayus, Dridayus, the son of Shalva, the Kalinga kings, and Kumara.

2. This is another incident Karna relates to describe his relationship with Duryodhana. This is from Tamil folklore.

Duryodhana and Karna are so close that Karna has access to Duryodhana's harem, and his wife's inner apartments.

One day, Karna is playing dice with Duryodhana's wife, and she is losing to him. Suddenly, Duryodhana enters the private chamber. Karna has his back to the door, while Duryodhana's wife is facing it. She sees Duryodhana and gets up.

Karna has not seen him yet, and saying, 'You can't leave just because you are losing!' pulls her to sit down again. Accidentally, he breaks her string of pearls.

She is embarrassed and confused, lest Duryodhana misunderstand this intimacy. She stands shaken and unsure.

Duryodhana calmly comes up to them, and says ... the Tamil version is 'Cherkkava, Korkkava?' which means, 'Shall I join your game, or string the pearls?'

When, just before the war, Kunti begs Karna to join the Pandavas, telling him he is their brother, this is one of the stories he relates to tell her to say that he could never abandon Duryodhana, who trusted him so completely and was closer than any brother to him.

Book 6. Bheeshma Parva

1. Vyasa describes some of the sinister omens seen, which presage an unthinkable slaughter, and the end of kshatriya kind. He is speaking to Dhritarashtra.

'Great will be the slaughter, O King. I see so many dreadful omens. Hawks, vultures, cranes, crows and herons swarm in the branches of the trees around Kurukshetra, delighted at the prospect of war. Carnivores of every kind teem in the woods, and will feast upon the flesh of elephants and horses. Other birds of ill omen wheel in dense flocks in the sky, drifting south, and utter terrible cries.

'At dawn and dusk, I see the face of the sun covered with the headless trunks of fighting men. At both sandhyas clouds of three colours, shaped like maces, cover the sun. At night, the moon and the stars seem to take fire and burn above. Even on the fifteenth night of the bright fortnight of Kartika, the full moon was either invisible or the colour of fire, and the sky the hue of a lotus.

'All night I hear the savage cries of fighting boars and cats. Surely, numberless heroes will perish during the war.

'In temples, the idols of the Gods and Goddesses laugh dementedly at times, then tremble. Often, they vomit blood, sweat, or even fall down. Without being beaten, great drums sound of themselves; without horses being yoked to them, kshatriya, chariots move on their own.

'At dawn, thick insect swarms cover the morning sky, obscuring the first light. Strange clouds appear suddenly and rain down showers of dust and pieces of flesh. The peerless Arundhati, renowned for her dharma, flies ahead of her lord Vasishta. Saturn, Shanaishchara afflicts the asterism Rohini. The deer upon the face of the Moon has strayed from his customary place. Thunder echoes in a perfectly clear sky, and lightning flashes.

'The cows and horses in their sheds and stables cry all day and night. Cows bring forth baby donkeys. Trees in the forest are laden with unseasonable flowers and fruit. Lotuses and lilies grow from trees! Women, both pregnant and not, give birth to hideous children, monsters. Animals, too, bring forth dreadful offspring—some with three horns, some four-eyed, some with two heads or five legs, some with two tails or phalluses. All these are born with gaping mouths, uttering profane cries.

'Crested horses are being born, many of them with just three legs, but horned.

'In your city, Dhritarashtra, the wives of brahmanas are giving birth to eaglets and peacocks. The mare brings forth the calf of the cow, and the bitch brings forth the jackals or the cockerel. Deer and parrots give ceaseless throat to the weirdest cries and songs.

'Some women give birth to four and five daughters, together, and these children sing, laugh and dance as soon as they are born. All those beyond the pale of the four varnas are celebrant—the scavengers and the lowest of the lowborn, as if in delight at the age of chaos that is dawning over the world.

'The smallest infants attack one another with wooden clubs, and are full of violence: as if Death sits on their hearts. Powerful winds blow without pause, and earthquakes are felt in every kingdom. Taking his position between Chitra and Swati, Rahu creeps upon the Sun, and the white planet Ketu, mixing fire and smoke, having passed the constellation of Chitra, stays where he is, and attacks Jyeshta, which is sacred to Indra. A fiery comet, big as a planet, has risen to afflict Pushyami. Mars wheels at Magha, and Jupiter toward Shravana. The Sun's child Saturn approaches the sign Bhaga, afflicting it. Shukra glitters brilliantly, rising toward Purva Bhadra, and gazes across at Uttara Bhadra, wheeling in his direction.

'Dhruva blazes, no longer stationary but spinning to the right. The Sun and Moon both afflict Rohini. Red Mars, Mangala, aligns himself with Shravana, and Brihaspati, Jupiter, there.

'Our sacred earth has burst forth in a plethora of crops of every season. Every stalk of barley has five ears, and each one of paddy, a hundred. Cows yield only blood, when milked after the calves have drunk.

'Bows and swords burn with uncanny light, without being touched—as if they already behold the war that is before them. The colour of water, weapons and armor is of fire. Ah, a great massacre will happen, and the earth will flow a frothing river of blood with the standards of kshatriyas for its rafts.

'The mandala of the Saptarishi is dim in the sky, as if in deep sorrow. For a whole year Saturn and Jupiter have entered Vishaka, and stood unmoving there. Extraordinary eclipses, of both Sun and Moon, and bizarre lunation, out of time—three full moons in a fortnight—have been seen, frequently. The four quarters and the intermediate directions all seem inauspicious, with filthy clouds of dust risen.

'Some midnight clouds appear in a moment, and pour down rains of blood. Rivers run blood mingled with water in their banks. Rakshasas drink from them, and are not sated. Deep natural wells bellow like bulls.

'Ferocious and savage Rahu constantly afflicts Krittika, too. What but a great slaughtering can all these omens portend? The rishis all say the Earth will drink the blood of thousands of kings, and their hosts.

'Kailasa and Mandara echo with strange explosions, and are swollen by submarine quakes, the oceans appear ready to break their shores and sweep across the continents. The howling winds that blow bear tiny pebbles, like hails of darts. Lightning strikes trees, great and small, in exceptional numbers, reducing them to pillars of ash.

'Sacrificial fires burn blue, crimson or yellow, when libations are poured into them. Their flames bend to the left, give off a fecal stench, and loud reports, sending sparks flying. Human senses seem to decay, change their very nature—touch, smell, and taste have become what they were not.'

2. Here is the hymn with which Arjuna worships the Goddess Durga, before his moment of crisis on Kurukshetra, before the war begins.

Arjuna said, 'I bow to you, Queen of yogins, who are one with the Brahman, who dwell in the Mandara forest, who are free from ageing and decay, O Kali, consort of the Kapalin, you who are black and red.

'I worship you, who bless your bhaktas, O Mahakaali, wife of the destroyer of the universe, proud one, who save from every danger, and who own every auspicious quality.

'You sprang from the Kata race, you that deserve the highest worship, fierce One, bestower of victory, O Victory personified, with the banner of peacock plumes, wearing every invaluable ornament, who bear the dreadful spear, with the sword and the shield, who are the younger sister of the chief of the cowherds, Eldest, who love quaffing the blood of the buffalo, born in the race of Kushika, who wear yellow robes.

'I worship you that have devoured demons, by assuming a great wolf's face. I bow to you who love battle! O Uma, Shakambari, you are white, Gauri, then black again, Kali. You slew the Demon Kaitabha. You have yellow eyes, you have many eyes, you have eyes the colour of smoke, and I worship you.

'You are the Vedas, the Srutis, and the highest dharma. You bless brahmanas that perform yagnas. You know the past and you dwell in all the sacred shrines built to you in every city in Jambudwipa. Ah, I adore you, Devi! Among sciences, you are the science of the Brahman, and you are the sleep of beings, from which there is no waking.

'Mother of Skanda, you own the six loftiest attributes. Durga, who dwell everywhere, in the most accessible places, you are Swaha, Swadha, Kala, Kashta, Saraswathi, Savitri mother of the Vedas. You are the Vedanta, too.

'With my heart clear, I bow again to you, O incomparable Goddess—I beg you let victory always ride with me during this war. You dwell in the most difficult and dangerous places, where there is fear, in the homes of your bhaktas and in patala. You are she that always slays the danavas.

'You are unconsciousness, sleep, illusion, modesty, and everything that is beautiful in all creatures. You are the twilight, you are the day, you are Savitri, and you are the Mother. You are contentment, you are growth, and you are light. You support the Sun and the Moon, and make them shine. You are the prosperity of the prosperous. The siddhas and charanas seek and find you in dhyana.'

The boon-giving Devi Durga appeared before Arjuna and blessed him, 'Soon you will vanquish your enemies, Pandava. Invincible one, Narayana himself is your sarathy, and not even Indra can defeat you in battle.'

And the glorious Mother vanished.

Book 7. Drona Parva

1. There is a colourful description of some of the kings' chariot horses.

'Bheema's chariot is drawn by horses dappled like the antelope. Satyaki has silvery steeds, Yudhamanyu has varicoloured horses, Dhrishtadyumna's are the hue of pigeons, covered by golden mail, his son Kshatradharman's are red, Shikhandi's son Kshatradeva's are the colour of lotus leaves, and have clear white eyes. Born in the land of the Valhikas, they are covered in rich crimson silk.

'Nakula's horses are of the Kamboja breed; they wear plumes with feathers of the green parrot. Uttamaujas rides against Drona in his chariot drawn by horses that are the colour of thunderheads. Sahadeva's horses are of many hues, Yudhishtira's are ivory-coloured, with black manes; Virata's horses are pale red, like the trumpet-flower, and are exceptionally beautiful.

'Uttara Kumara's horses are yellow; the five Kekaya brothers have deep red steeds. Shikhandi's are gandharva horses, given him by Tumburu. Sishupala has mottled horses, again like the antelope, Dhrishtaketu's are of different colours. Brihadkshatra's horses are of the Sindhu breed, the colour of the smoke of burning straw.

'Covered in golden armour, their skins the hue of red silk, Senabindu has quiet, swift horses. The young and delicate prince of the Kasis, powerful warrior, has horses the hue of cranes. Like his father Yudhishtira, Prativindhya has white horses with black manes, swift as the mind and obedient to their sarathy's very thought. Bheema's son Sutasoma, radiant as a thousand moons, has wheatish coloured horses, which he got from Soma Deva. Nakula's son Sataneeka's horses are the hue of the sala flower, or the morning sun. Sahadeva's son, Srutakarman's, chariot is pulled by steeds the hue of a peacock's throat, while Arjuna's son Srutakirti has horses the colour of kingfishers.

'Tawny horses bear Abhimanyu into war. Yuyutsu's horses are gigantic. Vardhakshemi's horses are plump, richly adorned, and the colour of the dried paddy stalk. The young Sauchitti's horses have black legs, golden breastplates, and are exceptionally obedient. Srenimat's steeds are also the hue of red silk, as are those of Satyadhriti.

'Chekitana's horses are like tawny silk. Arjuna's maternal uncle Kuntibhoja has rainbow-hued horses, while Rochamana's horses resemble the star-spangled night sky. The Panchala prince Singhasena, son of Gopati, has steeds like the red deer, with streaks of white, and Janamejaya's horses are the colour of mustard flowers. Quick as light, huge, and deep blue, with backs the colour of curd, are the horses of Drupada, and they are decked with golden chains.

'Bold and with beautiful heads, are the horses of Dandadhara; they are as white as the stalks of reeds, and splendid as the lotus or the firmament. Vyaghradatta's horses are light brown, their backs a mousy hue, and they hold their necks up more proudly than perhaps any other steeds. The Panchala prince Sudhanwan has horses with dark speckles.

'Chitrayudha's horses are fierce and beautiful, having the colour of the indragopakas, with variegated patches. The Kosala prince Sukshatra's chariot is yoked to horses whose bellies are the colour of the chakravaka. Long-legged and large, many-coloured, and most docile are the chariot-horses of Satyadhriti. Shukla's armor, standard, bow and horses are all the same white hue.

'The ferociously energetic Chandrasena, son of Samudrasena, rides with steeds born on the seacoast, white as the moon. Saiva's exquisite ratha is drawn by horses of the colour of the blue lotus, adorned with golden mail and beautiful wreaths of flowers. Rathasena tilts into battle in his chariot yoked to pedigreed horses the colour of kalaya flowers, with red and white streaks.

'Chitrayudha has steeds of superior bloodlines, their hue of kimsuka flowers. Nile has blue horses, armour, flag and weapons. Chitra's horses are extravagantly bejewelled. Rochamana's son. Hemavarna's horses are also the colour of the lotus. The hue of the hen's egg, their testicles white, and their spines the colour of reeds, are the steeds of Dandaketu.

'The Pandya king, Sarangadhwaja, had horses the hue of the rays of the full moon yoked. A hundred and forty-thousand warriors that followed this king owned horses the hue of the atrusa flower.

'Strange and varicoloured horses bore the rakshasas of Ghatotkacha. Red-eyed Brihatna's chariot was drawn by outsized horses of the Aratta breed. This king was a devotee of Yudhishtira and had come to fight for him, against the wishes of his people and his ilk, and abandoning all else he owned. The Prabhadrakas had steeds of many amazing colours. Dhrishtadyumna favored these kshatriyas greatly.'

Now for the flags and standards of some of the heroes:

'A black deer-skin waving above it, Drona's standard excelled those of all the enemy. It bore a lovely water-pot. Bheema's splendent standard bore a huge silver lion, its eyes of lapis. The great Yudhishtira's banner had the golden moon, with the planets around it, and it was luminous indeed. Two kettle-drums, named Nanda and Upananda, were tied to it, and had sticks attached that beat them with the wind.

'Nakula has an eight-legged Sarabha upon his banner, to terrify his foes; the mythic creature's back is made of gold. Sahadeva's flag bears a silver swan, which magically strikes fear into his adversaries' hearts. The standards of the five sons of Panchali bore the images of Dharma, Vayu, Indra, and the two Aswins.

'Abhimanyu's banner bears a peacock, the hue of molten gold. When he rode in his chariot, it flew a flag of a bright vulture, and his horses could fly anywhere at his will, even as those of Ravana of old.'

And later:

'The maharathikas had standards that blazed like fire, for they were often made of gold like Meru, or adorned with golden emblems; also, they were of many resonant colours—all those of the rainbow. Flying in the wind, they were as graceful as dancing courtesans.

'Of course, Arjuna's standard bears Hanuman himself. Aswatthama's flag was bright as a rising sun, and had a lion's tail above it. Karna flew a banner with a golden 'elephant rope'; wonderfully splendid, it seemed to dance upon his flagstaff and was adorned with gold and garlands. Kripa had a fighting bull on his banner, awesome as Nandiswara.

'Vrishasena flies a peacock, as magnificent as Skanda's, as well as a plowshare. Shalya of the Madras flew the image of a Devi as lovely as the Goddess of the field, who creates every seed of the harvest. He also flew a massive silver elephant, with peacocks surrounding it. A silver boar adorns the standard of the Sindhu king, and it glitters like crystal.

'Somadatta's son flies a yupastamba, a sacrificial stake, on his banner— one as resplendent as the stamba at a Rajasuya yagna. On his golden banner, Duryodhana flew an elephant as magnificent as Airavata, encrusted with precious jewels all over.'

As for weapons:

'Yudhishtira's bow was called the Mahendra, and Bheema's the Vayavya. Arjuna wielded the Gandiva, which Brahma once bore to protect the three worlds. Nakula wielded the Vaishnavi, and Sahadeva the Aswan.

'Ghatotkacha came into battle with the unearthly bow, the Paulastya. Draupadi's five sons wielded the Raudra, the Agneya, the Kauverya, the Yamya, and the Girisa.'

It is also told (in the Ganguli translation) that Bheema obtained the Raudra, and that it was Subhadra's son Abhimanyu who had it from his uncle.

3. Aswatthama asks in despair, 'Why did my Agneyastra not slay Arjuna and Krishna?'

Vyasa replies, 'Narayana is older than the oldest times. He, the Creator of the universe, once incarnated himself as Dharma's son. He sat upon the Himalaya in the most awesome tapasya. Splendid as fire or the sun, he stood upon the mountain, with his arms raised heavenward. For sixty-six thousand years, he stood without eating or drinking, living only on the air he breathed. His eyes shone like the petals of the mystic lotus.

'His energy spread through the earth. Then he stood in another, sterner, penance for twice that time, and now his great energy filled the space between heaven and earth. With this tapasya, Narayana Muni shone forth like Brahma, and then suddenly he saw the Master, the Origin, and Guardian of the Universe, the Lord of all the Gods, the Final Deity, smaller than the smallest, bigger than the greatest, who is almost impossible to gaze upon for his splendour, who is called Rudra, the terrible One. He who is also called Hara and Sambhu wore matted jata upon his head—he who infuses life into all things, who is the primal Cause, who is irresistible and also frightful, whose wrath consumes the cosmos, whose Soul encompasses everything, whose heart is boundless, who wields the bow Pinaka and twin quivers, who wears golden armour, whose energy is infinite, who bears a huge sword, a thunderbolt, a blazing trident, a battle-axe, and a mace.

The Lord Siva's eyebrows were fair, his matted locks black, he wielded a short club, he bore the crescent moon on his head, he wore a tiger-skin, and snakes were the sacred threads on his ash-covered body. All sorts of strange and wonderful creatures from across the universe surrounded him, as well as goblins and ghouls, ghosts and spirits.

'He is the One, the abode of yoga and dhyana, whom the eldest in the world always revere, who is water, heaven, sky, earth, sun, moon, wind and fire, who is the measure of the duration of the universe. Never do the evil-hearted obtain a vision of the Un-born One, the slayer of those that hate brahmanas, he that bestows moksha.

Only those purified of all their sins, men of dharma, ever see the Lord Siva with their mind's eye. After his long tapasya, Narayana saw the unfading One, Dharma's embodiment, the adorable One, who has the universe for his form. Vasudeva saw that final abode of every kind of splendour, the God with the garland of ashes round his neck, and Narayana Muni was filled with ecstasy, which he sought to express with his understanding, his body, his heart and by words.

Narayana worshipped the Divine Siva, First cause of creation, giver of boons, the puissant One who sports with the exquisite Parvati, he that is always surrounded by bhutas and pramathas, who is the Parabrahman manifest, the essence of all causes, the One of infinite power. Prostrating before Rudra, who slew the Asura Andhaka, Narayana of the lotus eyes began to fervently hymn the blue-throated, three-eyed Lord.

"Adorable One, first of all Gods, Creator of the Prajapatis, regents of the earth, who entered the world and protected it before all the universe, with its Devas, asuras, nagas, rakshasas, pisachas, humans, birds, gandharvas, yakshas, and every other creature, sprang from you.

"All worship of Indra, Yama, Varuna, Kubera, the Pitrs, Tvashtri, and Soma is in truth only worship of you. Form and light, sound and sky, wind and touch, taste and water, scent and earth, time, Brahma himself, the Vedas, the brahmanas, all things that move and are still have come from you.

"The wise man observes the birth and the passing of all things, and realizes that you are the only truth, the single unity, and the sacred ground. You created two birds, Iswara and jiva, four aswathha trees with their branches of holy words—the Vedas—, seven guardians—the five elements, the heart and the intellect—, and the ten senses and their objects. You are apart from all these.

"The past, the present and the future flow from you, as do the seven realms and the universe. I am your devoted bhakta; Lord, be gracious to me. Let evil never penetrate my heart. You are unknowable, the Soul of souls. He that knows you are the seed of the stars finds the Parabrahman. Lord, not all the Gods can fathom you. I am here to realize your true nature; Siva, reveal yourself to me, do not hide behind your illusion."

Then the blue-throated Lord, the Pinakin, whom the rishis always hymn, blessed Vasudeva with the rare boons he sought, for he deserved to receive them.

Mahadeva said, "Narayana, I bless you that among men, Devas, and gandharvas, you shall have untold, immeasurable power and soul. Not the gods, the asuras, the great uragas, the pisachas, gandharvas, men, rakshasas, birds, beasts, nagas, or any creature in the universe shall be able to resist you, or withstand your prowess. None among the gods or demons shall ever be able to vanquish you in battle. By my grace, not Indra's vajra shall be able to harm you. No weapon, wet, dry, unmoving or mobile will ever cause you pain.

"If you ever come to battle against me, you shall triumph!"

These were the boons that Narayana acquired from Lord Siva in another yuga. It is that Narayana who walks the earth today as Krishna.

While he performed his tapasya of old, another great muni was born from him—equal to him in every way. He was called Nara, and Arjuna is none other than that Nara. These two rishis, said to be older than the eldest of the Gods, incarnate themselves into the world, from age to age, to protect dharma, when it is threatened.'

Vyasa paused, then continued, 'You, Aswatthama, of great heart and tapasya of yore, were born yourself as an amsa of Siva—with the Lord's own energy and wrath! In a previous life, you were as wise as a Deva. You thought of the universe as being only Siva, and emaciated yourself in a fierce penance to gratify that God. You worshipped him with mantras, homa, and other offerings. Siva, who is always easily pleased, granted you several boons, which you have cherished in your heart.

'Your tapasya, like Nara and Narayana's, was also superior. As they have, you, too, have adored Mahadeva in your every life, as the sacred Linga. Krishna is Rudra's greatest bhakta, sprung from Siva himself, and he worships the Linga as the root of the universe. The knowledge of the Linga is always in him, and by it, he sees the identity of creation with the Brahman. He see everything, past, present, and future, the near and the remote, whole and undivided before his eyes. The Devas, the rishis, and the siddhas all worship Krishna because he has attained to Siva, the highest goal of all.

'Krishna is also the creator of all things; he must be worshipped. He always worships the Lord Siva, and Siva has even greater adoration for him!'

The light of understanding dawned on Aswatthama's heart, and Drona's son bowed to Siva, and realized who Krishna was. Divine delight filled him, and his body shone. He returned to the field of battle, and asked Duryodhana to withdraw the Kuru army for the night.

The next chapter deals again with Siva. Now, the victorious Arjuna speaks to Vyasa.

'Muni, while I was killing the enemy with storms of arrows, I always saw a blazing, refulgent figure before my chariot and my eyes. He was bright as fire, and held a spear in his hands. Wherever he went, with that weapon raised, the enemy fell like flies before him, though I do not think they ever saw him. Indeed, every soldier that I seemed to kill was in fact slain by the mysterious figure. I merely followed him, and loosed my arrows at those whom he had already killed.

'Great Vyasa, who was that figure, to my eyes brilliant as the sun? His feet never touched the earth, and he never cast his spear or pierced anyone with it—yet I saw a million sulas fly out from his single weapon.'

Vyasa replied, 'Arjuna, you saw Siva, the First cause, from whom the Prajapatis came—Shankara, who is the embodiment of Swarga, Bhumi and Patala, the Divine Lord, who protects the universe, the Great Master, also known as Isana.

'He is also Mahadeva, the greatest God, the Supreme Soul, and the only true Lord, with matted jata, the home of all that is auspicious. With three eyes and mighty arms, his locks tied above his head like a crown, his body covered in skins, he is Rudra. The boon giver, sovereign of the universe, he is called Hara and Sthanu. He is the foremost of all beings, invincible, who brings joy to the worlds, and the supreme monarch.

'He is the first cause, the light and the refuge of the worlds, and always triumphant. He is the soul and the maker, and having the universe for his body, his fame is eternal and infinite. He is the master of karma.

Called Sambhu, he is self-born, lord of all creatures, the source of the three times. He is yoga and the Lord of yoga, the Mahayogin. He is Sarva, all things.

'The highest One, he is Paramesthin. He is the soul of knowledge, and knowledge can never encompass him. He is the greatest, most munificent granter of boons to his bhaktas.

'Siva's companions are his ganas—weird and divine beings, many of them macabre and hideous to behold. Some are dwarves, some have jata, some are hairless of body and head, some have no necks, others huge bellies, others immense bodies, some are enormously strong and others have very long ears. All the ganas dress strangely indeed, and have deformed faces, mouths, and bent legs.

'This is Siva, who went before you in battle, Arjuna, through his kindness and ancient love for you. How else would you have razed an army which Karna, Kripa and Aswatthama protected? But the warrior before whom Siva walks is always triumphant. Why, the very scent of Maheswara, when he is angry, makes any enemy tremble and fall senseless on the field. For this do the Devas of heaven worship him. So, too, men of this earth that worship the Lord Siva find joy here and moksha in the hereafter.

'O son of Kunti, do you also bow down to Him that is Peace, Rudra of the blue throat, terrible beyond imagining, effulgent, called Kapardin, skull-bearer, of tawny eyes, the boon-giver, the great ordainer, of red hair and perfect dharma, who is always an object of desire, who is the Purusha, who is boldness itself, who is the subtlest, who gives light, who embodies all sacred waters, who is the God of gods, who is impetuous, who is manifest, handsome, the mountain his home, who is peace, who wears valkala, golden ornaments upon his arms, who is fierce, Lord of all the directions, of the clouds and all created beings, lord of plants and trees, and of kine, whose body is shrouded by the trees of the tapovana, who inspires every thought, who has the sacrificial ladle in his hand, who is ablaze, who wields the Pinaka, is Rama's self, has many forms, wears munja grass, has a thousand heads, a thousand eyes, arms, and legs.

'O Kaunteya, seek the protection of Umapati, who destroyed Daksha's yagna, the always cheerful Siva, whose navel is like that of a bull, who rides the bull, and whose emblem is the mighty bull. He is proud as a bull; he is the Lord of bulls, and the Bull of bulls. He has a bull on his banner, is liberal to the righteous, can be approached only by yoga, his eyes are like a bull's, his weapons superior, whose arrow is Vishnu himself, who personifies dharma, who is called Maheswara, who has a vast belly and a vast body, who sits on a leopard skin, Lord of the worlds, devoted to Brahma, who loves the brahmanas, wields the trisula, who gave his battle-axe to Parasurama.

'I place myself in the hands of this God, who wears the skin of the deer. Kubera is his friend, the greatest archers his companions, who himself is the greatest of them all, of stern vows and immaculate austerity, whose favourite weapon is the bow, who is himself the shaft discharged from his bow, who is the bow and bowstring, and the guru that teaches the use of the bow.

'I bow to the God whose weapons are awesome, the foremost of all Gods. I bow to him of many forms, with myriad bowmen around him. I salute him, who consumed the Tripura, who slew the Asura Bhaga, who is the Lord of trees and men, of the divine mothers, and of the spirit tribes called the ganas. He is the Lord of cattle and sacrifices, of the waters, of the Devas, who knocked out Surya's teeth, Hara who has a blue throat and golden hair.'

Vyasa goes on to describe some of the legends about Siva—how he destroyed Sati's father, Daksha's, yagna, where Surya was devouring the main offering, when Siva knocked out his teeth. Vyasa tells how all the Devas and rishis together, who had defied Siva, could not face his wrath in battle, and finally, terrified, sought his mercy and protection.

Vyasa tells of the marvellous triune cities of Mayaa Danava, the great Asura artisan, and how Siva burned them, when dharma left those cities.

He continues, 'He is Rudra, Siva, Agni; he is everything and knows everything. He is Indra, Vayu, the Aswin twins, and he is lightning. He is Bhava, Parjannya, Mahadeva, and he is sinless. He is Soma, Isana, Surya, and Varuna. He is Kala, Antaka, Mrityu and Yama. He is the day, and he is the night. He is the fortnight, the month, and the seasons. He is the sandhyas; he is the year.

'He is Dhatri, Vidhatri, the Soul of the universe and he that does all things that happen in the universe. He is formless himself, yet all these endless forms are him. He is infinitely splendid and glorious, and all the gods hymn him.

He is one, he is many; he is a hundred, and a thousand. Brahmanas who know the Veda say that Siva has two forms—the terrible and the auspicious. These two forms, again, are many. The gentle forms are water, light, and the moon, all that is most profoundly mysterious in all the branches of the Vedas, the Upanishads. And the Puranas, and every science that deals with the Soul—all these are Maheswara. This God, Mahadeva, was never born; he always existed.

Arjuna, not if I were to speak without pausing for a thousand years, can I begin to enumerate all the attributes of Siva. He is the One who delivers those that seek him, be they afflicted by malignant planets, and tainted by every dreadful sin. He grants and takes away life, health, prosperity, wealth, and all the diverse objects of desire. Indra's fortune and prosperity belong to Siva, as do those of the other devas. He is ever engaged in the welfare and detriment of men of the earth. He can do whatever he pleases, for he is the ultimate Lord. He is perfectly just; he is dharma embodied.

He pervades creation in many forms—his mouth is the ocean, and the wise know that mouth assumes the form of a mare's head to drink the sacrificial libations of holy water. Siva dwells in crematoria, burning ghats, and his bhaktas worship him in those places, where only the brave venture. Countless are the blazing and savage forms of the Lord Siva of which men speak, and worship in this world. Countless, also, are his sacred names, each one a salvational mantra. The main names are found in the Veda, in the hymn called the Satarudriya.

The brahmanas and munis all say he is the First-born of all creatures. He is the first of the Gods, too. Vayu was born from Siva's mouth. Since Rudra created all the animals of the worlds, and always loves and sports with them, he is Pasupati. His Linga is an emblem of brahmacharya. Since he always brings joy to the worlds, he is Maheswara. The Devas, rishis, gandharvas, and apsaras adore the erect Linga, and that pleases the God Siva as no other worship.

Being multi-formed, he is Bahurupa. He is all the worlds, hence he is Sarva. He is Dhurjjati, since his form is like that of smoke. The Gods of the cosmos, the Viswadevas, dwell inside Siva, so he is Viswarupa. He is called Tryambaka, because the Goddesses of the universe—sky, water, and earth—adore and have recourse to him. Since he is always auspicious toward men, in every way, he is Siva, the Auspicious One.

He is Mahadeva, being the Great God. Since he is steadfast and everlasting, he is Sthanu. Since the light of the sun and the moon that fall onto the earth are said to be his hair, he is Vyomakesa. Finally, he destroys even Brahma, Indra, Varuna, Yama and Kubera—so he is Hara. Since he is the three times, and their origin and end, he is Bhava. Kapi means the supreme one, and Vrisha, the just; Siva is Vrishakapi. He is all the vital breaths of living beings, and their health and sickness too.

The one that worships Siva as a Linga always finds unimaginable prosperity resulting. Half of the Lord is fierce like fire, and half of him cool and gentle as the moon. Blazing with cosmic energy, he burns more brightly than all the gods do. With his burning form, he practises brahmacharya. With this apocalyptic form, he devours the universe when the time of the end comes. Because he burns, because he is fierce, powerful, and devours flesh, blood and marrow, he is Rudra.

Worship Siva with the Satarudriya, Arjuna, and the Lord will go before you, wherever you ride.' Vyasa said. 'Defeat is not for you, because Krishna is your sarathy!'

Book 8. Karna Parva

1. The Devas, the Danavas, the gandharvas, the pisachas, the nagas, the rakshasas—all these took different sides in the battle between Karna and Arjuna. The sky was anxious for Karna; the earth was anxious for Arjuna, even as a mother for her son. The rivers, mountains, trees, deciduous plants and herbs took Arjuna, the Kiritin's, side.

The asuras, yatudhanas, and guhyakas were with Karna, as were ravens and other sky-rangers. All the precious gemstones and jewels, the four Vedas, the Upavedas, the Upanishads, with all their mysteries, Vasuki, Chitrasena, Takshaka and Upatakshaka, all the children of Kadru, all great serpents and nagas were for Arjuna, as were Airavata, the children of Surabhi, those of Vaisali, and the bhogins.

The smaller snakes sided with Karna, while wolves, wild stags, and all sorts of auspicious birds and beasts took Arjuna's part. The Vasus, the Maruts, the Sadhyas, the Rudras, the Viswedevas, the Aswins, Agni, Indra, Soma, Vayu, and the ten points of the compass—all these were for Arjuna. The Adityas were for Karna.

The vaisyas, sudras, sutas, all mixed castes, took the side of Radha's son. All the Devas, and the pitrs, with their followers, Yama, Kubera, and Varuna were for Arjuna's victory, as were the brahmanas, kshatriyas, the yagnas, and the dakshinas. Pisachas, pretas, most carnivores—animal and bird—the rakshasas, all the great monsters of the deep blue sea, dogs and jackals were for Karna. The rishis, of this world and the heavens, were for the Pandava, as were the gandharvas of Tumburu.

The Devas and the great Asuras adopted opposing sides. All the celestials, or darkness and light gathered invisibly in the firmament to watch the duels of duels. Brahma was there, and even Bhava, Siva in his vimana.

Indra said, 'Let Arjuna kill Karna today!'

Surya cried hotly, 'Let my son triumph and spill the Pandava's blood!'

They almost battled themselves, until Brahma intervened. The three worlds trembled when Karna and Arjuna faced each other, as did the rishis, the Devas and every other creature. The Devas and the Asuras said to Brahma, 'Let the encounter be equal, and let the universe not be destroyed by the duel between Arjuna and Karna!'

But Indra bowed to his Sire, and said, 'You once averred that victory would always belong to the two Krishnas. Let your words not prove false today. Holy father, be pleased with me!'

At which, Brahma and Rudra both replied, 'Be assured that Savyasachin, Arjuna, shall triumph today, for he is on the side of dharma, while Karna fights for evil.'

Brahma said, 'Siva is for Arjuna and Krishna; how can they be defeated? Moreover, Arjuna is a master of the four kinds of astras. Krishna and he are Nara and Narayana—all the gods, the charanas, and devarishis walk behind them. There is none that can vanquish them anywhere.

Yet, when Karna, that bull among men, dies, let him attain the highest worlds of bliss. Let him be equal to the Vasus and the Maruts. Vikartana's (Surya) son is a great hero—let him be worshipped in heaven, even as Bheeshma and Drona are.'

Book 9. Shalya Parva

1. Maharathika Aswatthama was like Rudra himself in battle. He had beautiful limbs, a handsome head covered with thick hair, a neck adorned

with three lines as on a conch-shell, sweet-spoken, eyes that resembled the petals of a full-blown lotus, a face as dignified as Meru. His neck, his eyes, tread and voice were like Nandiswara's. His arms were powerful, well-jointed, his chest broad and well-formed, he was Garuda's equal in speed and strength, splendid as the sun's rays, as intelligent as Shukra, as handsome as Soma. His body seemed to be made of a number of golden lotuses. His thighs were powerful and well-formed, as were his waist and hips. His hands and fingers were elegant and beautiful, as were his fingernails. Why, Brahma seemed to have made Aswatthama after collecting the finest features of man in all his creation. His learning was oceanic, and he bore every auspicious mark upon his person. He always vanquished his enemy with stunning swiftness, while they were helpless against his prowess.

He was a master of astras—their four padas, and ten angas. He was equally a master of the four Vedas, with all their branches, and the Akhyanas. It must be remembered that Drona, who was not born of a woman and had great ascetic punya, worshipped Lord Siva for a son. He begot Aswatthama upon Kripi, who also was not born of a woman. Aswatthama is often considered an amsa of Siva, and unrivalled were his beauty his erudition, and his feats.

Book 14. Aswamedha Parva

1. King Janamejaya wants to know about the mysterious mongoose, and Vaisampayana tells him.

'I will tell who the blue-eyed mongoose was, and how he could speak in a human voice and tongue. Once, the Rishi Jamadagni wanted to perform a yagna. His homa cow came to him, and the sage milked her himself. He poured the milk into a pure new vessel. Dharma Deva, assuming the form of Krodha, Anger, entered the vessel, for the God of dharma wanted to see how Jamadagni would react if provoked. Dharma spilt and spolit that milk. Jamadagni knew who had done this, and evinced no annoyance.

Then, Krodha became a brahmana and appeared before the rishi. He said, 'Greatest among all the race of Bhrigu, you have conquered me! The entire world says that the Bhrigus are known for their rage, but I find now that they lie. You have subdued me, O Mahatman, and you possess the rare virtue of forgiveness. I stand before you as a supplicant, O Muni. I fear your tapasya; puissant one, be kind to me.'

Jamadagni said, 'I have seen you, O Krodha, in your embodied form. Go where you wish, without any fear. You have not done me any injury today, and I bear no grudge against you. However, the milk you spoilt was for the Pitrs. You must go before them, and see what they do.'

In some terror, Anger vanished from the presence of the sage. But the manes cursed him to become a mongoose. Krodha began to worship the Pitrs, to end the curse. They spoke to him in an asariri, 'You shall end the curse if you denigrate Dharma Deva.'

Thus, the mongoose wandered the wide world, criticizing every great yagna he found. Finally, he arrived at Yudhishtira's Aswamedha yagna, and by censuring Dharma's son, his very self, Krodha was released from the curse of the manes.'

Ganguli observes that, in his opinion, the entire incident of the mongoose might well be an interpolation.

Book 16. Mausala parva

1. The omens seen in Dwaraka:

'Every day, Death, embodied, wandered through the homes of the Yadavas. He had the form of a fierce and terrible man, bald and black-skinned, as well as tawny. The bowmen of Dwaraka shot thousands of arrows at him, but none pierced that macabre figure.

'Day by day, the sea winds blew more roughly, and all manners of other evil portents arose—foreboding the end of the Vrishnis and the Andhakas. The streets swarmed with rats and mice. Earthen vessels cracked on their own, spilling what they contained. At nights, the rats and mice gnawed away the hair and the nails of sleeping men. Sarikas chirped incessantly, inside the houses of the sea city. Sarasas called like owls, and goats bayed like jackals.

'The strangest birds appeared, Death's messengers, never seen before—pale feathered, with bright red legs. At every hour, pigeons disported in the homes of the Yadus. Cows gave birth to asses, mules to elephants, and bitches littered kittens. The mouse was born to the mongoose.

'The Vrishnis became sinners, all of them except Balarama and Krishna. They grew shameless, insulted and humiliated their gurus and elders. They showed disrespect toward brahmanas, the manes, and the Gods. Wives deceived their husbands, and husbands their wives. Sacred fires always cast their flames to the left. At times, they burned with unnatural brilliance, in bright red and blue.

'As the sun rose or set over the city, it seemed shrouded by headless figures of men. Wriggling beds of worms, of many kinds, appeared in clean, cooked food, as soon as it was served. When brahmanas blessed the hour of day, as they received gifts or alms, countless heavy footfalls would be heard, running helter-skelter, everywhere. But no one could be seen making that sound.

'The planets appeared to repeatedly attack and strike the constellations in the sky. However, no Yadava could ever see, at any time, the sign under which he was born. When they blew their auspicious conches, a dissonant chorus of donkeys brayed in the solemn echo of the bass.

'Every night, Vrishni women dreamt of a black hag with white teeth, who laughed maniacally, ran through Dwaraka and their homes, and snatched the sacred threads from their wrists. Men dreamt of crimson-eyed vultures entering their houses and yagnashalas, and feeding on their bodies.

'They saw hideous rakshasas steal their ornaments, standards, armour, and other insignia. One day, in plain sight of all the Yadus, the Sudarshana Chakra flashed up into the sky and vanished. Then, the Jaitra, Krishna's chariot, in Daruka, his sarathy's, sight, disappeared in the most unusual manner. The four great horses, Saibya, Sugriva, Meghapushpa, and Balahaka, flew off with it at the speed of thought, dragging it across the surface of the sea!

'Krishna's Garuda standard, and Balarama's with the palmyra, were taken by apsaras, who called day and night in their sweet, sweet voices to the Yadavas to set out on a yatra to some holy tirtha.'

Book 18. Swargarohanika Parva

1. When they die, most of the great characters of the legend are absorbed, or reabsorbed, as in Bheeshma's case, into the God or Gods of whom they were amsas.

Bheeshma, of course, again becomes the Vasu Prabhasa, or Dyu, when he dies. Drona enters into Brihaspati, Kritavarman enters the Maruts, Pradyumna again becomes part of Sanatkumara, whose amsa he was, (though it is also told that he was Kama Deva incarnate!), Dhritarashtra attains to Kubera's realm, and Gandhari with him. Pandu, Kunti and Madri attain Indra's world. Virata, Drupada, Dhrishtaketu, Nishatha, Akrura, Samba, Bhanukampa, Viduratha, Bhoorisravas, Sala, Bhoori, Kamsa, Ugrasena, Vasudeva, and Uttara Kumara are all absorbed into the various Devas.

Soma's mighty son Varchas was born as Abhimanyu. Abhimanyu becomes Varchas again, when he dies. Karna enters into Surya, Shakuni is absorbed into Dwapara, and Dhrishtadyumna into Agni Deva. Vidura and Yudhishtira are both absorbed in Dharma Deva. The rakshasas born as Dhritarashtra's sons all found heaven for themselves, by dying on the field of war.

Balarama became Ananta and went down into patala, where he is the support of Vishnu and the worlds. Krishna, of course, became Vishnu again.

When their time came, the sixteen thousand that had been Krishna's wives, entered the Saraswati, and returned to Vishnuloka as unearthly apsaras. Ghatotkacha and his rakshasas all became lofty yakshas, Bheema's son himself was equal to a God. Of the other warriors who perished on Kurukshetra, some went to the world of Indra, some to the realm of Kubera of matchless intellect, and others to the marine world of Varuna.

Called Sambhu, he is self-born, lord of all creatures, the source of the three times. He is yoga and the Lord of yoga, the Mahayogin. He is Sarva, all things.

'The highest One, he is Paramesthin. He is the soul of knowledge, and knowledge can never encompass him. He is the greatest, most munificent granter of boons to his bhaktas.

'Siva's companions are his ganas—weird and divine beings, many of them macabre and hideous to behold. Some are dwarves, some have jata, some are hairless of body and head, some have no necks, others huge bellies, others immense bodies, some are enormously strong and others have very long ears. All the ganas dress strangely indeed, and have deformed faces, mouths, and bent legs.

'This is Siva, who went before you in battle, Arjuna, through his kindness and ancient love for you. How else would you have razed an army which Karna, Kripa and Aswatthama protected? But the warrior before whom Siva walks is always triumphant. Why, the very scent of Maheswara, when he is angry, makes any enemy tremble and fall senseless on the field. For this do the Devas of heaven worship him. So, too, men of this earth that worship the Lord Siva find joy here and moksha in the hereafter.

'O son of Kunti, do you also bow down to Him that is Peace, Rudra of the blue throat, terrible beyond imagining, effulgent, called Kapardin, skull-bearer, of tawny eyes, the boon-giver, the great ordainer, of red hair and perfect dharma, who is always an object of desire, who is the Purusha, who is boldness itself, who is the subtlest, who gives light, who embodies all sacred waters, who is the God of gods, who is impetuous, who is manifest, handsome, the mountain his home, who is peace, who wears valkala, golden ornaments upon his arms, who is fierce, Lord of all the directions, of the clouds and all created beings, lord of plants and trees, and of kine, whose body is shrouded by the trees of the tapovana, who inspires every thought, who has the sacrificial ladle in his hand, who is ablaze, who wields the Pinaka, is Rama's self, has many forms, wears munja grass, has a thousand heads, a thousand eyes, arms, and legs.

'O Kaunteya, seek the protection of Umapati, who destroyed Daksha's yagna, the always cheerful Siva, whose navel is like that of a bull, who rides the bull, and whose emblem is the mighty bull. He is proud as a bull; he is the Lord of bulls, and the Bull of bulls. He has a bull on his banner, is liberal to the righteous, can be approached only by yoga, his eyes are like a bull's, his weapons superior, whose arrow is Vishnu himself, who personifies dharma, who is called Maheswara, who has a vast belly and a vast body, who sits on a leopard skin, Lord of the worlds, devoted to Brahma, who loves the brahmanas, wields the trisula, who gave his battle-axe to Parasurama.

'I place myself in the hands of this God, who wears the skin of the deer. Kubera is his friend, the greatest archers his companions, who himself is the greatest of them all, of stern vows and immaculate austerity, whose favourite weapon is the bow, who is himself the shaft discharged from his bow, who is the bow and bowstring, and the guru that teaches the use of the bow.

'I bow to the God whose weapons are awesome, the foremost of all Gods. I bow to him of many forms, with myriad bowmen around him. I salute him, who consumed the Tripura, who slew the Asura Bhaga, who is the Lord of trees and men, of the divine mothers, and of the spirit tribes called the ganas. He is the Lord of cattle and sacrifices, of the waters, of the Devas, who knocked out Surya's teeth, Hara who has a blue throat and golden hair.'

Vyasa goes on to describe some of the legends about Siva—how he destroyed Sati's father, Daksha's, yagna, where Surya was devouring the main offering, when Siva knocked out his teeth. Vyasa tells how all the Devas and rishis together, who had defied Siva, could not face his wrath in battle, and finally, terrified, sought his mercy and protection.

Vyasa tells of the marvellous triune cities of Mayaa Danava, the great Asura artisan, and how Siva burned them, when dharma left those cities.

He continues, 'He is Rudra, Siva, Agni; he is everything and knows everything. He is Indra, Vayu, the Aswin twins, and he is lightning. He is Bhava, Parjannya, Mahadeva, and he is sinless. He is Soma, Isana, Surya, and Varuna. He is Kala, Antaka, Mrityu and Yama. He is the day, and he is the night. He is the fortnight, the month, and the seasons. He is the sandhyas; he is the year.

'He is Dhatri, Vidhatri, the Soul of the universe and he that does all things that happen in the universe. He is formless himself, yet all these endless forms are him. He is infinitely splendid and glorious, and all the gods hymn him.

He is one, he is many; he is a hundred, and a thousand. Brahmanas who know the Veda say that Siva has two forms—the terrible and the auspicious. These two forms, again, are many. The gentle forms are water, light, and the moon, all that is most profoundly mysterious in all the branches of the Vedas, the Upanishads. And the Puranas, and every science that deals with the Soul—all these are Maheswara. This God, Mahadeva, was never born; he always existed.

Arjuna, not if I were to speak without pausing for a thousand years, can I begin to enumerate all the attributes of Siva. He is the One who delivers those that seek him, be they afflicted by malignant planets, and tainted by every dreadful sin. He grants and takes away life, health, prosperity, wealth, and all the diverse objects of desire. Indra's fortune and prosperity belong to Siva, as do those of the other devas. He is ever engaged in the welfare and detriment of men of the earth. He can do whatever he pleases, for he is the ultimate Lord. He is perfectly just; he is dharma embodied.

He pervades creation in many forms—his mouth is the ocean, and the wise know that mouth assumes the form of a mare's head to drink the sacrificial libations of holy water. Siva dwells in crematoria, burning ghats, and his bhaktas worship him in those places, where only the brave venture. Countless are the blazing and savage forms of the Lord Siva of which men speak, and worship in this world. Countless, also, are his sacred names, each one a salvational mantra. The main names are found in the Veda, in the hymn called the Satarudriya.

The brahmanas and munis all say he is the First-born of all creatures. He is the first of the Gods, too. Vayu was born from Siva's mouth. Since Rudra created all the animals of the worlds, and always loves and sports with them, he is Pasupati. His Linga is an emblem of brahmacharya. Since he always brings joy to the worlds, he is Maheswara. The Devas, rishis, gandharvas, and apsaras adore the erect Linga, and that pleases the God Siva as no other worship.

Being multi-formed, he is Bahurupa. He is all the worlds, hence he is Sarva. He is Dhurjjati, since his form is like that of smoke. The Gods of the cosmos, the Viswadevas, dwell inside Siva, so he is Viswarupa. He is called Tryambaka, because the Goddesses of the universe—sky, water, and earth—adore and have recourse to him. Since he is always auspicious toward men, in every way, he is Siva, the Auspicious One.

He is Mahadeva, being the Great God. Since he is steadfast and everlasting, he is Sthanu. Since the light of the sun and the moon that fall onto the earth are said to be his hair, he is Vyomakesa. Finally, he destroys even Brahma, Indra, Varuna, Yama and Kubera—so he is Hara. Since he is the three times, and their origin and end, he is Bhava. Kapi means the supreme one, and Vrisha, the just; Siva is Vrishakapi. He is all the vital breaths of living beings, and their health and sickness too.

The one that worships Siva as a Linga always finds unimaginable prosperity resulting. Half of the Lord is fierce like fire, and half of him cool and gentle as the moon. Blazing with cosmic energy, he burns more brightly than all the gods do. With his burning form, he practises brahmacharya. With this apocalyptic form, he devours the universe when the time of the end comes. Because he burns, because he is fierce, powerful, and devours flesh, blood and marrow, he is Rudra.

Worship Siva with the Satarudriya, Arjuna, and the Lord will go before you, wherever you ride.' Vyasa said. 'Defeat is not for you, because Krishna is your sarathy!'

Book 8. Karna Parva

1. The Devas, the Danavas, the gandharvas, the pisachas, the nagas, the rakshasas—all these took different sides in the battle between Karna and Arjuna. The sky was anxious for Karna; the earth was anxious for Arjuna, even as a mother for her son. The rivers, mountains, trees, deciduous plants and herbs took Arjuna, the Kiritin's, side.

The asuras, yatudhanas, and guhyakas were with Karna, as were ravens and other sky-rangers. All the precious gemstones and jewels, the four Vedas, the Upavedas, the Upanishads, with all their mysteries, Vasuki, Chitrasena, Takshaka and Upatakshaka, all the children of Kadru, all great serpents and nagas were for Arjuna, as were Airavata, the children of Surabhi, those of Vaisali, and the bhogins.

The smaller snakes sided with Karna, while wolves, wild stags, and all sorts of auspicious birds and beasts took Arjuna's part. The Vasus, the Maruts, the Sadhyas, the Rudras, the Viswedevas, the Aswins, Agni, Indra, Soma, Vayu, and the ten points of the compass—all these were for Arjuna. The Adityas were for Karna.

The vaisyas, sudras, sutas, all mixed castes, took the side of Radha's son. All the Devas, and the pitrs, with their followers, Yama, Kubera, and Varuna were for Arjuna's victory, as were the brahmanas, kshatriyas, the yagnas, and the dakshinas. Pisachas, pretas, most carnivores—animal and bird—the rakshasas, all the great monsters of the deep blue sea, dogs and jackals were for Karna. The rishis, of this world and the heavens, were for the Pandava, as were the gandharvas of Tumburu.

The Devas and the great Asuras adopted opposing sides. All the celestials, or darkness and light gathered invisibly in the firmament to watch the duels of duels. Brahma was there, and even Bhava, Siva in his vimana.

Indra said, 'Let Arjuna kill Karna today!'

Surya cried hotly, 'Let my son triumph and spill the Pandava's blood!'

They almost battled themselves, until Brahma intervened. The three worlds trembled when Karna and Arjuna faced each other, as did the rishis, the Devas and every other creature. The Devas and the Asuras said to Brahma, 'Let the encounter be equal, and let the universe not be destroyed by the duel between Arjuna and Karna!'

But Indra bowed to his Sire, and said, 'You once averred that victory would always belong to the two Krishnas. Let your words not prove false today. Holy father, be pleased with me!'

At which, Brahma and Rudra both replied, 'Be assured that Savyasachin, Arjuna, shall triumph today, for he is on the side of dharma, while Karna fights for evil.'

Brahma said, 'Siva is for Arjuna and Krishna; how can they be defeated? Moreover, Arjuna is a master of the four kinds of astras. Krishna and he are Nara and Narayana—all the gods, the charanas, and devarishis walk behind them. There is none that can vanquish them anywhere.

Yet, when Karna, that bull among men, dies, let him attain the highest worlds of bliss. Let him be equal to the Vasus and the Maruts. Vikartana's (Surya) son is a great hero—let him be worshipped in heaven, even as Bheeshma and Drona are.'

Book 9. Shalya Parva

1. Maharathika Aswatthama was like Rudra himself in battle. He had beautiful limbs, a handsome head covered with thick hair, a neck adorned with three lines as on a conch-shell, sweet-spoken, eyes that resembled the petals of a full-blown lotus, a face as dignified as Meru. His neck, his eyes, tread and voice were like Nandiswara's. His arms were powerful, well-jointed, his chest broad and well-formed, he was Garuda's equal in speed and strength, splendid as the sun's rays, as intelligent as Shukra, as handsome as Soma. His body seemed to be made of a number of golden lotuses. His thighs were powerful and well-formed, as were his waist and hips. His hands and fingers were elegant and beautiful, as were his fingernails. Why, Brahma seemed to have made Aswatthama after collecting the finest features of man in all his creation. His learning was oceanic, and he bore every auspicious mark upon his person. He always vanquished his enemy with stunning swiftness, while they were helpless against his prowess.

He was a master of astras—their four padas, and ten angas. He was equally a master of the four Vedas, with all their branches, and the Akhyanas. It must be remembered that Drona, who was not born of a woman and had great ascetic punya, worshipped Lord Siva for a son. He begot Aswatthama upon Kripi, who also was not born of a woman. Aswatthama is often considered an amsa of Siva, and unrivalled were his beauty his erudition, and his feats.

Book 14. Aswamedha Parva

1. King Janamejaya wants to know about the mysterious mongoose, and Vaisampayana tells him.

'I will tell who the blue-eyed mongoose was, and how he could speak in a human voice and tongue. Once, the Rishi Jamadagni wanted to perform a yagna. His homa cow came to him, and the sage milked her himself. He poured the milk into a pure new vessel. Dharma Deva, assuming the form of Krodha, Anger, entered the vessel, for the God of dharma wanted to see how Jamadagni would react if provoked.

Dharma spilt and spolit that milk. Jamadagni knew who had done this, and evinced no annoyance.

Then, Krodha became a brahmana and appeared before the rishi. He said, 'Greatest among all the race of Bhrigu, you have conquered me! The entire world says that the Bhrigus are known for their rage, but I find now that they lie. You have subdued me, O Mahatman, and you possess the rare virtue of forgiveness. I stand before you as a supplicant, O Muni. I fear your tapasya; puissant one, be kind to me.'

Jamadagni said, 'I have seen you, O Krodha, in your embodied form. Go where you wish, without any fear. You have not done me any injury today, and I bear no grudge against you. However, the milk you spoilt was for the Pitrs. You must go before them, and see what they do.'

In some terror, Anger vanished from the presence of the sage. But the manes cursed him to become a mongoose. Krodha began to worship the Pitrs, to end the curse. They spoke to him in an asariri, 'You shall end the curse if you denigrate Dharma Deva.'

Thus, the mongoose wandered the wide world, criticizing every great yagna he found. Finally, he arrived at Yudhishtira's Aswamedha yagna, and by censuring Dharma's son, his very self, Krodha was released from the curse of the manes.'

Ganguli observes that, in his opinion, the entire incident of the mongoose might well be an interpolation.

Book 16. Mausala parva

1. The omens seen in Dwaraka:

'Every day, Death, embodied, wandered through the homes of the Yadavas. He had the form of a fierce and terrible man, bald and black-skinned, as well as tawny. The bowmen of Dwaraka shot thousands of arrows at him, but none pierced that macabre figure.

'Day by day, the sea winds blew more roughly, and all manners of other evil portents arose—foreboding the end of the Vrishnis and the Andhakas. The streets swarmed with rats and mice. Earthen vessels cracked on their own, spilling what they contained. At nights, the rats and mice gnawed away the hair and the nails of sleeping men. Sarikas chirped incessantly, inside the houses of the sea city. Sarasas called like owls, and goats bayed like jackals.

'The strangest birds appeared, Death's messengers, never seen before—pale feathered, with bright red legs. At every hour, pigeons disported in the homes of the Yadus. Cows gave birth to asses, mules to elephants, and bitches littered kittens. The mouse was born to the mongoose.

'The Vrishnis became sinners, all of them except Balarama and Krishna. They grew shameless, insulted and humiliated their gurus and elders. They showed disrespect toward brahmanas, the manes, and the Gods. Wives deceived their husbands, and husbands their wives. Sacred fires always cast their flames to the left. At times, they burned with unnatural brilliance, in bright red and blue.

'As the sun rose or set over the city, it seemed shrouded by headless figures of men. Wriggling beds of worms, of many kinds, appeared in clean, cooked food, as soon as it was served. When brahmanas blessed the hour of day, as they received gifts or alms, countless heavy footfalls would be heard, running helter-skelter, everywhere. But no one could be seen making that sound.

'The planets appeared to repeatedly attack and strike the constellations in the sky. However, no Yadava could ever see, at any time, the sign under which he was born. When they blew their auspicious conches, a dissonant chorus of donkeys brayed in the solemn echo of the bass.

'Every night, Vrishni women dreamt of a black hag with white teeth, who laughed maniacally, ran through Dwaraka and their homes, and snatched the sacred threads from their wrists. Men dreamt of crimson-eyed vultures entering their houses and yagnashalas, and feeding on their bodies.

'They saw hideous rakshasas steal their ornaments, standards, armour, and other insignia. One day, in plain sight of all the Yadus, the Sudarshana Chakra flashed up into the sky and vanished. Then, the Jaitra, Krishna's chariot, in Daruka, his sarathy's, sight, disappeared in the most unusual manner. The four great horses, Saibya, Sugriva, Meghapushpa, and Balahaka, flew off with it at the speed of thought, dragging it across the surface of the sea!

'Krishna's Garuda standard, and Balarama's with the palmyra, were taken by apsaras, who called day and night in their sweet, sweet voices to the Yadavas to set out on a yatra to some holy tirtha.'

Book 18. Swargarohanika Parva

1. When they die, most of the great characters of the legend are absorbed, or reabsorbed, as in Bheeshma's case, into the God or God of whom they were amsas.

Bheeshma, of course, again becomes the Vasu Prabhasa, or Dyu, when he dies. Drona enters into Brihaspati, Kritavarman enters the Maruts, Pradyumna again becomes part of Sanatkumara, whose amsa he was, (though it is also told that he was Kama Deva incarnate!), Dhritarashtra attains to Kubera's realm, and Gandhari with him. Pandu, Kunti and Madri attain Indra's world. Virata, Drupada, Dhrishtaketu, Nishatha, Akrura, Samba, Bhanukampa, Viduratha, Bhoorisravas, Sala, Bhoori, Kamsa, Ugrasena, Vasudeva, and Uttara Kumara are all absorbed into the various Devas.

Soma's mighty son Varchas was born as Abhimanyu. Abhimanyu becomes Varchas again, when he dies. Karna enters into Surya, Shakuni is absorbed into Dwapara, and Dhrishtadyumna into Agni Deva. Vidura and Yudhishtira are both absorbed in Dharma Deva. The rakshasas born as Dhritarashtra's sons all found heaven for themselves, by dying on the field of war.

Balarama became Ananta and went down into patala, where he is the support of Vishnu and the worlds. Krishna, of course, became Vishnu again.

When their time came, the sixteen thousand that had been Krishna's wives, entered the Saraswati, and returned to Vishnuloka as unearthly apsaras. Ghatotkacha and his rakshasas all became lofty yakshas, Bheema's son himself was equal to a God. Of the other warriors who perished on Kurukshetra, some went to the world of Indra, some to the realm of Kubera of matchless intellect, and others to the marine world of Varuna.